Here's What the Experts Have to Say About
CALIFORNIA GOLF

"For golfers who wonder if the grasses are greener on the other side of the state, (CALIFORNIA GOLF) fits you to a tee."
*Escondido Times-Advocate*

"(These) insightful descriptions of California courses are a must-read for any avid golfer."
*Roger Maltbie, Five-time PGA Tour Winner*

"An excellent reference guide for golf enthusiasts."
*Sacramento Bee*

"An excellent resource book for any golfer who's looking to test his or her skills at a new course."
*Golf Today*

"It's the perfect book not only for the good golfer but the average player as well. It's something every golfer should have."
*Julie Inkster,*
*Three-time U.S. Women's Amateur Champion and LPGA Touring Pro*

Here's What Readers Have to Say About
CALIFORNIA GOLF

"Our typical weekend includes camping, exploring back roads, and trying different golf courses. This book is our bible!"
*Bob Summers, Walnut Creek*

"Great book—a wealth of well-researched data!"
*Pat Falcaro, La Crescenta*

"Appreciate your women's yardages and slopes."
*Mary Jobson, Sonoma*

"A great book. Will keep in my car for use as I travel around the state."
*Bill Page, Coalinga*

ISBN 0-935701-18-4

# CALIFORNIA GOLF

1993-94 Edition

Ray A. March, Editor

Contributing Authors:
Bob Burns, Ted Johnson, Ray A. March,
John Strege, T.R. Reinman

Foghorn Press
555 De Haro Street, Suite 220
San Francisco, CA 94107
Telephone: (415) 241-9550

**Managing Editor**—Ann-Marie Brown
**Copy Editors**—Howard Rabinowitz, Samantha Trautman, Emily Marks
**Book Design and Maps**—David Ergo, Luke Thrasher

**Cover Photo**—PGA West—17th Hole TPC™ Stadium™
Course, designed by Pete Dye
**Back Cover Photo**—La Costa Resort and Spa, Carlsbad, CA
South Course—18th Hole green

Library of Congress
Cataloging-In-Publication Data:
March, Ray A.

CALIFORNIA GOLF: The Complete Guide/ Ray A. March, Ed.
1993-94 edition
p. cm.
Rev. ed. of: California golf 1991
Includes index
ISBN 0-935701-18-4: $17.95
1. Golf courses—California—Directories. 2. California-Description and travel—1993—Guide Books. I. California golf. II. Title

GV982.C2C35 1993
796.352'06'8794—dc20

91-37989 CIP

Printed in the United States

## About the Authors

*California Golf* was written by five golf writers across California and edited by Ray A. March.

**Bob Burns** researched Northern California pages 32-89, 126-183, and 268-310. Bob has been a sports writer at the *Sacramento Bee* for eight years and covering golf for six years.

**Ted Johnson** researched the San Francisco Bay Area, pages 90-125 and 184-267. He has been covering golf for ten years for the Lesher chain of newspapers in the East Bay.

**Ray A. March** researched Central California, pages 311-462. He is the author of *A Paradise Called Pebble Beach* and the 1992 edition of *California Golf.* He also writes about golf for *Western Links* and the *San Francisco Chronicle.*

**T.R. Reinman** researched Southern California pages 506-583 and pages 668-726. He has been a golf writer for the *San Diego Union Tribune* for eight years.

**John Strege** researched Southern California pages 463-505 and pages 584-667. He writes about golf for the *Orange County Register.*

We've done the most possible to ensure that the information in this book is completely accurate and updated. However, many golf courses frequently change their fees, times and rules of play. We recommend that before traveling to any golf course in this book, you call the course and make sure you have all the information you need.

If you have any commments, corrections or suggestions about the content of this book, please write to us at Foghorn Press, 555 DeHaro Street #220, The Boiler Room, San Francisco, CA 94107.

Happy golfing!

# ABOUT THIS BOOK

If you've ever waited for a tee time, no one has to remind you that golf is still gaining in popularity. Yet all across the state, there are courses—public, semi-private, private, resort and military—that are uncrowded and available when you want to play. You just have to know where to find them.

To help you in this process, we have tracked down and mapped more than 700 golf courses in California, organized them into Northern, Central and Southern California zones and detailed each of them in the corresponding listings. This easy-to-use format will allow you to explore the great diversity of courses that California has to offer.

In these listings, you will find courses that challenge your skill level, are in your budget, and are located in the setting you desire. Each course listing includes par, play policy, yardage and rating. Names and numbers are included so you can easily make tee time reservations. In addition, there are written directions to each course as well as detailed maps. Most courses feature detailed descriptions of holes, and many include exact replications of course scorecards.

This book includes listings of the following types of golf courses:

**PUBLIC COURSES**: Public courses offer the most variety. Overall, they are less expensive and often offer twilight, senior and junior rates. Some offer motorized carts, others only pull carts. Some are short par-3 courses and others are challenging 18-hole layouts. The prices are low when compared to private course fees. Municipal courses are listed in this category.

**SEMI-PRIVATE COURSES**: Most semi-private courses are open to the public. They may also offer memberships that are available to the public. In some cases, though, memberships are restricted to property owners within the residential community where the course is located.

**RESORT COURSES**: Most resort courses are open to the public, but offer lower fees to hotel guests. In many cases, these are among the best courses in the state, and the easiest to get onto.

**MILITARY COURSES**: Some military courses allow civilian play, but most limit play to active and retired military personnel and their guests. Every military base has a golf course.

**PRIVATE COURSES**: Private courses are divided into two categories: those that are reciprocal with members of other private clubs and those that are not. Non-reciprocal clubs are the most exclusive, with only members and their guests allowed. The majority of private clubs, however, are reciprocal with members of other private clubs. Prior arrangements almost always are required. Most clubs ask that the pro from your club make the contact. Reciprocal private clubs have special rates for members of other private clubs and are cited in this book as the fees "without a member or unaccompanied by a member." Fees can range from $15 to $85 for 18 holes. If you already belong to a club, reciprocal play provides an opportunity to explore the rest of California.

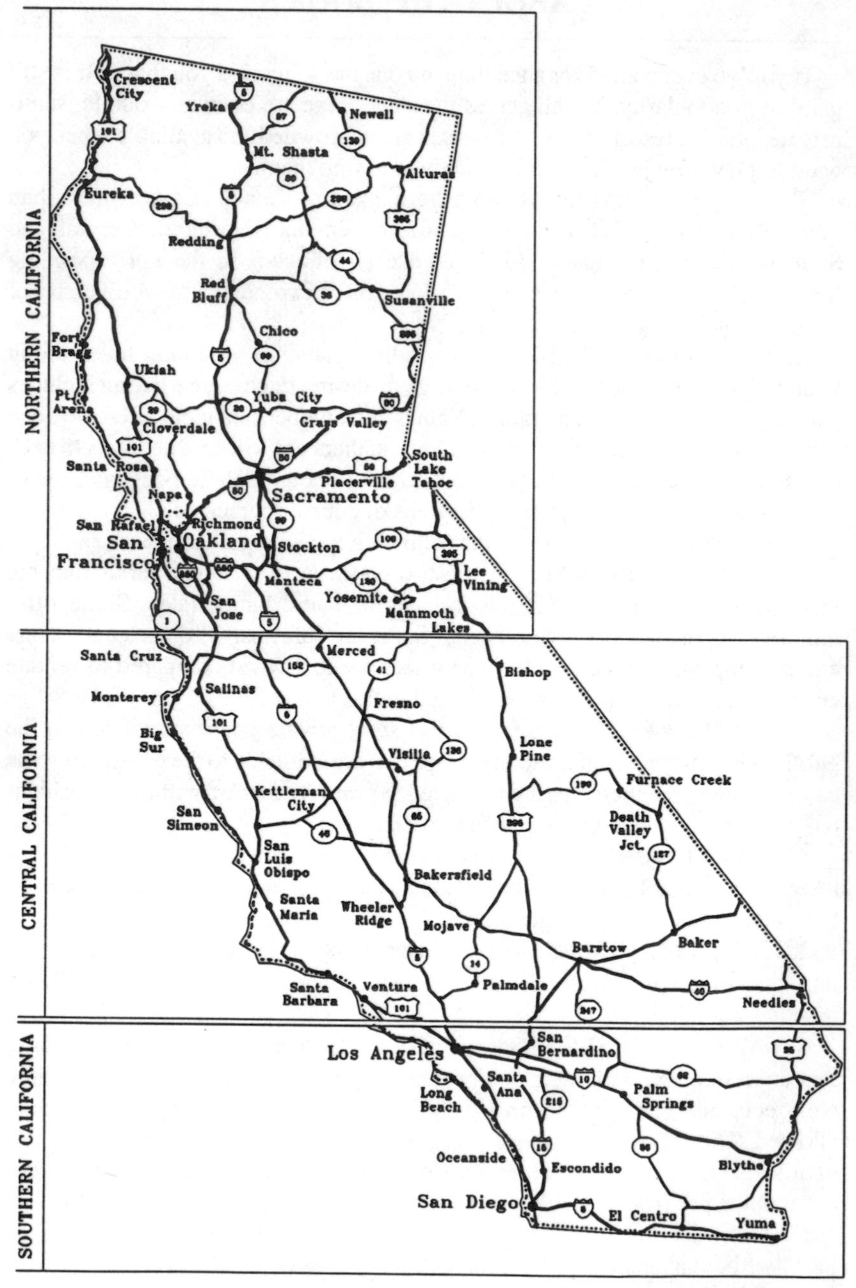

NORTHERN CALIFORNIA
CENTRAL CALIFORNIA
SOUTHERN CALIFORNIA
Crescent City
Yreka
Newell
Mt. Shasta
Alturas
Eureka
Redding
Red Bluff
Susanville
Chico
Fort Bragg
Ukiah
Pt. Arena
Yuba City
Grass Valley
Cloverdale
Santa Rosa
South Lake Tahoe
Placerville
Napa
Sacramento
San Rafael
Richmond
San Francisco
Oakland
Stockton
Lee Vining
Manteca
Yosemite
Mammoth Lakes
San Jose
Santa Cruz
Merced
Bishop
Monterey
Salinas
Fresno
Big Sur
Lone Pine
Visalia
Furnace Creek
Kettleman City
San Simeon
Death Valley Jct.
San Luis Obispo
Bakersfield
Santa Maria
Wheeler Ridge
Mojave
Barstow
Baker
Palmdale
Santa Barbara
Ventura
Needles
Los Angeles
San Bernardino
Santa Ana
Long Beach
Palm Springs
Oceanside
Escondido
Blythe
San Diego
El Centro
Yuma

# TABLE OF CONTENTS

# Palm Springs: The Golfer's Candy Store

by Ray A. March

Circling above the Palm Springs Regional Airport, the Coachella Valley below looks like a tiny bright green dot in an endless desert.

Once on the ground, the perception of this arid region— where even a jacket rabbit would die of exposure if it wandered too far without a flask—is just the opposite. The Coachella Valley is an oasis and there is no desert.

Both views have their merit.

The Coachella Valley, also known by its principle settlements as Palm Springs, Palm Desert, Rancho Mirage, Indian Wells and La Quinta, is the desert home to the greatest concentration of golf courses found anywhere.

There are so many golf courses that no one knows for certain how many there actually are.

"It's hard to keep track," admits Dan Poppers, editor of *GOLF NEWS Magazine* in nearby Cathedral City. "If you try to keep count, you're a half dozen behind at the end of the year."

By current estimates there are more than 90 golf courses in 150 square miles of Coachella Valley desert. That adds up to one golf course every 1.6 miles, which means you can go two miles in any direction and run into a golf course. Golf courses have been multiplying on this desert floor at such a startling rate that there hasn't been time to even call it a "boom." In the 1980s, for example, at least a dozen courses opened for play; that's more than one a year for 10 years.

If there's space for golf courses, there seems to be ample room for golf course architects. Once dominated by such established designers as Ted Robinson, the field has now been infiltrated by the "names"—Robert Trent Jones, Jr., Jack Nicklaus, Arnold Palmer, Pete Dye, Gary Player and Tom Fazio.

Golf—even in the hot summer months—is the area's leading industry. There are golf communities, golf resorts, golf clubs, golf courses for the sake of golf only, and the in-depth support services necessary to keep it all running. Golf is so popular that even the 891-room Marriott Desert Springs with 36 holes has been rumored to farm guests out to other golf courses.

The area virtually celebrates golf as a recreation, sport and source of income.

In Palm Desert each November, the locals dress up their golf carts as floats and form a parade that stretches for one and a half miles along El Paseo. One year, Linda Gray of "Dallas" was the grand marshal. That's just to get folks in the mood.

In a three-month stretch, January through March each year, there are four major golf tournaments in the Coachella Valley. They are the Bob Hope Chrysler Classic, Frank Sinatra Celebrity Invitational, Vintage Arco Seniors Invitational and Nabisco Dinah Shore LPGA. And that doesn't include the Skins Game, the Golden State or Nike Tours.

Why golf in the desert?

Skip the fact that golfers will go anywhere, anytime to play a round. The Coachella Valley, with its sandy soil, has all the necessary ingredients for becoming the successful golf refuge that it has.

"First, it has the climate, then the water and finally the ambience," explains Dennis Orsborn, Vice President of Golf Operations for Sunrise Company, the largest developer of golf communities in the area. "What more can you ask for?"

Orsborn is right on target. Beginning with Palm Springs, the area has been a hideaway for Hollywood's rich for more than 60 years. The climate, while scorching during the summer, is especially welcoming in the fall and winter months when other sections of the country are under snow. The water? Well, now that's another matter.

There have been all kinds of estimates on how much water lies under the Coachella Valley surface—all on the high side. While California has suffered from drought for some time, the Coachella Valley is water wealthy. Beneath those 90-some golf courses is an aquifer estimated to contain 11 million acre feet, a 400-year supply of water under current usage. There's water for fountains, pools, spas, patio micromists, whiskey chasers and golf course irrigation. It's no wonder the area looks like a green dot from the air and an enticing oasis at ground level. There is so much water in the air, the talk at outdoor cocktail parties is that the climate may change from dry to wet, heaven forbid.

There are other reasons for golf's success here. A major factor is supply-and-demand. The National Golf Foundation estimates that in California there are nearly three million golfers. That averages out to 4,000 golfers for every 18-hole golf course in the state. Considering that Palm Springs and its neighboring cities are about 100 miles from overpopulated Greater Los Angeles, the picture is perfect.

With those statistics in mind, can there be hope for four friends looking for a tee time at a top course? You bet.

What was once an exclusive retreat for Charlie Farrell, Palm Springs' first celebrity-mayor and his tennis playing pals from Hollywood in the 1930s, has now become the golfer's candy store. Of course, some people never get the message. Likeable Sonny Bono, today's mayor of Palm Springs, still prefers tennis to golf.

The best courses here are equal to the best anywhere. PGA West, for example, is rated one of the top 100 courses in the United States. Fortunately, the beauty of golf courses, like original art, is in the eye of the beholder.

Michael Roseto of Carmel, California and owner of Wide World of Golf Tours, is an acknowledged expert on the quality of courses and their popularity. He ranks PGA West and its four courses (Nicklaus Resort, Nicklaus Private, Arnold Palmer and TPC Stadium), The Club at Morningside, La Quinta Hotel Golf Club and Indian Wells Country Club as the most desirable courses accessible to outside play in the Coachella Valley. His first choice in the strictly-private category is Thunderbird Country Club.

To that list of courses open to outside play, Dan Poppers of *GOLF NEWS Magazine* adds Desert Falls Country Club, Lawrence Welk Desert Oasis (formerly Cathedral Canyon Country Club) and Westin Mission Hills Resort. His private course selections include Big Horn, Vintage Club, Mission Hills Country Club Old Course and Indian Ridge Country Club, which will open this year with two Arnold Palmer courses.

The characteristics of these courses are a good example of the variety of layouts golfers encounter when they tee off in the Coachella Valley. The Thunderbird is gently rolling and easy on the older players; they go to the 19th hole feeling that at least they had a chance to do well. The Nicklaus-designed Morningside gives players a choice between gambling and playing it safe on every hole, so they have only themselves to blame. At the Vintage, players have a choice of desert or mountain terrain.

*Golf Digest* has rated the par-4 17th at La Quinta's Dunes one of America's toughest holes; that should be warning enough. The Monterey Country Club is a tight target course, which means bring plenty of balls. For a course called Desert Princess, there is an unusual amount of water; there are also four sets of tees for bailing out. Don't be confused with the Scottish-look of Desert Falls: the greens are big enough to play U.S.-style football. The Lawrence Welk Desert Oasis is for shot-makers, so come prepared. The TPC Stadium is packed with pot bunkers, sand, water and sidehill lies, giving the golfer little choice but to play tough or go home.

Access to most golf courses in the area varies from totally public to resort to totally private, but in most instances even private clubs are available for play through a host member or home pro.

Green fees range wildly on a seasonal basis, but expect peak season rates to hover close to $100 a round at the best clubs. During the May through October season, local players take advantage of "golf passes," and visitors can do the same. Charities and some entrepreneurs sell golf cards for $60 to $75. For the one-time price of the card, or pass, a golfer has unlimited play on about 40 to 50 different courses—all summer. The only additional fee is for a cart.

"You can play yourself to death," one wag snorted.

On the tournament scale, Mission Hills Country Club is home to the Dinah Shore; Desert Springs Resort and Desert Falls Country Club hosts the Frank Sinatra; the Vintage Seniors is at the Vintage Club; the Bob Hope is played across the board at various clubs including Indian Wells, PGA-Palmer, La Quinta and Bermuda Dunes and the Skins has been seen at the TPC Stadium and Big Horn.

If that's not enough, there is also the Don Drysdale Hall of Fame Golf Classic each January.

Hot spot accommodations during tournament time include the La Quinta Hotel and its three courses, Hyatt Grand Champions with 36 holes of golf, Stouffer Esmeralda Resort with another 36 holes and the Marriott Desert Springs with still another 36 holes.

For those in the party who don't play golf (and they may wonder why they are in the Palm Springs area), a great compromise is La Mancha. If the name is a stranger, it's because La Mancha, with its private villas and pools behind electronic gates and security systems, is a hidden jewel.

Owned and run by Ken Irwin, La Mancha is so private the individual villas don't even have room numbers. Sound proofing is off the chart and every amenity, from projection TV to Heirloom custom beds, is absolutely state of the art. This is where Liz went to get her tan before the Oscars, where John Dean wrote his memoirs after Watergate and where Willie Shoemaker celebrated his 7,000th horse racing victory.

As if the ultimate in private accommodations isn't enough, there is also golf at La Mancha. Well, golf the La Mancha way, that is. In addition to tennis and tournament croquet, the secluded resort features "El Diablo," a nine-hole pitch and putt warm up course with two regulation practice greens. Another reason for staying at La Mancha: they can get you on almost any golf course with a telephone call.

If it seems that golf permeates everything it touches in these desert communities, it is no mirage. There's no question that the area will eventually boast more than 100 golf courses.

Real estate developments such as Desert Island and Mission Hills in Rancho Mirage, Lake La Quinta and Brock Desert Fairways in La Quinta, the Vintage Club in Indian Wells and Big Horn in Palm Desert are ultra-luxurious, secure and well-located. And all are golf oriented.

Big Horn, for example, is a Westinghouse Desert Community plan related to Coral Springs near Fort Lauderdale and Pelican Bay and Pelican Nest in Naples, Florida—individual residences within what they call a "golfer's golf club." Expect membership on the golf side to be separate from the condo or detached home, but know in advance that golf surrounds it all.

The major builder, Sunrise Company, has built nearly 7,000 homes in the Coachella Valley in the last 20 years. All are golf communities, and there is another preparing to open in early 1993: Indian Ridge Country Club in Palm Desert. Plans include two Arnold Palmer championship courses to accompany home sites on 640 acres. Sales began in early 1992.

Parades, new golf course homes, new golf courses, serious golf tournaments, social golf tournaments, endless play on endless courses, special summer golf passes—wow! Golf is certainly on a killer pace, but even the Coachella Valley takes a break from the game once in awhile.

Each fall, usually from mid-September into October, a majority of the courses shut down for reseeding. And then it's golf as usual starting in November—just in time for the golf cart parade. And then the Skins, and then the Hope, and then the Sinatra, and then the Dinah, and then the...

Typically, when golfers die, their pals think of them as passing on to the big golf course in the sky, for surely heaven is the ideal 18-hole challenge. Until that final day, however, they may want to settle for Palm Springs and the Coachella Valley. It's got to be the next best thing.

# Ten Confidence Builders For Beginners

by Janet Coles

One of the greatest challenges I've faced when working with students, especially beginners, is helping them maintain their enthusiasm for playing the game. Often new players, particularly women, feel intimidated during the early stages of the learning process.

Here are 10 suggestions to help maintain your enthusiasm while playing golf:

**1. Set your pace in relationship to the group in front of you, not the group behind you.**

The Rules of Golf state that you are responsible for maintaining pace with the group ahead of you and for not falling more than one hole behind. If you are more than one hole behind, you should offer to let the group behind you play through. Then relax, and get ready to play.

**2. Hurry between shots, but do not hurry your shot.**

Concentrate on getting to your next shot as soon as possible; however, once you arrive take time to think about your shot, make the proper club selection, then set-up and swing smoothly.

**3. When it's your turn, be ready to hit your shot.**

During the time other players in your group are preparing and hitting their shots, it is best for you to be figuring your yardage, selecting your club and planning your shot. Then, when it is your turn, you are ready to play.

**4. Play the course when it is least congested.**

Consider late afternoon rounds of golf when there are fewer people playing. Most players who are playing at off-hours are not rushing to finish and are more accepting of beginning players.

**5. Begin by playing with players of the same skill level and begin by playing just nine holes.**

If at all possible, play with friends who will be understanding and supportive. And don't think you have to play 18 holes or even nine. Play just a few holes to start out and then increase the number as your skill and confidence increase. Also, don't feel you have to keep score!

**6. To build confidence, play the same course often and to start, play a course of lesser difficulty.**

As a beginner you may feel the "perfect" course has no wind, no trees, no sand, no water. This may be difficult to find; however, a place to start would be an executive course which typically has shorter yardage with few hazards. To build confidence play this type of course often.

**7. Focus on your target, not the fact that you are the target of on-lookers.**

First-hole jitters are common to all players. You are not alone. To overcome this tendency focus more attention on your target. Concentrate on relaxing and let it rip!

**8. As you become more comfortable begin to play with more advanced players.**

As you improve your game and feel more confident on the golf course, choose players, men or women, who encourage your progress and challenge your skills.

**9. To be ready to play, be physically fit.**

Remember, physical fitness is essential. As you play more you will recognize the importance of physical endurance. Make this your goal: finish the 18th with the same energy as you played hole number one.

**10. Have fun!**

Golf is a game. Do not be distracted by mechanics or shots that are not perfect. With time, practice and patience you will improve. Enjoy the challenge of this process. Above all else, remember that golf is a game to played, not labored over.

# Golf Clubs: The Ultimate Passion In Collecting

by Michael Roseto

As the general interest in collecting golf antiques and memorabilia continues to boom throughout a diversified world, it's predictable that there is an equally diverse range of specialties and types of collectors.

There are hobbyists, historians, commercial and home designers, most certainly the investor, and more frequently the newcomer. What they collect ranges from old clubs, balls, printed materials, porcelains and silver, trophies, art and posters, and any kind of tidbit that has become part of the game.

Typically, collectors approaching their hobby with true zeal often find it necessary to funnel their efforts in one specific direction: the golf club. It's the collectors of golf clubs who have the most sustaining passion for their hobby or investment.

The development of the golf club, in contrast to the golf ball, took many years and many turns which resulted in hundreds of variations. There are different sizes of lofts of clubs, a variety of manufacturers and a tremendous number of patented clubs.

Although there is as varied a price structure on golf clubs as there is in types of clubs offered or purchased, collectors should consider these sales at major British and U.S. golf auctions:

• In 1992 a rare 18th century square toe iron circa 1760, with a concave face and a replaced grip and shaft, sold in the U.S. for $77,000. The club was used by early Scottish golfers at a time when quite heavy irons and very wide shafts were necessary.

• Of modest condition, a Hugh Philp (the first professional at St. Andrews) long nose putter dating circa 1845 sold for $88,000. A Philp driver or spoon in superb condition would most likely fetch between $10,000 and $18,000.

• At that same auction in the summer of '92, an 1830 Rut Iron sold as low as $1,200. The cleeks can go for about $800, at the lower level.

But antique clubs, much like other collectors' precious items, can fluctuate in value. Collectors must be aware that the market can change dramatically in a short period of time. But investment speculation is not the only reason for collecting, so don't stop going to garage sales, flea markets, auctions or antique shops in hopes of making a discovery that just might be an $80,000 club.

So, how does one start a collection? If you have a family heirloom, or perhaps a golf item that has been handed down (it doesn't necessarily have to be a golf club), keep it. Whether it is an old book, painting, unusual club, silver trophy or autograph, build your collection around that personal piece. That's your keystone to a successful collection.

Skip an appraisal of that first—sometimes inherited—golf collectible. The value may be in its personal worth, not in the price it may bring. Besides, if you're starting a collection, you should not be planning on selling it—at least not initially.

Research the background of the golf items you plan to collect. There are some excellent books that will assist you. Titles that should be in every collector's library include "Golf in the Making" and "The History of an Obsession," both by David Stirk; "A History of Golf," by Robert Browning; "The Game of Golf and the Printed Word 1566-1985," by Joseph S.F. Murdoch; and "Art of Golf 1754-1940," by Gary H. Schwartz.

Do not speculate. Golf collecting should be a personal matter, and should not be based on the speculation that a particular item will increase in value. Leave that to the experts.

Through collecting, you will discover a whole new world of golf, whether you're an accomplished player or a beginner.

# There's More Than One Way To Play Golf On The Monterey Peninsula

by Ray A. March

Granted, it is the goal of every golfer to some day play Pebble Beach, site of three U.S. Open Championships, but for the locals who live and play in its shadow, there are some attractive alternatives to this mecca.

There are 17 18-hole courses on the Monterey Peninsula and one nine-hole, par-3 course. Of the regular-length courses, only three are actually private layouts while five fall generally into the resort category and six are fully public. Another three are under military jurisdiction.

Considering that Pebble Beach will more than challenge the average golfer (if he or she doesn't run out of balls first), the wise golfer will try out the Monterey Peninsula's safer golf courses before challenging Pebble. Three of the more receptive layouts are the following:

**Old Del Monte.** This is the oldest course in continuous use west of the Mississippi but, because of excellent care, it does not show its age. This is a public, 18-hole course rated 69.5 with a slope rating of 119 from the regular tees.

Located in Monterey, Old Del Monte is a meandering, hilly layout with lots of trees and tight doglegs. The par-3 No. 14 and par-4 No. 18 are considered exceptionally difficult holes by locals who know.

**Pacific Grove Golf Course.** There are unsubstantiated reports that the original nine holes at this municipal course were designed by Jack Neville, who laid out Pebble Beach back in 1918-19. Even if unfounded, there are similarities between the two courses. The back nine, while not clinging to ocean bluffs like Pebble, has a distinct Scottish-links flavor.

The course is in the city of Pacific Grove. The front nine weaves through the forest and portions of residential areas. For two distinct styles of play—similar to the inland and sand dune character of Spyglass Hill Golf Course—Pacific Grove Golf Course is a great nine-hole or 18-hole experience. It is rated 66.3 with a slope of 115 from the regular tees.

**Rancho Canada Golf Course (East).** Beginning and intermediate golfers will be well received at Rancho's hospitable East Course. This is a layout frequently recommended by local teaching pros because it won't totally destroy one's confidence. The course is rated 67.3 with a slope of 111 from the regular tees.

Rancho Canada is in lower Carmel Valley, an easy drive from Carmel or other Monterey Peninsula locations. There are four lakes on the East Course, but think nothing of it.

# Golfing the Wine Country

by Pat Sullivan

To golf or not to golf. That's never really the question for the true believer. The question for the California golfer in the advanced stage of devotion to this royal and ancient game usually boils down to setting.

Whether 'tis nobler to play Palm Springs or Pebble Beach, Pasatiempo or Pismo Beach, the choices are endless. And, by the way, let's make sure to get reservations for dinner at that hot new restaurant before teeing up.

In essence, all of California is divided into three parts when it comes to destination golf: the warm Southern California desert, the cool Monterey Peninsula coastline and Northern California's temperate valleys, more popularly known as "Wine Country." This story is about that last area, which—with the introduction of the whimsical, new Club Shakespeare—has become even more alluring than ever.

Other improved courses in the North Bay, such as Sonoma Golf Club and Bodega Harbour Golf Links, have added to the growing sense that the area has a huge golfing future in the '90s and beyond.

In the past, if one were searching for a championship test with all the amenities, golf in Napa Valley pretty much meant Silverado Country Club. Opened in 1955, Silverado rapidly became a focus of North Bay golf through its association with the PGA Tour, serving as the site of the annual Kaiser International and Anheuser-Busch Classic Tournaments through 1980.

Today, Silverado remains a premier resort and conference center, annually scoring high in magazine polls of "the Best in the West." And it has assured its position as a golf institution in Northern California by becoming the site of the Senior PGA Tour's Transamerica Senior Championship, which will be played for the fifth time in October 1993.

How well do the pros like Silverado? During the 1992 event, at least one referred to it as "heaven," among other highly complimentary terms.

But the wheels of progress keep turning, and this year, at least, Silverado will have to share the North Bay spotlight with a new entrant in the world-class golf arena, Club Shakespeare.

The private, 18-hole course, designed by Algie Pully, is located at the Chardonnay Golf Club, which has been in operation since 1987. Nine of Chardonnay's 27 holes—the Vineyards Course—were appropriated to form nine of Shakespeare's 18, and a spectacular new nine were added.

While Chardonnay's original 27 holes sat amid rolling hills and vineyards, the new nine is a departure, featuring a waterfall, native stone rock walls and impressive views. (You can almost see Restaurant Row in Yountville.)

The signature hole for the new nine—and for Club Shakespeare—is the highly unusual 13th, a 163-yard par-3. The elevated tee box is situated next to a soothing waterfall; the shot, however, is not so soothing. It's to an island green, and in the afternoon you must play directly into what is at times quite strong wind. The 13th is a golf hole each player will recall vividly for years.

Here are a few other examples from Shakespearean Golf 101, taken from the official Shakespearean Club's document on the layout:

**No. 1 (King Lear)**, 391 yards, par-4: "The three bunkers on this good-sized golf hole signify the relationship Lear, King of Britain, held with his three daughters, Goneril, Regan and Cordelia. The green-side bunker sits precariously close to the heart of the green and is thus named after Cordelia, who held a close bond with her father even after being disinherited."

**No. 4 (Venus and Adonis)**, 429 yards, par-4: "The prodigious rock out-croppings (Venus and Adonis) on either side of the fairway provide a narrow landing area for tee shots."

**No. 7 (Romeo and Juliet)**, 569 yards, par-5: "The two featured lakes represent young, passionate lovers, Romeo and Juliet. A well-placed drive leaves a demanding shot between the bodies of water hugging both sides of the fairway. A naive attempt on the approach will painfully lead you to tragedy."

**No. 13 (A Midsummer Night's Dream)**, 163 yards, par-3: "Named after the story of fantasy and fairy tales. Many tales will be told about this par-3."

**No. 18 (All's Well That End's Well)**, 435 yards, par-4: "All's well that ends well only for those who play it smart here. A narrow shot off the tee opens up a tenuous approach shot over a much-heralded oak tree on this classic finishing hole."

Club Shakespeare also includes a 69-yard pitch-and-putt hole near the clubhouse, the better to settle ties and playoffs or to play for a round of drinks. The hole is modeled after one at Club Shakespeare in Sapporo, Japan. Sister Shakespeare clubs are being built in Atlanta, Georgia and Izmir, Turkey. Club Shakespeare and the Chardonnay Club are strictly golf-oriented; the plunking of fuzzy tennis balls will not be heard during one's round. No lodging is available on site, but staff members will direct visitors to a variety of bed and breakfasts and several hotels within easy driving distance. The toll free number is (800) 788-0136.

No trip to the area would be complete without a visit to the wineries of Napa Valley, Sonoma Valley or the Russian River. Guidebooks are everywhere. One might even discover a small boutique winery in one's own name, as I did. At the Sullivan Winery, the daughter of the winemaker broke off her delightful practice of the harp—we could hear her clearly from the driveway—to pour a Cabernet for my wife and me. An unforgettable experience.

For an especially memorable time, try the Napa Valley Wine Train. It offers an enhanced dining experience during a slow, three-house roundtrip up and down the spine of the valley from downtown Napa. The Winemaker's Dinner Series includes tastings and explanations of the wine-making process, in addition to a sumptuous, multi-course, gourmet meal.

Railroad buffs will get an added kick from the experience. The train's dining cars are restored Pullmans from the early 20th century, the Golden Age of American railroading. For information on Wine Train luncheons and dinners, call (800) 427-4124.

For travelers continuing on, the refurbished Sonoma Golf Club is definitely worth a stop. Opened in 1925, it was redesigned by Robert Muir Graves and reopened two years ago. Sonoma maintains a working relationship with the luxurious Sonoma Mission Inn and Spa. For information, call (707) 996-0300.

Farther west, across Highway 101, is the scenic, rural area stretching toward the Sonoma coast and Bodega Harbour Golf Links, featuring 94 (!) pot bunkers. For tee times, call (707) 875-3538.

To golf or not to golf? In the Napa Valley, that's never the question.

# Northern California Golf Courses

# NORTHERN CALIFORNIA COURSES

The golf courses of Northern California are remarkable for the sheer diversity of their landscape. In the upper reaches of the state, near Crescent City and the border with Oregon, are courses which play through huge stands of ancient redwoods, subject to eerie winter mists and rain—a most unusual atmosphere for golf!

Then, over near the Klamath River, you can play golf and then cast into one of the best fly-fishing rivers in the West.

You can play a relaxed game of golf in a place you've probably never heard of—like Weaverville, Montague, or Fall River Mills—and then tell all your friends about one of the best-kept golfing secrets in the state.

On the other hand, as you enter the more heavily-traveled resort areas, such as the Napa Valley, you can find courses of unexcelled manicure and hotels with decided panache.

Of course the San Francisco Bay area boasts the prestigious Presidio, Olympic, San Francisco, and Burlingame golf clubs, tracts with more than an abundance of history, which count the movers and shakers of Northern California among their members today as they have for generations.

That's not to say that public golf is not popular or good—it is. Public access layouts such as Arbuckle, Graeagle, Edgewood (Tahoe), and Ancil Hoffman (near Sacramento) receive abundant praise and enthusiastic support.

Sierra courses, though not open year-round because of weather, are among the most scenic courses in the world—and they can challenge you severely with their slopes and lies.

In all, it is fair to say that the courses of Northern California operate at a far more relaxed pace than many of the more impacted courses you'll find in other parts of the state. Combine that with the fact that many Northern California courses offer entirely affordable tee times as well, and a golf excursion through the north becomes quite an attractive proposition.

# NOR-CAL BY AREA

### (MAP, COURSES, PAGES)



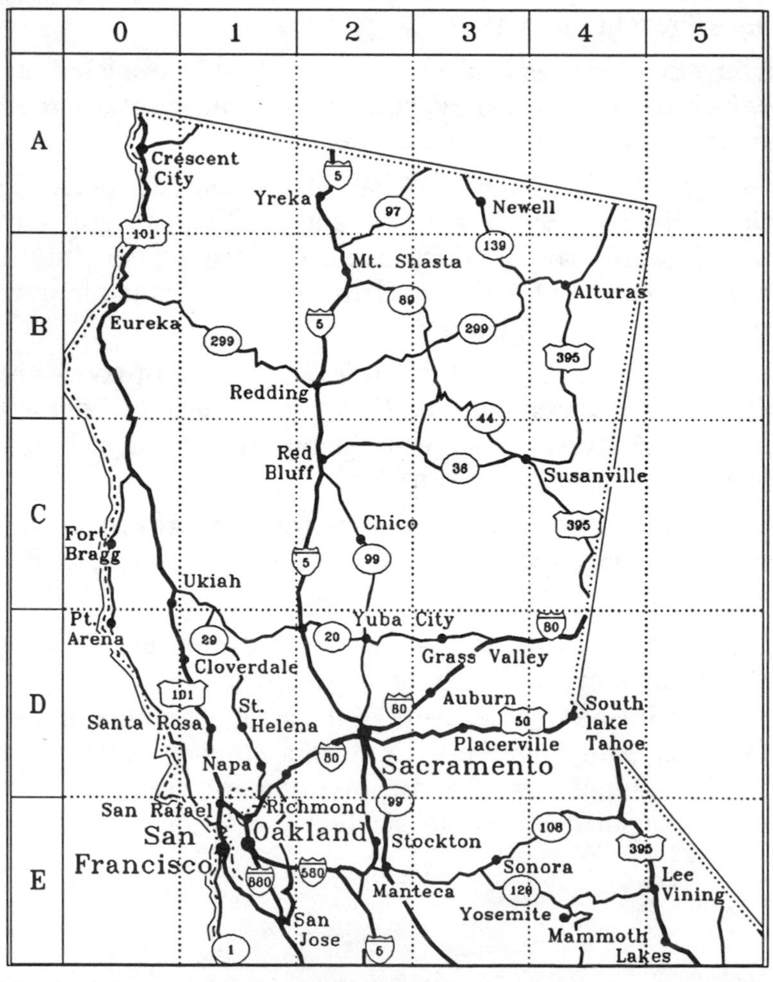

NORTHERN

# NOR-CAL BY CITY

**(CITY and MAP PAGE)**

# MAP AO
(2 COURSES)

PAGES.......32-35

NOR-CAL MAP.....see page 30
adjoining maps
NORTH ........................no map
EAST ............................no map
SOUTH (B0) .........see page 42
WEST ............................no map

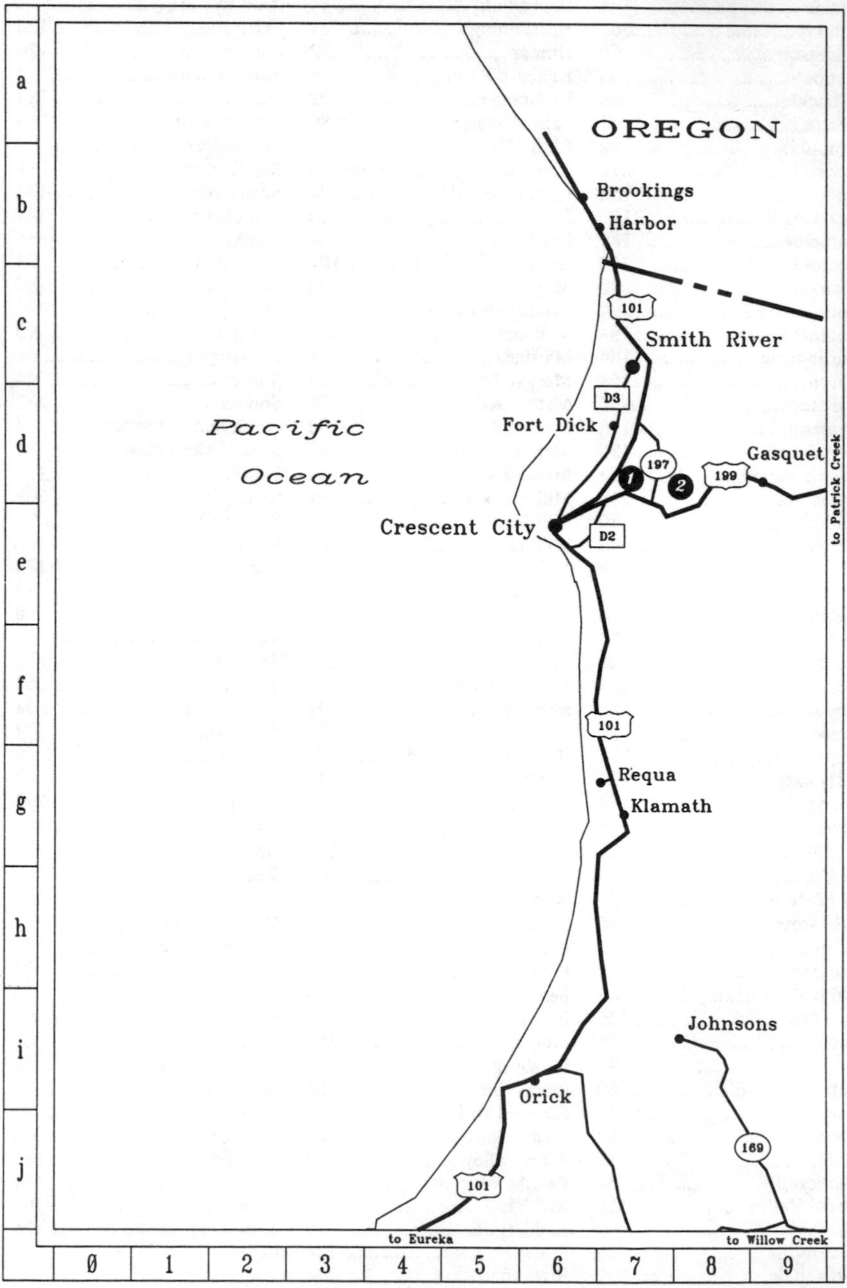

OREGON
Brookings
Harbor
101
Smith River
D3
Fort Dick
Pacific Ocean
197
1
2
199
Gasquet
to Patrick Creek
Crescent City
D2
101
Requa
Klamath
Johnsons
Orick
169
101
to Eureka
to Willow Creek

a b c d e f g h i j

0 1 2 3 4 5 6 7 8 9

# KINGS VALLEY GOLF COURSE

**Course 1**
MAP A0 grid d7



***Course information:*** This public course has nine holes. See card below for yardage and rating information.

***Play policy and fees:*** Green fees are $4 for nine holes and $7 for 18 on weekdays, $5 and $8 on weekends.

***Location:*** From Highway 101 in Crescent City, drive east on Highway 199 to Kings Valley Road North. Turn left on Lesina Road and follow it to the course. The course is 18 miles south of the Oregon line.

***Course description:*** Situated in a country setting, this short course is flat with only two par-4s. It's a good course for the average player. Redwoods abound and it's walkable. The men's course record is 49, held by Jim Bantrup, and the women's record is 58, held by Phyllis Hall.

**1965**
3030 Lesina Road
Crescent City, CA 95531

Pro shop (707) 464-2886

- ✓ **driving range**
- ✓ **practice greens**
- ✓ **power cart**
- ✓ **pull carts**
- ✓ **golf club rental**
- locker rooms
- showers
- executive course
- accommodations
- ✓ **food and beverages**
- ✓ **clubhouse**

**Keith Fields**
Owner/Manager

**Scott Fields**
Superintendent

| Hole | 1 | 2 | 3 | 4 | 5 | 6 | 7 | 8 | 9 | Out | BLUE | Rating: -- |
|---|---|---|---|---|---|---|---|---|---|---|---|---|
| BLUE | - | - | - | - | - | - | - | - | - | - | | Slope: -- |
| WHITE | 125 | 102 | 128 | 232 | 170 | 140 | 107 | 132 | 123 | 1259 | | |
| Par | 3 | 3 | 3 | 4 | 3 | 3 | 3 | 3 | 3 | 28 | WHITE | Rating: 51.8 |
| Handicap | 5 | 15 | 11 | 3 | 1 | 13 | 17 | 7 | 9 | x | | Slope: 70 |
| RED | 125 | 102 | 128 | 200 | 155 | 140 | 107 | 132 | 123 | 1212 | | |
| Par | 3 | 3 | 3 | 4 | 3 | 3 | 3 | 3 | 3 | 28 | RED | Rating: 54.1 |
| Handicap | 5 | 15 | 13 | 1 | 3 | 11 | 17 | 7 | 9 | x | | Slope: 77 |

| Hole | 10 | 11 | 12 | 13 | 14 | 15 | 16 | 17 | 18 | In | Totals | |
|---|---|---|---|---|---|---|---|---|---|---|---|---|
| BLUE | - | - | - | - | - | - | - | - | - | - | BLUE | -- |
| WHITE | 125 | 102 | 128 | 232 | 170 | 140 | 107 | 132 | 123 | 1259 | WHITE | 2518 |
| Par | 3 | 3 | 3 | 4 | 3 | 3 | 3 | 3 | 3 | 28 | Par | 56 |
| Handicap | 6 | 16 | 12 | 4 | 2 | 14 | 18 | 8 | 10 | x | | |
| RED | 125 | 102 | 128 | 200 | 155 | 140 | 107 | 132 | 123 | 1212 | RED | 2424 |
| Par | 3 | 3 | 3 | 4 | 3 | 3 | 3 | 3 | 3 | 28 | Par | 56 |
| Handicap | 6 | 16 | 14 | 2 | 4 | 12 | 18 | 8 | 10 | x | | |

# DEL NORTE GOLF COURSE

**Course 2**
MAP A0 grid d8

***Course information:*** This semi-private course has nine holes. Par is 71 for 18 holes. The course is 6,117 yards and rated 66.5 from the regular tees. The slope rating is 106. Women's tees are 6,117 yards and rated 74.0 from the forward tees. The slope rating is 124.

***Play policy and fees:*** Green fees are $8 for nine holes and $13 for 18 holes weekdays, $10 and $15 weekends. Carts are $8 for nine holes, $15 for 18. Outside play is accepted, although calling ahead for a time is recommended.

***Location:*** From Highway 101 in Crescent City, drive east across the Smith River on Highway 199. Turn right on Club Drive and head north to the course.

***Course description:*** Del Norte, the northwestern most course in the state, is cut into a beautiful setting with redwoods lining each fairway and two creeks winding back and forth across the course. Number four is known as the Bell Hole since golfers up ahead must ring a bell to inform those on the tee that they are out of the way. It's best to call ahead for a tee time in the summer, when the course is effectively closed on three weekends for member tournaments. The men's course record is 64, held by Chris Wegand and Gary Parkhurst. The women's course record is 72, held by Vivienne Moran (72).

130 Club Drive
Crescent City, CA 95531

Pro shop (707) 458-3214

- ✓ **driving range**
- ✓ **practice greens**
- ✓ **power carts**
- ✓ **pull carts**
- ✓ **golf club rental**
- locker rooms
- showers
- executive course
- accommodations
- ✓ **food and beverages**
- ✓ **clubhouse**

**Owen Westbrook**
Manager

**Dan Blackburn**
Superintendent

MAP ON PAGE 32

# MAP A2
(4 COURSES)

PAGES.......36-39

NOR-CAL MAP......................30
adjoining maps
NORTH ..........................no map
EAST (A3).............see page 40
SOUTH (B2) .........see page 50
WEST............................no map

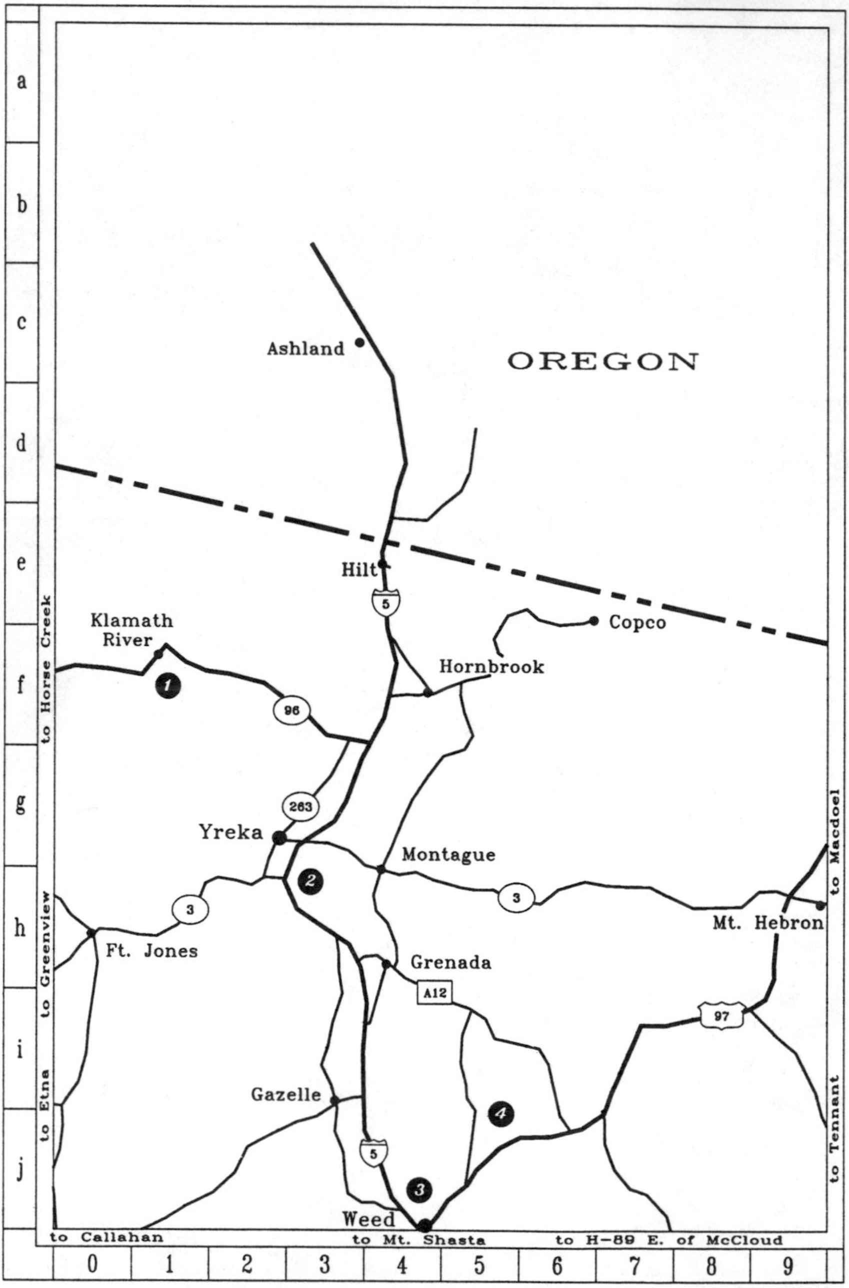

## EAGLE NEST GOLF COURSE

**Course 1**
MAP A2 grid f1

*Course information:* This public course has nine holes. Par is 64 for 18 holes. The course is 3,634 yards and rated 58.7 from the regular tees. The slope rating is 96. Women's tees are 3,634 yards and rated 61.1. The slope rating is 99.

*Play policy and fees:* Green fees are $10 weekdays and $15 weekends.

*Location:* From Yreka, drive eight miles north on Interstate 5. Take Highway 96 west to the city of Klamath River. On the east side of town, take the Lockhaven exit south across the Klamath River to Klamath River Road. The course is on the right.

*Course description:* Located just south of the Oregon border, this course is tricky with numerous trees and overhanging limbs that make fairways even narrower. The sixth hole is the most scenic, following alongside the Klamath River.

**1971**

22112 Klamath River Road
Klamath River, CA 96050

Pro shop (916) 465-2424
Clubhouse (916) 465-2277

- driving range
- ✓ **practice greens**
- power carts
- ✓ **pull carts**
- golf club rental
- locker rooms
- showers
- executive course
- accommodations
- food and beverages
- clubhouse

**Jeremy Bonnano**
Manager

**Nuno Bonnano**
Superintendent

## SHASTA VALLEY GOLF COURSE

**Course 2**
MAP A2 grid h3

*Course information:* This public course has nine holes. Par is 36 for nine holes. The course is 6,000 yards for 18 holes and rated 67.7 from the regular tees. The slope rating is 110. Women's tees are 5,435 yards and rated 69.4 from the regular tees. The slope rating is 105.

*Play policy and fees:* Green fees are $8 for nine holes and $12 for 18 holes weekdays, and $9 for nine holes and $14 for 18 holes weekends. Carts are $8 for nine holes and $16 for 18 holes. Shirts and shoes must be worn in the clubhouse.

*Location:* From Interstate 5 in Yreka, drive east on Highway 3 to Montague. Exit south onto Golf Course Road.

*Course description:* There's a lot of water to contend with on this short course, so there's a premium on accuracy. The course is the home of the Yreka City Golf Tournament, which takes place in September. The men's course record is 68, set in 1979 by host pro Paul Kirchen and tied by Darien Tucker in 1991, and the women's record is 72.

500 Golf Course Road
Montague, CA 96064

Pro shop (916) 842-2302

- ✓ **driving range**
- ✓ **practice greens**
- ✓ **power carts**
- ✓ **pull carts**
- ✓ **golf club rental**
- locker rooms
- showers
- executive course
- accommodations
- ✓ **food and beverages**
- ✓ **clubhouse**

**Paul Kirchen**
Professional

**John Howe**
Superintendent

# WEED GOLF COURSE

**Course 3**
MAP A2 grid j4

***Course information:*** This semi-private course has nine holes. See card below for yardage and rating information.

***Play policy and fees:*** Outside play is accepted. Summer green fees are $12 for nine holes and $15 for 18 holes on weekdays, and $14 for nine holes and $17 for 18 holes weekends. After 3 p.m. green fees are $8 for unlimited play. Carts are $10 for nine holes and $15 for 18 holes. Shoes and shirts must be worn. The course is open year-round depending on weather conditions. Winter rates are $8 and $10 for 18 holes on weekdays, $10 and $12 on weekends.

***Location:*** From Weed, drive one half mile north on Interstate 5. Take the North Weed exit. You will run right into the golf course.

***Course description:*** This rolling course, bordered by trees and a creek, has magnificent views of Mount Shasta and the Eddy Mountains. The greens are fast and water comes into play on four of the nine holes. The first hole, a tricky, 327-yard par-4, doglegs left and tests players from the very start. The course is the site of the Siskiyou Open Invitational each August. The men's course record is 62.

**1929**

PO Box 204
Weed, CA 96094

27730 Old Edgewood Road
Weed, CA 96094

Pro shop (916) 938-9971
Clubhouse (916) 235-2640

- driving range
- ✓ **practice greens**
- ✓ **power carts**
- ✓ **pull carts**
- ✓ **golf club rental**
- locker rooms
- showers
- executive course
- accommodations
- ✓ **food and beverages**
- ✓ **clubhouse**

**Dixie Nehring**
Manager

**Donald Nehring**
Superintendent

| Hole | 1 | 2 | 3 | 4 | 5 | 6 | 7 | 8 | 9 | Out | BLUE | Rating: -- |
|---|---|---|---|---|---|---|---|---|---|---|---|---|
| BLUE | - | - | - | - | - | - | - | - | - | - | | Slope: -- |
| WHITE | 327 | 151 | 489 | 155 | 327 | 365 | 491 | 304 | 187 | 2796 | | |
| Par | 4 | 3 | 5 | 3 | 4 | 4 | 5 | 4 | 3 | 35 | WHITE | Rating: 65.5 |
| Handicap | 5 | 17 | 3 | 13 | 11 | 7 | 1 | 15 | 9 | x | | Slope: 105 |
| RED | 327 | 129 | 418 | 133 | 325 | 300 | 404 | 238 | 163 | 2437 | | |
| Par | 4 | 3 | 5 | 3 | 4 | 4 | 5 | 4 | 3 | 35 | RED | Rating: 68.0 |
| Handicap | 5 | 17 | 1 | 15 | 7 | 9 | 3 | 11 | 13 | x | | Slope: 113 |

| Hole | 10 | 11 | 12 | 13 | 14 | 15 | 16 | 17 | 18 | In | Totals | |
|---|---|---|---|---|---|---|---|---|---|---|---|---|
| BLUE | - | - | - | - | - | - | - | - | - | - | BLUE | -- |
| WHITE | 327 | 132 | 468 | 134 | 327 | 329 | 491 | 304 | 161 | 2673 | WHITE | 5469 |
| Par | 4 | 3 | 5 | 3 | 4 | 4 | 5 | 4 | 3 | 35 | Par | 70 |
| Handicap | 6 | 18 | 4 | 14 | 8 | 12 | 2 | 16 | 10 | x | | |
| RED | 329 | 145 | 418 | 72 | 322 | 286 | 404 | 238 | 161 | 2375 | RED | 4812 |
| Par | 4 | 3 | 5 | 3 | 4 | 4 | 5 | 4 | 3 | 35 | Par | 70 |
| Handicap | 6 | 16 | 2 | 18 | 8 | 10 | 4 | 12 | 14 | x | | |

# LAKE SHASTINA GOLF COURSE

**Course 4**
MAP A2 grid j5

**1973**
**Robert Trent Jones, Jr.**

5925 Country Club Drive
Weed, CA 96094

Pro shop (916) 938-3201

- ✓ **driving range**
- ✓ **practice greens**
- ✓ **power carts**
- pull carts
- ✓ **golf club rental**
- locker rooms
- showers
- ✓ **executive course**
- ✓ **accommodations**
- ✓ **food and beverages**
- ✓ **clubhouse**

**Dave Schoenmann**
Professional

**Ed Irwin**
Superintendent

***Course information:*** This resort course has 27 holes. Par is 72 for the 18 hole course. The second is a short, nine-hole Scottish links course.

The 18-hole layout is 6,594 yards and rated 70.9 with a slope of 122 from the gold tees. See card below for additional yardage and rating information.

The Scottish links course is 3,009 yards and rated 34.7 from the regular tees. The slope rating is 52.

***Play policy and fees:*** Green fees are $36 for 18 holes and $9 for the Scottish links course. Carts are $12 per person. Reservations are accepted 30 days in advance. Summer rules are played here year-round.

***Location:*** From Interstate 5, take the exit for Weed. Drive four miles east on Highway 97 and turn left on Big Springs Road.

***Course description:*** These courses, designed by Robert Trent Jones, Jr., are located at the base of Mount Shasta. There are spectacular views from both courses. The large course is sprawling and long with five lakes. It's challenging and requires proficiency with irons. The 16th hole is one of the toughest par-3s in Northern California, measuring 209 yards over water. PGA Tour pro Peter Jacobsen earned his first pro win here at the 1976 Northern California Open. Craig Howard of Redding holds the course record at 63. The course is usually closed for about two months in the winter.

| Hole | 1 | 2 | 3 | 4 | 5 | 6 | 7 | 8 | 9 | Out | BLUE | Rating: 72.6 |
|---|---|---|---|---|---|---|---|---|---|---|---|---|
| BLUE | 562 | 345 | 181 | 402 | 342 | 442 | 399 | 190 | 572 | 3435 | | Slope: 126 |
| WHITE | 538 | 322 | 159 | 378 | 302 | 401 | 377 | 145 | 525 | 3147 | | |
| Par | 5 | 4 | 3 | 4 | 4 | 4 | 4 | 3 | 5 | 36 | WHITE | Rating: 69.5 |
| Handicap | 5 | 11 | 17 | 1 | 13 | 3 | 7 | 15 | 9 | x | | Slope: 119 |
| RED | 496 | 297 | 123 | 313 | 283 | 374 | 339 | 97 | 457 | 2779 | | |
| Par | 5 | 4 | 3 | 4 | 4 | 4 | 4 | 3 | 5 | 36 | RED | Rating: 70.2 |
| Handicap | 1 | 11 | 17 | 7 | 13 | 5 | 9 | 15 | 3 | x | | Slope: 109 |

| Hole | 10 | 11 | 12 | 13 | 14 | 15 | 16 | 17 | 18 | In | Totals | |
|---|---|---|---|---|---|---|---|---|---|---|---|---|
| BLUE | 596 | 222 | 444 | 190 | 592 | 337 | 209 | 412 | 532 | 3534 | BLUE | 6969 |
| WHITE | 566 | 157 | 413 | 141 | 520 | 300 | 183 | 360 | 504 | 3144 | WHITE | 6291 |
| Par | 5 | 3 | 4 | 3 | 5 | 4 | 3 | 4 | 5 | 36 | Par | 72 |
| Handicap | 2 | 18 | 4 | 16 | 6 | 14 | 10 | 8 | 12 | x | | |
| RED | 540 | 106 | 344 | 111 | 491 | 260 | 142 | 303 | 454 | 2751 | RED | 5530 |
| Par | 5 | 3 | 4 | 3 | 5 | 4 | 3 | 4 | 5 | 36 | Par | 72 |
| Handicap | 2 | 18 | 8 | 16 | 4 | 12 | 14 | 10 | 6 | x | | |

MAP ON PAGE 36

# MAP A3
(1 COURSE)

PAGES.......40-41

NOR-CAL MAP.....see page 30
adjoining maps
NORTH .........................no map
EAST ............................no map
SOUTH (B3) .........see page 60
WEST (A2)...........see page 36

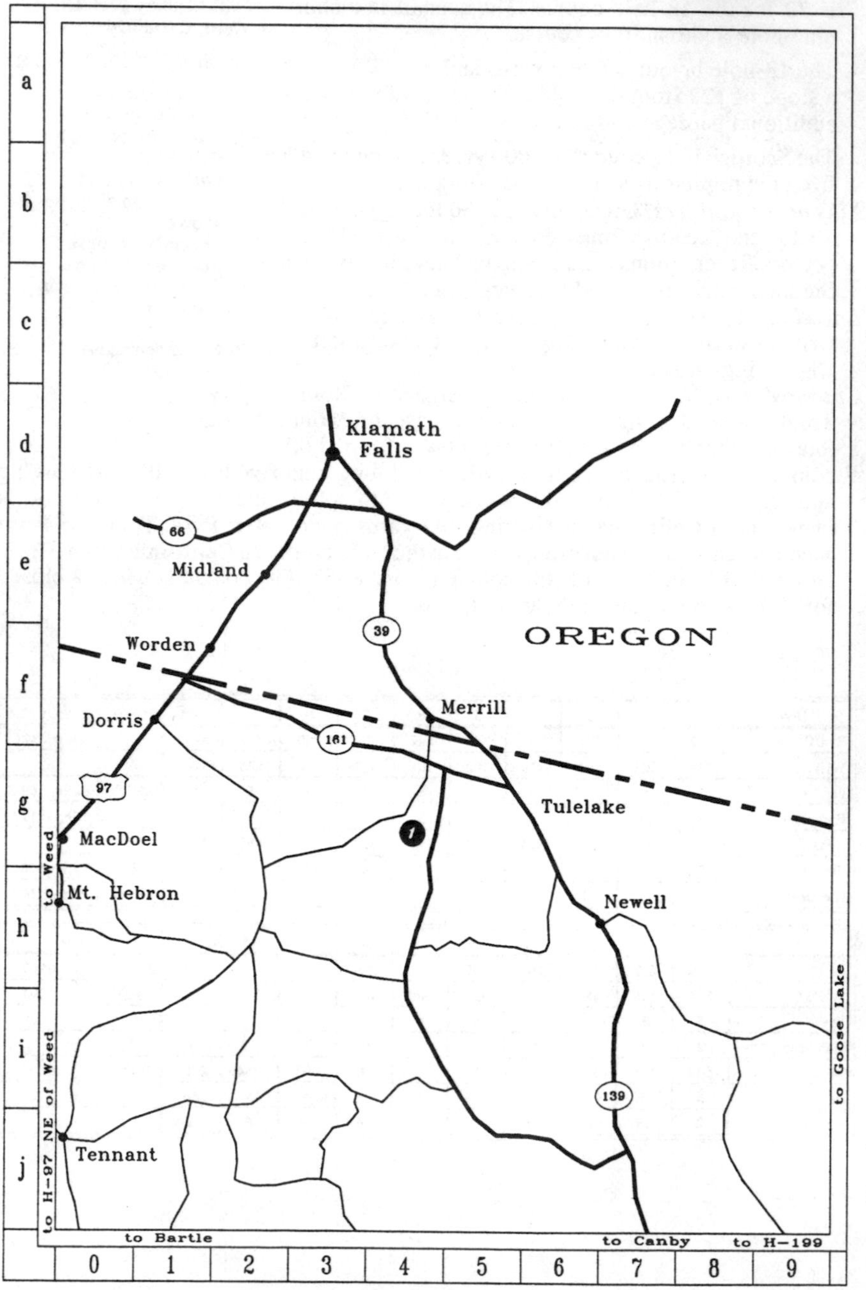

a b c d e f g h i j

0 1 2 3 4 5 6 7 8 9

Klamath Falls
66
Midland
39
Worden
OREGON
Merrill
Dorris
161
97
Tulelake
1
MacDoel
Mt. Hebron
Newell
139
Tennant
to Weed
to H-97 NE of Weed
to Bartle
to Canby
to H-199
to Goose Lake

# INDIAN CAMP GOLF COURSE

**Course 1**
MAP A3 grid g4

***Course information:*** This public course has nine holes. See card below for yardage information.

***Play policy and fees:*** Green fees are $5 for nine holes and $4 for the second nine holes. There is a special $15 all-day fee.

***Location:*** From Tulelake, take Highway 139 north to Highway 161 (State Line Road). Turn west onto Highway 161 and drive to Hill Road. Turn south (left) on Hill Road and drive to the course.

***Course description:*** Indian Camp is the northernmost golf course in California. As a matter of fact, it's less than 300 yards from the Oregon border. According to archaeologists, the course is on the site of an age-old hunting and fishing camp. It is said that Captain Jack of the Modoc Indian tribe fished and hunted here in the 1870s when he wasn't skirmishing with the U.S. Army. The course is mostly flat with scenic views and eight par-3 holes. The only par-4 is the 255-yard second hole.

**1982**
**Malcolm Crawford**

Box 46-A
Tulelake, CA 96134

Route 1
Tulelake, CA 96134

Pro shop (916) 667-2922

- driving range
- ✓ **practice greens**
- power carts
- ✓ **pull carts**
- ✓ **golf club rental**
- locker rooms
- showers
- ✓ **executive course**
- accommodations
- food and beverages
- clubhouse

**Dan Crawford**
Owner

**Jim Walker**
Manager/Superintendent

| Hole | 1 | 2 | 3 | 4 | 5 | 6 | 7 | 8 | 9 | Out | BLUE | Rating: -- |
|---|---|---|---|---|---|---|---|---|---|---|---|---|
| BLUE | - | - | - | - | - | - | - | - | - | - | | Slope: -- |
| WHITE | 179 | 255 | 153 | 186 | 146 | 100 | 180 | 157 | 156 | 1512 | | |
| Par | 3 | 4 | 3 | 3 | 3 | 3 | 3 | 3 | 3 | 28 | WHITE | Rating: -- |
| Handicap | - | - | - | - | - | - | - | - | - | x | | Slope: -- |
| RED | 169 | 225 | 153 | 160 | 146 | 100 | 155 | 157 | 156 | 1421 | | |
| Par | 3 | 4 | 3 | 3 | 3 | 3 | 3 | 3 | 3 | 28 | RED | Rating: -- |
| Handicap | - | - | - | - | - | - | - | - | - | x | | Slope: -- |

| Hole | 10 | 11 | 12 | 13 | 14 | 15 | 16 | 17 | 18 | In | Totals | |
|---|---|---|---|---|---|---|---|---|---|---|---|---|
| BLUE | - | - | - | - | - | - | - | - | - | - | BLUE | -- |
| WHITE | 179 | 255 | 153 | 186 | 146 | 100 | 180 | 157 | 156 | 1512 | WHITE | 3024 |
| Par | 3 | 4 | 3 | 3 | 3 | 3 | 3 | 3 | 3 | 28 | Par | 56 |
| Handicap | - | - | - | - | - | - | - | - | - | x | | |
| RED | 169 | 225 | 153 | 160 | 146 | 100 | 155 | 157 | 156 | 1512 | RED | 2933 |
| Par | 3 | 4 | 3 | 3 | 3 | 3 | 3 | 3 | 3 | 28 | Par | 56 |
| Handicap | - | - | - | - | - | - | - | - | - | x | | |

MAP ON PAGE 40

# MAP BO
(4 COURSES)

PAGES.......42-47

NOR-CAL MAP.....see page 30
adjoining maps
NORTH (A0).........see page 32
EAST (B1)............see page 48
SOUTH (C0).........see page 64
WEST............................no map

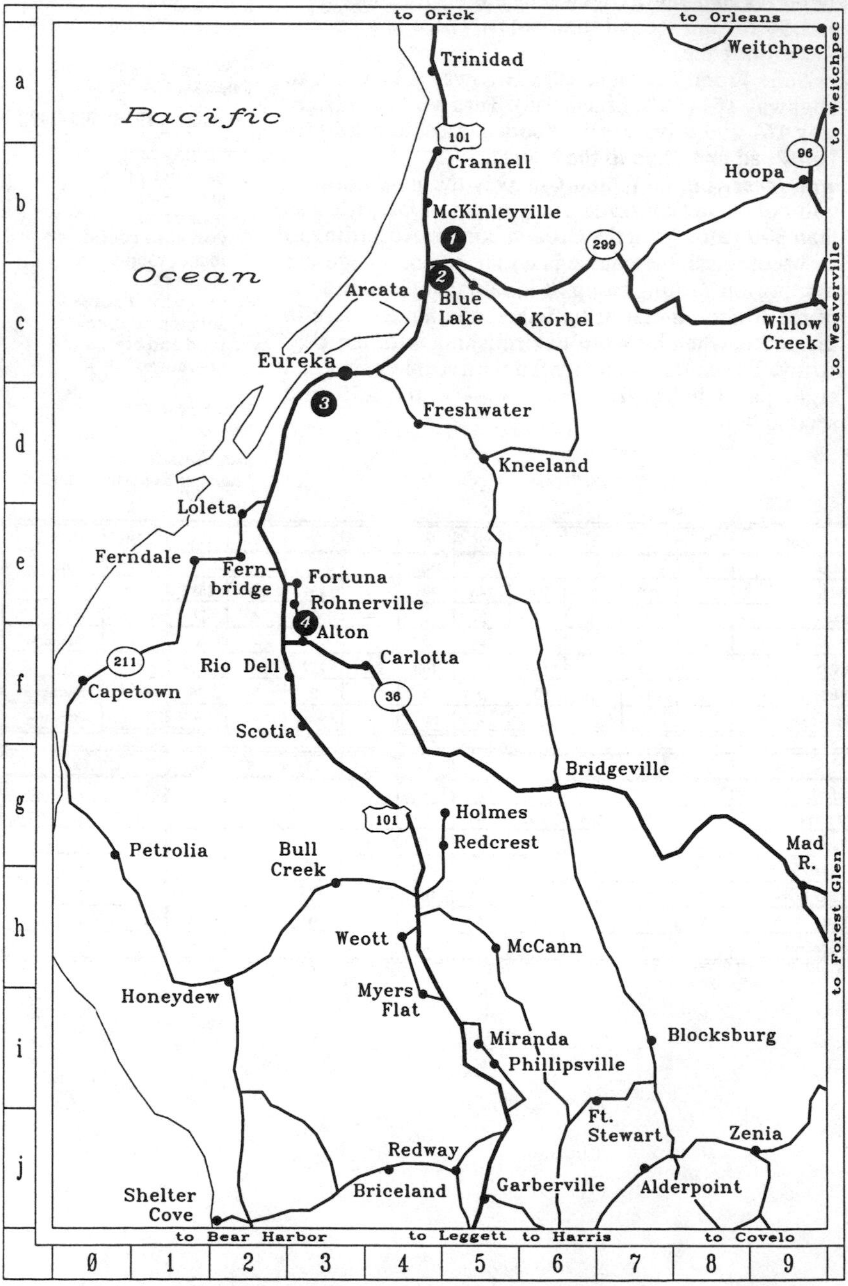

to Orick
to Orleans
Weitchpec
Trinidad
Pacific
101
Crannell
to Weitchpec
96
Hoopa
McKinleyville
1
299
2
Ocean
Arcata
Blue
Lake
Korbel
Willow
Creek
to Weaverville
Eureka
3
Freshwater
Kneeland
Loleta
Ferndale
Fern-
bridge
Fortuna
Rohnerville
4
Alton
Carlotta
211
Rio Dell
Capetown
36
Scotia
Bridgeville
101
Holmes
Redcrest
Mad
R.
Petrolia
Bull
Creek
to Forest Glen
Weott
McCann
Honeydew
Myers
Flat
Miranda
Blocksburg
Phillipsville
Ft.
Stewart
Zenia
Redway
Shelter
Cove
Briceland
Garberville
Alderpoint
to Bear Harbor
to Leggett
to Harris
to Covelo

a
b
c
d
e
f
g
h
i
j

Ø
1
2
3
4
5
6
7
8
9

# BEAU PRE GOLF COURSE

**Course 1**
MAP B0 grid b5

***Course information:*** This semi-private course has 18 holes. See card below for yardage and rating information.

***Play policy and fees:*** Outside guests are welcome. Green fees are $14 on weekdays and $18 on weekends. Twilight rates are $8 after 3 p.m. any day. Carts are $15. Reservations are recommended, especially on the weekends.

***Location:*** From Highway 101 in McKinleyville, take the Murray Road exit to Central Avenue. Turn north on Central Avenue to Norton Road. Turn right on Norton Road and drive to the course.

***Course description:*** Over the years this scenic course has gradually expanded from a nine-hole layout into 18 holes. It has lush fairways and ocean views. Pine and spruce trees line most of the fairways on each side; sometimes too many of them. Water comes into play on nine holes and the bunkers are strategically placed. The par-5 seventh hole offers an excellent view of the Pacific. The men's course record is 64, set by Fred Schrieber in 1989. The women's course record of 70 is held by Donna Stephens.

**1967**
**Don Harling**

PO Box 2278
McKinleyville, CA 95221

1777 Norton Road
McKinleyville, CA 95221

Pro shop (707) 839-3412
Clubhouse (707) 839-2342

- ✓ **driving range**
- ✓ **practice greens**
- ✓ **power carts**
- ✓ **pull carts**
- ✓ **golf club rental**
- ✓ **locker rooms**
- showers
- executive course
- accommodations
- ✓ **food and beverages**
- ✓ **clubhouse**

**Don Harling**
Manager/Professional

**Paul Egbert**
Superintendent

| Hole | 1 | 2 | 3 | 4 | 5 | 6 | 7 | 8 | 9 | Out | | |
|---|---|---|---|---|---|---|---|---|---|---|---|---|
| BLUE | 402 | 331 | 387 | 149 | 422 | 151 | 469 | 329 | 344 | 2984 | BLUE | Rating: 68.1 |
| WHITE | 367 | 301 | 354 | 135 | 403 | 125 | 442 | 308 | 328 | 2763 | | Slope: 116 |
| Par | 4 | 4 | 4 | 3 | 5 | 3 | 5 | 4 | 4 | 36 | WHITE | Rating: 66.2 |
| Handicap | 1 | 3 | 5 | 17 | 7 | 15 | 9 | 13 | 11 | x | | Slope: 112 |
| RED | 367 | 294 | 354 | 105 | 347 | 107 | 382 | 308 | 308 | 2572 | | |
| Par | 4 | 4 | 4 | 3 | 5 | 3 | 5 | 4 | 4 | 36 | RED | Rating: 67.6 |
| Handicap | 1 | 3 | 5 | 17 | 7 | 15 | 9 | 13 | 11 | x | | Slope: 116 |

| Hole | 10 | 11 | 12 | 13 | 14 | 15 | 16 | 17 | 18 | In | Totals | |
|---|---|---|---|---|---|---|---|---|---|---|---|---|
| BLUE | 558 | 426 | 197 | 293 | 143 | 459 | 377 | 142 | 331 | 2926 | BLUE | 5910 |
| WHITE | 538 | 403 | 175 | 275 | 125 | 425 | 353 | 111 | 280 | 2685 | WHITE | 5448 |
| Par | 5 | 4 | 3 | 4 | 3 | 5 | 4 | 3 | 4 | 35 | Par | 71 |
| Handicap | 4 | 2 | 8 | 12 | 16 | 10 | 6 | 18 | 14 | x | | |
| RED | 412 | 403 | 160 | 263 | 98 | 401 | 302 | 98 | 267 | 2404 | RED | 4976 |
| Par | 5 | 5 | 3 | 4 | 3 | 5 | 4 | 3 | 4 | 36 | Par | 72 |
| Handicap | 4 | 2 | 12 | 10 | 16 | 8 | 6 | 18 | 14 | x | | |

# BAYWOOD GOLF AND COUNTRY CLUB

**Course 2**
MAP B0 grid c4

**1956**
**R.E. Baldock**

3600 Buttermilk Lane
Arcata, CA 95521

Pro shop (707) 822-3688
Clubhouse (707) 822-3686

- ✓ **driving range**
- ✓ **practice greens**
- ✓ **power carts**
- ✓ **pull carts**
- ✓ **golf club rental**
- ✓ **locker rooms**
- ✓ **showers**
- executive course
- accommodations
- ✓ **food and beverages**
- ✓ **clubhouse**

**Bob Shubrook**
Manager

**Jim Hosley**
Professional

**Pete Williams**
Superintendent

***Course information:*** This private course has 18 holes. See card below for yardage and rating information.

***Play policy and fees:*** Reciprocal play is accepted with members of other private clubs. Guest fees are $15 when accompanied by a member, $25 when sponsored by a member and $35 for reciprocal players. Carts are $18. Reservations are recommended. No blue jeans, T-shirts, or short shorts may be worn.

***Location:*** From Highway 101 in Arcata, take the Sunny Brae exit east. Pass the California Highway Patrol station. Turn left on Buttermilk Lane and drive to the course.

***Course description:*** Situated in the midst of towering redwoods, this scenic course offers a challenging, tree-guarded layout. It's often foggy or misty. Hole number 11 is a par-4, 445-yard challenge. It's long, with a downhill green surrounded by bunkers. Count on a good drive to get there in two, and the green's not easy to stick. The men's course record is 63, set in 1984 by host pro Jim Hosley, and the women's record is 72. The back nine is much tighter than the front.

| Hole | 1 | 2 | 3 | 4 | 5 | 6 | 7 | 8 | 9 | Out | | |
|---|---|---|---|---|---|---|---|---|---|---|---|---|
| BLUE | 504 | 534 | 323 | 329 | 166 | 387 | 398 | 201 | 398 | 3240 | BLUE | Rating: 70.8 |
| WHITE | 453 | 512 | 305 | 318 | 137 | 373 | 384 | 185 | 381 | 3048 | | Slope: 124 |
| Par | 5 | 5 | 4 | 4 | 3 | 4 | 4 | 3 | 4 | 36 | WHITE | Rating: 69.6 |
| Handicap | 11 | 5 | 9 | 15 | 17 | 1 | 3 | 13 | 7 | x | | Slope: 122 |
| RED | 482 | 477 | 290 | 307 | 90 | 353 | 370 | 171 | 364 | 2904 | | |
| Par | 5 | 5 | 4 | 4 | 3 | 4 | 4 | 3 | 4 | 36 | RED | Rating: 74.0 |
| Handicap | 3 | 5 | 9 | 11 | 15 | 7 | 1 | 17 | 13 | x | | Slope: 125 |

| Hole | 10 | 11 | 12 | 13 | 14 | 15 | 16 | 17 | 18 | In | Totals | |
|---|---|---|---|---|---|---|---|---|---|---|---|---|
| BLUE | 345 | 451 | 169 | 338 | 464 | 207 | 460 | 280 | 403 | 3117 | BLUE | 6357 |
| WHITE | 324 | 444 | 158 | 333 | 459 | 198 | 444 | 254 | 395 | 3009 | WHITE | 6057 |
| Par | 4 | 4 | 3 | 4 | 5 | 3 | 5 | 4 | 4 | 36 | Par | 72 |
| Handicap | 14 | 2 | 16 | 6 | 10 | 12 | 8 | 18 | 4 | x | | |
| RED | 319 | 429 | 144 | 328 | 401 | 153 | 430 | 241 | 390 | 2835 | RED | 5739 |
| Par | 4 | 5 | 3 | 4 | 5 | 3 | 5 | 4 | 5 | 38 | Par | 74 |
| Handicap | 12 | 4 | 16 | 14 | 8 | 18 | 2 | 10 | 6 | x | | |

# EUREKA GOLF COURSE

**Course 3**
MAP B0 grid d3

***Course information:*** This public course has 18 holes and par is 70. See card below for yardage and rating information.

***Play policy and fees:*** Green fees are $8 weekdays and $11 weekends. Twilight rates are $4 weekdays and $6 weekends. Senior rates are $5.50 weekdays and $8 weekends. Carts are $9 for nine holes and $14 for 18 holes. Reservations recommended during the summer.

***Location:*** From Highway 101 in Eureka, take the Herrick exit east. Drive one–quarter mile to the golf course.

***Course description:*** An interesting layout with a creek that meanders across it, Eureka Golf Course plays longer than its yardage due to climatic conditions. The 10th hole doglegs 90 degrees and measures 400 yards. Most of the fairways are generously wide, but not number 10.

**1958**
**Robert Dean Putman**

4750 Fairway Drive
Eureka, CA 95501

Pro shop (707) 443-4808

- ✓ **driving range**
- ✓ **practice greens**
- ✓ **power carts**
- ✓ **pull carts**
- ✓ **golf club rental**
- locker rooms
- showers
- executive course
- accommodations
- ✓ **food and beverages**
- ✓ **clubhouse**

**Don Roller, Jr.**
Superintendent

**Mike Ash**
Head Professional/
Manager



| Hole | 1 | 2 | 3 | 4 | 5 | 6 | 7 | 8 | 9 | Out | | |
|---|---|---|---|---|---|---|---|---|---|---|---|---|
| BLUE | 323 | 181 | 469 | 380 | 186 | 321 | 408 | 177 | 484 | 2929 | BLUE | Rating: 66.8 |
| WHITE | 315 | 174 | 456 | 362 | 164 | 305 | 395 | 157 | 469 | 2797 | | Slope: 109 |
| Par | 4 | 3 | 5 | 4 | 3 | 4 | 4 | 3 | 5 | 35 | WHITE | Rating: 66.8 |
| Handicap | 15 | 9 | 3 | 7 | 13 | 11 | 1 | 17 | 5 | x | | Slope: 100 |
| RED | 287 | 167 | 447 | 350 | 152 | 286 | 377 | 121 | 453 | 2640 | | |
| Par | 4 | 3 | 5 | 4 | 3 | 4 | 4 | 3 | 5 | 35 | RED | Rating: 69.8 |
| Handicap | 11 | 13 | 3 | 7 | 15 | 9 | 1 | 17 | 5 | x | | Slope: 117 |

| Hole | 10 | 11 | 12 | 13 | 14 | 15 | 16 | 17 | 18 | In | Totals | |
|---|---|---|---|---|---|---|---|---|---|---|---|---|
| BLUE | 407 | 314 | 139 | 471 | 417 | 160 | 304 | 553 | 174 | 2939 | BLUE | 5868 |
| WHITE | 400 | 304 | 110 | 462 | 398 | 143 | 280 | 536 | 159 | 2792 | WHITE | 5589 |
| Par | 4 | 4 | 3 | 5 | 4 | 3 | 4 | 5 | 3 | 35 | Par | 70 |
| Handicap | 2 | 10 | 18 | 8 | 6 | 16 | 14 | 4 | 12 | x | | |
| RED | 443 | 322 | 127 | 309 | 350 | 104 | 280 | 413 | 287 | 2661 | RED | 5180 |
| Par | 5 | 4 | 3 | 5 | 4 | 3 | 4 | 5 | 3 | 36 | Par | 71 |
| Handicap | 4 | 10 | 18 | 8 | 8 | 2 | 16 | 14 | 6 | 12x | | |

MAP ON PAGE 42

# REDWOOD EMPIRE GOLF AND COUNTRY CLUB

**Course 4**
MAP B0 grid e3

**1954**

***Course information:*** This private course has nine holes. See card below for yardage and rating information.

***Play policy and fees:*** Reciprocal play is accepted with members of other private clubs. Fees are $20 for reciprocal players. Guest fees are $10 weekdays and $16 weekends when accompanied by a member. Carts are $14.

***Location:*** From Highway 101 in Fortuna, take the Kenmar Road exit to Fortuna Boulevard. Drive east past Rhonerville Road to Mill Street and turn right on Mill Street. Then turn right on Country Club Drive.

***Course description:*** This course plays much longer than the yardage indicates. Situated on a ridge, it's tight and hilly with lots of trees, sidehill lies, prevailing winds and not much roll. It's a great test of the short game. The greens are fast, but they hold well. Greg Senestrato's 65 is the course record. It's not uncommon to have more deer on the course than golfers.

352 Country Club Drive
Fortuna, CA 95540

Pro shop (707) 725-5194
Clubhouse (707) 725-5195

- ✓ **driving range**
- ✓ **practice greens**
- ✓ **power carts**
- ✓ **pull carts**
- ✓ **golf club rental**
- ✓ **locker rooms**
- showers
- executive course
- accommodations
- ✓ **food and beverages**
- ✓ **clubhouse**

**Henry Sandler**
Professional

**Mark Van Lienden**
Superintendent

| Hole | 1 | 2 | 3 | 4 | 5 | 6 | 7 | 8 | 9 | Out | BLUE | Rating:-- |
|---|---|---|---|---|---|---|---|---|---|---|---|---|
| BLUE | - | - | - | - | - | - | - | - | - | - | | Slope: -- |
| WHITE | 375 | 529 | 120 | 367 | 199 | 357 | 475 | 491 | 141 | 3054 | | |
| Par | 4 | 5 | 3 | 4 | 3 | 4 | 5 | 5 | 3 | 36 | WHITE | Rating: 68.2 |
| Handicap | 1 | 5 | 13 | 3 | 7 | 11 | 9 | 15 | 17 | x | | Slope: 109 |
| RED | 322 | 430 | 120 | 367 | 204 | 330 | 436 | 358 | 141 | 2708 | | |
| Par | 4 | 5 | 3 | 4 | 4 | 4 | 5 | 4 | 3 | 36 | RED | Rating: 70.7 |
| Handicap | 11 | 3 | 17 | 5 | 13 | 9 | 1 | 7 | 15 | x | | Slope: 115 |

| Hole | 10 | 11 | 12 | 13 | 14 | 15 | 16 | 17 | 18 | In | Totals | |
|---|---|---|---|---|---|---|---|---|---|---|---|---|
| BLUE | - | - | - | - | - | - | - | - | - | - | BLUE | -- |
| WHITE | 410 | 461 | 99 | 442 | 139 | 372 | 476 | 414 | 133 | 2946 | WHITE | 6000 |
| Par | 4 | 5 | 3 | 5 | 3 | 4 | 5 | 4 | 3 | 36 | Par | 72 |
| Handicap | 2 | 10 | 18 | 12 | 16 | 6 | 8 | 4 | 14 | x | | |
| RED | 371 | 422 | 99 | 423 | 139 | 302 | 341 | 414 | 133 | 2644 | RED | 5352 |
| Par | 4 | 5 | 3 | 5 | 3 | 4 | 4 | 5 | 3 | 36 | Par | 72 |
| Handicap | 10 | 2 | 18 | 4 | 14 | 12 | 6 | 8 | 16 | x | | |

MAP ON PAGE 42

# MAP B1

(2 COURSES)

PAGES.......48-49

NOR-CAL MAP.....see page 30
adjoining maps
NORTH ..........................no map
EAST (B2)............see page 50
SOUTH...........................no map
WEST (B0)...........see page 42

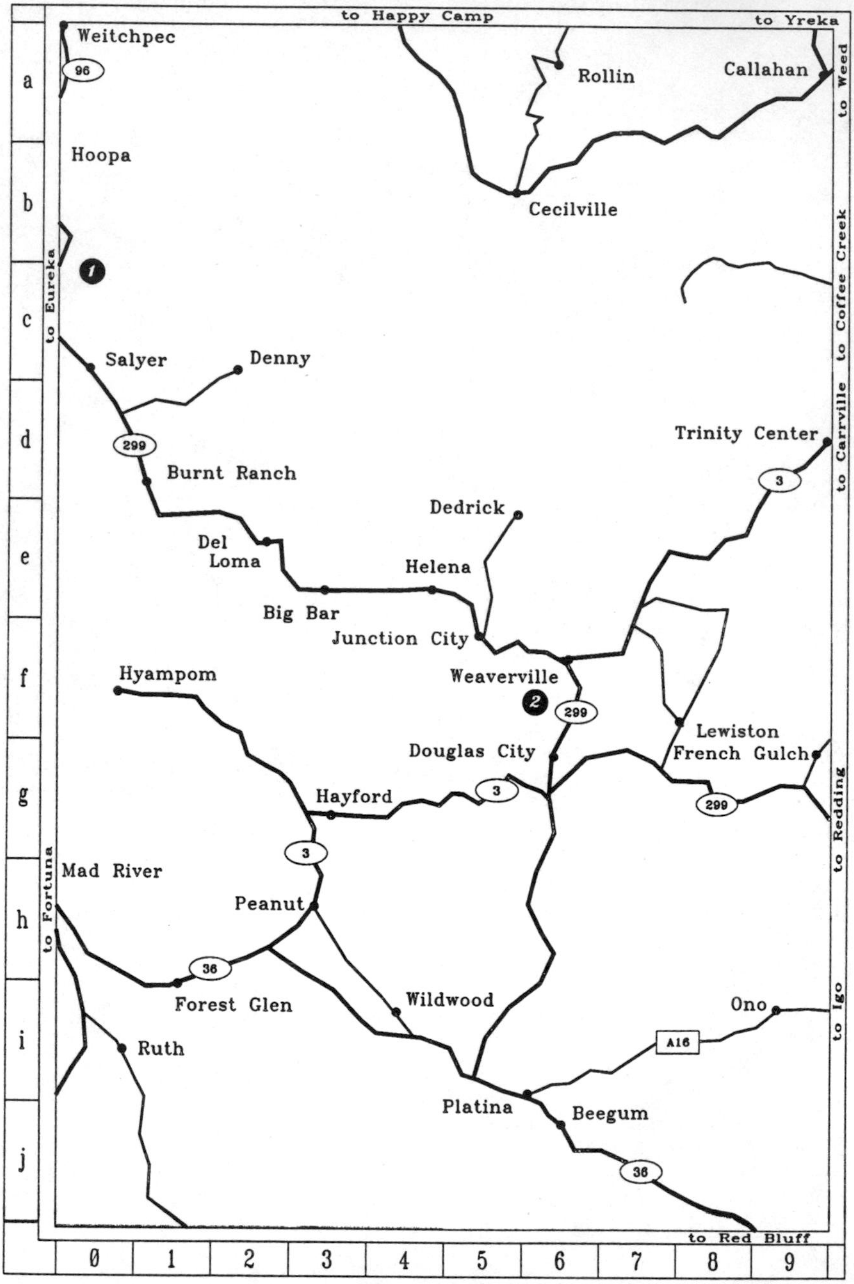

to Happy Camp
to Yreka
to Weed
to Coffee Creek
to Carrville
to Redding
to Igo
to Red Bluff
to Eureka
to Fortuna

Weitchpec
96
Hoopa
Rollin
Callahan
Cecilville
1
Salyer
Denny
299
Burnt Ranch
Trinity Center
3
Dedrick
Del Loma
Helena
Big Bar
Junction City
Hyampom
Weaverville
2
299
Lewiston
Douglas City
French Gulch
Hayford
3
299
3
Mad River
Peanut
36
Forest Glen
Wildwood
Ono
Ruth
A16
Platina
Beegum
36

a
b
c
d
e
f
g
h
i
j

0 1 2 3 4 5 6 7 8 9

# BIGFOOT GOLF AND COUNTRY CLUB

**Course 1**
MAP B1 grid c0

*Course information:* This semi-private course has nine holes. Par is 70 for 18 holes. The course is 5,007 yards and rated 63.9 from the regular tees. The slope rating is 103. Women's tees are 5,007 yards and rated 67.9 from the regular tees. The slope rating is 112.

*Play policy and fees:* Outside play is accepted. Green fees are $8 for nine holes and $12 for 18 holes weekdays, and $10 for nine holes and $14 for 18 holes weekends. Carts are $7 per ninc holes. No spectators are allowed.

*Location:* From Highway 101 in Arcata, take Highway 299 east to Willow Creek. Turn left on Country Club Road and cross the Trinity River. Turn left on Patterson at the "T." Turn right on Bigfoot Avenue.

*Course description:* Although short from a yardage standpoint, Bigfoot requires accuracy with its small greens and water on five of nine holes. The seventh hole, for instance, is reachable for big hitters at 277 yards, but out-of-bounds lurks both to the left and behind the green. The par-5 fourth hole, just 477 yards, features a green that is just 16 yards deep from front to back, and water encircles three-quarters of the putting surface. The course record is 60, set by Don Nelson, Jr.

PO Box 836
Patterson Road
Willow Creek, CA 95573

Pro shop (916) 629-2977
Clubhouse (916) 629-2193

- ✓ **driving range**
- practice greens
- ✓ **power carts**
- ✓ **pull carts**
- ✓ **golf club rental**
- locker rooms
- showers
- executive course
- accommodations
- ✓ **food and beverages**
- ✓ **clubhouse**

**Bob Newell**
Professional

**Cappy Kramer**
Superintendent

**Carol Tonkin**
Manager

# TRINITY ALPS GOLF AND COUNTRY CLUB

**Course 2**
MAP B1 grid f6

*Course information:* This semi-private course has nine holes. Par is 62 for 18 holes. The course is 3,702 yards and rated 59.1 from the regular tees. The slope rating is 93. Women's tees are 3,474 yards and rated 59.0 from the regular tees. The slope rating is 96.

*Play policy and fees:* Outside play is accepted. Green fees are $8 for nine holes and $10 for 18 holes. Power carts are $5 per nine holes.

*Location:* From Redding, drive 49 miles west on Highway 299 to Weaverville. Exit south onto Glen Road, travel to Golf Course Drive to the course.

*Course description:* There are two water hazards on this rolling, short and walkable course. It's picturesque, with lots of trees and views of the Trinity Alps. The par-3 seventh hole has two water hazards. Four of the nine holes have water, in fact, and the greens are small. The course record of 55 is shared by Felix Claveran and bright young junior Jay Berowitz. The course was designed by Fred Eastwood, father of PGA tour pro Bob Eastwood.

PO Box 582
111 Golf Course Drive
Weaverville, CA 96093

Pro shop (916) 623-5411

- ✓ **driving range**
- ✓ **practice greens**
- ✓ **power carts**
- ✓ **pull carts**
- ✓ **golf club rental**
- ✓ **locker rooms**
- showers
- ✓ **executive course**
- accommodations
- ✓ **food and beverages**
- ✓ **clubhouse**

**Felix Claveran**
Owner/Professional

**Bobby Tyler**
Superintendent

MAP ON PAGE 48

# MAP B2
(9 COURSES)

PAGES.......50-59

NOR-CAL MAP.....see page 30
adjoining maps
NORTH (A2).........see page 36
EAST (B3)............see page 60
SOUTH (C2).........see page 70
WEST (B1)...........see page 48

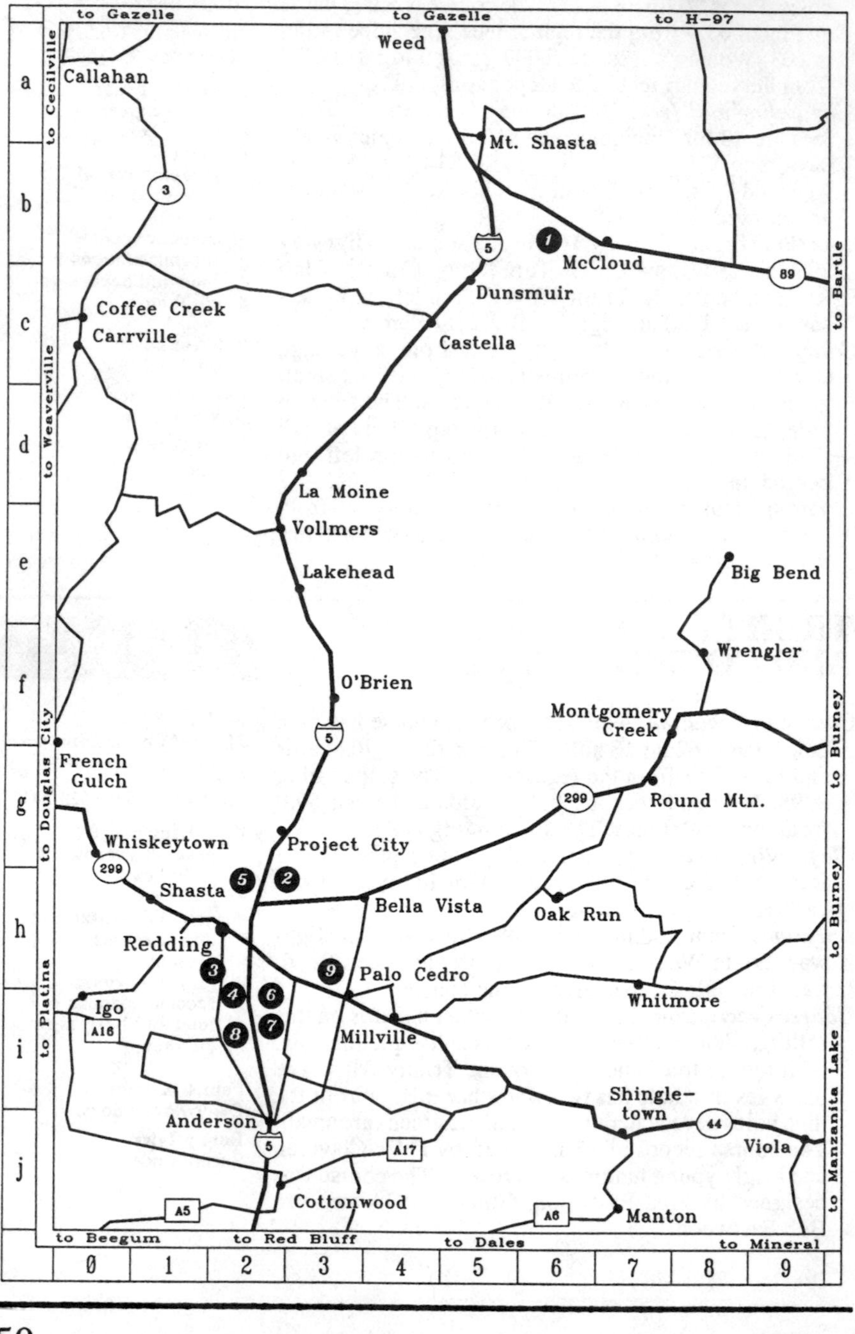

to Gazelle
to Gazelle
to H-97
to Cecilville
to Weaverville
to Douglas City
to Platina
to Bartle
to Burney
to Burney
to Manzanita Lake
to Beegum
to Red Bluff
to Dales
to Mineral

Weed
Callahan
Mt. Shasta
3
5
1
McCloud
89
Dunsmuir
Coffee Creek
Carrville
Castella
La Moine
Vollmers
Lakehead
Big Bend
Wrengler
O'Brien
Montgomery Creek
5
French Gulch
299
Round Mtn.
Whiskeytown
Project City
299
5
2
Shasta
Bella Vista
Oak Run
Redding
3
9
Palo Cedro
4
6
Whitmore
Igo
A16
8
7
Millville
Shingle-town
44
Anderson
5
A17
Viola
Cottonwood
A5
A6
Manton

a
b
c
d
e
f
g
h
i
j

0 1 2 3 4 5 6 7 8 9

# McCLOUD GOLF COURSE

**Course 1**
MAP B2 grid b6

***Course information:*** This public course has nine holes. See card below for yardage and rating information.

***Play policy and fees:*** Green fees are $10 for nine holes and $12 for 18 holes weekdays, and $12 for nine holes and $15 for 18 holes weekends and holidays. Carts are $10 per nine holes and $15 for 18 holes. The course is open April through November. Senior citizens pay $2 less on Mondays.

***Location:*** From Interstate 5 north of Redding and Dunsmuir, take the Highway 89 exit. Drivc east to McCloud. In McCloud, turn right on to Squaw Valley Road south and follow it to the course.

***Course description:*** On a clear day McCloud Golf Course offers one of the most beautiful sites in California golf: a majestic, bird's eye view of Mt. Shasta. The course features native pine and quaking aspen with Squaw Creek menadering through it. Water comes into play on six of the nine holes. The par-3 seventh hole has a fountain offering 40-degree water from Mt. Shasta that is piped onto the course. The men's course record of 63 was set by PGA Tour pro Rod Curl.

**1927**

PO Box 728
McCloud, CA 96057

1001 Squaw Valley Road
McCloud, CA 96057

Pro shop (916) 964-2535

- ✓ **driving range**
- ✓ **practice greens**
- ✓ **power carts**
- ✓ **pull carts**
- ✓ **golf club rental**
- locker rooms
- showers
- executive course
- accommodations
- ✓ **food and beverages**
- ✓ **clubhouse**

**Charles Nutt**
Manager

**Earl Martin**
Superintendent

| Hole | 1 | 2 | 3 | 4 | 5 | 6 | 7 | 8 | 9 | Out | BLUE | Rating: -- |
|---|---|---|---|---|---|---|---|---|---|---|---|---|
| BLUE | - | - | - | - | - | - | - | - | - | - | | Slope:-- |
| WHITE | 346 | 354 | 482 | 154 | 274 | 477 | 167 | 222 | 507 | 2983 | | |
| Par | 4 | 4 | 5 | 3 | 4 | 5 | 3 | 3 | 5 | 36 | WHITE | Rating:67.5 |
| Handicap | 12 | 6 | 10 | 16 | 18 | 8 | 14 | 2 | 4 | x | | Slope: 109 |
| RED | 341 | 341 | 409 | 107 | 266 | 375 | 142 | 221 | 411 | 2623 | | |
| Par | 4 | 4 | 5 | 3 | 4 | 4 | 3 | 4 | 5 | 36 | RED | Rating: 68.4 |
| Handicap | 5 | 3 | 9 | 13 | 17 | 1 | 7 | 15 | 11 | x | | Slope: 102 |

| Hole | 10 | 11 | 12 | 13 | 14 | 15 | 16 | 17 | 18 | In | Totals | |
|---|---|---|---|---|---|---|---|---|---|---|---|---|
| BLUE | - | - | - | - | - | - | - | - | - | - | BLUE | -- |
| WHITE | 346 | 354 | 502 | 197 | 274 | 497 | 167 | 323 | 417 | 3077 | WHITE | 6060 |
| Par | 4 | 4 | 5 | 3 | 4 | 5 | 3 | 4 | 4 | 36 | Par | 72 |
| Handicap | 13 | 3 | 9 | 5 | 17 | 7 | 15 | 11 | 1 | x | | |
| RED | 345 | 342 | 413 | 150 | 269 | 379 | 100 | 221 | 418 | 2645 | RED | 5268 |
| Par | 4 | 4 | 5 | 3 | 4 | 4 | 3 | 4 | 5 | 36 | Par | 72 |
| Handicap | 4 | 6 | 8 | 10 | 12 | 2 | 18 | 16 | 14 | x | | |

# GOLD HILLS COUNTRY CLUB

**Course 2**
MAP B2 grid h2

***Course information:*** This semi-private course has 18 holes. See card below for yardage and rating information.

***Play policy and fees:*** Green fees are $15 weekdays and $20 weekends. Carts are $16.

***Location:*** From Interstate 5 on the north side of Redding, take the Oasis Road exit east and drive one–half mile. Turn right on Gold Hills Drive and follow it to the course.

***Course description:*** Head pro Thurm Krater calls this a "player's course," meaning it offers a challenging but not overly severe test in a beautiful setting. Golfers have views of Mt. Lassen and Mt. Shasta on nice days. Carts are recommended due to the hilly terrain. The opening hole is formidable—419 yards with out-of-bounds left, Churn Creek right. The course record is set by Doren Granberry, a deaf-mute with a zero handicap.

**1978**
**Phil Holcomb**

1950 Gold Hills Drive
Redding, CA 96003

Pro shop (916) 246-7867

- ✓ **driving range**
- ✓ **practice greens**
- ✓ **power carts**
- ✓ **pull carts**
- ✓ **golf club rental**
- locker rooms
- showers
- executive course
- accommodations
- ✓ **food and beverages**
- ✓ **clubhouse**

**Steve Adams**
Manager

**Thurm Krater**
Professional

**Larry Johnson**
Superintendent

| Hole | 1 | 2 | 3 | 4 | 5 | 6 | 7 | 8 | 9 | Out | BLUE | Rating: 71.0 |
|---|---|---|---|---|---|---|---|---|---|---|---|---|
| BLUE | 419 | 529 | 134 | 378 | 363 | 421 | 367 | 208 | 508 | 3327 | | Slope: 127 |
| WHITE | 387 | 479 | 105 | 363 | 350 | 393 | 358 | 188 | 487 | 3110 | | |
| Par | 4 | 5 | 3 | 4 | 4 | 4 | 4 | 3 | 5 | 36 | WHITE | Rating: 69.4 |
| Handicap | 3 | 9 | 15 | 5 | 13 | 1 | 17 | 7 | 11 | x | | Slope: 123 |
| RED | 357 | 398 | 92 | 334 | 331 | 384 | 345 | 155 | 393 | 2789 | | |
| Par | 4 | 5 | 3 | 4 | 4 | 4 | 4 | 3 | 5 | 36 | RED | Rating: 71.6 |
| Handicap | 3 | 13 | 17 | 9 | 7 | 1 | 5 | 11 | 15 | x | | Slope: 124 |

| Hole | 10 | 11 | 12 | 13 | 14 | 15 | 16 | 17 | 18 | In | Totals | |
|---|---|---|---|---|---|---|---|---|---|---|---|---|
| BLUE | 391 | 366 | 402 | 344 | 214 | 512 | 427 | 112 | 508 | 3276 | BLUE | 6603 |
| WHITE | 370 | 354 | 366 | 333 | 167 | 501 | 392 | 105 | 467 | 3055 | WHITE | 6165 |
| Par | 4 | 4 | 4 | 4 | 3 | 5 | 4 | 3 | 5 | 36 | Par | 72 |
| Handicap | 16 | 6 | 10 | 12 | 14 | 4 | 2 | 18 | 8 | x | | |
| RED | 351 | 341 | 352 | 311 | 124 | 434 | 303 | 101 | 436 | 2753 | RED | 5542 |
| Par | 4 | 4 | 4 | 4 | 3 | 5 | 4 | 3 | 5 | 36 | Par | 72 |
| Handicap | 14 | 8 | 4 | 2 | 16 | 10 | 6 | 18 | 12 | x | | |

# RIVERVIEW GOLF AND COUNTRY CLUB

**Course 3**
MAP B2 grid h2



4200 Bechelli Lane
Redding, CA 96002

Pro shop (916) 224-2250
Clubhouse (916) 224-2255

- ✓ **driving range**
- ✓ **practice greens**
- ✓ **power carts**
- ✓ **pull carts**
- ✓ **golf club rental**
- ✓ **locker rooms**
- ✓ **showers**
- executive course
- accommodations
- ✓ **food and beverages**
- ✓ **clubhouse**

**Gary Kellogg**
Manager

**Kim Thurman**
Professional

**Dick Howe**
Superintendent

***Course information:*** This private course has 18 holes and par is 72. The course is 6,450 yards and rated 70.1 from the regular tees. The slope rating is 118. Women's tees are 5,900 yards and rated 73.0. The slope rating is 121.

***Play policy and fees:*** Reciprocal play is accepted with members of other private clubs. Reciprocal fees are $40. Carts are $20 for guests. The course is closed Mondays.

***Location:*** From Interstate 5 in Redding, take the Bonneyview Road/Churn Creek exit. Go over the overpass and turn right on Bechelli Lane. Follow it to the course on the left.

***Course description:*** Head pro Kim Thurman calls the first hole—a par-5 of 572 yards—"the most scenic in California." The Sacramento River borders the left side with a spectacular view of the mountains in the background. The course is narrow with countless trees and the greens are mostly small. The par-3s measure 217, 206, 185 and 132 yards. Some golfers throw a ball into the Sacramento River as an act of resignation.

# ALLEN'S GOLF COURSE

**Course 4**
MAP B2 grid h2

***Course information:*** This public course has nine holes See card below for yardage and rating information.

***Play policy and fees:*** Green fees are $5 for nine holes and $9.50 for 18 holes weekdays, and $5.50 for nine holes and $10.50 for 18 holes weekends. Senior and junior rates are $4 for nine holes and $7.25 for 18 holes on weekdays. Wednesday specials for seniors are $3.50 for nine holes and $6.50 for 18 holes.

***Location:*** From Interstate 5 in Redding, take the Bonneyview Road/Churn Creek exit. Turn left on Bonneyview Road and left on East Side Road. Turn left on Star Drive, which becomes Sacramento Drive. The course is on the left, just past Olney Creek.

***Course description:*** Set in a rolling terrain with lots of trees, Allens's Golf Course has out-of-bounds on every hole. Bob Allen bought this course in 1975—hence the name—and operates it with his wife. The course has a regular clientele.

2780 Sacramento Drive
Redding, CA 96001

Pro shop (916) 241-5055

- driving range
- ✓ **practice greens**
- power carts
- ✓ **pull carts**
- ✓ **golf club rental**
- locker rooms
- showers
- ✓ **executive course**
- accommodations
- food and beverages
- ✓ **clubhouse**

**Greg Anderson**
Manager

**Bob Allen**
**Pat Allen**
Superintendents

| Hole | 1 | 2 | 3 | 4 | 5 | 6 | 7 | 8 | 9 | Out | | |
|---|---|---|---|---|---|---|---|---|---|---|---|---|
| BLUE | - | - | - | - | - | - | - | - | - | - | BLUE | Rating:-- |
| WHITE | 284 | 285 | 107 | 126 | 240 | 167 | 151 | 236 | 110 | 1706 | | Slope:-- |
| Par | 4 | 4 | 3 | 3 | 4 | 3 | 3 | 4 | 3 | 31 | WHITE | Rating:56.9 |
| Handicap | 3 | 5 | 17 | 15 | 1 | 7 | 9 | 11 | 13 | x | | Slope: 92 |
| RED | 284 | 285 | 107 | 126 | 196 | 167 | 151 | 236 | 110 | 1662 | | |
| Par | 4 | 4 | 3 | 3 | 4 | 3 | 3 | 4 | 3 | 31 | RED | Rating: 58.2 |
| Handicap | 3 | 5 | 17 | 15 | 1 | 7 | 9 | 11 | 13 | x | | Slope: 89 |

| Hole | 10 | 11 | 12 | 13 | 14 | 15 | 16 | 17 | 18 | In | Totals | |
|---|---|---|---|---|---|---|---|---|---|---|---|---|
| BLUE | - | - | - | - | - | - | - | - | - | - | BLUE | -- |
| WHITE | 284 | 285 | 107 | 126 | 240 | 167 | 151 | 236 | 110 | 1706 | WHITE | 3412 |
| Par | 4 | 4 | 3 | 3 | 4 | 3 | 3 | 4 | 3 | 31 | Par | 62 |
| Handicap | 4 | 6 | 18 | 16 | 2 | 8 | 10 | 12 | 14 | x | | |
| RED | 284 | 285 | 107 | 126 | 240 | 167 | 151 | 236 | 110 | 1706 | RED | 3368 |
| Par | 4 | 4 | 3 | 3 | 4 | 3 | 3 | 4 | 3 | 31 | Par | 62 |
| Handicap | 4 | 6 | 18 | 16 | 2 | 8 | 10 | 12 | 14 | x | | |

# LAKE REDDING GOLF COURSE

**Course 5**
MAP B2 grid h2

**1959**

*Course information:* This public course has nine holes. Par is 62 for 18 holes. The course is 3,757 yards and rated 57.3 from the regular tees. The slope rating is 87. Women's tees are 3,757 yards and rated 60.5 from the regular tees. The slope rating is 88.

*Play policy and fees:* Green fees are $6 for nine holes and $11 for 18 holes. Green fees for seniors are $4 Monday through Friday before noon, and $5.50 for nine holes and $10 for 18 holes after noon and on Saturdays and Sundays. Carts are $8 for nine holes and $15 for 18 holes.

*Location:* Heading north on Interstate 5 in Redding, take the Highway 299 East exit. Turn left and drive to the second stop light and turn left again. At the bottom of the hill take the first right, which is Benton Drive. Take Benton Drive to the course.

*Course description:* This short executive course is known for requiring accuracy because of its narrow fairways lined with trees. There are four lakes that come into play. Bunkers have been added for more challenge. There are new tee boxes, the fairways are double cut and some of the greens have been rebuilt. A nice setting in a river valley, with a train trestle running nearby, this course is popular with seniors and beginners because of its modest length, although it is demanding in terms of accuracy. There are three par-4s, the most interesting being number one—218 yards to a green with water in front—and number nine, a 240-yarder with another small green. A new clubhouse was recently built.

1795 Benton Drive
Redding, CA 96003

Pro shop (916) 243-5531

- driving range
- ✓ **practice greens**
- ✓ **power carts**
- ✓ **pull carts**
- ✓ **golf club rental**
- locker rooms
- showers
- ✓ **executive course**
- accommodations
- ✓ **food and beverages**
- ✓ **clubhouse**

**Peggy Sutterfield**
Owner/Manager

**Cesar Serrano**
Superintendent

# CHURN CREEK GOLF COURSE

**Course 6**
MAP B2 grid i2

***Course information:*** This public course has nine holes. Par is 72 for 18 holes. The course is 6,206 yards and rated 68.6 from the regular tees. The slope rating is 108. Women's tees are 5,516 yards and rated 71.4 with a slope rating of 117.

***Play policy and fees:*** Green fees are $6 for nine holes and $12 for 18 holes all year. Carts are $7 for nine holes and $14 for 18 holes.

***Location:*** From Interstate 5 in Redding, take the Knighton Road exit east. Knighton Road turns into Churn Creek Road, which leads to the course.

***Course description:*** The course is primarily flat, but numerous trees separate adjoining fairways, and there is out-of-bounds on all but two holes. Churn Creek opened in 1982 and is becoming popular enough that golfers should call ahead to reserve a time. It's a good test, of moderate length, with trees and small greens giving it a distinctive flavor.

7355 Churn Creek Road
Redding, CA 96002

Pro shop (916) 222-6353

✓ **driving range**
✓ **practice greens**
✓ **power carts**
✓ **pull carts**
✓ **golf club rental**
locker rooms
showers
executive course
accommodations
✓ **food and beverages**
✓ **clubhouse**

**Steven Divine**
**Robert Divine**
Manager

**Bob Blackwell**
**Lisa Kelley**
Professional

**Robert Divine**
Superintendent

# TUCKER OAKS GOLF COURSE

**Course 7**
MAP B2 grid i2

*Course information:* This public course has nine holes with alternate tee boxes for those desiring to play 18 holes. Par is 72 for 18 holes. The course is 6,371 yards and rated 67.2 from the regular tees (18 holes). The slope rating is 98. Women's tees are 5,896 yards and rated 70.9. The slope rating is 109.

*Play policy and fees:* Green fees are $6 for nine holes and $12 for 18 holes any day. Carts are $7 for nine holes and $14 for 18 holes. Closed the third Monday of each month during the summer.

*Location:* From Interstate 5 in Anderson, take the Riverside exit to Airport Road north. Drive across the Sacramento River and turn left on Churn Creek Road. Continue to the course.

*Course description:* Like most Redding area courses, Tucker Oaks is distinguised by numerous trees. There are bunkers on every hole as well as two lakes that come into play. The best hole is probably number three, a 434-yarder that doglegs left. Out-of-bounds comes into play on the final three holes. The men's course record is 63, shared by four golfers, and Betty Bennett has the women's course record of 68.

PO Box 654
Anderson, CA 96007

6241 Churn Creek Road
Redding, CA 96002

Pro shop (916) 365-3350
Clubhouse (916) 365-6622

- ✓ **driving range**
- ✓ **practice greens**
- ✓ **power carts**
- ✓ **pull carts**
- ✓ **golf club rental**
- locker rooms
- showers
- executive course
- accommodations
- ✓ **food and beverages**
- ✓ **clubhouse**

**Al Banuelos**
Manager

**Chuck Sherman**
Professional

**Mike Ervin**
Superintendent

# RIVER BEND GOLF AND COUNTRY CLUB

**Course 8**
MAP B2 grid i2

**1991**
**Bill Ralston**

1863 Keystone Court
Redding, CA 96003

5369 Indianwood Drive
Redding, CA 96001

Pro shop (916) 246-9077
Office (916) 222-8101

- driving range
- ✓ **practice greens**
- ✓ **power carts**
- ✓ **pull carts**
- ✓ **golf club rental**
- ✓ **locker rooms**
- showers
- ✓ **executive course**
- accommodations
- ✓ **food and beverages**
- clubhouse

**Bill Ralston**
Manager

**Tony Luerra**
Professional

**Rick White**
Superintendent

***Course information:*** This semi-private course has nine holes. Par is 64 for 18 holes. The course is 3,999 yards for 18 holes and rated 59. Women's tees are 3466 yards and rated 59. The slope for men and women is 93.

***Play policy and fees:*** Members and guests only. Only players with NCGA, SCGA or out-of-state golf association handicaps or guests of members are allowed to play the course. Green fees are $6 for nine holes and $12 for 18 holes daily. Reservations are recommended. Carts are $5 for nine holes, $10 for 18 holes.

***Location:*** From Interstate 5, take the Churn Creek/Bechelli exit and turn west. Cross over the Sacramento River and turn right onto Indianwood Drive, which leads to the River Bend Estate. Drive through the subdivision. The course is at the rear of the residential area.

***Course description:*** This course was designed and built by Bill Ralston with the assistance of retired pro Eric Batten. With its tight layout, two ponds and the Sacramento River slough coming into play on five holes, consider this a target course of the most demanding dimensions. The course is in outstanding condition. The eighth hole, a par-4 of 326 yards, is deceptively difficult with out-of-bounds right, water left and a green that slopes heavily left.

# PALO CEDRO GOLF CLUB

**Course 9**
MAP B2 grid h3



**1992**
**Bert Stamps**

222499 Golf Time Drive
Palo Cedro, CA 96073

Pro shop (916)547-3012

- driving range
- practice greens
- ✓ **power carts**
- ✓ **pull carts**
- ✓ **golf club rental**
- locker rooms
- showers
- executive course
- accommodations
- ✓ **food and beverages**
- ✓ **clubhouse**

**Todd Sickles**
Professional

**Jim Adsit**
Superintendent

***Course information:*** This private course has 9 holes and par is 72 for 18. The course is 6,198 yards and rated 68.7 from the championship tees, and 5,812 yards and rated 67.0 from the regular tees. The slope ratings are 116 championship and 113 regular. The women's tees are 5,432 yards and rated 67.9. The slope rating is 114.

***Play policy and fees:*** Outside play is accepted. It is reciprocal with members of other private clubs. Green fees are $8 for nine and $15 for 18 holes. Carts are $8 for nine and $15 for 18 holes.

***Location:*** Take Interstate 5 to De Shoots Road in Palo Cedro. Go south to Highway 44. Turn left. Go east to Silver Bridge Road. Turn left. The course is on the left.

***Course description:*** There is lots of water on this slightly hilly layout. There are many maturing trees on this course. The par-5, 9th hole is 481 yards. It has a dogleg left over a stream. The green is guarded on both sides by bunkers that will catch any errant shots. The signature hole is the par-3, 6th. It is 165 yards. It is guarded on the left by pine and oak trees and a creek, and on the right by two huge oak trees. Playing from the raised tree box, you have to channel your ball through the narrow fairway in order to reach the green. If you're short off the tee, there are bunkers guarding the front left and right of the green.

# MAP B3
(1 COURSE)

PAGES.......60-61

NOR-CAL MAP.....see page 30
adjoining maps
NORTH (A3).........see page 40
EAST (B4)............see page 62
SOUTH (C3).........see page 80
WEST (B2)...........see page 50

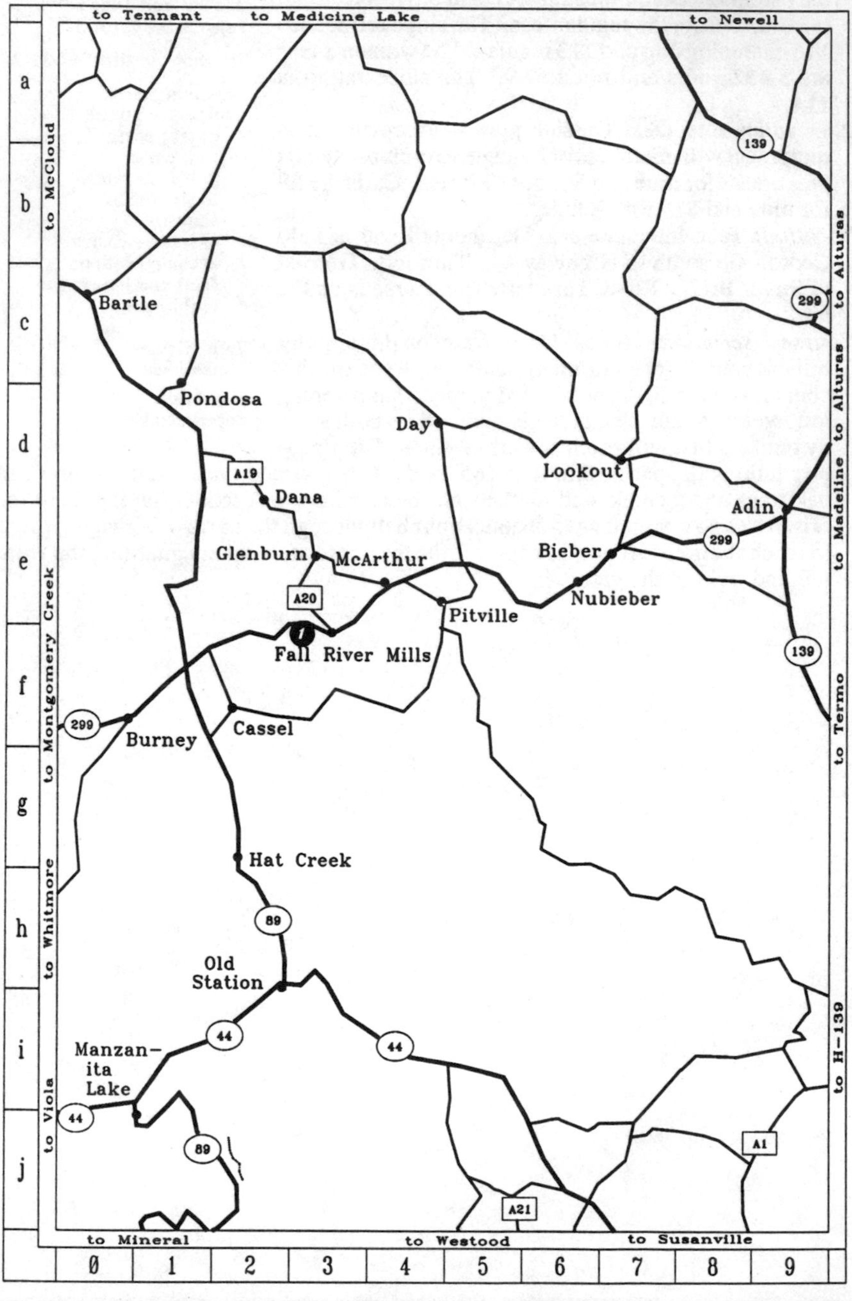

to Tennant
to Medicine Lake
to Newell
to McCloud
to Montgomery Creek
to Whitmore
to Viola
to Alturas
to Madeline to Alturas
to Termo
to H-139
to Mineral
to Westood
to Susanville

a
b
c
d
e
f
g
h
i
j

Ø 1 2 3 4 5 6 7 8 9

Bartle
Pondosa
Day
Lookout
Adin
A19
Dana
Glenburn
McArthur
Bieber
299
139
A20
Nubieber
Pitville
1
Fall River Mills
139
299
Burney
Cassel
Hat Creek
89
Old Station
44
44
Manzanita Lake
44
89
A1
A21

# FALL RIVER GOLF AND COUNTRY CLUB

**Course 1**
MAP B3 grid f3

*Course information:* This public course has 18 holes. See card below for yardage and rating information.

*Play policy and fees:* Green fees are $15 on weekdays and $19 on weekends. Senior rates are $10 on Fridays. The Monday fee is $13. Carts are $18.

*Location:* From Interstate 5 in Redding, drive east on Highway 299 to Fall River Mills. The course is on the right.

*Course description:* One of California's longest and toughest courses, at least when played from the blue tees, Fall River is located in a mountain valley best known for its first-rate fishing. But the golf course is a jewel, winding its way through the trees with a wide variety of holes. The eighth hole, a par-3 over a marshy lake, is named "Bing's Bluff" in honor of the old crooner. Clark Glasson was building the course when he noticed Bing Crosby watching from a distance. Crosby owned the nearby Rising River Ranch, now owned by Clint Eastwood.

**1980**
**Clark Glasson**

PO Box PAR
Fall River Mills, CA 96028

Highway 299 East
Fall River Mills, CA 96028

Pro shop (916) 336-5555

- ✓ **driving range**
- ✓ **practice greens**
- ✓ **power carts**
- ✓ **pull carts**
- ✓ **golf club rental**
- locker rooms
- showers
- executive course
- accommodations
- ✓ **food and beverages**
- ✓ **clubhouse**

**Karen Estes**
Manager

**Mike Glasson**
Superintendent

NORHTERN B3

| Hole | 1 | 2 | 3 | 4 | 5 | 6 | 7 | 8 | 9 | Out | BLUE | Rating: 75.2 |
|---|---|---|---|---|---|---|---|---|---|---|---|---|
| BLUE | 392 | 442 | 666 | 227 | 400 | 449 | 435 | 198 | 579 | 3788 | | Slope: 131 |
| WHITE | 370 | 425 | 642 | 200 | 375 | 424 | 395 | 164 | 518 | 3513 | | |
| Par | 4 | 4 | 5 | 3 | 4 | 4 | 4 | 3 | 5 | 36 | WHITE | Rating: 72.5 |
| Handicap | 15 | 5 | 1 | 13 | 17 | 3 | 7 | 9 | 11 | x | | Slope: 176 |
| RED | 357 | 382 | 620 | 179 | 332 | 406 | 364 | 136 | 456 | 3171 | | |
| Par | 4 | 4 | 5 | 3 | 4 | 4 | 4 | 3 | 5 | 36 | RED | Rating: 74.0 |
| Handicap | 15 | 5 | 1 | 13 | 17 | 3 | 7 | 9 | 11 | x | | Slope: 115 |

| Hole | 10 | 11 | 12 | 13 | 14 | 15 | 16 | 17 | 18 | In | Totals | |
|---|---|---|---|---|---|---|---|---|---|---|---|---|
| BLUE | 401 | 178 | 432 | 429 | 615 | 175 | 450 | 380 | 517 | 3577 | BLUE | 7365 |
| WHITE | 377 | 166 | 407 | 390 | 561 | 151 | 421 | 354 | 492 | 3319 | WHITE | 6832 |
| Par | 4 | 3 | 4 | 4 | 5 | 3 | 4 | 4 | 5 | 36 | Par | 72 |
| Handicap | 10 | 12 | 6 | 8 | 2 | 16 | 4 | 18 | 14 | x | | |
| RED | 354 | 162 | 386 | 364 | 473 | 118 | 390 | 333 | 449 | 3029 | RED | 6200 |
| Par | 4 | 3 | 4 | 4 | 5 | 3 | 4 | 4 | 5 | 36 | Par | 72 |
| Handicap | 10 | 12 | 6 | 8 | 2 | 16 | 4 | 18 | 14 | x | | |

# MAP B4

(1 COURSE)

PAGES.......62-63

NOR-CAL MAP.....see page 30
adjoining maps
NORTH .........................no map
EAST .............................no map
SOUTH (C4) .........see page 88
WEST (B3)............see page 60

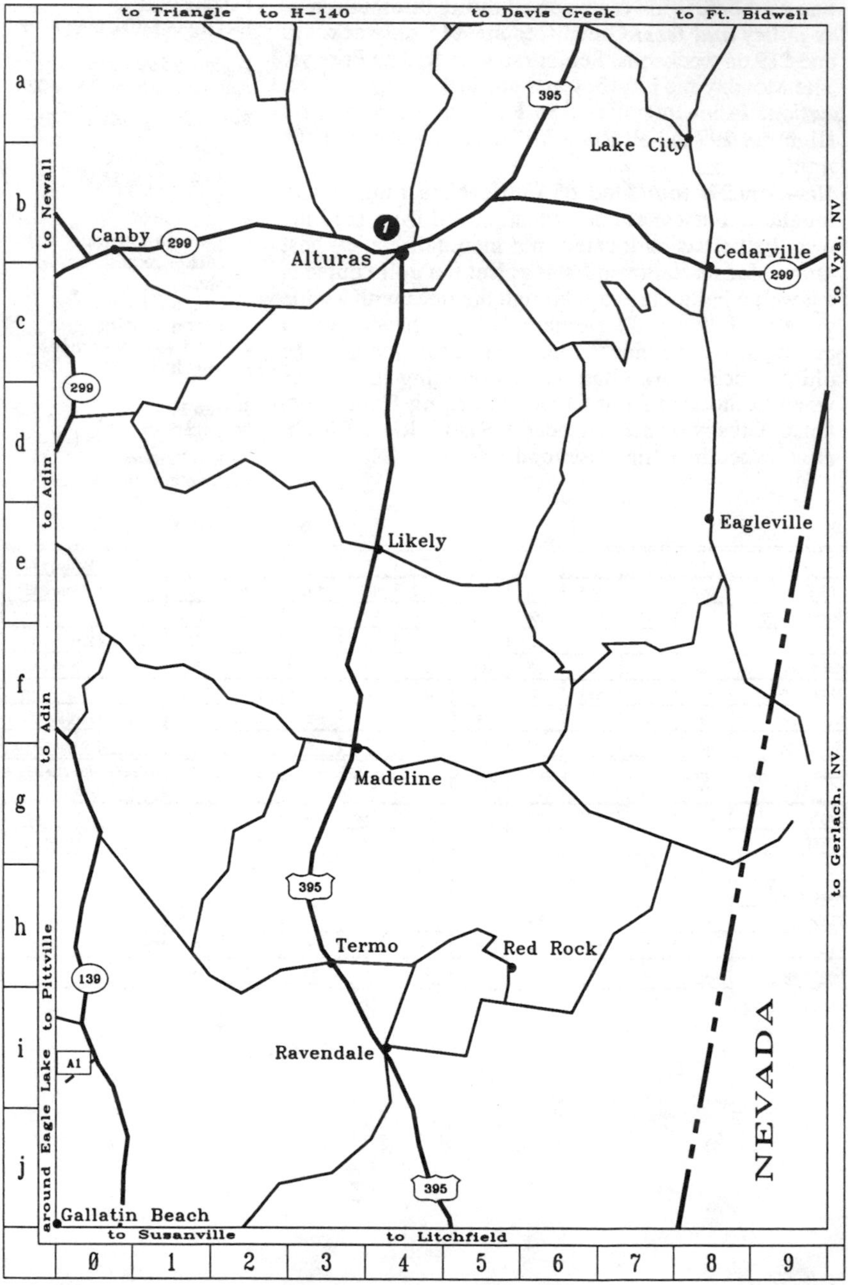

to Triangle
to H-140
to Davis Creek
to Ft. Bidwell
to Newall
to Adin
to Adin
around Eagle Lake to Pittville
to Vya, NV
to Gerlach, NV
to Susanville
to Litchfield

a
b
c
d
e
f
g
h
i
j

395
Lake City
Canby
299
1
Alturas
Cedarville
299
299
Eagleville
Likely
Madeline
395
Termo
Red Rock
139
A1
Ravendale
NEVADA
395
Gallatin Beach

0 1 2 3 4 5 6 7 8 9

# ARROWHEAD GOLF COURSE

**Course 1**
MAP B4 grid b4

**1949**
**William Park Bell**

1901 North Warner Street
Alturas, CA 96101

Pro shop (916) 233-3404

- ✓ **driving range**
- ✓ **practice greens**
- ✓ **power carts**
- ✓ **pull carts**
- ✓ **golf club rental**
- locker rooms
- showers
- executive course
- accommodations
- ✓ **food and beverages**
- ✓ **clubhouse**

**Gary McClellan**
**Lynn McClellan**
Managers

**Bud Porter**
Professional

**Gary McClellan**
Superintendent

NORTHERN B4

***Course information:*** This public course has nine holes. See card below for yardage and rating information.

***Play policy and fees:*** Green fees are $6 for nine holes and $10 for 18 holes weekdays, and $7 and $12 weekends. Memberships are available. Carts are $6 for nine holes and $10 for 18 holes. The clubhouse is closed November through February, but there is a drop box for collecting fees.

***Location:*** From Interstate 5 in Redding, drive east on Highway 299 to Alturas. Take the Warner Street exit, and drive north to the course.

***Course description:*** This course has wide fairways and elevated greens. Irrigation ditches come into play on every hole, but there are no bunkers. There is a long par-4 from the men's tees and two par-5 holes from the women's tees. The northeasternmost course in the state, Arrowhead is one of those rare courses where you can almost always drive up and tee off within minutes. It is wide-open in design as well, with small, elevated greens and a drainage ditch that comes into play on all but two holes. The toughest hole is number eight, a par-4, which measures 450 yards for men. Millard Porter holds the course record with a 66.

| Hole | 1 | 2 | 3 | 4 | 5 | 6 | 7 | 8 | 9 | Out | | |
|---|---|---|---|---|---|---|---|---|---|---|---|---|
| BLUE | - | - | - | - | - | - | - | - | - | - | BLUE | Rating:-- |
| | | | | | | | | | | | | Slope:-- |
| WHITE | 336 | 340 | 346 | 186 | 304 | 369 | 422 | 450 | 315 | 3068 | | |
| Par | 4 | 4 | 4 | 3 | 4 | 4 | 4 | 4 | 4 | 35 | WHITE | Rating:67.9 |
| Handicap | 13 | 3 | 15 | 5 | 17 | 7 | 9 | 1 | 11 | x | | Slope: 109 |
| RED | 320 | 331 | 346 | 93 | 149 | 363 | 422 | 445 | 325 | 2794 | | |
| Par | 4 | 4 | 4 | 3 | 3 | 4 | 5 | 5 | 4 | 36 | RED | Rating: 71.0 |
| Handicap | 5 | 1 | 7 | 15 | 13 | 3 | 17 | 9 | 11 | x | | Slope: 112 |

| Hole | 10 | 11 | 12 | 13 | 14 | 15 | 16 | 17 | 18 | In | Totals | |
|---|---|---|---|---|---|---|---|---|---|---|---|---|
| BLUE | - | - | - | - | - | - | - | - | - | - | BLUE | -- |
| WHITE | 346 | 330 | 358 | 170 | 314 | 359 | 420 | 446 | 325 | 3068 | WHITE | 6136 |
| Par | 4 | 4 | 4 | 3 | 4 | 4 | 4 | 4 | 4 | 35 | Par | 70 |
| Handicap | 14 | 4 | 16 | 10 | 18 | 6 | 8 | 2 | 12 | x | | |
| RED | 336 | 331 | 272 | 93 | 149 | 318 | 422 | 445 | 325 | 2691 | RED | 5485 |
| Par | 4 | 4 | 4 | 3 | 3 | 4 | 5 | 5 | 4 | 36 | Par | 72 |
| Handicap | 6 | 2 | 16 | 14 | 12 | 4 | 18 | 8 | 10 | x | | |

# MAP C0
(4 COURSES)

PAGES.......64-69

NOR-CAL MAP.....see page 30
adjoining maps
NORTH (B0).........see page 42
EAST...........................no map
SOUTH (D0).........see page 90
WEST...........................no map

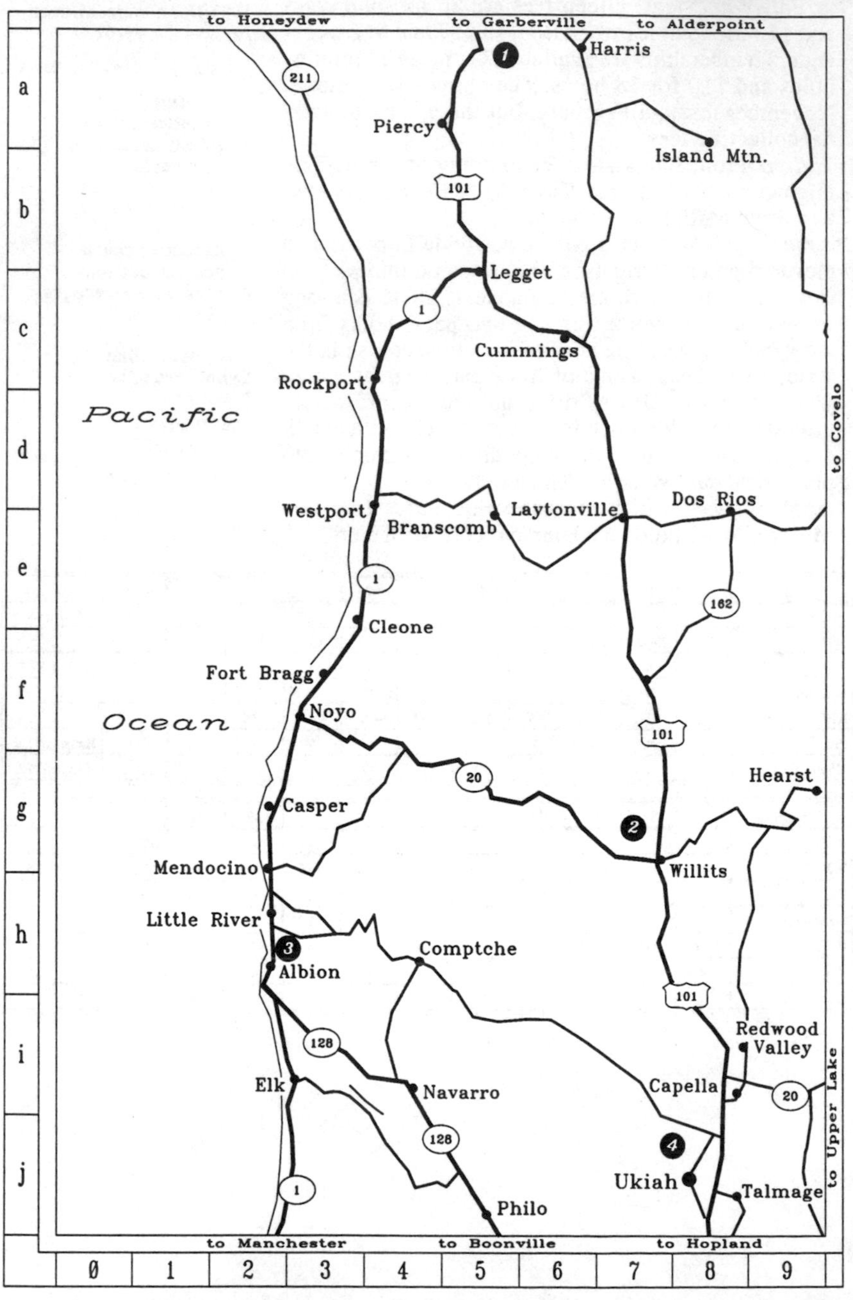

# BENBOW GOLF COURSE

**Course 1**
MAP C0 grid j5

**1925**

7000 Benbow Drive
Garberville, CA 95442

Pro shop (707) 923-2777

- driving range
- ✓ **practice greens**
- ✓ **power carts**
- ✓ **pull carts**
- ✓ **golf club rental**
- locker rooms
- showers
- executive course
- accommodations
- ✓ **food and beverages**
- clubhouse

**Don Hunt**
Manager

**John Wheeler**
Superintendent

*Course information:* This public course has nine holes with two sets of tees for those wishing to play 18. Par is 70. The course is 5,098 yards and rated 64.1 from the regular tees. The slope rating is 101. Women's tees are 5,098 and rated 68.5 with a slope rating of 114.

*Play policy and fees:* Green fees are $10 for nine holes and $13 for 18 holes for those staying in the adjacent R.V. park; $10 and $15 for non-park guests on weekdays, $13 and $18 on weekends. Carts are $9 for nine holes, $18 for 18.

*Location:* On Highway 101 two miles south of Garberville take the Benbow exit directly to the course.

*Course description:* Called "The Bowling Alley" for its tree-lined fairways, Benbow is pretty much closed in the peak summer months to those not staying in the adjacent recreational vehicle park. Several fairways slope severely left to right, making it extremely difficult to keep the ball in play. Though it has its share of hills, the course is walkable.

# BROOKTRAILS GOLF COURSE

**Course 2**
MAP C0 grid g7

***Course information:*** This public course has nine holes. Par is 56 for 18 holes. The course is 2,653 yards and rated 53.0 from the regular tees. The slope rating is 80. Women's tees are 2,653 yards and unrated.

***Play policy and fees:*** Green fees are $4.50 for nine holes and $6.50 for 18 holes weekdays, and $5.50 for nine holes and $9 for 18 holes weekends.

***Location:*** Drive north on Highway 101 through Willits, take the Sherwood exit northwest. Drive 2.5 miles to Birch Street. The course is on the right.

***Course description:*** A wonderfully scenic course set in the redwoods, Brooktrails is short but tricky, with a creek winding across four fairways. The greens are small but quick. The only par-4 is number five, a dogleg measuring 273 yards. The par-3s range in distance from 87 yards (number one) to 179 yards (number nine.) Eric McKillican holds this course record with a 51.

24860 Birch Street
Willits, CA 95490

Pro shop (707) 459-6761

- driving range
- ✓ **practice greens**
- power carts
- ✓ **pull carts**
- ✓ **golf club rental**
- locker rooms
- showers
- ✓ **executive course**
- ✓ **accommodations**
- ✓ **food and beverages**
- ✓ **clubhouse**

**Ron Runberg**
Owner

**Doug Pohlson**
Superintendent

| Hole | 1 | 2 | 3 | 4 | 5 | 6 | 7 | 8 | 9 | Out | BLUE | Rating: -- |
|---|---|---|---|---|---|---|---|---|---|---|---|---|
| BLUE | - | - | - | - | - | - | - | - | - | - | | Slope: -- |
| WHITE | 87 | 125 | 94 | 135 | 273 | 128 | 156 | 139 | 179 | 1316 | | |
| Par | 3 | 3 | 3 | 3 | 4 | 3 | 3 | 3 | 3 | 28 | WHITE | Rating: 53.0 |
| Handicap | 18 | 13 | 15 | 6 | 1 | 11 | 5 | 12 | 4 | x | | Slope: 80 |
| RED | 87 | 125 | 94 | 135 | 273 | 128 | 156 | 139 | 179 | 1316 | | |
| Par | 3 | 3 | 3 | 3 | 4 | 3 | 3 | 3 | 3 | 28 | RED | Rating: -- |
| Handicap | 18 | 10 | 15 | 8 | 1 | 12 | 6 | 11 | 4 | x | | Slope: -- |

| Hole | 10 | 11 | 12 | 13 | 14 | 15 | 16 | 17 | 18 | In | Totals | |
|---|---|---|---|---|---|---|---|---|---|---|---|---|
| BLUE | - | - | - | - | - | - | - | - | - | - | BLUE | -- |
| WHITE | 98 | 195 | 103 | 135 | 200 | 140 | 116 | 199 | 151 | 1337 | WHITE | 2653 |
| Par | 3 | 3 | 3 | 3 | 4 | 3 | 3 | 3 | 3 | 28 | Par | 56 |
| Handicap | 17 | 3 | 14 | 10 | 7 | 9 | 16 | 2 | 8 | x | | |
| RED | 98 | 195 | 103 | 135 | 200 | 140 | 116 | 199 | 151 | 1337 | RED | 2653 |
| Par | 3 | 4 | 3 | 3 | 4 | 3 | 3 | 4 | 3 | 30 | Par | 58 |
| Handicap | 17 | 3 | 14 | 9 | 5 | 7 | 16 | 2 | 13 | x | | |

# LITTLE RIVER INN GOLF AND TENNIS RESORT

**Course 3**
MAP CO grid h2

PO Box Drawer B
Little River, CA 95456

7750 North Highway 1
Little River, CA 95456

Pro shop (707) 937-5667

- ✓ **driving range**
- ✓ **practice greens**
- ✓ **power carts**
- ✓ **pull carts**
- ✓ **golf club rental**
- locker rooms
- showers
- executive course
- ✓ **accommodations**
- ✓ **food and beverages**
- ✓ **clubhouse**

**Tim Finn**
Manager

**Doug Howe**
Pro/Superintendent

***Course information:*** This resort course has nine holes. Par is 71 for 18 holes. The course is 5,458 yards and rated 66.6 from the regular tees (18 holes). The slope rating is 115. Women's tees are 4,995 yards and rated 68.6 from the regular tees. The slope rating is 111.

***Play policy and fees:*** Outside play is accepted. Green fees are $12 for nine holes and $15 for 18 holes on weekdays, and $15 for nine holes and $20 for 18 holes on weekends and holidays. Carts are $13 for nine holes and $20 for 18 holes. Golfers staying at the Inn receive a 10 percent discount on green fees and merchandise.

***Location:*** The course is located on Highway 1, south of Mendocino, in the town of Little River.

***Course description:*** This favorite of Mendocino County tourists is tight and hilly with lots of sidehill, uphill and downhill lies. Little River is known as an "11-hole course" because the seventh and ninth holes have two sets of tee boxes. The best hole is number four, a sharp dogleg par-5 of 510 yards.

# UKIAH MUNICIPAL GOLF COURSE

**Course 4**
MAP C0 grid j8

599 Park Boulevard
Ukiah, CA 95482

Pro shop (707) 462-8857

- driving range
- ✓ **practice greens**
- ✓ **power carts**
- ✓ **pull carts**
- ✓ **golf club rental**
- locker rooms
- showers
- executive course
- accommodations
- ✓ **food and beverages**
- ✓ **clubhouse**

**Jeff McMillen**
Professional

**Ken Woods**
Assistant Professional

**McCormick, Tad**
Assistant Professional

**Reed Carpenter**
Superintendent

***Course information:*** This public course has 18 holes and par is 70. The course is 5,850 yards and rated 67.4 from the championship tees, and 5,657 yards and rated 66.2 from the regular tees. The slope ratings are 120 championship and 118 regular. Women's tees are 5,657 yards and rated 71.4 from the championship tees, and 5,312 yards and rated 69.5 from the regular tees. The slope ratings are 125 championship and 120 regular.

***Play policy and fees:*** Green fees are $7 for nine holes and $9 for 18 holes weekdays, and $11 for nine holes and $13 for 18 holes weekends. Carts are $9 for nine holes and $18 for 18 holes. Reservations are recommended and accepted daily. Twilights fees are $5 weekdays, $6 weekends. All rates are $3 and $5 higher on weekdays and weekends, respectively, for non-Mendocino County residents.

***Location:*** From Highway 101 in Ukiah, take the Perkins Street exit west to North State Street. Turn left on Scott Street and follow it two blocks to Walnut Street. Walnut Street turns into Park Boulevard.

***Course description:*** Ukiah means "deep valley," and this municipal course does nothing to refute that definition. The course is short and relies on hills and oak trees to keep scores honest. The first hole is the most picturesque, a par-4 of 275 yards heading straight uphill to an elevated green. The Mendocino County Men's Amateur is held here each spring. John McMullen has the course record with a 63.

MAP ON PAGE 64

# MAP C2
(10 COURSES)

PAGES.......70-79

NOR-CAL MAP.....see page 30
adjoining maps
NORTH (B2).........see page 50
EAST (C3) ............see page 80
SOUTH (D2).......see page 126
WEST............................no map

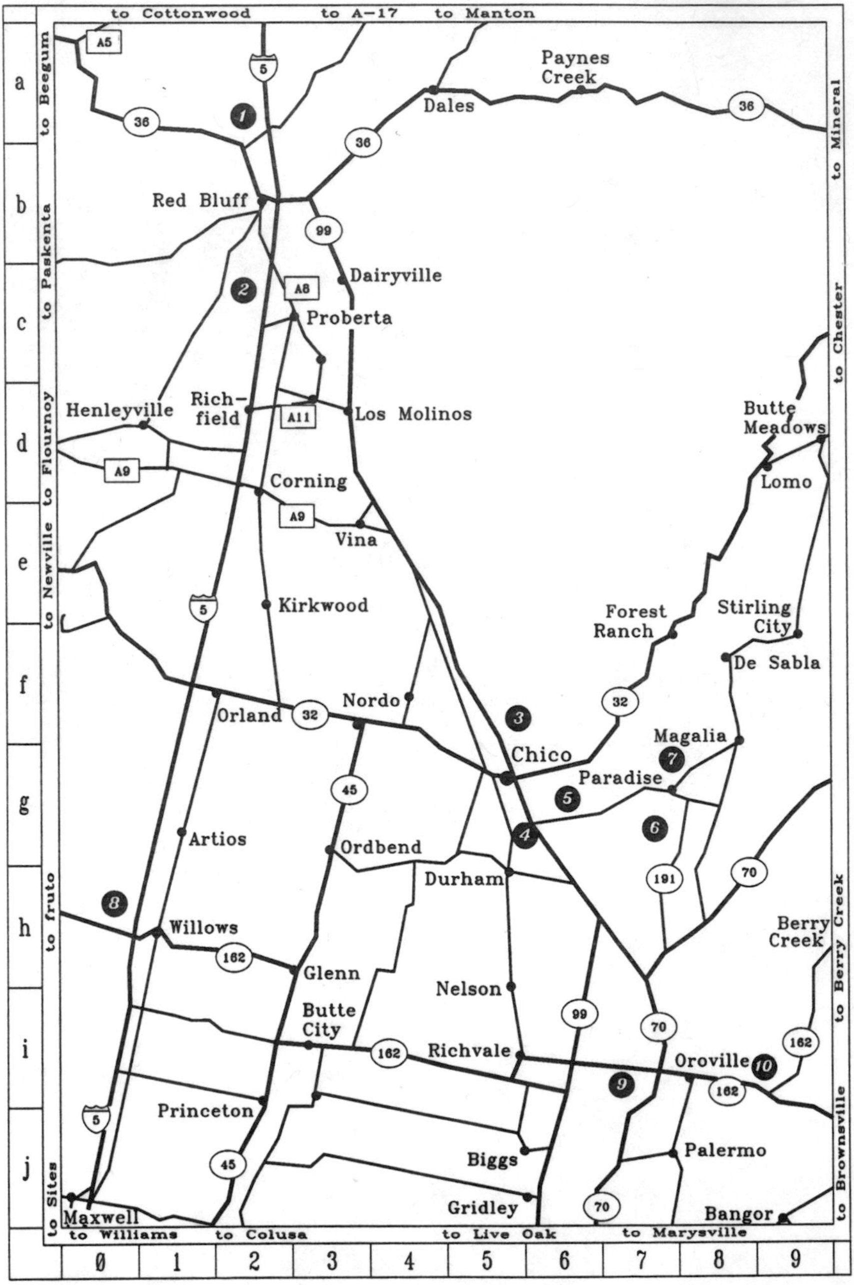

to Cottonwood
to A-17
to Manton
to Beegum
to Paskenta
to Newville to Flournoy
to fruto
to Sites
to Mineral
to Chester
to Berry Creek
to Brownsville
to Williams
to Colusa
to Live Oak
to Marysville

A5
5
36
1
Paynes Creek
Dales
36
36
Red Bluff
99
Dairyville
2
A8
Proberta
Henleyville
Rich-field
A11
Los Molinos
Butte Meadows
Lomo
A9
Corning
A9
Vina
5
Kirkwood
Forest Ranch
Stirling City
De Sabla
Nordo
3
32
Orland
32
Magalia
7
Chico
Paradise
5
45
6
Artios
4
Ordbend
Durham
191
70
8
Willows
Berry Creek
162
Glenn
Nelson
Butte City
99
70
162
162
Richvale
Oroville
10
9
162
Princeton
5
Palermo
45
Biggs
Gridley
70
Bangor
Maxwell

a
b
c
d
e
f
g
h
i
j

0 1 2 3 4 5 6 7 8 9

# WILCOX OAKS GOLF COURSE

**Course 1**
MAP C2 grid a2

*Course information:* This private course has 18 holes. Women's tees are 6,102 yards, and rated 74.5 with a slope of 127 from the championship tees. See card below for additional yardage and rating information.

*Play policy and fees:* Reciprocal play is accepted with members of other private clubs for $30. Guest fees are $15 when accompanied by a member. Carts are $14.

*Location:* From Interstate 5 just north of Red Bluff, take the Wilcox Oaks Golf Road exit. The course is on the west side of Interstate 5.

*Course description:* "The toughest 6,100-yard course in Northern California," head pro Bill DeWildt calls Wilcox Oaks. The back nine is appreciably more difficult than the front side, starting with the 300-yard tenth hole that doglegs up a steep hill. Wild turkeys frequent this course. The record is 64, held by three men.

PO Box 127
Red Bluff, CA 96080

Wilcox Oaks Golf Road
Red Bluff, CA 96080

Pro shop (916) 527-7087
Clubhouse (916) 527-6680

- ✓ **driving range**
- ✓ **practice greens**
- ✓ **power carts**
- ✓ **pull carts**
- ✓ **golf club rental**
- ✓ **locker rooms**
- ✓ **showers**
- executive course
- accommodations
- ✓ **food and beverages**
- ✓ **clubhouse**

**Linda Cristiansen**
Manager

**Bill DeWildt**
Professional

**Lin Westmoreland**
Superintendent

| Hole | 1 | 2 | 3 | 4 | 5 | 6 | 7 | 8 | 9 | Out | BLUE | Rating:-- |
|---|---|---|---|---|---|---|---|---|---|---|---|---|
| BLUE | - | - | - | - | - | - | - | - | - | - | | Slope:-- |
| WHITE | 309 | 489 | 323 | 189 | 504 | 378 | 311 | 144 | 395 | 3042 | | |
| Par | 4 | 5 | 4 | 3 | 5 | 4 | 4 | 3 | 4 | 36 | WHITE | Rating: 69.2 |
| Handicap | 12 | 4 | 14 | 16 | 2 | 6 | 10 | 18 | 8 | x | | Slope: 115 |
| RED | 302 | 462 | 314 | 180 | 464 | 366 | 303 | 135 | 375 | 2901 | | |
| Par | 4 | 5 | 4 | 3 | 5 | 4 | 4 | 3 | 4 | 36 | RED | Rating: 72.7 |
| Handicap | 13 | 1 | 9 | 15 | 3 | 5 | 11 | 17 | 7 | x | | Slope: 122 |

| Hole | 10 | 11 | 12 | 13 | 14 | 15 | 16 | 17 | 18 | In | Totals | |
|---|---|---|---|---|---|---|---|---|---|---|---|---|
| BLUE | - | - | - | - | - | - | - | - | - | - | BLUE | -- |
| WHITE | 311 | 335 | 513 | 378 | 383 | 188 | 379 | 479 | 130 | 3096 | WHITE | 6140 |
| Par | 4 | 4 | 5 | 4 | 4 | 3 | 4 | 5 | 3 | 36 | Par | 72 |
| Handicap | 7 | 13 | 3 | 9 | 1 | 15 | 5 | 11 | 17 | x | | |
| RED | 270 | 288 | 501 | 370 | 368 | 182 | 367 | 469 | 94 | 2911 | RED | 5813 |
| Par | 4 | 4 | 5 | 4 | 4 | 3 | 4 | 5 | 3 | 36 | Par | 72 |
| Handicap | 8 | 14 | 2 | 10 | 6 | 16 | 12 | 4 | 18 | x | | |

# OAK CREEK GOLF COURSE

**Course 2**
MAP C2 grid c2

***Course information:*** This public layout has nine holes. Par is 70 for 18 holes. The course is 5,350 yards and rated 64.4 from the championship tees, and 5,140 yards and rated 63.2 from the regular tees (18 holes). The slope ratings are 105 championship and 103 regular. Women's tees are 5,062 yards and rated 66.2 from the regular tees. The slope rating is 106.

***Play policy and fees:*** Green fees are $7 for nine holes and $13 for 18 holes. Senior rates are $6 for nine and $11 for 18 holes. Twilight rates are $6. Reservations are recommended. The "Thursday special" offers 18 holes for $6.

***Location:*** From Interstate 5 in Red Bluff traveling north, take the Main Street exit (first exit in Red Bluff). At the end of the exit ramp, turn north onto Main Street. When you reach Montgomery Road, turn left and follow it to the course.

***Course description:*** Mount Shasta and Mount Lassen are visible from this flat course. Annual tournaments include the Red Bluff Junior Golf Championship, Cinco De Mayo Tournament, Polar Bear, Oak Creek Challenge Cup (two-man low net) and the Project Santa Invitational. The course is in fine shape—fairly flat with two par-4s and one par-5. The seventh hole is 319 yards, but playing the left side off the tee requires a carry of 200 yards, and out-of-bounds right beckons on the other side.

2620 Montgomery Road
Red Bluff, CA 96080

Pro shop (916) 529-0674

- ✓ **driving range**
- ✓ **practice greens**
- ✓ **power carts**
- ✓ **pull carts**
- ✓ **golf club rental**
- locker rooms
- showers
- executive course
- accommodations
- ✓ **food and beverages**
- ✓ **clubhouse**

**Chris Goddard**
Manager

**Don Moore**
Superintendent

# BIDWELL PARK GOLF COURSE

Course 3
MAP C2 grid f5

**1929**

***Course information:*** This public course has 18 holes. Women's tees are 6,178 yards, and rated 74.9 with a slope of 126 from the championship tees. See card below for additional yardage and rating information.

***Play policy and fees:*** Green fees are $13 weekdays and $17 weekends. This is an all day rate; you can play as much or as little as you want. Carts are $9 for nine holes and $16 for 18 holes.

***Location:*** From Highway 99 in Chico, take the East Avenue exit and drive east to Wildwood Avenue north.

***Course description:*** Situated in a beautiful part of upper Bidwell Park, this tight course is flanked by trees and water. The front nine is set in the foothills, and the back nine is flat and longer. Accuracy is important. The third and fourth holes offer an excellent tandem of par-4s. Number three is 365 yards, a slight dogleg left over water. Number four is 403 yards with a downhill fairway shot into the green. The Chico City Amateur, one of the few match-play events left, is held here. The course record is 63, shared by three golfers.

PO Box 7750
Chico, CA 95927

Wildwood Avenue
Chico, CA 95927

Pro shop (916) 891-8417
Clubhouse (916) 894-2667

- ✓ **driving range**
- ✓ **practice greens**
- ✓ **power carts**
- ✓ **pull carts**
- ✓ **golf club rental**
- locker rooms
- showers
- executive course
- accommodations
- ✓ **food and beverages**
- ✓ **clubhouse**

**Susan Bruzza**
Manager

**John Pease, Jr.**
Professional

**Russ Krok**
Superintendent

| Hole | 1 | 2 | 3 | 4 | 5 | 6 | 7 | 8 | 9 | Out | | |
|---|---|---|---|---|---|---|---|---|---|---|---|---|
| BLUE | - | - | - | - | - | - | - | - | - | - | BLUE | Rating: |
| | | | | | | | | | | | | Slope: -- |
| WHITE | 390 | 171 | 365 | 403 | 390 | 366 | 398 | 354 | 376 | 3213 | | |
| Par | 4 | 3 | 4 | 4 | 4 | 4 | 4 | 4 | 4 | 35 | WHITE | Rating: 68.6 |
| Handicap | 3 | 17 | 7 | 1 | 5 | 9 | 11 | 13 | 15 | x | | Slope: 115 |
| RED | 377 | 145 | 353 | 415 | 376 | 357 | 393 | 339 | 362 | 3117 | | |
| Par | 4 | 3 | 4 | 5 | 4 | 4 | 4 | 4 | 4 | 36 | RED | Rating: 73.1 |
| Handicap | 2 | 18 | 8 | 16 | 4 | 10 | 12 | 6 | 14 | x | | Slope: 123 |

| Hole | 10 | 11 | 12 | 13 | 14 | 15 | 16 | 17 | 18 | In | Totals | |
|---|---|---|---|---|---|---|---|---|---|---|---|---|
| BLUE | - | - | - | - | - | - | - | - | - | - | BLUE | -- |
| WHITE | 188 | 396 | 123 | 364 | 385 | 399 | 140 | 452 | 497 | 2944 | WHITE | 6157 |
| Par | 3 | 4 | 3 | 4 | 4 | 4 | 3 | 5 | 5 | 35 | Par | 70 |
| Handicap | 10 | 4 | 16 | 8 | 2 | 6 | 18 | 14 | 12 | x | | |
| RED | 180 | 391 | 106 | 355 | 375 | 385 | 126 | 419 | 401 | 2738 | RED | 5855 |
| Par | 3 | 4 | 3 | 4 | 4 | 4 | 3 | 5 | 5 | 35 | Par | 71 |
| Handicap | 13 | 5 | 17 | 7 | 3 | 1 | 15 | 11 | 9 | x | | |

# BUTTE CREEK COUNTRY CLUB

**Course 4**
MAP C2 grid g5

**1965**
**R.E. Baldock**

175 Estates Drive
Chico, CA 95928

Pro shop (916) 343-8292
Clubhouse (916) 343-7979

- ✓ **driving range**
- ✓ **practice greens**
- ✓ **power carts**
- ✓ **pull carts**
- ✓ **golf club rental**
- ✓ **locker rooms**
- ✓ **showers**
- executive course
- accommodations
- ✓ **food and beverages**
- ✓ **clubhouse**

**Larry Reynolds**
Manager

**Ed Hester**
Professional

**Curtis Carrico**
Superintendent

***Course information:*** This private course has 18 holes and par is 72. The course is 6,897 yards and rated 72.8 from the tournament tees, and 6,663 yards and rated 71.7 from the championship tees, and 6,103 yards and rated 69.3 from the regular tees. The slope ratings are: 125 tournament, 122 championship and 117 regular. Women's tees are 6,086 yards and rated 74.8 from the regular tees. The slope rating is 126.

***Play policy and fees:*** Members and guests only. Reciprocal fees are the same as those charged by the visitor's course. Guest fees are $15 when accompanied by a member and $25 without. Carts are $14.

***Location:*** From Highway 99 in Chico, take the Estates Drive exit. Drive one mile west to the course.

***Course description:*** Butte Creek is inarguably one of the top courses in the Sacramento Valley. The creek for which the course is named comes into play on five holes. Relatively open for the most part, this course has enough old oak trees to cause trouble, and the greens are large and undulating. The par-3 17th is a beauty, over water with flowers and railroad ties surrounding the green. Butte Creek played host to U.S. Open local qualifying in 1992.

# CANYON OAKS COUNTRY CLUB

**Course 5**
MAP C2 grid g6

**1990**
999 Yosemite Drive
Chico, CA 95928

Pro shop (916) 345-1622

- ✓ **driving range**
- ✓ **practice greens**
- ✓ **power carts**
- ✓ **pull carts**
- ✓ **golf club rental**
- locker rooms
- showers
- executive course
- accommodations
- ✓ **food and beverages**
- clubhouse

**Ron Davis**
Manager

**Paul Bullock**
Professional

**Bill Fosnot**
Superintendent

***Course information:*** This public course has 18 holes and par is 72. The course is 6,779 yards and rated 72.9 with a slope of 133 from the tournament tees, 6,221 yards and rated 70.5 with a slope of 128 from the championship tees, and 5,701 yards and rated 68.1 with a slope of 123 from the regular tees. Women's tees are 5,701 and rated 73.6 with a slope of 137 from the championship tees, and 5,030 yards and rated 70.4 with a slope of 127 from the regular tees.

***Play policy and fees:*** Green fees are $17 weekdays and $22 weekends. Carts are $16. Reservations recommended one week in advance. This course is available for outside tournaments. There is a dress code.

***Location:*** From Highway 99 in Chico, take Highway 32 east. Turn left on Bruce Road and drive past the California Park Pavilion to the course.

***Course description:*** On the site of a former driving range, this hilly course has narrow fairways and greens of varying size and contour. The course is tree-lined and a creek bed runs throughout. Water is everywhere but only comes into play on three holes. The sixth hole is a par-3 of 180 yards over water and number 18, a par-4, measures 486 yards from the back tees. Many call the large greens some of the finest in the north state. Definitely a course worth playing.

# TALL PINES GOLF COURSE

**Course 6**
MAP C2 grid g7

**1965**
**Joe Balch**

5325 Clark Road
Paradise, CA 95969

Pro shop (916) 877-5816

- ✓ **driving range**
- ✓ **practice greens**
- ✓ **power carts**
- ✓ **pull carts**
- ✓ **golf club rental**
- locker rooms
- showers
- executive course
- accommodations
- ✓ **food and beverages**
- ✓ **clubhouse**

**Joe Balch**
Owner/Professional

**John McHargue**
Superintendent

***Course information:*** This public course has nine holes. Par is 68 for 18 holes. The course is 4,209 yards and rated 60.1 from the regular tees. The slope rating is 84. Women's tees are 4,209 yards and rated 65.2 from the regular tees. The slope rating is 110.

***Play policy and fees:*** Green fees are $8 for nine holes and $10 for 18 holes weekdays, and $9 for nine holes and $12 for 18 holes weekends. Carts are $13 for 18 holes weekdays and $14 for 18 holes weekends and holidays. Pull carts are $1.50.

***Location:*** Drive north on Highway 70, through Oroville. Take the Highway 191/Clark Road exit toward Paradise. Drive 11 miles north on Highway 191 (Clark Road) to Paradise. The course is on the left.

***Course description:*** This course is characterized by rolling, elevated greens. Like most foothill courses, Tall Pines is tight with plenty of trees. The signature hole is number one, the number one handicap hole with an elevated green nestled into—what else—tall pines. Randy Gath and Mark Pata hold the men's course record with a 60, and Deborah Baker holds the women's with a 69.



MAP ON PAGE 70

# PARADISE PINES GOLF COURSE

Course 7
MAP C2 grid g7

***Course information:*** This public course has nine holes. See card below for yardage and rating information.

***Play policy and fees:*** Green fees are $9 for nine holes and $12 for 18 holes on weekdays, and $10 for nine holes and $13 for 18 holes weekends. Carts are $9 for nine holes and $14 for 18 holes. Reservations are recommended. Tee time reservations are accepted two days in advance. Shirts are required.

***Location:*** From Highway 99 in Chico, take the Skyway exit and drive to Magalia. In Magalia, turn left on South Park Drive.

***Course description:*** This short course has tight, tree-lined fairways and offers diversity from hole to hole. Holes five through seven are the course's best. Number five is a par-3 of 190 yards; number six is a narrow, dogleg par-4 measuring 364 yards; and number seven is a dogleg par-5 of 500 yards. An interesting course with plenty of undulating lies and small greens.

PO Box 1538
Magalia, CA 95954

13917 South Park Drive
Magalia, CA 95954

Pro shop (916) 873-1111

- ✓ **driving range**
- ✓ **practice greens**
- ✓ **power carts**
- ✓ **pull carts**
- ✓ **golf club rental**
- locker rooms
- showers
- executive course
- accommodations
- ✓ **food and beverages**
- ✓ **clubhouse**

**Chuck Overmyer**
Manager/ Professional

**Bob Fortina**
Owner

**Dave Roberts**
Superintendent

| Hole | 1 | 2 | 3 | 4 | 5 | 6 | 7 | 8 | 9 | Out | | |
|---|---|---|---|---|---|---|---|---|---|---|---|---|
| BLUE | - | - | - | - | - | - | - | - | - | - | BLUE | Rating:-- |
| | | | | | | | | | | | | Slope:-- |
| WHITE | 295 | 234 | 201 | 323 | 188 | 364 | 486 | 265 | 139 | 2495 | | |
| Par | 4 | 4 | 3 | 4 | 3 | 4 | 5 | 4 | 3 | 34 | WHITE | Rating:64.6 |
| Handicap | 12 | 16 | 8 | 10 | 6 | 4 | 2 | 14 | 18 | x | | Slope: |
| RED | 290 | 241 | 193 | 314 | 178 | 336 | 477 | 268 | 130 | 2427 | | |
| Par | 4 | 4 | 3 | 4 | 3 | 4 | 5 | 4 | 3 | 34 | RED | Rating: 68.4 |
| Handicap | 12 | 16 | 8 | 10 | 6 | 4 | 2 | 14 | 18 | x | | Slope: |

| Hole | 10 | 11 | 12 | 13 | 14 | 15 | 16 | 17 | 18 | In | Totals | |
|---|---|---|---|---|---|---|---|---|---|---|---|---|
| BLUE | - | - | - | - | - | - | - | - | - | - | BLUE | -- |
| WHITE | 313 | 255 | 196 | 347 | 198 | 385 | 500 | 284 | 149 | 2627 | WHITE | 5122 |
| Par | 4 | 4 | 3 | 4 | 3 | 4 | 5 | 4 | 3 | 34 | Par | 68 |
| Handicap | 11 | 15 | 7 | 9 | 5 | 3 | 1 | 13 | 17 | x | | |
| RED | 295 | 234 | 201 | 323 | 188 | 364 | 486 | 265 | 139 | 2495 | RED | 4922 |
| Par | 4 | 4 | 3 | 4 | 3 | 4 | 5 | 4 | 3 | 34 | Par | 68 |
| Handicap | 11 | 15 | 7 | 9 | 5 | 3 | 1 | 13 | 17 | x | | |

# GLENN GOLF AND COUNTRY CLUB

Course 8
MAP C2 grid h0

**1960**

*Course information:* This semi-private course has nine holes. Par is 72 for 18 holes. The course is 6,509 yards and rated 69.6 from the regular tees. The slope rating is 106. Women's tees are 5,917 yards and rated 72.4. The slope rating is 114.

*Play policy and fees:* Outside play is accepted. Green fees are $10 on weekdays and $15 weekends. Senior rates are $5 during the week. Carts are $15 for f18 holes, $9 for nine holes.

*Location:* The course is five miles north of Willows on Bayliss Blue Gum Road. From Interstate 5, take the Bayliss Blue Gum Road exit west.

*Course description:* This long course is lined with weeping willows and eucalyptus. It has outstanding greens and a great view of the Sierra. There are four par-5 holes. The number-one handicap hole is the fourth, a par-3 of 215 yards. There is out-of-bounds to the left and in the back of the green, which is guarded by bunkers in the front. If you hit on the back of the green you are out-of-bounds. The average score on this par-3 is 4.3. The men's course record is 63, set by Ken Dunn in 1988. Glenn head pro Tony De Napoli calls it "a player's course because you're not fighting traps and water all the time."

6226 Country Road 39
Willows, CA 95988

Bayliss Blue Gum Road
Willows, CA 95988

Pro shop (916) 934-9918

- ✓ **driving range**
- ✓ **practice greens**
- ✓ **power carts**
- ✓ **pull carts**
- ✓ **golf club rental**
- locker rooms
- showers
- executive course
- accommodations
- ✓ **food and beverages**
- ✓ **clubhouse**

**Don Bowes**
Manager

**Tony De Napoli**
Professional

**David Delay**
Superintendent

NORTHERN C2

# TABLE MOUNTAIN GOLF COURSE

**Course 9**
MAP C2 grid i7

**1956**
**R.E. Baldock**

PO Box 2767
Oroville, CA 95965

2700 West Oro Dam Blvd.
Oroville, CA 95965

Pro shop (916) 533-3922
Clubhouse (916) 533-3924

- ✓ **driving range**
- ✓ **practice greens**
- ✓ **power carts**
- ✓ **pull carts**
- ✓ **golf club rental**
- locker rooms
- showers
- executive course
- accommodations
- ✓ **food and beverages**
- ✓ **clubhouse**

**Ron Anderson**
Professional

**Dean Olson**
Superintendent

***Course information:*** This municipal course has 18 holes. See card below for yardage and rating information.

***Play policy and fees:*** Green fees are $13 for 18 holes weekdays, $10 and $15 weekends. Carts are $10 for nine holes and $16 for 18 holes.

***Location:*** This course is located in Oroville on Highway 162 (West Oro Dam Boulevard) between Highway 99 and Highway 70.

***Course description:*** Table Mountain is a wide-open course with fast fairways, considerable hardpan and quick greens. Forty bunkers and four ponds make things difficult in lieu of numerous trees that were killed by winter frost. The signature hole is number 18, a par-4 covering 417 yards.

| Hole | 1 | 2 | 3 | 4 | 5 | 6 | 7 | 8 | 9 | Out | | |
|---|---|---|---|---|---|---|---|---|---|---|---|---|
| BLUE | - | - | - | - | - | - | - | - | - | - | BLUE | Rating: -- |
| | | | | | | | | | | | | Slope: -- |
| WHITE | 350 | 502 | 137 | 419 | 389 | 434 | 166 | 404 | 477 | 3278 | | |
| Par | 4 | 5 | 3 | 4 | 4 | 4 | 3 | 4 | 5 | 36 | WHITE | Rating:70.1 |
| Handicap | 15 | 13 | 17 | 3 | 7 | 1 | 9 | 5 | 11 | x | | Slope: 116 |
| RED | 337 | 486 | 92 | 380 | 377 | 393 | 143 | 380 | 457 | 3045 | | |
| Par | 4 | 5 | 3 | 4 | 4 | 4 | 3 | 4 | 5 | 36 | RED | Rating: 72.8 |
| Handicap | 13 | 1 | 17 | 9 | 11 | 5 | 15 | 7 | 3 | x | | Slope: 112 |

| Hole | 10 | 11 | 12 | 13 | 14 | 15 | 16 | 17 | 18 | In | Totals | |
|---|---|---|---|---|---|---|---|---|---|---|---|---|
| BLUE | - | - | - | - | - | - | - | - | - | - | BLUE | -- |
| WHITE | 366 | 491 | 140 | 376 | 500 | 344 | 166 | 394 | 417 | 3194 | WHITE | 6472 |
| Par | 4 | 5 | 3 | 4 | 5 | 4 | 3 | 4 | 4 | 36 | Par | 72 |
| Handicap | 8 | 12 | 18 | 6 | 14 | 16 | 10 | 4 | 2 | x | | |
| RED | 355 | 450 | 124 | 357 | 412 | 313 | 129 | 357 | 340 | 2837 | RED | 5882 |
| Par | 4 | 5 | 3 | 4 | 5 | 4 | 3 | 4 | 4 | 36 | Par | 72 |
| Handicap | 8 | 2 | 18 | 6 | 4 | 12 | 16 | 10 | 14 | x | | |

# KELLY RIDGE GOLF LINKS

**Course 10**
MAP C2 grid i9

**1974**
**Homer Flint**

5131 Royal Oaks Drive
Oroville, CA 95966

Pro shop (916) 589-0777

- driving range
- ✓ **practice greens**
- ✓ **power carts**
- ✓ **pull carts**
- ✓ **golf club rental**
- locker rooms
- showers
- executive course
- accommodations
- ✓ **food and beverages**
- ✓ **clubhouse**

**Paul Mares**
Manager/Professional

**Barry Roderick**
Superintendent

NORTHERN C2

***Course information:*** This semi-private course has nine holes. Par is 66 for 18 holes. The course is 4,160 yards and rated 62.5 at 18 holes. The slope rating is 106. Women's tees are also 4,160 yards, with a rating of 64.6. The slope rating is 120.

***Play policy and fees:*** Reciprocal play is accepted with members of other private clubs. Just show your NCGA card. Outside play is accepted. Green fees are $7 for nine holes and $9 for 18 holes weekdays; $9 and $11 weekends and holidays. On Tuesdays and Wednesdays after 2 p.m., nine holes and a cart costs $17 for two people, $27 for 18 holes. Carts are $8 for nine holes and $14 for 18 holes weekdays, and $10 for nine holes and $14 for 18 holes weekends and holidays. Reservations are recommended at least 24 hours in advance on weekends. Shirts are required.

***Location:*** From Highway 70 in Oroville, take the Oro Dam Boulevard exit east 1.5 miles to Olive Highway. Turn right and drive 5.5 miles to Kelly Ridge Road. Turn left and go left again at Royal Oaks Drive.

***Course description:*** Situated in the Sierra Alton foothills on the Oro Dam, this short course is hilly and tight with narrow fairways and well bunkered greens. Balls tend to roll to the right. Many players are intimidated by the 135-yard par-3 third hole, which requires a carry over a deep ravine. There are six par-4 and three par-3 holes.

MAP ON PAGE 70

# MAP C3
(7 COURSES)

PAGES.......80-87

NOR-CAL MAP.....see page 30
adjoining maps
NORTH (B3) .........see page 60
EAST (C4) ............see page 88
SOUTH (D3) .......see page 158
WEST (C2) ...........see page 70

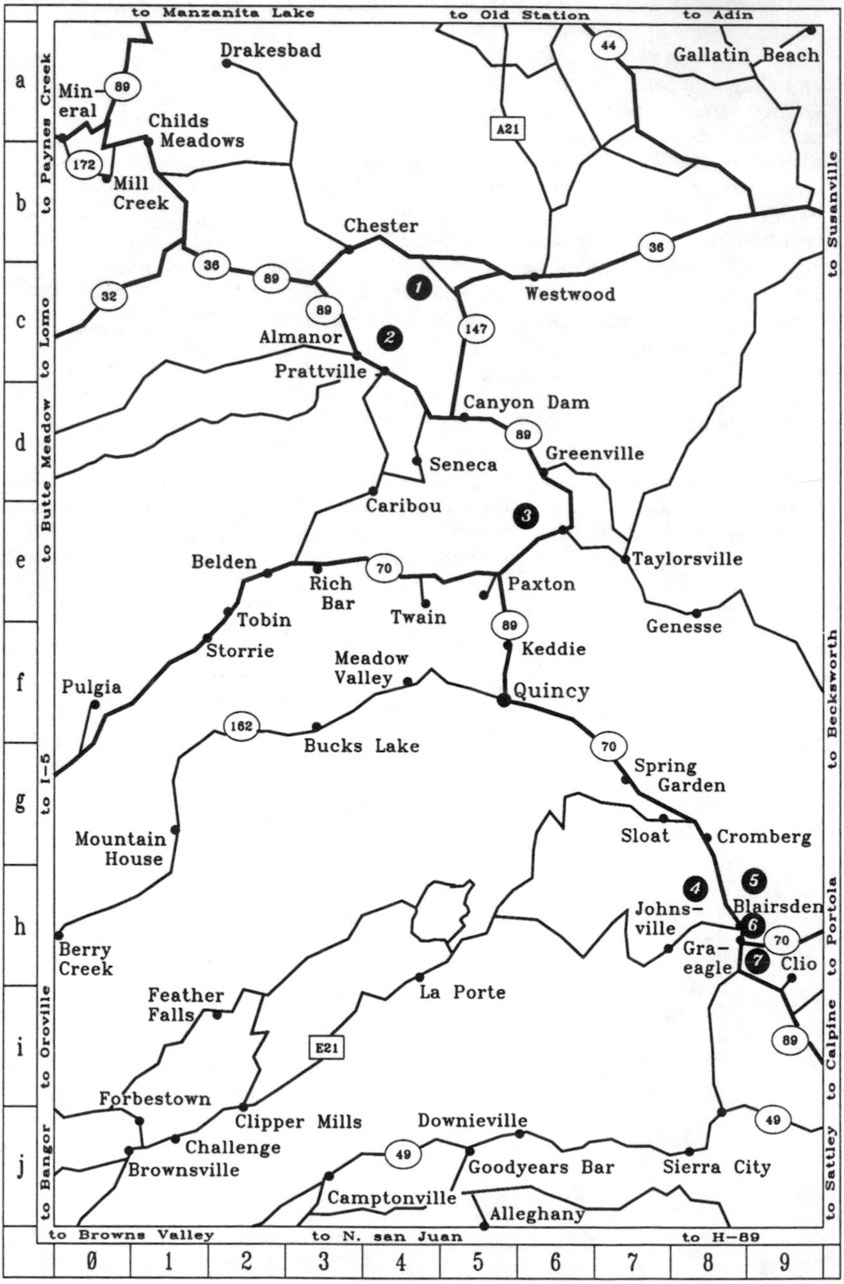

to Manzanita Lake
to Old Station
to Adin
to Paynes Creek
to Butte Meadow to Lomo
to I-5
to Oroville
to Bangor
to Susanville
to Becksworth
to Portola
to Calpine
to Sattley
to Browns Valley
to N. san Juan
to H-89

Drakesbad
Gallatin Beach
Mineral
Childs Meadows
Mill Creek
Chester
Westwood
Almanor
Prattville
Canyon Dam
Seneca
Greenville
Caribou
Belden
Rich Bar
Twain
Paxton
Taylorsville
Tobin
Storrie
Genesse
Keddie
Meadow Valley
Quincy
Pulgia
Bucks Lake
Spring Garden
Mountain House
Sloat
Cromberg
Johnsville
Blairsden
Graeagle
Clio
Berry Creek
Feather Falls
La Porte
Forbestown
Clipper Mills
Downieville
Challenge
Brownsville
Goodyears Bar
Sierra City
Camptonville
Alleghany

89, 172, 36, 32, 89, 89, 147, 36, 44, A21, 89, 70, 89, 162, 70, 70, 89, E21, 49, 49

1 2 3 4 5 6 7

a b c d e f g h i j

0 1 2 3 4 5 6 7 8 9

# LAKE ALMANOR COUNTRY CLUB

**Course 1**
MAP C3 grid c4

**1958**

PO Box 3323
Lake Almanor, CA 96137

951 Clifford Drive
Lake Almanor, CA 96137

Pro shop (916) 259-2868
Clubhouse (916) 259-2141

✓ **driving range**
✓ **practice greens**
✓ **power carts**
✓ **pull carts**
golf club rental
locker rooms
showers
executive course
accommodations
✓ **food and beverages**
✓ **clubhouse**

**Tom Maumoynier,**
Superintendent

NORTHERN C3

***Course information:*** This private course has nine holes. See card below for yardage and rating information.

***Play policy and fees:*** Public play is accepted after 3 p.m. in July and August. Green fees are $14 for nine holes and $23 for 18 holes for non-members. Carts are $8.50 per nine holes. Outside players will not be permitted through the gate without a pre-arranged tee time. Reservations should be made on the day of play.

***Location:*** From Interstate 5 in Red Bluff, take Highway 36 through Chester. Turn on County Road A13 and drive about one mile. Turn right on Walker Road and drive to the gate.

***Course description:*** This rolling, scenic mountain course has big trees and undulating greens. The par-4 second hole provides a breathtaking view of Mount Lassen and the seventh hole offers a view of Lake Almanor. Mark Soltau's 63 is the course record.

| Hole | 1 | 2 | 3 | 4 | 5 | 6 | 7 | 8 | 9 | Out | BLUE | Rating:-- |
|---|---|---|---|---|---|---|---|---|---|---|---|---|
| BLUE | - | - | - | - | - | - | - | - | - | - | | Slope:-- |
| WHITE | 506 | 331 | 321 | 194 | 387 | 220 | 474 | 131 | 355 | 2919 | | |
| Par | 5 | 4 | 4 | 3 | 4 | 3 | 5 | 3 | 4 | 35 | WHITE | Rating: 68.3 |
| Handicap | 5 | 11 | 13 | 13 | 1 | 9 | 7 | 17 | 3 | x | | Slope: 114 |
| RED | 427 | 321 | 313 | 173 | 374 | 275 | 464 | 120 | 348 | 2815 | | |
| Par | 5 | 4 | 4 | 3 | 4 | 4 | 5 | 3 | 4 | 36 | RED | Rating: 71.9 |
| Handicap | 1 | 13 | 11 | 15 | 5 | 7 | 9 | 17 | 3 | x | | Slope: 117 |

| Hole | 10 | 11 | 12 | 13 | 14 | 15 | 16 | 17 | 18 | In | Totals | |
|---|---|---|---|---|---|---|---|---|---|---|---|---|
| BLUE | - | - | - | - | - | - | - | - | - | - | BLUE | -- |
| WHITE | 506 | 331 | 321 | 194 | 387 | 220 | 509 | 131 | 355 | 2954 | WHITE | 5873 |
| Par | 5 | 4 | 4 | 3 | 4 | 3 | 5 | 3 | 4 | 35 | Par | 70 |
| Handicap | 6 | 12 | 14 | 16 | 2 | 10 | 8 | 18 | 4 | x | | |
| RED | 427 | 321 | 313 | 173 | 374 | 275 | 464 | 120 | 348 | 2815 | RED | 5630 |
| Par | 5 | 4 | 4 | 3 | 4 | 4 | 5 | 3 | 4 | 36 | Par | 72 |
| Handicap | 2 | 14 | 12 | 16 | 6 | 8 | 10 | 18 | 4 | x | | |

# ALMANOR WEST GOLF COURSE

**Course 2**
MAP C3 grid c4

***Course information:*** This public course has nine holes. See card below for yardage and rating information.

***Play policy and fees:*** Green fees are $15 for nine holes and $22 for 18 holes. Carts are $20.

***Location:*** From Interstate 5 in Red Bluff, take Highway 36 to Highway 89. Drive south on Highway 89 to Lake Almanor west. Turn left on Slim Drive and you'll find the course.

***Course description:*** This picturesque mountain layout offers a dramatic view of Mount Lassen. It has towering pines and large, undulating greens. The fairways are wide-open. The third hole—a par-3 of 176 yards for men and 136 yards for women—requires a firm shot over water. Club pro June Szody holds the women's course record with a 68.

PO Box 1040
Chester, CA 96020

111 Slim Drive
Chester, CA 96020

Pro shop (916) 259-4555

- ✓ **driving range**
- ✓ **practice greens**
- ✓ **power carts**
- ✓ **pull carts**
- golf club rental
- locker rooms
- showers
- executive course
- accommodations
- ✓ **food and beverages**
- ✓ **clubhouse**

**June Szody**
Manager/Professional

**Gary Boatwright**
Superintendent

| Hole | 1 | 2 | 3 | 4 | 5 | 6 | 7 | 8 | 9 | Out | BLUE | Rating: -- |
|---|---|---|---|---|---|---|---|---|---|---|---|---|
| BLUE | - | - | - | - | - | - | - | - | - | - | | Slope:-- |
| WHITE | 489 | 341 | 176 | 389 | 354 | 162 | 470 | 440 | 323 | 3144 | | |
| Par | 5 | 4 | 3 | 4 | 4 | 3 | 5 | 4 | 4 | 36 | WHITE | Rating: 69.6 |
| Handicap | 11 | 17 | 5 | 3 | 9 | 15 | 7 | 1 | 13 | x | | Slope:-- |
| RED | 454 | 308 | 131 | 364 | 306 | 120 | 411 | 324 | 266 | 2684 | | |
| Par | 5 | 4 | 3 | 4 | 4 | 3 | 5 | 4 | 4 | 364 | RED | Rating: 69.6 |
| Handicap | 1 | 9 | 5 | 3 | 13 | 17 | 11 | 7 | 15 | x | | Slope: -- |

| Hole | 10 | 11 | 12 | 13 | 14 | 15 | 16 | 17 | 18 | In | Totals | |
|---|---|---|---|---|---|---|---|---|---|---|---|---|
| BLUE | - | - | - | - | - | - | - | - | - | - | BLUE | -- |
| WHITE | 474 | 375 | 137 | 402 | 329 | 155 | 411 | 522 | 369 | 3174 | WHITE | 6318 |
| Par | 5 | 4 | 3 | 4 | 4 | 3 | 4 | 5 | 4 | 36 | Par | 72 |
| Handicap | 8 | 14 | 18 | 2 | 16 | 12 | 4 | 6 | 10 | x | | |
| RED | 408 | 318 | 97 | 345 | 304 | 109 | 363 | 488 | 279 | 2711 | RED | 5395 |
| Par | 5 | 4 | 3 | 4 | 4 | 3 | 4 | 5 | 4 | 36 | Par | 72 |
| Handicap | 2 | 12 | 16 | 6 | 14 | 18 | 8 | 4 | 10 | x | | |

# MOUNT HUFF

**Course 3**
MAP C3 grid e6

*Course information:* This public course has nine holes. Par is 66 for 18 holes. The course is 4,409 yards and rated 60.2 from the regular tees. The slope rating is 92. Women's tees are 3,794 yards and rated 61.1 from the regular tees. The slope rating is 93.

*Play policy and fees:* Green fees are $6 for nine holes and $10 for 18 holes weekdays, and $7 and $12 weekends and holidays. Carts are $7 for nine holes and $12 for 18 holes.

*Location:* From Interstate 5 in Red Bluff, take Highway 36 to Highway 89. Follow Highway 89 to Crescent Mills (between Greenville and Quincy). The course is located on Highway 89 at the Taylorsville "T" Coming from Oroville take Highway 70 east to Highway 89. Turn left on Highway 89 and drive six miles to the course.

*Course description:* The course originated as a six-hole layout about 25 years ago, and was designated nine holes in 1981. Many seniors enjoy this course because it isn't too hilly. However, flat doesn't mean easy. The par-3s are long, though the best one might be number four, which measures just 135 yards but plays much tougher because of water. The course record is 57, set by Greg Hockenson.

PO Box 569
Greenville, CA 95947

Highway 89 at the
Taylorsville "T"
Crescent Mills, CA 95934

Pro shop (916) 284-6204

- ✓ **driving range**
- practice greens
- ✓ **power carts**
- ✓ **pull carts**
- ✓ **golf club rental**
- locker rooms
- showers
- ✓ **executive course**
- accommodations
- ✓ **food and beverages**
- ✓ **clubhouse**

**Loren Lindner**
Manager

**Clyde Alexander**
**Loren Lindner**
Professionals

**Todd Posch**
Superintendent

# GRAEAGLE MEADOWS GOLF COURSE

**Course 4**
MAP C3 grid h9

**1968**

*Course information:* This public course has 18 holes. See card below for yardage and rating information.

*Play policy and fees:* Green fees are $25 seven days a week. The twilight rate (after 4 p.m.) is $16. Carts are $22. Reservations are recommended. This course is available for outside tournaments. The course is open from April until about mid-November.

*Location:* From Truckee, drive 50 miles north on Highway 89. The course is on Highway 89 in Graeagle, three miles south of Highway 70.

*Course description:* This popular mountain course is set in a picturesque valley with the Feather River running through it. Though pine trees abound, most holes are fairly wide-open off the tee. Graeagle's signature hole is number six, a 386-yarder with a bunker across the fairway and a stunning view of Eureka Peak. The course record of 62 is held by Dick Lotz.

PO Box 68
Graeagle, CA 96103

Highway 89
Graeagle, CA 96103

Pro shop (916) 836-2323
Clubhouse (916) 836-2348

- ✓ **driving range**
- ✓ **practice greens**
- ✓ **power carts**
- ✓ **pull carts**
- ✓ **golf club rental**
- locker rooms
- showers
- executive course
- accommodations
- ✓ **food and beverages**
- ✓ **clubhouse**

**Don West**
Manager

**Bob Klein Jr.**
Professional

**Ross Ripple**
Superintendent

| Hole | 1 | 2 | 3 | 4 | 5 | 6 | 7 | 8 | 9 | Out | BLUE | Rating:-- |
|---|---|---|---|---|---|---|---|---|---|---|---|---|
| BLUE | - | - | - | - | - | - | - | - | - | - | | Slope: -- |
| WHITE | 435 | 394 | 110 | 413 | 512 | 386 | 543 | 139 | 357 | 3289 | | |
| Par | 4 | 4 | 3 | 4 | 5 | 4 | 5 | 3 | 4 | 36 | WHITE | Rating: 70.7 |
| Handicap | 3 | 11 | 17 | 1 | 7 | 9 | 5 | 13 | 15 | x | | Slope:118 |
| RED | 370 | 284 | 110 | 366 | 440 | 354 | 481 | 139 | 290 | 2834 | | |
| Par | 4 | 4 | 3 | 4 | 5 | 4 | 5 | 3 | 4 | 36 | RED | Rating: 71.3 |
| Handicap | 7 | 13 | 17 | 5 | 3 | 9 | 1 | 15 | 11 | x | | Slope: 118 |

| Hole | 10 | 11 | 12 | 13 | 14 | 15 | 16 | 17 | 18 | In | Totals | |
|---|---|---|---|---|---|---|---|---|---|---|---|---|
| BLUE | - | - | - | - | - | - | - | - | - | - | BLUE | -- |
| WHITE | 437 | 504 | 135 | 431 | 401 | 422 | 161 | 395 | 505 | 3391 | WHITE | 6680 |
| Par | 4 | 5 | 3 | 4 | 4 | 4 | 3 | 4 | 5 | 36 | Par | 72 |
| Handicap | 4 | 16 | 18 | 2 | 12 | 6 | 8 | 10 | 14 | x | | |
| RED | 369 | 416 | 135 | 351 | 307 | 358 | 139 | 304 | 427 | 2806 | RED | 5640 |
| Par | 4 | 5 | 3 | 4 | 4 | 4 | 3 | 4 | 5 | 36 | Par | 72 |
| Handicap | 4 | 2 | 18 | 10 | 12 | 6 | 14 | 16 | 8 | x | | |

# PLUMAS PINES COUNTRY CLUB

**Course 5**
MAP C3 grid h8



**1980**
**Homer Flint**

402 Poplar Valley Road
Blairsden, CA 96103

Pro shop (916) 836-1420
Clubhouse (916) 836-1305

- ✓ **driving range**
- ✓ **practice greens**
- ✓ **power carts**
- pull carts
- ✓ **golf club rental**
- ✓ **locker rooms**
- ✓ **showers**
- executive course
- ✓ **accommodations**
- ✓ **food and beverages**
- ✓ **clubhouse**

**Tony DiLoreto**
Manager

**Gregory Katerba**
Professional

**Ben Keechler II**
Superintendent

***Course information:*** This public course has 18 holes. Women's tees are 5,824 yards and rated 74.1 with a slope of 136 from the championship tees. See card below for additional yardage and rating information.

***Play policy and fees:*** Green fees are $40, Monday through Thursday including cart. Fees are $45 Friday through Sunday. There is a $45 mid-week and $55 weekend golfers' special that includes dinner for tee times after 2 p.m. Twilight rates begin at 3:30 p.m. and are $30. Reservations are recommended and should be made three weeks in advance. Shirts and shoes must be worn at all times. The course is open from April to November.

***Location:*** The course is located in Blairsden just off Highway 70.

***Course description:*** This scenic, hilly course is situated in the midst of Plumas National Forest and is bordered by the Middle Fork of the Feather River. The fairways are tight with lots of trees. One notable hole is the second, a 419-yard par-4 with the river to the left and trees to the right. Another tough hole is the 201-yard, par-3 third over water. This is a regular qualifying site of the USGA Women's Mid-Amateur Championship Tournament. Plumas Pines is the sort of course that takes a different mindset to play because many holes demand an iron off the tee. It may sound like a cliche, but accuracy is more important than length here.

| Hole | 1 | 2 | 3 | 4 | 5 | 6 | 7 | 8 | 9 | Out | | |
|---|---|---|---|---|---|---|---|---|---|---|---|---|
| BLUE | 591 | 419 | 201 | 484 | 378 | 310 | 157 | 414 | 395 | 3349 | BLUE | Rating: 71.6 |
| WHITE | 548 | 359 | 155 | 458 | 364 | 293 | 126 | 362 | 363 | 3028 | | Slope: 127 |
| Par | 5 | 4 | 3 | 5 | 4 | 4 | 3 | 4 | 4 | 36 | WHITE | Rating: 69.0 |
| Handicap | 9 | 3 | 5 | 11 | 13 | 15 | 17 | 7 | 1 | x | | Slope: 120 |
| RED | 469 | 309 | 135 | 318 | 344 | 254 | 109 | 410 | 312 | 2660 | | |
| Par | 5 | 4 | 3 | 4 | 4 | 4 | 3 | 5 | 4 | 36 | RED | Rating: 68.5 |
| Handicap | 1 | 9 | 17 | 11 | 7 | 13 | 15 | 3 | 5 | x | | Slope: 122 |

| Hole | 10 | 11 | 12 | 13 | 14 | 15 | 16 | 17 | 18 | In | Totals | |
|---|---|---|---|---|---|---|---|---|---|---|---|---|
| BLUE | 295 | 177 | 379 | 460 | 398 | 155 | 354 | 398 | 539 | 3155 | BLUE | 6504 |
| WHITE | 257 | 135 | 349 | 450 | 352 | 139 | 298 | 373 | 513 | 2866 | WHITE | 5894 |
| Par | 4 | 3 | 4 | 5 | 4 | 3 | 4 | 4 | 5 | 36 | Par | 72 |
| Handicap | 16 | 14 | 4 | 12 | 10 | 18 | 8 | 6 | 2 | x | | |
| RED | 233 | 98 | 329 | 360 | 265 | 128 | 267 | 340 | 426 | 2446 | RED | 5106 |
| Par | 4 | 3 | 4 | 4 | 4 | 3 | 4 | 4 | 5 | 35 | Par | 71 |
| Handicap | 14 | 18 | 6 | 8 | 16 | 10 | 12 | 4 | 2 | x | | |

MAP ON PAGE 80

# FEATHER RIVER GOLF COURSE

**Course 6**
MAP C3 grid h9

**1915**

***Course information:*** This public course has nine holes. See card below for yardage and rating information.

***Play policy and fees:*** Green fees are $12 weekdays and $15 weekends. Senior rates are $9 weekdays and $11 weekends. Carts are $9 for nine holes and $13 for 18 holes weekdays, and $13 for nine holes and $16 for 18 holes weekends. The course is open from April to about mid-October.

***Location:*** The course is located on Highway 70 in Blairsden.

***Course description:*** This scenic, flat course is tight with lots of trees. It opened in 1915, making it the oldest course in the Mohawk Valley. The ninth hole has character. It measures 275 yards but plays longer to an elevated green. Harry Weiss, the former head pro, holds the course record with a 58.

PO Box 67
Blairsden, CA 96103

Highway 70
Blairsden, CA 96103

Pro shop (916) 836-2722

- driving range
- ✓ **practice greens**
- ✓ **power carts**
- ✓ **pull carts**
- ✓ **golf club rental**
- locker rooms
- showers
- executive course
- ✓ **accommodations**
- ✓ **food and beverages**
- clubhouse

**Steve Davis**
Manager

**Hal Janney**
Professional

**Mary Leal**
Superintendent

| Hole | 1 | 2 | 3 | 4 | 5 | 6 | 7 | 8 | 9 | Out | BLUE | Rating: -- |
|---|---|---|---|---|---|---|---|---|---|---|---|---|
| BLUE | - | - | - | - | - | - | - | - | - | - | | Slope: -- |
| WHITE | 394 | 411 | 320 | 350 | 350 | 368 | 126 | 150 | 275 | 2744 | | |
| Par | 4 | 4 | 4 | 4 | 4 | 4 | 3 | 3 | 4 | 34 | WHITE | Rating:66.2 |
| Handicap | 5 | 1 | 13 | 7 | 9 | 3 | 17 | 15 | 11 | x | | Slope: 98 |
| RED | 394 | 411 | 320 | 350 | 350 | 368 | 126 | 150 | 275 | 2744 | | |
| Par | 4 | 5 | 4 | 4 | 4 | 4 | 3 | 3 | 4 | 35 | RED | Rating: 68.8 |
| Handicap | 5 | 1 | 13 | 7 | 9 | 3 | 17 | 15 | 11 | x | | Slope: 110 |

| Hole | 10 | 11 | 12 | 13 | 14 | 15 | 16 | 17 | 18 | In | Totals | |
|---|---|---|---|---|---|---|---|---|---|---|---|---|
| BLUE | - | - | - | - | - | - | - | - | - | - | BLUE | -- |
| WHITE | 394 | 411 | 320 | 350 | 350 | 368 | 126 | 150 | 275 | 2744 | WHITE | 5488 |
| Par | 4 | 4 | 4 | 4 | 4 | 4 | 3 | 3 | 4 | 34 | Par | 68 |
| Handicap | 6 | 2 | 14 | 8 | 10 | 4 | 18 | 16 | 12 | x | | |
| RED | 394 | 411 | 320 | 350 | 350 | 368 | 126 | 150 | 275 | 2744 | RED | 5488 |
| Par | 4 | 5 | 4 | 4 | 4 | 4 | 3 | 3 | 4 | 35 | Par | 70 |
| Handicap | 6 | 2 | 14 | 8 | 10 | 4 | 18 | 16 | 12 | x | | |

# FEATHER RIVER PARK RESORT

**Course 7**
MAP C3 grid h9

**1922**

*Course information:* This public course has nine holes. Par is 70 for 18 holes. The course is 5,164 yards at 18 holes and unrated.

*Play policy and fees:* Green fees are $13 weekdays and $15 weekends and holidays; the senior rate is $10 weekdays. Carts are $10 for nine holes and $14 for 18 holes. No reservations necessary. The course is open from April to mid-October.

*Location:* From Interstate 80 in Truckee, drive north on Highway 89. The course is a one-hour drive from Truckee and is past the town of Graeagle. The course is right on Highway 89.

*Course description:* This scenic course is flat, open and walkable. There are two par-5s, both reachable in two; there are three par-3s, the 179-yard third hole being the longer one. Feather River Park Resort generally gets the overflow from Graeagle and Plumas Pines. It is particularly poular with women, seniors and juniors, who can learn in a low-pressure environment.

PO Box 37
Blairsden, CA 96103

8339 Highway 89
Blairsden, CA 96103

Pro shop (916) 836-2328

- driving range
- practice greens
- ✓ **power carts**
- ✓ **pull carts**
- ✓ **golf club rental**
- locker rooms
- showers
- executive course
- ✓ **accommodations**
- ✓ **food and beverages**
- ✓ **clubhouse**

**Mike Boyd**
Manager/Professional/
Superintendent

# MAP C4
(1 COURSE)

PAGES.......88-89

NOR-CAL MAP.....see page 30
adjoining maps
NORTH (B4).............see page 62
EAST ............................no map
SOUTH (D4) .......see page 174
WEST (C3) ..........see page 80

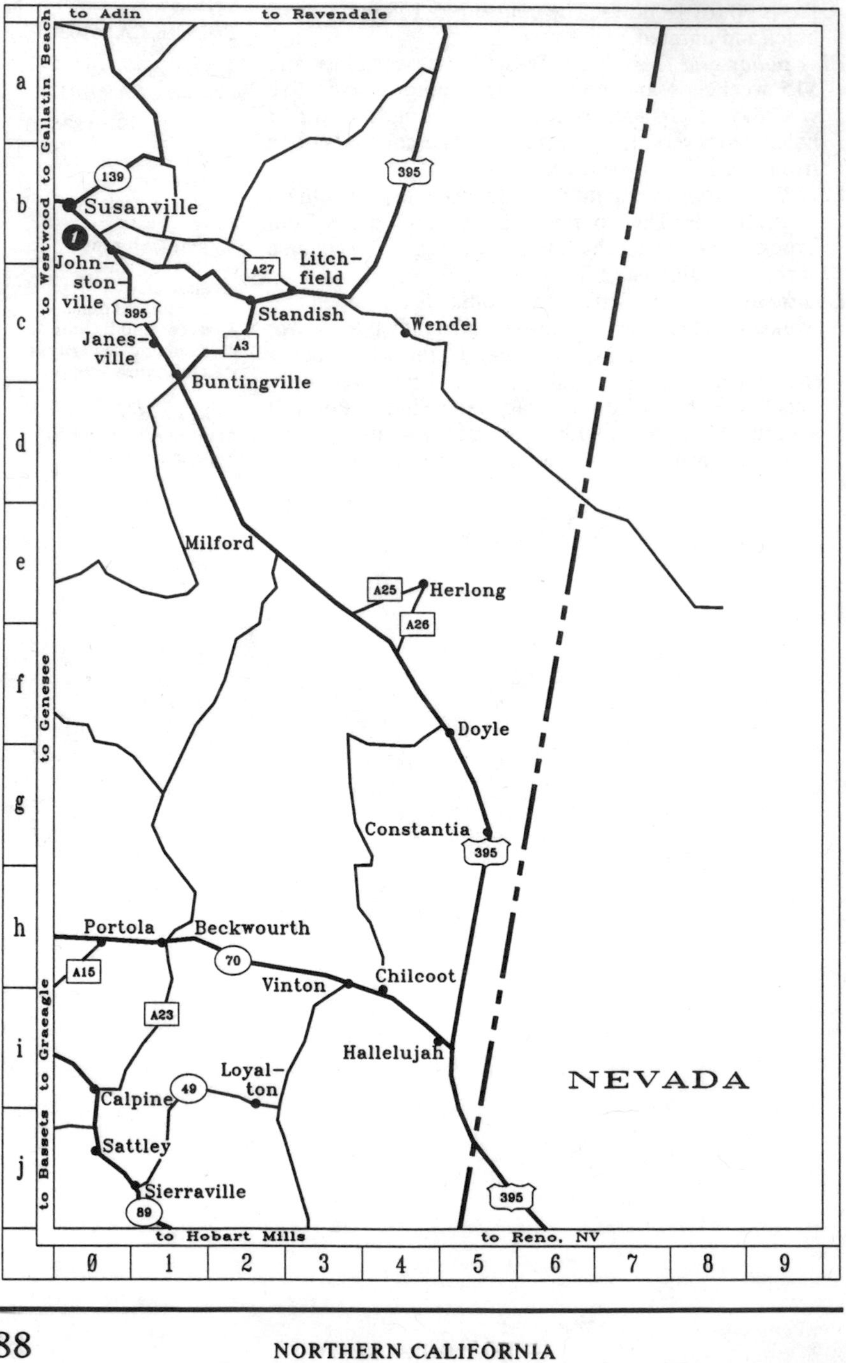

to Adin
to Ravendale
to Westwood to Gallatin Beach
to Genesee
to Bassets to Graeagle
to Hobart Mills
to Reno, NV

a
b
c
d
e
f
g
h
i
j

Ø 1 2 3 4 5 6 7 8 9

139
Susanville
1
Johnstonville
395
Janesville
A27
Litchfield
Standish
A3
Wendel
395
Buntingville
Milford
A25
Herlong
A26
Doyle
Constantia
395
Portola
Beckwourth
70
A15
Vinton
Chilcoot
A23
Hallelujah
Loyalton
Calpine
49
Sattley
Sierraville
89
395
NEVADA

# EMERSON LAKE GOLF COURSE

**Course 1**
MAP C4 grid b0

**1967**

*Course information:* This public course has nine holes. See card below for yardage and rating information.

*Play policy and fees:* Green fees are $7 for nine holes and $12 for 18 holes. Carts are $8 for nine holes and $14 for 18 holes. Reservations recommended one week in advance. This course is available for outside tournaments.

*Location:* From Interstate 5 in Red Bluff, take Highway 36 to Susanville. Turn right on Weatherlow in Susanville, which turns into Richmond Road. Turn right on Wingfield Road. From Reno, take Highway 395 to Susanville. Turn left on Richmond Road at Mount Lassen Motors Drive and drive about three miles. Turn left on Wingfield Road and drive one-quarter mile to the club house.

*Course description:* This rolling course is well maintained and walkable. It has two creeks, one lake, which is frequently dry, and some hills. Evergreens flank the entire course. The greens are excellent and there is a beautiful view of Diamond Mountain. The men's record is 64, set by Tom Swickard. Expect to see this course grow to 18 holes in the next three years, as an additional nine holes, designed by Jack Bridges, are on the drawing board. The Susanville Open is held here each August, drawing a full field of 150 golfers.

470-835 Wingfield Rd. N.
Susanville, CA 96130

Pro shop (916) 257-6303

- ✓ **driving range**
- ✓ **practice greens**
- ✓ **power carts**
- ✓ **pull carts**
- ✓ **golf club rental**
- locker rooms
- ✓ **showers**
- executive course
- accommodations
- ✓ **food and beverages**
- ✓ **clubhouse**

**Bob Genasci**
Manager

**Walt DeWitt**
Superintendent

| Hole | 1 | 2 | 3 | 4 | 5 | 6 | 7 | 8 | 9 | Out | | |
|---|---|---|---|---|---|---|---|---|---|---|---|---|
| BLUE | - | - | - | - | - | - | - | - | - | - | BLUE | Rating: -- |
| | | | | | | | | | | | | Slope: -- |
| WHITE | 313 | 218 | 391 | 284 | 156 | 370 | 378 | 513 | 362 | 3185 | | |
| Par | 5 | 3 | 4 | 4 | 3 | 4 | 4 | 5 | 4 | 36 | WHITE | Rating:68.8 |
| Handicap | 7 | 9 | 3 | 17 | 13 | 15 | 1 | 5 | 11 | x | | Slope: 107 |
| RED | 497 | 208 | 283 | 273 | 118 | 296 | 298 | 443 | 261 | 2677 | | |
| Par | 5 | 3 | 4 | 4 | 3 | 4 | 4 | 5 | 4 | 36 | RED | Rating: 68.9 |
| Handicap | 1 | 5 | 11 | 13 | 17 | 9 | 7 | 3 | 15 | x | | Slope: 112 |

| Hole | 10 | 11 | 12 | 13 | 14 | 15 | 16 | 17 | 18 | In | Totals | |
|---|---|---|---|---|---|---|---|---|---|---|---|---|
| BLUE | - | - | - | - | - | - | - | - | - | - | BLUE | -- |
| WHITE | 488 | 157 | 379 | 296 | 218 | 402 | 339 | 513 | 371 | 3163 | WHITE | 6384 |
| Par | 5 | 3 | 4 | 4 | 3 | 4 | 4 | 5 | 4 | 36 | Par | 72 |
| Handicap | 8 | 16 | 2 | 18 | 6 | 4 | 14 | 10 | 12 | x | | |
| RED | 416 | 147 | 365 | 283 | 152 | 327 | 284 | 408 | 339 | 2721 | RED | 5398 |
| Par | 5 | 3 | 4 | 4 | 3 | 4 | 4 | 5 | 4 | 36 | Par | 72 |
| Handicap | 8 | 16 | 2 | 18 | 12 | 10 | 14 | 6 | 4 | x | | |

# MAP D0

(3 COURSES)

PAGES.......90-93

NOR-CAL MAP.....see page 30
adjoining maps
NORTH (C0).........see page 64
EAST (D1) ...........see page 94
SOUTH.........................no map
WEST...........................no map

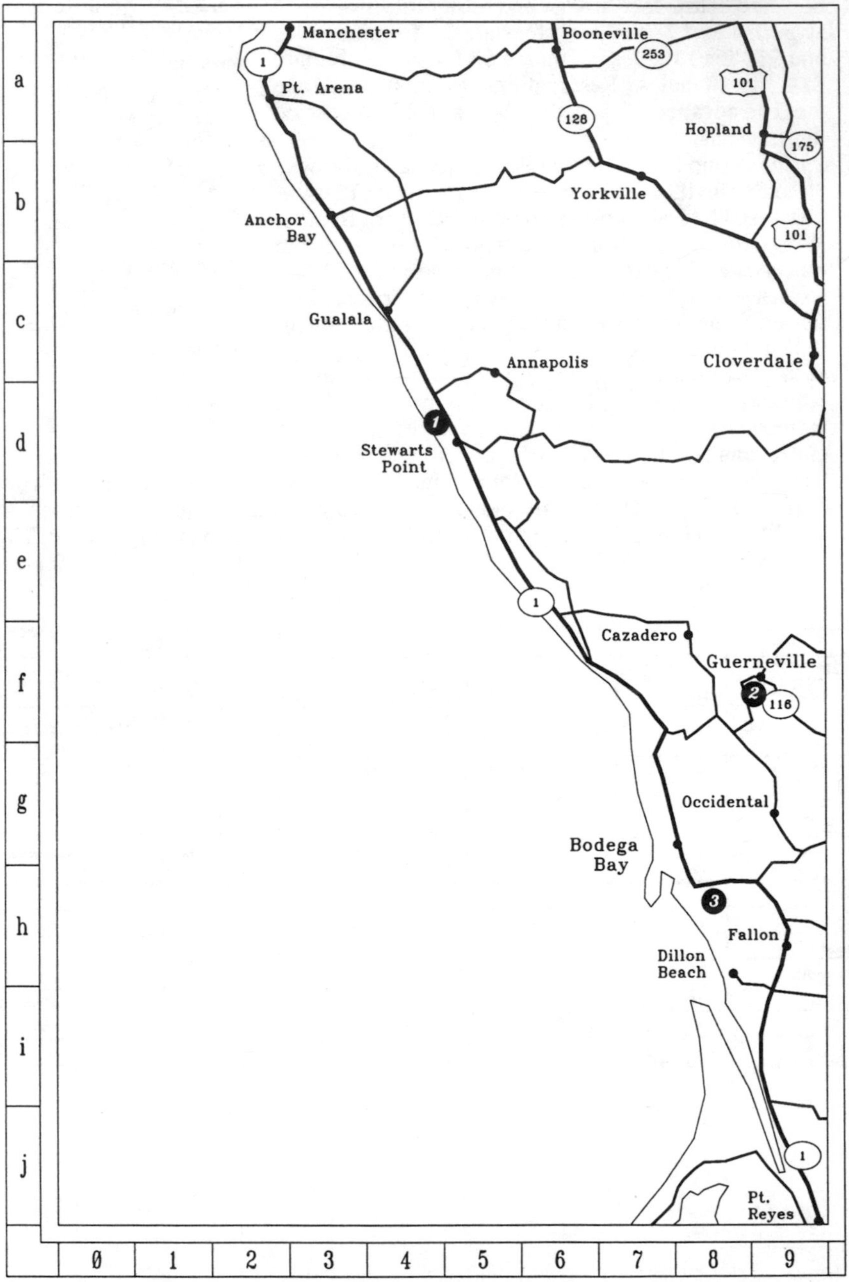

Manchester
Booneville
253
1
101
Pt. Arena
128
Hopland
175
Yorkville
Anchor Bay
101
Gualala
Annapolis
Cloverdale
1
Stewarts Point
1
Cazadero
Guerneville
2
116
Occidental
Bodega Bay
3
Fallon
Dillon Beach
1
Pt. Reyes

a b c d e f g h i j

0 1 2 3 4 5 6 7 8 9

# SEA RANCH GOLF LINKS

**Course 1**
MAP D0 grid d4

***Course information:*** This resort course has nine holes but final permits are in the works for a second nine. Construction could begin in 1994. The current nine are 6,740 yards and rated 73.5 from the championship tees, and 6,276 yards and rated 71.4 from the regular tees. The slope ratings are 133 championship and 128 regular. Women's tees are 5,544 yards and rated 72.4 from the regular tees. The slope rating is 128.

***Play policy and fees:*** Green fees are $18 for nine holes and $22 for 18 holes weekdays, and $24 for nine holes and $35 for 18 holes weekends. Carts are $15 for nine holes and $24 for 18 holes.

***Location:*** From Jenner, drive 40 miles northwest on Highway 1 to course in the Sea Ranch development.

***Course description:*** This is a scenic, seaside links with a traditional Scottish layout. The prevailing winds out of the northwest make several holes play considerably longer. For example, the 502-yard par-5 number one hole forces players to think about laying up short on the non-contiguous fairway. Holes one, four, five and six all have water. This is a fun course from the white tees, a killer in the wind from the blues.

**1973**
**Robert Muir Graves**

PO Box 10
Sea Ranch, CA 95497

49300 Highway 1
Sea Ranch, CA 95497

Pro shop (707) 785-2468

- ✓ **driving range**
- ✓ **practice greens**
- ✓ **power carts**
- ✓ **pull carts**
- ✓ **golf club rental**
- locker rooms
- showers
- executive course
- ✓ **accommodations**
- ✓ **food and beverages**
- ✓ **clubhouse**

**Rich Bland**
Professional

**Greg Sherwood**
Superintendent



MAP ON PAGE 90

# NORTHWOOD GOLF COURSE

**Course 2**
MAP D0 grid f9

*Course information:* This public course has nine holes. Par is 72 for 18 holes. The course is 5,746 yards and rated 68.8 from the regular tees (18 holes). The slope rating is 115. Women's tees are 5,596 yards and rated 71.6 with a slope rating of 116.

*Play policy and fees:* Green fees are $12 for nine holes and $18 for 18 holes weekdays, and $16 for nine holes and $25 for 18 holes weekends. There is a twilight rate of $9 after 4 p.m. any day. Carts are $10 on weekdays and $16 on weekends. Reservations are recommended two weeks in advance. Ask about rates for seniors.

*Location:* From Guerneville, drive three miles west on Highway 116. The course is on the left.

*Course description:* Situated in the Russian River resort area near the Bohemian Grove, this course was designed in 1928 by Alister MacKenzie. The huge redwoods and firs give this course a quiet peaceful feeling. It's flat and narrow with lots of redwood trees. The 525-yard ninth hole has been voted the toughest par-5 in Sonoma County. Numerous doglegs make play longer than the yardage suggests.

**1929**
**Alister MacKenzie**

19400 Highway 116
Monte Rio, CA 95462

Pro shop (707) 865-1116

- ✓ **driving range**
- ✓ **practice greens**
- ✓ **power carts**
- ✓ **pull carts**
- ✓ **golf club rental**
- locker rooms
- showers
- executive course
- ✓ **accommodations**
- ✓ **food and beverages**
- ✓ **clubhouse**

**Gaylord R. Schaap**
Manager

**John Moore**
Professional

**Edwin Bale**
Superintendent

# BODEGA HARBOUR GOLF LINKS

**Course 3**
MAP D0 grid h8

**1977**
**Robert Trent Jones, Jr.**

PO Box 368
Bodega Bay, CA 94923

21301 Heron Drive
Bodega Bay, CA 94923

Pro shop (707) 875-3538

- driving range
- ✓ **practice greens**
- ✓ **power carts**
- ✓ **pull carts**
- ✓ **golf club rental**
- ✓ **locker rooms**
- ✓ **showers**
- executive course
- ✓ **accommodations**
- ✓ **food and beverages**
- ✓ **clubhouse**

**Dennis Kalkowski**
Professional

**Chester Manni**
Superintendent

*Course information:* This semi-private course has 18 holes. Women's tees are 5630 yards and are rated 73.8 with a slope of 131 from the white tees. See card below for additional yardage and rating information.

*Play policy and fees:* Outside play is accepted. Property owners on the golf course are eligible for membership. Green fees are $35 on weekdays and $53 on weekends. Carts are $12 per person. Reservations are required. Reservations are accepted 60 days in advance. There is a dress code; shirts must have collars.

*Location:* From Bodega Bay, drive south on Highway 1. Take the South Harbour Way exit to the right and drive 150 yards to Heron Drive. Turn right on Heron Drive and drive one-half mile to the course.

*Course description:* This course originated as a nine-hole layout and was expanded to 18 holes in 1988. It is a challenging, oceanside links course. The fairways are narrow with scenic views. The front nine is hilly and the back nine is flat. There are 58 pot bunkers (count 'em) on the front nine and 36 on the back. The par-4 16th, par-3 17th and par-4 18th all border the ocean and cross a fresh water marsh. This three-hole sequence makes for an excellent finish. The course record for men is 68, set by Charlie Gibson in 1988 and tied by Bob Borowicz in 1991. The women's record is 71, held by Lois Hodge.

| Hole | 1 | 2 | 3 | 4 | 5 | 6 | 7 | 8 | 9 | Out | | |
|---|---|---|---|---|---|---|---|---|---|---|---|---|
| BLUE | 407 | 334 | 203 | 407 | 491 | 155 | 216 | 487 | 327 | 3027 | BLUE | Rating: 71.9 |
| WHITE | 389 | 308 | 175 | 371 | 448 | 136 | 172 | 451 | 301 | 2751 | | Slope: 130 |
| Par | 4 | 4 | 3 | 4 | 5 | 3 | 3 | 5 | 4 | 35 | WHITE | Rating: 69.2 |
| Handicap | 3 | 7 | 5 | 1 | 15 | 17 | 11 | 13 | 9 | x | | Slope: 125 |
| RED | 283 | 251 | 135 | 305 | 415 | 88 | 128 | 400 | 270 | 2275 | | |
| Par | 4 | 4 | 3 | 4 | 5 | 3 | 3 | 5 | 4 | 35 | RED | Rating: 68.9 |
| Handicap | 3 | 7 | 5 | 1 | 11 | 17 | 15 | 13 | 9 | x | | Slope: 120 |

| Hole | 10 | 11 | 12 | 13 | 14 | 15 | 16 | 17 | 18 | In | Totals | |
|---|---|---|---|---|---|---|---|---|---|---|---|---|
| BLUE | 332 | 399 | 186 | 413 | 443 | 510 | 291 | 152 | 467 | 3193 | BLUE | 6220 |
| WHITE | 292 | 363 | 158 | 377 | 400 | 476 | 271 | 137 | 405 | 2879 | WHITE | 5630 |
| Par | 4 | 4 | 3 | 4 | 4 | 5 | 4 | 3 | 4 | 35 | Par | 70 |
| Handicap | 18 | 6 | 12 | 8 | 4 | 14 | 16 | 10 | 2 | x | | |
| RED | 267 | 346 | 117 | 353 | 355 | 458 | 164 | 88 | 326 | 2474 | RED | 4749 |
| Par | 4 | 4 | 3 | 4 | 4 | 5 | 4 | 3 | 5 | 36 | Par | 71 |
| Handicap | 10 | 6 | 14 | 8 | 2 | 12 | 18 | 16 | 4 | x | | |

# MAP D1

(33 COURSES)

PAGES.... 94-125

NOR-CAL MAP.....see page 30
adjoining maps
NORTH ........................no map
EAST (D2) ..........see page 126
SOUTH (E1) .......see page 184
WEST (D0) ..........see page 90

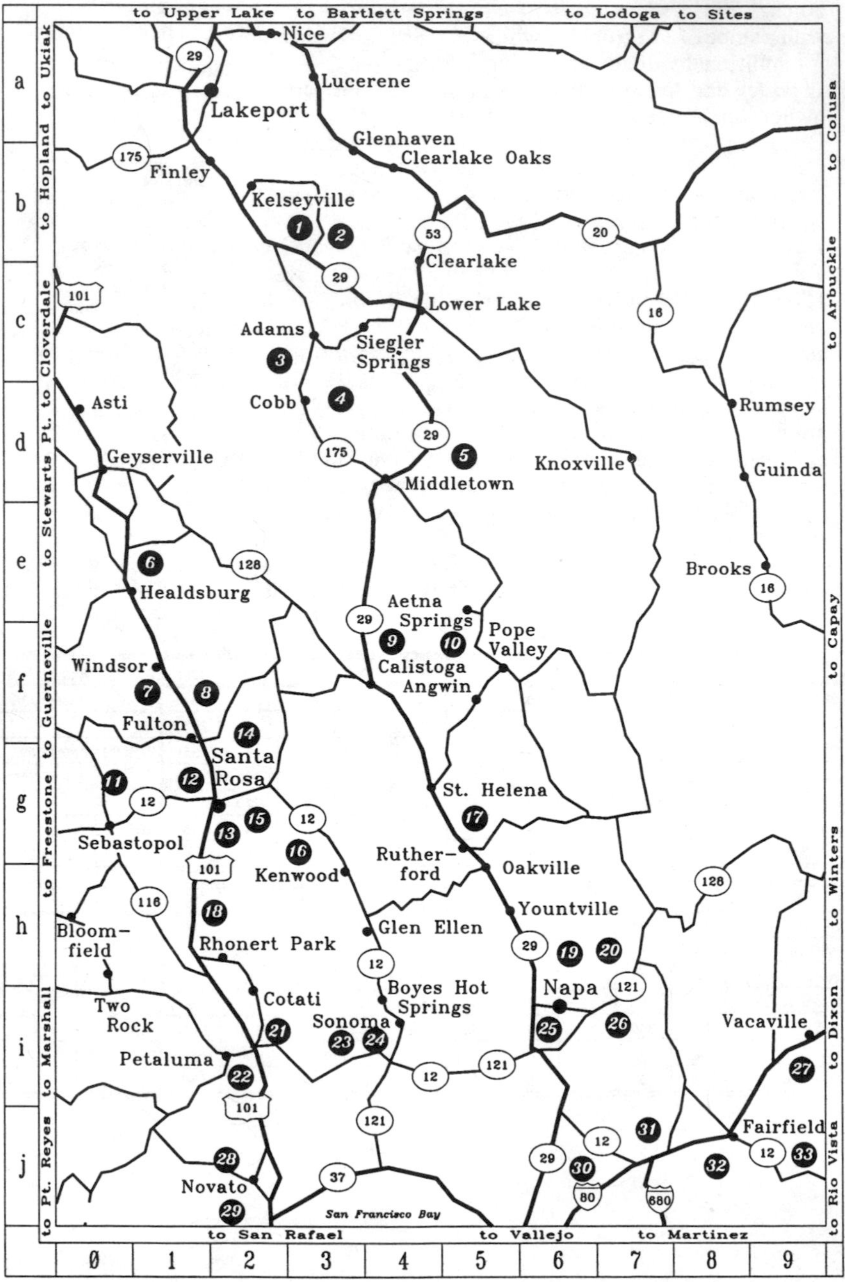

to Upper Lake to Bartlett Springs to Lodoga to Sites

to Hopland to Ukiak

to Cloverdale

to Stewarts Pt.

to Guerneville

to Freestone

to Marshall

to Pt. Reyes

to Colusa

to Arbuckle

to Capay

to Winters

to Dixon

to Rio Vista

to San Rafael to Vallejo to Martinez

a b c d e f g h i j

0 1 2 3 4 5 6 7 8 9

Nice
Lucerene
Lakeport
Glenhaven
Clearlake Oaks
Finley
Kelseyville
Clearlake
Lower Lake
Adams
Siegler Springs
Cobb
Asti
Geyserville
Middletown
Knoxville
Rumsey
Guinda
Brooks
Healdsburg
Aetna Springs
Pope Valley
Calistoga
Angwin
Windsor
Fulton
Santa Rosa
St. Helena
Sebastopol
Kenwood
Rutherford
Oakville
Yountville
Bloomfield
Rhonert Park
Glen Ellen
Cotati
Boyes Hot Springs
Napa
Two Rock
Sonoma
Vacaville
Petaluma
Fairfield
Novato
San Francisco Bay

29 175 53 20 101 16 29 175 128 29 16 12 12 101 116 128 29 12 121 121 12 101 121 37 12 29 12 80 680

1 2 3 4 5 6 7 8 9 10 11 12 13 14 15 16 17 18 19 20 21 22 23 24 25 26 27 28 29 30 31 32 33

# BUCKINGHAM GOLF AND COUNTRY CLUB

**Course 1**
MAP D1 grid b3

*Course information:* This is a nine hole private course, but outside play is accepted. Call the pro. See card below for yardage and rating information.

*Play policy and fees:* Reciprocal play is accepted with members of other private clubs. Guests of the Konocti Harbor Inn are also welcome. Green fees are $10 for nine holes and $17 for 18 on weekdays, $14 for nine holes and $25 for 18 holes on weekends.

*Location:* From Highway 101 north, exit on Highway 20, then Highway 29 to Lakeport. Take Soda Bay Road east one mile to East Lake Drive.

*Course description:* This flat course circles a 25-acre lake called Little Borax. Pine and oak trees come into play, and large boulders dot the fairways. The par-5 fourth features a sand trap around an oak tree 50 yards short of the green. The par-3 sixth will be lengthened to 251 yards. New bunkers and cart paths will be added this year. The course record is 63, by Paul Wilcox, the Diablo Country Club pro.

2855 Eastlake Drive
Kelseyville, CA 95451

Pro shop (707) 279-4863

- ✓ **driving range**
- ✓ **practice greens**
- ✓ **power carts**
- ✓ **pull carts**
- ✓ **golf club rental**
- ✓ **locker rooms**
- ✓ **showers**
- executive course
- ✓ **accommodations**
- ✓ **food and beverages**
- ✓ **clubhouse**

**Bill Dykstra**
Manager

**Mark Wotherspoon**
Owner/Professional

**Hepalito Perez**
Superintendent

NORTHERN D1

| Hole | 1 | 2 | 3 | 4 | 5 | 6 | 7 | 8 | 9 | Out | | |
|---|---|---|---|---|---|---|---|---|---|---|---|---|
| BLUE | - | - | - | - | - | - | - | - | - | - | BLUE | Rating: -- |
| | | | | | | | | | | | | Slope: -- |
| WHITE | 366 | 172 | 160 | 508 | 241 | 197 | 422 | 382 | 532 | 2980 | | |
| Par | 4 | 3 | 3 | 5 | 4 | 3 | 5 | 4 | 5 | 36 | WHITE | Rating: 68.1 |
| Handicap | 3 | 17 | 15 | 9 | 13 | 7 | 11 | 1 | 5 | x | | Slope: 144 |
| RED | 366 | 149 | 162 | 480 | 199 | 179 | 423 | 401 | 473 | 2832 | | |
| Par | 4 | 3 | 3 | 5 | 4 | 3 | 5 | 5 | 5 | 37 | RED | Rating: 71.9 |
| Handicap | 5 | 17 | 13 | 1 | 15 | 11 | 7 | 9 | 3 | x | | Slope: 124 |

| Hole | 10 | 11 | 12 | 13 | 14 | 15 | 16 | 17 | 18 | In | Totals | |
|---|---|---|---|---|---|---|---|---|---|---|---|---|
| BLUE | - | - | - | - | - | - | - | - | - | - | BLUE | -- |
| WHITE | 345 | 160 | 258 | 493 | 210 | 211 | 423 | 382 | 496 | 2978 | WHITE | 5958 |
| Par | 4 | 3 | 4 | 5 | 3 | 3 | 5 | 4 | 5 | 36 | Par | 72 |
| Handicap | 8 | 18 | 16 | 12 | 2 | 6 | 14 | 4 | 10 | x | | |
| RED | 351 | 146 | 156 | 471 | 196 | 172 | 418 | 401 | 473 | 2784 | RED | 5616 |
| Par | 4 | 3 | 3 | 5 | 4 | 3 | 5 | 5 | 5 | 37 | Par | 74 |
| Handicap | 6 | 18 | 14 | 2 | 16 | 12 | 8 | 10 | 4 | x | | |

# CLEAR LAKE RIVIERA YACHT AND GOLF CLUB

**Course 2**
MAP D1 grid b3

**1965**
**Ed DeFelice**

10200 Fairway Drive
Kelseyville, CA 95451

Pro shop (707) 277-7129
Restaurant (707) 277-7575

- driving range
- ✓ **practice greens**
- ✓ **power carts**
- ✓ **pull carts**
- ✓ **golf club rental**
- locker rooms
- showers
- ✓ **executive course**
- accommodations
- ✓ **food and beverages**
- ✓ **clubhouse**

**Garvey Blanc**
General Manager

**Rex Thrasher**
Superintendent

***Course information:*** This semi-private course has nine holes. See card below for yardage and rating information. There is also a six-hole pitch-and-putt course.

***Play policy and fees:*** Outside play is accepted. Memberships are available. Green fees are $11 for nine holes and $15 for 18 holes on weekdays, and $12 for nine holes and $20 for 18 holes on weekends. Carts are $9 for nine holes and $13 for 18 holes weekdays. $11 and $18 weekends. Reservations are recommended.

***Location:*** From Napa on Highway 29 drive to Lower Lake, turn left and drive to Soda Bay Road. Turn right and drive to Fairway Drive. From Ukiah take Highway 20 to Lakeport and Kelseyville. Turn left on Soda Bay Road and travel to Fairway Drive.

***Course description:*** This hilly, picturesque course offers views of Clear Lake. It has sidehill lies, big greens and elevated tees. This is a panoramic course, but tough. Manager Garvey Blanc used to think people who rode in carts were finks. "Now I own my own cart," he says. The course isn't long, but features dramatic elevation changes, which offer breathtaking views. It's a one-way track, with no adjacent fairways.

| Hole | 1 | 2 | 3 | 4 | 5 | 6 | 7 | 8 | 9 | Out | BLUE | Rating: -- |
|---|---|---|---|---|---|---|---|---|---|---|---|---|
| BLUE | - | - | - | - | - | - | - | - | - | - | | Slope: -- |
| WHITE | 276 | 387 | 303 | 273 | 151 | 439 | 283 | 254 | 362 | 2728 | | |
| Par | 4 | 4 | 4 | 4 | 3 | 5 | 4 | 4 | 4 | 36 | WHITE | Rating: 67.5 |
| Handicap | 9 | 3 | 7 | 13 | 11 | 5 | 17 | 15 | 1 | x | | Slope: 112 |
| RED | 227 | 370 | 304 | 210 | 152 | 431 | 276 | 232 | 361 | 2563 | | |
| Par | 4 | 4 | 4 | 3 | 3 | 5 | 4 | 4 | 5 | 36 | RED | Rating: 69.9 |
| Handicap | 15 | 5 | 7 | 11 | 13 | 1 | 17 | 9 | 3 | x | | Slope: 125 |

| Hole | 10 | 11 | 12 | 13 | 14 | 15 | 16 | 17 | 18 | In | Totals | |
|---|---|---|---|---|---|---|---|---|---|---|---|---|
| BLUE | - | - | - | - | - | - | - | - | - | - | BLUE | -- |
| WHITE | 309 | 519 | 321 | 213 | 161 | 459 | 353 | 262 | 313 | 2910 | WHITE | 5638 |
| Par | 4 | 5 | 4 | 3 | 3 | 5 | 4 | 4 | 4 | 36 | Par | 72 |
| Handicap | 12 | 2 | 8 | 14 | 16 | 10 | 4 | 18 | 6 | x | | |
| RED | 273 | 368 | 304 | 238 | 151 | 431 | 279 | 238 | 260 | 2542 | RED | 5105 |
| Par | 4 | 4 | 4 | 4 | 3 | 5 | 4 | 4 | 4 | 36 | Par | 72 |
| Handicap | 10 | 8 | 4 | 12 | 16 | 2 | 18 | 14 | 6 | x | | |

# ADAMS SPRINGS GOLF COURSE

Course 3
MAP D1 grid c3

**1962**
**Jack Fleming**

PO Box 2088
14347 Snead Court
Loch Lomond, CA 95426

Pro shop (707) 928-9992

- driving range
- ✓ **practice greens**
- ✓ **power carts**
- ✓ **pull carts**
- ✓ **golf club rental**
- locker rooms
- showers
- executive course
- accommodations
- ✓ **food and beverages**
- ✓ **clubhouse**

**V.S. Doucette**
Owner/Manager

**F.H. Doucette**
Superintendent

***Course information:*** This public course has nine holes. Par is 68 for 18 holes. The course is 5,280 yards and rated 64.6 from the regular tees (18 holes). The slope rating is 111. Women's tees are 4,998 yards and rated 68.1. The slope rating is 119.

***Play policy and fees:*** Green fees are $7 for nine holes and $10 for 18 holes weekdays, and $8 for nine holes and $12 for 18 holes weekends. Carts are $15.

***Location:*** From Highway 29 in Middletown, take Highway 175 west. Drive 11 miles to the course (one mile past Hoberg and one mile south of Loch Lomond). There are signs on the road to direct you.

***Course description:*** One thing this course has going for it are the green fees: they haven't increased in the last few years. Better yet, this mountain-setting course has a rolling terrain with generous fairways and is walkable. Three lakes come into play on five holes. The par-3 fourth hole, 181 yards long, has a great view. You'll see lots of wildlife. Plans call for overnight lodging.

# HOBERG'S FOREST LAKE GOLF AND COUNTRY CLUB

Course 4
MAP D1 grid d3

PO Box 2325
Cobb, CA 95436

10200 Golf Road
Cobb, CA 95436

Pro shop (707) 928-5276

- driving range
- ✓ **practice greens**
- ✓ **power carts**
- ✓ **pull carts**
- ✓ **golf club rental**
- locker rooms
- showers
- executive course
- accommodations
- ✓ **food and beverages**
- clubhouse

**Les Russo**
Professional

**Helmut Knorn**
Superintendent

***Course information:*** This public course has nine holes. Par is 66 for 18 holes. The course is 4,482 yards and rated 61.5 from the regular tees. The slope rating is 109. Women's tees are 4,482 yards and rated 64.6. The slope rating is 107.

***Play policy and fees:*** Green fees are $8 for nine holes and $11 for 18 holes weekdays, and $10 for nine holes and $13 for 18 holes weekends. Carts are $8 for nine holes and $15 for 18 holes.

***Location:*** Drive north on Highway 29 to Highway 175. Take Highway 175 to the town of Cobb. The course is set at Highway 175 and Golf Road.

***Course description:*** A creek meanders through this pretty mountain course located 3,600 feet above sea level. There are bunkers on every hole and many pine trees come into play. This course is open for play year-round, weather permitting. There are 6 par-4s and 3 par-3s. The eighth is a 398-yarder, and it's very pretty.

MAP ON PAGE 94

# HIDDEN VALLEY LAKE GOLF AND COUNTRY CLUB

**Course 5**
MAP D1 grid d4

***Course information:*** This semi-private course has 18 holes. See card below for yardage and rating information.

***Play policy and fees:*** Green fees are $10 for nine holes and $15 for 18 holes on weekdays, and $15 for nine holes and $24 for 18 holes on weekends. Fees could change by June. Property owners are eligible for special rates. There is a senior rate on Wednesdays for $8. Seniors get a $3 discount on Monday, Tuesday and Wednesday. Carts are $18 on weekdays and $20 on weekends. Reservations are recommended. Shirts must be worn at all times. No tank tops, halter tops, short shorts or street shoes may be worn.

***Location:*** From Middletown, drive five miles north on Highway 29. The course is on the right.

***Course description:*** This sprawling course is scenic and hilly. The front nine is long and flat. The back nine is shorter with elevated tees. Water comes into play on 10 of the holes, mostly during the winter months. The most dramatic hole is the 404-yard, par-4 15th. The tee is 200 feet above the fairway. It's a spectacular shot, with Sutter Home Winery on the left, and Mount St. Helena in the background. It looks like you have to hit it a country mile, but you don't. If you over-hit, you're likely to land in the trees on the right, which just proves that going for the green will get you in trouble. Insiders suggest aiming for the swimming pool and you're safe. Pro Charlie Gibson set the course record, with a 64.

**1970**
**William Francis Bell**

PO Box 628
Middletown, CA 95461

1 Hartman Road
Middletown, CA 95461

Pro shop (707) 987-3035
Restaurant (707) 987-3146

- ✓ **driving range**
- ✓ **practice greens**
- ✓ **power carts**
- ✓ **pull carts**
- ✓ **golf club rental**
- ✓ **locker rooms**
- ✓ **showers**
- executive course
- accommodations
- ✓ **food and beverages**
- ✓ **clubhouse**

**Rob Kenny**
Professional

**Dana Waldor**
Superintendent

| Hole | 1 | 2 | 3 | 4 | 5 | 6 | 7 | 8 | 9 | Out | BLUE | Rating: 71.6 |
|---|---|---|---|---|---|---|---|---|---|---|---|---|
| BLUE | 433 | 482 | 444 | 188 | 346 | 568 | 449 | 208 | 390 | 3508 | | Slope: 118 |
| WHITE | 418 | 472 | 434 | 140 | 338 | 494 | 443 | 200 | 339 | 3278 | | |
| Par | 4 | 5 | 4 | 3 | 4 | 5 | 4 | 3 | 4 | 36 | WHITE | Rating: 70.1 |
| Handicap | 5 | 17 | 1 | 15 | 13 | 7 | 3 | 9 | 11 | x | | Slope: 115 |
| RED | 328 | 427 | 432 | 121 | 334 | 484 | 413 | 133 | 330 | 3002 | | |
| Par | 4 | 5 | 5 | 3 | 4 | 5 | 5 | 3 | 4 | 38 | RED | Rating: 71.5 |
| Handicap | 11 | 5 | 9 | 17 | 1 | 3 | 15 | 13 | 7 | x | | Slope: 123 |

| Hole | 10 | 11 | 12 | 13 | 14 | 15 | 16 | 17 | 18 | In | Totals | |
|---|---|---|---|---|---|---|---|---|---|---|---|---|
| BLUE | 425 | 123 | 467 | 392 | 120 | 386 | 490 | 338 | 341 | 3082 | BLUE | 6590 |
| WHITE | 400 | 111 | 455 | 383 | 100 | 377 | 471 | 331 | 331 | 2959 | WHITE | 6237 |
| Par | 4 | 3 | 5 | 4 | 3 | 4 | 5 | 4 | 4 | 36 | Par | 72 |
| Handicap | 4 | 18 | 8 | 2 | 16 | 12 | 6 | 10 | 14 | x | | |
| RED | 385 | 102 | 407 | 317 | 100 | 239 | 436 | 323 | 282 | 2591 | RED | 5593 |
| Par | 4 | 3 | 5 | 4 | 3 | 4 | 5 | 4 | 4 | 36 | Par | 74 |
| Handicap | 4 | 18 | 2 | 6 | 16 | 14 | 10 | 8 | 12 | x | | |

# TAYMAN PARK GOLF COURSE

**Course 6**
MAP D1 grid e1

*Course information:* This public course has nine holes. Par is 70 for 18 holes. The course is 5,304 yards and rated 65.6 from the regular tees (18 holes). The slope rating is 112. Women's tees are 4,884 yards and rated 68.4. The slope rating is 113.

*Play policy and fees:* Green fees are $9 for nine holes and $11 for 18 holes weekdays, and $11 for nine holes and $13 for 18 holes weekends. There is a $7 senior rate for nine holes. Carts are $9 for nine holes and $16 for 18 holes.

*Location:* Driving north on Highway 101 into Healdsburg, take the Central Healdsburg exit onto Healdsburg Avenue. Drive on Healdsburg Avenue through two lights before turning right on Matheson Street. You'll see the course on the left.

*Course description:* This is a hilly, tree-lined course with small greens. It's walkable. The 324-yard ninth stands out into the wind, the tee shot is across a creek, down into a sloping fairway. The approach goes back uphill to the green next to the clubhouse. The course offers picturesque views of Healdsburg and the surrounding area. The greens are fast, and many have two tiers.

PO Box 1193
Healdsburg, CA 95448

927 S. Fitch Mountain Road
Healdsburg, CA 95448

Pro shop (707) 433-4275

driving range
✓ **practice greens**
✓ **power carts**
✓ **pull carts**
✓ **golf club rental**
locker rooms
showers
executive course
accommodations
✓ **food and beverages**
✓ **clubhouse**

**Andy Wakefield**
Manager/Professional

**John Rader**
Superintendent



MAP ON PAGE 94

# WINDSOR GOLF CLUB

**Course 7**
MAP D1 grid f1

**1989**
**Fred Bliss**

6555 Skylane Boulevard
Windsor, CA 95492

Pro shop (707) 838-7888

✓ **driving range**
✓ **practice greens**
✓ **power carts**
✓ **pull carts**
✓ **golf club rental**
locker rooms
showers
executive course
accommodations
✓ **food and beverages**
clubhouse

**Charlie Gibson**
Professional

**Rick Hansen**
Superintendent

***Course information:*** This public course has 18 holes and par is 72. The course is 6,650 yards and rated 72.3 from the tournament tees, 6,169 yards and rated 70.1 from the championship tees, and 5,628 yards and rated 67.0 from the regular tees. The slope ratings are 126 tournament, 121 championship and 118 regular. Women's tees are 5,628 yards and rated 72.5 from the championship tees, and 5,116 yards and rated 69.3 from the regular tees. The slope ratings are 136 championship and 125 regular.

***Play policy and fees:*** Green fees are $21 on weekdays, and $31 on weekends. Twilight rates are $15 on weekdays and $21 on weekends. Senior rates are $12 weekdays. Junior rates are $7 weekdays. Carts are $20 for 18 holes and $15 for a single rider. Twilighters get the carts for $15. Pull carts are $2. Reserve a tee time seven days in advance.

***Location:*** From Highway 101 in Santa Rosa, take the Shiloh Road exit. Drive one-half of a mile west of the freeway. The course is on the right.

***Course description:*** This course boasts a winding creek, four lakes and many mature oaks. The nines have been switched. The pride of the course is the par-3 13th, formerly the fourth hole, a 194-yarder to a rock-banked green. The par-4 number two, at 432 yards, and the 217-yard par-3 seventh, are among the toughest holes on the old Ben Hogan Tour. Now the tour is sponsored by Nike, and again will be played here in October. As the clubhouse tale goes, a hole-in-one was once sunk like this: the ball bounced off a rock in the lake, rebounded up onto the green and found the hole! Hole 17 is also notable. It's 368 yards from an elevated tee, with bunkers to the left and a lake to the right. The second shot is over a lake to a small green (par is four). It's a beauty. Former PGA Tour player Charlie Gibson is both the pro and director of golf operations.

# WIKIUP GOLF COURSE

**Course 8**
MAP D1 grid f1

**1963**

5001 Carriage Lane
Santa Rosa, CA 95401

Pro shop (707) 546-8787

- driving range
- ✓ **practice greens**
- ✓ **power carts**
- ✓ **pull carts**
- ✓ **golf club rental**
- locker rooms
- showers
- executive course
- accommodations
- ✓ **food and beverages**
- clubhouse

**Tom Langbein**
Manager/Superintendent

*Course information:* This public course has nine holes. Par is 58 for 18 holes. The course is 3,223 yards and rated 54.8 from the regular tees (18 holes). The slope rating is 80. Women's yardage and ratings are the same.

*Play policy and fees:* Green fees are $7 for nine holes and $10 for 18 holes on weekdays, and $9 for nine holes and $12 for 18 holes on weekends and holidays. Student and senior rates are $7 for 18 holes. Carts are $9 for nine holes and $12 for 18 holes.

*Location:* From Santa Rosa, drive four miles north on Highway 101 to River Road. Turn east on River Road. Turn north on Old Redwood Highway and drive one-half mile. Turn east on Wikiup Drive and drive one-half mile to the course.

*Course description:* This is a challenging, short course with no adjacent holes. It is scenic and well bunkered with two par-4s. The short 268-yard, par-4 second hole is a temptation. It makes players choose between laying up or carrying a water hazard. The gentle slopes make the course easily walkable.

# MOUNT SAINT HELENA GOLF COURSE

**Course 9**
MAP D1 grid f4

PO Box 344
Calistoga, CA 94515

Grant Street,
Napa Co. Fairgrounds
Calistoga, CA 94515

Pro shop (707) 942-9966

- driving range
- practice greens
- ✓ **power carts**
- ✓ **pull carts**
- ✓ **golf club rental**
- locker rooms
- showers
- executive course
- accommodations
- ✓ **food and beverages**
- clubhouse

**Roy Wells**
Manager

**Dick Hall**
Superintendent

*Course information:* This public course has nine holes. Par is 68 for 18 holes. The course is 5,496 yards and rated 65.9 from the regular tees (18 holes). The slope rating is 105. Women's tees are 5,294 yards and rated 69.1. The slope rating is 113.

*Play policy and fees:* Green fees are $10 on weekdays and $14 on weekends. Senior rates are $8 on weekdays and $10 weekends. Carts are $8 for nine holes and $14 for 18 holes. Shirts must be worn at all times. No rubber spikes are allowed.

*Location:* Driving north toward Calistoga on Highway 29, take the Lincoln exit north to Grant Street. Turn left and follow the road to the course at the fairgrounds on the left.

*Course description:* This course is located in the middle of the Napa County Fairgrounds. It's short and flat with narrow fairways. Accuracy is important. There are no par-5s. The sixth hole, formerly a par-5, is now a 435-yard par-4. Water comes into play on two holes.

# AETNA SPRINGS GOLF COURSE

**Course 10**
MAP D1 grid f5

1600 Aetna Springs Road
Pope Valley, CA 94567

Pro shop (707) 965-2115

- ✓ **driving range**
- ✓ **practice greens**
- ✓ **power carts**
- ✓ **pull carts**
- ✓ **golf club rental**
- locker rooms
- showers
- executive course
- accommodations
- ✓ **food and beverages**
- ✓ **clubhouse**

**Kent Stuth**
Manager/Professionl

**Ron Fukuyama**
Superintendent

***Course information:*** This public course has nine holes. See card below for yardage and rating information.

***Play policy and fees:*** Green fees are $9 weekdays and $10 for nine holes or $12 for 18 holes weekends. Seniors and juniors are $6 on weekdays. All day play is permitted for the same price on weekdays. Twilight green fee is $5 after 4 p.m. weekdays. Carts are $8 for nine holes and $15 for 18 holes. This course is available for tournaments.

***Location:*** From Highway 29 heading north toward Calistoga, drive one mile past Saint Helena. Turn right on Deer Park Road North. Stay on this road and drive through Angwin. The road turns into Howell Mountain Road. Once in Pope Valley veer to the left where the road branches at the service station. Drive four miles to Aetna Springs Road (just past the Hub Cap Ranch). Turn onto Aetna and drive one mile to the course.

***Course description:*** Built around the turn of the century, this is one of the oldest courses in California. It's nestled in the mountains with gentle hills and two creeks running through it. It has six par-4s, two par-3s and one par-5. Bring the family—picnic tables border the course. There is also a barbecue area. Stuth is working to re-shape some holes with elevated tees. "It might take three years to do," he said. The course is remote. The population is 300, but it's quiet and serene, and the course is marked by towering oak trees and meandering creeks. It's a good course for beignners.

| Hole | 1 | 2 | 3 | 4 | 5 | 6 | 7 | 8 | 9 | Out | | |
|---|---|---|---|---|---|---|---|---|---|---|---|---|
| BLUE | - | - | - | - | - | - | - | - | - | - | BLUE | Rating: -- |
| WHITE | 330 | 281 | 332 | 317 | 315 | 379 | 136 | 456 | 140 | 2686 | | Slope: -- |
| Par | 4 | 4 | 4 | 4 | 4 | 4 | 3 | 5 | 3 | 35 | WHITE | Rating: 64.7 |
| Handicap | 7 | 15 | 5 | 9 | 3 | 1 | 17 | 11 | 13 | x | | Slope: 102 |
| RED | 290 | 248 | 332 | 298 | 315 | 338 | 136 | 430 | 140 | 2527 | | |
| Par | 4 | 4 | 4 | 4 | 4 | 4 | 3 | 5 | 3 | 35 | RED | Rating: 69.2 |
| Handicap | 7 | 15 | 3 | 11 | 5 | 1 | 17 | 9 | 13 | x | | Slope: 113 |

| Hole | 10 | 11 | 12 | 13 | 14 | 15 | 16 | 17 | 18 | In | Totals | |
|---|---|---|---|---|---|---|---|---|---|---|---|---|
| BLUE | - | - | - | - | - | - | - | - | - | - | BLUE | -- |
| WHITE | 330 | 281 | 332 | 317 | 315 | 379 | 136 | 456 | 140 | 2686 | WHITE | 5372 |
| Par | 4 | 4 | 4 | 4 | 4 | 4 | 3 | 5 | 3 | 35 | Par | 70 |
| Handicap | 8 | 16 | 6 | 10 | 4 | 2 | 18 | 12 | 14 | x | | |
| RED | 290 | 248 | 332 | 298 | 315 | 338 | 136 | 430 | 140 | 2527 | RED | 5054 |
| Par | 4 | 4 | 4 | 4 | 4 | 4 | 3 | 5 | 3 | 35 | Par | 70 |
| Handicap | 8 | 16 | 4 | 12 | 6 | 2 | 18 | 10 | 14 | x | | |

# SEBASTOPOL GOLF COURSE

**Course 11**
MAP D1 grid g0

***Course information:*** This public course has nine holes. See card below for yardage and rating information.

***Play policy and fees:*** Green fees are $7 for nine holes and $10 for 18 holes weekdays, and $9 for nine holes and $12 for 18 holes weekends. Senior rates are $6 on weekdays. Carts are $8 for nine holes and $12 for 18 holes.

***Location:*** From Sebastopol, drive three miles north on Highway 116 to Scotts Right-of-Way to the course.

***Course description:*** This short course is all par-3s and par-4s, with the longest hole measuring 240 yards. The most notable is the 195-yard, par-3 second hole, which requires an uphill shot to a two-tiered green. Water comes into play on the 195-yard, par-4 eighth hole.

2881 Scotts Right-of-Way
Sebastopol, CA 95472

Pro shop (707) 823-9852
Clubhouse (707) 823-2003

- driving range
- ✓ **practice greens**
- ✓ **power carts**
- ✓ **pull carts**
- ✓ **golf club rental**
- locker rooms
- showers
- executive course
- accommodations
- ✓ **food and beverages**
- ✓ **clubhouse**

**Lee Farris**
Manager

**Wade Farris**
Superintendent

| Hole | 1 | 2 | 3 | 4 | 5 | 6 | 7 | 8 | 9 | Out | BLUE | Rating: -- |
|---|---|---|---|---|---|---|---|---|---|---|---|---|
| BLUE | - | - | - | - | - | - | - | - | - | - | | Slope: -- |
| WHITE | 147 | 195 | 190 | 200 | 206 | 140 | 150 | 195 | 240 | 1663 | | |
| Par | 3 | 3 | 3 | 4 | 4 | 3 | 3 | 4 | 4 | 31 | WHITE | Rating: 55.0 |
| Handicap | 15 | 11 | 9 | 5 | 7 | 17 | 13 | 3 | 1 | x | | Slope: 86 |
| RED | 147 | 195 | 190 | 200 | 206 | 140 | 150 | 195 | 240 | 1663 | | |
| Par | 3 | 4 | 4 | 4 | 4 | 3 | 3 | 4 | 4 | 33 | RED | Rating: 55.0 |
| Handicap | 15 | 11 | 9 | 5 | 7 | 17 | 13 | 3 | 1 | x | | Slope: 86 |

| Hole | 10 | 11 | 12 | 13 | 14 | 15 | 16 | 17 | 18 | In | Totals | |
|---|---|---|---|---|---|---|---|---|---|---|---|---|
| BLUE | - | - | - | - | - | - | - | - | - | - | BLUE | -- |
| WHITE | 147 | 195 | 190 | 200 | 206 | 140 | 150 | 195 | 240 | 1663 | WHITE | 3326 |
| Par | 3 | 3 | 3 | 4 | 4 | 3 | 3 | 4 | 4 | 31 | Par | 62 |
| Handicap | 16 | 12 | 10 | 6 | 8 | 18 | 14 | 4 | 2 | x | | |
| RED | 147 | 195 | 190 | 200 | 206 | 140 | 150 | 195 | 240 | 1663 | RED | 3326 |
| Par | 3 | 4 | 4 | 4 | 4 | 3 | 3 | 4 | 4 | 33 | Par | 66 |
| Handicap | 16 | 12 | 10 | 6 | 8 | 18 | 14 | 4 | 2 | x | | |

MAP ON PAGE 94

# SANTA ROSA GOLF AND COUNTRY CLUB

**Course 12**
MAP D1 grid g1

**1958**
**Ben Harmen**

5110 Oak Meadow Drive
Santa Rosa, CA 95401

Pro shop (707) 546-6617
Clubhouse (707) 546-3485

- ✓ **driving range**
- ✓ **practice greens**
- ✓ **power carts**
- ✓ **pull carts**
- ✓ **golf club rental**
- ✓ **locker rooms**
- ✓ **showers**
- executive course
- accommodations
- ✓ **food and beverages**
- ✓ **clubhouse**

**Val Verhunce**
Professional

**Ed Stocke**
Superintendent

***Course information:*** This private course has 18 holes. See card below for yardage and rating information.

***Play policy and fees:*** Members and guests only. Reciprocal play is accepted with members of other private clubs. Reciprocal fees are $40 on weekdays and $50 on weekends. Guest fees are $25 when accompanied by a club member. Carts are $10 and are mandatory. Reservations recommended. Shirts must have a collar and shorts must have a six-inch inseam. No blue jeans, halter tops or tank tops may be worn.

***Location:*** From Highway 101, take the Highway 12 west toward Sebastopol. Turn right on Fulton Road and left on Hall Road. Turn left on Country Club road and drive to the parking lot.

***Course description:*** This sprawling course is lined with beautiful oak trees and is tougher than it looks. The course record for men is 63, set by member Tom Costello. New traps and three new lakes mark an improvement project by Fred Bliss. Oak trees line the fairways, and out-of-bounds comes into play on six holes. Good tee shots set up the course, which requires precise iron shots. On the par-4 eighth, 426 yards, the tee shot carries over a lake. An oak tree comes into play on approach. The course has small greens, which make putting a chore.

| Hole | 1 | 2 | 3 | 4 | 5 | 6 | 7 | 8 | 9 | Out | BLUE | Rating: 72.5 |
|---|---|---|---|---|---|---|---|---|---|---|---|---|
| BLUE | 378 | 490 | 439 | 194 | 537 | 174 | 400 | 426 | 367 | 3405 | | Slope: 128 |
| WHITE | 361 | 474 | 422 | 184 | 508 | 158 | 391 | 390 | 352 | 3240 | | |
| Par | 4 | 5 | 4 | 3 | 5 | 3 | 4 | 4 | 4 | 36 | WHITE | Rating: 70.5 |
| Handicap | 7 | 13 | 1 | 15 | 11 | 17 | 5 | 3 | 9 | x | | Slope: 124 |
| RED | 350 | 413 | 416 | 142 | 480 | 124 | 381 | 340 | 342 | 2988 | | |
| Par | 4 | 5 | 5 | 3 | 5 | 3 | 4 | 4 | 4 | 37 | RED | Rating: 72.7 |
| Handicap | 11 | 3 | 5 | 17 | 1 | 15 | 7 | 13 | 9 | x | | Slope: 123 |

| Hole | 10 | 11 | 12 | 13 | 14 | 15 | 16 | 17 | 18 | In | Totals | |
|---|---|---|---|---|---|---|---|---|---|---|---|---|
| BLUE | 367 | 584 | 401 | 344 | 368 | 213 | 355 | 197 | 515 | 3344 | BLUE | 6749 |
| WHITE | 347 | 540 | 373 | 312 | 362 | 188 | 319 | 150 | 490 | 3081 | WHITE | 6321 |
| Par | 4 | 5 | 4 | 4 | 4 | 3 | 4 | 3 | 5 | 36 | Par | 72 |
| Handicap | 14 | 2 | 6 | 16 | 4 | 10 | 12 | 18 | 8 | x | | |
| RED | 337 | 495 | 341 | 305 | 352 | 144 | 304 | 121 | 411 | 2810 | RED | 5798 |
| Par | 4 | 5 | 4 | 4 | 4 | 3 | 4 | 3 | 5 | 36 | Par | 73 |
| Handicap | 12 | 2 | 8 | 10 | 6 | 16 | 14 | 18 | 4 | x | | |

# BENNETT VALLEY GOLF COURSE

**Course 13**
MAP D1 grid g2

3330 Yulupa Avenue
Santa Rosa, CA 95405

Pro shop (707) 528-3673

- ✓ **driving range**
- ✓ **practice greens**
- ✓ **power carts**
- ✓ **pull carts**
- ✓ **golf club rental**
- locker rooms
- showers
- executive course
- accommodations
- ✓ **food and beverages**
- ✓ **clubhouse**

**John Flachman**
Manager

**Bob Borowicz**
Professional

**Steve Tiedeman**
Superintendent

NORTHERN D1

***Course information:*** This public course has 18 holes. See card below for yardage and rating information.

***Play policy and fees:*** Green fees are $6 for nine holes and $9 for 18 holes weekdays, and $8 and $12 weekends. Senior rates are $5 for nine holes and $6 for 18 holes and available on weekdays only. Carts are $18 for 18 holes. Reservations are recommended. Fees should change by June, up a couple of dollars a round.

***Location:*** Take Highway 12 east off Highway 101. At the fairgrounds veer right onto Bennett Valley Road, which will take you to Yulupa Avenue.

***Course description:*** This is a flat, well conditioned course with lots of trees. The greens are fast and the course is walkable. A creek wanders through the course, and provides some water hazard encounters. Bennett Valley Golf Course hosts the first leg of the Santa Rosa City Championship. In the summer, the course averages 350 to 400 players a day, a very busy course. Tee times are given out a week in advance. The 433-yard 17th hole is the toughest hole on the course, but overall it's a good test for all golfers.

| Hole | 1 | 2 | 3 | 4 | 5 | 6 | 7 | 8 | 9 | Out | BLUE | Rating: 70.6 |
|---|---|---|---|---|---|---|---|---|---|---|---|---|
| BLUE | 491 | 441 | 368 | 309 | 519 | 176 | 365 | 212 | 377 | 3258 | | Slope: 112 |
| WHITE | 444 | 432 | 347 | 297 | 501 | 156 | 340 | 201 | 365 | 3083 | | |
| Par | 5 | 4 | 4 | 4 | 5 | 3 | 4 | 3 | 4 | 36 | WHITE | Rating: 69.0 |
| Handicap | 3 | 1 | 9 | 17 | 5 | 15 | 7 | 13 | 11 | x | | Slope: 109 |
| RED | 420 | 422 | 340 | 293 | 449 | 143 | 331 | 191 | 337 | 2926 | | |
| Par | 5 | 5 | 4 | 4 | 5 | 3 | 4 | 3 | 4 | 37 | RED | Rating: 72.5 |
| Handicap | 3 | 5 | 9 | 15 | 1 | 17 | 7 | 13 | 11 | x | | Slope:116 |

| Hole | 10 | 11 | 12 | 13 | 14 | 15 | 16 | 17 | 18 | In | Totals | |
|---|---|---|---|---|---|---|---|---|---|---|---|---|
| BLUE | 499 | 171 | 424 | 393 | 392 | 168 | 367 | 433 | 478 | 3325 | BLUE | 6583 |
| WHITE | 482 | 160 | 413 | 359 | 369 | 138 | 356 | 425 | 436 | 3138 | WHITE | 6221 |
| Par | 5 | 3 | 4 | 4 | 4 | 3 | 4 | 4 | 5 | 36 | Par | 72 |
| Handicap | 12 | 18 | 4 | 10 | 6 | 16 | 8 | 2 | 14 | x | | |
| RED | 458 | 148 | 403 | 350 | 359 | 133 | 343 | 420 | 418 | 3032 | RED | 5958 |
| Par | 5 | 3 | 5 | 4 | 4 | 3 | 4 | 5 | 5 | 38 | Par | 75 |
| Handicap | 2 | 18 | 14 | 12 | 10 | 16 | 4 | 6 | 8 | x | | |

MAP ON PAGE 94

# FOUNTAINGROVE RESORT AND COUNTRY CLUB

**Course 14**
MAP D1 grid g2

**1985**
**Ted Robinson**

1525 Fountaingrove Parkway
Santa Rosa, CA 95403

Pro shop (707) 579-4653
Clubhouse (707) 544-1330

✓ **driving range**
✓ **practice greens**
✓ **power carts**
pull carts
✓ **golf club rental**
✓ **locker rooms**
✓ **showers**
executive course
✓ **accommodations**
✓ **food and beverages**
✓ **clubhouse**

**Mike Jonas**
Professional

**Robert Tyler**
Superintendent

***Course information:*** This semi-private course has 18 holes. See card below for yardage and rating information.

***Play policy and fees:*** Outside play is accepted. Green fees are $45 on weekdays, $55 on Fridays, and $70 on weekends. Carts are mandatory and included in the green fees. Reservations are recommended up to a week in advance. Carts are allowed on paths only.

***Location:*** In Santa Rosa on Highway 101, take the Mendocino Avenue/Old Redwood Highway exit. Drive east and turn left on Fountaingrove Parkway. Continue up the hill to the course, which is on the left.

***Course description:*** This Ted Robinson design is a tight, hilly layout with lots of trees and good greens. The 17th hole is picturesque. It is a par-3 that requires a 218-yard shot downhill over water. The course records are 67 for men and 73 for women. This offers some challenging holes, and it's a very pretty setting in North Santa Rosa. The 403-yard 13th hole requires a lay-up tee shot. The green is bordered by a bunker. Oak trees are everywhere. Don't stray too far off the fairway. Rattlesnakes have been known to sunbathe on the rocks.

| Hole | 1 | 2 | 3 | 4 | 5 | 6 | 7 | 8 | 9 | Out | | |
|---|---|---|---|---|---|---|---|---|---|---|---|---|
| BLUE | 379 | 396 | 390 | 496 | 145 | 388 | 367 | 604 | 174 | 3339 | BLUE | Rating: 72.8 |
| WHITE | 359 | 366 | 374 | 485 | 125 | 358 | 337 | 586 | 150 | 3140 | | Slope: 132 |
| Par | 4 | 4 | 4 | 5 | 3 | 4 | 4 | 5 | 3 | 36 | WHITE | Rating: 70.9 |
| Handicap | 9 | 3 | 13 | 7 | 17 | 5 | 11 | 1 | 15 | x | | Slope: 128 |
| RED | 299 | 326 | 333 | 453 | 107 | 322 | 302 | 518 | 126 | 2786 | | |
| Par | 4 | 4 | 4 | 5 | 3 | 4 | 4 | 5 | 3 | 36 | RED | Rating: 72.1 |
| Handicap | 13 | 7 | 5 | 3 | 17 | 9 | 11 | 1 | 15 | x | | Slope: 128 |

| Hole | 10 | 11 | 12 | 13 | 14 | 15 | 16 | 17 | 18 | In | Totals | |
|---|---|---|---|---|---|---|---|---|---|---|---|---|
| BLUE | 396 | 558 | 176 | 403 | 541 | 396 | 389 | 218 | 381 | 3458 | BLUE | 6797 |
| WHITE | 378 | 538 | 161 | 374 | 520 | 361 | 364 | 178 | 366 | 3240 | WHITE | 6380 |
| Par | 4 | 5 | 3 | 4 | 5 | 4 | 4 | 3 | 4 | 36 | Par | 72 |
| Handicap | 12 | 8 | 16 | 2 | 10 | 6 | 4 | 14 | 18 | x | | |
| RED | 306 | 490 | 131 | 336 | 484 | 308 | 330 | 133 | 340 | 2858 | RED | 5644 |
| Par | 4 | 5 | 3 | 4 | 5 | 4 | 4 | 3 | 4 | 36 | Par | 72 |
| Handicap | 14 | 2 | 18 | 8 | 4 | 12 | 10 | 16 | 6 | x | | |

# FAIRGROUNDS GOLF CENTER

Course 15
MAP D1 grid g2

*Course information:* This public course has nine holes. Par is 58 for 18 holes. The course is 3,296 yards and rated 54.6 (18 holes). The slope rating is 73. Women's yardage and ratings were unavailable. The course will undergo remodeling to add two or three holes by summer.

*Play policy and fees:* Green fees are $6 for nine holes and $7 for 18 holes weekdays, and $7 and $8 weekends. Senior and junior rates are $5 for nine holes and $6 for 18 holes weekdays. Twilight rates are $6 after three p.m. for nine holes and $7 for 18 holes on weekends. Pull carts are $2.

*Location:* In Santa Rosa on Highway 101 north, take the Santa Rosa Fairgrounds exit which will take you to the fairgrounds and the course on your right.

*Course description:* This course, situated in the center of the Santa Rosa Fairgrounds race track, is a good practice course. There are two water hazards and some sand traps. The course is flat and the greens are fairly small. A night driving range is open to 8 p. m.

1350 Bennett Valley Road
Santa Rosa, CA 95404

Pro shop (707) 577-0755

- ✓ **driving range**
- ✓ **practice greens**
- power carts
- ✓ **pull carts**
- ✓ **golf club rental**
- locker rooms
- showers
- executive course
- accommodations
- ✓ **food and beverages**
- clubhouse

**Rod Metzler**
Director of Golf

**Brian Metzler**
Professional

NORTHERN D1

| Hole | 1 | 2 | 3 | 4 | 5 | 6 | 7 | 8 | 9 | Out | | |
|---|---|---|---|---|---|---|---|---|---|---|---|---|
| BLUE | - | - | - | - | - | - | - | - | - | - | BLUE | Rating: -- |
| | | | | | | | | | | | | Slope: -- |
| WHITE | 184 | 94 | 138 | 133 | 168 | 302 | 308 | 118 | 205 | 1650 | | |
| Par | 3 | 3 | 3 | 3 | 3 | 4 | 4 | 3 | 3 | 29 | WHITE | Rating: 54.6 |
| Handicap | 4 | 18 | 12 | 16 | 6 | 14 | 10 | 8 | 2 | x | | Slope: 73 |
| RED | - | - | - | - | - | - | - | - | - | - | | |
| Par | - | - | - | - | - | - | - | - | - | - | RED | Rating: -- |
| Handicap | - | - | - | - | - | - | - | - | - | x | | Slope: -- |

| Hole | 10 | 11 | 12 | 13 | 14 | 15 | 16 | 17 | 18 | In | Totals | |
|---|---|---|---|---|---|---|---|---|---|---|---|---|
| BLUE | - | - | - | - | - | - | - | - | - | - | BLUE | -- |
| WHITE | 184 | 94 | 138 | 133 | 168 | 302 | 308 | 118 | 205 | 1650 | WHITE | 3300 |
| Par | 3 | 3 | 3 | 3 | 3 | 4 | 4 | 3 | 3 | 29 | Par | 58 |
| Handicap | 4 | 18 | 12 | 16 | 6 | 14 | 10 | 8 | 2 | x | | |
| RED | - | - | - | - | - | - | - | - | - | - | RED | -- |
| Par | - | - | - | - | - | - | - | - | - | - | Par | -- |
| Handicap | | - | - | - | - | - | - | - | - | x | | |

## OAKMONT GOLF COURSE

**Course 16**
MAP D1 grid g3

**1963**
**Ted Robinson**

7025 Oakmont Drive
Santa Rosa, CA 95409

West course(707) 539-0415
East course (707) 538-2454

- ✓ **driving range**
- ✓ **practice greens**
- ✓ **power carts**
- ✓ **pull carts**
- ✓ **golf club rental**
- ✓ **locker rooms**
- ✓ **showers**
- ✓ **executive course** accommodations
- ✓ **food and beverages**
- ✓ **clubhouse**

**Dean F. James**
Professional

**Mike Clark**
Superintendent

***Course information:*** This semi-private facility has 36 holes. Par is 72 for the West Course and 63 for the East Course.

The West Course is 6,379 yards and rated 70.5 from the championship tees, and 6,059 yards and rated 69.0 from the regular tees. The slope ratings are 120 championship and 117 regular. Women's tees are 5,573 yards and rated 71.9. The slope rating is 128.

The East Course is 4,293 yards and rated 59.8 from the regular tees. The slope rating is 94. Women's tees are 4,067 yards and rated 62.2. The slope rating is 94.

***Play policy and fees:*** Outside play is accepted. West Course green fees are $22 on weekdays and $28 on weekends. East Course green fees are $17 on weekdays and $22 on weekends. Carts are $22. Reservations are recommended, one day in advance for weekdays and one week for weekends. Shirts must have collars. No tank tops may be worn.

***Location:*** From Santa Rosa, drive east on Highway 12 toward Sonoma. Turn right on Oakmont Drive into the community of Oakmont. The course is on the right, eight miles east of Highway 101.

***Course description:*** The West Course is short with lots of trees. There is water on 14 holes. The pride of the West Course is the 381-yard, par-4 eighth hole, which boasts two lakes and out-of-bounds on both sides. The East Course is a short, executive course with some challenging par-3s. The 171-yard, par-3 14th hole, for example, requires a longish carry over a creek. Oakmont co-hosts the Santa Rosa City Championship. Both courses are busy; 140,000 rounds are played here a year.

# MEADOWOOD RESORT HOTEL GOLF COURSE

**Course 17**
MAP D1 grid g5

**1963**

*Course information:* This private resort course has nine holes. Par is 62 for 18 holes. The course is 4,106 yards and rated 59.5 from the regular tees (18 holes). The slope rating is 92. Women's tees are 3,982 yards and rated 61.9. The slope rating is 94.

*Play policy and fees:* Reciprocal play is accepted with members of other private clubs. Hotel guests are welcome. Green fees are $35 for hotel guests, and $35 for reciprocators on weekdays, $40 on weekends. Shirts with collars must be worn.

*Location:* From Napa, drive north on Highway 29. Turn right on Pope Street and take Pope Street to Silverado Trail. Jog left then right on Silverado Trial to Howell Mountain Road. Follow Howell Mountain Road to Meadowood Lane.

*Course description:* This is a short, tight and tricky course with lots of trees. There are some hills and undulating greens. It's an excellent course for beginners and intermediates. The 348-yard number three is a par-4 that doglegs to the right. Although Meadowood is a short course, the setting in the oaks with the beautiful resort nearby is very pretty and peaceful. Note the world-class croquet pitch next to the golf course.

900 Meadowood Lane
Saint Helena, CA 94574

Pro shop (707) 963-3646

- driving range
- ✓ **practice greens**
- power carts
- ✓ **pull carts**
- ✓ **golf club rental**
- locker rooms
- showers
- ✓ **executive course**
- ✓ **accommodations**
- ✓ **food and beverages**
- clubhouse

**Thomas Hill**
Head Professional

**Gary Williams**
Superintendent

# MOUNTAIN SHADOWS GOLF COURSE

**Course 18**
MAP D1 grid h1

**1963**
**R.E. Baldock**

100 Golf Course Drive
Rohnert Park, CA 94928

Pro shop (707) 584-7766

- ✓ **driving range**
- ✓ **practice greens**
- ✓ **power carts**
- ✓ **pull carts**
- ✓ **golf club rental**
- locker rooms
- showers
- executive course
- accommodations
- ✓ **food and beverages**
- ✓ **clubhouse**

**Greg Anderson**
Professional

**Sam Singh**
Superintendent

***Course information:*** This public facility has two 18-hole courses. Par is 72 for each.

The North Course is 6,690 yards and rated 69.7 from the championship tees, and 6,160 yards and rated 67.5 from the regular tees. The slope ratings are 112 championship and 108 regular. Women's tees are 5,543 yards and rated 70.5 from the regular tees. The slope rating is 117.

The South Course is 6,490 yards and rated 70.1 from the championship tees, and 6,086 yards and rated 68.0 from the regular tees. The slope ratings are 115 championship and 111 regular. Women's tees are 5,806 yards and rated 71.4 from the regular tees. The slope rating is 117.

***Play policy and fees:*** The North Course weekday green fees are $29 before 2 p.m., $20 from 2 p.m. to 4 p.m., $15 from 4 p.m. to 6 p.m., and $10 after 6 p.m. Green fees for Fridays, weekends and holidays are $45 before 3 p.m., $25 from 3 p.m. to 5 p.m., $15 from 5 p.m. to 7 p.m., and $10 after 7 p.m. Rates could change.

South Course weekday green fees are $16 without cart or $27 with cart before 2 p.m., $13 without cart or $18 with cart from 2 p.m. to 4 p.m., $8 without cart or $15 with cart from 4 p.m. to 6 p.m., and $5 without cart and $8 with cart after 6 p.m. Weekend and holiday green fees are $25 until 3 p.m., $13 without cart or $20 with cart from 3 p.m. to 5 p.m., $8 without cart and $15 with cart from 5 p.m. to 7 p.m., and $5 without cart or $8 with cart after 7 p.m. Call for mandatory cart policy.

***Location:*** From Santa Rosa, drive seven miles south on Highway 101. Take the Wilfred exit east to Golf Course Drive.

***Course description:*** Both courses are tight with a rolling terrain and large, undulating greens. Notable is the seventh hole on the North Course. It's 380 yards, and every shot is trouble to negotiate. It was rated one of the most difficult holes in Northern California with out-of-bounds to the left and a lake running down the entire right side. The green sits on a well bunkered peninsula. It's a beauty. The Redwood Empire Championship-Golden State Tour and the Sonoma County Men's Amateur Championship tournaments are held here annually.

# CHIMNEY ROCK GOLF COURSE

**Course 19**
MAP D1 grid h7



**1966**
**R.E. Baldock**

5320 Silverado Trail
Napa, CA 94559

Pro shop (707) 255-3363
Fax (707)257-2036

- driving range
- ✓ **practice greens**
- ✓ **power carts**
- ✓ **pull carts**
- ✓ **golf club rental**
- locker rooms
- showers
- executive course
- accommodations
- ✓ **food and beverages**
- ✓ **clubhouse**

**Jay Rasband**
Manager

**Scott Pajak**
Superintendent

***Course information:*** This public course has nine holes. See card below for yardage and rating information.

***Play policy and fees:*** Green fees are $12 for nine holes and $18 for 18 holes weekdays, and $15 and $22 weekends. Senior rates are $8.50 for unlimited play weekdays only. Carts are $13 for nine holes and $20 for 18 holes. Napa County seniors can enjoy a special rate of $8.50, but only on weekdays. Twilight rates are available.

***Location:*** From Napa heading north on Highway 29, go right on Oak Knoll Ave. At the end, turn left and make an immediate right again onto Oak Knoll. Turn left onto Silverado Trail and travel 1.5 miles to the course.

***Course description:*** Located in the Soda Canyon Hills, the course offers beauty and some challenging holes, as three lakes come into play on the flat layout. The best hole is the par-4 second, a dogleg over a lake, with a green nestled among the oaks and pines.

| Hole | 1 | 2 | 3 | 4 | 5 | 6 | 7 | 8 | 9 | Out | BLUE | Rating: 71.0 |
|---|---|---|---|---|---|---|---|---|---|---|---|---|
| BLUE | 384 | 424 | 221 | 534 | 418 | 311 | 200 | 505 | 421 | 3418 | | Slope: 110 |
| WHITE | 373 | 414 | 208 | 527 | 408 | 294 | 188 | 497 | 400 | 3309 | | |
| Par | 4 | 4 | 3 | 5 | 4 | 4 | 3 | 5 | 4 | 36 | WHITE | Rating: 70.0 |
| Handicap | 9 | 1 | 15 | 7 | 5 | 11 | 17 | 13 | 3 | x | | Slope: 108 |
| RED | 361 | 299 | 154 | 479 | 396 | 266 | 140 | 472 | 375 | 2942 | | |
| Par | 4 | 4 | 3 | 5 | 4 | 4 | 3 | 5 | 4 | 36 | RED | Rating: 72.9 |
| Handicap | 9 | 13 | 15 | 1 | 5 | 11 | 17 | 3 | 7 | x | | Slope: 124 |

| Hole | 10 | 11 | 12 | 13 | 14 | 15 | 16 | 17 | 18 | In | Totals | |
|---|---|---|---|---|---|---|---|---|---|---|---|---|
| BLUE | 384 | 424 | 221 | 534 | 418 | 311 | 200 | 505 | 421 | 3418 | BLUE | 6836 |
| WHITE | 373 | 414 | 208 | 527 | 408 | 294 | 188 | 497 | 400 | 3309 | WHITE | 6618 |
| Par | 4 | 4 | 3 | 5 | 4 | 4 | 3 | 5 | 4 | 36 | Par | 72 |
| Handicap | 10 | 2 | 16 | 8 | 6 | 12 | 18 | 14 | 4 | x | | |
| RED | 361 | 299 | 154 | 479 | 396 | 266 | 140 | 472 | 375 | 2942 | RED | 5884 |
| Par | 4 | 4 | 3 | 5 | 4 | 4 | 3 | 5 | 4 | 36 | Par | 72 |
| Handicap | 10 | 14 | 16 | 2 | 6 | 12 | 18 | 4 | 8 | x | | |

# SILVERADO COUNTRY CLUB

**Course 20**
MAP D1 grid h7

***Course information:*** This private resort facility has two 18-hole courses. Par is 72 for each.

The North Course is 6,900 yards and rated 73.4 from the championship tees, and 6,351 yards and rated 70.9 from the regular tees. The slope ratings are: 131 championship and 126 regular. Women's tees are 5,857 yards and rated 73.1. The slope rating is 128.

The South Course is 6,685 yards and rated 72.4 from the championship tees, and 6,243 yards and rated 70.5 from the regular tees. The slope ratings are 129 championship and 124 regular. Women's tees are 5,672 yards and rated 72.7. The slope rating is 128.

***Play policy and fees:*** Reciprocal play is accepted with members of other private clubs. Hotel guests are welcome. Green fees are $90 for hotel guests and $100 for reciprocal players. Carts are mandatory and included in the green fees. Reservations are recommended two days in advance unless you are a hotel guest.

***Location:*** From Napa, drive north on Highway 121. Take the Atlas Peak Road exit north. Drive less than a mile to the course.

**1955**
**Johnny Dawson**

1600 Atlas Peak Road
Napa, CA 94558

Pro shop (707) 257-5460
Clubhouse (707) 257-0200

- ✓ **driving range**
- ✓ **practice greens**
- ✓ **power carts**
- pull carts
- ✓ **golf club rental**
- ✓ **locker rooms**
- ✓ **showers**
- executive course
- ✓ **accommodations**
- ✓ **food and beverages**
- ✓ **clubhouse**

**Jeff Goodwin**
Professional

**Brian Morris**
Superintendent

***Course description:*** The North Course is a longer, championship course, while the South Course is shorter and requires more finesse shots. Both have sprawling layouts with large, undulating greens. Water and large oak trees guard the courses. Remodeled by Robert Trent Jones, Jr. in 1966, the North Course was formerly used for the PGA Tour's Kaiser International and Anheuser-Busch Classic. The South Course is the site of the Senior PGA Tour's Transamerica Open. The back nine on the North Course offers demanding par-4s. The South Course is not as long, but it's very enjoyable. The 380-yard tenth, the 14th, and the 360-yard 16th prove good holes don't necessarily have to be long.

# ADOBE CREEK GOLF COURSE

**Course 21**
**MAP D1 grid i2**

***Course information:*** This public course has 18 holes and par is 72. The course is 6,815 yards and rated 72.6 with a slope of 126 from the tournament tees. See card below for additional yardage and rating information.

***Play policy and fees:*** Green fees are $35 weekdays and $55 weekends, carts included. Reservations are accepted two weeks in advance.

***Location:*** From Highway 101 in Petaluma, take the Highway 116 exit east and drive 1.25 miles. Turn left on Frates Road and drive three-fourths of a mile to the course on the left.

***Course description:*** This sprawling course, situated in the Sonoma County countryside, has many mounds. Five lakes, a stream and 70 bunkers make accuracy a must. Beware of the seventh hole: It's a par-4, 405-yard challenge with a creek on the right and a creek fronting the large green. Two creeks equal trouble. This course can get very wet, so during the rainy season call ahead. The ninth, 16th, 17th and 18th holes are very good holes. A total of 40,000 to 50,000 rounds are played here per year.

**1990**
**Robert Trent Jones, Jr.**

1901 Frates Road
Petaluma, CA 94954

Pro shop (707) 765-3000

- ✓ **driving range**
- ✓ **practice greens**
- ✓ **power carts**
- pull carts
- ✓ **golf club rental**
- locker rooms
- showers
- executive course
- accommodations
- ✓ **food and beverages**
- ✓ **clubhouse**

**Dana Banke**
Professional

**Peter Dempsey**
Superintendent

NORTHERN D1

| Hole | 1 | 2 | 3 | 4 | 5 | 6 | 7 | 8 | 9 | Out | BLUE | Rating: 70.0 |
|---|---|---|---|---|---|---|---|---|---|---|---|---|
| BLUE | 501 | 390 | 367 | 483 | 132 | 320 | 388 | 160 | 352 | 3093 | | Slope: 120 |
| WHITE | 454 | 363 | 339 | 444 | 118 | 276 | 363 | 124 | 322 | 2803 | | |
| Par | 5 | 4 | 4 | 5 | 3 | 4 | 4 | 3 | 4 | 36 | WHITE | Rating: 67.5 |
| Handicap | 3 | 9 | 13 | 5 | 17 | 15 | 1 | 11 | 7 | x | | Slope: 115 |
| RED | 422 | 330 | 313 | 405 | 94 | 255 | 298 | 98 | 267 | 2482 | | |
| Par | 5 | 4 | 4 | 5 | 3 | 4 | 4 | 3 | 4 | 36 | RED | Rating: 68.3 |
| Handicap | 2 | 6 | 10 | 8 | 18 | 14 | 4 | 16 | 12 | x | | Slope: 115 |

| Hole | 10 | 11 | 12 | 13 | 14 | 15 | 16 | 17 | 18 | In | Totals | |
|---|---|---|---|---|---|---|---|---|---|---|---|---|
| BLUE | 357 | 533 | 128 | 382 | 476 | 379 | 140 | 326 | 407 | 3128 | BLUE | 6221 |
| WHITE | 318 | 503 | 97 | 349 | 442 | 344 | 135 | 303 | 374 | 2865 | WHITE | 5668 |
| Par | 4 | 5 | 3 | 4 | 5 | 4 | 3 | 4 | 4 | 36 | Par | 72 |
| Handicap | 10 | 2 | 18 | 8 | 4 | 12 | 16 | 14 | 6 | x | | |
| RED | 277 | 463 | 85 | 299 | 416 | 297 | 96 | 280 | 332 | 2545 | RED | 5027 |
| Par | 4 | 5 | 3 | 4 | 5 | 4 | 3 | 4 | 4 | 36 | Par | 72 |
| Handicap | 9 | 3 | 15 | 7 | 1 | 13 | 17 | 11 | 5 | x | | |

MAP ON PAGE 94

# PETALUMA GOLF AND COUNTRY CLUB

Course 22
MAP D1 grid i2

***Course information:*** This private course has nine holes. Par is 70 for 18 holes. The course is 5,574 yards and rated 66.0 from the regular tees (18 holes). The slope rating is 107. Women's tees are 5,426 yards and rated 70.5 from the regular tees. The slope rating is 119.

***Play policy and fees:*** Reciprocal play is accepted with members of other private clubs. Call to make arrangements.

***Location:*** Heading north on Highway 101 toward Petaluma, take the Petaluma Boulevard South exit northwest into town. Take McNear Avenue south to Country Club Drive to the course.

***Course description:*** This short, hilly course is called "Goat Hill." It has lots of bunkers, no water and is walkable but it's a workout. The sixth hole is a 148-yard par-3 to the green, guarded on the right by a huge oak tree. A total of 19,000 rounds are played here per year.

PO Box 26
Petaluma, CA 94953

1500 Country Club Drive
Petaluma, CA 94953

Pro shop (707) 762-7041

✓ **driving range**
✓ **practice greens**
✓ **power carts**
✓ **pull carts**
✓ **golf club rental**
locker rooms
showers
executive course
accommodations
✓ **food and beverages**
✓ **clubhouse**

**Terry Cline**
Manager

**Alan Brownlie**
Professional

**Bill Maeder**
Superintendent

# SONOMA GOLF CLUB



**1926**
**Sam Whiting**

**1991**
**Robert Muir Graves**
**Re-Design**

17700 Arnold Drive
Sonoma, CA 95476

Pro shop (707) 996-0300
Clubhouse (707) 996-4852

- ✓ **driving range**
- ✓ **practice greens**
- ✓ **power carts**
- pull carts
- ✓ **golf club rental**
- ✓ **locker rooms**
- ✓ **showers**
- executive course
- accommodations
- ✓ **food and beverages**
- ✓ **clubhouse**

**Steve Shimano**
Manager

**Don Tarvid**
Professional

**Larry Norman**
Superintendent

***Course information:*** This public course has 18 holes. See card below for yardage and rating information.

***Play policy and fees:*** Green fees include cart and are $45 Monday through Thursday, $55 Fridays, and $65 weekends. Twilight green fees are half price.

***Location:*** Travel north on Highway 101; take Highway 37 east to Highway 121. Travel north on Highway 121 to the Arnold Drive exit. Drive about seven miles on Arnold Drive to the golf course.

***Course description:*** This course has undergone a major renovation under the design guidance of Robert Muir Graves. It reopened in March, 1991 to rave reviews, and is considered one of the top public courses in the country. A driving range was added, causing some realignment, but the hole sequence remains the same. It's mostly flat but there is a lot of mounding and subtle elevation changes. The greens were totally rebuilt and enlarged during the 15-month, $10 million renovation period, but are well established. They are also very subtle and maintain a traditional flavor. There is nothing tricky about the greens. The 433-yard fifth is a monster, a drive and long iron into a prevailing wind. The 432-yard 15th, a dogleg right, is tougher, due to an uphill approach into the wind. Because it is an old, mature course, there are lots of oaks and redwoods guarding several tight doglegs. Two new lakes were added, but they don't come noticeably into play unless your shot is particularly errant. The rough has just been stripped and redone. This is definitely the new course to play in Northern California. A total of 40,000 rounds are played here a year

| Hole | 1 | 2 | 3 | 4 | 5 | 6 | 7 | 8 | 9 | Out | BLUE | Rating: 74.9 |
|---|---|---|---|---|---|---|---|---|---|---|---|---|
| BLUE | 389 | 555 | 410 | 206 | 433 | 430 | 222 | 597 | 346 | 3588 | | Slope: 135 |
| WHITE | 367 | 523 | 388 | 186 | 414 | 408 | 179 | 576 | 327 | 3368 | | |
| Par | 4 | 5 | 4 | 3 | 4 | 4 | 3 | 5 | 4 | 36 | WHITE | Rating: 72.2 |
| Handicap | 15 | 3 | 9 | 13 | 1 | 11 | 7 | 5 | 17 | x | | Slope: 130 |
| RED | 303 | 444 | 322 | 142 | 346 | 338 | 131 | 496 | 263 | 2785 | | |
| Par | 4 | 5 | 4 | 3 | 4 | 4 | 3 | 5 | 4 | 36 | RED | Rating: 71.5 |
| Handicap | 15 | 5 | 9 | 13 | 1 | 7 | 11 | 3 | 17 | x | | Slope:128 |

| Hole | 10 | 11 | 12 | 13 | 14 | 15 | 16 | 17 | 18 | In | Totals | |
|---|---|---|---|---|---|---|---|---|---|---|---|---|
| BLUE | 429 | 360 | 429 | 527 | 219 | 442 | 539 | 140 | 396 | 3481 | BLUE | 7069 |
| WHITE | 381 | 343 | 395 | 498 | 193 | 417 | 485 | 130 | 373 | 3215 | WHITE | 6583 |
| Par | 4 | 4 | 4 | 5 | 3 | 4 | 5 | 3 | 4 | 36 | Par | 72 |
| Handicap | 10 | 14 | 4 | 12 | 6 | 2 | 16 | 18 | 8 | x | | |
| RED | 306 | 271 | 330 | 455 | 149 | 347 | 448 | 106 | 322 | 2734 | RED | 5519 |
| Par | 4 | 4 | 4 | 5 | 3 | 4 | 5 | 3 | 4 | 36 | Par | 72 |
| Handicap | 14 | 16 | 8 | 6 | 10 | 2 | 4 | 18 | 12 | x | | |

# LOS ARROYOS GOLF CLUB

**Course 24**
MAP D1 grid i4

*Course information:* This public course has nine holes and par is 58 for 18 holes. The course is 3,078 yards and not rated.

*Play policy and fees:* Green fees are $7 weekdays and $10 weekends. This is an all-day rate. Pull carts are $2.

*Location:* From San Francisco heading north on Highway 101, take the Highway 116 exit east to Sonoma. The course is at the intersection of Highway 116 and Highway 121.

*Course description:* This tree-lined executive course is fairly flat and makes a good iron course. There are two par-4s. The best hole on the course is the par-3 eighth, 160 yards. A total of 32,000 rounds are played here each year.

5000 Stage Gulch Road
Sonoma, CA 95476

Pro shop (707) 938-8835

- ✓ **driving range**
- practice greens
- power carts
- ✓ **pull carts**
- ✓ **golf club rental**
- locker rooms
- showers
- ✓ **executive course**
- accommodations
- ✓ **food and beverages**
- ✓ **clubhouse**

**Karen Sequeria**
Manager

| Hole | 1 | 2 | 3 | 4 | 5 | 6 | 7 | 8 | 9 | Out | BLUE | Rating: -- |
|---|---|---|---|---|---|---|---|---|---|---|---|---|
| BLUE | - | - | - | - | - | - | - | - | - | - | | Slope: -- |
| WHITE | 143 | 150 | 285 | 95 | 305 | 100 | 144 | 160 | 157 | 1539 | | |
| Par | 3 | 3 | 4 | 3 | 4 | 3 | 3 | 3 | 3 | 29 | WHITE | Rating: -- |
| Handicap | 11 | 5 | 3 | 15 | 9 | 17 | 7 | 1 | 13 | x | | Slope: -- |
| RED | 143 | 150 | 285 | 95 | 305 | 100 | 144 | 160 | 157 | 1539 | | |
| Par | 3 | 3 | 4 | 3 | 4 | 3 | 3 | 3 | 3 | 29 | RED | Rating: -- |
| Handicap | 11 | 5 | 3 | 15 | 9 | 17 | 7 | 1 | 13 | x | | Slope: -- |

| Hole | 10 | 11 | 12 | 13 | 14 | 15 | 16 | 17 | 18 | In | Totals | |
|---|---|---|---|---|---|---|---|---|---|---|---|---|
| BLUE | - | - | - | - | - | - | - | - | - | - | BLUE | -- |
| WHITE | 143 | 150 | 285 | 95 | 305 | 100 | 144 | 160 | 157 | 1539 | WHITE | 3708 |
| Par | 3 | 3 | 4 | 3 | 4 | 3 | 3 | 3 | 3 | 29 | Par | 58 |
| Handicap | 12 | 6 | 4 | 16 | 10 | 18 | 8 | 2 | 14 | x | | |
| RED | 143 | 150 | 285 | 95 | 305 | 100 | 144 | 160 | 157 | 1539 | RED | 3708 |
| Par | 3 | 3 | 4 | 3 | 4 | 3 | 3 | 3 | 3 | 29 | Par | 58 |
| Handicap | 12 | 6 | 4 | 16 | 10 | 18 | 8 | 2 | 14 | x | | |

# NAPA GOLF COURSE

**Course 25**
MAP D1 grid i6



***Course information:*** This public course has 18 holes. Women's tees are 4,958 yards and rated 68.5 with a slope of 120 from the gold tees. See card below for additional yardage and rating information.

***Play policy and fees:*** The city of Napa now has a resident/non-resident green fee policy for this course. Green fees for non-residents are $17 weekdays, $23 weekends and holidays, and $12 after 3 p.m. any day. Resident green fees are $13 weekdays, $17 weekends and holidays, and $10 after 3 p.m. any day. Carts are $17 for 18 holes and $10 for nine holes. Reservations are recommended seven days or less in advance. No single play is allowed. No spectators.

***Location:*** From Highway 12 in Napa, take Highway 29 north. Take the Lake Berryessa exit at the fork. Drive two miles to Streblow Drive and turn left to get to the course.

***Course description:*** This underrated course is long, tough and tight. It has many trees and water occurs on 14 holes. Nicknamed Kennedy Park because the course is situated in Napa's John F. Kennedy Park, this course was used for U.S. Open qualifying in 1972 and formerly for PGA Tour events at Silverado Country Club.

**1958**
**Jack Fleming**

Kennedy Parkway,
2295 Streblow Drive
Napa, CA 94558

Pro shop (707) 255-4333

- ✓ **driving range**
- ✓ **practice greens**
- ✓ **power carts**
- ✓ **pull carts**
- ✓ **golf club rental**
- locker rooms
- showers
- executive course
- accommodations
- ✓ **food and beverages**
- ✓ **clubhouse**

**Bob Swan**
Manager/Professional

| Hole | 1 | 2 | 3 | 4 | 5 | 6 | 7 | 8 | 9 | Out | | |
|---|---|---|---|---|---|---|---|---|---|---|---|---|
| BLUE | 391 | 422 | 409 | 199 | 510 | 433 | 164 | 350 | 527 | 3405 | BLUE | Rating: 71.7 |
| WHITE | 371 | 408 | 401 | 188 | 494 | 417 | 148 | 336 | 513 | 3276 | | Slope: 118 |
| Par | 4 | 4 | 4 | 3 | 5 | 4 | 3 | 4 | 5 | 36 | WHITE | Rating: 70.7 |
| Handicap | 7 | 1 | 5 | 9 | 11 | 3 | 17 | 15 | 13 | x | | Slope: 115 |
| RED | 359 | 398 | 388 | 143 | 438 | 335 | 133 | 323 | 461 | 2978 | | |
| Par | 4 | 5 | 4 | 3 | 5 | 4 | 3 | 4 | 5 | 37 | RED | Rating: 73.6 |
| Handicap | 3 | 13 | 5 | 15 | 9 | 7 | 17 | 11 | 1 | x | | Slope: -- |

| Hole | 10 | 11 | 12 | 13 | 14 | 15 | 16 | 17 | 18 | In | Totals | |
|---|---|---|---|---|---|---|---|---|---|---|---|---|
| BLUE | 415 | 329 | 429 | 202 | 549 | 372 | 161 | 490 | 378 | 3325 | BLUE | 6730 |
| WHITE | 405 | 318 | 418 | 187 | 538 | 362 | 157 | 478 | 367 | 3230 | WHITE | 6506 |
| Par | 4 | 4 | 4 | 3 | 5 | 4 | 3 | 5 | 4 | 36 | Par | 72 |
| Handicap | 4 | 18 | 2 | 8 | 12 | 10 | 16 | 14 | 6 | x | | |
| RED | 395 | 307 | 338 | 139 | 474 | 351 | 154 | 464 | 356 | 2978 | RED | 5956 |
| Par | 4 | 4 | 4 | 3 | 5 | 4 | 3 | 5 | 4 | 36 | Par | 73 |
| Handicap | 2 | 14 | 10 | 18 | 12 | 8 | 16 | 4 | 6 | x | | |

# NAPA VALLEY COUNTRY CLUB

**Course 26**
MAP D1 grid i7

***Course information:*** This private course has 18 holes and par is 72. The course is 6,051 yards and rated 70.0 from the championship tees, and 5,718 yards and rated 69.0 from the regular tees. The slope ratings are 125 championship and 122 regular. Women's tees are 5,230 yards and rated 69.8. The slope rating is 123.

***Play policy and fees:*** Reciprocal play is accepted with members of other private clubs. Green fees for reciprocators are $60, including cart. Guest fees are $25 when accompanied by a member weekdays, and $30 weekends. Call to make arrangements. Carts are $8 per rider. Rates could change by summer.

***Location:*** From Highway 121 in Napa, drive 1.5 miles on Hagen Road to the course.

***Course description:*** This scenic course has tight fairways and small, undulating greens. There are many oak trees. The course was expanded in the spring of 1990 to 18 holes under the design guidance of Ron Fream, and the new nine is beautiful. From it you can see the entire Bay Area and Napa Valley. From the 11th tee you can see the Golden Gate Bridge. When you're not looking at the view, check out this par-3. It's 135 yards to an island green. If you miss the green you're not in water, but you are in a mean barranca. Rocks and a hazard surround the green. It helps to know how to chip. The course has small greens on the front, but they're bigger on the back. It's a member's course, where local knowledge can win out over talent.

**1914**
**(Front Nine)**
**1990**
**Ron Fream**
**(Back Nine)**

PO Box 3177
Napa, CA 94558

3385 Hagen Road
Napa, CA 94558

Pro shop (707) 252-1114
Clubhouse (707) 252-1111

- ✓ **driving range**
- ✓ **practice greens**
- ✓ **power carts**
- ✓ **pull carts**
- ✓ **golf club rental**
- ✓ **locker rooms**
- ✓ **showers**
- executive course
- accommodations
- ✓ **food and beverages**
- ✓ **clubhouse**

**Mitch Johnson**
Professional

**Ron Forsythe**
Superintendent

# GREEN TREE GOLF COURSE

**Course 27**
MAP D1 grid i9

*Course information:* This public facility has 27 holes and par is 71. The course is 6,017 yards and rated 68.2 from the championship tees, and 5,809 yards and rated 67.3 from the regular tees. The slope ratings are 114 championship and 112 regular. Women's tees are 5,396 yards and rated 69.5. The slope rating is 117. The Executive Course is 3,120 yards and par is 29.

*Play policy and fees:* Green fees are $12 on weekdays and $17 on weekends. Senior and junior green fees are discounted $2. Carts are $16 on weekdays and $19 on weekends and holidays. Reservations are recommended one week in advance.

*Location:* From Vacaville, drive east on Interstate 80, past the Nut Tree restaurant. Take the Leisure Town Road exit to the course.

*Course description:* The course is picturesque and well maintained. The tee shot on the unusual par-3 first hole must carry over a lake. The men's course record is 62. While the course has undergone a complete face-lift, more changes are scheduled to occur. They will switch number nine, 390 yards, par-4, to a finishing hole. This hole has out-of-bounds right and mounds in the fairway. It's very narrow and plays hard into the wind, which comes up nearly everyday.

PO Box 1056
Vacaville, CA 95688

999 Leisure Town Road
Vacaville, CA 95688

Pro shop (707) 448-1420

- ✓ **driving range**
- ✓ **practice greens**
- ✓ **power carts**
- ✓ **pull carts**
- ✓ **golf club rental**
- locker rooms
- showers
- ✓ **executive course**
- accommodations
- ✓ **food and beverages**
- ✓ **clubhouse**

**Thom Casey**
Manager

**Dave Wiseman**
Professional

**Mike Scolaro**
Superintendent



MAP ON PAGE 94

# INDIAN VALLEY GOLF CLUB

**Course 28**
MAP D1 grid j2

**1957**

***Course information:*** This public course has 18 holes. See card below for yardage and rating information.

***Play policy and fees:*** Green fees are $25 on weekdays and $35 on weekends. Carts are $20. Reservations are recommended. This course is available for tournaments.

***Location:*** From Highway 101 in Novato, take the San Marin Drive exit west to Novato Boulevard. Turn right on Novato Boulevard to the course.

***Course description:*** This scenic course is challenging and diverse. There are rolling hills and many trees. Water comes into play on 10 holes. A premium is placed on chipping and putting. One of the best holes is the 16th. It's a par-5 and drops 250 feet from the tee. There is an elevator from the 13th to the 14th hole. The pro shop offers Henry Griffitts custom clubs, among other things, which are fitted in the pro shop by Hoyt and Mike Moore. A total of 80,000 rounds are played here per year.

PO Box 351
Novato, CA 94948

3035 Novato Boulevard
Novato, CA 94947

Pro shop (415) 897-1118

- ✓ **driving range**
- ✓ **practice greens**
- ✓ **power carts**
- ✓ **pull carts**
- ✓ **golf club rental**
- ✓ **locker rooms**
- ✓ **showers**
- executive course
- accommodations
- ✓ **food and beverages**
- ✓ **clubhouse**

**Ron Hoyt**
Professional

**Jeff McAndrew**
Director

**Terry Leach**
Superintendent

| Hole | 1 | 2 | 3 | 4 | 5 | 6 | 7 | 8 | 9 | Out | | |
|---|---|---|---|---|---|---|---|---|---|---|---|---|
| BLUE | 528 | 408 | 485 | 120 | 289 | 367 | 420 | 158 | 365 | 3140 | BLUE | Rating: 69.2 |
| WHITE | 523 | 389 | 464 | 110 | 261 | 332 | 387 | 148 | 323 | 2937 | | Slope: 119 |
| Par | 5 | 4 | 5 | 3 | 4 | 4 | 4 | 3 | 4 | 36 | WHITE | Rating: 67.8 |
| Handicap | 1 | 5 | 9 | 18 | 13 | 3 | 7 | 15 | 11 | x | | Slope: 116 |
| RED | 504 | 374 | 454 | 96 | 239 | 298 | 327 | 138 | 264 | 2694 | | |
| Par | 5 | 4 | 5 | 3 | 4 | 4 | 4 | 3 | 4 | 36 | RED | Rating: 70.9 |
| Handicap | 1 | 7 | 3 | 17 | 15 | 9 | 5 | 13 | 11 | x | | Slope: 128 |

| Hole | 10 | 11 | 12 | 13 | 14 | 15 | 16 | 17 | 18 | In | Totals | |
|---|---|---|---|---|---|---|---|---|---|---|---|---|
| BLUE | 360 | 324 | 425 | 146 | 395 | 365 | 475 | 148 | 475 | 3113 | BLUE | 6253 |
| WHITE | 300 | 313 | 415 | 134 | 379 | 323 | 450 | 139 | 452 | 2905 | WHITE | 5842 |
| Par | 4 | 4 | 4 | 3 | 4 | 4 | 5 | 3 | 5 | 36 | Par | 72 |
| Handicap | 14 | 12 | 2 | 16 | 4 | 6 | 8 | 17 | 10 | x | | |
| RED | 232 | 301 | 374 | 119 | 359 | 250 | 429 | 123 | 357 | 2544 | RED | 5238 |
| Par | 4 | 4 | 4 | 3 | 5 | 4 | 5 | 3 | 4 | 36 | Par | 72 |
| Handicap | 16 | 6 | 4 | 14 | 10 | 8 | 12 | 18 | 2 | x | | |

# MARIN COUNTRY CLUB

Course 29
MAP D1 grid j2

NORTHERN D1

*Course information:* This private course has 18 holes. See card below for yardage and rating information.

*Play policy and fees:* Reciprocal play is accepted with members of other private clubs. Guest fees are $50. Carts are $22.

*Location:* From Highway 101 in Novato, take the Ignacio Boulevard exit west. Drive 1.5 miles. Turn left on Country Club Drive to the course.

*Course description:* This sprawling course winds through a posh suburban neighborhood, offering tight fairways, fast and undulating greens, and sidehill lies. Wind can become a factor, but club selection is the key here on any day. The 411-yard fifth hole is a dogleg right, with water on the right, and out-of-bounds on the left. All the par-3s are demanding, and the greens are typically fast, putting lots of pressure on the short game.

**1959**

500 Country Club Drive
Novato, CA 94949

Pro shop (415) 382-6707
Clubhouse (415) 382-6700

- ✓ **driving range**
- ✓ **practice greens**
- ✓ **power carts**
- ✓ **pull carts**
- ✓ **golf club rental**
- ✓ **locker rooms**
- ✓ **showers**
- executive course
- accommodations
- ✓ **food and beverages**
- ✓ **clubhouse**

**Gil Bennett**
Professional

**Stanley Burgess**
Superintendent

| Hole | 1 | 2 | 3 | 4 | 5 | 6 | 7 | 8 | 9 | Out | | |
|---|---|---|---|---|---|---|---|---|---|---|---|---|
| BLUE | 481 | 167 | 388 | 357 | 411 | 352 | 178 | 394 | 506 | 3234 | BLUE | Rating: 71.9 |
| WHITE | 475 | 145 | 373 | 343 | 395 | 342 | 160 | 368 | 490 | 3091 | | Slope: 126 |
| Par | 5 | 3 | 4 | 4 | 4 | 4 | 3 | 4 | 5 | 36 | WHITE | Rating: 70.7 |
| Handicap | 17 | 15 | 5 | 7 | 1 | 13 | 11 | 3 | 9 | x | | Slope: 124 |
| RED | 460 | 134 | 371 | 330 | 301 | 331 | 146 | 320 | 479 | 2872 | | |
| Par | 5 | 3 | 4 | 4 | 4 | 4 | 3 | 4 | 5 | 36 | RED | Rating: 73.7 |
| Handicap | 3 | 17 | 7 | 5 | 13 | 9 | 15 | 11 | 1 | x | | Slope: 133 |

| Hole | 10 | 11 | 12 | 13 | 14 | 15 | 16 | 17 | 18 | In | Totals | |
|---|---|---|---|---|---|---|---|---|---|---|---|---|
| BLUE | 370 | 385 | 385 | 319 | 360 | 150 | 479 | 364 | 382 | 3194 | BLUE | 6428 |
| WHITE | 362 | 377 | 375 | 307 | 352 | 135 | 472 | 349 | 368 | 3097 | WHITE | 6188 |
| Par | 4 | 4 | 4 | 4 | 4 | 3 | 5 | 4 | 4 | 36 | Par | 72 |
| Handicap | 2 | 12 | 4 | 16 | 6 | 18 | 10 | 8 | 14 | x | | |
| RED | 357 | 370 | 368 | 297 | 303 | 114 | 437 | 327 | 359 | 2932 | RED | 5804 |
| Par | 4 | 4 | 4 | 4 | 4 | 3 | 5 | 4 | 4 | 36 | Par | 72 |
| Handicap | 4 | 14 | 6 | 16 | 12 | 18 | 2 | 8 | 10 | x | | |

# CHARDONNAY GOLF CLUB

**Course 30**
MAP D1 grid j6

***Course information:*** The Club Shakespeare Course is a private 18 hole course, with a par 72 for all tees. The championship tees are 6,593 yards, the regular tees are 6,147 yards, and the womens's tees are 5,448 yards. No ratings were available at press time.

The Vineyards Course is a public 18 hole course. The black tees are 6811 yards, are rated 73.7 with a slope of 133. The gold tees are 5,571 yards, are rated 68.1 (72.5 women) and have a slope rating of 118 (131 women). See card below for additional yardage and rating information.

***Play policy and fees:*** For the Vineyards Course, green fees are $50. Carts and range balls are included. Reservations may be made seven days in advance. For the Club Shakespeare Course, reciprocal play is accepted and the green fee is $75. Guests of members pay $48 on weekends and holidays and $32 on weekdays.

***Location:*** From Highway 29 south of Napa, take Highway 12 east. The entrance to the course is 1.3 miles from the intersection.

***Course description:*** The Club Shakespeare Course opened in the fall of 1992. It features open par-4s, back-to-back par-3s and par-5s, and plenty of character. The course was blended with the old Meadows Course, so some holes are familiar. The 200-yard sixth, with the pin-tucked left, is a great par-3. The 392-yard 14th offers a severe descent to a dogleg left fairway. The course is a good test that can be made brutal by an incessant wind. The 160-yard 13th, which descends over a waterfall and lake into a huge green, is the signature hole. The Vineyards has a rougher feel to it and seems more exposed to the wind. It has long carries over crevasses and creeks, with punishing par-4s on eight and nine.

**1987**
**Algie M. Pulley, Jr.**

PO Box 3779
Napa, CA 94558

2555 Jameson Canyon Road
Napa, CA 94559

Pro shop (707) 257-8950

- ✓ **driving range**
- ✓ **practice greens**
- ✓ **power carts**
- pull carts
- ✓ **golf club rental**
- ✓ **locker rooms**
- ✓ **showers**
- executive course
- accommodations
- ✓ **food and beverages**
- ✓ **clubhouse**

**Murray Blaire**
Professional

**Roger Billings**
Director

**Dick McAllister**
Superintendent

Vineyards Course

| Hole | 1 | 2 | 3 | 4 | 5 | 6 | 7 | 8 | 9 | Out | | |
|---|---|---|---|---|---|---|---|---|---|---|---|---|
| BLUE | 493 | 383 | 182 | 389 | 151 | 539 | 164 | 421 | 445 | 3167 | BLUE | Rating: 71.7 |
| WHITE | 466 | 343 | 151 | 374 | 132 | 505 | 151 | 401 | 429 | 2952 | | Slope: 127 |
| Par | 5 | 4 | 3 | 4 | 3 | 5 | 3 | 4 | 4 | 35 | WHITE | Rating: 69.8 |
| Handicap | 11 | 5 | 13 | 9 | 15 | 7 | 17 | 3 | 1 | x | | Slope: 122 |
| RED | 443 | 299 | 109 | 337 | 104 | 410 | 126 | 325 | 345 | 2498 | | |
| Par | 5 | 4 | 3 | 4 | 3 | 5 | 3 | 4 | 4 | 35 | RED | Rating: 70.1 |
| Handicap | 3 | 13 | 15 | 5 | 17 | 1 | 11 | 9 | 7 | x | | Slope: 126 |

| Hole | 10 | 11 | 12 | 13 | 14 | 15 | 16 | 17 | 18 | In | Totals | |
|---|---|---|---|---|---|---|---|---|---|---|---|---|
| BLUE | 441 | 162 | 516 | 176 | 348 | 441 | 492 | 154 | 513 | 3243 | BLUE | 6410 |
| WHITE | 427 | 155 | 482 | 153 | 341 | 392 | 478 | 138 | 465 | 3031 | WHITE | 5983 |
| Par | 4 | 3 | 5 | 3 | 4 | 4 | 5 | 3 | 5 | 36 | Par | 71 |
| Handicap | 4 | 16 | 10 | 14 | 6 | 2 | 8 | 18 | 12 | x | | |
| RED | 388 | 129 | 452 | 124 | 333 | 321 | 416 | 115 | 424 | 2702 | RED | 5200 |
| Par | 4 | 3 | 5 | 3 | 4 | 4 | 5 | 3 | 5 | 36 | Par | 71 |
| Handicap | 10 | 16 | 2 | 14 | 6 | 12 | 4 | 18 | 8 | x | | |

# GREEN VALLEY COUNTRY CLUB

**Course 31**
MAP D1 grid j7

35 Country Club Drive
Suisun City, CA 94585

Pro shop (707) 864-0473
Clubhouse (707) 864-1101

- ✓ **driving range**
- ✓ **practice greens**
- ✓ **power carts**
- ✓ **pull carts**
- ✓ **golf club rental**
- ✓ **locker rooms**
- ✓ **showers**
- executive course
- accommodations
- ✓ **food and beverages**
- ✓ **clubhouse**

**Mike Sherman**
Professional

**Ray Story**
Superintendent

***Course information:*** This private course has 18 holes. See card below for yardage and rating information.

***Play policy and fees:*** Reciprocal play is accepted with members of other private clubs. Guest fees are $20 with a member any day, and $30 without a member weekdays, and $40 without a member weekends. Carts are $18 with a member and $22 without.

***Location:*** From Vallejo, take Interstate 80 to Green Valley Road. Head north to Country Club Drive and turn left to the course.

***Course description:*** This is a real nice course, with a rolling, tree-lined layout and good greens. The front nine is flat, the back winding through the hills. The 349-yard 12th requires a long-iron off the tee, then a mid- to short-iron in the green is severely scored. It's a good example of Green Valley's charms, which includes a creek running through four holes. The wind can become a factor.

| Hole | 1 | 2 | 3 | 4 | 5 | 6 | 7 | 8 | 9 | Out | BLUE | Rating: 70.7 |
|---|---|---|---|---|---|---|---|---|---|---|---|---|
| BLUE | 450 | 344 | 524 | 366 | 196 | 349 | 148 | 385 | 389 | 3150 | | Slope: 125 |
| WHITE | 443 | 337 | 513 | 355 | 175 | 340 | 132 | 371 | 382 | 3061 | | |
| Par | 5 | 4 | 5 | 4 | 3 | 4 | 3 | 4 | 4 | 36 | WHITE | Rating: 69.6 |
| Handicap | 14 | 10 | 12 | 2 | 8 | 16 | 18 | 6 | 4 | x | | Slope: 122 |
| RED | 428 | 340 | 516 | 364 | 132 | 341 | 128 | 351 | 382 | 2982 | | |
| Par | 5 | 4 | 5 | 4 | 3 | 4 | 3 | 4 | 4 | 36 | RED | Rating: 73.7 |
| Handicap | 7 | 9 | 1 | 3 | 15 | 13 | 17 | 11 | 5 | x | | Slope: 131 |

| Hole | 10 | 11 | 12 | 13 | 14 | 15 | 16 | 17 | 18 | In | Totals | |
|---|---|---|---|---|---|---|---|---|---|---|---|---|
| BLUE | 464 | 400 | 349 | 168 | 378 | 519 | 445 | 209 | 388 | 3320 | BLUE | 6470 |
| WHITE | 457 | 382 | 335 | 149 | 378 | 486 | 420 | 172 | 378 | 3188 | WHITE | 6249 |
| Par | 5 | 4 | 4 | 3 | 4 | 5 | 4 | 3 | 4 | 36 | Par | 72 |
| Handicap | 15 | 7 | 3 | 17 | 11 | 13 | 1 | 9 | 5 | x | | |
| RED | 440 | 365 | 304 | 143 | 318 | 442 | 381 | 144 | 362 | 2899 | RED | 5881 |
| Par | 5 | 4 | 4 | 3 | 4 | 5 | 4 | 3 | 4 | 36 | Par | 72 |
| Handicap | 2 | 12 | 10 | 14 | 16 | 6 | 4 | 18 | 8 | x | | |

# RANCHO SOLANO GOLF COURSE

**Course 32**
MAP D1 grid i8

**1990**
**Gary Roger Baird**

3250 Rancho Solano Parkway
Fairfield, CA 94533

Pro shop (707) 429-4653

- ✓ **driving range**
- ✓ **practice greens**
- ✓ **power carts**
- ✓ **pull carts**
- ✓ **golf club rental**
- locker rooms
- showers
- executive course
- accommodations
- ✓ **food and beverages**
- ✓ **clubhouse**

**Dale Bradley**
Manager/Professional

**Tim McCoy**
Superintendent

***Course information:*** This public course has 18 holes. The men's tees are 5701 yards and rated 68.5 with a slope of 120 from the gold tees. See card below for additional yardage and rating information.

***Play policy and fees:*** Green fees are $24 weekdays and $30 weekends for non-residents. Half price rates are available after 4 p.m. Carts are $24.

***Location:*** On Interstate 80 in Fairfield, exit on Waterman Boulevard west and follow it two miles. Go right on Rancho Solano Parkway to the course.

***Course description:*** It's an open course that allows one to use a driver on nearly all the par-4s and par-5s. The par-3s, however, are challenging and the course has the largest greens in California, so club selection is tough. The fifth (189) and 12th (250) play over water, and the 154-yard 15th has several mounds in the green. All three are fun, pretty and frustrating. This is great value for the money.

| Hole | 1 | 2 | 3 | 4 | 5 | 6 | 7 | 8 | 9 | Out | | |
|---|---|---|---|---|---|---|---|---|---|---|---|---|
| BLUE | 502 | 348 | 384 | 382 | 194 | 370 | 482 | 217 | 387 | 3266 | BLUE | Rating: 72.0 |
| WHITE | 479 | 330 | 364 | 366 | 170 | 339 | 466 | 176 | 345 | 3035 | | Slope: 125 |
| Par | 5 | 4 | 4 | 4 | 3 | 4 | 5 | 3 | 4 | 36 | WHITE | Rating: 69.9 |
| Handicap | 3 | 9 | 1 | 13 | 7 | 17 | 5 | 11 | 15 | x | | Slope: 121 |
| RED | 417 | 297 | 272 | 323 | 138 | 289 | 388 | 114 | 307 | 2545 | | |
| Par | 5 | 4 | 4 | 4 | 3 | 4 | 5 | 3 | 4 | 36 | RED | Rating: 69.6 |
| Handicap | 3 | 7 | 11 | 9 | 15 | 13 | 1 | 17 | 5 | x | | Slope: 117 |

| Hole | 10 | 11 | 12 | 13 | 14 | 15 | 16 | 17 | 18 | In | Totals | |
|---|---|---|---|---|---|---|---|---|---|---|---|---|
| BLUE | 572 | 429 | 233 | 372 | 375 | 158 | 355 | 522 | 356 | 3372 | BLUE | 6638 |
| WHITE | 528 | 376 | 197 | 336 | 370 | 147 | 331 | 494 | 345 | 3124 | WHITE | 6159 |
| Par | 5 | 4 | 3 | 4 | 4 | 3 | 4 | 5 | 4 | 36 | Par | 72 |
| Handicap | 8 | 2 | 4 | 16 | 6 | 18 | 14 | 12 | 10 | x | | |
| RED | 443 | 322 | 127 | 309 | 350 | 104 | 280 | 413 | 287 | 2635 | RED | 5180 |
| Par | 5 | 4 | 3 | 4 | 4 | 3 | 4 | 5 | 4 | 36 | Par | 72 |
| Handicap | 8 | 6 | 16 | 12 | 2 | 18 | 14 | 10 | 4 | x | | |

# CYPRESS LAKES GOLF COURSE

**Course 33**
MAP D1 grid j9

NORTHERN D1

*Course information:* This military course has 18 holes. See card below for yardage and rating information.

*Play policy and fees:* Green fees are $15 weekdays, $20 weekends, and are available to the public if sponsored by active or retired military personnel. Carts are $12 on weekdays and $14 on weekends. Reservations are recommended. Golf attire must be worn.

*Location:* From Vallejo, drive east on Interstate 80. Take the Elmira exit east. Turn right on Meridian to the course.

*Course description:* This course boasts big greens, seven lakes and lots of trees. It's flat and easily walkable. Plan to play into the wind. The greens are usually in great condition, and the course can become quite a challenge from the blue tees. The last three holes are the best: the par-4 16th, which doglegs right over a lake; the par-5 17th is a dogleg left over a lake; and the par-4 18th requires an approach shot over a lake.

**5601 Meridian Road**
**Bldg 2012, Travis AFB,**
**CA 94535**

Pro shop (707) 448-7186

- ✓ **driving range**
- ✓ **practice greens**
- ✓ **power carts**
- ✓ **pull carts**
- ✓ **golf club rental**
- ✓ **locker rooms**
- ✓ **showers**
- executive course
- accommodations
- ✓ **food and beverages**
- ✓ **clubhouse**

**Kenneth W. Cochran**
Manager/Professional

**Joe Goldbronn**
Superintendent

| Hole | 1 | 2 | 3 | 4 | 5 | 6 | 7 | 8 | 9 | Out | BLUE | Rating: 72.6 |
|---|---|---|---|---|---|---|---|---|---|---|---|---|
| BLUE | 503 | 383 | 176 | 403 | 523 | 376 | 362 | 194 | 405 | 3325 | | Slope: 122 |
| WHITE | 461 | 363 | 151 | 383 | 512 | 351 | 342 | 163 | 383 | 3109 | | |
| Par | 5 | 4 | 3 | 4 | 5 | 4 | 4 | 3 | 4 | 36 | WHITE | Rating: 71.0 |
| Handicap | 11 | 5 | 17 | 1 | 9 | 7 | 13 | 15 | 3 | x | | Slope: 119 |
| RED | 448 | 343 | 138 | 345 | 443 | 327 | 327 | 154 | 368 | 2893 | | |
| Par | 5 | 4 | 3 | 4 | 5 | 4 | 4 | 3 | 4 | 36 | RED | Rating: 72.9 |
| Handicap | 1 | 11 | 17 | 7 | 3 | 9 | 13 | 15 | 5 | x | | Slope: 120 |

| Hole | 10 | 11 | 12 | 13 | 14 | 15 | 16 | 17 | 18 | In | Totals | |
|---|---|---|---|---|---|---|---|---|---|---|---|---|
| BLUE | 522 | 179 | 429 | 427 | 141 | 367 | 408 | 553 | 445 | 3471 | BLUE | 6796 |
| WHITE | 508 | 148 | 413 | 410 | 123 | 342 | 391 | 523 | 417 | 3275 | WHITE | 6384 |
| Par | 5 | 3 | 4 | 4 | 3 | 4 | 4 | 5 | 4 | 36 | Par | 72 |
| Handicap | 12 | 16 | 6 | 10 | 18 | 14 | 2 | 8 | 4 | x | | |
| RED | 404 | 118 | 338 | 341 | 115 | 323 | 311 | 422 | 404 | 2776 | RED | 5669 |
| Par | 5 | 3 | 4 | 4 | 3 | 4 | 4 | 5 | 5 | 37 | Par | 73 |
| Handicap | 4 | 16 | 14 | 12 | 18 | 10 | 8 | 2 | 6 | x | | |

# MAP D2

(31 COURSES)

PAGES.. 126-157

NOR-CAL MAP.....see page 30
adjoining maps
NORTH (C2).........see page 70
EAST (D3) ..........see page 158
SOUTH (E3) .......see page 292
WEST (D1) ..........see page 94

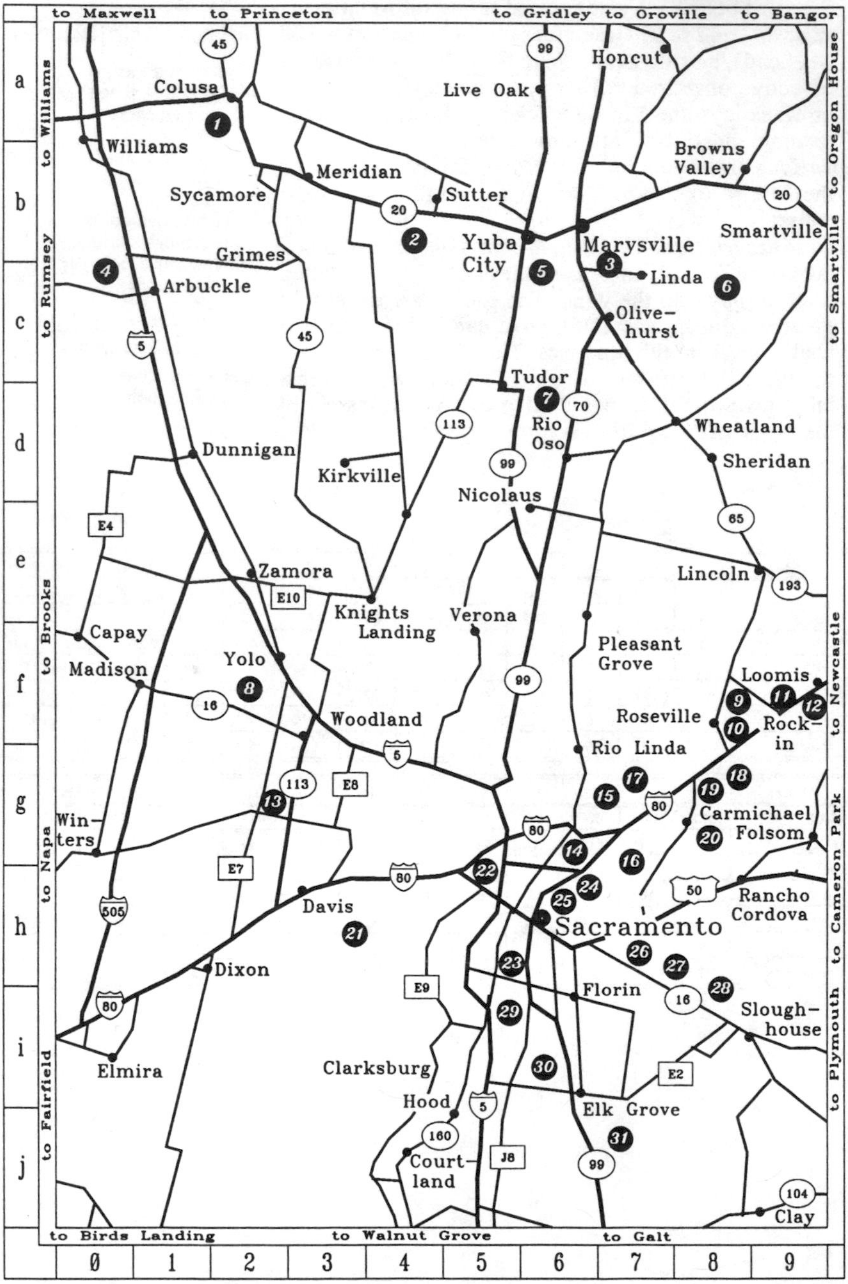

to Maxwell
to Princeton
to Gridley
to Oroville
to Bangor
to Williams
to Rumsey
to Brooks
to Napa
to Fairfield
to Oregon House
to Smartville
to Newcastle
to Cameron Park
to Plymouth
to Birds Landing
to Walnut Grove
to Galt

a
b
c
d
e
f
g
h
i
j

45
99
Honcut
Colusa
Live Oak
1
Williams
Browns Valley
Meridian
Sycamore
Sutter
20
20
Smartville
2
Yuba City
Marysville
Grimes
4
Arbuckle
5
3
Linda
6
Olivehurst
5
45
Tudor
7
70
Rio Oso
113
Wheatland
Dunnigan
Sheridan
99
Kirkville
Nicolaus
65
E4
Zamora
Lincoln
193
E10
Knights Landing
Verona
Capay
Pleasant Grove
Yolo
Madison
Loomis
99
8
9
11
12
16
Roseville
Woodland
Rock-in
10
5
Rio Linda
113
E8
17
18
13
15
19
80
Carmichael
Winters
80
Folsom
20
14
E7
22
16
80
24
50
25
Rancho Cordova
505
Davis
Sacramento
21
26
27
Dixon
23
E9
Florin
28
80
16
29
Slough-house
Elmira
30
Clarksburg
E2
Hood
5
Elk Grove
160
31
J8
99
Court-land
104
Clay

0
1
2
3
4
5
6
7
8
9

# COLUSA COUNTRY CLUB

**Course 1**
MAP D2 grid a2

**1956**

*Course information:* This semi-private course has nine holes. Par is 72 for 18 holes. The course is 6,617 yards and rated 71.1 from the regular tees (18 holes). The slope rating is 118. Women's tees are 5,853 yards and rated 73.1 from the forward tees. The slope rating is 120.

*Play policy and fees:* Outside play is accepted. Green fees are $10 for nine holes and $14 for 18 holes weekdays, and $20 for nine or 18 holes weekends and holidays. Carts are $18.

*Location:* From Interstate 5 in Williams, drive east on Highway 20 to Colusa. The course is on Highway 20 on the right.

*Course description:* This flat, tree-lined course is tight and walkable. It's more challenging than meets the eye. A new sprinkler system has improved fairway conditions. The par-5 sixth hole (517 yards) is a toughie, requiring a difficult second shot to avoid trees in the fairway.

PO Box 686
Colusa, CA 95932

Highway 20 East
Colusa, CA 95932

Pro shop (916) 458-5577

- ✓ **driving range**
- ✓ **practice greens**
- ✓ **power carts**
- ✓ **pull carts**
- ✓ **golf club rental**
- ✓ **locker rooms**
- showers
- executive course
- accommodations
- ✓ **food and beverages**
- ✓ **clubhouse**

**Rick Burgess**
Professional

**Gene Dommer**
Superintendent



MAP ON PAGE 126

# SOUTHRIDGE GOLF COURSE

**Course 2**
MAP D2 grid b4

***Course information:*** This semi-private course has 18 holes. The men's tees are 7,047 yards and rated 72.9 with a slope of 134 from the gold tees. See card below for additional yardage and rating information.

***Play policy and fees:*** Outside play is accepted. Green fees are $20 with an additional $10 for a cart for 18 holes weekdays. Weekend rates are $25 ($35 with cart). Carts are a necessity due to severe terrain.

***Location:*** From Yuba City drive west on Highway 20. The course is seven miles west of Yuba City and can be seen from the highway.

***Course description:*** A most interesting layout, Southridge features one nine that would fatigue a mountain goat—currently the front, but soon to be the back—and one links-style nine. The Sutter Buttes nine features one of the most diffcult (and exasperating) holes in Northern California, a par-5 of 637 yards that requires a radar-straight drive and a well-placed second shot, among other skills. Love it or loathe it, you'll remember it. The links side is easier, though not by much with water coming into play on eight holes. If you want diversity, this is the course.

**1991**
**Cal Olson**

9413 South Butte Road
Sutter, CA 95982

Pro shop (916) 755-4653
(916) 755-4685

- ✓ **driving range**
- ✓ **practice greens**
- ✓ **power carts**
- ✓ **pull carts**
- ✓ **golf club rental**
- locker rooms
- showers
- executive course
- accommodations
- ✓ **food and beverages**
- clubhouse

**Steve Miles**
Manager/Professional

| Hole | 1 | 2 | 3 | 4 | 5 | 6 | 7 | 8 | 9 | Out | BLUE | Rating: 71.0 |
|---|---|---|---|---|---|---|---|---|---|---|---|---|
| BLUE | 423 | 515 | 347 | 357 | 184 | 118 | 619 | 417 | 396 | 3376 | | Slope: 129 |
| WHITE | 414 | 477 | 309 | 341 | 168 | 109 | 556 | 400 | 362 | 3136 | | |
| Par | 4 | 5 | 4 | 4 | 3 | 3 | 5 | 4 | 4 | 36 | WHITE | Rating: 68.7 |
| Handicap | 9 | 15 | 3 | 11 | 13 | 17 | 1 | 5 | 7 | x | | Slope: 123 |
| RED | 382 | 443 | 273 | 325 | 150 | 92 | 530 | 373 | 332 | 2900 | | |
| Par | 4 | 5 | 4 | 4 | 3 | 3 | 5 | 4 | 4 | 36 | RED | Rating: 69.8 |
| Handicap | 9 | 15 | 3 | 11 | 13 | 17 | 1 | 5 | 7 | x | | Slope: 123 |

| Hole | 10 | 11 | 12 | 13 | 14 | 15 | 16 | 17 | 18 | In | Totals | |
|---|---|---|---|---|---|---|---|---|---|---|---|---|
| BLUE | 406 | 383 | 372 | 177 | 495 | 358 | 150 | 416 | 478 | 3235 | BLUE | 6611 |
| WHITE | 375 | 356 | 306 | 146 | 471 | 330 | 131 | 382 | 472 | 2969 | WHITE | 6105 |
| Par | 4 | 4 | 4 | 3 | 5 | 4 | 3 | 4 | 5 | 36 | Par | 72 |
| Handicap | 4 | 6 | 10 | 16 | 14 | 8 | 18 | 2 | 12 | x | | |
| RED | 345 | 336 | 261 | 98 | 439 | 283 | 95 | 364 | 420 | 2641 | RED | 5541 |
| Par | 4 | 4 | 4 | 3 | 5 | 4 | 3 | 4 | 5 | 36 | Par | 72 |
| Handicap | 4 | 6 | 10 | 16 | 14 | 8 | 18 | 2 | 12 | x | | |

# PEACH TREE GOLF AND COUNTRY CLUB

**Course 3**
MAP D2 grid b7

**1958**
**R.E. Baldock**

PO Box 231
Marysville, CA 95901

2043 Simpson-Dantoni Road
Marysville, CA 95901

Pro shop (916) 743-2039
Clubhouse (916) 743-1897

- ✓ **driving range**
- ✓ **practice greens**
- ✓ **power carts**
- ✓ **pull carts**
- ✓ **golf club rental**
- ✓ **locker rooms**
- ✓ **showers**
- executive course
- accommodations
- ✓ **food and beverages**
- ✓ **clubhouse**

**Ed Lewis**
Professional

**Tim Philo**
Superintendent

*Course information:* This private course has 18 holes. Women's tees are 5,865 yards and rated 74.0 with a slope of 131 from the yellow tees. See card below for additional yardage and rating information.

*Play policy and fees:* Reciprocal play is accepted with members of other private clubs. Guest fees are $25 weekdays and $30 weekends when accompanied by a member. The fee for reciprocal players is $50. Carts are $18.

*Location:* From Sacramento, take Highway 70 through Marysville to Highway 20. Turn right on Ramirez Road and drive to Simpson-Dantoni Road. Turn left and drive to the course.

*Course description:* This course is characterized by its mature trees—walnut and cypress, but only one peach. The fairways are bermuda and the greens are bent grass. Peach Tree is a very tight course with fairway bunkers strategically placed. The greens are fast and bowl-shaped. Number seven, a par-3 of 218 yards from the blues, is the signature hole. It requires a carry over water that fronts about half the green, and there's a bunker on the left side. The course record of 62 was set before the trees matured; since then, the best is a 66.

| Hole | 1 | 2 | 3 | 4 | 5 | 6 | 7 | 8 | 9 | Out | | |
|---|---|---|---|---|---|---|---|---|---|---|---|---|
| BLUE | 402 | 527 | 165 | 432 | 450 | 503 | 218 | 384 | 360 | 3441 | BLUE | Rating: 72.8 |
| | | | | | | | | | | | | Slope: 125 |
| WHITE | 387 | 511 | 150 | 414 | 432 | 485 | 203 | 364 | 342 | 3288 | | |
| Par | 4 | 5 | 3 | 4 | 4 | 5 | 3 | 4 | 4 | 36 | WHITE | Rating: 71.4 |
| Handicap | 7 | 9 | 17 | 3 | 1 | 15 | 5 | 13 | 11 | x | | Slope: 122 |
| RED | 374 | 494 | 139 | 397 | 418 | 466 | 147 | 346 | 329 | 3110 | | |
| Par | 4 | 5 | 3 | 4 | 5 | 5 | 3 | 4 | 4 | 37 | RED | Rating:76.0 |
| Handicap | 9 | 1 | 17 | 5 | 7 | 3 | 15 | 11 | 13 | x | | Slope: 136 |

| Hole | 10 | 11 | 12 | 13 | 14 | 15 | 16 | 17 | 18 | In | Totals | |
|---|---|---|---|---|---|---|---|---|---|---|---|---|
| BLUE | 363 | 513 | 429 | 380 | 181 | 378 | 401 | 184 | 541 | 3370 | BLUE | 6811 |
| WHITE | 351 | 488 | 411 | 358 | 167 | 366 | 389 | 169 | 519 | 3218 | WHITE | 6506 |
| Par | 4 | 5 | 4 | 4 | 3 | 4 | 4 | 3 | 5 | 36 | Par | 72 |
| Handicap | 16 | 10 | 2 | 8 | 18 | 14 | 4 | 12 | 6 | x | | |
| RED | 341 | 461 | 395 | 342 | 158 | 353 | 381 | 157 | 505 | 3093 | RED | 6203 |
| Par | 4 | 5 | 4 | 4 | 3 | 4 | 4 | 3 | 5 | 36 | Par | 73 |
| Handicap | 12 | 2 | 4 | 14 | 18 | 10 | 8 | 16 | 6 | x | | |

# ARBUCKLE GOLF COURSE

**Course 4**
MAP D2 grid c0

**1924**

***Course information:*** This semi-private course has nine holes. See card below for yardage and rating information.

***Play policy and fees:*** Outside play is accepted. Green fees are $14 weekdays and $20 weekends. Carts are $18. Reservations recommended.

***Location:*** From Interstate 5 in Arbuckle, exit on Arbuckle College City and drive to Hillgate Road west. Drive 4.5 miles on Hillgate Road to the course.

***Course description:*** This challenging course has a rolling layout with a few tight doglegs. The greens are true, smooth and fast. The club has been in existence since 1924, but the greens weren't changed from sand to grass until 1960. The par-4 third hole (416 yards) presents a spectacular view of the Sutter Buttes and the valley. Arbuckle is one of the finest nine-hole courses in the state—challenging and exceptionally conditioned.

PO Box 975
Arbuckle, CA 95912

Hillgate Road
Arbuckle, CA 95912

Pro shop (916) 476-2470

- ✓ **driving range**
- ✓ **practice greens**
- ✓ **power carts**
- ✓ **pull carts**
- ✓ **golf club rental**
- locker rooms
- showers
- executive course
- accommodations
- ✓ **food and beverages**
- ✓ **clubhouse**

**Carl Funk**
Manager/Professional

**Abel Gomez**
Superintendent

| Hole | 1 | 2 | 3 | 4 | 5 | 6 | 7 | 8 | 9 | Out | BLUE | Rating: -- |
|---|---|---|---|---|---|---|---|---|---|---|---|---|
| BLUE | - | - | - | - | - | - | - | - | - | - | | Slope: -- |
| WHITE | 502 | 167 | 416 | 383 | 548 | 338 | 182 | 390 | 336 | 3262 | | |
| Par | 5 | 3 | 4 | 4 | 5 | 4 | 3 | 4 | 4 | 36 | WHITE | Rating:69.9 |
| Handicap | 3 | 15 | 7 | 9 | 1 | 11 | 17 | 5 | 13 | x | | Slope: 111 |
| RED | 408 | 132 | 393 | 360 | 509 | 314 | 182 | 368 | 317 | 2983 | | |
| Par | 5 | 3 | 4 | 4 | 5 | 4 | 3 | 4 | 4 | 36 | RED | Rating: 72.7 |
| Handicap | 7 | 17 | 5 | 3 | 1 | 13 | 15 | 9 | 11 | x | | Slope: 120 |

| Hole | 10 | 11 | 12 | 13 | 14 | 15 | 16 | 17 | 18 | In | Totals | |
|---|---|---|---|---|---|---|---|---|---|---|---|---|
| BLUE | - | - | - | - | - | - | - | - | - | - | BLUE | -- |
| WHITE | 486 | 132 | 403 | 371 | 521 | 326 | 197 | 379 | 383 | 3198 | WHITE | 6460 |
| Par | 5 | 3 | 4 | 4 | 5 | 4 | 3 | 4 | 4 | 36 | Par | 72 |
| Handicap | 4 | 18 | 8 | 10 | 2 | 14 | 16 | 12 | 6 | x | | |
| RED | 408 | 122 | 403 | 371 | 426 | 326 | 169 | 379 | 325 | 2929 | RED | 5912 |
| Par | 5 | 3 | 4 | 4 | 5 | 4 | 3 | 4 | 4 | 36 | Par | 72 |
| Handicap | 6 | 18 | 4 | 2 | 14 | 12 | 16 | 8 | 10 | x | | |

# MALLARD LAKE GOLF COURSE

**Course 5**
MAP D2 grid c6



*Course information:* This public course has nine holes. See card below for yardage and rating information.

*Play policy and fees:* Green fees are $7 for nine holes and $12 for 18 holes weekdays, and $9 for nine holes and $14 for 18 holes on weekends. Carts are $9 for nine holes and $13 for 18 holes.

*Location:* From Yuba City, drive south on Highway 99. The course is a quarter mile south of Oswald Road on Sawtelle Avenue (Highway 99).

*Course description:* This mostly flat course has water on all nine holes. It's short and tough with small, well maintained greens. The toughest hole is number four (357 yards), with out-of-bounds on both sides of the fairway and a pond situated right where an average hitter usually drives. The clientele is approximately 50 percent seniors with the remaining half all varieties of skill.

4238 South Highway 99
Yuba City, CA 95991

Pro shop (916) 674-0475

- ✓ **driving range**
- ✓ **practice greens**
- ✓ **power carts**
- ✓ **pull carts**
- ✓ **golf club rental**
- locker rooms
- showers
- executive course
- accommodations
- ✓ **food and beverages**
- ✓ **clubhouse**

**Dirk Ekey**
Manager

**Ernest Carranza**
Superintendent

| Hole | 1 | 2 | 3 | 4 | 5 | 6 | 7 | 8 | 9 | Out | BLUE | Rating: -- |
|---|---|---|---|---|---|---|---|---|---|---|---|---|
| BLUE | - | - | - | - | - | - | - | | - | - | | Slope: -- |
| WHITE | 361 | 148 | 385 | 357 | 327 | 329 | 301 | 160 | 344 | 2712 | | |
| Par | 4 | 3 | 4 | 4 | 4 | 4 | 4 | 3 | 4 | 34 | WHITE | Rating.64.2 |
| Handicap | 5 | 17 | 3 | 1 | 7 | 11 | 13 | 15 | 9 | x | | Slope: 103 |
| RED | 342 | 133 | 313 | 336 | 276 | 314 | 286 | 150 | 320 | 2470 | | |
| Par | 4 | 3 | 4 | 4 | 4 | 4 | 4 | 3 | 4 | 34 | RED | Rating: 67.6 |
| Handicap | 1 | 17 | 5 | 11 | 9 | 13 | 7 | 15 | 3 | x | | Slope: 112 |

| Hole | 10 | 11 | 12 | 13 | 14 | 15 | 16 | 17 | 18 | In | Totals | |
|---|---|---|---|---|---|---|---|---|---|---|---|---|
| BLUE | - | - | - | - | - | - | - | - | - | - | BLUE | -- |
| WHITE | 361 | 148 | 385 | 357 | 327 | 329 | 301 | 160 | 344 | 2712 | WHITE | 5424 |
| Par | 4 | 3 | 4 | 4 | 4 | 4 | 4 | 3 | 4 | 34 | Par | 68 |
| Handicap | 6 | 18 | 4 | 2 | 8 | 12 | 14 | 16 | 10 | x | | |
| RED | 342 | 133 | 313 | 336 | 276 | 314 | 286 | 150 | 320 | 2470 | RED | 4940 |
| Par | 4 | 3 | 4 | 4 | 4 | 4 | 4 | 3 | 4 | 34 | Par | 68 |
| Handicap | 2 | 18 | 6 | 12 | 10 | 14 | 8 | 16 | 4 | x | | |

# BEALE AIR FORCE BASE GOLF COURSE

**Course 6**
MAP D2 grid c8

***Course information:*** This military course has nine holes. Par is 70 for 18 holes. The course is 6,146 yards and rated 69.6 from the regular tees (18 holes). The slope rating is 118. Women's tees are 5,326 yards and rated 69.7. The slope rating is 119.

***Play policy and fees:*** Outside play is accepted with prior arrangement. Guest fees are $12 weekdays and $15 weekends for civilians. Green fees are $7 weekdays and $10 weekends for military ranked E-5 and above and Department of Defense personnel. Carts are $14.

***Location:*** From Highway 70 in Marysville, take the North Beale Road east exit. Drive to the main gate of Beale Air Force Base.

***Course description:*** Beale is a flat course with elevated greens. There are enough trees to make things challenging, and the fifth hole is distinguished by a large lake, one of just two on the course. Bob Anderson holds the course record with a 66.

SSRG Building 2241
Beale AFB, CA 95903

Pro shop (916) 634-2124
Clubhouse (916) 634-2127

✓ **driving range**
✓ **practice greens**
✓ **power carts**
✓ **pull carts**
✓ **golf club rental**
✓ **locker rooms**
✓ **showers**
executive course
accommodations
✓ **food and beverages**
✓ **clubhouse**

**Bob Anderson**
Manager/Professional

**Marvin Grisson**
Superintendent

# PLUMAS LAKE GOLF AND COUNTRY CLUB

**Course 7**
**MAP D2 grid d6**

**1929**

*Course information:* This semi-private layout has 18 holes. See card below for yardage and rating information.

*Play policy and fees:* Outside play is accepted. Green fees are $15 Mondays through Thursday and $20 Friday through Sunday. Carts are $18. Closed Mondays during the winter.

*Location:* From Marysville, drive south on Highway 70. Take the Feather River Boulevard exit and drive about 6.5 miles. Turn left on Country Club Avenue.

*Course description:* Plumas Lake is well-known among golf insiders throughout Northern California as a jewel. It is mostly flat and not exceedingly tight, but there are a number of monster holes, starting with number eight, a 399-yarder with a giant oak blocking entrance to the green. Holes 12 (423 yards), 13 (208) and 14 (414) are Pluma Lake's answer to Amen Corner. The course record is a superb 60 by Ray Arinno. LPGA star Alice Miller grew up playing Plumas Lake—from the men's tecs.

1551 Country Club Ave.
Marysville, CA 95901

Pro shop (916) 742-3201
Clubhouse (916) 742-3202

- ✓ **driving range**
- ✓ **practice greens**
- ✓ **power carts**
- ✓ **pull carts**
- ✓ **golf club rental**
- ✓ **locker rooms**
- ✓ **showers**
- executive course
- accommodations
- ✓ **food and beverages**
- ✓ **clubhouse**

**Ken Galbraith**
Manager

**Pat Gould**
Professional

**Cotton Triplett**
Superintendent

NORTHERN D2

| Hole | 1 | 2 | 3 | 4 | 5 | 6 | 7 | 8 | 9 | Out | | |
|---|---|---|---|---|---|---|---|---|---|---|---|---|
| BLUE | 421 | 407 | 188 | 348 | 520 | 341 | 161 | 408 | 340 | 3134 | BLUE | Rating: 70.5 |
| WHITE | 406 | 386 | 158 | 339 | 509 | 329 | 161 | 399 | 327 | 3014 | | Slope: 122 |
| Par | 4 | 4 | 3 | 4 | 5 | 4 | 3 | 4 | 4 | 35 | WHITE | Rating: 69.3 |
| Handicap | 3 | 5 | 15 | 13 | 9 | 7 | 17 | 1 | 11 | x | | Slope: 120 |
| RED | 392 | 377 | 146 | 329 | 414 | 310 | 161 | 337 | 316 | 2782 | | |
| Par | 4 | 4 | 3 | 4 | 5 | 4 | 3 | 4 | 4 | 35 | RED | Rating: 73.2 |
| Handicap | 4 | 8 | 18 | 6 | 2 | 10 | 16 | 12 | 14 | x | | Slope: 126 |

| Hole | 10 | 11 | 12 | 13 | 14 | 15 | 16 | 17 | 18 | In | Totals | |
|---|---|---|---|---|---|---|---|---|---|---|---|---|
| BLUE | 486 | 374 | 433 | 219 | 424 | 501 | 162 | 335 | 332 | 3266 | BLUE | 6400 |
| WHITE | 473 | 361 | 423 | 208 | 414 | 490 | 142 | 319 | 309 | 3139 | WHITE | 6153 |
| Par | 5 | 4 | 4 | 3 | 4 | 5 | 3 | 4 | 4 | 36 | Par | 71 |
| Handicap | 8 | 6 | 2 | 12 | 4 | 10 | 18 | 16 | 14 | x | | |
| RED | 457 | 350 | 413 | 195 | 351 | 479 | 128 | 305 | 299 | 2977 | RED | 5759 |
| Par | 5 | 4 | 5 | 3 | 4 | 5 | 3 | 4 | 4 | 37 | Par | 72 |
| Handicap | 3 | 5 | 7 | 13 | 9 | 1 | 17 | 15 | 11 | x | | |

MAP ON PAGE 126

# YOLO FLIERS COUNTRY CLUB

**Course 8**
MAP D2 grid f2

**1919**

***Course information:*** This private course has 18 holes. See card below for yardage and rating information.

***Play policy and fees:*** Reciprocal play is accepted with members of other private clubs. Guest fees are $20 with a member. Carts are $20. Reciprocal fees are $50 per person.

***Location:*** From Interstate 505 in Woodland, take Highway 16 East. Drive four miles and turn north on Road 94B. The course is located by the Woodland Municipal Airport.

***Course description:*** It has the feel of an old course—it is old—with mature trees and well-maintained greens. The number one handicap hole is the 14th, a par-4 measuring 444 yards. There is a fair amount of out-of-bounds. The name of the course came from the adjacent airport. It's not uncommon for people to fly in for a round of golf, hence Yolo Fliers.

PO Box 1366
Woodland, CA 95695

Off Highway 16, Rd. 94–B
Woodland, CA 95695

Pro shop (916) 662-8050
Clubhouse (916) 662-0281

- ✓ **driving range**
- ✓ **practice greens**
- ✓ **power carts**
- ✓ **pull carts**
- ✓ **golf club rental**
- ✓ **locker rooms**
- ✓ **showers**
- executive course
- accommodations
- ✓ **food and beverages**
- ✓ **clubhouse**

**Ernie Fatta**
Manager

**Bob Badger**
Professional

**Donald Baker**
Superintendent

| Hole | 1 | 2 | 3 | 4 | 5 | 6 | 7 | 8 | 9 | Out | BLUE | Rating: -- |
|---|---|---|---|---|---|---|---|---|---|---|---|---|
| BLUE | - | - | - | - | - | - | - | - | - | - | | Slope: -- |
| WHITE | 522 | 380 | 360 | 190 | 400 | 500 | 136 | 347 | 355 | 3190 | | |
| Par | 5 | 4 | 4 | 3 | 4 | 5 | 3 | 4 | 4 | 36 | WHITE | Rating:70.1 |
| Handicap | 6 | 8 | 12 | 4 | 2 | 16 | 18 | 14 | 10 | x | | Slope: 119 |
| RED | 491 | 329 | 357 | 178 | 388 | 481 | 130 | 331 | 331 | 3016 | | |
| Par | 5 | 4 | 4 | 3 | 4 | 5 | 3 | 4 | 4 | 36 | RED | Rating: 74.2 |
| Handicap | 5 | 13 | 3 | 15 | 1 | 7 | 17 | 11 | 9 | x | | Slope: 122 |

| Hole | 10 | 11 | 12 | 13 | 14 | 15 | 16 | 17 | 18 | In | Totals | |
|---|---|---|---|---|---|---|---|---|---|---|---|---|
| BLUE | - | - | - | - | - | - | - | - | - | - | BLUE | -- |
| WHITE | 440 | 495 | 151 | 331 | 444 | 130 | 332 | 510 | 405 | 3238 | WHITE | 6428 |
| Par | 4 | 5 | 3 | 4 | 4 | 3 | 4 | 5 | 4 | 36 | Par | 72 |
| Handicap | 3 | 7 | 13 | 9 | 1 | 17 | 15 | 11 | 5 | x | | |
| RED | 432 | 423 | 143 | 333 | 420 | 119 | 320 | 493 | 382 | 3065 | RED | 6081 |
| Par | 5 | 5 | 3 | 4 | 5 | 3 | 4 | 5 | 4 | 38 | Par | 74 |
| Handicap | 12 | 14 | 16 | 4 | 8 | 18 | 10 | 2 | 6 | x | | |

# DIAMOND OAKS GOLF COURSE

**Course 9**
MAP D2 grid f8



349 Diamond Oaks Road
Roseville, CA 95678

Pro shop (916 )783-4947
Clubhouse (916) 782-3513

- ✓ **driving range**
- ✓ **practice greens**
- ✓ **power carts**
- ✓ **pull carts**
- ✓ **golf club rental**
- locker rooms
- showers
- executive course
- accommodations
- ✓ **food and beverages**
- ✓ **clubhouse**

**Ed Vasconcellos**
Professional

**Henry Singh**
Superintendent

***Course information:*** This public course has 18 holes. See card below for yardage and rating information.

***Play policy and fees:*** Green fees are $9 for nine holes and $16 for 18 holes weekdays, and $9.75 and $17 weekends. Carts are $8 for nine holes and $16 for 18 holes. The twilight rate is $4.50 after 5:30 p.m. during the summer. Reservations are recommended one week in advance for weekdays and the Monday before for weekend tee times. There is a $1 reservation fee.

***Location:*** From Interstate 80 in Roseville, take the Atlantic Street exit to Yosemite Street. Turn right and drive to Diamond Oaks Road. Turn left and drive 400 yards to the course.

***Course description:*** Mature oaks line the fairways of this rolling course. Diamond Oaks is fairly forgiving for the most part, and the greens are in excellent shape for a municipal course numbering 90,000 rounds a year. The ninth hole (par 4, 405 yards) has oak trees right and left. Number 18 is a superb finishing hole, measuring 430 yards uphill with a large oak tree dominating the right side of the fairway. Sacramento Valley amateur champ Lou Alvarez calls this his home course and owns the lowest score here, a 62. Diamond Oaks plays host to a number of amateur events, including the Roseville City.

| Hole | 1 | 2 | 3 | 4 | 5 | 6 | 7 | 8 | 9 | Out | BLUE | Rating: 68.2 |
|---|---|---|---|---|---|---|---|---|---|---|---|---|
| BLUE | 366 | 486 | 143 | 358 | 162 | 475 | 374 | 375 | 405 | 3144 | | Slope: 110 |
| WHITE | 356 | 476 | 134 | 348 | 144 | 465 | 363 | 360 | 390 | 3036 | | |
| Par | 4 | 5 | 3 | 4 | 3 | 5 | 4 | 4 | 4 | 36 | WHITE | Rating: -- |
| Handicap | 7 | 13 | 17 | 5 | 15 | 9 | 3 | 11 | 1 | x | | Slope: -- |
| RED | 331 | 449 | 123 | 268 | 133 | 414 | 344 | 342 | 381 | 2785 | | |
| Par | 4 | 5 | 3 | 4 | 3 | 5 | 4 | 4 | 4 | 36 | RED | Rating: 70.5 |
| Handicap | 9 | 3 | 15 | 13 | 17 | 1 | 7 | 11 | 5 | x | | Slope: 112 |

| Hole | 10 | 11 | 12 | 13 | 14 | 15 | 16 | 17 | 18 | In | Totals | |
|---|---|---|---|---|---|---|---|---|---|---|---|---|
| BLUE | 497 | 357 | 136 | 370 | 319 | 177 | 473 | 370 | 440 | 3139 | BLUE | 6283 |
| WHITE | 470 | 345 | 120 | 360 | 314 | 170 | 465 | 355 | 430 | 3029 | WHITE | 6065 |
| Par | 5 | 4 | 3 | 4 | 4 | 3 | 5 | 4 | 4 | 36 | Par | 72 |
| Handicap | 10 | 6 | 18 | 4 | 16 | 8 | 14 | 12 | 2 | x | | |
| RED | 407 | 340 | 119 | 336 | 312 | 137 | 412 | 340 | 420 | 2823 | RED | 5608 |
| Par | 5 | 4 | 3 | 4 | 4 | 3 | 5 | 4 | 5 | 37 | Par | 73 |
| Handicap | 4 | 12 | 18 | 8 | 14 | 16 | 2 | 10 | 6 | x | | |

# SIERRA VIEW COUNTRY CLUB

**Course 10**
MAP D2 grid f8

*Course information:* This private layout has 18 holes and par is 72. The course is 6,481 yards and rated 70.6 from the regular tees. The slope rating is 121. Women's tees are 5,936 yards and rated 74.5 from the forward tees. The slope rating is 129.

*Play policy and fees:* Reciprocal play is accepted with members of other private clubs, otherwise members and guests only. Guest fees are $30 weekdays and $35 weekends when accompanied by a member. Carts are $16. Green fees for reciprocal play are the same as the visitor's home course fees.

*Location:* Off Interstate 80 in Roseville, exit at Atlantic Street and take the second right onto Yosemite Street. Drive a few blocks until the road bends. Look for Alta Vista and go left to the course.

*Course description:* Sierra View is located at the base of the foothills, a rolling course with mature trees and exceptional greens. Designed by Jack Fleming, the right-hand man of famed architect Alister MacKenzie, it offers a wide variety of short and long par-4s. The toughest is number three, a 463-yarder, which plays like a par-5 for all but the biggest hitters. The par-5 18th hole (554 yards) is an outstanding test, tightening as it goes along. Robert Meyer holds the course record with a 62. Sierra View has served as a qualifying site for the U. S. Senior Open and the U.S. Women's Amateur.

**1956**
**Jack Fleming**

105 Alta Vista
Roseville, CA 95661

Pro shop (916) 783-4600
Clubhouse (916) 782-3741

- ✓ **driving range**
- ✓ **practice greens**
- ✓ **power carts**
- ✓ **pull carts**
- ✓ **golf club rental**
- ✓ **locker rooms**
- ✓ **showers**
- executive course
- accommodations
- ✓ **food and beverages**
- ✓ **clubhouse**

**Bill Wampler**
Manager

**James Salazar**
Professional

**Ben Hartley**
Superintendent

# SUNSET WHITNEY COUNTRY CLUB

**Course 11**
MAP D2 grid f9

PO Box 788
Rocklin, CA 95677

4201 Midas Avenue
Rocklin, CA 95677

Pro shop (916) 624-2610
Clubhouse (916) 624-2402

- ✓ **driving range**
- ✓ **practice greens**
- ✓ **power carts**
- ✓ **pull carts**
- ✓ **golf club rental**
- locker rooms
- showers
- executive course
- accommodations
- ✓ **food and beverages**
- ✓ **clubhouse**

**Eric Pohl**
Professional

**Mike Kaveney**
Superintendent

***Course information:*** This private course has 18 holes. See card below for yardage and rating information.

***Play policy and fees:*** Reciprocal play is accepted with members of other private clubs. Guest fees are $25 weekdays and $35 weekends with a member. Green fees for reciprocal players are $50 weekdays and $60 weekends, carts included. Carts are $20. Reservations are recommended seven days in advance. This course is available for outside tournaments.

***Location:*** From Interstate 80 in Rocklin, take the Taylor Road North exit. Turn left on Midas Avenue and drive to the course.

***Course description:*** Situated in the Sierra Nevada foothills, this tight, twisting course has water, bunkers and undulating greens. It plays longer than the scorecard since fairways allow minimal roll. Sunset has one of Northern California's best short par-3s in number nine, a 113-yarder. From the elevated tee, it seems as though the golfer can almost reach across the small pond and touch the green. But the two-tiered green is wide and shallow. The tee shot better bite or it's sand city. Then there is the par-4 12th, a 411-yarder requiring a tee shot to carry over a large pond. Some of the best amateurs in Sacramento play out of Sierra View, and San Francisco 49ers Joe Montana and Steve Young drop by during training camp up the road at Sierra College.

| Hole | 1 | 2 | 3 | 4 | 5 | 6 | 7 | 8 | 9 | Out | BLUE | Rating: 71.8 |
|---|---|---|---|---|---|---|---|---|---|---|---|---|
| BLUE | 463 | 423 | 183 | 346 | 410 | 529 | 167 | 346 | 128 | 2995 | | Slope: 124 |
| WHITE | 452 | 404 | 169 | 316 | 375 | 504 | 146 | 331 | 113 | 2810 | | |
| Par | 5 | 4 | 3 | 4 | 4 | 5 | 3 | 4 | 3 | 35 | WHITE | Rating: 70.0 |
| Handicap | 7 | 1 | 13 | 11 | 3 | 5 | 15 | 9 | 17 | x | | Slope: 120 |
| RED | 444 | 385 | 141 | 304 | 326 | 411 | 87 | 317 | 88 | 2503 | | |
| Par | 5 | 4 | 3 | 4 | 4 | 5 | 3 | 4 | 3 | 35 | RED | Rating: 72.0 |
| Handicap | 3 | 1 | 16 | 13 | 10 | 14 | 18 | 6 | 17 | x | | Slope: 128 |

| Hole | 10 | 11 | 12 | 13 | 14 | 15 | 16 | 17 | 18 | In | Totals | |
|---|---|---|---|---|---|---|---|---|---|---|---|---|
| BLUE | 458 | 380 | 439 | 541 | 371 | 373 | 194 | 447 | 409 | 3612 | BLUE | 6607 |
| WHITE | 446 | 359 | 411 | 516 | 351 | 345 | 171 | 428 | 381 | 3408 | WHITE | 6218 |
| Par | 5 | 4 | 4 | 5 | 4 | 4 | 3 | 4 | 4 | 37 | Par | 72 |
| Handicap | 18 | 14 | 2 | 6 | 10 | 12 | 16 | 4 | 8 | x | | |
| RED | 433 | 339 | 311 | 447 | 342 | 303 | 152 | 319 | 358 | 3004 | RED | 5507 |
| Par | 5 | 4 | 4 | 5 | 4 | 4 | 3 | 4 | 4 | 37 | Par | 72 |
| Handicap | 9 | 7 | 4 | 5 | 2 | 11 | 15 | 12 | 8 | x | | |

# INDIAN CREEK COUNTRY CLUB

**Course 12**
MAP D2 grid f9

**1966**

PO Box 303
Loomis, CA 95650

4487 Barton Road
Loomis, CA 95650

Pro shop (916) 652-5546
Clubhouse (916) 652-3147

- ✓ **driving range**
- ✓ **practice greens**
- ✓ **power carts**
- ✓ **pull carts**
- ✓ **golf club rental**
- locker rooms
- showers
- ✓ **executive course**
- accommodations
- ✓ **food and beverages**
- ✓ **clubhouse**

**Peter Nash**
Manager

**Brent Jensen**
Professional

***Course information:*** This public course has nine holes. Par is 64 for 18 holes. The course is 4,140 yards and rated 59.2 from the regular tees. The slope rating is 98. Women's tees are 4,140 yards and rated 63.1.

***Play policy and fees:*** Green fees are $7 for nine holes and $12 for 18 holes weekdays, and $8 for nine holes and $14 for 18 holes weekends. Senior (65 and over) rates are $6 for nine holes and $10 for 18 holes weekdays, and $7 for nine holes and $11 for 18 holes weekends. Carts are $6 per nine holes.

***Location:*** From Interstate 80 east in Rocklin, take the Rocklin Road exit (not the exit for the town of Rocklin). Turn right on Rocklin Road and drive about two miles to the end. Turn left on Barton Road and drive one mile to the course.

***Course description:*** A short course, Indian Creek is a natural layout set in the rolling hills of Placer County. Low-handicappers are often surprised at the difficulty of these holes. Number two is a downhill dogleg over water with the second shot going up again to an elevated green.

# DAVIS GOLF COURSE

**Course 13**
MAP D2 grid g2

**1964**

PO Box 928
Davis, CA 95617

Highway 113 and Road 29
Davis, CA 95616

Pro shop (916) 756-4010

- ✓ **driving range**
- ✓ **practice greens**
- ✓ **power carts**
- ✓ **pull carts**
- ✓ **golf club rental**
- locker rooms
- showers
- executive course
- accommodations
- ✓ **food and beverages**
- clubhouse

**Jerry Lilliedoll**
Manager/Professional

**Tim Conner**
Superintendent

NORTHERN D2

***Course information:*** This public course has 18 holes and par is 66. The course is 4,895 yards and rated 62.3 from the championship tees, and 4,422 yards and rated 60.0 from the regular tees. The slope ratings are 97 championship and 92 regular. Women's tees are 4,422 yards and rated 64.3. The slope rating is 96.

***Play policy and fees:*** Green fees are $10 weekdays, $11 weekends. Seniors and juniors during the weekday pay $7 and $6 respectively. Carts are $16 for 18 holes. Reservations are recommended one week in advance.

***Location:*** From Interstate 80 in Davis, take the Highway 113 exit. Drive five miles north to County Road 29. The course is on the left.

***Course description:*** This short, flat course has strategically placed trees, lots of out-of-bounds and requires accuracy. There are six par-3s and 12 par-4s, the longest being 440 yards. The course's condition has improved markedly over the last 10 years despite 90,000 rounds annually. Water and bunkers abound. Chris Hallee and Bob Neri share the course record of 56.

| Hole | 1 | 2 | 3 | 4 | 5 | 6 | 7 | 8 | 9 | Out | BLUE | Rating: 66.7 |
|---|---|---|---|---|---|---|---|---|---|---|---|---|
| BLUE | 343 | 331 | 158 | 293 | 142 | 352 | 121 | 318 | 237 | 2295 | | Slope: 102 |
| WHITE | 322 | 306 | 132 | 261 | 128 | 328 | 103 | 274 | 216 | 2070 | | |
| Par | 4 | 4 | 3 | 4 | 3 | 4 | 3 | 4 | 4 | 33 | WHITE | Rating: 60.1 |
| Handicap | 4 | 6 | 10 | 8 | 12 | 2 | 16 | 14 | 18 | x | | Slope: 93 |
| RED | 322 | 306 | 132 | 261 | 128 | 328 | 103 | 274 | 216 | 2070 | | |
| Par | 4 | 4 | 3 | 4 | 3 | 4 | 3 | 4 | 4 | 33 | RED | Rating: 63.9 |
| Handicap | 4 | 6 | 12 | 16 | 14 | 2 | 8 | 10 | 18 | x | | Slope: 95 |

| Hole | 10 | 11 | 12 | 13 | 14 | 15 | 16 | 17 | 18 | In | Totals | |
|---|---|---|---|---|---|---|---|---|---|---|---|---|
| BLUE | 324 | 176 | 295 | 438 | 200 | 287 | 141 | 350 | 389 | 2600 | BLUE | 4895 |
| WHITE | 306 | 154 | 272 | 394 | 167 | 259 | 120 | 313 | 367 | 2352 | WHITE | 4422 |
| Par | 4 | 3 | 4 | 4 | 3 | 4 | 3 | 4 | 4 | 33 | Par | 66 |
| Handicap | 13 | 7 | 15 | 1 | 5 | 17 | 11 | 9 | 3 | x | | |
| RED | 306 | 154 | 272 | 394 | 167 | 259 | 120 | 313 | 367 | 2352 | RED | 4422 |
| Par | 4 | 3 | 4 | 4/5 | 3 | 4 | 3 | 4 | 4 | 33/34 | Par | 66/67 |
| Handicap | 5 | 15 | 13 | 1 | 9 | 11 | 17 | 7 | 3 | x | | |

# HAGGIN OAKS GOLF COURSE

**Course 14**
MAP D2 grid g6

**1932**
**Alister MacKenzie**

3645 Fulton Avenue
Sacramento, CA 95821

Pro shop
North (916) 481-4508
South (916) 481-4506
Clubhouse (916) 965-5970

- ✓ **driving range**
- ✓ **practice greens**
- ✓ **power carts**
- ✓ **pull carts**
- ✓ **golf club rental**
- locker rooms
- showers
- executive course
- accommodations
- ✓ **food and beverages**
- ✓ **clubhouse**

**Ken Morton**
Professional

**Joe Andrade**
Superintendent

***Course information:*** This public facility has 36 holes and par is 72 on both.

The South Course is detailed below.

The North Course is 6,985 yards and rated 71.4 from with a slope of 115 the championship tees, and 6,660 yards and rated 69.9 with a slope of 112 from the regular tees. Women's tees are 5,853 yards and rated 70.6 with a slope of 107 from the forward tees.

***Play policy and fees:*** Green fees are $11.50 weekdays and $14 weekends. Nine-hole rates on the north course are $5.75 weekdays, $7 weekends. Carts are $9 for nine holes, $18 for 18 holes. There is a $2 reservation fee for tee-off times.

***Location:*** Take the Fulton Road exit north off Business 80 in Sacramento and follow it to the course.

***Course description:*** The South Course was originally designed by legendary architect Alister Mackenzie and played host to the Sacramento Open in the late 1930s. Among the pros who competed were Sam Snead, Walter Hagen, Gene Sarazen and Ben Hogan. The South Course is tree-lined with large greens and extensive bunkering. Most recently Haggin Oaks held the 1992 US Women's Amateur Public Links, won by Amy Fruhwirth. Heather Hughes set the women's course record of 67 in stroke-play qualifying. The best hole on the course is either number 16, a par-3 of 165 yards or the par-5 18th hole. The North Course, consisting of the red and blue nines, is much longer but more wide open. The 18th hole (number nine on the blue nine) is an outstanding par-5. It measures 499 yards and is a double dogleg requiring either a bold second shot over towering trees or a precise lay-up. On both courses, reservations are a must because each numbers about 90,000 rounds a year.

South Course

| Hole | 1 | 2 | 3 | 4 | 5 | 6 | 7 | 8 | 9 | Out | BLUE | Rating: 70.6 |
|---|---|---|---|---|---|---|---|---|---|---|---|---|
| BLUE | 521 | 402 | 410 | 343 | 129 | 383 | 381 | 155 | 330 | 3054 | | Slope: 113 |
| WHITE | 512 | 390 | 395 | 333 | 114 | 373 | 370 | 139 | 320 | 2946 | | |
| Par | 5 | 4 | 4 | 4 | 3 | 4 | 4 | 3 | 4 | 35 | WHITE | Rating: 69.3 |
| Handicap | 11 | 3 | 1 | 9 | 17 | 5 | 7 | 15 | 13 | x | | Slope: 110 |
| RED | 482 | 375 | 373 | 325 | 111 | 308 | 335 | 140 | 311 | 2760 | | |
| Par | 5 | 4 | 4 | 4 | 3 | 4 | 4 | 3 | 4 | 35 | RED | Rating: 71.4 |
| Handicap | 6 | 4 | 8 | 2 | 18 | 12 | 10 | 16 | 14 | x | | Slope: 113 |

| Hole | 10 | 11 | 12 | 13 | 14 | 15 | 16 | 17 | 18 | In | Totals | |
|---|---|---|---|---|---|---|---|---|---|---|---|---|
| BLUE | 389 | 387 | 548 | 350 | 176 | 422 | 191 | 560 | 515 | 3538 | BLUE | 6592 |
| WHITE | 375 | 371 | 534 | 336 | 147 | 395 | 165 | 528 | 499 | 3350 | WHITE | 6296 |
| Par | 4 | 4 | 5 | 4 | 3 | 4 | 3 | 5 | 5 | 37 | Par | 72 |
| Handicap | 10 | 14 | 12 | 4 | 16 | 2 | 8 | 6 | 18 | x | | |
| RED | 285 | 345 | 520 | 304 | 125 | 364 | 132 | 495 | 426 | 2996 | RED | 5756 |
| Par | 4 | 4 | 5 | 4 | 3 | 4 | 3 | 5 | 5 | 37 | Par | 72 |
| Handicap | 13 | 9 | 5 | 1 | 15 | 7 | 17 | 3 | 11 | x | | |

# LAWRENCE LINKS GOLF COURSE

**Course 15**
MAP D2 grid g7

NORTHERN D2

McClellan AFB, 7823
Blackfoot Way
North Highlands, CA 95660

Pro shop (916) 643-3313

- driving range
- ✓ **practice greens**
- ✓ **power carts**
- ✓ **pull carts**
- ✓ **golf club rental**
- ✓ **locker rooms**
- ✓ **showers**
- executive course
- accommodations
- ✓ **food and beverages**
- ✓ **clubhouse**

**Wes Cline**
Manager

***Course information:*** This military course has nine holes. Par is 72 for 18 holes. The course is 6,062 yards and rated 69.7 from the regular tees (18 holes). The slope rating is 123. Women's tees are 5,176 yards and rated 70.2 from the forward tees. The slope rating is 120.

***Play policy and fees:*** Reciprocal play is accepted with members of other military clubs. Green fees for military personnel are $6 for nine holes and $9 for 18 holes weekdays, and $7 nine holes and $11 for 18 holes weekends. Guest fees for civilians are $7 for nine holes and $12 for 18 holes weekdays, and $8 for nine holes and $12 for 18 holes weekends. Carts are $14 for 18 holes.

***Location:*** From Interstate 80 in Sacramento, take the Watt Avenue exit north and drive past the entrance to McClellan Air Force Base. Turn right on Blackfoot Way and drive to the end. The course is about 5.5 miles from Interstate 80.

***Course description:*** This tough, demanding course has four lakes that provide water hazards on every hole. Golfers play the red tees the first nine and the blue tees the next time around. Number 10 is the longest hole, a par-5 stretching out to 603 yards, and the best par-3 is number six, a 160-yarder over a hazard. Steve Taylor holds the course record with a 10-under 62.

# ANCIL HOFFMAN GOLF COURSE

**Course 16**
MAP D2 grid g7

**1965**
**William Francis Bell**

PO Box 790
Carmichael, CA 95608

6700 Tarshes Drive
Carmichael, CA 95608

Pro shop (916) 482-5660

- ✓ **driving range**
- ✓ **practice greens**
- ✓ **power carts**
- pull carts
- ✓ **golf club rental**
- locker rooms
- showers
- executive course
- accommodations
- ✓ **food and beverages**
- ✓ **clubhouse**

**Steve Price**
Professional

**Rich Sizelove**
Superintendent

***Course information:*** This public course has 18 holes and par is 72. The course is 6,794 yards and rated 72.5 from the championship tees, and 6,434 yards and rated 71.0 from the regular tees. The slope ratings are 123 championship and 119 regular. Women's tees are 5,954 yards and rated 73.4. The slope rating is 123.

***Play policy and fees:*** Green fees for county residents are $13 weekdays, $15 weekends. The 18-hole rates for non-residents are $16.50 weekdays, $20 weekends. The twilight rate for residents is $8, for non-residents $10. Carts are $18 for 18 holes.

***Location:*** From Business 80 in Sacramento, take the Marconi Avenue exit east. Drive five miles to Fair Oaks Boulevard and turn right. Turn left on Kenneth Avenue. Turn right on California Avenue and left on Ancil Hoffman Park Road (Tarshes Drive) and follow to the course.

***Course description:*** Golf Digest ranks it among the top 75 public courses in the country. Situated in Ancil Hoffman Park on the American River, oak and pine trees come into play on nearly every hole. The fairways are tight and the greens are contoured. Although it shows the wear of nearly 100,000 rounds each year, Hoffman is one of the premier public courses in Northern California. The seventh hole, a par-5 of 542 yards, is an outstanding hole, requiring a pinpoint drive down a tree-lined fairway. The second shot is almost as difficult to place, and the green is big. Perhaps the finest holes are 15 and 16, two par-4s of superb character. Number 15 is just 318 yards but bends severely to the left and has a well-bunkered green with overhanging oaks. Number 16 is a monster of 422 yards featuring a narrow driving area.

# CHERRY ISLAND GOLF COURSE

**Course 17**
MAP D2 grid g7

**1990**
**Robert Muir Graves**

2360 Elverta Road
Elverta, CA 95626

Pro shop (916) 991-7293
Starter (916) 991-0770
Clubhouse (916) 991-0655

- ✓ **driving range**
- ✓ **practice greens**
- ✓ **power carts**
- ✓ **pull carts**
- ✓ **golf club rental**
- locker rooms
- showers
- executive course
- accommodations
- ✓ **food and beverages**
- ✓ **clubhouse**

**Blair Kline**
Professional

**George Quinday**
Superintendent

*Course information:* This public course has 18 holes and par is 72. The course is 6,562 yards and rated 71.1 from the tournament tees, and 6,201 and rated 69.5 from the championship tees, and 5,556 yards and rated 67.8 from the regular tees. The slope ratings are 124 tournament, 121 championship and 117 regular. Women's tees are 5,163 yards and rated 70.0 from the forward tees. The slope rating is 117.

*Play policy and fees:* Green fees for county residents are $13 weekdays, $15 weekends. The 18-hole rates for non-residents are $16.50 weekdays, $20 weekends. The twilight rate for residents is $8, for non-residents $10. Carts are $18 for 18 holes.

*Location:* From Interstate 80 in Sacramento, take the Watt Avenue exit north. Drive five miles to Elverta Road and turn left. Drive one mile to the course on the left.

*Course description:* Cherry Island is an unusual course in the sense that it forces a golfer with average or above-average length to leave the driver in the bag on several holes. Water comes into play on 10 holes, requiring numerous lay-up shots off the tee. The front nine has several instances of in-course out-of-bounds. The third hole (par-5, 543 yards) wraps around a large lake and forces a difficult decision on the second shot. The par-3s are excellent, including the 158-yard 14th hole over a creek into a green framed by trees. The 15th hole, a par-5 of 543 yards, is a tough nut: There is out-of-bounds left, water on the right, and an elevated green surrounded by bunkers.

# ROSEVILLE ROLLING GREENS GOLF COURSE

**Course 18**
MAP D2 grid g8

**1950**

***Course information:*** This public course has nine holes. See card below for yardage and rating information.

***Play policy and fees:*** Green fees are $7 for nine holes and $11 for 18 holes weekdays, and $8 for nine holes and $13 for 18 holes weekends. Play is on a first come, first served basis.

***Location:*** From Interstate 80 in Roseville, take the Douglas Street exit east. Turn right on Sierra College Boulevard and left on Eureka Road.

***Course description:*** This short, par-3 course has rolling terrain and can be tough, especially the 235-yard par-3 sixth, which has only been aced once. The course record is 50 for 18 holes.

5572 Eureka Road
Roseville, CA 95661

Pro shop (916) 797-9986

driving range
✓ **practice greens**
power carts
✓ **pull carts**
golf club rental
locker rooms
showers
✓ **executive course**
accommodations
✓ **food and beverages**
clubhouse

**Bob Peterson**
Manager/Professional

**Jerry Levesque**
Superintendent

| Hole | 1 | 2 | 3 | 4 | 5 | 6 | 7 | 8 | 9 | Out | | |
|---|---|---|---|---|---|---|---|---|---|---|---|---|
| BLUE | - | - | - | - | - | - | - | - | - | - | BLUE | Rating: -- |
| | | | | | | | | | | | | Slope: -- |
| WHITE | 187 | 127 | 141 | 117 | 234 | 223 | 181 | 155 | 135 | 1500 | | |
| Par | 3 | 3 | 3 | 3 | 3 | 3 | 3 | 3 | 3 | 27 | WHITE | Rating: 53.9 |
| Handicap | 5 | 17 | 11 | 15 | 3 | 1 | 7 | 9 | 13 | x | | Slope: 79 |
| RED | 190 | 130 | 144 | 120 | 235 | 225 | 185 | 160 | 140 | 1529 | | |
| Par | 3 | 3 | 3 | 3 | 4 | 4 | 3 | 3 | 3 | 29 | RED | Rating: 56.5 |
| Handicap | 3 | 17 | 7 | 15 | 11 | 13 | 1 | 5 | 9 | x | | Slope: 92 |

| Hole | 10 | 11 | 12 | 13 | 14 | 15 | 16 | 17 | 18 | In | Totals | |
|---|---|---|---|---|---|---|---|---|---|---|---|---|
| BLUE | - | - | - | - | - | - | - | - | - | - | BLUE | -- |
| WHITE | 187 | 127 | 141 | 117 | 234 | 223 | 181 | 155 | 135 | 1500 | WHITE | 3000 |
| Par | 3 | 3 | 3 | 3 | 3 | 3 | 3 | 3 | 3 | 27 | Par | 54 |
| Handicap | 6 | 18 | 12 | 16 | 4 | 2 | 8 | 10 | 14 | x | | |
| RED | 190 | 130 | 144 | 120 | 235 | 225 | 185 | 160 | 140 | 1529 | RED | 3058 |
| Par | 3 | 3 | 3 | 3 | 4 | 4 | 3 | 3 | 3 | 29 | Par | -- |
| Handicap | 4 | 18 | 8 | 16 | 12 | 14 | 2 | 6 | 10 | x | | |

# SUNRISE GOLF COURSE

*Course information:* This private facility has nine holes. Par is 64 for 18 holes. The course is 4,094 yards and rated 59.7 from the regular tees. The slope rating is 95. Women's tees are 4,094 and rated 64.2. The slope rating is 96.

*Play policy and fees:* Reciprocal play is accepted with members of other private clubs. Guest and reciprocal fees are $7 and $11 weekdays and $8 and $15 weekends when accompanied by a member.

*Location:* From Interstate 80 in Citrus Heights (northeast of Sacramento), take the Greenback Lane exit east. Drive four miles to Sunrise Boulevard and turn left. The course is located on your right.

*Course description:* This executive-style course has rolling hills, tree-lined fairways and small greens. The par-4 ninth hole has a creek running through the fairway and is very tight, a demanding finish. While the course is private, the driving range is open to the public until 10 p.m. nightly.

**Course 19**
MAP D2 grid g8

**1981**

6412 Sunrise Boulevard
Citrus Heights, CA 95610

Pro shop (916) 723-8854
Starter (916) 723-0481

- ✓ **driving range**
- ✓ **practice greens**
- ✓ **power carts**
- ✓ **pull carts**
- ✓ **golf club rental**
- locker rooms
- showers
- ✓ **executive course**
- accommodations
- ✓ **food and beverages**
- ✓ **clubhouse**

**Steve Barrett**
Manager

**Mike Griggs**
Professional

**Gary Mills**
Superintendent

# NORTH RIDGE COUNTRY CLUB

**Course 20**
MAP D2 grid g8

**1952**
**Robert Muir Graves**

PO Box 326
Fair Oaks, CA 95628

7600 Madison Avenue
Fair Oaks, CA 95628

Pro shop (916) 967-5716
Clubhouse (916) 967-5717

- ✓ **driving range**
- ✓ **practice greens**
- ✓ **power carts**
- ✓ **pull carts**
- ✓ **golf club rental**
- ✓ **locker rooms**
- ✓ **showers**
- executive course
- accommodations
- ✓ **food and beverages**
- ✓ **clubhouse**

**Ron Witt**
Manager

**Nate Pomeroy**
Professional

**Fritz Howell**
Superintendent

***Course information:*** This private course has 18 holes. See card below for yardage and rating information.

***Play policy and fees:*** Reciprocal play is accepted with members of other private clubs for $70, including cart. Guest fees are $25 with a member and $70 without. Carts are $18.

***Location:*** From Sacramento, drive east on Interstate 80. Take the Madison Avenue exit east. Follow Madison Avenue for five miles to Mariposa.

***Course description:*** This tree-lined course has Bermuda grass fairways and long par-4s. It tends to play longer than the yardage due to the number of uphill holes. North Ridge features a classic par-5, number 15. It narrows each step of the way and demands a precise second shot to the left of the tree line. The small green caps things off. "Most par-5s are kind of cheap," North Ridge pro Nate Peroy said. "But 15 places a real premium on the second shot. Most par-5s don't." Robert Meyer holds the course record with a 62.

| Hole | 1 | 2 | 3 | 4 | 5 | 6 | 7 | 8 | 9 | Out | BLUE | Rating: 71.9 |
|---|---|---|---|---|---|---|---|---|---|---|---|---|
| BLUE | 510 | 402 | 202 | 426 | 456 | 154 | 329 | 191 | 521 | 3191 | | Slope: 125 |
| WHITE | 501 | 391 | 180 | 405 | 445 | 131 | 309 | 183 | 497 | 3042 | | |
| Par | 5 | 4 | 3 | 4 | 5 | 3 | 4 | 3 | 5 | 36 | WHITE | Rating: 70.6 |
| Handicap | 8 | 4 | 10 | 2 | 14 | 18 | 16 | 12 | 6 | x | | Slope: 122 |
| RED | 495 | 352 | 169 | 386 | 419 | 116 | 296 | 172 | 465 | 2870 | | |
| Par | 5 | 4 | 3 | 4 | 5 | 3 | 4 | 3 | 5 | 36 | RED | Rating: 74.1 |
| Handicap | 6 | 8 | 16 | 2 | 10 | 18 | 12 | 14 | 4 | x | | Slope: 129 |

| Hole | 10 | 11 | 12 | 13 | 14 | 15 | 16 | 17 | 18 | In | Totals | |
|---|---|---|---|---|---|---|---|---|---|---|---|---|
| BLUE | 369 | 182 | 430 | 388 | 344 | 523 | 358 | 208 | 559 | 3361 | BLUE | 6552 |
| WHITE | 354 | 176 | 411 | 381 | 327 | 512 | 341 | 176 | 538 | 3216 | WHITE | 6258 |
| Par | 4 | 3 | 4 | 4 | 4 | 5 | 4 | 3 | 5 | 36 | Par | 72 |
| Handicap | 9 | 15 | 1 | 5 | 17 | 3 | 13 | 7 | 11 | x | | |
| RED | 341 | 169 | 383 | 371 | 317 | 494 | 316 | 172 | 445 | 3008 | RED | 5878 |
| Par | 4 | 3 | 4 | 4 | 4 | 5 | 4 | 3 | 5 | 36 | Par | 72 |
| Handicap | 9 | 15 | 5 | 3 | 13 | 1 | 7 | 17 | 11 | x | | |

# EL MACERO COUNTRY CLUB

**Course 21**
**MAP D2 grid h3**

*Course information:* This private course has 18 holes. See card below for yardage and rating information.

*Play policy and fees:* Reciprocal play is accepted with members of other private clubs. Guest fees are $30. Reciprocal fees are $55. Carts are $20 for 18 holes.

*Location:* From Davis, drive two miles east on Interstate 80. Take the Mace Boulevard exit south in El Macero. Drive south to Clubhouse Road.

*Course description:* This long, narrow course has lots of out-of-bounds and challenging fairway bunkers. There are three lakes. The talk of this course is hole number 15. It is 512 yards and par-5. There are two fairway bunkers in the right landing zone and if you survive those the undulating green is surrounded by more bunkers. Trees are everywhere. Out-of-bounds mark both sides of the wide fairway. If you stray, you have to hit out of the trees. El Macero lost its greens five years ago and has since undergone a dramatic transformation supervised by Robert Muir Graves. The course is narrow and fairly long with excellent greens. Two holes of note are numbers six and 15. The par-4 sixth is 414 yards requiring a pinpoint drive out of a narrow chute. Number 15 is a par-5 of 512 yards with several well-placed bunkers. Joe Acosta of Visalia set the course record of 63 in U.S. Amateur qualifying.

**1961**
**R.E. Baldock**

PO Box 2005
El Macero, CA 95618

1 Clubhouse Road
El Macero, CA 95618

Pro shop (916) 753-5621

- ✓ **driving range**
- ✓ **practice greens**
- ✓ **power carts**
- ✓ **pull carts**
- golf club rental
- ✓ **locker rooms**
- ✓ **showers**
- executive course
- accommodations
- ✓ **food and beverages**
- ✓ **clubhouse**

**Nick Nicoloudis**
**Mike Henry**
Professionals

**Campbell Turner**
Assistant Professional

| Hole | 1 | 2 | 3 | 4 | 5 | 6 | 7 | 8 | 9 | Out | BLUE | Rating: 72.3 |
|---|---|---|---|---|---|---|---|---|---|---|---|---|
| BLUE | 356 | 515 | 226 | 467 | 560 | 437 | 157 | 381 | 389 | 3488 | | Slope: 12[illegible] |
| WHITE | 346 | 503 | 210 | 443 | 543 | 407 | 133 | 363 | 367 | 3315 | | |
| Par | 4 | 5 | 3 | 4 | 5 | 4 | 3 | 4 | 4 | 36 | WHITE | Rating: 70.4 |
| Handicap | 15 | 13 | 5 | 1 | 7 | 3 | 17 | 11 | 9 | x | | Slope: 119 |
| RED | 322 | 480 | 194 | 356 | 528 | 330 | 112 | 350 | 357 | 3029 | | |
| Par | 4 | 5 | 3 | 4 | 5 | 4 | 3 | 4 | 4 | 36 | RED | Rating: 73.3 |
| Handicap | 11 | 5 | 15 | 9 | 1 | 13 | 17 | 3 | 7 | x | | Slope: 119 |

| Hole | 10 | 11 | 12 | 13 | 14 | 15 | 16 | 17 | 18 | In | Totals | |
|---|---|---|---|---|---|---|---|---|---|---|---|---|
| BLUE | 408 | 416 | 177 | 382 | 354 | 516 | 176 | 398 | 520 | 3347 | BLUE | 6837 |
| WHITE | 386 | 402 | 152 | 361 | 338 | 468 | 162 | 384 | 501 | 3174 | WHITE | 6489 |
| Par | 4 | 4 | 3 | 4 | 4 | 5 | 3 | 4 | 5 | 36 | Par | 72 |
| Handicap | 4 | 2 | 18 | 8 | 12 | 14 | 16 | 6 | 10 | x | | |
| RED | 346 | 366 | 133 | 347 | 325 | 474 | 143 | 371 | 476 | 2981 | RED | 6010 |
| Par | 4 | 4 | 3 | 4 | 4 | 5 | 3 | 4 | 5 | 36 | Par | 72 |
| Handicap | 10 | 2 | 16 | 12 | 14 | 6 | 18 | 8 | 4 | x | | |

# LIGHTHOUSE GOLF COURSE

**Course 22**
MAP D2 grid h5

***Course information:*** This public course has 18 holes. See card below for yardage and rating information.

***Play policy and fees:*** Green fees are $15 weekdays and $20 weekends. Carts are $18 for 18 holes, $9 for nine.

***Location:*** From the Interstate 80 Business Loop in West Sacramento, take the Jefferson exit north. Turn right on Sacramento Avenue. Drive 1.5 blocks to Douglas Street and turn left. The course is at the end of Douglas.

***Course description:*** This course is young, but growing. The old course, formerly the Riverbend Golf and Country Club, was plowed up and redesigned. There is now water on 15 holes. Mature trees were retained as part of the new course, and others have been planted. Surfacing as a spectacularly tough hole is the par-4, 418-yard 15th. There is water left and right. The elevated green is narrow in the front and deep in the back. Pin position often makes this a particularly difficult hole. This course is shaping up as a real challenge. The greens are excellent.

**1990**
**Bert Stamps**

500 Douglas Street
West Sacramento, CA 95605

Pro shop (916) 372-4949
Clubhouse (916) 372-0800

- ✓ **driving range**
- ✓ **practice greens**
- ✓ **power carts**
- ✓ **pull carts**
- ✓ **golf club rental**
- locker rooms
- showers
- executive course
- accommodations
- ✓ **food and beverages**
- ✓ **clubhouse**

**Don Howton**
General Manager

**Robert Halpenny**
Professional

**Pargan Singh**
Superintendent

| Hole | 1 | 2 | 3 | 4 | 5 | 6 | 7 | 8 | 9 | Out | BLUE | Rating: 64.0 |
|---|---|---|---|---|---|---|---|---|---|---|---|---|
| BLUE | 416 | 416 | 256 | 197 | 374 | 346 | 161 | 136 | 163 | 2465 | | Slope: 107 |
| WHITE | 416 | 401 | 256 | 188 | 348 | 332 | 144 | 131 | 145 | 2361 | | |
| Par | 5 | 4 | 4 | 3 | 4 | 4 | 3 | 3 | 3 | 33 | WHITE | Rating: 62.8 |
| Handicap | 9 | 3 | 17 | 1 | 7 | 5 | 11 | 15 | 13 | x | | Slope: 104 |
| RED | 403 | 401 | 219 | 174 | 325 | 320 | 121 | 100 | 126 | 2189 | | |
| Par | 5 | 5 | 4 | 3 | 4 | 4 | 3 | 3 | 3 | 34 | RED | Rating: 62.5 |
| Handicap | 1 | 7 | 17 | 3 | 5 | 9 | 11 | 15 | 13 | x | | Slope: 103 |

| Hole | 10 | 11 | 12 | 13 | 14 | 15 | 16 | 17 | 18 | In | Totals | |
|---|---|---|---|---|---|---|---|---|---|---|---|---|
| BLUE | 464 | 161 | 143 | 155 | 169 | 418 | 137 | 268 | 349 | 2264 | BLUE | 4729 |
| WHITE | 464 | 155 | 123 | 135 | 158 | 404 | 122 | 251 | 330 | 2142 | WHITE | 4503 |
| Par | 5 | 3 | 3 | 3 | 3 | 4 | 3 | 4 | 4 | 32 | Par | 65 |
| Handicap | 12 | 4 | 16 | 10 | 8 | 2 | 14 | 18 | 6 | x | | |
| RED | 412 | 101 | 107 | 115 | 125 | 409 | 107 | 234 | 321 | 1931 | RED | 4120 |
| Par | 5 | 3 | 3 | 3 | 3 | 5 | 3 | 4 | 4 | 33 | Par | 67 |
| Handicap | 12 | 8 | 10 | 18 | 6 | 2 | 14 | 16 | 4 | x | | |

# WILLIAM LAND PARK GOLF COURSE

**Course 23**
MAP D2 grid h5

1701 Sutterville Road
Sacramento, CA 95822
Pro shop (916) 455-5014

- driving range
- ✓ **practice greens**
- power carts
- ✓ **pull carts**
- ✓ **golf club rental**
- locker rooms
- showers
- executive course
- accommodations
- ✓ **food and beverages**
- ✓ **clubhouse**

**Steve Feliciano**
Professional

**Frank Acosta**
Superintendent

NORTHERN D2

***Course information:*** This public course has nine holes. See card below for yardage and rating information.

***Play policy and fees:*** Green fees are $5.75 for nine holes and $11.50 for 18 holes weekdays, and $7 and $14 weekends and holidays. Senior (65 and over) rates are $4.75 for nine holes and $9 for 18 holes weekdays. Juniors are $3.50 for nine holes weekdays. Pull carts only.

***Location:*** From Business 80 in Sacramento, exit on 16th Street and drive south. 16th Street turns into Land Park Drive. At the Sacramento Zoo entrance take a left turn to the clubhouse.

***Course description:*** Set in beautiful William Land Park, this course is a favoritc of women, seniors and locals interested in a peaceful round of golf. The par-3 third hole (152 yards) has long been considered one of the area's best, wtih its two huge conttonwoods guarding thc green. Former U.S. Women's Amateur champion Barbara Romack learned how to play here, as did "Mr. 59" Al Geiberger. When the city threatened to close thc golf course in the early 1950s, one of its staunchest defenders was Sis Kennedy, mother of future Supreme Court Justice Anthony Kennedy.

| Hole | 1 | 2 | 3 | 4 | 5 | 6 | 7 | 8 | 9 | Out | | |
|---|---|---|---|---|---|---|---|---|---|---|---|---|
| BLUE | - | - | - | - | - | - | - | - | - | - | BLUE | Rating: -- |
| | | | | | | | | | | | | Slope: -- |
| WHITE | 144 | 328 | 153 | 358 | 383 | 296 | 147 | 456 | 334 | 2599 | | |
| Par | 3 | 4 | 3 | 4 | 4 | 4 | 3 | 5 | 4 | 34 | WHITE | Rating: 63.0 |
| Handicap | 15 | 3 | 9 | 11 | 1 | 13 | 17 | 7 | 5 | x | | Slope: 96 |
| RED | 144 | 328 | 153 | 358 | 383 | 296 | 147 | 436 | 334 | 2579 | | |
| Par | 3 | 4 | 3 | 4 | 4 | 4 | 3 | 5 | 4 | 34 | RED | Rating: 63.0 |
| Handicap | 15 | 3 | 9 | 11 | 1 | 13 | 17 | 5 | 7 | x | | Slope: 100 |

| Hole | 10 | 11 | 12 | 13 | 14 | 15 | 16 | 17 | 18 | In | Totals | |
|---|---|---|---|---|---|---|---|---|---|---|---|---|
| BLUE | - | - | - | - | - | - | - | - | - | - | BLUE | -- |
| WHITE | 144 | 328 | 153 | 358 | 383 | 296 | 147 | 456 | 334 | 2599 | WHITE | 5198 |
| Par | 3 | 4 | 3 | 4 | 4 | 4 | 3 | 5 | 4 | 34 | Par | 68 |
| Handicap | 16 | 4 | 10 | 12 | 2 | 14 | 18 | 8 | 6 | x | | |
| RED | 144 | 328 | 153 | 358 | 383 | 296 | 147 | 436 | 334 | 2579 | RED | 5158 |
| Par | 3 | 4 | 3 | 4 | 4 | 4 | 3 | 5 | 4 | 34 | Par | 68 |
| Handicap | 16 | 4 | 10 | 12 | 2 | 14 | 18 | 6 | 8 | x | | |

# DEL PASO COUNTRY CLUB

**Course 24**
MAP D2 grid h6

**1916**
**Herbert Fowler**

3333 Marconi Avenue
Sacramento, CA 95821

Pro shop (916) 483-0401
Clubhouse (916) 489-3681

- ✓ **driving range**
- ✓ **practice greens**
- ✓ **power carts**
- ✓ **pull carts**
- golf club rental
- ✓ **locker rooms**
- ✓ **showers**
- executive course
- accommodations
- ✓ **food and beverages**
- ✓ **clubhouse**

**Les Streeper**
Professional

**Tom Unruh**
Superintendent

***Course information:*** This private course has 18 holes and par is 72. The course is 6,300 yards and rated 70.0 from the regular tees. The slope is 117. Women's tees are 5,931 yards and rated 74.4 from the forward tees. The slope rating is 130.

***Play policy and fees:*** Reciprocal play is accepted only with clubs at least 50 miles away. Call for specifics. Guest fees are $30 with a member and $75 without.

***Location:*** From Business 80 in Sacramento, take the Marconi Avenue exit east. Drive 1.5 miles to the course, which is on the left. From Interstate 80 take the Watt Avenue exit. Travel on Watt Avenue to Marconi Avenue, turn right on Marconi and follow it to the course.

***Course description:*** This rolling, tree-lined layout is narrow with small, undulating greens. The fairways and greens are well bunkered. The men's course record is 63, set by Lee Elder and Bob E. Smith during the old "Swing at Cancer" benefits. Del Paso has hosted several USGA events: the 1957 and 1976 U.S. Women's Amateur and the 1964 Senior Women's Amateur. The 1982 U.S. Women's Open was held here. The most distinct holes are number two, a par-5 of 488 yards that horseshoes around a creek and trees; number 16, a 200-yard par-3; number 17, a par-4 of 403 yards into a well-bunkered green; and 18, a 396-yarder with the stately clubhouse serving as a backdrop.

# CAMPUS COMMONS GOLF COURSE

**Course 25**
MAP D2 grid h6

**1973**
**Bill McDowell**

2 Cadillac Drive
Sacramento, CA 95825

Pro shop (916) 922-5861

- driving range
- ✓ **practice greens**
- ✓ **power carts**
- ✓ **pull carts**
- ✓ **golf club rental**
- locker rooms
- showers
- ✓ **executive course**
- accommodations
- ✓ **food and beverages**
- clubhouse

**Ray Arinno**
Manager/Professional

**Dale Arinno**
Superintendent



***Course information:*** This public course has nine holes. See card below for yardage and rating information.

***Play policy and fees:*** Outside play is accepted. Green fees are $6.50 for nine holes and $10.50 for 18 holes weekdays, and $7.50 for nine holes and $11.50 for 18 holes weekends. Carts are $8 per nine holes. Reservations are recommended.

***Location:*** From Highway 50 in Sacramento, take the Howe Avenue North exit. Take a left on Fair Oaks Boulevard, and a right on Cadillac Drive. Follow Cadillac Drive to the course.

***Course description:*** This rolling executive course is bordered by the American River. The greens are elevated and there is a lot of roll to the fairways. The river comes into play on the fifth, seventh and eighth holes. Number five plays about 220 yards, with the river an intimidating presence on the right. Pro Ray Arinno says the greens are "the best in Sacramento." A popular course for seniors and women, Campus Commons also attracts some of the area's better amateurs for Monday afternoon games. A new clubhouse with patio opened in 1992. The course record is 53, set by Rex Smothers.

| Hole | 1 | 2 | 3 | 4 | 5 | 6 | 7 | 8 | 9 | Out | BLUE | Rating: -- |
|---|---|---|---|---|---|---|---|---|---|---|---|---|
| BLUE | - | - | - | - | - | - | - | - | - | - | | Slope: -- |
| WHITE | 150 | 138 | 276 | 135 | 187 | 168 | 160 | 287 | 172 | 1673 | | |
| Par | 3 | 3 | 4 | 3 | 3 | 3 | 3 | 4 | 3 | 29 | WHITE | Rating: 54.0 |
| Handicap | 16 | 18 | 6 | 12 | 1 | 8 | 4 | 14 | 10 | x | | Slope: -- |
| RED | 127 | 116 | 264 | 118 | 187 | 152 | 142 | 260 | 142 | 1508 | | |
| Par | 3 | 3 | 4 | 3 | 4 | 3 | 3 | 4 | 3 | 30 | RED | Rating: 56.0 |
| Handicap | 13 | 15 | 1 | 17 | 5 | 11 | 7 | 3 | 9 | x | | Slope: -- |

| Hole | 10 | 11 | 12 | 13 | 14 | 15 | 16 | 17 | 18 | In | Totals | |
|---|---|---|---|---|---|---|---|---|---|---|---|---|
| BLUE | - | - | - | - | - | - | - | - | - | - | BLUE | -- |
| WHITE | 150 | 138 | 276 | 135 | 187 | 168 | 160 | 287 | 172 | 1673 | WHITE | 3246 |
| Par | 3 | 3 | 4 | 3 | 3 | 3 | 3 | 4 | 3 | 29 | Par | 58 |
| Handicap | 16 | 18 | 6 | 12 | 1 | 8 | 4 | 14 | 10 | x | | |
| RED | 127 | 116 | 264 | 118 | 187 | 152 | 142 | 260 | 142 | 1508 | RED | 3016 |
| Par | 3 | 3 | 4 | 3 | 4 | 3 | 3 | 4 | 3 | 30 | Par | 60 |
| Handicap | 13 | 15 | 1 | 17 | 5 | 11 | 7 | 3 | 9 | x | | |

# BRADSHAW RANCH GOLF COURSE

**Course 26**
MAP D2 grid h7

**1989**

***Course information:*** This nine-hole course is 1,084 yards for men and women. It is not rated. Par is 27.

***Play policy and fees:*** Green fees are $4 weekdays and $4.50 weekends. Pull carts are $1.

***Location:*** Either take Bradshaw exit south off Highway 50 or take Florin Road east off Highway 99 and drive several miles to Bradshaw. Turn left on Bradshaw.

***Course description:*** A short course that is particularly popular with seniors and women, it is well-maintained with good greens. The 111-yard fourth hole has a lake and features the only real sloping green on the course.

7350 Bradshaw Road
Sacramento, CA 95828

Pro shop (916)363-6549

- driving range
- ✓ **practice greens**
- power carts
- ✓ **pull carts**
- ✓ **golf club rental**
- locker rooms
- showers
- ✓ **executive course**
- accommodations
- ✓ **food and beverages**
- ✓ **clubhouse**

**Marshall Cain**
Professional

**Steve Legarra**
Owner/Superintendent

# MATHER GOLF COURSE

**Course 27**
MAP D2 grid h7

**1958**

*Course information:* This military course has 18 holes. See card below for yardage and rating information.

*Play policy and fees:* Military personnel and invited guests only. Military personnel and retirees pay $8.50 on weekdays, $10 on weekends. Guest fees are $18. Carts are $14.

*Location:* From Sacramento, drive east on Highway 50. Take the Mather Air Force Base exit and follow Mather Base Drive inside the gate.

*Course description:* This long course is lined with mature trees and a creek runs through the third hole. It demands length off the tee. There are six par-4s that are 420 yards or longer. The final two holes are a tough finish. Number 17 is 458 yards and par-4. It is straight away and long with trees left and right. The front of the relatively large green is open but there is a bunker to the left. Hit it long and straight. Number 18 is 420 yards and par-4. It features a dogleg left and trees down both sides. With Mather Air Force Base targeted for closure in September 1993, the golf course is being pursued by several groups, including the Northern California Golf Association and a group of retired military personnel. Pentagon closure guidelines indicate it will probably be open to the public.

Building 8855, Mather AFB
CA 95655–5000

Pro shop (916) 364-4462

- ✓ **driving range**
- ✓ **practice greens**
- ✓ **power carts**
- ✓ **pull carts**
- ✓ **golf club rental**
- locker rooms
- showers
- executive course
- accommodations
- ✓ **food and beverages**
- ✓ **clubhouse**

**Les Wright**
Manager

**Jack Emmons**
Professional

**Larry Johnson**
Superintendent

| Hole | 1 | 2 | 3 | 4 | 5 | 6 | 7 | 8 | 9 | Out | | |
|---|---|---|---|---|---|---|---|---|---|---|---|---|
| BLUE | 395 | 534 | 156 | 423 | 426 | 353 | 183 | 382 | 522 | 3374 | BLUE | Rating: 70.6 |
| WHITE | 385 | 521 | 144 | 388 | 416 | 342 | 162 | 371 | 503 | 3232 | | Slope: 115 |
| Par | 4 | 5 | 3 | 4 | 4 | 4 | 3 | 4 | 5 | 36 | WHITE | Rating: 69.2 |
| Handicap | 5 | 7 | 17 | 3 | 1 | 13 | 15 | 11 | 9 | x | | Slope: 111 |
| RED | 377 | 473 | 135 | 374 | 409 | 308 | 150 | 331 | 471 | 3028 | | |
| Par | 4 | 5 | 3 | 4 | 5 | 4 | 3 | 4 | 5 | 37 | RED | Rating: 72.4 |
| Handicap | 5 | 1 | 13 | 7 | 15 | 11 | 17 | 9 | 3 | x | | Slope: 119 |

| Hole | 10 | 11 | 12 | 13 | 14 | 15 | 16 | 17 | 18 | In | Totals | |
|---|---|---|---|---|---|---|---|---|---|---|---|---|
| BLUE | 448 | 168 | 473 | 296 | 182 | 356 | 541 | 463 | 420 | 3347 | BLUE | 6721 |
| WHITE | 417 | 144 | 458 | 281 | 167 | 345 | 523 | 428 | 402 | 3165 | WHITE | 6397 |
| Par | 4 | 3 | 5 | 4 | 3 | 4 | 5 | 4 | 4 | 36 | Par | 72 |
| Handicap | 4 | 18 | 10 | 16 | 12 | 14 | 6 | 2 | 8 | x | | |
| RED | 376 | 134 | 452 | 273 | 157 | 328 | 427 | 415 | 386 | 2948 | RED | 5976 |
| Par | 4 | 3 | 5 | 4 | 3 | 4 | 5 | 5 | 4 | 37 | Par | 74 |
| Handicap | 6 | 12 | 2 | 14 | 18 | 10 | 8 | 16 | 4 | x | | |



MAP ON PAGE 126

# CORDOVA GOLF COURSE

**Course 28**
MAP D2 grid h8

***Course information:*** This public course has 18 holes. See card below for yardage and rating information.

***Play policy and fees:*** Green fees are $7 weekdays and $8 weekends. Carts are $7 for nine holes and $14 for 18 holes. Reservations are recommended 24 to 48 hours in advance. This course is available for tournaments. Arrangements must be made through the Cordova Park District.

***Location:*** From Highway 50 in Sacramento, take the Highway 16/Jackson Road exit. Drive five miles to the course. It is between Bradshaw Road and South Watt Avenue.

***Course description:*** Cordova is a flat course with small greens and tough par-3s. The third hole, for instance, is 201 yards in length, and number 18 is 191 yards. The only par-5 is number six. This is the busiest course in the Sacramento area, numbering 120,000 rounds a year, popular because of its rates and short yardage. Dave Keck's 56 is the lowest round ever shot here.

9425 Jackson Road
Sacramento, CA 95826

Pro shop (916) 362-1196

- ✓ **driving range**
- ✓ **practice greens**
- ✓ **power carts**
- ✓ **pull carts**
- ✓ **golf club rental**
- locker rooms
- showers
- executive course
- accommodations
- ✓ **food and beverages**
- ✓ **clubhouse**

**Jim Marta**
Professional

**Stanley Flood**
Superintendent

| Hole | 1 | 2 | 3 | 4 | 5 | 6 | 7 | 8 | 9 | Out | | |
|---|---|---|---|---|---|---|---|---|---|---|---|---|
| BLUE | | | | | | | | | | | BLUE | Rating: |
| | | | | | | | | | | | | Slope: |
| WHITE | 390 | 265 | 201 | 170 | 211 | 471 | 381 | 154 | 389 | 2632 | | |
| Par | 4 | 4 | 3 | 3 | 3 | 5 | 4 | 3 | 4 | 33 | WHITE | Rating: 61.2 |
| Handicap | 7 | 17 | 1 | 13 | 5 | 11 | 9 | 15 | 3 | x | | Slope: 90 |
| RED | 390 | 265 | 214 | 170 | 221 | 471 | 381 | 154 | 389 | 2655 | | |
| Par | 4 | 4 | 4 | 3 | 4 | 5 | 4 | 3 | 4 | 35 | RED | Rating: 64.9 |
| Handicap | 3 | 13 | 17 | 9 | 15 | 7 | 5 | 11 | 1 | x | | Slope: 96 |

| Hole | 10 | 11 | 12 | 13 | 14 | 15 | 16 | 17 | 18 | In | Totals | |
|---|---|---|---|---|---|---|---|---|---|---|---|---|
| BLUE | | | | | | | | | | | BLUE | |
| WHITE | 383 | 178 | 190 | 180 | 407 | 306 | 143 | 177 | 191 | 2157 | WHITE | 4755 |
| Par | 4 | 3 | 3 | 3 | 4 | 4 | 3 | 3 | 3 | 30 | Par | 63 |
| Handicap | 4 | 12 | 8 | 14 | 2 | 18 | 16 | 10 | 6 | x | | |
| RED | 301 | 178 | 190 | 180 | 407 | 306 | 143 | 177 | 191 | 2073 | RED | 4728 |
| Par | 4 | 3 | 3 | 3 | 5 | 4 | 3 | 3 | 3 | 31 | Par | 66 |
| Handicap | 6 | 10 | 4 | 8 | 14 | 18 | 16 | 12 | 2 | x | | |

# BING MALONEY GOLF COURSE

**Course 29**
MAP D2 grid i5

**1952**

PO Box 23031
Sacramento, CA 95823

6801 Freeport Boulevard
Sacramento, CA 95822

Pro shop (916) 428-9401

- ✓ **driving range**
- ✓ **practice greens**
- ✓ **power carts**
- ✓ **pull carts**
- ✓ **golf club rental**
- locker rooms
- showers
- ✓ **executive course**
- accommodations
- ✓ **food and beverages**
- clubhouse

**Tom Doris**
Professional



***Course information:*** This public course has 18 holes and par is 72. The course is 6,281 yards and rated 69.7 from the regular tees. The slope rating is 108. Women's tees are 5,972 yards and rated 72.6. The slope rating is 119. There is also a short executive course that is 1,332 yards and rated 58.0. See card below for yardage and rating information.

***Play policy and fees:*** Green fees are $11.50 weekdays and $14 weekends. Twilight rates are $7 weekdays and $8 weekends after 5 p.m. during the summer season. Carts are $18. Reservations are recommended and there is a $2 reservation fee. This course is available for outside tournaments.

***Location:*** From Sacramento, drive six miles south on Interstate 5. Take the Florin Road exit east. Turn left on Freeport Road and drive toward the Sacramento International Airport. The course is on the right.

***Course description:*** A flat course, Bing Maloney requires accurate tee shots because large trees border each fairway. Site of the Sacramento Regional Four-Ball Championship each year, this heavily used course (upwards of 95,000 rounds a year) has large greens surrounded by bunkers. The most difficult hole without question is number 12, a par-4 measuring 414 yards (a par-5 for women). A huge cottonwood tree stands out like a sore thumb directly in front of the tee, forcing the golfer to (A) bale out right; (B) hook it around the tree and risk going out-of-bounds; or (C) hit a sharp cut shot. Good luck. Bing is a shotmaker's course.

| Hole | 1 | 2 | 3 | 4 | 5 | 6 | 7 | 8 | 9 | Out | BLUE | Rating: 68.5 |
|---|---|---|---|---|---|---|---|---|---|---|---|---|
| BLUE | 392 | 385 | 123 | 355 | 169 | 493 | 400 | 352 | 516 | 3185 | | Slope: 106 |
| WHITE | - | - | - | - | - | - | - | - | - | - | | |
| Par | 4 | 4 | 3 | 4 | 3 | 5 | 4 | 4 | 5 | 36 | WHITE | Rating: -- |
| Handicap | 2 | 6 | 16 | 14 | 18 | 8 | 4 | 12 | 10 | x | | Slope: -- |
| RED | 383 | 380 | 100 | 345 | 157 | 450 | 342 | 349 | 493 | 2999 | | |
| Par | 4 | 4 | 3 | 4 | 3 | 5 | 4 | 4 | 5 | 36 | RED | Rating: 72.6 |
| Handicap | 5 | 3 | 15 | 13 | 17 | 7 | 9 | 11 | 1 | x | | Slope: 121 |

| Hole | 10 | 11 | 12 | 13 | 14 | 15 | 16 | 17 | 18 | In | Totals | |
|---|---|---|---|---|---|---|---|---|---|---|---|---|
| BLUE | 372 | 490 | 414 | 130 | 462 | 379 | 149 | 344 | 356 | 3096 | BLUE | 6281 |
| WHITE | - | - | - | - | - | - | - | - | - | - | WHITE | – |
| Par | 4 | 5 | 4 | 3 | 5 | 4 | 3 | 4 | 4 | 36 | Par | 72 |
| Handicap | 3 | 5 | 1 | 11 | 15 | 9 | 13 | 17 | 7 | x | | |
| RED | 363 | 475 | 413 | 128 | 468 | 295 | 145 | 340 | 346 | 2973 | RED | 5972 |
| Par | 4 | 5 | 5 | 3 | 5 | 4 | 3 | 4 | 4 | 37 | Par | 73 |
| Handicap | 4 | 6 | 12 | 18 | 2 | 14 | 16 | 10 | 8 | x | | |

# VALLEY HI COUNTRY CLUB

**Course 30**
MAP D2 grid i6

***Course information:*** This private course has 18 holes. See card below for yardage and rating information.

***Play policy and fees:*** Reciprocal play is accepted with members of other private clubs. Guest fees are $20 with a member and reciprocal fees are $40. Carts are $17 per cart.

***Location:*** From Sacramento, drive south on Highway 99, take the Elk Grove Boulevard exit west. Drive 3.5 miles until it deadends at Franklin Boulevard. Turn right. The course is on the right.

***Course description:*** Valley Hi's reputation grows with each year as the trees and the course mature. It has three large lakes that seem to crop up everywhere. The toughest holes are number two (434 yards), number 11 (409 yards) and number 15 (412 yards). Those par-4s invariably play into the wind. The greens are bent grass, without much undulation but fairly fast and most difficult to read. Valley Hi holds numerous amateur tournaments for men and women. It will serve as a local qualifying site for the 1993 U.S. Open.

PO Box 850
Elk Grove, CA 95624

9595 Franklin Boulevard
Elk Grove, CA 95624

Pro shop (916) 423-2170
Clubhouse (916) 423-2093

✓ **driving range**
✓ **practice greens**
✓ **power carts**
pull carts
✓ **golf club rental**
✓ **locker rooms**
✓ **showers**
executive course
accommodations
✓ **food and beverages**
✓ **clubhouse**

**Nick West**
Manager

**Jim Collart**
Professional

**Mike Jones**
Superintendent

| Hole | 1 | 2 | 3 | 4 | 5 | 6 | 7 | 8 | 9 | Out | | |
|---|---|---|---|---|---|---|---|---|---|---|---|---|
| BLUE | 366 | 445 | 389 | 488 | 153 | 371 | 194 | 538 | 376 | 3320 | BLUE | Rating: 71.6 |
| WHITE | 358 | 434 | 380 | 478 | 140 | 360 | 183 | 528 | 367 | 3228 | | Slope: 120 |
| Par | 4 | 4 | 4 | 5 | 3 | 4 | 3 | 5 | 4 | 36 | WHITE | Rating: 70.5 |
| Handicap | 9 | 1 | 3 | 13 | 17 | 7 | 15 | 11 | 5 | x | | Slope: 117 |
| RED | 340 | 381 | 337 | 465 | 112 | 344 | 172 | 480 | 328 | 2959 | | |
| Par | 4 | 4 | 4 | 5 | 3 | 4 | 3 | 5 | 4 | 36 | RED | Rating: 73.9 |
| Handicap | 9 | 5 | 11 | 1 | 17 | 7 | 16 | 2 | 13 | x | | Slope: 126 |

| Hole | 10 | 11 | 12 | 13 | 14 | 15 | 16 | 17 | 18 | In | Totals | |
|---|---|---|---|---|---|---|---|---|---|---|---|---|
| BLUE | 334 | 424 | 365 | 566 | 168 | 436 | 185 | 396 | 571 | 3445 | BLUE | 6765 |
| WHITE | 326 | 409 | 352 | 549 | 158 | 412 | 170 | 381 | 558 | 3315 | WHITE | 6543 |
| Par | 4 | 4 | 4 | 5 | 3 | 4 | 3 | 4 | 5 | 36 | Par | 72 |
| Handicap | 14 | 2 | 12 | 10 | 18 | 4 | 16 | 8 | 6 | x | | |
| RED | 311 | 403 | 341 | 468 | 106 | 361 | 147 | 372 | 485 | 2994 | RED | 5953 |
| Par | 4 | 5 | 4 | 5 | 3 | 4 | 3 | 4 | 5 | 37 | Par | 73 |
| Handicap | 12 | 14 | 10 | 3 | 18 | 8 | 15 | 6 | 4 | x | | |

# EMERALD LAKES GOLF CENTRE

**Course 31**
MAP D2 grid j7



**1991**
**Rick Yount**

10651 East Stockton
Boulevard
Elk Grove, CA 95624

Pro shop (916) 685-4653

- ✓ **driving range**
- ✓ **practice greens**
- ✓ **power carts**
- ✓ **pull carts**
- ✓ **golf club rental**
- locker rooms
- showers
- executive course
- accommodations
- ✓ **food and beverages**
- clubhouse

**John Hoag**
Professional

**Larry Feliciano**
Superintendent

***Course information:*** This public course has nine holes. See card below for yardage and rating information.

***Play policy and fees:*** Green fees are $6 for nine holes and $12 for 18 holes weekdays, and $7 for nine holes and $14 for 18 holes weekends. The senior rate is $4 for nine holes weekdays. The rate for juniors holding an etiquette card is $3 for nine holes weekdays. Carts are $8 for nine holes. Reservations are recommended weekday evenings and weekends. There is a $1 reservation fee. This course is available for outside tournaments. The lighted driving range is open summer months until 10 p.m.

***Location:*** From Highway 99 in Elk Grove take the Grant Line Road exit east. Drive south on Stockton Boulevard (frontage road). Stockton Boulevard deadends in the parking lot of the course.

***Course description:*** This course opened in May, 1991. The layout consists of one par-5, four par-4s and four par-3s. The fairways are relatively narrow. There are three lakes which come into play on six holes. The greens, which are the best part of this young course, are undulating and fast. Two of the greens are two-tiered. The signature hole is the par-3 fifth, a 123-yard drive with an island green. Pat Terpak holds the nine-hole course record with a 29. A total of 60,000 rounds are played each year.

| Hole | 1 | 2 | 3 | 4 | 5 | 6 | 7 | 8 | 9 | Out | | |
|---|---|---|---|---|---|---|---|---|---|---|---|---|
| BLUE | - | - | - | - | - | - | - | - | - | - | BLUE | Rating: -- |
| | | | | | | | | | | | | Slope: -- |
| WHITE | 300 | 206 | 129 | 505 | 123 | 353 | 173 | 285 | 342 | 2416 | | |
| Par | 4 | 3 | 3 | 5 | 3 | 4 | 3 | 4 | 4 | 33 | WHITE | Rating: 62.7 |
| Handicap | 9 | 13 | 17 | 1 | 7 | 3 | 15 | 11 | 5 | x | | Slope: 98 |
| RED | 236 | 148 | 100 | 461 | 97 | 333 | 148 | 250 | 244 | 2017 | | |
| Par | 4 | 3 | 3 | 5 | 3 | 4 | 3 | 4 | 4 | 33 | RED | Rating: 61.4 |
| Handicap | 9 | 15 | 17 | 3 | 7 | 1 | 13 | 11 | 5 | x | | Slope: 97 |

| Hole | 10 | 11 | 12 | 13 | 14 | 15 | 16 | 17 | 18 | In | Totals | |
|---|---|---|---|---|---|---|---|---|---|---|---|---|
| BLUE | | | | | | | | | | | BLUE | -- |
| WHITE | 300 | 206 | 129 | 505 | 123 | 353 | 173 | 285 | 342 | 2416 | WHITE | 4832 |
| Par | 4 | 3 | 3 | 5 | 3 | 4 | 3 | 4 | 4 | 33 | Par | 66 |
| Handicap | 10 | 14 | 18 | 2 | 8 | 4 | 16 | 12 | 6 | x | | |
| RED | 236 | 148 | 100 | 461 | 97 | 333 | 148 | 250 | 244 | 2017 | RED | 4034 |
| Par | 4 | 3 | 3 | 5 | 3 | 4 | 3 | 4 | 4 | 33 | Par | 66 |
| Handicap | 10 | 16 | 18 | 6 | 8 | 2 | 14 | 12 | 4 | x | | |

# MAP D3
(14 COURSES)

PAGES.. 158-173

NOR-CAL MAP.....see page 30
adjoining maps
NORTH (C3).........see page 80
EAST (D4) .........see page 174
SOUTH (E4) .......see page 306
WEST (D2) .........see page 126

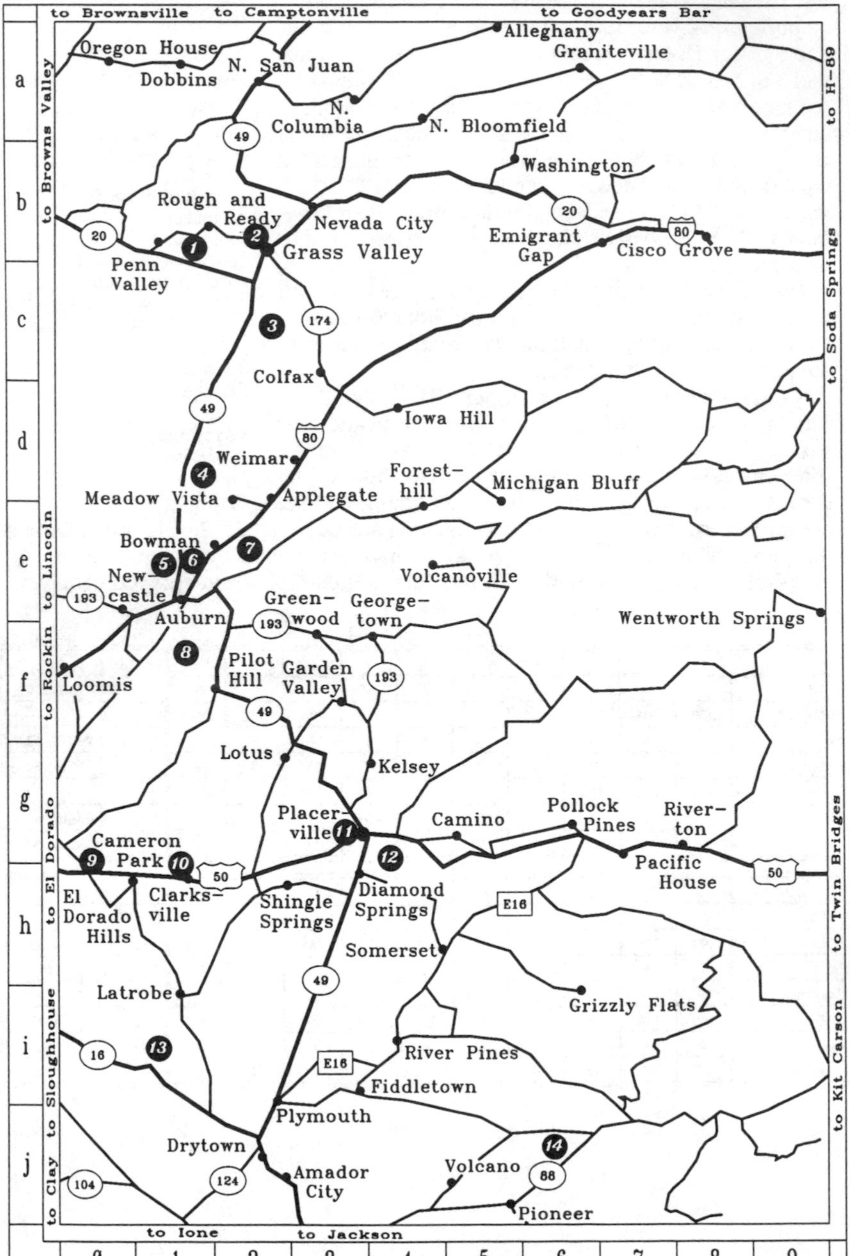

# LAKE WILDWOOD COUNTRY CLUB

**Course 1**
MAP D3 grid b1

*Course information:* This private course has 18 holes and par is 72. The course is 6,500 yards and rated 71.0 from the championship tees, and 6,248 yards and rated 69.7 from the regular tees. The slope ratings are 125 championship and 123 regular. Women's tees are 5,743 yards and rated 73.0 from the forward tees. The slope rating is 130.

*Play policy and fees:* Reciprocal play is accepted with members of other private clubs. Guest fees are $16 for nine holes and $27 for 18 holes when accompanied by a member. Reciprocal fees are $34 for 18 holes. Carts are $10 for nine holes and $15 for 18.

*Location:* From Marysville, drive 30 miles east on Highway 20 to Pleasant Valley Road. Turn left and drive one mile to the four-way stop. Turn right onto Cottontail Way.

*Course description:* This rolling course is lined with mature oaks. Water comes into play on five holes and the back nine is hilly. The most memorable hole is number 12, a par-4 measuring 364 yards from the white tees. It requires a difficult carry over water on the second shot. Perhaps appropriately, there is an old "hanging" tree behind the green. Three of the course's par-5s are reachable in two for good players. Lake Wildwood member Kirk Lyford claims the course record of 62.

11255 Cottontail Way
Penn Valley, CA 95946

Pro shop (916) 432-1163
Clubhouse (916) 432-1152

- ✓ **driving range**
- ✓ **practice greens**
- ✓ **power carts**
- ✓ **pull carts**
- ✓ **golf club rental**
- ✓ **locker rooms**
- ✓ **showers**
- executive course
- accommodations
- ✓ **food and beverages**
- ✓ **clubhouse**

**John Klein**
Professional

**Dave Wilber**
Superintendent

# NEVADA COUNTY COUNTRY CLUB

**Course 2**
MAP D3 grid b2

**1925**

***Course information:*** This semi-private course has nine holes. See card below for yardage and rating information.

***Play policy and fees:*** Outside play is accepted. Green fees are $12 for nine holes and $18 for 18 holes. Carts are $12 for nine holes and $18 for 18 holes seven days a week.

***Location:*** From Highway 49 in Grass Valley, take the Idaho Maryland exit. At the end of the ramp turn left and drive to East Main Street. Turn right and drive to the course on the left.

***Course description:*** This course is relatively wide open except for holes five and six. The greens are small and tricky, invariably breaking toward the nearby (but unseen) hospital. The par-4 eighth hole is far and way the toughest, a 423-yard hole with a tiny green. Some of the older members caddied here in the 1920s, and many of them were miners.

1040 East Main Street
Grass Valley, CA 95945

Pro shop (916) 273-6436

- ✓ **driving range**
- ✓ **practice greens**
- ✓ **power carts**
- ✓ **pull carts**
- ✓ **golf club rental**
- locker rooms
- showers
- executive course
- accommodations
- food and beverages
- ✓ **clubhouse**

**Jeff Fish**
Manager/Professional

**Robert Brueggeman**
Superintendent

| Hole | 1 | 2 | 3 | 4 | 5 | 6 | 7 | 8 | 9 | Out | BLUE | Rating: -- |
|---|---|---|---|---|---|---|---|---|---|---|---|---|
| BLUE | - | - | - | - | - | - | - | - | - | - | | Slope: -- |
| WHITE | 315 | 152 | 324 | 318 | 150 | 309 | 353 | 416 | 357 | 2694 | | |
| Par | 4 | 3 | 4 | 4 | 3 | 4 | 4 | 5 | 4 | 35 | WHITE | Rating:65.6 |
| Handicap | 6 | 18 | 16 | 8 | 10 | 14 | 12 | 2 | 4 | x | | Slope: 110 |
| RED | 318 | 153 | 328 | 328 | 147 | 264 | 370 | 417 | 277 | 2602 | | |
| Par | 4 | 3 | 4 | 4 | 3 | 4 | 4 | 5 | 4 | 35 | RED | Rating: 68.1 |
| Handicap | 5 | 17 | 9 | 7 | 15 | 13 | 3 | 1 | 11 | x | | Slope: 112 |

| Hole | 10 | 11 | 12 | 13 | 14 | 15 | 16 | 17 | 18 | In | Totals | |
|---|---|---|---|---|---|---|---|---|---|---|---|---|
| BLUE | - | - | - | - | - | - | - | - | - | - | BLUE | -- |
| WHITE | 320 | 152 | 330 | 328 | 170 | 309 | 353 | 423 | 384 | 2769 | WHITE | 5463 |
| Par | 4 | 3 | 4 | 4 | 3 | 4 | 4 | 4 | 4 | 34 | Par | 68 |
| Handicap | 5 | 17 | 15 | 7 | 9 | 13 | 11 | 1 | 3 | x | | |
| RED | 299 | 156 | 315 | 316 | 129 | 311 | 356 | 408 | 261 | 2551 | RED | 5153 |
| Par | 4 | 3 | 4 | 4 | 3 | 4 | 4 | 5 | 4 | 35 | Par | 70 |
| Handicap | 8 | 16 | 12 | 6 | 18 | 10 | 4 | 2 | 14 | x | | |

# ALTA SIERRA GOLF AND COUNTRY CLUB

**Course 3**
MAP D3 grid c2

**1965**
**R.E. Baldock**

11897 Tammy Way
Grass Valley, CA 95949

Pro shop (916) 273-2010
Clubhouse (916) 273-2041

✓ **driving range**
✓ **practice greens**
✓ **power carts**
✓ **pull carts**
✓ **golf club rental**
locker rooms
showers
executive course
accommodations
✓ **food and beverages**
✓ **clubhouse**

**Bill Dorville**
Manager

**Jeff Chleboun**
Professional

**Sean O'Brian**
Superintendent

NORTHERN D3

***Course information:*** This semi-private course has 18 holes. See card below for yardage and rating infomation.

***Play policy and fees:*** Outside play is accepted after 11:30 a.m. or noon. Green fees are $25 for 18 holes weekdays and $30 for 18 holes weekends. Green fees for nine holes are $15 weekdays and $20 weekends. Carts are $18 for 18 holes, $10 for nine holes. Reservations are recommended. Reserve tee times one to four weeks in advance. Proper golf attire required.

***Location:*** From Highway 49 between Grass Valley and Auburn, take the Alta Sierra Drive East exit. Drive two miles to the course on Tammy Way. Follow the signs.

***Course description:*** This hilly, scenic course has a links-style layout with big greens. There are no parallel fairways. Deer and other wildlife are plentiful. The 18th hole is a par-5 of 508 yards from the championship tee (493 from the whites). It doglegs right with water on the right and a hazard that interferes with the second shot. Alta Sierra is a well-conditioned course that is particularly challenging for women, who receive minimal break in yardage on several tough holes. Brian Pemberton's 61 is the course record.

| Hole | 1 | 2 | 3 | 4 | 5 | 6 | 7 | 8 | 9 | Out | | |
|---|---|---|---|---|---|---|---|---|---|---|---|---|
| BLUE | 497 | 444 | 184 | 344 | 365 | 503 | 180 | 389 | 402 | 3308 | BLUE | Rating: 71.6 |
| WHITE | 487 | 426 | 176 | 330 | 355 | 498 | 172 | 379 | 394 | 3217 | | Slope: 124 |
| Par | 5 | 4 | 3 | 4 | 4 | 5 | 3 | 4 | 4 | 36 | WHITE | Rating: 70.5 |
| Handicap | 3 | 1 | 15 | 13 | 11 | 9 | 17 | 5 | 7 | x | | Slope: 122 |
| RED | 446 | 371 | 170 | 322 | 326 | 482 | 170 | 369 | 369 | 3025 | | |
| Par | 5 | 4 | 3 | 4 | 4 | 5 | 3 | 4 | 4 | 36 | RED | Rating: 74.6 |
| Handicap | 3 | 1 | 15 | 11 | 13 | 5 | 17 | 9 | 7 | x | | Slope: 128 |

| Hole | 10 | 11 | 12 | 13 | 14 | 15 | 16 | 17 | 18 | In | Totals | |
|---|---|---|---|---|---|---|---|---|---|---|---|---|
| BLUE | 384 | 365 | 142 | 351 | 515 | 204 | 367 | 393 | 508 | 3229 | BLUE | 6537 |
| WHITE | 375 | 355 | 137 | 341 | 505 | 195 | 356 | 370 | 493 | 3127 | WHITE | 6344 |
| Par | 4 | 4 | 3 | 4 | 5 | 3 | 4 | 4 | 5 | 36 | Par | 72 |
| Handicap | 2 | 16 | 18 | 12 | 8 | 14 | 6 | 10 | 4 | x | | |
| RED | 363 | 325 | 135 | 324 | 483 | 164 | 336 | 352 | 477 | 2959 | RED | 5984 |
| Par | 4 | 4 | 3 | 4 | 5 | 3 | 4 | 4 | 5 | 36 | Par | 72 |
| Handicap | 2 | 16 | 18 | 12 | 6 | 14 | 8 | 10 | 4 | x | | |

MAP ON PAGE 158

# LAKE OF THE PINES COUNTRY CLUB

**Course 4**
MAP D3 grid d1

11665 Lakeshore North
Auburn, CA 95603

Pro shop (916) 269-1544
Clubhouse (916) 269-1133

- ✓ **driving range**
- ✓ **practice greens**
- ✓ **power carts**
- pull carts
- ✓ **golf club rental**
- locker rooms
- showers
- executive course
- accommodations
- ✓ **food and beverages**
- ✓ **clubhouse**

**Richard Conroy**
Director/Head Professional

**Craig Thomas**
Superintendent

***Course information:*** This private course has 18 holes and par is 71.The course is 6,150 yards and rated 69.3 from the championship tees, and 5,843 yards and rated 68.2 from the regular tees. The slope ratings are 119 championship and 117 regular. Women's tees are 5,598 yards and rated 71.5. The slope rating is 127.

***Play policy and fees:*** Reciprocal play is accepted with members of other private clubs, otherwise members and guests only. Green fees for reciprocators are $30. Guest fees are $20 weekdays and $25 weekends. Mandatory carts are $15 for nine holes and $20 for 18 holes.

***Location:*** In Auburn, drive north on Highway 49 to Combie Road East. Turn right and drive to Lakeshore North. Turn right and drive to the course.

***Course description:*** This hilly course is about 25 years old. It's narrow with lots of out-of-bounds. Water comes into play on seven holes. The number eight hole can be a headache. At 505 yards, it's a tough par-5. There are hazards everywhere on this hole. Your drive must clear a creek. The fairway doglegs to the left and there are out-of-bounds stakes on both sides. The green is small but thankfully holds well.

# AUBURN VALLEY GOLF AND COUNTRY CLUB

**Course 5**
MAP D3 grid e1

*NORTHERN D3*

***Course information:*** This private course has 18 holes. See card below for yardage and rating information.

***Play policy and fees:*** Reciprocal play is accepted with members of other private clubs. Guest fees are $20 weekdays and $30 weekends. Carts are $16. Reciprocal green fees are $30 weekdays and $50 weekends.

***Location:*** From Auburn, drive 10 miles north on Highway 49. Take the Lone Star Road exit west to Auburn Valley Road.

***Course description:*** This is a long, hilly, challenging course with fast greens and 11 lakes that come into play. This is a beautiful course, set in the foothills with numerous elevated tees that afford excellent views. The fairways are generally narrow and the greens fast. Auburn Valley has one of the most difficult starting holes around; number one measures 410 yards into an elevated green. "It's the best hole on the golf course," head pro Greg French said. "What makes it tough is that it's the first hole." This is one of Northern California's hidden jewels.

8800 Auburn Valley Road
Auburn, CA 95603

Pro shop (916) 269-1837
Clubhouse (916) 269-2775

- ✓ **driving range**
- ✓ **practice greens**
- ✓ **power carts**
- ✓ **pull carts**
- ✓ **golf club rental**
- ✓ **locker rooms**
- ✓ **showers**
- executive course
- accommodations
- ✓ **food and beverages**
- ✓ **clubhouse**

**Nancie Ann Mans**
Manager

**Greg French**
Professional

**Dan Nordell**
Superintendent

| Hole | 1 | 2 | 3 | 4 | 5 | 6 | 7 | 8 | 9 | Out | | |
|---|---|---|---|---|---|---|---|---|---|---|---|---|
| BLUE | 423 | 320 | 507 | 377 | 576 | 143 | 408 | 218 | 357 | 3329 | BLUE | Rating: 72.6 |
| WHITE | 415 | 292 | 483 | 367 | 369 | 134 | 397 | 207 | 326 | 3179 | | Slope: 126 |
| Par | 4 | 4 | 5 | 4 | 5 | 3 | 4 | 3 | 4 | 36 | WHITE | Rating: 71.1 |
| Handicap | 1 | 17 | 11 | 5 | 9 | 15 | 7 | 3 | 13 | x | | Slope: 123 |
| RED | 412 | 265 | 422 | 356 | 548 | 111 | 386 | 102 | 312 | 2914 | | |
| Par | 5 | 4 | 5 | 4 | 5 | 3 | 4 | 3 | 4 | 37 | RED | Rating: 73.0 |
| Handicap | 9 | 13 | 5 | 3 | 1 | 17 | 7 | 15 | 11 | x | | Slope: 130 |

| Hole | 10 | 11 | 12 | 13 | 14 | 15 | 16 | 17 | 18 | In | Totals | |
|---|---|---|---|---|---|---|---|---|---|---|---|---|
| BLUE | 425 | 433 | 190 | 507 | 397 | 435 | 219 | 376 | 508 | 3490 | BLUE | 6819 |
| WHITE | 419 | 424 | 163 | 500 | 364 | 409 | 186 | 367 | 495 | 3327 | WHITE | 6506 |
| Par | 4 | 4 | 3 | 5 | 4 | 4 | 3 | 4 | 5 | 36 | Par | 72 |
| Handicap | 8 | 4 | 10 | 18 | 14 | 2 | 12 | 6 | 16 | x | | |
| RED | 402 | 317 | 142 | 414 | 297 | 393 | 128 | 295 | 475 | 2863 | RED | 5777 |
| Par | 4 | 4 | 3 | 5 | 4 | 4 | 3 | 4 | 5 | 36 | Par | 73 |
| Handicap | 6 | 14 | 16 | 10 | 12 | 4 | 18 | 8 | 2 | x | | |

# BLACK OAK GOLF COURSE

**Course 6**
MAP D3 grid e1

**1984**
**John Walker**

2455 Black Oak Road
Auburn, CA 95603

Pro shop (916) 878-1900
Clubhouse (916) 878-8568

- ✓ **driving range**
- ✓ **practice greens**
- ✓ **power carts**
- ✓ **pull carts**
- ✓ **golf club rental**
- locker rooms
- showers
- executive course
- accommodations
- ✓ **food and beverages**
- ✓ **clubhouse**

**Norman Morrice**
General Manager

**Philip Himes**
Professional

**Matt Dillon**
Superintendent

***Course information:*** This public course has nine holes. See card below for yardage and rating information.

***Play policy and fees:*** Green fees are $9 for nine holes and $15 for 18 holes weekdays, and $10 for nine holes and $18 for 18 holes weekends. Senior and junior rates are $7 for nine holes and $13 for 18 holes weekdays. Reservations are recommended one week in advance. Carts are $9 per nine holes.

***Location:*** From Interstate 80, five miles east of Auburn, take the Dry Creek Road exit west and drive two miles. Turn right on Black Oak Road and follow it to the course.

***Course description:*** This challenging, nine-hole course is one of the toughest of its kind in Northern California. It has an up and down, wide-open terrain with mature oaks, water and sand. The greens are fast and undulating. Every hole is a killer, but a standout is the par-4, 376-yard number two. It plays uphill and is longer than it looks. The green is guarded by a bunker on the right and everything slopes to the left. You can three- or four-putt this hole easily if you're careless. The course is open year-round unless it's rained out or there is snow.

| Hole | 1 | 2 | 3 | 4 | 5 | 6 | 7 | 8 | 9 | Out | BLUE | Rating: 69.8 |
|---|---|---|---|---|---|---|---|---|---|---|---|---|
| BLUE | 348 | 376 | 530 | 134 | 336 | 530 | 202 | 297 | 360 | 3113 | | Slope: -- |
| WHITE | 330 | 355 | 503 | 117 | 318 | 514 | 186 | 277 | 345 | 2945 | | |
| Par | 4 | 4 | 5 | 3 | 4 | 5 | 3 | 4 | 4 | 34 | WHITE | Rating: 69.8 |
| Handicap | 15 | 1 | 7 | 17 | 11 | 9 | 15 | 13 | 3 | x | | Slope: - |
| RED | 314 | 309 | 450 | 109 | 285 | 468 | 141 | 259 | 285 | 2620 | | |
| Par | 4 | 4 | 5 | 3 | 4 | 5 | 3 | 4 | 4 | 36 | RED | Rating: 69.8 |
| Handicap | 15 | 1 | 7 | 17 | 11 | 9 | 5 | 13 | 3 | x | | Slope: -- |

| Hole | 10 | 11 | 12 | 13 | 14 | 15 | 16 | 17 | 18 | In | Totals | |
|---|---|---|---|---|---|---|---|---|---|---|---|---|
| BLUE | 348 | 376 | 530 | 134 | 336 | 530 | 202 | 297 | 360 | 3113 | BLUE | 6226 |
| WHITE | 330 | 355 | 503 | 117 | 318 | 514 | 186 | 277 | 345 | 2945 | WHITE | 5890 |
| Par | 4 | 4 | 5 | 3 | 4 | 5 | 3 | 4 | 4 | 36 | Par | 72 |
| Handicap | 16 | 2 | 8 | 18 | 12 | 10 | 6 | 14 | 4 | x | | |
| RED | 314 | 309 | 450 | 109 | 285 | 468 | 141 | 259 | 285 | 2620 | RED | 5240 |
| Par | 4 | 4 | 5 | 3 | 4 | 5 | 3 | 4 | 4 | 36 | Par | 72 |
| Handicap | 16 | 2 | 8 | 18 | 12 | 10 | 6 | 14 | 4 | x | | |

## ANGUS HILLS GOLF COURSE

**Course 7**
MAP D3 grid e2

**1982**

14520 Musso Road
Auburn, CA 95603

Pro shop (916) 878-7818

- ✓ **driving range**
- ✓ **practice greens**
- power carts
- ✓ **pull carts**
- ✓ **golf club rental**
- locker rooms
- showers
- executive course
- accommodations
- ✓ **food and beverages**
- ✓ **clubhouse**

**Fred Strong**
Manager/Superintendent+

***Course information:*** This public course has nine holes. Par is 58 for 18 holes. The course is 3,066 yards and rated 54.3 from the regular tees. The slope rating is 78. Women's yardage is the same but is not rated.

***Play policy and fees:*** Green fees are $5 weekdays and $6 weekends. Eighteen-hole rates are $8 weekdays, $12 weekends. Reserve a tee time two to three days in advance. Shoes and shirts are required.

***Location:*** From Interstate 80 in Auburn, take the Bell Road exit. Drive to Musso Road and continue to the course.

***Course description:*** This short course has several water hazards and is tougher than it looks. There are twilight tournaments every other Friday from April to November. Angus Hills has small greens that require accurate approaches. There is a moderate amount of water. The toughest hole is number two, a 200-yarder that demands a long iron or wood downhill to a small target. The men's course record is 26 (9 holes), set by Fred Strong in 1989; and the women's course record is 27, set by Aileen Purdy in 1982.

# AUBURN LAKE TRAILS GOLF COURSE

**Course 8**
MAP D3 grid f1

**1970**

PO Box 728
Auburn, CA 95614

2277 Westville Trail
Auburn, CA 95614

Pro shop (916) 885-6526

- driving range
- ✓ **practice greens**
- power carts
- ✓ **pull carts**
- golf club rental
- locker rooms
- showers
- ✓ **executive course**
- accommodations
- food and beverages
- clubhouse

**Bill Nigh**
Superintendent

***Course information:*** This private course has nine holes. See card below for yardage and rating information.

***Play policy and fees:*** Members and guests only. Guest fees are $9 weekdays and $10 weekends per nine holes when accompanied by a property owner.

***Location:*** From Auburn, drive six miles south on Highway 49.

***Course description:*** This course is an executive-type course that is maintained for and by the local property owners. The course is short and hilly with lots of out-of-bounds. There are two par-4s, one of which, number nine, is the most compelling hole. It measures 296 yards with a slight bend to the right around oak trees.

| Hole | 1 | 2 | 3 | 4 | 5 | 6 | 7 | 8 | 9 | Out | BLUE | Rating: -- |
|---|---|---|---|---|---|---|---|---|---|---|---|---|
| BLUE | - | - | - | - | - | - | - | - | - | - | | Slope: -- |
| WHITE | 266 | 111 | 153 | 133 | 70 | 139 | 80 | 104 | 296 | 1352 | | |
| Par | 4 | 3 | 3 | 3 | 3 | 3 | 3 | 3 | 4 | 29 | WHITE | Rating: 52.5 |
| Handicap | 5 | 13 | 1 | 7 | 15 | 11 | 17 | 9 | 3 | x | | Slope: 77 |
| RED | 266 | 111 | 153 | 133 | 70 | 139 | 80 | 104 | 296 | 1352 | | |
| Par | 4 | 3 | 3 | 3 | 3 | 3 | 3 | 3 | 4 | 29 | RED | Rating: 54.8 |
| Handicap | 5 | 13 | 1 | 7 | 15 | 11 | 17 | 9 | 3 | x | | Slope: 80 |

| Hole | 10 | 11 | 12 | 13 | 14 | 15 | 16 | 17 | 18 | In | Totals | |
|---|---|---|---|---|---|---|---|---|---|---|---|---|
| BLUE | - | - | - | - | - | - | - | | - | - | BLUE | -- |
| WHITE | 286 | 99 | 134 | 168 | 131 | 108 | 92 | 104 | 271 | 1393 | WHITE | 2745 |
| Par | 4 | 3 | 3 | 3 | 3 | 3 | 3 | 3 | 4 | 29 | Par | 58 |
| Handicap | 4 | 18 | 10 | 2 | 8 | 14 | 16 | 12 | 6 | x | | |
| RED | 286 | 99 | 134 | 168 | 131 | 108 | 92 | 104 | 271 | 1393 | RED | 2745 |
| Par | 4 | 3 | 3 | 3 | 3 | 3 | 3 | 3 | 4 | 29 | Par | 58 |
| Handicap | 4 | 18 | 10 | 2 | 8 | 14 | 16 | 12 | 6 | x | | |

# EL DORADO HILLS GOLF COURSE

**Course 9**
MAP D3 grid g0

**Robert Trent Jones, Sr.**

3775 El Dorado Hills Blvd.
El Dorado Hills, CA 95630

Pro shop (916) 933-6552

- ✓ **driving range**
- ✓ **practice greens**
- ✓ **power carts**
- ✓ **pull carts**
- ✓ **golf club rental**
- locker rooms
- showers
- executive course
- accommodations
- ✓ **food and beverages**
- clubhouse

**Ted R. Fitzpatrick**
Professional

**Ram Bali**
Superintendent

*Course information:* This public course has 18 holes. See card below for yardage and rating information.

*Play policy and fees:* Green fees are $16 weekdays and $20 weekends. Nine hole rates are $9 weekdays, $12 weekends. Twilight rates are available. Carts are $16 weekdays and $18 weekends. There are monthly fees ranging fron $70 (seniors) to $125.

*Location:* From Sacramento, drive 25 miles east on Highway 50. Take the El Dorado Hills Boulevard exit north and drive to the course, which is on the right.

*Course description:* Although primarily a test for irons, this course does have five par-4s and one par-5. The front nine is hilly. The course is well maintained and has lots of trees and water. The par-3 14th (176 yards) is one of the Sacramento area's finest, a challenging shot into a green fronted by a bunker with water on the left. As the yardages indicate, El Dorado Hills is even more demanding of women golfers.

| Hole | 1 | 2 | 3 | 4 | 5 | 6 | 7 | 8 | 9 | Out | | |
|---|---|---|---|---|---|---|---|---|---|---|---|---|
| BLUE | - | - | - | - | - | - | - | - | - | - | BLUE | Rating: -- |
| | | | | | | | | | | | | Slope: -- |
| WHITE | 310 | 460 | 184 | 174 | 116 | 186 | 155 | 184 | 290 | 2059 | | |
| Par | 4 | 5 | 3 | 3 | 3 | 3 | 3 | 3 | 4 | 31 | WHITE | Rating: 58.3 |
| Handicap | 17 | 11 | 1 | 3 | 13 | 5 | 7 | 9 | 15 | x | | Slope: 93 |
| RED | 310 | 460 | 184 | 174 | 116 | 186 | 155 | 139 | 290 | 2014 | | |
| Par | 4 | 5 | 3 | 3 | 3 | 3 | 3 | 3 | 4 | 31 | RED | Rating: 60.9 |
| Handicap | 3 | 1 | 9 | 7 | 17 | 11 | 13 | 15 | 5 | x | | Slope: 91 |

| Hole | 10 | 11 | 12 | 13 | 14 | 15 | 16 | 17 | 18 | In | Totals | |
|---|---|---|---|---|---|---|---|---|---|---|---|---|
| BLUE | - | - | - | - | - | - | - | - | - | - | BLUE | -- |
| WHITE | 170 | 311 | 120 | 297 | 176 | 189 | 196 | 140 | 286 | 1885 | WHITE | 3944 |
| Par | 3 | 4 | 3 | 4 | 3 | 3 | 3 | 3 | 4 | 30 | Par | 61 |
| Handicap | 8 | 18 | 14 | 10 | 2 | 4 | 6 | 12 | 16 | x | | |
| RED | 170 | 311 | 120 | 297 | 176 | 137 | 196 | 140 | 286 | 1833 | RED | 3847 |
| Par | 3 | 4 | 3 | 4 | 3 | 3 | 3 | 3 | 4 | 30 | Par | 61 |
| Handicap | 12 | 4 | 18 | 2 | 10 | 14 | 6 | 16 | 8 | x | | |

# CAMERON PARK COUNTRY CLUB

**Course 10**
MAP D3 grid g0

**1963**
**Bert Stamps**

3201 Royal Drive
Cameron Park, CA 95682

Pro shop (916) 672-7920
Clubhouse (916) 933-0270

- ✓ **driving range**
- ✓ **practice greens**
- ✓ **power carts**
- ✓ **pull carts**
- ✓ **golf club rental**
- ✓ **locker rooms**
- ✓ **showers**
- executive course
- accommodations
- ✓ **food and beverages**
- ✓ **clubhouse**

**Al Johnson**
Manager

**Steve Frye**
Professional

**Amby Mrozek**
Superintendent

***Course information:*** This private course has 18 holes. See card below for yardage and rating information.

***Play policy and fees:*** Reciprocal play is accepted with members of other private clubs. Green fees for reciprocal players are $50, plus $16 for a cart. Guest fees are $25 weekdays and $30 weekends. Carts are $16.

***Location:*** From Sacramento, drive 30 miles east on Highway 50. Take the Cameron Park Drive exit. Turn left and drive under the overpass. Make the first left (don't get back on the freeway) onto Country Club Drive. Drive about one-half mile, just past the driving range. Make the first right past the driving range (Royal Drive) and drive to the course entrance.

***Course description:*** Cameron Park would be a tough course due to its tightness alone, but the real trick to scoring well is in mastering the greens. They are fast, so fast that some putts simply won't stop short of the hole. The holes of particular note are numbers 14 and 17. The 14th is a par-3 of 210 yards over water, and number 17 is a par-4 measuring 389 yards with out-of-bounds to the right. Bert Stamps, the original designer of Rancho Murieta's North Course, was the architect. He now lives near the course. Kevin Sutherland, an All-American at Fresno State, holds the course record at 62.

| Hole | 1 | 2 | 3 | 4 | 5 | 6 | 7 | 8 | 9 | Out | | |
|---|---|---|---|---|---|---|---|---|---|---|---|---|
| BLUE | 322 | 521 | 176 | 516 | 427 | 379 | 142 | 394 | 346 | 3223 | BLUE | Rating: 71.0 |
| WHITE | 314 | 507 | 156 | 509 | 413 | 369 | 142 | 382 | 337 | 3129 | | Slope: 127 |
| Par | 4 | 5 | 3 | 5 | 4 | 4 | 3 | 4 | 4 | 36 | WHITE | Rating: 70.2 |
| Handicap | 13 | 7 | 15 | 9 | 1 | 3 | 17 | 5 | 11 | x | | Slope: 125 |
| RED | 280 | 494 | 133 | 506 | 415 | 292 | 135 | 326 | 330 | 2911 | | |
| Par | 4 | 5 | 3 | 5 | 5 | 4 | 3 | 4 | 4 | 37 | RED | Rating: 74.1 |
| Handicap | 9 | 1 | 15 | 3 | 13 | 11 | 17 | 7 | 5 | x | | Slope: 134 |

| Hole | 10 | 11 | 12 | 13 | 14 | 15 | 16 | 17 | 18 | In | Totals | |
|---|---|---|---|---|---|---|---|---|---|---|---|---|
| BLUE | 443 | 322 | 128 | 370 | 395 | 504 | 363 | 215 | 481 | 3221 | BLUE | 6444 |
| WHITE | 433 | 315 | 120 | 358 | 389 | 504 | 347 | 204 | 471 | 3141 | WHITE | 6270 |
| Par | 4 | 4 | 3 | 4 | 4 | 5 | 4 | 3 | 5 | 36 | Par | 72 |
| Handicap | 2 | 16 | 18 | 8 | 6 | 12 | 10 | 4 | 14 | x | | |
| RED | 392 | 279 | 107 | 349 | 393 | 494 | 344 | 153 | 461 | 2972 | RED | 5883 |
| Par | 4 | 4 | 3 | 4 | 4 | 5 | 4 | 3 | 5 | 36 | Par | 73 |
| Handicap | 2 | 14 | 18 | 8 | 4 | 12 | 10 | 16 | 6 | x | | |

# COLD SPRINGS GOLF AND COUNTRY CLUB

**Course 11**
MAP D3 grid g3

**1960/1979**

6500 Clubhouse Drive
Placerville, CA 95667

Pro shop (916) 622-4567
Clubhouse (916) 622-9948

- ✓ **driving range**
- ✓ **practice greens**
- ✓ **power carts**
- ✓ **pull carts**
- ✓ **golf club rental**
- ✓ **locker rooms**
- ✓ **showers**
- executive course
- accommodations
- ✓ **food and beverages**
- ✓ **clubhouse**

**Randy Thomas**
Professional

**Robert Leas**
Superintendent

***Course information:*** This private course has 18 holes. See card below for yardage and rating information.

***Play policy and fees:*** Reciprocal play is accepted with members of other private clubs, otherwise members and guests only. The green fees for reciprocal players are $35. Guest fees are $20 weekdays and $25 weekends. Carts are $16.

***Location:*** From Highway 50 in Placerville, take the Placerville Drive/Forni Road exit. Drive over the overpass to the second stop sign. Turn left on Cole Springs Road. Drive three miles and turn left on Richard Avenue, which turns into Clubhouse Drive.

***Course description:*** Weber Creek winds through this course, which is very tight with a preponderance of short, dogleg par-4s. Cold Springs is moderately hilly and has plenty of oaks and pines. The fourth hole (par 4, 402 yards) is a handful. It doglegs right with out-of-bounds right and hardpan left for those driving through the fairway. There is a huge oak on the right side of the green, which slopes severely. The course record is 64 for men, set by Jim Sorum, and Karen Beckman's 77 is the women's record.

| Hole | 1 | 2 | 3 | 4 | 5 | 6 | 7 | 8 | 9 | Out | BLUE | Rating: -- |
|---|---|---|---|---|---|---|---|---|---|---|---|---|
| BLUE | - | - | - | - | - | - | - | - | - | - | | Slope: -- |
| WHITE | 310 | 259 | 271 | 402 | 308 | 462 | 209 | 158 | 545 | 2924 | | |
| Par | 4 | 4 | 4 | 4 | 4 | 5 | 3 | 3 | 5 | 36 | WHITE | Rating: 69.2 |
| Handicap | 5 | 17 | 13 | 1 | 9 | 11 | 7 | 15 | 3 | x | | Slope: -- |
| RED | 276 | 237 | 269 | 362 | 302 | 452 | 182 | 127 | 495 | 2702 | | |
| Par | 4 | 4 | 4 | 4 | 4 | 5 | 3 | 3 | 5 | 36 | RED | Rating: 73.2 |
| Handicap | 9 | 15 | 11 | 5 | 7 | 3 | 13 | 17 | 1 | x | | Slope: -- |

| Hole | 10 | 11 | 12 | 13 | 14 | 15 | 16 | 17 | 18 | In | Totals | |
|---|---|---|---|---|---|---|---|---|---|---|---|---|
| BLUE | - | - | - | - | - | - | - | - | - | - | BLUE | -- |
| WHITE | 377 | 371 | 159 | 413 | 552 | 325 | 442 | 185 | 412 | 3236 | WHITE | 6160 |
| Par | 4 | 4 | 3 | 4 | 5 | 4 | 5 | 3 | 4 | 36 | Par | 72 |
| Handicap | 6 | 12 | 16 | 4 | 8 | 10 | 18 | 14 | 2 | x | | |
| RED | 351 | 359 | 147 | 349 | 459 | 323 | 428 | 124 | 355 | 2895 | RED | 5597 |
| Par | 4 | 4 | 3 | 4 | 5 | 4 | 5 | 3 | 4 | 36 | Par | 72 |
| Handicap | 6 | 10 | 16 | 14 | 2 | 4 | 12 | 18 | 8 | x | | |

# SIERRA GOLF COURSE

**Course 12**
MAP D3 grid g4

**1959**

*Course information:* This public course has nine holes. See card below for yardage and rating information.

*Play policy and fees:* Green fees are $7 for nine holes and $10 for 18 holes on weekdays, and $8 for nine holes and $12 for 18 holes weekends. Junior rate is $5 for nine holes and $6 for 18 holes. Reservations are not required.

*Location:* From Highway 50 in Placerville, take the Main Street exit. Take Cedar Ravine to Country Club Drive and the course. Watch for the airport sign and you'll find the course.

*Course description:* This short course is flat with sloping greens. Oak, pine and cedar trees line the fairways, but there is no water. The eighth hole is a tough green. Most of the regulars at Sierra are seniors.

1822 Country Club Drive
Placerville, CA 95667

Pro shop (916) 622-0760

driving range
✓ **practice greens**
power carts
✓ **pull carts**
golf club rental
locker rooms
showers
executive course
accommodations
✓ **food and beverages**
✓ **clubhouse**

**Dean Peterson,**
Manager/Professional

**Frank Herrera**
Superintendent

| Hole | 1 | 2 | 3 | 4 | 5 | 6 | 7 | 8 | 9 | Out | BLUE | Rating: -- |
|---|---|---|---|---|---|---|---|---|---|---|---|---|
| BLUE | - | - | - | - | - | - | - | - | - | - | | Slope: -- |
| WHITE | 148 | 115 | 248 | 176 | 120 | 213 | 242 | 176 | 236 | 1674 | | |
| Par | 3 | 3 | 4 | 3 | 3 | 4 | 4 | 3 | 4 | 31 | WHITE | Rating: 55.4 |
| Handicap | 5 | 13 | 11 | 3 | 7 | 15 | 17 | 1 | 9 | x | | Slope: 82 |
| RED | 130 | 105 | 232 | 157 | 114 | 207 | 204 | 166 | 213 | 1528 | | |
| Par | 3 | 3 | 4 | 3 | 3 | 4 | 4 | 3 | 4 | 31 | RED | Rating: 58.1 |
| Handicap | 5 | 13 | 15 | 3 | 9 | 11 | 17 | 1 | 7 | x | | Slope: 92 |

| Hole | 10 | 11 | 12 | 13 | 14 | 15 | 16 | 17 | 18 | In | Totals | |
|---|---|---|---|---|---|---|---|---|---|---|---|---|
| BLUE | - | - | - | - | - | - | - | - | - | - | BLUE | -- |
| WHITE | 148 | 115 | 248 | 176 | 120 | 213 | 242 | 176 | 236 | 1674 | WHITE | 3348 |
| Par | 3 | 3 | 4 | 3 | 3 | 4 | 4 | 3 | 4 | 31 | Par | 62 |
| Handicap | 6 | 14 | 12 | 4 | 8 | 16 | 18 | 2 | 10 | x | | |
| RED | 130 | 105 | 232 | 157 | 114 | 207 | 204 | 166 | 213 | 1528 | RED | 3056 |
| Par | 3 | 3 | 4 | 3 | 3 | 4 | 4 | 3 | 4 | 31 | Par | 62 |
| Handicap | 6 | 14 | 16 | 4 | 10 | 12 | 18 | 2 | 8 | x | | |

# RANCHO MURIETA COUNTRY CLUB

**Course 13**
MAP D3 grid i1

**1980**
**Bert Stamps (North)**

**1971**
**Ted Robinson (South)**

14813 Jackson Road
Rancho Murieta, CA 95683

Pro shop (916) 354-2400
Clubhouse (916) 354-3400

- ✓ **driving range**
- ✓ **practice greens**
- ✓ **power carts**
- pull carts
- ✓ **golf club rental**
- ✓ **locker rooms**
- ✓ **showers**
- executive course
- ✓ **accommodations**
- ✓ **food and beverages**
- ✓ **clubhouse**

**Steve Bryant**
Manager

**David Hall**
Professional

**Rich Scholes**
Superintendent

NORTHERN D3

***Course information:*** This private facility has two 18 hole championship golf courses. Par is 72 on both.

The North Course is 6,839 yards and rated 72.8 with a slope of 131 from the championship tees, and 6,335 yards and rated 70.6 with a slope of 126 from the regular tees. Women's tees are 5,607 yards and rated 74.2 with a slope of 136.

The South Course is detailed on the scorecard below.

***Play policy and fees:*** Reciprocal play is accepted with members of other private clubs. Guests fees are $40 and must be invited and accompanied by a member. Reciprocator green fees are $75, including cart. Carts are $22 and mandatory. Reservations are required. Reciprocal guests should have their golf pro call three days in advance. Shirts must have collars and shorts must have a five-inch inseam.

***Location:*** From Sacramento drive east on Highway 50. Take Bradshaw Road exit south. Turn left on Highway 16/Jackson Road to Rancho Murieta. The club entrance is on the left.

***Course description:*** The North Course is generally considered to be the Sacramento area's top layout. The Raley's Senior Gold Rush, a regular stop on the Senior PGA Tour, is held here each fall. It features out-of-bounds on virtually every hole and the gigantic greens are severely undulated. The fourth, 10th, and 18th holes are outstanding par-4s, and the third and 15th holes are rugged par-5s. While overshadowed by its neighbor, the South Course holds its own. Water comes into play on 10 of 18 holes and scoring is almost as difficult on the South Course as it is on the North. Senior pros Simon Holoday, Don Bies and Bob Charles share the competitive North Course record at 65. Dave Sutherland holds the South Course record at 63.

South Course

| Hole | 1 | 2 | 3 | 4 | 5 | 6 | 7 | 8 | 9 | Out | | |
|---|---|---|---|---|---|---|---|---|---|---|---|---|
| BLUE | 395 | 395 | 553 | 182 | 385 | 514 | 190 | 402 | 423 | 3431 | BLUE | Rating: 72.6 |
| WHITE | 375 | 350 | 523 | 157 | 360 | 494 | 156 | 362 | 387 | 3164 | | Slope: 127 |
| Par | 4 | 4 | 5 | 3 | 4 | 5 | 3 | 4 | 4 | 36 | WHITE | Rating: 70.0 |
| Handicap | 7 | 9 | 13 | 17 | 5 | 11 | 15 | 1 | 3 | x | | Slope: 121 |
| RED | 334 | 310 | 445 | 119 | 329 | 434 | 126 | 325 | 325 | 2747 | | |
| Par | 4 | 4 | 5 | 3 | 4 | 5 | 3 | 4 | 4 | 36 | RED | Rating: 71.6 |
| Handicap | 5 | 7 | 3 | 17 | 13 | 1 | 15 | 9 | 11 | x | | Slope: 122 |

| Hole | 10 | 11 | 12 | 13 | 14 | 15 | 16 | 17 | 18 | In | Totals | |
|---|---|---|---|---|---|---|---|---|---|---|---|---|
| BLUE | 201 | 400 | 543 | 404 | 538 | 175 | 386 | 392 | 416 | 3455 | BLUE | 6886 |
| WHITE | 166 | 356 | 513 | 364 | 490 | 150 | 361 | 367 | 376 | 3143 | WHITE | 6307 |
| Par | 3 | 4 | 5 | 4 | 5 | 3 | 4 | 4 | 4 | 36 | Par | 72 |
| Handicap | 10 | 2 | 12 | 8 | 16 | 18 | 14 | 4 | 6 | x | | |
| RED | 140 | 314 | 438 | 312 | 454 | 122 | 325 | 355 | 320 | 2780 | RED | 5527 |
| Par | 3 | 4 | 5 | 4 | 5 | 3 | 4 | 4 | 4 | 36 | Par | 72 |
| Handicap | 16 | 8 | 2 | 14 | 6 | 18 | 10 | 4 | 12 | x | | |

# MACE MEADOW GOLF AND COUNTRY CLUB

**Course 14**
MAP D3 grid j6

**1966**
**Jack Fleming**

26570 Fairway Drive
Pioneer, CA 95666

Pro shop (209) 295-7020
Clubhouse (209) 295-4443

- ✓ **driving range**
- practice greens
- ✓ **power carts**
- ✓ **pull carts**
- ✓ **golf club rental**
- locker rooms
- showers
- executive course
- accommodations
- ✓ **food and beverages**
- ✓ **clubhouse**

**Jack Fox**
Professional

**Larry Anderson**
President

***Course information:*** This semi-private course has 18 holes. See card below for yardage and rating information.

***Play policy and fees:*** Outside play is accepted. Green fees are $14 weekdays and $20 weekends. Carts are $18.

***Location:*** The course is located 18 miles east of Jackson on Highway 88, and five miles east of Pioneer in Buckhorn. In Buckhorn, look for Meadow Drive at the parking lot. Fairway Drive is right there.

***Course description:*** Originally a nine-hole course designed by Jack Fleming, greens superintendent at San Francisco's fabled Olympic Club, Mace Meadow was expanded into 18 holes in 1988 by the club membership. The old and new nines were mixed together. The most picturesque hole on a beautiful course is number one, a par-5 with a red barn and a noisy rooster behind the green.

| Hole | 1 | 2 | 3 | 4 | 5 | 6 | 7 | 8 | 9 | Out | | |
|---|---|---|---|---|---|---|---|---|---|---|---|---|
| BLUE | 508 | 155 | 342 | 184 | 316 | 483 | 334 | 390 | 368 | 3080 | BLUE | Rating: 70.1 |
| WHITE | 491 | 130 | 330 | 158 | 304 | 471 | 327 | 367 | 360 | 2938 | | Slope: 122 |
| Par | 5 | 3 | 4 | 3 | 4 | 5 | 4 | 4 | 4 | 36 | WHITE | Rating: 68.8 |
| Handicap | 3 | 15 | 9 | 17 | 11 | 1 | 5 | 7 | 13 | x | | Slope: 120 |
| RED | 425 | 90 | 280 | 142 | 267 | 421 | 316 | 353 | 352 | 2646 | | |
| Par | 5 | 3 | 4 | 3 | 4 | 5 | 4 | 4 | 4 | 36 | RED | Rating: 70.0 |
| Handicap | 4 | 18 | 12 | 16 | 14 | 2 | 10 | 6 | 8 | x | | Slope: 114 |

| Hole | 10 | 11 | 12 | 13 | 14 | 15 | 16 | 17 | 18 | In | Totals | |
|---|---|---|---|---|---|---|---|---|---|---|---|---|
| BLUE | 357 | 379 | 176 | 361 | 490 | 404 | 332 | 181 | 525 | 3205 | BLUE | 6285 |
| WHITE | 336 | 370 | 165 | 350 | 473 | 382 | 323 | 172 | 501 | 3072 | WHITE | 6010 |
| Par | 4 | 4 | 3 | 4 | 5 | 4 | 4 | 3 | 5 | 36 | Par | 72 |
| Handicap | 14 | 6 | 18 | 8 | 4 | 2 | 12 | 16 | 10 | x | | |
| RED | 294 | 331 | 143 | 321 | 401 | 317 | 307 | 160 | 467 | 2741 | RED | 5387 |
| Par | 4 | 4 | 3 | 4 | 5 | 4 | 4 | 3 | 5 | 36 | Par | 72 |
| Handicap | 13 | 7 | 17 | 5 | 3 | 11 | 9 | 15 | 1 | x | | |

# MAP D4

(10 COURSES)

PAGES.. 174-183

NOR-CAL MAP.....see page 30
adjoining maps
NORTH (C4).........see page 88
EAST............................no map
SOUTH (E4) .......see page 306
WEST (D3) .........see page 158

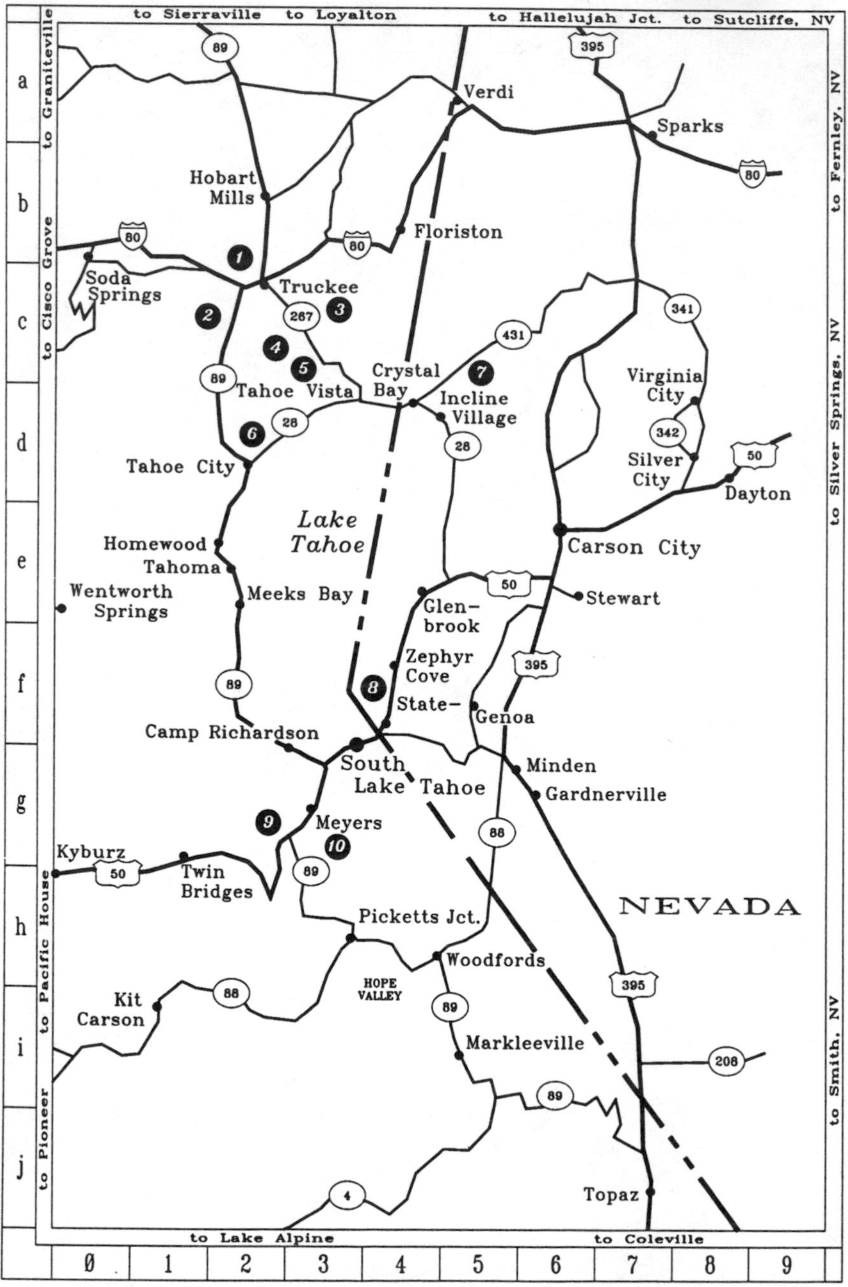

to Sierraville to Loyalton to Hallelujah Jct. to Sutcliffe, NV
to Graniteville
to Cisco Grove
to Fernley, NV
to Silver Springs, NV
to Pioneer to Pacific House
to Smith, NV
to Lake Alpine to Coleville

89 395 Verdi Sparks 80
Hobart Mills
80 80 Floriston
1
Soda Springs
Truckee
2 267 3
4 341
5 431
89 Crystal Bay 7
Tahoe Vista Incline Village Virginia City
28 28 342
6 Silver City 50
Tahoe City Dayton
Lake Tahoe
Homewood Carson City
Tahoma
Wentworth Springs Meeks Bay 50 Stewart
Glenbrook
Zephyr Cove 395
89 8
State- Genoa
Camp Richardson
South Lake Tahoe Minden
Gardnerville
9 Meyers
10 88
Kyburz
50 Twin Bridges 89
NEVADA
Picketts Jct.
Woodfords
HOPE VALLEY
Kit Carson 88 395
89
Markleeville
208
89
4
Topaz

| | 0 | 1 | 2 | 3 | 4 | 5 | 6 | 7 | 8 | 9 |
|---|---|---|---|---|---|---|---|---|---|---|

a b c d e f g h i j

# TAHOE DONNER GOLF AND COUNTRY CLUB

**Course 1**
MAP D4 grid c2

**1976**

*Course information:* This resort course has 18 holes. See card below for yardage and rating information.

*Play policy and fees:* Outside play is accepted. Green fees are $75, including cart. Reservations are required. Call 14 days in advance to reserve a tee time. No rubber spikes may be worn, and only shirts with collars are acceptable. The course is open from mid-April to October and is available for outside tournaments.

*Location:* From Interstate 80 east, take the first Truckee exit (Donner Pass Road). Turn left on Donner Pass Road and drive to the blinking red light. Turn left on Northwoods Boulevard. The course is located three miles from Interstate 80.

*Course description:* A golfer must search high and low to find a tighter golf course than Tahoe Donner. Pines line both sides of all 18 fairways, none of which run parallel to one another. There is no out-of-bounds and the course is walkable despite its 6,600-foot altitude. The 18th hole (401 yards from regular tees, 380 for women) features a vertical drop of 180 feet. Members joke about having to walk single-file down the fairways of this spectacular course.

11509 Northwoods Blvd.
Truckee, CA 96161

12850 Northwoods Blvd.
Truckee, CA 96161

Pro shop (916) 587-9440
Clubhouse (916) 587-9400

- ✓ **driving range**
- ✓ **practice greens**
- ✓ **power carts**
- ✓ **pull carts**
- ✓ **golf club rental**
- ✓ **locker rooms**
- ✓ **showers**
- executive course
- accommodations
- ✓ **food and beverages**
- ✓ **clubhouse**

**William Stewart**
Manager

**Bruce Towle**
Professional

**Joel Blaker**
Superintendent

| Hole | 1 | 2 | 3 | 4 | 5 | 6 | 7 | 8 | 9 | Out | BLUE | Rating: 73.3 |
|---|---|---|---|---|---|---|---|---|---|---|---|---|
| BLUE | 450 | 313 | 439 | 201 | 377 | 357 | 163 | 464 | 550 | 3514 | | Slope: 130 |
| WHITE | 432 | 483 | 430 | 192 | 369 | 349 | 146 | 439 | 532 | 3372 | | |
| Par | 4 | 5 | 4 | 3 | 4 | 4 | 3 | 4 | 5 | 36 | WHITE | Rating: 71.5 |
| Handicap | 1 | 9 | 5 | 11 | 17 | 13 | 15 | 3 | 7 | x | | Slope: 127 |
| RED | 422 | 471 | 359 | 147 | 308 | 340 | 132 | 429 | 453 | 3061 | | |
| Par | 5 | 5 | 4 | 3 | 4 | 4 | 3 | 5 | 5 | 38 | RED | Rating: 73.4 |
| Handicap | 3 | 1 | 5 | 13 | 11 | 7 | 17 | 15 | 9 | x | | Slope: 127 |

| Hole | 10 | 11 | 12 | 13 | 14 | 15 | 16 | 17 | 18 | In | Totals | |
|---|---|---|---|---|---|---|---|---|---|---|---|---|
| BLUE | 424 | 449 | 200 | 320 | 391 | 519 | 453 | 226 | 421 | 3403 | BLUE | 6917 |
| WHITE | 394 | 441 | 152 | 310 | 369 | 503 | 442 | 203 | 401 | 3215 | WHITE | 6587 |
| Par | 4 | 5 | 3 | 4 | 4 | 5 | 4 | 3 | 4 | 36 | Par | 72 |
| Handicap | 4 | 6 | 12 | 18 | 14 | 8 | 2 | 16 | 10 | x | | |
| RED | 349 | 430 | 130 | 301 | 352 | 491 | 356 | 182 | 380 | 2971 | RED | 6032 |
| Par | 4 | 5 | 3 | 4 | 4 | 5 | 4 | 3 | 4 | 36 | Par | 74 |
| Handicap | 4 | 10 | 16 | 12 | 8 | 6 | 14 | 18 | 2 | x | | |

MAP ON PAGE 174

# RESORT AT SQUAW CREEK

**Course 2**
MAP D4 grid c1

***Course information:*** Squaw Creek measures 6,931 yards from the gold tees. Par is 71. The course rating and slope from the gold tees are 72.9 and 140. There are no ratings or handicaps available yet for the women's tees.

***Play policy and fees:*** This 18-hole resort course is open to the public. The 18-hole rate for hotel guests is $79 (includes cart) and $99 for non-guests. Squaw Creek is generally open from May 15 through October 15, depending on the weather.

***Location:*** Take Highway 89 south toward Squaw Valley. Turn right on Squaw Valley Road, then left on Squaw Valley Creek Road.

***Course description:*** The front nine opened in September 1991, followed by the back nine on July 1, 1992. The first four holes are set up against the mountains, after which the course meanders through the meadow in a wetlands setting. Squaw Creek is very tight with precise landing areas and plenty of water. Senior PGA Tour pro George Archer has played it several times and says it makes him think like few courses do. The par-4 17th requires a long drive over wetlands, followed by an equally difficult second shot to a green bordered by Squaw Creek.

**1991**
**Robert Trent Jones, Jr.**

300 Squaw Creek Road
PO Box 3883
Olympic Valley, CA 96146

Clubhouse (916) 583-6300
Reservation (800) 3CREEK3

- ✓ **driving range**
- ✓ **practice greens**
- ✓ **power carts**
- pull carts
- ✓ **golf club rental**
- ✓ **locker rooms**
- showers
- executive course
- ✓ **accommodations**
- ✓ **food and beverages**
- ✓ **clubhouse**

**Mancil Davis**
Director of Golf

**Chip McCraney**
Head Professional

**Carl Rygg**
Superintendent

| Hole | 1 | 2 | 3 | 4 | 5 | 6 | 7 | 8 | 9 | Out | BLUE | Rating: 70.9 |
|---|---|---|---|---|---|---|---|---|---|---|---|---|
| BLUE | 368 | 404 | 205 | 525 | 371 | 176 | 343 | 318 | 488 | 3198 | | Slope: 132 |
| WHITE | 339 | 379 | 181 | 495 | 335 | 153 | 333 | 290 | 467 | 2972 | | |
| Par | 4 | 4 | 3 | 5 | 4 | 3 | 4 | 4 | 5 | 36 | WHITE | Rating: 69.1 |
| Handicap | 7 | 5 | 15 | 1 | 9 | 17 | 11 | 13 | 3 | x | | Slope: 129 |
| RED | 305 | 344 | 150 | 467 | 281 | 124 | 286 | 243 | 436 | 2636 | | |
| Par | 4 | 4 | 3 | 5 | 4 | 3 | 4 | 4 | 5 | 36 | RED | Rating: -- |
| Handicap | - | - | - | - | - | - | - | - | - | x | | Slope: -- |

| Hole | 10 | 11 | 12 | 13 | 14 | 15 | 16 | 17 | 18 | In | Totals | |
|---|---|---|---|---|---|---|---|---|---|---|---|---|
| BLUE | 365 | 387 | 412 | 496 | 202 | 378 | 184 | 407 | 424 | 3255 | BLUE | 6453 |
| WHITE | 325 | 349 | 395 | 480 | 179 | 348 | 166 | 385 | 411 | 3038 | WHITE | 6010 |
| Par | 4 | 4 | 4 | 5 | 3 | 4 | 3 | 4 | 4 | 35 | Par | 71 |
| Handicap | 14 | 10 | 8 | 2 | 16 | 12 | 18 | 6 | 4 | x | | |
| RED | 300 | 213 | 346 | 441 | 126 | 273 | 124 | 312 | 326 | 2461 | RED | 5097 |
| Par | 4 | 4 | 4 | 5 | 3 | 4 | 3 | 4 | 4 | 35 | Par | 71 |
| Handicap | - | - | - | - | - | - | - | - | - | x | | |

# PONDEROSA GOLF CLUB

**Course 3**
MAP D4 grid c3

**1961**

*Course information:* This public course has nine holes. See card below for yardage and rating information.

*Play policy and fees:* Green fees $30 for 18 holes weekdays and weekends. Nine-hole rates are $27. Carts are $12 for nine holes, $20 for 18. It is open from April to October.

*Location:* From Interstate 80 in Truckee, take the Northshore Boulevard (Highway 267) exit south and drive to the course. The course is a 12-minute drive from Lake Tahoe.

*Course description:* Baseball great Jackie Jensen was one of the original investors in this course when it was sold to a privately-owned group. A number of celebrities, including football coaches Bill Walsh and Mike Walsh, play an occasional round here. The first three holes are heavily wooded, after which things open up a bit. The ninth hole is a par-5 covering 492 yards from the white tees that doglegs right. Ponderosa is popular with golfers of all ages and abilites. Check out the beautiful view of Mt. Rose as well.

PO Box 729
Truckee, CA 95734

Hwy. 267 & Reynold Way
Truckee, CA 95734

Pro shop (916) 587-3501

- driving range
- ✓ **practice greens**
- ✓ **power carts**
- ✓ **pull carts**
- ✓ **golf club rental**
- locker rooms
- showers
- executive course
- accommodations
- ✓ **food and beverages**
- clubhouse

**Al Bailey**
General Manager

**Greg Carter**
Professional

**Don Colton**
Superintendent

| Hole | 1 | 2 | 3 | 4 | 5 | 6 | 7 | 8 | 9 | Out | BLUE | Rating: 67.0 |
|---|---|---|---|---|---|---|---|---|---|---|---|---|
| BLUE | 389 | 300 | 145 | 360 | 354 | 174 | 436 | 353 | 507 | 3018 | | Slope: 109 |
| WHITE | 375 | 289 | 135 | 350 | 337 | 163 | 424 | 331 | 492 | 2896 | | |
| Par | 4 | 4 | 3 | 4 | 4 | 3 | 5 | 4 | 5 | 36 | WHITE | Rating: 65.8 |
| Handicap | 5 | 13 | 17 | 3 | 11 | 9 | 7 | 15 | 1 | x | | Slope: 106 |
| RED | 309 | 266 | 118 | 327 | 313 | 134 | 347 | 281 | 461 | 2556 | | |
| Par | 4 | 4 | 3 | 4 | 4 | 3 | 5 | 4 | 5 | 36 | RED | Rating: 68.2 |
| Handicap | 5 | 13 | 17 | 3 | 11 | 9 | 7 | 15 | 1 | x | | Slope: 108 |

| Hole | 10 | 11 | 12 | 13 | 14 | 15 | 16 | 17 | 18 | In | Totals | |
|---|---|---|---|---|---|---|---|---|---|---|---|---|
| BLUE | 389 | 300 | 145 | 360 | 354 | 174 | 436 | 353 | 507 | 3018 | BLUE | 6036 |
| WHITE | 375 | 289 | 135 | 350 | 337 | 163 | 424 | 331 | 492 | 2896 | WHITE | 5792 |
| Par | 4 | 4 | 3 | 4 | 4 | 3 | 5 | 4 | 5 | 36 | Par | 72 |
| Handicap | 6 | 14 | 18 | 4 | 12 | 10 | 8 | 16 | 2 | x | | |
| RED | 309 | 266 | 118 | 327 | 313 | 134 | 347 | 281 | 461 | 2556 | RED | 5112 |
| Par | 4 | 4 | 3 | 4 | 4 | 3 | 5 | 4 | 5 | 36 | Par | 72 |
| Handicap | 5 | 13 | 17 | 3 | 11 | 9 | 7 | 15 | 1 | x | | |

# OLD BROCKWAY GOLF COURSE

**Course 4**
MAP D4 grid c3

**1924**

***Course information:*** This resort course has nine holes. Par is 70 for 18 holes. The course is 6,474 yards and rated 71.1 from the championship tees, and 6,076 yards and rated 69.8 from the regular tees (18 holes). The slope ratings are 116 championship and 113 regular. Women's tees are 5,596 yards and rated 66.9. The slope rating is 113.

***Play policy and fees:*** Green fees are $22 for nine holes and $32 for 18 holes. Off-season rates are $20 and $28. Carts are $14 for nine and $21 for 18 holes. Reservations are taken any time. The course is open from about April 15 to November 1.

***Location:*** This course is located on the north shore of Lake Tahoe where Highway 28 (North Lake Boulevard) and Highway 267 intersect.

***Course description:*** This scenic mountain course, flanked by trees, is tight with narrow fairways and small greens. The most notable hole is the seventh, a par-5 of 555 yards. The course was originally known as Woodvista.

PO Box 1269
Kings Beach, CA 95719

7900 North Lake Boulevard
Kings Beach, CA 95719

Pro shop (916) 546-9909

- ✓ **driving range**
- ✓ **practice greens**
- ✓ **power carts**
- ✓ **pull carts**
- ✓ **golf club rental**
- locker rooms
- showers
- executive course
- accommodations
- ✓ **food and beverages**
- clubhouse

**Gary Cursio**
Manager

**Garrett Good**
Professional

**Dave Laurie**
Superintendent

# NORTHSTAR-AT-TAHOE GOLF COURSE

Course 5
MAP D4 grid c3

**1975**
**Robert Muir Graves**

PO Box 129
Truckee, CA 96160

Basque Drive
Truckee, CA 96160

Pro shop (916) 562-2490
Office (916) 562-1010
Clubhouse (916) 562-2460

- ✓ **driving range**
- ✓ **practice greens**
- ✓ **power carts**
- pull carts
- ✓ **golf club rental**
- ✓ **locker rooms**
- ✓ **showers**
- executive course
- ✓ **accommodations**
- ✓ **food and beverages**
- ✓ **clubhouse**

**Bill Jensen**
General Manager

**Jim Anderson**
Professional

NORTHERN D4

***Course information:*** This resort course has 18 holes and par is 72. The course is 6,897 yards and rated 72.0 from the tournament tees, and 6,337 yards and rated 69.3 from the championship tees, and 6,015 yards and rated 67.4 from the regular tees. The slope ratings are 135 tournament, 130 championship and 125 regular. Women's tees are 5,470 yards and rated 71.2. The slope rating is 134 regular.

***Play policy and fees:*** Green fees are $65, cart included. Carts are mandatory until after 12:30 p.m. Twilight fees were $27 in 1992, but will go up in 1993. Reservations are recommended up to 21 days in advance. This course is open from May to October 30, depending on the weather.

***Location:*** In Truckee, drive six miles south on Highway 267. Exit at Northstar Drive. Turn right on Basque Drive and follow it to the clubhouse.

***Course description:*** The difference between the two nines is night and day, or open tee shots and tree-lined fairways. The front side is set in a meadow with few trees; the back nine is extremely tight and demanding. Water comes into play on 14 holes. The 15th hole (par-3, 180 yards from back tees) features a 120-foot drop to a green that looks no bigger than a postage stamp. Among the celebrities who have played this interesting course are Bill Murray, Bobby Riggs and Bill Walsh. Former U.S. Women's champ Susie Berning once lost eight balls on the back nine.

# TAHOE CITY GOLF AND COUNTRY CLUB

**Course 6**
MAP D4 grid d2

**1917**
**May Dunn**

PO Box 226
251 North Lake Boulevard
Tahoe City, CA 95730

Pro shop (916) 583-1516

- ✓ **driving range**
- ✓ **practice greens**
- ✓ **power carts**
- ✓ **pull carts**
- ✓ **golf club rental**
- locker rooms
- showers
- executive course
- accommodations
- ✓ **food and beverages**
- ✓ **clubhouse**

**Bobby Bonino**
Manager

**Don Hay**
Professional

**Brad Bonino**
Superintendent

***Course information:*** This public course has nine holes. Par is 66 for 18 holes. The course is 5,261 yards and rated 63.4 from the regular tees (18 holes). The slope rating is 108. Women's tees are 4,806 yards and rated 65.7 from the regular tees. The slope rating is 105.

***Play policy and fees:*** Green fees are $20 for nine holes and $30 for 18 holes. Carts are $13 for nine holes and $20 for 18 holes. Reservations recommended up to two weeks in advance. The course is open from April to November, depending on the weather.

***Location:*** This course is located near the intersection of Highway 89 and Highway 28 in Tahoe City. At the junction, turn onto Highway 28 (North Lake Boulevard) and follow it to the course.

***Course description:*** This layout has the rare distinction of being designed by a woman. It is the oldest course on Lake Tahoe. Offering great views of Lake Tahoe, Tahoe City Golf and Country Club is a scenic mountain course lined with pine, fir and cedar. The greens are well maintained and the fairways are tight. Among the luminaries who have played here are Bob Hope, Bing Crosby and Frank Sinatra.

# INCLINE VILLAGE GOLF COURSE

**Course 7**
MAP D4 grid d5

**1964**
**Robert Trent Jones, Sr.**

PO Box 7590
Incline Village, NV 89452

Information (702) 832-1143
Clubhouse (702) 832-1144

- ✓ **driving range**
- ✓ **practice greens**
- ✓ **power carts**
- ✓ **pull carts**
- ✓ **golf club rental**
- locker rooms
- showers
- ✓ **executive course**
- accommodations
- ✓ **food and beverages**
- ✓ **clubhouse**

**John Hughes**
Director of Golf

**Mike Hair**
Superintendent

***Course information:*** This semi-private course has 18 holes. Par is 72. The course is 6,910 yards and rated 72.6 from the blue tees, with a 129 slope, and 6,446 yards and rated 70.5 from the white tees, with a 124 slope. Forward tees are 5,350 yards with a 70.3 rating and a slope of 126.

***Play policy and fees:*** The course is open from May through mid-October, dependent on the weather. Green fees are $85 weekdays and weekends all season. Carts are included. No tennis shorts, cut-offs, tank tops or T shirts allowed. It gets very busy mid-season, so reservations are strongly encouraged.

***Location:*** Located in Nevada just five miles across the California border, the course can be reached by following Highway 267 to Lake Tahoe. Turn left onto Highway 28 and go six miles into Incline Village.

***Course description:*** This very hilly mountain course is cut out of the Sierras and runs through pine tree-laden terrain. A creek runs through a number of holes. Hole number 16 is par-4, 356 yards from the white tees, and offers a spectacular view of Lake Tahoe.

# EDGEWOOD TAHOE GOLF COURSE

**Course 8**
MAP D4 grid f3

Lake Parkway Drive
and Hwy 50
Stateline, NV 89449

Pro shop (702) 588-3566

- ✓ **driving range**
- ✓ **practice greens**
- ✓ **power carts**
- pull carts
- ✓ **golf club rental**
- ✓ **locker rooms**
- ✓ **showers**
- executive course
- accommodations
- ✓ **food and beverages**
- ✓ **clubhouse**

**Lou Eiguren**
Professional

**Steve Seibel**
Superintendent

***Course information:*** This public course has 18 holes and par is 72. The course is 7,491 yards and rated 76.0 with a slope of 139 from the gold tees. See card below for addtional yardage and rating information.

***Play policy and fees:*** Green fees are $125, including cart.

***Location:*** From Highway 50 in South Lake Tahoe, take the Lake Parkway Drive exit north and drive to the course.

***Course description:*** Edgewood, site of the 1985 U.S. Senior Open won by Miller Barber, is rated among the nation's top 100 courses by *Golf Digest*. Situated at 6,200 feet with breathtaking views of Lake Tahoe on several holes, it requires accurate approach shots and an ability to putt undulated, fast greens. Some holes are wide-open off the tee; others, such as the beautiful par-5 16th, require length and precision. The 17th and 18th holes border the lake. All of the par-3s—particularly number 12, which measures 167 yards (white tees) over a pond to a narrow green—are outstanding. The course is actually in Nevada, though the state line is no more than a few yards from the eighth green.

| Hole | 1 | 2 | 3 | 4 | 5 | 6 | 7 | 8 | 9 | Out | | |
|---|---|---|---|---|---|---|---|---|---|---|---|---|
| BLUE | 414 | 400 | 563 | 552 | 178 | 405 | 154 | 416 | 434 | 3516 | BLUE | Rating: 72.7 |
| WHITE | 399 | 383 | 555 | 523 | 139 | 394 | 144 | 370 | 416 | 3343 | | Slope: 133 |
| Par | 4 | 4 | 5 | 5 | 3 | 4 | 3 | 4 | 4 | 36 | WHITE | Rating: 70.8 |
| Handicap | 15 | 9 | 1 | 7 | 11 | 5 | 17 | 13 | 3 | x | | Slope: 128 |
| RED | 383 | 366 | 501 | 411 | 102 | 350 | 112 | 312 | 398 | 2935 | | |
| Par | 4 | 4 | 5 | 5 | 3 | 4 | 3 | 4 | 4 | 36 | RED | Rating: 71.5 |
| Handicap | 7 | 5 | 11 | 13 | 17 | 1 | 15 | 9 | 3 | x | | Slope: 130 |

| Hole | 10 | 11 | 12 | 13 | 14 | 15 | 16 | 17 | 18 | In | Totals | |
|---|---|---|---|---|---|---|---|---|---|---|---|---|
| BLUE | 415 | 374 | 192 | 421 | 407 | 363 | 545 | 169 | 558 | 3444 | BLUE | 6960 |
| WHITE | 401 | 357 | 167 | 383 | 388 | 340 | 532 | 141 | 492 | 3201 | WHITE | 6544 |
| Par | 4 | 4 | 3 | 4 | 4 | 4 | 5 | 3 | 5 | 36 | Par | 72 |
| Handicap | 6 | 12 | 10 | 2 | 4 | 16 | 8 | 18 | 14 | x | | |
| RED | 386 | 312 | 126 | 339 | 333 | 313 | 452 | 108 | 445 | 2814 | RED | 5749 |
| Par | 4 | 4 | 3 | 4 | 4 | 4 | 5 | 3 | 5 | 36 | Par | 72 |
| Handicap | 4 | 14 | 12 | 2 | 8 | 16 | 6 | 18 | 10 | x | | |

# LAKE TAHOE GOLF COURSE AND COUNTRY CLUB

**Course 9**
MAP D4 grid g2

PO Box 10406
S. Lake Tahoe, CA 95618

Highway 50 West
S. Lake Tahoe, CA 96150

Pro shop (916) 577-0788

- ✓ **driving range**
- ✓ **practice greens**
- ✓ **power carts**
- ✓ **pull carts**
- ✓ **golf club rental**
- locker rooms
- showers
- executive course
- accommodations
- ✓ **food and beverages**
- ✓ **clubhouse**

**Dave Rowe**
Manager

**Russell Lee**
Professional

**John Stanowski**
Superintendent

***Course information:*** This public course has 18 holes. See card below for yardage and rating information. The course is open from mid-April to mid-October. It is available for outside tournaments.

***Play policy and fees:*** Green fees are $30. Carts are $12. Twilight rates are also available.

***Location:*** This course is located on Highway 50 between South Lake Tahoe and Meyers. Reservations are recommended up to 30 days with a major credit card.

***Course description:*** The Truckee River runs through this scenic course. With the river and five ponds, water comes into play on 16 holes. The greens are smooth and true, particularly in late summer and early fall. The front nine is relatively wide open, though water comes into play on six holes. The back nine is the strength of the course, beginning with a tee shot against the mountain backdrop on number 10. The 14th, 15th, 16th, and 17th holes are a wonderful series of tight, scenic holes alongside the river. Lake Tahoe Golf Course plays quite a bit shorter than the yardage due to the 6,200-foot altitude.

| Hole | 1 | 2 | 3 | 4 | 5 | 6 | 7 | 8 | 9 | Out | BLUE | Rating: 70.6 |
|---|---|---|---|---|---|---|---|---|---|---|---|---|
| BLUE | 505 | 202 | 410 | 417 | 409 | 186 | 364 | 414 | 589 | 3496 | | Slope: 117 |
| WHITE | 495 | 158 | 362 | 377 | 362 | 154 | 338 | 384 | 515 | 3145 | | |
| Par | 5 | 3 | 4 | 4 | 4 | 3 | 4 | 4 | 5 | 36 | WHITE | Rating: 67.9 |
| Handicap | 10 | 12 | 14 | 4 | 2 | 16 | 18 | 8 | 6 | x | | Slope: 110 |
| RED | 485 | 154 | 356 | 362 | 350 | 120 | 300 | 376 | 433 | 2936 | | |
| Par | 5 | 3 | 4 | 4 | 4 | 3 | 4 | 4 | 5 | 36 | RED | Rating: 70.1 |
| Handicap | 1 | 17 | 9 | 5 | 11 | 15 | 13 | 7 | 3 | x | | Slope: 115 |

| Hole | 10 | 11 | 12 | 13 | 14 | 15 | 16 | 17 | 18 | In | Totals | |
|---|---|---|---|---|---|---|---|---|---|---|---|---|
| BLUE | 427 | 208 | 393 | 447 | 379 | 280 | 357 | 160 | 560 | 3211 | BLUE | 6707 |
| WHITE | 406 | 182 | 375 | 427 | 363 | 270 | 351 | 123 | 527 | 3024 | WHITE | 6169 |
| Par | 4 | 3 | 4 | 4 | 4 | 4 | 4 | 3 | 5 | 35 | Par | 71 |
| Handicap | 3 | 13 | 5 | 1 | 7 | 17 | 11 | 15 | 9 | x | | |
| RED | 285 | 143 | 355 | 415 | 353 | 269 | 341 | 101 | 489 | 2751 | RED | 5687 |
| Par | 4 | 3 | 4 | 5 | 4 | 4 | 4 | 3 | 5 | 36 | Par | 72 |
| Handicap | 12 | 18 | 6 | 14 | 8 | 10 | 4 | 16 | 2 | x | | |

# TAHOE PARADISE GOLF COURSE

**Course 10**
MAP D4 grid g3

*Course information:* This public course has 18 holes and par is 66. The course is 4,021 yards and rated 59.9 from the regular tees. The slope rating is 94. Women's tees are 3,886 and rated 61.7. The slope rating is 96.

*Play policy and fees:* Green fees were $14 for nine holes and $22 for 18 holes any day of the week but will go up in 1993. Twilight rates are available. Carts are $11.50 for ninc holes and $18 for 18 holes. Reservations recommended two to three days in advance. This course is available for tournaments.

*Location:* This course is located in Meyers on Highway 50, three miles south of the Lake Tahoe Airport.

*Course description:* This valley course has hilly, rolling terrain with narrow, tree-lined fairways. The greens are small and well maintained. There are very few bunkers on this short course.

PO Box 11074
Tahoe Paradise, CA 95708

3021 Highway 50
Meyers, CA 95708

Pro shop (916) 577-2121
Clubhouse (916) 577-2233

- ✓ **driving range**
- ✓ **practice greens**
- ✓ **power carts**
- ✓ **pull carts**
- ✓ **golf club rental**
- locker rooms
- showers
- ✓ **executive course**
- accommodations
- ✓ **food and beverages**
- ✓ **clubhouse**

**Dave Beeman**
Manager/Professional/
Superintendent

# MAP E1
(90 COURSES)

PAGES.. 184-267

NOR-CAL MAP.....see page 30
adjoining maps
NORTH (D1).........see page 94
EAST (E2)...........see page 268
SOUTH (F1) .......see page 316
WEST ............................no map

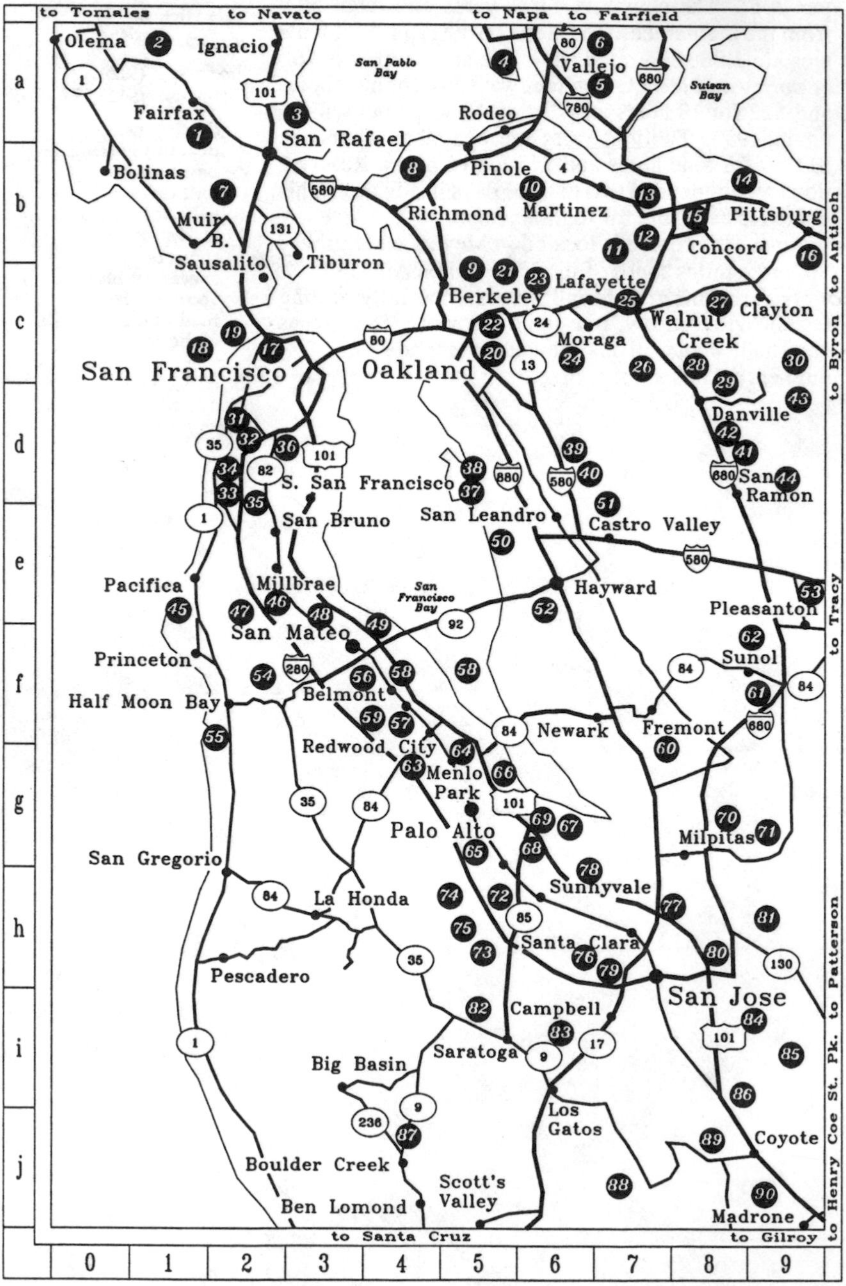

to Tomales
to Navato
to Napa
to Fairfield
to Byron to Antioch
to Tracy
to Henry Coe St. Pk. to Patterson
to Santa Cruz
to Gilroy

a b c d e f g h i j
0 1 2 3 4 5 6 7 8 9

Olema
Ignacio
San Pablo Bay
Vallejo
Suisun Bay
Fairfax
Rodeo
San Rafael
Bolinas
Pinole
Richmond
Martinez
Pittsburg
Muir B.
Concord
Sausalito
Tiburon
Berkeley
Lafayette
Walnut Creek
Clayton
Moraga
San Francisco
Oakland
Danville
S. San Francisco
San Ramon
San Bruno
San Leandro
Castro Valley
Pacifica
Millbrae
San Francisco Bay
Hayward
Pleasanton
San Mateo
Princeton
Sunol
Half Moon Bay
Belmont
Newark
Fremont
Redwood City
Menlo Park
Palo Alto
Milpitas
San Gregorio
Sunnyvale
La Honda
Santa Clara
Pescadero
San Jose
Campbell
Saratoga
Big Basin
Los Gatos
Coyote
Boulder Creek
Scott's Valley
Ben Lomond
Madrone

# MEADOW CLUB

**Course 1**
MAP E1 grid a1

*NORTHERN E1*

***Course information:*** This private course has 18 holes. See card below for yardage and rating information.

***Play policy and fees:*** Limited reciprocal play is accepted with members of other private clubs. Reciprocal fees are $75 with a mandatory $30 cart fee. Guest fees are $40 on weekdays and $45 on weekends when accompanied by a member. Carts are $22.

***Location:*** From Highway 101, take the Sir Francis Drake Boulevard exit west (toward Fairfax). Turn left on Bolinas Road and follow it to the course.

***Course description:*** This is a tight course nestled in the foothills of Mount Tamalpais; it's built on light rolling terrain that used to be on Marin County Water District property. All the bunkers have been re-done, and the greens are tricky. Five par-4s over 400 yards make the course. The par-4 333-yard 16th requires tight shot placement with a creek down the right side, willow trees and a two-tiered green, which is heavily bunkered. Huey Lewis is a member here. Former club pro Ray Leach shot the course record, a 60. A total of 39,000 rounds are played here per year.

**1926**
**Alister MacKenzie**

1001 Bolinas Road
Fairfax, CA 94930

Pro shop (415) 456-9393
Clubhouse (415) 453-3274

- ✓ **driving range**
- ✓ **practice greens**
- ✓ **power carts**
- ✓ **pull carts**
- ✓ **golf club rental**
- ✓ **locker rooms**
- ✓ **showers**
- executive course
- accommodations
- ✓ **food and beverages**
- ✓ **clubhouse**

**Steven Snyder**
Professional

**Dave Sexton**
Superintendent

| Hole | 1 | 2 | 3 | 4 | 5 | 6 | 7 | 8 | 9 | Out | | |
|---|---|---|---|---|---|---|---|---|---|---|---|---|
| BLUE | 494 | 444 | 382 | 379 | 202 | 410 | 416 | 159 | 450 | 3336 | BLUE | Rating: 71.2 |
| WHITE | 482 | 424 | 369 | 365 | 172 | 397 | 404 | 146 | 434 | 3193 | | Slope: 125 |
| Par | 5 | 4 | 4 | 4 | 3 | 4 | 4 | 3 | 4 | 35 | WHITE | Rating: 70.1 |
| Handicap | 15 | 5 | 9 | 11 | 13 | 1 | 7 | 17 | 3 | x | | Slope: 122 |
| RED | 481 | 420 | 361 | 356 | 150 | 349 | 345 | 141 | 373 | 2976 | | |
| Par | 5 | 5 | 4 | 4 | 3 | 4 | 4 | 3 | 4 | 36 | RED | Rating: 74.2 |
| Handicap | 5 | 13 | 1 | 11 | 15 | 7 | 9 | 17 | 3 | x | | Slope: 134 |

| Hole | 10 | 11 | 12 | 13 | 14 | 15 | 16 | 17 | 18 | In | Totals | |
|---|---|---|---|---|---|---|---|---|---|---|---|---|
| BLUE | 378 | 153 | 389 | 524 | 203 | 502 | 333 | 415 | 363 | 3260 | BLUE | 6596 |
| WHITE | 347 | 144 | 360 | 505 | 171 | 494 | 311 | 399 | 347 | 3078 | WHITE | 6271 |
| Par | 4 | 3 | 4 | 5 | 3 | 5 | 4 | 4 | 4 | 36 | Par | 71 |
| Handicap | 4 | 18 | 14 | 10 | 8 | 6 | 16 | 2 | 12 | x | | |
| RED | 345 | 139 | 349 | 485 | 132 | 488 | 293 | 393 | 342 | 2966 | RED | 5942 |
| Par | 4 | 3 | 4 | 5 | 3 | 5 | 4 | 5 | 4 | 37 | Par | 73 |
| Handicap | 8 | 18 | 12 | 4 | 16 | 2 | 10 | 14 | 6 | x | | |

# SAN GERONIMO VALLEY GOLF COURSE

**Course 2**
MAP E1 grid a1

**1965**
**A. Vernon Macan**

*Course information:* This semi-private course has 18 holes. See card below for yardage and rating information.

*Play policy and fees:* Green fees before 2 p.m. are $35 Monday through Thursday, $40 Fridays and $45 weekends. Call for twilight hour rates. Carts are $20. Reservations are recommended one week in advance.

*Location:* Driving on Highway 101 south of San Rafael, take the San Anselmo exit to Sir Francis Drake Boulevard and drive 15 miles west to the course.

*Course description:* A lot of work was put into the course three years ago. Renovations include a new irrigation system, re-contoured greens, and the addition of 50 bunkers and seven lakes. The greens are tough and there are a few blind holes. The 400-yard sixth requires a 210-yard carry off the tee. Trees and a creek guard the right side. It plays into a prevailing wind. The 11th hole is one of the toughest holes in the area. It's 420 yards, and the tee shot has to be left-center to open up an approach shot to the green, which is guarded on the right and front by a creek and trees. The 358-yard 16th gets to be a challenge when the pin is tucked left, behind a hazard.

PO Box 130
San Geronimo, CA 94963

5800 Sir Francis Drake Blvd.
San Geronimo, CA 94963

Pro shop (415) 488-4030
Clubhouse (415) 488-9849

- driving range
- ✓ **practice greens**
- ✓ **power carts**
- pull carts
- ✓ **golf club rental**
- locker rooms
- showers
- executive course
- accommodations
- ✓ **food and beverages**
- ✓ **clubhouse**

**Doug Talley**
Professional

**Dave Michael**
Manager

**David Michael**
Superintendent

| Hole | 1 | 2 | 3 | 4 | 5 | 6 | 7 | 8 | 9 | Out | BLUE | Rating: 72.0 |
|---|---|---|---|---|---|---|---|---|---|---|---|---|
| BLUE | 387 | 482 | 190 | 515 | 450 | 394 | 190 | 374 | 357 | 3339 | | Slope: 125 |
| WHITE | 372 | 473 | 182 | 502 | 437 | 374 | 174 | 344 | 327 | 3185 | | |
| Par | 4 | 5 | 3 | 5 | 4 | 4 | 3 | 4 | 4 | 36 | WHITE | Rating: 70.7 |
| Handicap | 5 | 17 | 11 | 13 | 1 | 3 | 9 | 7 | 15 | x | | Slope: 122 |
| RED | 345 | 456 | 172 | 491 | 389 | 319 | 155 | 306 | 260 | 2893 | | |
| Par | 4 | 5 | 3 | 5 | 5 | 4 | 3 | 4 | 4 | 37 | RED | Rating: 73.4 |
| Handicap | 9 | 3 | 15 | 1 | 5 | 11 | 17 | 7 | 13 | x | | Slope: 126 |

| Hole | 10 | 11 | 12 | 13 | 14 | 15 | 16 | 17 | 18 | In | Totals | |
|---|---|---|---|---|---|---|---|---|---|---|---|---|
| BLUE | 516 | 421 | 415 | 150 | 397 | 220 | 358 | 485 | 406 | 3368 | BLUE | 6707 |
| WHITE | 490 | 401 | 402 | 136 | 388 | 184 | 347 | 476 | 367 | 3191 | WHITE | 6376 |
| Par | 5 | 4 | 4 | 3 | 4 | 3 | 4 | 5 | 4 | 36 | Par | 72 |
| Handicap | 14 | 2 | 8 | 18 | 4 | 10 | 12 | 16 | 6 | x | | |
| RED | 336 | 355 | 393 | 116 | 289 | 163 | 327 | 467 | 349 | 2795 | RED | 5688 |
| Par | 4 | 4 | 5 | 3 | 4 | 3 | 4 | 5 | 4 | 36 | Par | 73 |
| Handicap | 10 | 4 | 8 | 18 | 12 | 16 | 14 | 2 | 6 | x | | |

# PEACOCK GAP GOLF AND COUNTRY CLUB





**1959**

333 Biscayne Drive
San Rafael, CA 94901

Pro shop (415) 453-4940

- ✓ **driving range**
- ✓ **practice greens**
- ✓ **power carts**
- ✓ **pull carts**
- ✓ **golf club rental**
- locker rooms
- showers
- executive course
- accommodations
- ✓ **food and beverages**
- ✓ **clubhouse**

**Al Hand**
Professional

**Richard Levine**
Superintendent

***Course information:*** This semi-private course has 18 holes. Women's tees are 5,994 yards and rated 73.6 with a slope of 128 from the white tees. See card below for additional yardage and rating information.

***Play policy and fees:*** Outside play is accepted. Memberships are available. Green fees are $25 on weekdays and $30 on weekends. Twilight rate is $18 weekdays and $23 weekends. Carts, which are mandatory on weekends before noon, are $20. Reservations are recommended seven days in advance for weekdays and by Thursday at noon for the following weekend. Men must wear shirts and golf shoes are required. No tank tops may be worn.

***Location:*** From Highway 101 in San Rafael, take the Central San Rafael exit. Turn east onto Second Street and drive five miles. Turn left on Biscayne Drive to the course.

***Course description:*** This sprawling, tree-lined course is mostly flat with water on 12 holes. A creek meanders through the course. On the 16th hole, there's a 157-yard shot over a water inlet of the San Pablo Bay. There are bunkers on the fairways and the greens. The course is well maintained and very forgiving. PGA Tour standout Raymond Floyd holds the course record at 63. The sixth, a dogleg left of 350 yards, asks for a mid-iron off the tee and an approach over a lagoon—a fun hole. The course offers the only driving range in Marin County.

| Hole | 1 | 2 | 3 | 4 | 5 | 6 | 7 | 8 | 9 | Out | BLUE | Rating: 69.7 |
|---|---|---|---|---|---|---|---|---|---|---|---|---|
| BLUE | 398 | 395 | 173 | 506 | 426 | 305 | 185 | 391 | 502 | 3281 | | Slope: 121 |
| WHITE | 366 | 382 | 159 | 500 | 413 | 292 | 158 | 367 | 489 | 3126 | | |
| Par | 4 | 4 | 3 | 5 | 4 | 4 | 3 | 4 | 5 | 36 | WHITE | Rating: 67.9 |
| Handicap | 3 | 9 | 5 | 13 | 1 | 15 | 11 | 17 | 7 | x | | Slope: 118 |
| RED | 358 | 371 | 136 | 453 | 403 | 232 | 128 | 354 | 471 | 2906 | | |
| Par | 4 | 4 | 3 | 5 | 5 | 4 | 3 | 4 | 5 | 37 | RED | Rating: 71.2 |
| Handicap | 5 | 9 | 11 | 3 | 13 | 15 | 17 | 7 | 1 | x | | Slope: 123 |

| Hole | 10 | 11 | 12 | 13 | 14 | 15 | 16 | 17 | 18 | In | Totals | |
|---|---|---|---|---|---|---|---|---|---|---|---|---|
| BLUE | 137 | 391 | 543 | 180 | 516 | 362 | 155 | 348 | 441 | 3073 | BLUE | 6354 |
| WHITE | 121 | 376 | 522 | 173 | 465 | 313 | 145 | 334 | 421 | 2870 | WHITE | 5996 |
| Par | 3 | 4 | 5 | 3 | 5 | 4 | 3 | 4 | 4 | 35 | Par | 71 |
| Handicap | 18 | 8 | 6 | 10 | 4 | 14 | 12 | 16 | 2 | x | | |
| RED | 119 | 359 | 469 | 138 | 464 | 302 | 138 | 326 | 408 | 2723 | RED | 5629 |
| Par | 3 | 4 | 5 | 3 | 5 | 4 | 3 | 4 | 5 | 36 | Par | 73 |
| Handicap | 18 | 6 | 4 | 16 | 2 | 14 | 12 | 8 | 10 | x | | |

MAP ON PAGE 184

# MARE ISLAND GOLF COURSE

**Course 4**
MAP E1 grid a5

***Course information:*** This military course has nine holes. See card below for yardage and rating information.

***Play policy and fees:*** Outside play is encouraged. Call the pro to make arrangements. Guest fees are $6.75 weekdays, $7.75 weekends for active duty servicemen, $8 for retirees, $8.75 for Department of Defense personnel, and $10 weekdays, $11 weekends for guests. Add $1 to all of above for weekend rates. Carts are $12 for active duty personnel and $16 for civilians.

***Location:*** From Highway 80, take the Tennessee exit and head west to the main entrance and to the course.

***Course description:*** On this course, water comes into play on four holes and it's very hilly. Look out for the 10th hole. This 434-yard, par-4 doglegs slightly right. The course forces players to be accurate with the irons. Locals like to think it is a small version of the Olympic Club. A total of 45,000 rounds are played here per year.

1800 Club Drive,
Mare Island
Vallejo, CA 94592

Pro shop (707) 644-3888

driving range
✓ **practice greens**
✓ **power carts**
✓ **pull carts**
✓ **golf club rental**
✓ **locker rooms**
✓ **showers**
executive course
accommodations
✓ **food and beverages**
✓ **clubhouse**

**Jim Johnson**
Manager/Professional

**Frank Moore**
Superintendent

| Hole | 1 | 2 | 3 | 4 | 5 | 6 | 7 | 8 | 9 | Out | | |
|---|---|---|---|---|---|---|---|---|---|---|---|---|
| BLUE | - | - | - | - | - | - | - | - | - | - | BLUE | Rating: -- |
| | | | | | | | | | | | | Slope: -- |
| WHITE | 374 | 188 | 521 | 257 | 386 | 193 | 510 | 335 | 348 | 3112 | | |
| Par | 4 | 3 | 5 | 4 | 4 | 3 | 5 | 4 | 4 | 36 | WHITE | Rating: 68,8 |
| Handicap | 7 | 17 | 3 | 9 | 1 | 11 | 5 | 15 | 13 | x | | Slope: -- |
| RED | 364 | 136 | 498 | 185 | 375 | 79 | 403 | 320 | 342 | 2702 | | |
| Par | 4 | 3 | 5 | 4 | 4 | 3 | 5 | 4 | 4 | 36 | RED | Rating: 69.6 |
| Handicap | 7 | 15 | 1 | 13 | 3 | 17 | 5 | 11 | 9 | x | | Slope: 116 |

| Hole | 10 | 11 | 12 | 13 | 14 | 15 | 16 | 17 | 18 | In | Totals | |
|---|---|---|---|---|---|---|---|---|---|---|---|---|
| BLUE | - | - | - | - | - | - | - | - | - | - | BLUE | -- |
| WHITE | 434 | 173 | 501 | 184 | 386 | 193 | 510 | 284 | 372 | 3037 | WHITE | 6149 |
| Par | 4 | 3 | 5 | 3 | 4 | 3 | 5 | 4 | 4 | 35 | Par | 71 |
| Handicap | 4 | 18 | 8 | 14 | 2 | 10 | 6 | 16 | 12 | x | | |
| RED | 345 | 136 | 430 | 137 | 367 | 79 | 403 | 279 | 342 | 2518 | RED | 5220 |
| Par | 4 | 3 | 5 | 3 | 4 | 3 | 5 | 4 | 4 | 35 | Par | 71 |
| Handicap | 8 | 16 | 2 | 14 | 4 | 18 | 6 | 12 | 10 | x | | |

# JOE MORTARA GOLF COURSE

**Course 5**
MAP E1 grid a6

*Course information:* This public course has nine holes. See card below for yardage and rating information.

*Play policy and fees:* Green fees are $5 for nine holes weekdays with $2 for each additional nine holes, and $6 for nine holes weekends with $2 for each additional nine holes. Pull carts are $1 for the day.

*Location:* From Interstate 80 on the north end of Vallejo, take the Redwood exit. Turn right on Fairgrounds Drive. The course is located at the Solano County Fairgrounds.

*Course description:* This short course is flat and a good test for beginners and brushing up on your iron game. There is only one par-4, the 320-yard seventh. The course is situated in the middle of the track of the Solano Country Fairgrounds. A total of 75,000 rounds are played here each year.

**1981**
**Joe Mortara, Sr.**
**Jack Flemming**

900 Fairgrounds Drive
Vallejo, CA 94590

Pro shop (707) 642-5146

- driving range
- ✓ **practice greens**
- power carts
- ✓ **pull carts**
- ✓ **golf club rental**
- locker rooms
- showers
- executive course
- accommodations
- ✓ **food and beverages**
- ✓ **clubhouse**

**Joe Mortara, Jr.**
Professional

**Bob Wagner**
Superintendent

NORTHERN E1

| Hole | 1 | 2 | 3 | 4 | 5 | 6 | 7 | 8 | 9 | Out | BLUE | Rating: -- |
|---|---|---|---|---|---|---|---|---|---|---|---|---|
| BLUE | - | - | - | - | - | - | - | - | - | - | | Slope: -- |
| WHITE | 200 | 150 | 160 | 172 | 212 | 140 | 320 | 126 | 112 | 1591 | | |
| Par | 3 | 3 | 3 | 3 | 3 | 3 | 4 | 3 | 3 | 28 | WHITE | Rating:54.4 |
| Handicap | 3 | 11 | 9 | 7 | 1 | 13 | 5 | 15 | 17 | x | | Slope: -- |
| RED | - | - | - | - | - | - | - | - | - | - | | |
| Par | - | - | - | - | - | - | - | - | - | - | RED | Rating: -- |
| Handicap | - | - | - | - | - | - | - | - | - | x | | Slope: -- |

| Hole | 10 | 11 | 12 | 13 | 14 | 15 | 16 | 17 | 18 | In | Totals | |
|---|---|---|---|---|---|---|---|---|---|---|---|---|
| BLUE | - | - | - | - | - | - | - | - | - | - | BLUE | -- |
| WHITE | 200 | 150 | 160 | 172 | 212 | 140 | 320 | 125 | 112 | 1591 | WHITE | 3182 |
| Par | 3 | 3 | 3 | 3 | 3 | 3 | 4 | 3 | 3 | 28 | Par | 56 |
| Handicap | 4 | 12 | 10 | 8 | 2 | 14 | 6 | 16 | 18 | x | | |
| RED | - | - | - | - | - | - | - | - | - | - | RED | -- |
| Par | - | - | - | - | - | - | - | - | - | - | Par | -- |
| Handicap | - | - | - | - | - | - | - | - | - | x | | |

# BLUE ROCK SPRINGS GOLF COURSE

**Course 6**
**MAP E1 grid a6**

**1941**
**Jack Flemming**
**Joe Mortara, Sr.**

PO Box 5207
Vallejo, CA 94591

Columbus Parkway
Vallejo, CA 94591

Pro shop (707) 643-8476

- ✓ **driving range**
- ✓ **practice greens**
- ✓ **power carts**
- ✓ **pull carts**
- ✓ **golf club rental**
- ✓ **locker rooms**
- ✓ **showers**
- executive course
- accommodations
- ✓ **food and beverages**
- ✓ **clubhouse**

**Ralph Harris**
Professional

**Bob Ludwig**
Club Secretary

**Bob Wagner**
Superintendent

***Course information:*** This public course has 18 holes and par is 70. The courses are about 6,100 yards and rated 68.2 from the regular tees. Women's tees are 5,879 yards and rated 72.9. The slope rating is 114.

***Play policy and fees:*** Green fees are $13 on weekdays and $16 on weekends; fees for residents are $11 weekdays, $14 weekends. The twilight rates are $6 weekdays and $7 weekends. Carts are $10 for nine holes and $17 for 18 holes. Spiked shoes and shirts with collars must be worn.

***Location:*** From Interstate 80 in Vallejo, take the Columbus Parkway exit and drive three miles east to the course on the right.

***Course description:*** The course is undergoing a major reconstruction to 36 holes. Both 18s are par-70s. They are expected to be up in 1994, but the course is now open. Some holes have temporary greens. The project is done piece by piece so it's tough to say which holes will be under construction at any time but 18 holes will always be open. It's the site of the Vallejo Open. A total of 105,000 rounds are played here each year.

# MILL VALLEY GOLF COURSE

**Course 7**
MAP E1 grid b2

**1919**

280 Buena Vista Avenue
Mill Valley, CA 94941
Pro shop (415) 388-9982

- driving range
- ✓ **practice greens**
- ✓ **power carts**
- ✓ **pull carts**
- ✓ **golf club rental**
- locker rooms
- showers
- executive course
- accommodations
- ✓ **food and beverages**
- ✓ **clubhouse**

**Stephen Yuhas**
Manager/Professional

**William Osborn**
Superintendent

*Course information:* This public course has nine holes. See card below for yardage and rating information.

*Play policy and fees:* Green fees are $9 for nine holes and $12 for 18 holes on weekdays, and $11 for nine holes and $14 for 18 holes on weekends. Senior rates are $6 for nine holes and $9 for 18 holes on weekdays only. Power carts are $8 for nine holes and $14 for 18 holes.

*Location:* From Highway 101 in Mill Valley, take the East Blithedale Avenue exit west. Turn right on Carmelita Avenue and then right again on Buena Vista Avenue to the course.

*Course description:* A creek comes into play on half the holes. This short, hilly course is walkable, but golf spikes are mandatory. The par-4 fourth, at 365 yards, has most players hitting long-irons off the tee and on the approach. It's a dogleg uphill. The redwood groves make this very pretty. The men's course record is 56 by Malcolm Brown and the women's is 64 by Karen Zielenski.

| Hole | 1 | 2 | 3 | 4 | 5 | 6 | 7 | 8 | 9 | Out | | |
|---|---|---|---|---|---|---|---|---|---|---|---|---|
| BLUE | - | - | - | - | - | - | - | - | - | - | BLUE | Rating: -- |
| | | | | | | | | | | | | Slope: -- |
| WHITE | 241 | 224 | 241 | 365 | 130 | 250 | 121 | 343 | 263 | 2178 | | |
| Par | 4 | 3 | 4 | 4 | 3 | 4 | 3 | 4 | 4 | 33 | WHITE | Rating: 60.6 |
| Handicap | 13 | 3 | 11 | 1 | 17 | 9 | 15 | 5 | 7 | x | | Slope: 100 |
| RED | 237 | 224 | 241 | 356 | 130 | 250 | 121 | 343 | 257 | 2159 | | |
| Par | 4 | 4 | 4 | 4 | 3 | 4 | 3 | 4 | 4 | 34 | RED | Rating: 63.7 |
| Handicap | 9 | 11 | 13 | 1 | 17 | 5 | 15 | 3 | 7 | x | | Slope: 103 |

| Hole | 10 | 11 | 12 | 13 | 14 | 15 | 16 | 17 | 18 | In | Totals | |
|---|---|---|---|---|---|---|---|---|---|---|---|---|
| BLUE | - | - | - | - | - | - | - | - | - | - | BLUE | -- |
| WHITE | 241 | 186 | 217 | 365 | 130 | 250 | 108 | 312 | 228 | 2037 | WHITE | 4215 |
| Par | 4 | 3 | 3 | 4 | 3 | 4 | 3 | 4 | 4 | 32 | Par | 65 |
| Handicap | 14 | 4 | 8 | 2 | 18 | 10 | 16 | 6 | 12 | x | | |
| RED | 237 | 176 | 217 | 356 | 130 | 250 | 103 | 296 | 228 | 1993 | RED | 4152 |
| Par | 4 | 3 | 4 | 4 | 3 | 4 | 3 | 4 | 4 | 33 | Par | 67 |
| Handicap | 10 | 12 | 14 | 2 | 18 | 6 | 16 | 4 | 8 | x | | |

# RICHMOND COUNTRY CLUB

**Course 8**
MAP E1 grid b4

**1924**

3900 Giant Road
Richmond, CA 94086

Pro shop (510) 232-7815
Clubhouse (510) 232-1080

- ✓ **driving range**
- ✓ **practice greens**
- ✓ **power carts**
- ✓ **pull carts**
- ✓ **golf club rental**
- ✓ **locker rooms**
- ✓ **showers**
- executive course
- accommodations
- ✓ **food and beverages**
- ✓ **clubhouse**

**Tom Zahradka**
Professional

**George Bartholomeu**
Superintendent

***Course information:*** This private course has 18 holes and par is 72. The course is 6,499 yards and rated 71.5 from the tournament tees, 6,316 yards and rated 70.7 from the championship tees, and 5,023 yards and rated 64.8 from the regular tees. The slope ratings are 122 tournament, 121 championship and 109 regular. Women's tees are 6,316 yards and rated 76.6 from the tournament tees, 6,066 yards and rated 75.0 from the championship tees, and 5,023 yards and rated 69.0 from the forward tees. The slope ratings are 132 tournament, 128 championship and 116 forward.

***Play policy and fees:*** Reciprocal play is accepted with members of other private clubs. Have your club pro call ahead. Green fees for guests accompanied by a member are $30 on weekdays and $50 on weekends. For unaccompanied guests, the fees are $50 on weekdays and $60 on weekends. Carts are $18. Make reservations one week in advance. Wear suitable golf attire. No tank tops, blue jeans or shorts of inappropriate length may be worn.

***Location:*** From Interstate 80 in Richmond, take the El Portal Drive exit west. El Portal turns into Broadway. Take Broadway to 11th Street. Turn right on 11th Street and go to the first stop sign, which is Stanton. Turn left and drive to Giant Road. Turn right to the course.

***Course description:*** This mature course is short and very secluded. The fairways are tight and tree lined. The terrain is gentle and rolling, and there are very tall and broad pine and eucalyptus trees. In the late 1940s and '50s, men's and women's pro tournaments were held here featuring such players as Patty Berg, Babe Zaharias, Ben Hogan and Sam Snead. The men's course record is 63; the women's is 64. This is the norm among old East Bay courses: short holes with slanted greens—very tricky. The 16th, 17th and 18th holes offer views of the Bay through the trees. Off the third tee you can catch a glimpse of the Golden Gate Bridge, fog permitting.

# MIRA VISTA COUNTRY CLUB

**Course 9**
MAP E1 grid b5

*Course information:* This private course has 18 holes and par is 71. The course is 6,157 yards and rated 70.2 from the regular tees. The slope rating is 123. Women's tees are 5,938 yards and rated 74.3. The slope rating is 130.

*Play policy and fees:* Reciprocal play is accepted with members of other private clubs. Have the golf pro from your club call in advance to arrange tee times. For guests accompanied by a member, green fees are $20 on weekdays and $30 on weekends. For unaccompanied guests, the fees are $40 on weekdays and $50 on weekends. Carts are $18 per person.

*Location:* From Interstate 80 in Oakland, take Portrero Exit 60 straight across San Pablo Avenue, up Hill Street to Elm; turn left. Elm flows into Cutting. Drive to the end of Cutting Boulevard.

*Course description:* This sprawling course has small, severe greens. There are great views of San Francisco. It often gets windy. The course is undulating with lots of trees. Water comes into play on one hole. Pretty on a pretty day; on a miserable day, it's miserable—fog and wind can make it seem like you're on top of San Francisco's Transamerica building. All the greens are elevated. The course plays much longer than yardage; precise shotmaking is essential. Stay below the cup. Some greens are almost unfair.

**1924**
**William "Willie" Watson**

PO Box 600
El Cerrito, CA 94530

7901 Cutting Boulevard
El Cerrito, CA 94530

Pro shop (510) 237-7045
Clubhouse (510) 233-7550

- ✓ **driving range**
- ✓ **practice greens**
- ✓ **power carts**
- ✓ **pull carts**
- ✓ **golf club rental**
- ✓ **locker rooms**
- ✓ **showers**
- executive course
- accommodations
- ✓ **food and beverages**
- ✓ **clubhouse**

**Carol Pence**
Professional

**Frank Barberio**
Superintendent

# FRANKLIN CANYON GOLF COURSE

**Course 10**
MAP E1 grid b6

**1968**
**Robert Muir Graves**

Highway 4
Rodeo, CA 94572

Pro shop (510) 799-6191

- ✓ **driving range**
- ✓ **practice greens**
- ✓ **power carts**
- ✓ **pull carts**
- ✓ **golf club rental**
- locker rooms
- showers
- executive course
- accommodations
- ✓ **food and beverages**
- ✓ **clubhouse**

**Brett Smithers**
Professional

**Abelardo Pacheco**
Superintendent

***Course information:*** This public course has 18 holes. See card below for yardage and rating information.

***Play policy and fees:*** Green fees are $18 weekdays and $30 weekends. Carts are $22 weekdays, $24 on weekends.

***Location:*** Located on Highway 4 in Rodeo, three miles east of Interstate 80.

***Course description:*** This hilly, sprawling course has two ponds that come into play on four holes. Several tight doglegs require accurate positioning. The wind often affects play, and the large undulating greens are difficult to read. Locals seem to prefer the back nine, which includes a 242-yard par-3 at 11. The par-4 12th, a dogleg right over a barranca, is also nice. The 373-yard 14th, downhill, with pine trees on the right side, seems easy, but bunkers and a tricky green can wreck a scorecard. The lateral hazards make this course, particularly the last three holes.

| Hole | 1 | 2 | 3 | 4 | 5 | 6 | 7 | 8 | 9 | Out | BLUE | Rating: 70.9 |
|---|---|---|---|---|---|---|---|---|---|---|---|---|
| BLUE | 532 | 193 | 368 | 183 | 383 | 207 | 528 | 420 | 519 | 3348 | | Slope: 118 |
| WHITE | 472 | 183 | 345 | 169 | 360 | 189 | 511 | 392 | 505 | 3126 | | |
| Par | 5 | 3 | 4 | 3 | 4 | 3 | 5 | 4 | 5 | 36 | WHITE | Rating: 68.9 |
| Handicap | 11 | 5 | 17 | 13 | 15 | 9 | 7 | 1 | 3 | x | | Slope: 114 |
| RED | 441 | 157 | 315 | 145 | 325 | 165 | 490 | 317 | 410 | 2765 | | |
| Par | 5 | 3 | 4 | 3 | 4 | 3 | 5 | 4 | 5 | 36 | RED | Rating: 71.2 |
| Handicap | 3 | 13 | 11 | 17 | 7 | 15 | 1 | 9 | 5 | x | | Slope: 123 |

| Hole | 10 | 11 | 12 | 13 | 14 | 15 | 16 | 17 | 18 | In | Totals | |
|---|---|---|---|---|---|---|---|---|---|---|---|---|
| BLUE | 396 | 242 | 370 | 525 | 373 | 457 | 373 | 157 | 535 | 3428 | BLUE | 6776 |
| WHITE | 356 | 189 | 338 | 504 | 335 | 401 | 353 | 138 | 461 | 3076 | WHITE | 6202 |
| Par | 4 | 3 | 4 | 5 | 4 | 4 | 4 | 3 | 5 | 36 | Par | 72 |
| Handicap | 4 | 8 | 12 | 2 | 14 | 6 | 10 | 16 | 18 | x | | |
| RED | 340 | 133 | 320 | 425 | 312 | 363 | 278 | 135 | 445 | 2751 | RED | 5516 |
| Par | 4 | 3 | 4 | 5 | 4 | 4 | 4 | 3 | 5 | 36 | Par | 72 |
| Handicap | 8 | 16 | 10 | 2 | 12 | 6 | 14 | 18 | 4 | x | | |

# PLEASANT HILL GOLF AND COUNTRY CLUB

**Course 11**
MAP E1 grid b7

***Course information:*** This course has been closed.

# PINE MEADOWS GOLF COURSE

**Course 12**
MAP E1 grid b7

***Course information:*** This public course has nine holes. Par is 54 for 18 holes. The course is 2,774 yards. No rating is available.

***Play policy and fees:*** Green fees are $6 for the first nine holes and $4 for the second nine holes weekdays. Weekday senior rates are $5 for the first nine holes and $3 for the second nine holes. Weekend green fees are $8 for the first nine holes and $6 for second nine holes.

***Location:*** From Interstate 80, take Highway 4 to the Morrelo exit in Martinez. Drive past two stop signs and turn left on Center. Turn left at Vine Hill Way. The course is on the left.

***Course description:*** A new irrigation system has greened up the course quite a bit. There is also the possibility of its being lengthened to qualify for NCGA ratings. This all-par-3 course has rolling hills and lots of trees. The longest hole is the 200-yard ninth. This is not an easy course. A total of 35,000 rounds are played here each year.

451 Vine Hill Way
Martinez, CA 94553

Pro shop (510) 228-2881

- driving range
- ✓ **practice greens**
- ✓ **power carts**
- ✓ **pull carts**
- ✓ **golf club rental**
- locker rooms
- showers
- executive course
- accommodations
- ✓ **food and beverages**
- ✓ **clubhouse**

**John Dodson**
Manager

# CONTRA COSTA COUNTRY CLUB

**Course 13**
MAP E1 grid b7

**1992**
**Remodeled**
**Robert Muir Graves**

801 Golf Club Road
Pleasant Hill, CA 94523

Pro shop (510) 685-8288
Clubhouse (510) 798-7135

- ✓ **driving range**
- ✓ **practice greens**
- ✓ **power carts**
- ✓ **pull carts**
- golf club rental
- ✓ **locker rooms**
- ✓ **showers**
- executive course
- accommodations
- ✓ **food and beverages**
- ✓ **clubhouse**

**Mike Roberts**
Head Professional

**Tony Steers**
Superintendent

***Course information:*** This private course has 18 holes and par is 72. The course is 6,473 yards and rated 70.7 from the championship tees, and 6,189 yards and rated 69.7 from the regular tees. The slope ratings are 125 championship and 123 regular. Women's tees are 5,598 and rated 71.9. The slope rating is 124.

***Play policy and fees:*** Reciprocal play is accepted with members of other private clubs. Have your club pro call for arrangements. In April, the course will re-open after renovation.

***Location:*** From Interstate 680 in Pleasant Hill, take either the Willow Pass or Concord Avenue exits, turning onto Contra Costa Boulevard and winding around Diablo Valley College. The course is one-half mile behind the college.

***Course description:*** The course has undergone major remodelling in 1992, and is slated to open in April of 1993. Re-designed greens, new tees and bunkers, coupled with a beautiful setting, should make this one of the best courses in the country. Designer Robert Muir Graves is in charge of the project. Originally, this course dates back to the 1920s and was designed and built by members. It offers scenic views of Mount Diablo. The greens are large with lots of undulation. Almost every green is bunkered, and there are barrancas on the 13th and 17th holes.

## DIABLO CREEK GOLF COURSE

**Course 14**
MAP E1 grid b8

NORTHERN E1

***Course information:*** This public course has 18 holes and par is 72. The course is 6,763 yards and rated 70.9 from the championship tees, and 6,344 yard and rated 69.3 from the regular tees. The slope ratings are 111 championship and 107 regular. Women's tees are a long 6,000 yards and rated 73.2 from the forward tees. The slope rating is 118.

***Play policy and fees:*** Green fees are $13.50 weekdays and $16.50 weekends for residents. Non-resident fees are $15.50 weekdays and $18.50 weekends. Carts are $16. Reservations are strongly recommended.

***Location:*** From Highway 4 in Concord, exit on Port Chicago and drive to the course.

***Course description:*** This is one of the best-kept municipal courses in Northern California. The course has its own water, so it's always in good shape, despite 100,000 rounds a year. There are five lakes on the front nine. The back nine is tight and narrow. The third hole is tough. At 660 yards from the back, this par-5 requires a shot into the wind around two ponds. The course is flat but wind can be a factor. The Concord City Championships are held here each October.

PO Box 129
Concord, CA 94522

4050 Port Chicago Hwy.
Concord, CA 94522

Pro shop (510) 686-6262
Clubhouse (510) 686-6266

✓ **driving range**
✓ **practice greens**
✓ **power carts**
✓ **pull carts**
✓ **golf club rental**
locker rooms
showers
executive course
accommodations
✓ **food and beverages**
✓ **clubhouse**

**Dan Brown**
Director of Golf

**Rod Kilcoyne**
Superintendent

## BUCHANAN FIELDS GOLF COURSE

**Course 15**
MAP E1 grid b8

**1960**
**Robert Muir Graves**

***Course information:*** This public course has nine holes. Par is 66 for 18 holes. The course is 5,164 yards and is rated 63.0 from the regular tees. The slope rating is 98. Women's tees are 5,142 yards and rated 66.5. The slope rating is 105. Course remodelling will finish in 1992; a new clubhouse is also in the works.

***Play policy and fees:*** Green fees are $8 for nine holes and $9.50 for 18 holes on weekdays, $9 for nine holes and $14 for 18 holes on weekends. Senior rates are $7 for nine holes and $11 for 18 holes on weekdays only. Carts are $9 per nine holes. Rates will change in 1993. Reservations are recommended three days in advance. Shirts and shoes must be worn.

***Location:*** From Interstate 80 in Concord, take the Concord Avenue exit east. Follow Concord Avenue to the course. Turn left just before reaching the Sheraton Inn.

***Course description:*** This course is relatively short and flat. There is a creek and a large lake. The greens are undulating. This is a great practice course for any golfer, but is an excellent test for seniors and women. With the new improvements, it should get even better.

3330 Concord Avenue
Concord, CA 94520

Pro shop (510) 682-1846

✓ **driving range**
✓ **practice greens**
✓ **power carts**
✓ **pull carts**
✓ **golf club rental**
locker rooms
showers
executive course
accommodations
✓ **food and beverages**
✓ **clubhouse**

**Resham Singh**
Manager

**Tim Sullivan**
Owner/Professional

**Ram Pal**
Superintendent

MAP ON PAGE 184

# DELTA VIEWS GOLF COURSE

**Course 16**
MAP E1 grid b9

***Course information:*** This public course has 18 holes. Par is 72 for 18 holes. The course is 6,359 yards from the championship tees, and 5,992 yards from the regular tees. Women's tees are 5,405 yards from the forward tees. The ratings and slope are: blue tees, 70.4 with a slope of 124; regular tees, 68.7, with a slope of 118; and women's tees, 70.1, with a slope of 120.

***Play policy and fees:*** Green fees for Pittsburg residents are $8 for nine holes and $10 for 18 holes weekdays, and $10 for nine holes and $12 for 18 holes weekends. Non-resident green fees are $10 for nine holes and $13 for 18 holes weekdays, and $13 for nine holes and $15 for 18 holes weekends. Carts are $13 for nine holes and $17 for 18 holes. The twilight rate for residents is $6 for nine holes and $8 for 18 holes, and $6 for nine holes and $9 for 18 holes for non-residents after 3:30 p.m. You must wear a shirt and shoes in and around the clubhouse and on the course.

***Location:*** From Concord, drive east on Highway 4. Take the Bailey Road exit south. Turn left on West Leland Road and drive to Golf Club Road.

***Course description:*** Formerly the Pittsburg Golf and Country Club, and now called Delta Views Golf Course, this layout expanded to a full 18 holes in June, 1991. The architect for the second nine was Robert Muir Graves. This sporty course gets windy, but it rewards the accurate driver. Hills abound as do an assortment of trees. The course plays harder than the yardage would indicate. It's murder for the slicer and gives you trouble on every hole to the right, particularly on the new nine. Every October the Pittsburg City Championships are held here. The par-4 17th, 395 yards with a dogleg right, requires a long carry over a gully 200 yards out. A real up and down course, walking is possible, but it's a strenuous work-out.

**1947**
**Alister MacKenzie**

**1991**
**Robert Muir Graves**

2222 Golf Club Road
Pittsburg, CA 94565

Pro shop (510) 427-4940
Clubhouse (510) 427-5852

- ✓ **driving range**
- ✓ **practice greens**
- ✓ **power carts**
- ✓ **pull carts**
- ✓ **golf club rental**
- locker rooms
- showers
- executive course
- ✓ **accommodations**
- ✓ **food and beverages**
- ✓ **clubhouse**

**Joe Fernandez**
Professional

**Carl King**
Superintendent

# PRESIDIO GOLF CLUB

**Course 17**
MAP E1 grid c2

**1895**

*Course information:* This private course has 18 holes. See card below for yardage and rating information.

*Play policy and fees:* Limited reciprocal play is accepted with members of other private clubs. Contact the golf professional for more information. Guest fees are $30 weekdays and $50 weekends. Carts are $16. Reservations are recommended one week in advance. Proper golf attire required. Closed Mondays.

*Location:* Driving into San Francisco over the Golden Gate Bridge on Highway 101, take the 19th Avenue exit south. At the first light after passing through the tunnel (Lake Street), turn right. Flip a U-turn and head east on Lake. Follow Lake Street up to Arguello Boulevard and turn left. The course is at the top of the hill.

*Course description:* As the second oldest golf course west of the Mississippi, this course originated as a member-built, nine-hole layout in 1895 and expanded to 18 holes in 1910. It was first known as the San Francisco Golf Club. The military has been the operator of the course since the 1950s. This hilly course meanders through the San Francisco Presidio and commands spectacular views of the city. Challenging and steep, it's heavily wooded with cypress and eucalyptus. The PGA Western Open was held here in 1956, with Mike Fetchik winning at 4-under. Beware of the 533-yard, par-5 11th hole. It has a blind elevated green that is completely lined with traps. The course record of 64, probably dating back to the late 1920s, is held by the late Lawson Little, who grew up playing this course. The course annually hosts major charity golf events, including Project Open Hand. The future of the course is somewhat cloudy. With the Department of Defense giving up the Presidio to the Department of the Interior, the course could go public with high fees.

PO Box 29103
San Francisco, CA 94129

8 Presidio Terrace
San Francisco, CA 94118

Pro shop (415) 751-4063
Clubhouse (415) 751-1322

- ✓ **driving range**
- ✓ **practice greens**
- ✓ **power carts**
- ✓ **pull carts**
- ✓ **golf club rental**
- ✓ **locker rooms**
- ✓ **showers**
- executive course
- accommodations
- ✓ **food and beverages**
- ✓ **clubhouse**

**John Murray**
Professional

**Jeff Yee**
Manager

**Louise Gibson**
Manager

**John Buckley**
Superintendent

NORTHERN E1

| Hole | 1 | 2 | 3 | 4 | 5 | 6 | 7 | 8 | 9 | Out | BLUE | Rating: 71.8 |
|---|---|---|---|---|---|---|---|---|---|---|---|---|
| BLUE | 508 | 398 | 453 | 173 | 349 | 182 | 368 | 353 | 524 | 3308 | | Slope: 129 |
| WHITE | 488 | 381 | 436 | 159 | 326 | 153 | 346 | 344 | 483 | 3116 | | |
| Par | 5 | 4 | 4 | 3 | 4 | 3 | 4 | 4 | 5 | 36 | WHITE | Rating: 70.2 |
| Handicap | 7 | 5 | 1 | 13 | 11 | 17 | 9 | 3 | 15 | x | | Slope: 126 |
| RED | 468 | 302 | 424 | 153 | 325 | 133 | 332 | 335 | 464 | 2936 | | |
| Par | 5 | 4 | 5 | 3 | 4 | 3 | 4 | 4 | 5 | 37 | RED | Rating: 73.5 |
| Handicap | 1 | 13 | 5 | 15 | 9 | 17 | 11 | 7 | 3 | x | | Slope: 128 |

| Hole | 10 | 11 | 12 | 13 | 14 | 15 | 16 | 17 | 18 | In | Totals | |
|---|---|---|---|---|---|---|---|---|---|---|---|---|
| BLUE | 398 | 528 | 385 | 145 | 312 | 363 | 245 | 379 | 526 | 3281 | BLUE | 6589 |
| WHITE | 385 | 433 | 379 | 127 | 302 | 350 | 195 | 365 | 491 | 3027 | WHITE | 6143 |
| Par | 4 | 5 | 4 | 3 | 4 | 4 | 3 | 4 | 5 | 36 | Par | 72 |
| Handicap | 8 | 16 | 2 | 18 | 14 | 4 | 6 | 10 | 12 | x | | |
| RED | 368 | 412 | 371 | 111 | 292 | 344 | 171 | 354 | 449 | 2872 | RED | 5808 |
| Par | 4 | 5 | 4 | 3 | 4 | 4 | 3 | 4 | 5 | 36 | Par | 73 |
| Handicap | 14 | 4 | 2 | 18 | 12 | 8 | 16 | 10 | 6 | x | | |

# GOLDEN GATE PARK GOLF COURSE

**Course 18**
MAP E1 grid c2

***Course information:*** This public course has nine holes. Par is 54 for 18 holes. The course is 2,714 yards for 18 holes. This course is unrated.

***Play policy and fees:*** Green fees are $8 weekdays and $11 weekends; San Francisco residents pay $5 weekdays, $7 weekends; senior cards are $4 weekdays, $7 weekends. Carts are $8 for nine holes. Pull carts are $3.50. Club rental is $6 per bag.

***Location:*** Located at the far west end of Golden Gate Park on Fulton Street off 47th Avenue. Take the 19th Avenue exit off Highway 101 into San Francisco. Follow 19th Avenue (Park Presidio) until you reach Fulton Street. Turn right and follow it along the park until 47th Avenue. Turn into the park and the course.

***Course description:*** Situated at the end of Golden Gate Park by the ocean, this short course is tight and twisty with lots of trees. The longest hole is the 193-yard fifth and the shortest is the 109-yard eighth. It offers good practice for your iron game. The course hosts the annual San Francisco Family Championship.

**1950**
**Jack Fleming**

McLaren Lodge
Golden Gate Park
San Francisco, CA 94117

47th Avenue & Fulton Street
San Francisco, CA 94117

Pro shop (415) 751-8987

driving range
✓ **practice greens**
✓ **power carts**
✓ **pull carts**
✓ **golf club rental**
locker rooms
showers
executive course
accommodations
✓ **food and beverages**
clubhouse

**Jim Thigpin**
Manager

# LINCOLN PARK GOLF COURSE

**Course 19**
MAP E1 grid c2

*Course information:* This public course has 18 holes and par is 68. The course is 5,131 yards and rated 64.4 from the regular tees. The slope rating is 106. Women's tees are 4,989 yards and rated 68.6 from the regular tees. The slope rating is 111.

*Play policy and fees:* Green fees are $17 weekdays and $21 weekends. Carts are $20. Residents of San Francisco still may purchase cards. Tee times can be made seven days in advance.

*Location:* Crossing over the Golden Gate Bridge on Highway 101 into San Francisco, take the 19th Avenue exit south, follow it through the tunnel and then turn right onto Clement Street. Follow Clement a few miles to the entrance of the course on the right.

*Course description:* Nestled around the Legion of Honor with views of San Francisco below, this extremely scenic course is tight and twisty. Part of the course runs along steep cliffs above the ocean. The 242-yard 17th hole is a brutal but spectacular par-3, with a stunning view of the Golden Gate Bridge. There are lots of trees and good placement shots are vital. It's hilly, but walkable. Pro golfers Johnny Miller and George Archer grew up playing here. This is a very busy course with a 100,000 rounds played annually.

**Jack Fleming**

3139 Clement Street
San Francisco, CA 94121

Pro shop (415) 221-9911
Clubhouse (415) 221-8727

driving range
✓ **practice greens**
✓ **power carts**
✓ **pull carts**
✓ **golf club rental**
locker rooms
showers
executive course
accommodations
✓ **food and beverages**
✓ **clubhouse**

**John Constantine**
Manager/Professional

**Jim Mannion**
Superintendent

# MONTCLAIR GOLF COURSE

**Course 20**
MAP E1 grid c5

*Course information:* This public course has nine holes. Par is 27. The course is 567 yards.

*Play policy and fees:* Green fees are $2.50 weekdays and $3 weekends.

*Location:* From Highway 13 in Oakland, take the Park Boulevard exit west. Follow it to Monterey Boulevard and drive one-quarter mile to the course.

*Course description:* This short, par-3 course is situated in the Oakland Hills and is mostly flat. It's a good beginner's course. There is a two-deck driving range. The 85-yard first hole is the longest.

**1973**

2477 Monterey Boulevard
Oakland, CA 94611

Pro shop (510) 482-0422
Clubhouse (510) 482-4444

✓ **driving range**
practice greens
power carts
pull carts
✓ **golf club rental**
locker rooms
showers
executive course
accommodations
✓ **food and beverages**
✓ **clubhouse**

**Pillim Lee**
Owner

# TILDEN PARK GOLF COURSE

**Course 21**
**MAP E1 grid c5**

**1935**
**William Park Bell**

8 Shasta Road
Berkeley, CA 94708

Pro shop (510) 848-7373

- ✓ **driving range**
- ✓ **practice greens**
- ✓ **power carts**
- ✓ **pull carts**
- ✓ **golf club rental**
- locker rooms
- showers
- executive course
- accommodations
- ✓ **food and beverages**
- ✓ **clubhouse**

**Paul Wyrybkowski**
Professional

**Dave Smith**
Superintendent

***Course information:*** This public course has 18 holes. See card below for yardage and rating information. The course is being re-rated.

***Play policy and fees:*** Green fees are $15 on weekdays and $20 on weekends. Carts are $12 for nine holes and $20 for 18 holes. The recommended lead time for tee time reservations is one week.

***Location:*** From Highway 24 in Berkeley, take the Fish Ranch Road exit (on the east side of the Caldecott Tunnel) and drive one mile north. Turn on Grizzly Peak Boulevard and follow it to the course.

***Course description:*** Situated in the Berkeley Hills, this course has squirrels, raccoons and deer. Overall, it's a tight, hilly course that allows little margin for error. There are lots of trees and the greens are tricky. The 411-yard, par-4 first hole is straight uphill and plays like a par-5. This has a lot of fun holes, with the 10th through the 12th run particularly satisfying. Hilly and tight, this course requires patience and accuracy. The first is the toughest, but the 400-yard 18th is no vacation. Almost all the shots carry to the greens. The Bay Regional Tournament and the 72-Hole event are held the last weekend in July and the first weekend in August. The men's record is 64 and is held jointly by Al Norris and Greg Anderson. A total of 85,000 rounds are played here each year.

| Hole | 1 | 2 | 3 | 4 | 5 | 6 | 7 | 8 | 9 | Out | BLUE | Rating: 69.9 |
|---|---|---|---|---|---|---|---|---|---|---|---|---|
| BLUE | 411 | 399 | 464 | 143 | 366 | 316 | 221 | 475 | 334 | 3129 | | Slope: 118 |
| WHITE | 404 | 385 | 377 | 137 | 327 | 297 | 201 | 467 | 320 | 2915 | | |
| Par | 4 | 4 | 4 | 3 | 4 | 4 | 3 | 5 | 4 | 35 | WHITE | Rating: 67.8 |
| Handicap | 3 | 11 | 9 | 15 | 1 | 13 | 17 | 5 | 7 | x | | Slope: 114 |
| RED | 401 | 376 | 356 | 123 | 316 | 270 | 170 | 460 | 286 | 2758 | | |
| Par | 5 | 4 | 4 | 3 | 4 | 4 | 3 | 5 | 4 | 36 | RED | Rating: 69.7 |
| Handicap | 3 | 13 | 17 | 11 | 5 | 9 | 15 | 1 | 7 | x | | Slope: 115 |

| Hole | 10 | 11 | 12 | 13 | 14 | 15 | 16 | 17 | 18 | In | Totals | |
|---|---|---|---|---|---|---|---|---|---|---|---|---|
| BLUE | 395 | 234 | 350 | 504 | 352 | 329 | 206 | 395 | 400 | 3165 | BLUE | 6294 |
| WHITE | 387 | 199 | 300 | 438 | 311 | 322 | 186 | 395 | 370 | 2908 | WHITE | 5823 |
| Par | 4 | 3 | 4 | 5 | 4 | 4 | 3 | 4 | 4 | 35 | Par | 70 |
| Handicap | 6 | 14 | 2 | 8 | 4 | 16 | 12 | 18 | 10 | x | | |
| RED | 381 | 120 | 264 | 431 | 284 | 309 | 138 | 379 | 335 | 2641 | RED | 5399 |
| Par | 4 | 3 | 4 | 5 | 4 | 4 | 3 | 4 | 4 | 35 | Par | 71 |
| Handicap | 6 | 18 | 4 | 2 | 12 | 14 | 16 | 8 | 10 | x | | |

# CLAREMONT COUNTRY CLUB

**Course 22**
MAP E1 grid c5

*NORTHERN E1*

***Course information:*** This private course has 18 holes. See card below for yardage and rating information.

***Play policy and fees:*** Members and guests only. Guests must be accompanied by a member. Green fees are $25 when accompanied by a member. Carts are $20.

***Location:*** From Highway 24 in Oakland, exit onto Broadway southwest. Turn left on Broadway Terrace. The course is one-half mile on the right. Or as an alternative, take Highway 13 and exit on Broadway Terrace west.

***Course description:*** Alister Mackenzie is credited with re-working this course. This is a tight, rolling course in the Oakland hills. It is one of the oldest courses in Northern California. The 230-yard par-3 13th requires a tee shot through a narrow opening. Snead is credited with saying it's the only fairway that requires players to walk single-file. The course looks easy on the card, but the par-3s (210-yard number two and 230-yard number 13) and the sloped, fast greens make this a tough test. It's also one of the few courses that still have caddies. Play the number 12 hole as smart as you can. It's 400 yards even and a par-4 with an uphill tee shot through a narrow fairway. There is out-of-bounds right and a drop-off to the left. The green is sloped and well trapped. Sam Snead won the Oakland Open here in 1937. 28,000 rounds are played here each year.

**1904**

5295 Broadway Terrace
Oakland, CA 94618

Pro shop (510) 655-2431
Clubhouse (510) 653-6789

driving range
✓ **practice greens**
✓ **power carts**
✓ **pull carts**
✓ **golf club rental**
✓ **locker rooms**
✓ **showers**
executive course
✓ **accommodations**
✓ **food and beverages**
✓ **clubhouse**

**John Fite**
Professional

**Randy Gai**
Superintendent

| Hole | 1 | 2 | 3 | 4 | 5 | 6 | 7 | 8 | 9 | Out | BLUE | Rating: |
|---|---|---|---|---|---|---|---|---|---|---|---|---|
| BLUE | | | | | | | | | | | | Slope: |
| WHITE | 430 | 215 | 126 | 341 | 332 | 260 | 385 | 170 | 391 | 2650 | | |
| Par | 5 | 3 | 3 | 4 | 4 | 4 | 4 | 3 | 4 | 34 | WHITE | Rating: 67.0 |
| Handicap | 10 | 8 | 18 | 4 | 14 | 12 | 2 | 16 | 6 | x | | Slope: 119 |
| RED | 430 | 215 | 126 | 341 | 332 | 260 | 385 | 170 | 376 | 2635 | | |
| Par | 5 | 4 | 3 | 4 | 4 | 4 | 5 | 3 | 4 | 36 | RED | Rating: 71.4 |
| Handicap | 8 | 16 | 18 | 6 | 10 | 12 | 2 | 14 | 4 | x | | Slope: 127 |

| Hole | 10 | 11 | 12 | 13 | 14 | 15 | 16 | 17 | 18 | In | Totals | |
|---|---|---|---|---|---|---|---|---|---|---|---|---|
| BLUE | | | | | | | | | | | BLUE | |
| WHITE | 160 | 391 | 400 | 225 | 291 | 345 | 372 | 130 | 505 | 2819 | WHITE | 5469 |
| Par | 3 | 4 | 4 | 3 | 4 | 4 | 4 | 3 | 5 | 34 | Par | 68 |
| Handicap | 15 | 3 | 1 | 11 | 13 | 7 | 5 | 17 | 9 | x | | |
| RED | 120 | 391 | 400 | 198 | 291 | 345 | 372 | 130 | 505 | 2752 | RED | 5387 |
| Par | 3 | 4 | 5 | 3 | 4 | 4 | 4 | 3 | 5 | 35 | Par | 71 |
| Handicap | 17 | 3 | 1 | 13 | 11 | 9 | 7 | 15 | 5 | x | | |

MAP ON PAGE 184

# ORINDA COUNTRY CLUB

**Course 23**
MAP E1 grid c6

***Course information:*** This private course has 18 holes. The course is 5,859 yards and rated 68.5 with a slope of 116 from the gold tees. Women's tees are rated 75.3 with a slope of 135 from the white tees. See card below for additional yardage and rating information.

***Play policy and fees:*** Reciprocal play is accepted with members of other private clubs. Guest fees vary, call ahead.

***Location:*** From Highway 24, take the Orinda-Moraga exit. Turn left on San Pablo Dam Road. Turn right at the second stop light at Camino Sobrante. Go through the stop sign and drive one mile up the winding road to the course on the left. Turn left at the lake.

***Course description:*** This tight, rolling course was built in 1924 and opened in 1925. It has traditional small greens and a creek winds through it. Two long par-4s, the ninth and 11th holes, create the most trouble. The ninth is a rolling 432-yard demon. You can see the green from the tee box, but you're driving over two mounds to a blind fairway. There is a slope from left to right. Long hitters can fly both hills on the fairway, but most will land in the second bank, requiring a long iron or wood for the second shot. It's considered the best hole on the course because everybody has a chance to par it if they play it smart and look for some roll. The 11th hole is 442 yards from the back and doglegs 220 yards out to the left. Trees border the right fairway and there is out-of-bounds on the left. There is a creek 75 yards short of the green you have to carry if you're going for it. But beware: The green has very interesting natural mounds all around it and there is out-of-bounds to the left. The par-5 569-yard sixth hole carries over Miner Road. Legend has it that only Tony Lema has ever reached the green in two shots. But it was done several times when the PAC 10 Conference held it's 1988 tournament there. So much for legends.

**1925**
**William "Willie" Watson**

315 Camino Sobrante
Orinda, CA 94563

Pro shop (510) 254-0811
Clubhouse (510) 254-4313

- driving range
- ✓ **practice greens**
- ✓ **power carts**
- ✓ **pull carts**
- ✓ **golf club rental**
- ✓ **locker rooms**
- ✓ **showers**
- executive course
- accommodations
- ✓ **food and beverages**
- ✓ **clubhouse**

**Shim Lagoy**
Professional

**David Rosenstraugh**
Superintendent

| Hole | 1 | 2 | 3 | 4 | 5 | 6 | 7 | 8 | 9 | Out | BLUE | Rating: 71.0 |
|---|---|---|---|---|---|---|---|---|---|---|---|---|
| BLUE | 354 | 321 | 244 | 458 | 354 | 569 | 337 | 120 | 432 | 3189 | | Slope: 125 |
| WHITE | 334 | 309 | 237 | 450 | 343 | 556 | 316 | 116 | 428 | 3089 | | |
| Par | 4 | 4 | 3 | 5 | 4 | 5 | 4 | 3 | 4 | 36 | WHITE | Rating: 70.0 |
| Handicap | 15 | 11 | 7 | 9 | 5 | 1 | 13 | 17 | 3 | x | | Slope: 123 |
| RED | 310 | 307 | 230 | 448 | 334 | 496 | 299 | 101 | 423 | 2948 | | |
| Par | 4 | 4 | 3 | 5 | 4 | 5 | 4 | 3 | 5 | 37 | RED | Rating: 73.0 |
| Handicap | 15 | 9 | 13 | 3 | 7 | 1 | 11 | 17 | 5 | x | | Slope: 129 |

| Hole | 10 | 11 | 12 | 13 | 14 | 15 | 16 | 17 | 18 | In | Totals | |
|---|---|---|---|---|---|---|---|---|---|---|---|---|
| BLUE | 308 | 442 | 463 | 192 | 290 | 186 | 414 | 347 | 521 | 3163 | BLUE | 6352 |
| WHITE | 298 | 434 | 441 | 178 | 282 | 162 | 394 | 339 | 510 | 3038 | WHITE | 6127 |
| Par | 4 | 4 | 5 | 3 | 4 | 3 | 4 | 4 | 5 | 36 | Par | 72 |
| Handicap | 16 | 2 | 12 | 14 | 18 | 8 | 4 | 10 | 6 | x | | |
| RED | 252 | 426 | 403 | 155 | 272 | 127 | 354 | 328 | 453 | 2770 | RED | 5718 |
| Par | 4 | 5 | 5 | 3 | 4 | 3 | 4 | 4 | 5 | 37 | Par | 74 |
| Handicap | 14 | 2 | 6 | 18 | 12 | 16 | 8 | 10 | 4 | x | | |

# MORAGA COUNTRY CLUB

**Course 24**
MAP E1 grid c6

***Course information:*** This private course is 18 holes. See card below for yardage and rating information.

***Play policy and fees:*** Reciprocal play is accepted with members of other private clubs in the area. Guest fees are $24 weekdays, and $45 for weekends. Carts are $20.

***Location:*** From Highway 24 in Moraga, take the Moraga Way exit south four miles to Saint Andrews Drive.

***Course description:*** This course demands a good short game. It's tight and hilly with bunkers and slick greens. The course expanded to 18 holes in the fall of 1992 under the design expertise of Algie Pulley. The new number nine, 505-yard par-5, has water on the right, big mounds on the left, and plays into a breeze. The green is long and narrow. The par-3 10th, a 167-yarder over a creek, is a beauty. From there, the course goes up the hills. Some deceptive par-4s, with unbelievable mounds in the greens, make this course memorable or exasperating or both. The 489-yard, par-5 14th, for example, has a five-tiered green. But the par-5 18th, a dogleg right with an approach over a green, is great.

**1974**
**Robert Muir Graves**

1600 Saint Andrews Drive
Moraga, CA 94556

Pro shop (510) 376-2253
Clubhouse (510) 376-2200

- ✓ **driving range**
- ✓ **practice greens**
- ✓ **power carts**
- ✓ **pull carts**
- ✓ **golf club rental**
- ✓ **locker rooms**
- ✓ **showers**
- executive course
- accommodations
- ✓ **food and beverages**
- ✓ **clubhouse**

**John Lundahl**
Manager/Professional

**Gary Ingram**
Superintendent

| Hole | 1 | 2 | 3 | 4 | 5 | 6 | 7 | 8 | 9 | Out | | |
|---|---|---|---|---|---|---|---|---|---|---|---|---|
| BLUE | 402 | 376 | 412 | 323 | 129 | 395 | 182 | 268 | 505 | 2992 | BLUE | Rating: 70.5 |
| WHITE | 391 | 366 | 382 | 305 | 124 | 384 | 174 | 259 | 480 | 2865 | | Slope: 127 |
| Par | 4 | 4 | 4 | 4 | 3 | 4 | 3 | 4 | 5 | 35 | WHITE | Rating: 68.9 |
| Handicap | 5 | 3 | 1 | 11 | 17 | 9 | 15 | 13 | 7 | x | | Slope: 124 |
| RED | 378 | 326 | 327 | 269 | 124 | 350 | 128 | 255 | 435 | 2392 | | |
| Par | 4 | 4 | 4 | 4 | 3 | 4 | 3 | 4 | 5 | 35 | RED | Rating: 69.9 |
| Handicap | 1 | 3 | 7 | 13 | 17 | 5 | 15 | 9 | 4 | x | | Slope: 128 |

| Hole | 10 | 11 | 12 | 13 | 14 | 15 | 16 | 17 | 18 | In | Totals | |
|---|---|---|---|---|---|---|---|---|---|---|---|---|
| BLUE | 167 | 302 | 353 | 503 | 489 | 224 | 391 | 170 | 560 | 3159 | BLUE | 6151 |
| WHITE | 155 | 268 | 340 | 460 | 448 | 185 | 333 | 147 | 510 | 2846 | WHITE | 5711 |
| Par | 3 | 4 | 4 | 5 | 5 | 3 | 4 | 3 | 5 | 36 | Par | 71 |
| Handicap | 10 | 16 | 4 | 14 | 6 | 8 | 12 | 18 | 2 | x | | |
| RED | 131 | 247 | 281 | 419 | 412 | 156 | 302 | 120 | 449 | 2517 | RED | 5109 |
| Par | 3 | 4 | 4 | 5 | 5 | 3 | 4 | 3 | 5 | 36 | Par | 71 |
| Handicap | 6 | 12 | 10 | 8 | 4 | 16 | 6 | 18 | 2 | x | | |

# DIABLO HILLS GOLF COURSE

**Course 25**
MAP E1 grid c7

***Course information:*** This public course has nine holes. See card below for yardage and rating information.

***Play policy and fees:*** Green fees are $10 for nine holes and $14 for 18 holes on weekdays, and $13 for nine holes and $25 for 18 holes on weekends and holidays. Senior rates are $4 for the back nine, $8 for 18 holes. Carts are $12 for nine holes and $24 for 18 holes. Shirts with collars must be worn.

***Location:*** From Interstate 680 in Walnut Creek, take the Ygnacio Valley Road exit to Marchbanks Drive. Drive two miles to the course.

***Course description:*** This flat course winds through condominiums, but is wide open. There are slightly rolling, yet walkable, hills with many sand traps. This is the ideal course for beginning and junior golfers, and there is a junior tournament every Tuesday for $6 in the spring and summer. The Singh Invitational takes place every fall. Host pro Nick Andrakin holds the course record with 60 for 18 holes and 29 for nine holes. A total of 70,000 rounds are played here each year.

**1975**
**Robert Muir Graves**

1551 Marchbanks Drive
Walnut Creek, CA 94598

Pro shop (510) 939-7372
Clubhouse (510) 937-1270

- driving range
- ✓ **practice greens**
- ✓ **power carts**
- ✓ **pull carts**
- ✓ **golf club rental**
- locker rooms
- showers
- executive course
- accommodations
- ✓ **food and beverages**
- ✓ **clubhouse**

**Nick Andrakin**
Professional

**Hardev Singh**
Owner

| Hole | 1 | 2 | 3 | 4 | 5 | 6 | 7 | 8 | 9 | Out | BLUE | Rating: -- |
|---|---|---|---|---|---|---|---|---|---|---|---|---|
| BLUE | - | - | - | - | - | - | - | - | - | - | | Slope: -- |
| WHITE | 264 | 328 | 106 | 88 | 323 | 254 | 140 | 489 | 310 | 2302 | | |
| Par | 4 | 4 | 3 | 3 | 4 | 4 | 3 | 5 | 4 | 34 | WHITE | Rating:62.5 |
| Handicap | 16 | 4 | 12 | 18 | 2 | 14 | 6 | 10 | 8 | x | | Slope: 100 |
| RED | 251 | 305 | 94 | 63 | 323 | 254 | 126 | 466 | 291 | 2173 | | |
| Par | 4 | 4 | 3 | 3 | 4 | 4 | 3 | 5 | 4 | 34 | RED | Rating: 65.7 |
| Handicap | 7 | 5 | 15 | 17 | 3 | 11 | 13 | 1 | 9 | x | | Slope: 104 |

| Hole | 10 | 11 | 12 | 13 | 14 | 15 | 16 | 17 | 18 | In | Totals | |
|---|---|---|---|---|---|---|---|---|---|---|---|---|
| BLUE | - | - | - | - | - | - | - | - | - | - | BLUE | -- |
| WHITE | 264 | 328 | 106 | 88 | 323 | 254 | 140 | 489 | 310 | 2302 | WHITE | 4604 |
| Par | 4 | 4 | 3 | 3 | 4 | 4 | 3 | 5 | 4 | 34 | Par | 68 |
| Handicap | 15 | 3 | 11 | 17 | 1 | 13 | 5 | 9 | 7 | x | | |
| RED | 251 | 305 | 94 | 63 | 323 | 254 | 126 | 466 | 291 | 2173 | RED | 4346 |
| Par | 4 | 4 | 3 | 3 | 4 | 4 | 3 | 5 | 4 | 34 | Par | 68 |
| Handicap | 8 | 6 | 16 | 18 | 4 | 12 | 14 | 2 | 10 | x | | |

# ROSSMOOR GOLF COURSE

**Course 26**
MAP E1 grid c7



***Course information:*** This private course has 27 holes and par is 72 on both combinations of 18.

The South Course is 6,058 yards and rated 68.8 from the championship tees, and 5,798 yards and rated 67.6 from the regular tees. The slope ratings are 118 championship and 115 regular. Women's tees are 5,510 yards and rated 70.3. The slope rating is 120.

The North Course is 5,950 yards and rated 67.6 from the regular tees. The slope rating is 115. Women's tees are 5,608 yards and rated 70.6. The slope rating is 117.

***Play policy and fees:*** Members and guests only. Guest fees are $10 for nine holes and $20 for 18 holes weekdays, and $15 for nine holes and $30 for 18 holes weekends and holidays. Carts are $18.

***Location:*** From Highway 24 east of Lafayette, take the Pleasant Hill Road exit south to Olympic Boulevard east. Then turn right on the Tice Valley Boulevard and right again on Rossmoor Parkway. Turn right onto Stanley Dollar Drive to the course.

***Course description:*** These are retirement community courses. They are mostly flat and walkable although the South Course has some hills. The South's 372-yard second hole requires an uphill approach. The par-5 10th hole doglegs left, with two big oak trees at the turn. Both layouts are a good test of irons and short game strategy. The greens are very tricky. The North Course may be short, but it can be tough.

**1965**
**Robert Muir Graves**

1010 Stanley Dollar Drive
Walnut Creek, CA 94595

Pro shop (510) 933-2607

- ✓ **driving range**
- ✓ **practice greens**
- ✓ **power carts**
- ✓ **pull carts**
- ✓ **golf club rental**
- locker rooms
- showers
- executive course
- accommodations
- ✓ **food and beverages**
- ✓ **clubhouse**

**Norm Oliver**
Professional

**Joe Rodriquez**
Superintendent

# BOUNDRY OAK GOLF COURSE

**Course 27**
MAP E1 grid c8

***Course information:*** This public course has 18 holes. See card below for yardage and rating information.

***Play policy and fees:*** Green fees are $15 weekdays and $20 weekends. Carts are $20.

***Location:*** From Interstate 680, take the Ygnacio Valley Road exit east. Drive three miles into Walnut Creek. Turn right on Oak Grove Road, then left on Valley Vista Road.

***Course description:*** This course has a sprawling, demanding layout with both trees and water coming into play. It's a good driving course. Coincidentally, head pro Bob Boldt led the Senior PGA Tour in driving distance in 1988. The re-designed 11th, at 444 yards, requires a huge drive to get an approach to the green. The second shot is over a lake. When the greens are in good condition, this is a fun, challenging course. But at times, the greens get bumpy, so putting these severely sloped surfaces becomes a real chore.

**1969**
**Robert Muir Graves**

PO Box 4759
Walnut Creek, CA 94596

3800 Valley Vista Road
Walnut Creek, CA 94598

Pro shop (510) 934-6211
Clubhouse (510) 935-8121

- ✓ **driving range**
- ✓ **practice greens**
- ✓ **power carts**
- ✓ **pull carts**
- ✓ **golf club rental**
- locker rooms
- showers
- executive course
- accommodations
- ✓ **food and beverages**
- ✓ **clubhouse**

**Bob Boldt**
Manager/Pro/Superintendent

**George Claus**
Course Manager

| Hole | 1 | 2 | 3 | 4 | 5 | 6 | 7 | 8 | 9 | Out | BLUE | Rating: 72.0 |
|---|---|---|---|---|---|---|---|---|---|---|---|---|
| BLUE | 418 | 152 | 528 | 410 | 504 | 200 | 367 | 337 | 390 | 3306 | | Slope: 124 |
| WHITE | 398 | 139 | 516 | 382 | 470 | 165 | 353 | 321 | 373 | 3117 | | |
| Par | 4 | 3 | 5 | 4 | 5 | 3 | 4 | 4 | 4 | 36 | WHITE | Rating: 70.2 |
| Handicap | 8 | 18 | 4 | 2 | 16 | 10 | 12 | 14 | 6 | x | | Slope: 120 |
| RED | 381 | 119 | 474 | 330 | 453 | 145 | 314 | 276 | 329 | 2821 | | |
| Par | 4 | 3 | 5 | 4 | 5 | 3 | 4 | 4 | 4 | 36 | RED | Rating: 72.1 |
| Handicap | 3 | 17 | 1 | 5 | 11 | 15 | 7 | 13 | 9 | x | | Slope: 123 |

| Hole | 10 | 11 | 12 | 13 | 14 | 15 | 16 | 17 | 18 | In | Totals | |
|---|---|---|---|---|---|---|---|---|---|---|---|---|
| BLUE | 362 | 394 | 183 | 419 | 562 | 416 | 419 | 209 | 518 | 3482 | BLUE | 6788 |
| WHITE | 345 | 373 | 167 | 391 | 549 | 397 | 389 | 190 | 488 | 3289 | WHITE | 6406 |
| Par | 4 | 4 | 3 | 4 | 5 | 4 | 4 | 3 | 5 | 36 | Par | 72 |
| Handicap | 17 | 13 | 15 | 7 | 1 | 5 | 3 | 9 | 11 | x | | |
| RED | 307 | 314 | 125 | 353 | 489 | 359 | 351 | 148 | 438 | 2884 | RED | 5705 |
| Par | 4 | 4 | 3 | 4 | 5 | 4 | 4 | 3 | 5 | 36 | Par | 72 |
| Handicap | 14 | 6 | 18 | 12 | 2 | 10 | 8 | 16 | 4 | x | | |

# ROUND HILL GOLF AND COUNTRY CLUB

**Course 28**
MAP E1 grid c8

**1978**
**William Francis Bell**

3169 Round Hill Road
Alamo, CA 94507

Pro shop (510) 837-7424
Clubhouse (510) 934-8211

- ✓ **driving range**
- ✓ **practice greens**
- ✓ **power carts**
- pull carts
- ✓ **golf club rental**
- ✓ **locker rooms**
- ✓ **showers**
- executive course
- accommodations
- ✓ **food and beverages**
- ✓ **clubhouse**

**Al Krueger**
Professional

**George Cherolis**
Superintendent

*Course information:* This private course has 18 holes. See card below for yardage and rating information.

*Play policy and fees:* Reciprocal play is accepted with members of other private clubs. Have your club pro call to make arrangements. Guest fees are $30 when accompanied by a member and $50 unaccompanied. Carts are $30 for guests. This course is available for outside tournaments on Mondays only.

*Location:* From Interstate 680 in Alamo, take the Stone Valley Road exit east to Round Hill Road north. The course is one mile from Interstate 680.

*Course description:* This tight, rolling course is located in San Ramon Valley. It has undulating greens, many trees, lots of side-hill lies, and narrow approach shots. In the past, LPGA events have taken place here. The 401-yard third is a great par-4. There's a lake in front of the tee and a huge oak in the middle of the fairway. Holes 12 through 16, a 424-yard severe dogleg right, a 188-yard par-3, a 488-yard par-5, a 384-yard par-4, and a 200-yard par-3, are the guts of the course. Always in immaculate shape, Round Hill has PGA-quality greens. Head pro Al Krueger has been at RHGC for 27 years.

| Hole | 1 | 2 | 3 | 4 | 5 | 6 | 7 | 8 | 9 | Out | | |
|---|---|---|---|---|---|---|---|---|---|---|---|---|
| BLUE | 398 | 349 | 401 | 499 | 206 | 455 | 142 | 339 | 387 | 3176 | BLUE | Rating: 71.2 |
| | | | | | | | | | | | | Slope: 127 |
| WHITE | 381 | 349 | 377 | 482 | 190 | 455 | 142 | 339 | 354 | 3069 | | |
| Par | 4 | 4 | 4 | 5 | 3 | 5 | 3 | 4 | 4 | 36 | WHITE | Rating: 70.3 |
| Handicap | 5 | 11 | 1 | 3 | 9 | 7 | 17 | 15 | 13 | x | | Slope: 125 |
| RED | 375 | 332 | 366 | 478 | 182 | 413 | 122 | 326 | 332 | 2926 | | |
| Par | 4 | 4 | 4 | 5 | 3 | 5 | 3 | 4 | 4 | 36 | RED | Rating: 74.1 |
| Handicap | 7 | 9 | 1 | 3 | 17 | 5 | 15 | 13 | 11 | x | | Slope: 134 |

| Hole | 10 | 11 | 12 | 13 | 14 | 15 | 16 | 17 | 18 | In | Totals | |
|---|---|---|---|---|---|---|---|---|---|---|---|---|
| BLUE | 388 | 318 | 424 | 188 | 488 | 384 | 200 | 417 | 488 | 3295 | BLUE | 6471 |
| WHITE | 377 | 300 | 412 | 173 | 488 | 367 | 192 | 399 | 481 | 3189 | WHITE | 6258 |
| Par | 4 | 4 | 4 | 3 | 5 | 4 | 3 | 4 | 5 | 36 | Par | 72 |
| Handicap | 10 | 18 | 2 | 12 | 8 | 6 | 14 | 4 | 16 | x | | |
| RED | 370 | 288 | 406 | 165 | 475 | 314 | 175 | 398 | 428 | 3019 | RED | 5945 |
| Par | 4 | 4 | 5 | 3 | 5 | 4 | 3 | 5 | 5 | 38 | Par | 74 |
| Handicap | 10 | 14 | 4 | 16 | 2 | 8 | 18 | 6 | 12 | x | | |



MAP ON PAGE 184

# DIABLO COUNTRY CLUB

**Course 29**
MAP E1 grid c8

***Course information:*** This private course has 18 holes. Women's tees are rated 76.2 with a slope of 136 from the white tees. See card below for additional yardage and rating information.

***Play policy and fees:*** Reciprocal play is accepted with members of other private clubs. Have your club pro call for arrangements. Guest fees are $30 weekdays and $40 weekends with a member. Reciprocal fees are $85. Carts are $10 per person.

***Location:*** From Interstate 680 in Danville, take the Diablo Road exit into Diablo Development; proceed one quarter of a mile, veering left at the fork in the road, the left on Clubhouse Road.

***Course description:*** This course has a tree-lined layout with small, demanding greens. It's an old course with tough par-3s. It's one of the best courses in the Bay Area. The 436-yard ninth, 536-yard 10th, 441-yard 11th, 430-yard 12th, and 238-yard par-3 13th is the best string of holes in the county. Jack Neville helped design some of the course back in 1917. Huge oak trees come into play often. The 397-yard 17th, and 479-yard 18th play through oaks that are 300 years old. A re-designed clubhouse gives this the feel of an old eastern country club.

PO Box 777
Diablo, CA 94528

1 Clubhouse Road
Diablo, CA 94528

Pro shop (510) 837-9233
Clubhouse (510) 837-4221

- driving range
- ✓ **practice greens**
- ✓ **power carts**
- pull carts
- golf club rental
- ✓ **locker rooms**
- ✓ **showers**
- executive course
- accommodations
- ✓ **food and beverages**
- ✓ **clubhouse**

**Paul Wilcox, Jr.**
Professional

**Sohan Singh**
Superintendent

| Hole | 1 | 2 | 3 | 4 | 5 | 6 | 7 | 8 | 9 | Out | BLUE | Rating: 71.5 |
|---|---|---|---|---|---|---|---|---|---|---|---|---|
| BLUE | 391 | 388 | 166 | 419 | 540 | 192 | 490 | 157 | 436 | 3179 | | Slope: 123 |
| WHITE | 358 | 378 | 157 | 401 | 529 | 179 | 485 | 141 | 401 | 3029 | | |
| Par | 4 | 4 | 3 | 4 | 5 | 3 | 5 | 3 | 4 | 35 | WHITE | Rating: 70.1 |
| Handicap | 7 | 5 | 13 | 1 | 9 | 11 | 17 | 15 | 3 | x | | Slope: 120 |
| RED | 360 | 373 | 141 | 347 | 453 | 158 | 472 | 113 | 369 | 2786 | | |
| Par | 4 | 4 | 3 | 4 | 5 | 3 | 5 | 3 | 4 | 35 | RED | Rating: 73.2 |
| Handicap | 9 | 7 | 15 | 11 | 1 | 13 | 3 | 17 | 5 | x | | Slope: 129 |

| Hole | 10 | 11 | 12 | 13 | 14 | 15 | 16 | 17 | 18 | In | Totals | |
|---|---|---|---|---|---|---|---|---|---|---|---|---|
| BLUE | 536 | 441 | 430 | 238 | 338 | 421 | 181 | 397 | 479 | 3461 | BLUE | 6640 |
| WHITE | 513 | 379 | 390 | 213 | 326 | 404 | 164 | 385 | 474 | 3248 | WHITE | 6277 |
| Par | 5 | 4 | 4 | 3 | 4 | 4 | 3 | 4 | 5 | 36 | Par | 71 |
| Handicap | 12 | 4 | 6 | 8 | 14 | 2 | 16 | 10 | 18 | x | | |
| RED | 429 | 373 | 376 | 160 | 310 | 408 | 145 | 334 | 431 | 2966 | RED | 5752 |
| Par | 5 | 4 | 4 | 3 | 4 | 5 | 3 | 4 | 5 | 37 | Par | 72 |
| Handicap | 2 | 8 | 12 | 16 | 14 | 4 | 18 | 10 | 6 | x | | |

# OAKHURST COUNTRY CLUB

**Course 30**
MAP E1 grid c9



**1990**
**Ron Fream**

PO Box 358
Clayton, CA 94517

8000 Clayton Road
Clayton, CA 94517

Pro shop (510) 672-9737

- ✓ **driving range**
- ✓ **practice greens**
- ✓ **power carts**
- pull carts
- ✓ **golf club rental**
- locker rooms
- showers
- executive course
- accommodations
- ✓ **food and beverages**
- ✓ **clubhouse**

**Dick Huff**
Director of Golf

**Dennis Simon**
Professional

***Course information:*** This semi-private course has 18 holes. Par is 72. The course is 6,739 yards and rated 73.1 with a slope of 132 from the black tees. Women's tees are rated 70.3 with a slope of 123 from the white tees. See card below for additional yardage and rating information.

***Play policy and fees:*** Outside play is accepted. Green fees are $50 weekdays and $70 weekends. Twilight fees are $39 weekends. Carts are included and required. Reservations are recommended three days in advance. This course is available for outside tournaments.

***Location:*** From Highway 680, take Ygnacio Valley exit east to Clayton Road. Turn right on Clayton Road and drive two miles to the course.

***Course description:*** This course has quickly become a solid test of any player's game. It's a highly rated semi-private layout, with lots of lateral hazards and out-of-bounds. The fairways are undulating with few even lies. The greens, although still maturing, are quick and true. You can count on reliable putting, considering their youth. The 580-yard 12th hole plays along a barranca on the right, and the next two par-4s require precision tee shots. The 18th hole, which plays over a huge barranca, can be misleading, if not downright deceptive. You have to play the tee shot just left of the right fairway bunkers. Be forewarned: The greens can be so tough, even club pros 4-putt. Up to 50,000 rounds are played here each year.

| Hole | 1 | 2 | 3 | 4 | 5 | 6 | 7 | 8 | 9 | Out | | |
|---|---|---|---|---|---|---|---|---|---|---|---|---|
| GOLD | 517 | 380 | 163 | 362 | 374 | 402 | 495 | 144 | 361 | 3198 | GOLD | Rating: 70.9 |
| WHITE | 488 | 340 | 123 | 342 | 351 | 372 | 466 | 123 | 340 | 2945 | | Slope: 127 |
| Par | 5 | 4 | 3 | 4 | 4 | 4 | 5 | 3 | 4 | 36 | WHITE | Rating: 69.1 |
| Handicap | 5 | 1 | 17 | 13 | 7 | 3 | 11 | 15 | 9 | x | | Slope: 122 |
| RED | 457 | 313 | 92 | 324 | 323 | 344 | 432 | 105 | 316 | 2706 | | |
| Par | 5 | 4 | 3 | 4 | 4 | 4 | 5 | 3 | 4 | 36 | RED | Rating: 70.3 |
| Handicap | 1 | 11 | 17 | 13 | 5 | 9 | 3 | 15 | 7 | x | | Slope: 123 |

| Hole | 10 | 11 | 12 | 13 | 14 | 15 | 16 | 17 | 18 | In | Totals | |
|---|---|---|---|---|---|---|---|---|---|---|---|---|
| GOLD | 405 | 181 | 535 | 122 | 340 | 274 | 480 | 325 | 415 | 3077 | GOLD | 6275 |
| WHITE | 381 | 160 | 513 | 118 | 315 | 258 | 471 | 302 | 380 | 2898 | WHITE | 5843 |
| Par | 4 | 3 | 5 | 3 | 4 | 4 | 5 | 4 | 4 | 36 | Par | 72 |
| Handicap | 4 | 10 | 8 | 18 | 6 | 14 | 12 | 16 | 2 | x | | |
| RED | 349 | 126 | 469 | 95 | 295 | 239 | 404 | 272 | 330 | 2579 | RED | 5285 |
| Par | 4 | 3 | 5 | 3 | 4 | 4 | 5 | 4 | 4 | 36 | Par | 72 |
| Handicap | 8 | 16 | 2 | 18 | 6 | 14 | 12 | 10 | 4 | x | | |

# HARDING PARK GOLF COURSE

**Course 31**
MAP E1 grid d2

**1925**
**William "Willie" Watson**

15 Morton Drive
Daly City, CA 94015

Pro shop (415) 664-4690
Clubhouse (415) 878-4427

- ✓ **driving range**
- ✓ **practice greens**
- ✓ **power carts**
- ✓ **pull carts**
- ✓ **golf club rental**
- locker rooms
- showers
- ✓ **executive course**
- accommodations
- ✓ **food and beverages**
- ✓ **clubhouse**

**Rodger Langlois**
Professional

**Jeff Wilson**
Director of Golf

**Raul Hernandez**
Superintendent

***Course information:*** This public course has 27 holes.

The Harding Course is detailed below.

The Fleming Course, a nine-hole, par-3, beginner layout, is 2,700 yards and par is 31.

***Play policy and fees:*** Green fees are $20 weekdays and $25 weekends at the Harding Course. Senior resident of San Francisco rates are available for $10 weekdays and $15 weekends. Residents with a card pay $14 weekdays, $17 weekends. The Fleming Course fees are $9 weekdays and $10 weekends. Residents with a card pay $7 weekdays, $12 weekends. Senior rates are also available. Carts are $10 for nine holes and $18 for 18 holes with a $5 deposit.

***Location:*** Heading north into San Francisco on Interstate 280 onto 19th Avenue, make a left on Skyline Boulevard. Follow Skyline to Morton Drive and turn left to the course.

***Course description:*** This underrated, sprawling course is surrounded by Lake Merced and is mostly flat but well guarded by trees. The latest nine was designed by Jack Fleming. The back nine is one of the best in Northern California. The course was formerly used for the PGA Tour's Lucky International Open and a Senior PGA Tour event. It is the annual site for Publinx Qualifying, and is used for the San Francisco City Golf Championship, the biggest and oldest city tournament in the country. The back nine finishes with great views as the 16th and 17th look over Lake Merced. The 384-yard 18th require a carry over a ravine. With 135,000 rounds a year, this might be the busiest course in Northern California.

| Hole | 1 | 2 | 3 | 4 | 5 | 6 | 7 | 8 | 9 | Out | BLUE | Rating: -- |
|---|---|---|---|---|---|---|---|---|---|---|---|---|
| BLUE | - | - | - | - | - | - | - | - | - | - | | Slope: -- |
| WHITE | 377 | 339 | 161 | 572 | 337 | 396 | 386 | 204 | 495 | 3267 | | |
| Par | 4 | 4 | 3 | 5 | 4 | 4 | 4 | 3 | 5 | 36 | WHITE | Rating: 71.3 |
| Handicap | 7 | 17 | 11 | 3 | 13 | 1 | 5 | 9 | 15 | x | | Slope: 119 |
| RED | 346 | 348 | 146 | 550 | 325 | 372 | 319 | 185 | 481 | 3072 | | |
| Par | 4 | 4 | 3 | 5 | 4 | 4 | 4 | 3 | 5 | 36 | RED | Rating: 74.5 |
| Handicap | 9 | 7 | 17 | 1 | 11 | 3 | 13 | 15 | 5 | x | | Slope: -- |

| Hole | 10 | 11 | 12 | 13 | 14 | 15 | 16 | 17 | 18 | In | Totals | |
|---|---|---|---|---|---|---|---|---|---|---|---|---|
| BLUE | - | - | - | - | - | - | - | - | - | - | BLUE | -- |
| WHITE | 552 | 182 | 492 | 401 | 401 | 404 | 334 | 169 | 384 | 3319 | WHITE | 6586 |
| Par | 5 | 3 | 5 | 4 | 4 | 4 | 4 | 3 | 4 | 36 | Par | 72 |
| Handicap | 4 | 10 | 16 | 2 | 8 | 6 | 18 | 14 | 12 | x | | |
| RED | 528 | 139 | 468 | 400 | 366 | 375 | 320 | 155 | 364 | 3115 | RED | 6187 |
| Par | 5 | 3 | 5 | 5 | 4 | 4 | 4 | 3 | 4 | 37 | Par | 73 |
| Handicap | 2 | 18 | 4 | 6 | 10 | 8 | 14 | 16 | 12 | x | | |

# SAN FRANCISCO GOLF CLUB

**Course 32**
MAP E1 grid d2

**1915**
**A.W. Tillinghast**

Junipero Serra Boulevard
and Brotherhood Way
San Francisco, CA 94132

Pro shop (415) 469-4122
Clubhouse (415) 469-4103

- ✓ **driving range**
- ✓ **practice greens**
- ✓ **power carts**
- pull carts
- ✓ **golf club rental**
- ✓ **locker rooms**
- ✓ **showers**
- executive course
- accommodations
- ✓ **food and beverages**
- ✓ **clubhouse**

**Roberta Foster**
Manager

**Rick Rhoads**
Professional

**Robert Klinesteker**
Superintendent

***Course information:*** This private course has 18 holes. Women's tees are 6,015 and rated 76.3 with a slope of 140. See card below for additional yardage and rating information.

***Play policy and fees:*** Reciprocal play is not accepted. Members and guests only. Guest fees when accompanied by a member are $35 and $100 unaccompanied. Carts are allowed only with a medical excuse and the fee is $20 with a member and $25 without.

***Location:*** From the Golden Gate Bridge into San Francisco, take the 19th Avenue exit and follow it through town until it turns into Junipero Serra Boulevard (past San Francisco State University). Turn right on Brotherhood Way and then take the first left onto Saint Thomas Moore Way to the course on the left.

***Course description:*** This serene, immaculate course is rated among the top in the country. It's a medium-length, sprawling course with fast, undulating greens and 100 bunkers. Every hole is a treat. Designed in 1915 by A.W. Tillinghast, the course has strategically placed pine trees that make accuracy essential. The 407-yard dogleg right on the 12th and the 421-yard dogleg right on the 17th are examples of Tillinghast's subtle touch. The course played host to the 1974 Curtis Cup Match and is a regular site of the U.S. Open sectional qualifying. By the 7th tee are monuments commemorating the last dueling spot in California. A great, fair course where every hole is a treat. A total of 20,000 rounds are played here a year.

| Hole | 1 | 2 | 3 | 4 | 5 | 6 | 7 | 8 | 9 | Out | BLUE | Rating: 72.9 |
|---|---|---|---|---|---|---|---|---|---|---|---|---|
| BLUE | 516 | 423 | 382 | 215 | 388 | 411 | 184 | 372 | 576 | 3467 | | Slope: 133 |
| WHITE | 497 | 410 | 354 | 207 | 380 | 403 | 166 | 333 | 536 | 3286 | | |
| Par | 5 | 4 | 4 | 3 | 4 | 4 | 3 | 4 | 5 | 36 | WHITE | Rating: 71.5 |
| Handicap | 15 | 1 | 5 | 11 | 7 | 3 | 17 | 9 | 13 | x | | Slope: 130 |
| RED | - | - | - | - | - | - | - | - | - | - | | |
| Par | | | | | | | | | | | RED | Rating: -- |
| Handicap | | | | | | | | | | x | | Slope: -- |

| Hole | 10 | 11 | 12 | 13 | 14 | 15 | 16 | 17 | 18 | In | Totals | |
|---|---|---|---|---|---|---|---|---|---|---|---|---|
| BLUE | 408 | 157 | 407 | 377 | 333 | 161 | 373 | 421 | 523 | 3160 | BLUE | 6627 |
| WHITE | 378 | 148 | 370 | 372 | 326 | 148 | 367 | 414 | 507 | 3030 | WHITE | 6316 |
| Par | 4 | 3 | 4 | 4 | 4 | 3 | 4 | 4 | 5 | 35 | Par | 71 |
| Handicap | 6 | 18 | 4 | 8 | 14 | 16 | 10 | 2 | 12 | x | | |
| RED | - | - | - | - | - | - | - | - | - | - | RED | -- |
| Par | | | | | | | | | | | Par | |
| Handicap | | | | | | | | | | x | | |

MAP ON PAGE 184

# LAKE MERCED GOLF AND COUNTRY CLUB

**Course 33**
MAP E1 grid d2

**1922**
**Will Lock**

2300 Junipero Serra Blvd.
Daly City, CA 94015

Pro shop (415) 755-2239
Clubhouse (415) 755-2233

✓ **driving range**
✓ **practice greens**
✓ **power carts**
pull carts
golf club rental
✓ **locker rooms**
✓ **showers**
executive course
accommodations
✓ **food and beverages**
✓ **clubhouse**

**Adair B. Chew**
Manager

**Woody Wright**
Professional

**Lou Tonelli**
Superintendent

***Course information:*** This private course has 18 holes and par is 72. The course is 6,786 yards and rated 72.8 from the championship tees, and 6,499 yards and rated 71.5 from the regular tees. The slope ratings are 128 championship and 125 regular. Women's tees are 5,968 and rated 75.1. The slope rating is 135.

***Play policy and fees:*** Reciprocal play is at the discretion of the pro. Guest fees when accompanied by a member are $35 weekdays and $40 weekends. Green fees for reciprocators are $80 with a member and $90 without a member. Carts are $10 with a member and $15 without.

***Location:*** On 19th Avenue in San Francisco or Highway 1, merge onto Junipero Serra Boulevard toward Daly City and follow to the course.

***Course description:*** This is a long, challenging course with big, undulating greens, huge pines and San Francisco weather. There are some difficult par-3s, especially the 15th hole. It's long at 200 yards and narrow. Designed by Will Lock in 1922 and remodeled in 1964 by Robert Muir Graves, this course is well maintained and walkable. It was the 1990 site of the USGA Boys' National Championship. It was also the site of the Western Open and the Northern California Junior Championship, as well as 1992 U.S. Open sectional qualifying. The uphill dogleg right fourth hole, 442 yards, is one of the toughest holes in the region. The 409-yard fifth, dogleg left, and the 458-yard seventh, which requires a tee shot around a huge eucalyptus tree, are great challenges.

# THE OLYMPIC CLUB

**Course 34**
MAP E1 grid d2

**1924**
**Wilfred Reid**
**Sam Whiting**

524 Post Street
San Francisco, CA 94102

Off Skyline Boulevard
Daly City, CA 94105

Pro shop (415) 587-8338
Clubhouse (415) 587-4800

- ✓ **driving range**
- ✓ **practice greens**
- ✓ **power carts**
- pull carts
- ✓ **golf club rental**
- ✓ **locker rooms**
- ✓ **showers**
- executive course
- accommodations
- ✓ **food and beverages**
- ✓ **clubhouse**

**Paul Kennedy**
General Manager

**David Nightingale**
Manager

**Jim Lucius**
Professional

**John Fleming**
Superintendent

***Course information:*** This private facility has 36 holes. Par on the Lake Course is 71. Par on the Ocean Course is 72.

The Lake Course is 6,812 yards and rated 74.0 from the championship tees, and 6,476 yards and rated 72.1 from the regular tees. The slope ratings are 135 championship and 133 regular. Women's tees are 6,134 yards and rated 75.4. The slope rating is 135.

The Ocean Course is 6,359 yards and rated 70.8 from the championship tees, and 6,024 yards and rated 69.0 from the regular tees. The slope ratings are 126 championship and 123 regular. Women's tees are 5,566 yards and rated 72.8. The slope rating is 128.

***Play policy and fees:*** Reciprocal play is accepted for members of some private clubs. All guests must be accompanied by a member. Guest fees are $60 for the Lake Course and $50 for the Ocean Course when accompanied by a member. Unaccompanied guest fees are $150 for the Lake Course and $90 for the Ocean Course. Carts are $15 per rider.

***Location:*** Driving south on 19th Avenue through San Francisco, turn right on Sloat Boulevard. Follow it until it splits into a "Y" (before the San Francisco Zoo). Turn left onto Skyline Boulevard. The course is at the top of the hill, obscured by a fence.

***Course description:*** Add William "Willie" Watson's designer influence to the Ocean Course. History also links him to the Lake Course. The Lake Course has been the site of three U.S Opens (1955, 1966 and 1987) and ranks among the top 10 courses in the country. It is long, tight and has lots of trees. The greens are small and undulating. The Lake Course was designed by Wilfred Reid and Sam Whiting in 1924. Two of the biggest upsets in U.S. Open history happened on this course. In 1955, Jack Fleck shocked Ben Hogan in a playoff. In 1966, Billy Casper made up a seven-stroke deficit with nine holes to play to tie Arnold Palmer, then defeated him in a playoff. The course was also the site of the 1981 U.S. Amateur, where Nathaniel Crosby pulled off an upset victory. Some of the famous holes include the 605-yard 16th, a huge crescent of a par-5. Long par-4s dominate the Lake Course, making it the longest 6,800 yards in golf: the 433-yard ninth, and the 430-yard 11th are two examples. The Ocean Course is shorter and tighter, but equally challenging. Wind and fog come into play.



MAP ON PAGE 184

# CYPRESS GOLF COURSE

**Course 35**
MAP E1 grid d2

***Course information:*** This public course has nine holes. Women's yardage was not available. The course is unrated. See card below for yardage information.

***Play policy and fees:*** Green fees are $10 Monday through Thursday, and $15 Fridays, weekends and holidays. Senior rates are $7 before 9 a.m. Monday through Friday. Carts are $10 for nine holes.

***Location:*** From Interstate 280 in South San Francisco, take the Serramonte Boulevard exit. Cross over to the east side of the freeway and drive south on Hillside Boulevard. Continue down about 500 yards to the course entrance on the left.

***Course description:*** This course is tight and well guarded by trees. It has a lake, two par-5s and only one par-3. The double dogleg par-5 fifth, at 530 yards, all uphill, is the toughest on the course.

**1961**
**Jack Fleming**

2001 Hillside Boulevard
Colma, CA 94014

Pro shop (415) 992-5155

- ✓ **driving range**
- ✓ **practice greens**
- ✓ **power carts**
- ✓ **pull carts**
- golf club rental
- locker rooms
- showers
- executive course
- accommodations
- ✓ **food and beverages**
- ✓ **clubhouse**

**David G. Newman**
Director of Golf

**Don Giovannini**
Professional

**Mike Castillo**
Superintendent

| Hole | 1 | 2 | 3 | 4 | 5 | 6 | 7 | 8 | 9 | Out | BLUE | Rating: -- |
|---|---|---|---|---|---|---|---|---|---|---|---|---|
| BLUE | - | - | - | - | - | - | - | - | - | - | | Slope: -- |
| WHITE | 365 | 460 | 163 | 478 | 530 | 372 | 394 | 355 | 326 | 3443 | | |
| Par | 4 | 4 | 3 | 5 | 5 | 4 | 4 | 4 | 4 | 37 | WHITE | Rating: -- |
| Handicap | 7 | 5 | 4 | 3 | 1 | 2 | 6 | 9 | 8 | x | | Slope: -- |
| RED | - | - | - | - | - | - | - | - | - | - | | |
| Par | - | - | - | - | - | - | - | - | - | - | RED | Rating: -- |
| Handicap | - | - | - | - | - | - | - | - | - | x | | Slope: -- |

| Hole | 10 | 11 | 12 | 13 | 14 | 15 | 16 | 17 | 18 | In | Totals | |
|---|---|---|---|---|---|---|---|---|---|---|---|---|
| BLUE | - | - | - | - | - | - | - | - | - | - | BLUE | -- |
| WHITE | 365 | 460 | 163 | 478 | 530 | 372 | 394 | 355 | 326 | 3443 | WHITE | 6886 |
| Par | 4 | 4 | 3 | 5 | 5 | 4 | 4 | 4 | 4 | 37 | Par | 74 |
| Handicap | 7 | 5 | 4 | 4 | 1 | 2 | 6 | 9 | 8 | x | | |
| RED | - | - | - | - | - | - | - | - | - | - | RED | -- |
| Par | - | - | - | - | - | - | - | - | - | - | Par | -- |
| Handicap | - | - | - | - | - | - | - | - | - | x | | |

# GLENEAGLES INTERNATIONAL GOLF COURSE

**Course 36**
MAP E1 grid d3

**1963**
**Jack Fleming**

2100 Sunnydale Avenue
San Francisco, CA 94134

Pro shop (415) 587-2425

- driving range
- ✓ **practice greens**
- ✓ **power carts**
- pull carts
- golf club rental
- locker rooms
- showers
- executive course
- accommodations
- ✓ **food and beverages**
- ✓ **clubhouse**

**Erik DeLambert**
Owner/Manager

**Mick Soli**
Professional

**Ben DeLambert**
Superintendent

NORTHERN E1

***Course information:*** This public course has nine holes. Par is 72 for 18 holes. The course is 6,642 yards and rated 73.6 from the championship tees, and 6,421 yards and rated 71.0 from the regular tees. The slope ratings are 136 championship and 129 regular. Women's yardage and ratings were unavailable.

***Play policy and fees:*** Green fees are $9 for nine holes and $15 for 18 holes weekdays, and $20 for 18 holes weekends. There is no nine-hole play on weekends or holidays. Carts are $10 for nine holes and $20 for 18 holes.

***Location:*** Driving south on Highway 101 on the way out of San Francisco, take the Paul Avenue exit. At the stop sign, proceed up the hill on Manzell and over the top to Sunnydale Avenue and turn left. The course is located 400 yards at the first driveway on the left. It's unmarked. Driving north on Highway 101 into San Francisco, take the Cow Palace/Brisbane exit to Old Bayshore and go left at Geneva Street. In 1.5 miles, turn right on Moscow and then right again on Persia. It's three blocks to Sunnydale Avenue.

***Course description:*** This sleeper course is patterned after a Scottish links-type course with a rolling terrain. You'll find tight, tree-lined fairways and tricky greens. Good target shots are required. It's well maintained and often foggy and windy. The greens and tee boxes are in great shape. The course record is 66, set by former PGA Tour player and host pro Mick Soli. An eight-stool, Scottish-style pub with ales and beers will soothe your frayed nerves after you finish. Lee Trevino played the course, according to legend, shooting 71 on his first try, then going back out and shooting 72. Legend has it that no one has broken par the first time out. The 400-yard seventh is the toughest: a tee shot uphill and into the wind. A total of 60,000 rounds are played here each year.

# LEW F. GALBRAITH GOLF COURSE

**Course 37**
MAP E1 grid d5

***Course information:*** This public course has 18 holes. See card below for yardage and rating information.

***Play policy and fees:*** Green fees are $12 weekdays and $16 weekends. Rates for seniors are $9, juniors are $6 and twilight rates are $8. Carts are $16.

***Location:*** From Interstate 880 in Oakland, exit at Hegenberger Road southwest. Drive one mile to Doolittle Drive. Turn left and drive to the course on the right.

***Course description:*** This flat course plays long. The fifth and 18th holes are two beautiful, challenging par-4s of 422 and 410 yards, respectively. Because the course is near the airport, wind can be a contributing element—that and a 727 descending near the top of your backswing. The 380-yard 12th hole and the 412-yard 16th are good holes. A total of 62,500 rounds are played here each year.

**1966**
**R.E. Baldock**

10505 Doolittle Drive
Oakland, CA 94603

Pro shop (510) 569-9411
Clubhouse (510) 562-7474

- ✓ **driving range**
- ✓ **practice greens**
- ✓ **power carts**
- ✓ **pull carts**
- ✓ **golf club rental**
- ✓ **locker rooms**
- showers
- executive course
- accommodations
- ✓ **food and beverages**
- ✓ **clubhouse**

**Hugh McKay**
Director of Golf

| Hole | 1 | 2 | 3 | 4 | 5 | 6 | 7 | 8 | 9 | Out | | |
|---|---|---|---|---|---|---|---|---|---|---|---|---|
| BLUE | 495 | 337 | 403 | 194 | 422 | 406 | 439 | 543 | 180 | 3419 | BLUE | Rating: 71.2 |
| WHITE | 478 | 312 | 380 | 178 | 397 | 384 | 416 | 518 | 164 | 3227 | | Slope: 117 |
| Par | 5 | 4 | 4 | 3 | 4 | 4 | 4 | 5 | 3 | 36 | WHITE | Rating: 69.6 |
| Handicap | 5 | 11 | 9 | 15 | 1 | 13 | 3 | 7 | 17 | x | | Slope: 115 |
| RED | 464 | 282 | 362 | 150 | 376 | 369 | 386 | 498 | 150 | 3037 | | |
| Par | 5 | 4 | 4 | 3 | 4 | 4 | 4 | 5 | 3 | 36 | RED | Rating: 71.5 |
| Handicap | 1 | 13 | 11 | 15 | 7 | 9 | 3 | 5 | 17 | x | | Slope: 117 |

| Hole | 10 | 11 | 12 | 13 | 14 | 15 | 16 | 17 | 18 | In | Totals | |
|---|---|---|---|---|---|---|---|---|---|---|---|---|
| BLUE | 364 | 478 | 380 | 161 | 287 | 500 | 412 | 168 | 410 | 3160 | BLUE | 6579 |
| WHITE | 351 | 463 | 364 | 145 | 273 | 489 | 377 | 149 | 395 | 3006 | WHITE | 6233 |
| Par | 4 | 5 | 4 | 3 | 4 | 5 | 4 | 3 | 4 | 36 | Par | 72 |
| Handicap | 10 | 12 | 6 | 14 | 18 | 4 | 2 | 16 | 8 | x | | |
| RED | 311 | 451 | 344 | 131 | 263 | 409 | 251 | 126 | 381 | 2667 | RED | 5704 |
| Par | 4 | 5 | 4 | 3 | 4 | 5 | 4 | 3 | 4 | 36 | Par | 72 |
| Handicap | 10 | 2 | 8 | 16 | 14 | 4 | 12 | 18 | 6 | x | | |

# CHUCK CORICA GOLF COURSE

**Course 38**
MAP E1 grid d5



**1927**
**William Park Bell**
**William Francis Bell**

1 Memorial Drive
Alameda, CA 94501

Pro shop (510) 522-4321

- ✓ **driving range**
- ✓ **practice greens**
- ✓ **power carts**
- ✓ **pull carts**
- ✓ **golf club rental**
- ✓ **locker rooms**
- showers
- executive course
- accommodations
- ✓ **food and beverages**
- ✓ **clubhouse**

**John Thialaid**
Professional

**Dennis Plato**
Superintendent

***Course information:*** This public facility has 36 holes and par is 71 for both. There is an adjacent par-3 course.

The Jack Clark Course is 6,559 yards and rated 70.8 from the championship tees, and 6,107 yards and rated 68.0 from the regular tees. The slope ratings are 114 championship and 110 regular. Women's tees are 5,473 yards and rated and rated 70.0 from the forward tees. The slope rating is 118 championship.

See card below for yardage and rating information for the Earl Fry Course.

***Play policy and fees:*** Green fees are $13 weekdays and $14 weekends, for residents. For non-residents, weekdays cost $14, weekends, $17. Carts are $16.

***Location:*** From Interstate 880 (Nimitz Freeway) south of the Oakland Coliseum, take the Hegenberger Road exit west one mile. Turn right on Doolittle Road and follow it to Island Drive and turn left. Turn left again on Memorial Drive to the course.

***Course description:*** These are flat, challenging courses. The Jack Clark Course is longer and more difficult. It was designed by William Francis Bell. It is the more popular, with the 192-yard 15th—bunkers left and right and a water hazard behind the green—serving as the best hole. The Jack Clark Pro Am is held here every September. The Earl Fry Course was designed by William "Billy" Park Bell. Both are well-maintained and walkable courses with lots of trees and some water. This is the site of the annual Alameda Commuters Tournament each April, one of Northern California's oldest and best-run amateur events.

Earl Fry Course

| Hole | 1 | 2 | 3 | 4 | 5 | 6 | 7 | 8 | 9 | Out | | |
|---|---|---|---|---|---|---|---|---|---|---|---|---|
| BLUE | 371 | 493 | 345 | 177 | 330 | 459 | 176 | 386 | 400 | 3137 | BLUE | Rating: 69.2 |
| WHITE | 358 | 479 | 335 | 169 | 317 | 446 | 160 | 363 | 367 | 2994 | | Slope: 119 |
| Par | 4 | 5 | 4 | 3 | 4 | 5 | 3 | 4 | 4 | 36 | WHITE | Rating: 67.6 |
| Handicap | 7 | 3 | 13 | 17 | 15 | 5 | 11 | 1 | 9 | x | | Slope: 110 |
| RED | 326 | 450 | 314 | 154 | 284 | 439 | 150 | 412 | 340 | 2869 | | |
| Par | 4 | 5 | 4 | 3 | 4 | 5 | 3 | 5 | 4 | 37 | RED | Rating: 71.0 |
| Handicap | 7 | 1 | 15 | 17 | 11 | 3 | 13 | 5 | 9 | x | | Slope: 114 |

| Hole | 10 | 11 | 12 | 13 | 14 | 15 | 16 | 17 | 18 | In | Totals | |
|---|---|---|---|---|---|---|---|---|---|---|---|---|
| BLUE | 389 | 166 | 364 | 403 | 450 | 192 | 393 | 281 | 366 | 3004 | BLUE | 6141 |
| WHITE | 367 | 139 | 356 | 385 | 434 | 154 | 385 | 268 | 344 | 2832 | WHITE | 5826 |
| Par | 4 | 3 | 4 | 4 | 5 | 3 | 4 | 4 | 4 | 35 | Par | 71 |
| Handicap | 12 | 18 | 10 | 8 | 4 | 2 | 6 | 16 | 14 | x | | |
| RED | 366 | 134 | 329 | 376 | 423 | 99 | 381 | 250 | 333 | 2691 | RED | 5560 |
| Par | 4 | 3 | 4 | 4 | 5 | 3 | 4 | 4 | 4 | 35 | Par | 72 |
| Handicap | 4 | 14 | 12 | 8 | 2 | 16 | 6 | 18 | 10 | x | | |

# SEQUOYAH COUNTRY CLUB

**Course 39**
MAP E1 grid d6

**1913**

***Course information:*** This private course has 18 holes. See card below for yardage and rating information.

***Play policy and fees:*** Reciprocal play is accepted with members of other private clubs weekdays only. Have your club pro call to make arrangements. Guest green fees are $55 weekdays and $65 weekends, including mandatory cart. The golf dress code is in effect.

***Location:*** From Interstate 580 in southern Oakland, take the 98th Avenue exit. Cross to the east side of the freeway. Turn left onto Mountain Boulevard. Turn right on Sequoyah Road and follow it for three-fourths of a mile. Turn right on Heafey Road and drive to the course.

***Course description:*** This mature course is short, hilly and tight. The elevated tees and fast greens make for exciting par-3s. It's very exclusive. This course was the site of the PGA Tour's Oakland Open in the 1930s, featuring players such as Ben Hogan and Sam Snead. This course is very tough, and local knowledge of the greens is the only way to survive. There are five par-3s, and member Dr. Wayne Wright has scored a hole-in-one on all of them. He's been a member for 43 years, but he had his aces by 1980. The 445-yard 11th with a panoramic view of the bay is a great challenge. The course record, set by Don Witt, is 62.

4550 Heafey Road
Oakland, CA 94605

Pro shop (510) 632-4069
Clubhouse (510) 632-2900

- ✓ **driving range**
- ✓ **practice greens**
- ✓ **power carts**
- pull carts
- golf club rental
- ✓ **locker rooms**
- ✓ **showers**
- executive course
- accommodations
- ✓ **food and beverages**
- ✓ **clubhouse**

**Stan Spraul**
Manager

**John R. Bearden**
Professional

**Chuck Pratt**
Superintendent

| Hole | 1 | 2 | 3 | 4 | 5 | 6 | 7 | 8 | 9 | Out | BLUE | Rating: 69.8 |
|---|---|---|---|---|---|---|---|---|---|---|---|---|
| BLUE | 311 | 191 | 400 | 374 | 137 | 528 | 329 | 389 | 348 | 3007 | | Slope: 126 |
| WHITE | 311 | 191 | 387 | 369 | 137 | 509 | 314 | 366 | 333 | 2917 | | |
| Par | 4 | 3 | 4 | 4 | 3 | 5 | 4 | 4 | 4 | 35 | WHITE | Rating: 69.1 |
| Handicap | 17 | 3 | 5 | 1 | 15 | 3 | 11 | 7 | 9 | x | | Slope: 124 |
| RED | 304 | 188 | 380 | 359 | 119 | 496 | 304 | 327 | 299 | 2776 | | |
| Par | 4 | 3 | 4 | 4 | 3 | 5 | 4 | 4 | 4 | 35 | RED | Rating: 73.3 |
| Handicap | 13 | 15 | 3 | 5 | 17 | 1 | 7 | 9 | 11 | x | | Slope: 131 |

| Hole | 10 | 11 | 12 | 13 | 14 | 15 | 16 | 17 | 18 | In | Totals | |
|---|---|---|---|---|---|---|---|---|---|---|---|---|
| BLUE | 380 | 445 | 172 | 337 | 238 | 330 | 482 | 220 | 450 | 3054 | BLUE | 6061 |
| WHITE | 380 | 421 | 154 | 324 | 217 | 323 | 469 | 192 | 441 | 2921 | WHITE | 5838 |
| Par | 4 | 4 | 3 | 4 | 3 | 4 | 5 | 3 | 5 | 35 | Par | 70 |
| Handicap | 4 | 2 | 16 | 12 | 10 | 14 | 6 | 8 | 18 | x | | |
| RED | 373 | 448 | 126 | 307 | 231 | 316 | 452 | 177 | 432 | 2862 | RED | 5638 |
| Par | 4 | 5 | 3 | 4 | 4 | 4 | 5 | 3 | 5 | 37 | Par | 72 |
| Handicap | 4 | 6 | 16 | 10 | 18 | 12 | 2 | 14 | 8 | x | | |

# LAKE CHABOT GOLF COURSE

**Course 40**
MAP E1 grid d6

***Course information:*** This public course has 18 holes and par is 71. The course is 6,018 yards and rated 68.6 from the regular tees. The slope rating is 115. Women's tees are 5,278 yards and rated 68.5. The slope rating is 116. A par-3 executive course is also available, measuring 1,040 yards.

***Play policy and fees:*** Green fees are $11 weekdays and $15 weekends. Twilight rates are $6 weekdays and $9 weekends. The recommended lead time for tee time reservations is one week. Carts are $16 weekdays and $18 weekends.

***Location:*** From Interstate 580 in Oakland, take the Golf Links Road exit and follow the road to the end.

***Course description:*** This course is hilly but walkable. The 18th hole is a unique 690-yard par-5, down (or is it up) from its former par of 6 at 665 yards. The hole starts off level and slopes down and then up. Out-of-bounds is to the left and trees are on the right. Take your complaints to course manager Raymond Chester, former All-Pro tight end with the Oakland Raiders. The course is one of the oldest in Northern California. Tony Lema, 1964 British Open champion, grew up near Lake Chabot. The course record of 60 is shared by John Fry and Gary Vanier. 80,000 rounds are played here per year.

**1923**

Golf Links Road
Oakland, CA 94605

Pro shop (510) 351-5812

✓ **driving range**
✓ **practice greens**
✓ **power carts**
pull carts
✓ **golf club rental**
locker rooms
showers
✓ **executive course**
accommodations
✓ **food and beverages**
✓ **clubhouse**

**Jeff Dennis**
Professional

**Raymond Chester**
Manager

**Bill Menear**
Superintendent

# CANYON LAKES COUNTRY CLUB

**Course 41**
MAP E1 grid d8

**1987**
**Ted Robinson**

640 Bollinger Canyon Way
San Ramon, CA 94583

Pro shop (510) 735-6511
Clubhouse (510) 735-6224

- driving range
- ✓ **practice greens**
- ✓ **power carts**
- pull carts
- ✓ **golf club rental**
- ✓ **locker rooms**
- ✓ **showers**
- executive course
- accommodations
- ✓ **food and beverages**
- ✓ **clubhouse**

**Russ Dicks**
Manager/Professional

**Bobby Cox**
Superintendent

***Course information:*** This public course has 18 holes and par is 71. The course is 6,379 yards and rated 70.1 from the championship tees, and 5,975 yards and rated 68.2 from the regular tees. The slope ratings are 116 championship and 113 regular. Women's tees are 5,230 yards and rated 69.9. The slope rating is 121.

***Play policy and fees:*** Green fees are $50 weekdays and $55 weekends, mandatory carts included. Reserve starting times a week in advance. This course is available for tournaments. Closed Mondays.

***Location:*** From Interstate 680 in San Ramon, take the Bollinger Canyon exit east over the freeway. Turn left on Canyon Lakes Drive, and left again on Bollinger Canyon Way to the course.

***Course description:*** Situated in the foothills of San Ramon, this course opened as a nine-hole layout in 1987 and expanded to 18 holes in the fall of 1989. It has lots of water, trees and bunkers. The fairways are contoured, and the greens undulate. The 400-yard eighth and 405-yard ninth are strong holes, but the 275-yard fourth, with its green surrounded by water, is a lot of fun. The 520-yard 14th, a par-5 that plays over a creek, requires a precise 250-yard shot to a narrow fairway. It's possible to reach the green in two shots, but the green is severely scored and fast—home of the four-putt. The par-5 17th is uphill and into the prevailing wind—a maddening hole. The 430-yard 18th has a blind second shot.

# CROW CANYON COUNTRY CLUB

**Course 42**
MAP E1 grid d8

**1977**
**Ted Robinson**

711 Silver Lake Drive
Danville, CA 94526

Pro shop (510) 735-8300
Clubhouse (510) 735-8200

- ✓ **driving range**
- ✓ **practice greens**
- ✓ **power carts**
- pull carts
- ✓ **golf club rental**
- ✓ **locker rooms**
- ✓ **showers**
- executive course
- accommodations
- ✓ **food and beverages**
- ✓ **clubhouse**

**Dave Anderson**
Professional

**Ernie Martin**
Superintendent

***Course information:*** This private course has 18 holes. See card below for yardage and rating information.

***Play policy and fees:*** Reciprocal play is accepted with members of other private clubs. Have your club pro call for arrangements. Guest fees are $30 Monday through Thursday and $45 Fridays and weekends. Reservations are recommended one week in advance. Golf shoes and shirts with collars are required. No jeans, tank tops, T-shirts, short shorts, gym shorts or tennis shorts may be worn. Closed Mondays.

***Location:*** From Interstate 680 in San Ramon, take the Crow Canyon exit east. Turn left on El Capitan and right on Silver Lake Drive.

***Course description:*** This is a hilly, tight, rolling course. The sixth hole is a notable par-3. It's 196 yards against the wind to an elevated green. The par-4 third can get you into trouble. The fairway is only 15 yards from out-of-bounds on the right. This course is known for being very well manicured with great drainage during the rainy season. The course is well bunkered with water coming into play on nine holes. The Diablo Advocates Pro-Am initially started at Crow Canyon, with such great golfers as Johnny Miller, George Archer, Larry Nelson, Bill Russell, Joe Morgan and Jim Rice. Watch out for the 400-yard, par-4 18th hole, which features an elevated tee and water along the left side of the hole. The men's and women's course records are held by Sean Clark (63) and Jane Crafter (64), respectively. A total of 80,000 rounds are played here per year.

| Hole | 1 | 2 | 3 | 4 | 5 | 6 | 7 | 8 | 9 | Out | | |
|---|---|---|---|---|---|---|---|---|---|---|---|---|
| BLUE | 370 | 544 | 401 | 165 | 326 | 196 | 373 | 167 | 384 | 2926 | BLUE | Rating: 68.6 |
| WHITE | 344 | 523 | 372 | 147 | 304 | 161 | 349 | 148 | 375 | 2723 | | Slope: 118 |
| Par | 4 | 5 | 4 | 3 | 4 | 3 | 4 | 3 | 4 | 34 | WHITE | Rating: 66.1 |
| Handicap | 9 | 7 | 3 | 13 | 15 | 1 | 11 | 17 | 5 | x | | Slope: 114 |
| RED | 344 | 523 | 372 | 147 | 304 | 161 | 349 | 148 | 375 | 2723 | | |
| Par | 4 | 5 | 4 | 3 | 4 | 3 | 4 | 3 | 4 | 34 | RED | Rating: 72.3 |
| Handicap | 7 | 1 | 5 | 15 | 13 | 11 | 9 | 17 | 3 | x | | Slope: 126 |

| Hole | 10 | 11 | 12 | 13 | 14 | 15 | 16 | 17 | 18 | In | Totals | |
|---|---|---|---|---|---|---|---|---|---|---|---|---|
| BLUE | 340 | 369 | 143 | 519 | 330 | 330 | 157 | 395 | 400 | 2983 | BLUE | 5909 |
| WHITE | 307 | 345 | 128 | 497 | 325 | 326 | 138 | 377 | 388 | 2831 | WHITE | 5554 |
| Par | 4 | 4 | 3 | 5 | 4 | 4 | 3 | 4 | 4 | 35 | Par | 69 |
| Handicap | 14 | 4 | 18 | 8 | 16 | 10 | 12 | 6 | 2 | x | | |
| RED | 307 | 345 | 128 | 497 | 325 | 326 | 138 | 377 | 388 | 2831 | RED | 5554 |
| Par | 4 | 4 | 3 | 5 | 4 | 4 | 3 | 4 | 5 | 36 | Par | 70 |
| Handicap | 14 | 10 | 16 | 2 | 12 | 4 | 18 | 6 | 8 | x | | |

# BLACKHAWK COUNTRY CLUB

**Course 43**
MAP E1 grid d9

***Course information:*** This private club has 36 holes and par is 72 on both courses.

The Lakeside Course is 6,845 yards and rated 74.2 from the championship tees, and 6,407 yards and rated 71.8 from the regular tees. The slope ratings are 135 championship and 132 regular. Women's tees are 5,424 and rated 71.3. The slope rating is 130.

The Falls Course is 6,731 yards and rated 72.8 from the championship tees, and 6,155 yards and rated 70.5 from the regular tees. The slope ratings are: 128 championship and 122 regular. Women's tees are 5,374 yards and rated 70.5. The slope rating is 128.

***Play policy and fees:*** Members and guests only. No reciprocal play. Guests must be accompanied by a member at time of play. Guest fees are $40 weekdays and $50 weekends. Carts are $20 and mandatory on both courses.

***Location:*** From Interstate 680 in Danville, take the Sycamore Valley Road exit. Turn right on Camino Tassajara and left on Blackhawk Road. Drive to Blackhawk Club Drive and turn right.

***Course description:*** The Lakeside Course is rolling and imaginative. Designed by Bruce Devlin and Robert Von Hagge, it has large, undulating greens, lots of water, and tight fairways. There are many up and down holes threading through oak trees. It requires shot making. The 400-yard 8th has a creek all the way down the right side. It is the tougher of the two courses. The Falls Course, designed by Ted Robinson, is a shorter version with emphasis on placement. It is rolling and hilly between holes. The first hole is a straight drop, but after that it flattens out. The Falls' 14th, a 392 dogleg, has a barranca on the right side. A moon crater in the green puts the precision on the approach. It's a fun course to play. Each course has a clubhouse and pro shop. Both Randy Haag and Ken Kluba shot 62 on the Lakeside, with Haag holding the Falls' record at 65.

**1981**
**Bruce Devlin**
**Robert Von Hagge**
**(Lakeside Course)**

**Ted Robinson**
**(Falls Course)**

599 Blackhawk Club Drive
Danville, CA 94526

Pro shop (510) 736-6565
Clubhouse (510) 736-6500

- ✓ **driving range**
- ✓ **practice greens**
- ✓ **power carts**
- pull carts
- ✓ **golf club rental**
- ✓ **locker rooms**
- ✓ **showers**
- executive course
- accommodations
- ✓ **food and beverages**
- ✓ **clubhouse**

**Rob Frederick**
Professional

**Charlie Johnson**
Superintendent

# SAN RAMON ROYAL VISTA GOLF COURSE

**Course 44**
MAP E1 grid d9

**1962**
**Clark Glasson**

9430 Fircrest Lane
San Ramon, CA 94583

Pro shop (510) 828-6100

- ✓ **driving range**
- ✓ **practice greens**
- ✓ **power carts**
- ✓ **pull carts**
- ✓ **golf club rental**
- ✓ **locker rooms**
- ✓ **showers**
- executive course
- accommodations
- ✓ **food and beverages**
- ✓ **clubhouse**

**Patty Largent**
Professional

**Edward Ferreira**
Superintendent

NORTHERN E1

***Course information:*** This semi-private course has 18 holes and par is 72. The course is 6,538 yards and rated 70.9 from the championship tees, and 6,300 yards and rated 69.8 from the regular tees. The slope ratings are 115 championship and 113 regular. Women's tees are 5,870 yards and rated 72.7. The slope rating is 119.

***Play policy and fees:*** This course is open to the public. Green fees are $17 weekdays and $27 weekends. There is a $10 rate for nine holes before 8 a.m. Twilight rate is $11 weekdays and $15 weekends. Carts are $12 for nine holes and $22 for 18 holes. Reservations are recommended one week in advance. Shirts with collars are required. No T-shirts or tank tops on the course or at the driving range. This course is available for outside tournaments.

***Location:*** Driving south on Interstate 680 in San Ramon, take the Alcosta Boulevard exit. Cross back over the freeway and drive one mile. Turn on Fircrest Lane to the course.

***Course description:*** This is a flat course with large greens. Homes line almost every fairway. More than 300 new trees have been planted. The course is in beautiful condition, thanks to on-site well water. The 400-yard 11th requires a lay-up off tee, due to a hazard halfway down. No. 16, at 420 yards, doglegs right, and has out-of-bounds on the right. A total of 85,000 rounds are played here each year.

# SHARP PARK GOLF COURSE

**Course 45**
MAP E1 grid e1

***Course information:*** This public course has 18 holes and par is 72. The course is 6,273 yards and rated 70.0 from regular the tees. The slope rating is 115. Women's tees are 6,095 yards and rated 73.0. The slope rating is 120.

***Play policy and fees:*** Green fees are $17 weekdays and $21 weekends. Half-price twilight rates are available. Carts are $20. Reservations are required one week in advance for weekday play, the prior Wednesday for Saturday play and the prior Thursday for Sunday play. This course is available for outside tournaments.

***Location:*** Heading south on Interstate 280 from San Francisco, take the second exit toward the town of Pacifica. Continue on to Pacifica on Highway 1. Turn to the course at Fairway Drive.

***Course description:*** This is a flat, tree-lined course located at sea level. The front nine is set inland, and the back nine runs along the ocean. The fairways are tight with large greens. This could be considered the poor man's Pebble Beach. There's sand, water, views and golf. The 13th hole is a par-5, 525-yard dogleg left over water and it's a doozie. The par-3 15th, at 150 yards over water, is also challenging. A total of 100,000 rounds are played here each year.

**1929**
**Alister Mackenzie**

PO Box 1275
Pacifica, CA 94044

Sharp Park Road and Hwy. 1
Pacifica, CA 94044

Pro shop (415) 359-3380
Clubhouse (415) 355-7900

- driving range
- ✓ **practice greens**
- ✓ **power carts**
- ✓ **pull carts**
- ✓ **golf club rental**
- locker rooms
- showers
- executive course
- accommodations
- ✓ **food and beverages**
- ✓ **clubhouse**

**Jack Gage**
Professional

**Joan W. Lantz**
Manager

**Sean Sweeney**
Superintendent

# GREEN HILLS COUNTRY CLUB

**Course 46**
MAP E1 grid e2



**1932**
**Alister MacKenzie**

End of Ludeman Lane
Millbrae, CA 94030

Pro shop (415) 583-0882
Clubhouse (415) 588-4616

- ✓ **driving range**
- ✓ **practice greens**
- ✓ **power carts**
- pull carts
- ✓ **golf club rental**
- ✓ **locker rooms**
- ✓ **showers**
- executive course
- accommodations
- ✓ **food and beverages**
- ✓ **clubhouse**

**Jack Mahoney**
Manager

**Steve Martino**
Professional

**Walt Barrett**
Superintendent

***Course information:*** This private course has 18 holes. See card below for yardage and rating information.

***Play policy and fees:*** Reciprocal play is accepted with members of other private clubs. Guest fees are $40 weekdays and $50 weekends when accompanied by a member, and $85 unaccompanied. Fees for reciprocators are $85. Carts are $10 per rider. Four-bagger prices are available if you'd like a cart to tow your bag while you walk.

***Location:*** Located between Interstate 280 and Highway 101 in Millbrae. Exit on Millbrae Avenue off Highway 101 and drive north on El Camino Real. Turn left on Ludeman Lane and drive up the hill to the course.

***Course description:*** This short, but tricky Alister MacKenzie course is situated in the foothills among the pine and cypress. It has small, undulating greens and is well bunkered. The pride of the course is the uphill 180-yard, par-3 15th hole, which crosses a ravine. You must hit to a two-level green with severe undulation between the levels. The green is slick and difficult. Count on the back level to be the toughest. Two lakes have been added to the par-5 16th, so it's no longer a gimmie birdie hole for long hitters. There is a 120-yard practice area for 8- and 9-iron play. It's hilly, but walkable. A new driving range is slated to open early in 1993. John Joseph holds the course record of 63; he's playing on the PGA Senior Tour. A total of 50,000 rounds are played here each year.

| Hole | 1 | 2 | 3 | 4 | 5 | 6 | 7 | 8 | 9 | Out | | |
|---|---|---|---|---|---|---|---|---|---|---|---|---|
| BLUE | 348 | 508 | 511 | 178 | 384 | 400 | 150 | 381 | 364 | 3224 | BLUE | Rating: 71.0 |
| WHITE | 341 | 487 | 501 | 165 | 352 | 388 | 138 | 364 | 356 | 3092 | | Slope: 126 |
| Par | 4 | 5 | 5 | 3 | 4 | 4 | 3 | 4 | 4 | 36 | WHITE | Rating: 70.0 |
| Handicap | 9 | 17 | 1 | 11 | 5 | 7 | 15 | 13 | 3 | x | | Slope: 124 |
| RED | 336 | 469 | 480 | 155 | 323 | 379 | 129 | 355 | 345 | 2971 | | |
| Par | 4 | 5 | 5 | 3 | 4 | 4 | 3 | 4 | 4 | 36 | RED | Rating: 73.7 |
| Handicap | 7 | 5 | 1 | 15 | 11 | 9 | 17 | 13 | 3 | x | | Slope: 138 |

| Hole | 10 | 11 | 12 | 13 | 14 | 15 | 16 | 17 | 18 | In | Totals | |
|---|---|---|---|---|---|---|---|---|---|---|---|---|
| BLUE | 361 | 353 | 364 | 166 | 349 | 180 | 520 | 358 | 442 | 3093 | BLUE | 6317 |
| WHITE | 348 | 343 | 358 | 150 | 336 | 146 | 507 | 338 | 435 | 2961 | WHITE | 6053 |
| Par | 4 | 4 | 4 | 3 | 4 | 3 | 5 | 4 | 4 | 35 | Par | 71 |
| Handicap | 8 | 12 | 10 | 18 | 2 | 16 | 14 | 4 | 6 | x | | |
| RED | 335 | 326 | 346 | 140 | 327 | 132 | 443 | 317 | 415 | 2781 | RED | 5752 |
| Par | 4 | 4 | 4 | 3 | 4 | 3 | 5 | 4 | 5 | 36 | Par | 72 |
| Handicap | 10 | 12 | 8 | 18 | 6 | 16 | 2 | 4 | 14 | x | | |

# CALIFORNIA GOLF CLUB

**Course 47**
MAP E1 grid e2

***Course information:*** This private course has 18 holes. See card below for yardage and rating information.

***Play policy and fees:*** Members and guests only. Guest fees are $60 with a member and $125 without. Carts are $10.

***Location:*** From San Francisco, take Interstate 280 South to the Westborough Avenue exit east. At the bottom of the hill, turn right on Orange Avenue and follow it to the course.

***Course description:*** This sprawling, challenging course is situated above San Francisco International Airport and is often windy. Head Pro Al Vaccaro likes to bet the over/under on first-timers at the course. Scratch golfers have to best 80. It's loaded with 185 bunkers and is hilly. Once you play here you'll understand why the San Francisco Giants want to move out of Candlestick Park. The par-5s and par-3s are especially challenging. Lakes have been added, one on the right side of the 11th, and another on the left of the 18th green. This is a real sleeper course, giving the best golfers everything they want. The par-5 4th is a 525-yard double dogleg, with heavy trees on the right—a true 3-shot hole, with six bunkers guarding the approach. The 14th dogleg, left through a chute, is 442 yards. The 489-yard 15th has players drive to the top of a hill. A total of 38,000 rounds are played here each year. 1991 member Dennis Trixler, now on the Nike Tour, set the record: 65.

**1920**
**Vernon Macan**

844 West Orange Avenue
South San Francisco
CA 94080

Pro shop (415) 589-0144
Clubhouse (415) 761-0210

- ✓ **driving range**
- ✓ **practice greens**
- ✓ **power carts**
- pull carts
- golf club rental
- ✓ **locker rooms**
- ✓ **showers**
- executive course
- accommodations
- ✓ **food and beverages**
- ✓ **clubhouse**

**Dennis Mahoney**
Manager

**Al Vaccaro**
Professional

**Charles Pratt**
Superintendent

| Hole | 1 | 2 | 3 | 4 | 5 | 6 | 7 | 8 | 9 | Out | | |
|---|---|---|---|---|---|---|---|---|---|---|---|---|
| BLUE | 510 | 363 | 154 | 525 | 370 | 338 | 183 | 387 | 422 | 3252 | BLUE | Rating: 72.9 |
| WHITE | 500 | 355 | 148 | 513 | 354 | 330 | 179 | 376 | 389 | 3144 | | Slope: 134 |
| Par | 5 | 4 | 3 | 5 | 4 | 4 | 3 | 4 | 4 | 36 | WHITE | Rating: 72.0 |
| Handicap | 5 | 7 | 17 | 1 | 11 | 9 | 13 | 15 | 3 | x | | Slope: 132 |
| RED | 485 | 321 | 122 | 475 | 300 | 311 | 166 | 357 | 336 | 2873 | | |
| Par | 5 | 4 | 3 | 5 | 4 | 4 | 3 | 4 | 4 | 36 | RED | Rating: 74.3 |
| Handicap | 3 | 7 | 17 | 1 | 11 | 9 | 15 | 13 | 5 | x | | Slope: 125 |

| Hole | 10 | 11 | 12 | 13 | 14 | 15 | 16 | 17 | 18 | In | Totals | |
|---|---|---|---|---|---|---|---|---|---|---|---|---|
| BLUE | 394 | 399 | 225 | 368 | 442 | 489 | 160 | 552 | 396 | 3425 | BLUE | 6677 |
| WHITE | 386 | 392 | 194 | 363 | 437 | 471 | 154 | 547 | 386 | 3330 | WHITE | 6474 |
| Par | 4 | 4 | 3 | 4 | 4 | 5 | 3 | 5 | 4 | 36 | Par | 72 |
| Handicap | 4 | 12 | 14 | 8 | 2 | 16 | 18 | 6 | 10 | x | | |
| RED | 380 | 358 | 177 | 354 | 388 | 416 | 117 | 535 | 330 | 3055 | RED | 5928 |
| Par | 4 | 4 | 3 | 4 | 4 | 5 | 3 | 5 | 4 | 36 | Par | 72 |
| Handicap | 6 | 10 | 16 | 2 | 12 | 8 | 18 | 4 | 14 | x | | |

# BURLINGAME COUNTRY CLUB

**Course 48**
MAP E1 grid e3

**1893**
**Tom Nicoll**

80 New Place Road
Hillsborough, CA 94010

Pro shop (415) 342-0750
Clubhouse (415) 343-1843

- ✓ **driving range**
- ✓ **practice greens**
- ✓ **power carts**
- ✓ **pull carts**
- ✓ **golf club rental**
- ✓ **locker rooms**
- ✓ **showers**
- executive course
- accommodations
- ✓ **food and beverages**
- ✓ **clubhouse**

**Maurice Ver Brugge**
Professional

**Arthur Frey**
Manager

**Terry Grasso**
Superintendent

***Course information:*** This private course has 18 holes and par is 70. The course is 6,394 yards and rated 70.3 from the regular tees. The slope rating is 126. Women's tees are 5,731 yards and rated 73.0. The slope rating is 125.

***Play policy and fees:*** Members and guests only. Guest fees are $25 when accompanied by a member and $75 unaccompanied. Carts are $25.

***Location:*** Driving on Highway 101 in Burlingame, take the Broadway exit southwest to El Camino Real. Go left and, in less than one mile, turn right on Floribunda Avenue. When it dead ends, turn left on Eucalyptus and then right on New Place Road. The course is on the right.

***Course description:*** This course is one of the oldest west of the Mississippi, dating back to 1893. It has a sprawling, tree-lined layout and the narrow fairways require precise shots off the tee. It's largely flat and walkable. Bing Crosby was one of the many prominent members of this highly exclusive club. This course has been used for U.S. Sectional qualifying. It's very tight, with par-4s averaging avout 400 yards. A good, solid test of golf. A total of 15,000 rounds are played here each year. Maurie Ver Brugge set the record of 60 on Nov. 25, 1968.

# SAN MATEO GOLF COURSE

**Course 49**
MAP E1 grid e4

***Course information:*** This public course has 18 holes and par is 70. The course is 5,917 yards and rated 67.0 from the championship tees, and 5,598 yards and rated 65.5 from the regular tees. The slope ratings are 104 championship and 101 regular. Women's tees are 5,498 and rated 70.4. The slope rating is 117.

***Play policy and fees:*** Green fees are $14 weekdays and $18 weekends and holidays. After 3 p.m., twilight rates are available for $9.50 weekdays and $11 weekends and holidays. There are special rates for seniors and high school students within the city of San Mateo. Carts are $14. Pull carts are available for $1 plus a $1 handle deposit. For tee times, call a week in advance at about 6 a.m.

***Location:*** This course is on the east side of Highway 101 in San Mateo and visible from the freeway. From the north, take the Poplar Avenue exit. From the south, take the Dore exit. Follow the signs marked Coyote Point Drive from both exits to the course.

***Course description:*** This course is short and flat with tight eucalyptus-lined fairways. The greens are in the traditional style: very small, elevated, well bunkered and well contoured. Because of this, there is a premium on approach shots and putting. The course is usually windy and has several water hazards. It's walkable. A total of 102,000 rounds are played here each year. Sil DeLuca set the course record of 59.

**1934**

Box 634
San Mateo, CA 94401

1700 Coyote Point Drive
San Mateo, CA 94401

Pro shop (415) 347-1461

driving range
✓ **practice greens**
✓ **power carts**
✓ **pull carts**
✓ **golf club rental**
locker rooms
showers
executive course
accommodations
✓ **food and beverages**
✓ **clubhouse**

**Jake Montes**
Manager/Professional

**John Grant**
Superintendent

# TONY LEMA GOLF COURSE

**Course 50**
MAP E1 grid e5

**1982**
**William Francis Bell**

13800 Neptune Drive
San Leandro, CA 94577

Pro shop (510) 895-2162

- ✓ **driving range**
- ✓ **practice greens**
- ✓ **power carts**
- ✓ **pull carts**
- ✓ **golf club rental**
- ✓ **locker rooms**
- ✓ **showers**
- ✓ **executive course**
- **accommodations**
- ✓ **food and beverages**
- ✓ **clubhouse**

**Steve Elbe**
Professional

**John Lloyd**
Superintendent

***Course information:*** This public course has 27 holes.

The Tony Lema Course is detailed below.

Par is 58 for 18 holes on the nine hole Marina Course. It is 3,316 yards and rated 53.8 from the regular tees. The slope rating is 73. Women's yardage and ratings were unavailable.

***Play policy and fees:*** Green fees are $12 weekdays and $16 weekends for the Tony Lema course, with a $2 discount for residents. Fees are $6 for nine holes weekdays and $7 for nine holes weekends for the Marina Course, with a $1 discount for residents. Call for discount rates. Carts are $18. Pull carts are $3.

***Location:*** From Interstate 880 in San Leandro, take the Marina Boulevard exit west, which curves left into Neptune Drive to the course.

***Course description:*** Named for the late Tony Lema, the 1964 British Open champion, this course and its facilities were remodeled in 1990. The course is mostly flat and windy. Play early to miss the prevailing southeast wind off the bay. One of the more difficult holes is the number six, par-4 and 420 yards dead into the wind with a lake on the left. The hole plays like a par-5 because of the wind. Keep the ball low if you can, but there is no sure way to conquer this hole. On good days, there are great views of San Francisco Bay. There is a lot of tournament play. A good course for the double-digit handicapper—flat and forgiving. A total of 85,000 rounds are played here each year. The course record is 63.

Tony Lema Course

| Hole | 1 | 2 | 3 | 4 | 5 | 6 | 7 | 8 | 9 | Out | | |
|---|---|---|---|---|---|---|---|---|---|---|---|---|
| BLUE | 413 | 397 | 358 | 146 | 505 | 420 | 537 | 191 | 381 | 3348 | BLUE | Rating: 70.7 |
| WHITE | 401 | 377 | 346 | 132 | 471 | 392 | 505 | 178 | 252 | 3054 | | Slope: 115 |
| Par | 4 | 4 | 4 | 3 | 5 | 4 | 5 | 3 | 4 | 36 | WHITE | Rating: 68.6 |
| Handicap | 5 | 7 | 15 | 17 | 13 | 1 | 3 | 9 | 11 | x | | Slope: 107 |
| RED | 395 | 365 | 348 | 119 | 452 | 359 | 451 | 148 | 242 | 2879 | | |
| Par | 4 | 4 | 4 | 3 | 5 | 4 | 5 | 3 | 4 | 36 | RED | Rating: 71.3 |
| Handicap | 1 | 5 | 9 | 17 | 7 | 3 | 11 | 13 | 15 | x | | Slope: 108 |

| Hole | 10 | 11 | 12 | 13 | 14 | 15 | 16 | 17 | 18 | In | Totals | |
|---|---|---|---|---|---|---|---|---|---|---|---|---|
| BLUE | 160 | 399 | 549 | 486 | 296 | 411 | 210 | 371 | 406 | 3288 | BLUE | 6636 |
| WHITE | 146 | 385 | 507 | 465 | 278 | 406 | 192 | 351 | 391 | 3121 | WHITE | 6175 |
| Par | 3 | 4 | 5 | 5 | 4 | 4 | 3 | 4 | 4 | 36 | Par | 72 |
| Handicap | 18 | 8 | 4 | 14 | 16 | 2 | 10 | 12 | 6 | x | | |
| RED | 123 | 369 | 373 | 465 | 267 | 400 | 169 | 338 | 335 | 2839 | RED | 5718 |
| Par | 3 | 4 | 4 | 5 | 4 | 5 | 3 | 4 | 4 | 36 | Par | 72 |
| Handicap | 18 | 4 | 2 | 8 | 12 | 14 | 16 | 10 | 6 | x | | |



MAP ON PAGE 184

# WILLOW PARK GOLF COURSE

**Course 51**
MAP E1 grid e6

**1967**

PO Box 2407
Castro Valley, CA 94546

17007 Redwood Road
Castro Valley, CA 94546

Pro shop (510) 537-2521
Clubhouse (510) 886-4810

- ✓ **driving range**
- ✓ **practice greens**
- ✓ **power carts**
- ✓ **pull carts**
- golf club rental
- ✓ **locker rooms**
- showers
- executive course
- accommodations
- ✓ **food and beverages**
- ✓ **clubhouse**

**Robert Bruce**
Professional

**Rene S. Viviani**
Superintendent

***Course information:*** This public course has 18 holes. See card below for yardage and rating information.

***Play policy and fees:*** Green fees are $10 for nine holes and $15 for 18 holes weekdays, and $12 for nine holes and $20 for 18 holes weekends. Carts are $14 for nine holes and $20 for 18 holes. Call a week ahead of time; reservations are needed every day of the week.

***Location:*** Located in Castro Valley, two miles north of Interstate 580 on Redwood Road.

***Course description:*** This course is mostly flat with narrow fairways. A creek borders the front nine holes. There are deer in the outlying areas. The driving range has an unusual feature: You hit into a lake about 175 yards out. Floater balls are provided. A total of 100,000 rounds are played here each year. Jimmy Caires set the course record of 63 in 1967.

| Hole | 1 | 2 | 3 | 4 | 5 | 6 | 7 | 8 | 9 | Out | BLUE | Rating: 69.2 |
|---|---|---|---|---|---|---|---|---|---|---|---|---|
| BLUE | 417 | 384 | 157 | 494 | 182 | 352 | 191 | 333 | 582 | 3092 | | Slope: 115 |
| WHITE | 377 | 362 | 120 | 440 | 140 | 310 | 150 | 291 | 487 | 2677 | | |
| Par | 4 | 4 | 3 | 5 | 3 | 4 | 3 | 4 | 5 | 35 | WHITE | Rating: 67.4 |
| Handicap | 1 | 7 | 13 | 3 | 11 | 15 | 9 | 17 | 5 | x | | Slope: 110 |
| RED | 365 | 340 | 112 | 430 | 127 | 296 | 136 | 283 | 472 | 2561 | | |
| Par | 4 | 4 | 3 | 5 | 3 | 4 | 3 | 4 | 5 | 35 | RED | Rating: 69.2 |
| Handicap | 5 | 7 | 17 | 3 | 15 | 9 | 13 | 11 | 1 | x | | Slope: 117 |

| Hole | 10 | 11 | 12 | 13 | 14 | 15 | 16 | 17 | 18 | In | Totals | |
|---|---|---|---|---|---|---|---|---|---|---|---|---|
| BLUE | 416 | 288 | 499 | 144 | 332 | 390 | 190 | 367 | 509 | 3135 | BLUE | 6227 |
| WHITE | 353 | 258 | 485 | 130 | 275 | 365 | 160 | 329 | 475 | 2830 | WHITE | 5507 |
| Par | 4 | 4 | 5 | 3 | 4 | 4 | 3 | 4 | 5 | 36 | Par | 71 |
| Handicap | 2 | 18 | 8 | 16 | 12 | 4 | 6 | 10 | 14 | x | | |
| RED | 328 | 237 | 450 | 120 | 258 | 358 | 148 | 318 | 415 | 2632 | RED | 5193 |
| Par | 4 | 4 | 5 | 3 | 4 | 4 | 3 | 4 | 5 | 36 | Par | 71 |
| Handicap | 10 | 14 | 2 | 18 | 12 | 6 | 16 | 8 | 4 | x | | |

# SKYWEST GOLF COURSE

**Course 52**
MAP E1 grid e6

**1964**
**R.E. Baldock**

1401 Golf Course Road
Hayward, CA 94541

Pro shop (510) 278-6188

- ✓ **driving range**
- ✓ **practice greens**
- ✓ **power carts**
- ✓ **pull carts**
- golf club rental
- locker rooms
- showers
- executive course
- accommodations
- ✓ **food and beverages**
- ✓ **clubhouse**

**Cheryl Pastore**
Professional

**Gale Wilson**
Manager

**Wes Sakamoto**
Superintendent

***Course information:*** This public course has 18 holes. See card below for yardage and rating information.

***Play policy and fees:*** Green fees are $8 for nine holes and $12 for 18 holes weekdays, and $10 for nine holes and $15 for 18 holes weekends. Carts are $10 for nine holes and $17 for 18 holes weekdays, and $11 and $18 weekends. Rates will change in July '93, so these figures could change by a couple of dollars. Call a week in advance at 6 a.m. to get tee time.

***Location:*** From Interstate 880 in Hayward, take the A Street exit west to Heperian, then the first left at Golf Course Road to get to the course (next to the Hayward Air Terminal.)

***Course description:*** This flat course has lush, well-maintained, wide fairways with lots of trees. It tests every club in the bag. The talked-about hole on this course is number 16. It's 192 yards and par-3, playing especially difficult against the wind. There is a lake on the right and out-of-bounds on the left. The green slopes back to front, but fortunately it holds well. This course holds many tournaments. Also, the Players West Tour for aspiring women pros stops here every summer. A total of 100,000 rounds are played here each year. Mike Powers set the men's record of 65, and Muffin Spencer-Devlin set the women's record of 68.

| Hole | 1 | 2 | 3 | 4 | 5 | 6 | 7 | 8 | 9 | Out | | |
|---|---|---|---|---|---|---|---|---|---|---|---|---|
| BLUE | 438 | 145 | 408 | 552 | 364 | 433 | 547 | 223 | 446 | 3556 | BLUE | Rating: 72.8 |
| WHITE | 412 | 121 | 387 | [illegible] | 338 | 406 | 520 | 199 | 421 | 3329 | | Slope: 121 |
| Par | 4 | 3 | 4 | 5 | 4 | 4 | 5 | 3 | 4 | 36 | WHITE | Rating: 70.9 |
| Handicap | 3 | 17 | 13 | 5 | 15 | 1 | 11 | 9 | 7 | x | | Slope: 116 |
| RED | 389 | 100 | 367 | 506 | 320 | 391 | 502 | 156 | 399 | 3130 | | |
| Par | 4 | 3 | 4 | 5 | 4 | 4 | 5 | 3 | 4 | 36 | RED | Rating: 74.3 |
| Handicap | 3 | 17 | 9 | 7 | 15 | 1 | 5 | 13 | 11 | x | | Slope: 123 |

| Hole | 10 | 11 | 12 | 13 | 14 | 15 | 16 | 17 | 18 | In | Totals | |
|---|---|---|---|---|---|---|---|---|---|---|---|---|
| BLUE | 391 | 441 | 162 | 409 | 484 | 394 | 192 | 520 | 381 | 3374 | BLUE | 6930 |
| WHITE | 367 | 422 | 147 | 396 | 475 | 379 | 166 | 490 | 369 | 3211 | WHITE | 6540 |
| Par | 4 | 4 | 3 | 4 | 5 | 4 | 3 | 5 | 4 | 36 | Par | 72 |
| Handicap | 10 | 2 | 18 | 4 | 16 | 14 | 8 | 12 | 6 | x | | |
| RED | 355 | 410 | 135 | 386 | 440 | 350 | 144 | 472 | 349 | 3041 | RED | 6171 |
| Par | 4 | 5 | 3 | 4 | 5 | 4 | 3 | 5 | 4 | 37 | Par | 73 |
| Handicap | 14 | 2 | 18 | 4 | 10 | 12 | 6 | 16 | 8 | x | | |

# PLEASANTON FAIRWAYS GOLF COURSE

**Course 53**
MAP E1 grid e9

**1974**
**Ron Curtola**

PO Box 123
Pleasanton, CA 94566

Alameda Fairgrounds
Pleasanton, CA 94566

Pro shop (510) 462-4653

- ✓ **driving range**
- ✓ **practice greens**
- power carts
- ✓ **pull carts**
- ✓ **golf club rental**
- locker rooms
- showers
- ✓ **executive course**
- accommodations
- ✓ **food and beverages**
- ✓ **clubhouse**

**Ron Curtola**
Owner/Manager

**Paul H. Marty**
Superintendent

***Course information:*** This public course has nine holes. Par is 60 for 18 holes. Irons only on the driving range. The course is 3,428 yards and rated 55.9 for 18 holes from the regular tees. The slope rating is 82. Women's tees are 3,172 yards. The ratings were unavailable.

***Play policy and fees:*** Green fees are $7 for nine holes and $13.50 for 18 holes weekdays, and $8 for nine holes and $15.50 for 18 holes weekends. Seniors' fees are $5.75 for nine holes and $11 for 18 holes on weekdays, and $11 for nine holes and $13 for 18 holes on weekends. Reservations are recommended. Closed Christmas and during the Alameda County Fair (late June to early July).

***Location:*** From Interstate 680 in Pleasanton driving south, take the Bernal exit to the right, make a loop and head east on Bernal. Turn left on Pleasanton Avenue and left at the fairgrounds entrance. Once in the fairgrounds, drive slowly to the tunnel to the track.

***Course description:*** This short, flat course is located in the middle of the racetrack at the Alameda County Fairgrounds. This is not a course for beginners. The greens are all elevated and a driver is needed on three holes. You must be accurate to stick the par-3 greens. Be of serious mind when you approach this course. Also, the same family runs a very nice, large driving range on the west end of the fairgrounds, about a half-mile from the course. A total of 65,000 rounds are played here each year.

# CRYSTAL SPRINGS GOLF COURSE

**Course 54**
MAP E1 grid f2



***Course information:*** This semi-private course has 18 holes. See card below for yardage and rating information.

***Play policy and fees:*** Green fees are $38 weekdays plus cart, and $56 weekends including cart. Carts are $11 per person and are mandatory on weekends and holidays from 7:30 a.m. to 2:30 p.m. Twilight rates after 2:30 p.m. are $29 weekdays plus cart, and $39 weekends plus cart. Carts are not mandatory for twilight play. Memberships are available.

***Location:*** On Interstate 280 heading south in Burlingame, take the Hayne and Black Mountain Road exit. Make a right on Skyline Boulevard and follow it to Golf Course Drive. The course is visible from the highway.

***Course description:*** This hilly, meandering course has sidehill lies and requires decent placement shots. Situated in the midst of a California State Game Preserve, wildlife abounds. The weather ranges from San Francisco fog to Peninsula sun. It has some steep holes, but is walkable. The view from the 6th tee opens up on the game preserve. Deer regularly come onto the course. The first hole is a hard dogleg left, 397 yards, requiring a 240-yard drive, and the green is severly sloped. The 413-yard second has a faster green. A total of 75,000 rounds are played here each year. Charlie Leider set the course record of 62.

**1924**
**Herbert Fowler**

6650 Golf Course Drive
Burlingame, CA 94010

Pro shop (415) 342-0603
Clubhouse (415) 342-4188

- ✓ **driving range**
- ✓ **practice greens**
- ✓ **power carts**
- ✓ **pull carts**
- ✓ **golf club rental**
- locker rooms
- showers
- executive course
- accommodations
- ✓ **food and beverages**
- ✓ **clubhouse**

**Roger Graves**
Professional

**Charles Leider**
Director of Golf

**Jeff Leider**
Business Manager

**Pete Galea**
Superintendent

| Hole | 1 | 2 | 3 | 4 | 5 | 6 | 7 | 8 | 9 | Out | | |
|---|---|---|---|---|---|---|---|---|---|---|---|---|
| BLUE | 397 | 413 | 234 | 499 | 390 | 431 | 483 | 226 | 402 | 3475 | BLUE | Rating: 72.1 |
| WHITE | 389 | 397 | 224 | 474 | 380 | 426 | 467 | 178 | 386 | 3321 | | Slope: 125 |
| Par | 4 | 4 | 3 | 5 | 4 | 4 | 5 | 3 | 4 | 36 | WHITE | Rating: 70.7 |
| Handicap | 7 | 5 | 9 | 17 | 1 | 13 | 15 | 11 | 3 | x | | Slope: 122 |
| RED | 372 | 384 | 204 | 467 | 379 | 419 | 451 | 168 | 366 | 3210 | | |
| Par | 4 | 4 | 3 | 5 | 4 | 4 | 5 | 3 | 4 | 36 | RED | Rating: 74.0 |
| Handicap | 5 | 1 | 15 | 13 | 3 | 9 | 11 | 17 | 7 | x | | Slope: 130 |

| Hole | 10 | 11 | 12 | 13 | 14 | 15 | 16 | 17 | 18 | In | Totals | |
|---|---|---|---|---|---|---|---|---|---|---|---|---|
| BLUE | 375 | 161 | 373 | 154 | 425 | 313 | 479 | 402 | 526 | 3208 | BLUE | 6683 |
| WHITE | 344 | 151 | 348 | 149 | 408 | 295 | 451 | 349 | 505 | 3000 | WHITE | 6321 |
| Par | 4 | 3 | 4 | 3 | 4 | 4 | 5 | 4 | 5 | 36 | Par | 72 |
| Handicap | 6 | 18 | 4 | 16 | 2 | 14 | 12 | 8 | 10 | x | | |
| RED | 335 | 103 | 276 | 142 | 342 | 274 | 422 | 342 | 474 | 2710 | RED | 5920 |
| Par | 4 | 3 | 4 | 3 | 4 | 4 | 5 | 4 | 5 | 36 | Par | 72 |
| Handicap | 12 | 18 | 6 | 16 | 10 | 14 | 4 | 8 | 2 | x | | |

# HALF MOON BAY GOLF LINKS

**Course 55**
MAP E1 grid f2

*Course information:* This public course has 18 holes. See card below for yardage and rating information.

*Play policy and fees:* Green fees are $68 weekdays and $88 weekends. The twilight fees are $45 weekdays and $49 weekends. Fees include a mandatory cart. Reservations are recommended one week in advance.

*Location:* Heading toward Half Moon Bay via Highway 1 or Highway 92, the course is located three miles south of the highway junction, south of Half Moon Bay on the oceanside.

*Course description:* This oceanside course is long and demanding. The 18th hole spans 428 yards along an ocean cliff and has been rated one of the top 100 holes in the country. Check out the pin placement on this hole. If the pin is on top of the green, the landing area will be very tight. Fog and wind often come into play. Big, undulating greens and long par-3s add to the challenge. Half Moon Bay boasts the highest course rating in the Bay Area, 74.5. The Lakeside at Olympic Club is 74.2. Arnold Palmer was a consultant on the design of this course. A total of 55,000 rounds are played here each year. Dennis Trixler and George Cadle co-hold the course record of 66.

**1973**
**Francis Duane**

2000 Fairway Drive
Half Moon Bay, CA 94019

Pro shop (415) 726-4438
Clubhouse (415) 726-6384

- driving range
- ✓ **practice greens**
- ✓ **power carts**
- pull carts
- ✓ **golf club rental**
- ✓ **locker rooms**
- ✓ **showers**
- executive course
- accommodations
- ✓ **food and beverages**
- ✓ **clubhouse**

**Jim Wagner**
Manager/Director

**Moon Mullins**
Professional

**Dan Miller**
Superintendent

| Hole | 1 | 2 | 3 | 4 | 5 | 6 | 7 | 8 | 9 | Out | | |
|---|---|---|---|---|---|---|---|---|---|---|---|---|
| BLUE | 546 | 409 | 232 | 378 | 496 | 418 | 207 | 435 | 365 | 3486 | BLUE | Rating: 74.5 |
| WHITE | 513 | 389 | 130 | 336 | 476 | 388 | 179 | 407 | 341 | 3159 | | Slope: 136 |
| Par | 5 | 4 | 3 | 4 | 5 | 4 | 3 | 4 | 4 | 36 | WHITE | Rating: 71.0 |
| Handicap | 11 | 5 | 7 | 17 | 9 | 3 | 13 | 1 | 15 | x | | Slope: 130 |
| RED | 468 | 322 | 123 | 335 | 416 | 338 | 112 | 397 | 330 | 2841 | | |
| Par | 5 | 4 | 3 | 4 | 5 | 4 | 3 | 4 | 4 | 36 | RED | Rating: 72.9 |
| Handicap | 3 | 11 | 15 | 7 | 1 | 13 | 17 | 5 | 9 | x | | Slope: 124 |

| Hole | 10 | 11 | 12 | 13 | 14 | 15 | 16 | 17 | 18 | In | Totals | |
|---|---|---|---|---|---|---|---|---|---|---|---|---|
| BLUE | 560 | 417 | 439 | 208 | 424 | 566 | 418 | 170 | 428 | 3630 | BLUE | 7116 |
| WHITE | 495 | 390 | 416 | 168 | 350 | 528 | 378 | 142 | 396 | 3263 | WHITE | 6422 |
| Par | 5 | 4 | 4 | 3 | 4 | 5 | 4 | 3 | 4 | 36 | Par | 72 |
| Handicap | 16 | 14 | 4 | 12 | 8 | 2 | 6 | 18 | 10 | x | | |
| RED | 432 | 356 | 358 | 107 | 325 | 473 | 360 | 112 | 348 | 2871 | RED | 5712 |
| Par | 5 | 4 | 4 | 3 | 4 | 5 | 4 | 3 | 4 | 36 | Par | 72 |
| Handicap | 6 | 14 | 10 | 16 | 12 | 4 | 2 | 18 | 8 | x | | |

# PENINSULA GOLF AND COUNTRY CLUB

**Course 56**
MAP E1 grid f3

**1911**
**Donald Ross**

701 Madera Drive
San Mateo, CA 94403

Pro shop (415) 345-9521
Clubhouse (415) 573-5511

- ✓ **driving range**
- ✓ **practice greens**
- ✓ **power carts**
- pull carts
- ✓ **golf club rental**
- ✓ **locker rooms**
- ✓ **showers**
- executive course
- accommodations
- ✓ **food and beverages**
- ✓ **clubhouse**

**Henry Johns**
Manager

**Tom Toschi**
Professional

**Marvin King**
Superintendent

*Course information:* This private course has 18 holes. See card below for yardage and rating information.

*Play policy and fees:* Reciprocal play is accepted with members of other private clubs. Have your club pro call to make arrangements. Guest fees are $30 when accompanied by a member. The green fee for reciprocators is $80 and includes a cart. Carts are $6.50 per person for nine holes and $11 per person for 18 holes.

*Location:* Located between Highway 101 and Interstate 280, take Highway 92 to Alameda De Las Pulgas south. Turn right on Madera Drive.

*Course description:* This mature course offers undulating greens and tight fairways lined with manzanita and eucalyptus trees. The par-4 10th hole measures 447 yards and is especially challenging. You hit from an elevated tee box to a fairly wide open fairway with trees on both sides and out-of-bounds on the left. The green is sizeable, but is surrounded by bunkers. Play center left off the tee and go for the center of the slightly undulating green. Stay below the hole if possible. The course overlooks the peninsula. The 425-yard 16th has a blind tee shot, then a downhill approach to a green bordered on the left by a huge stand of eucalyptus. From a few other tee boxes you can see a full view of Mt. Diablo in the East Bay. Bud Ward holds the record here; 63. A total of 40,000 rounds are played here each year.

| Hole | 1 | 2 | 3 | 4 | 5 | 6 | 7 | 8 | 9 | Out | BLUE | Rating: 71.7 |
|---|---|---|---|---|---|---|---|---|---|---|---|---|
| BLUE | 374 | 423 | 468 | 193 | 461 | 364 | 183 | 328 | 445 | 3239 | | Slope: 128 |
| WHITE | 365 | 395 | 463 | 173 | 445 | 358 | 174 | 319 | 432 | 3124 | | |
| Par | 4 | 4 | 5 | 3 | 4 | 4 | 3 | 4 | 4 | 35 | WHITE | Rating: 70.5 |
| Handicap | 7 | 3 | 11 | 15 | 1 | 9 | 17 | 13 | 5 | x | | Slope: 126 |
| RED | 349 | 363 | 445 | 102 | 421 | 339 | 155 | 309 | 404 | 2879 | | |
| Par | 4 | 4 | 5 | 3 | 5 | 4 | 3 | 4 | 4 | 36 | RED | Rating: 73.0 |
| Handicap | 9 | 11 | 1 | 17 | 5 | 3 | 15 | 13 | 7 | x | | Slope: 126 |

| Hole | 10 | 11 | 12 | 13 | 14 | 15 | 16 | 17 | 18 | In | Totals | |
|---|---|---|---|---|---|---|---|---|---|---|---|---|
| BLUE | 447 | 521 | 164 | 457 | 354 | 151 | 425 | 294 | 527 | 3340 | BLUE | 6579 |
| WHITE | 438 | 496 | 158 | 457 | 342 | 134 | 411 | 288 | 507 | 3231 | WHITE | 6355 |
| Par | 4 | 5 | 3 | 4 | 4 | 3 | 4 | 4 | 5 | 36 | Par | 71 |
| Handicap | 2 | 10 | 16 | 4 | 8 | 18 | 6 | 14 | 12 | x | | |
| RED | 431 | 415 | 126 | 439 | 325 | 125 | 334 | 275 | 433 | 2903 | RED | 5782 |
| Par | 5 | 5 | 3 | 5 | 4 | 3 | 4 | 4 | 5 | 38 | Par | 74 |
| Handicap | 8 | 2 | 18 | 10 | 6 | 16 | 14 | 12 | 4 | x | | |

# MENLO COUNTRY CLUB

**Course 57**
MAP E1 grid f4

**1900**
**Tom Nicoll**

2300 Woodside Road
Woodside, CA 94062

Pro shop (415) 366-9910
Clubhouse (415) 366-5751

✓ **driving range**
✓ **practice greens**
✓ **power carts**
pull carts
golf club rental
✓ **locker rooms**
✓ **showers**
executive course
accommodations
✓ **food and beverages**
✓ **clubhouse**

**Michel Dubes**
Manager

**Mark Smithwick**
Professional

**Scott Lewis**
Superintendent

*Course information:* This private course has 18 holes and par is 70. The course is 6,320 yards and rated 70.1 from the championship tees, and 6,042 yards and rated 69.0 from the regular tees. The slope ratings are 126 championship and 123 regular. Women's tees are 5,641 yards and rated 72.6. The slope rating is 128.

*Play policy and fees:* Reciprocal play is not accepted. Guest fees are $25 weekdays and $30 weekends when accompanied by a member. Guests must be accompanied by a member. Carts are $20.

*Location:* Located between Interstate 280 and Highway 101 in Redwood City, take either freeway, exiting on Woodside Road or Highway 84. The course is on the north side of the street, seven-tenths of a mile from Interstate 280.

*Course description:* This is a short but sneaky course. Overhanging old oaks add character and line the fairways. Beware of the 16th hole where there's a massive oak in the middle of the fairway. The course mixes the old-style, traditional, small greens with recent innovations by Robert Trent Jones, Jr. It's mostly flat and walkable. A very exclusive club, this course is known for its pristine condition and traditional presence. It's a good example of a true old-style club. A total of 35,000 rounds are played here each year.

# BAY MEADOWS GOLF COURSE

**Course 58**
MAP E1 grid f4

PO Box 5050
Delaware Street
San Mateo, CA

Pro shop (415) 341-7204

driving range
✓ **practice greens**
power carts
✓ **pull carts**
✓ **golf club rental**
locker rooms
showers
executive course
accommodations
✓ **food and beverages**
✓ **clubhouse**

**Bill Finlay**
Professional

**R. Roberts**
Superintendent

*Course information:* This public course has nine holes. Par is 56 for 18 holes. The course is 2,730 yards for 18 holes. No rating is available.

*Play policy and fees:* Green fees are $5 for nine holes and $10 for 18 holes. Special 10-play books are available for $40. Carts are $2 and club rental is $3. During racing season, the course is only open Mondays and Tuesdays from 7 a.m. to 6 p.m., and Fridays from 7 a.m. to 1 p.m. Because the hours may vary, call ahead for tee times.

*Location:* From Highway 101 in San Mateo, take the Delaware Street exit, which will lead you to the fairgrounds and the race track. Just follow the signs. Park in the race track parking lot and walk to the center of the track.

*Course description:* This course is situated in the middle of Bay Meadows race track. It's in good condition and a nice course for beginners with eight par-3s and one par-4. It's flat and open.

# EMERALD HILLS GOLF CLUB

**Course 59**
MAP E1 grid f4

1059 Wilmington Way
Redwood City, CA 94062

Pro shop (415) 368-7820
Driving cage (415) 366-4760

- ✓ **driving range**
- ✓ **practice greens**
- power carts
- ✓ **pull carts**
- ✓ **golf club rental**
- locker rooms
- showers
- executive course
- accommodations
- food and beverages
- clubhouse

**Bob Gaspar**
Manager

**Bruce Olsen**
Superintendent

*Course information:* This public course has nine holes. Par is 54 for 18 holes. The course is 2,326 yards for 18 holes and rated 50.9 from the regular tees. The slope rating is 67. Women's tees are 2,276 yards and unrated.

*Play policy and fees:* Green fees are $6 for nine holes and $10 for 18 holes weekdays, and $7 for nine holes and $12 for 18 holes weekends. Senior rates are $4 for nine holes weekdays only.

*Location:* From Interstate 280 in Redwood City, exit on Edgewood Road southwest. Turn left on Canada Road. Drive 1.5 miles to Jefferson Avenue and turn left again, following it to Wilmington Way. Turn right to the course.

*Course description:* This is a short, starter course composed of par-3s. It's hilly but walkable and has a perfect layout for juniors, seniors and beginners. The course is owned by the Redwood City Elks Lodge. The driving range and putting green make this a good course to learn the game on. A total of 45,000 rounds are played here each year.

# PARKWAY GOLF COURSE

**Course 60**
MAP E1 grid f7

**1971**

3400 Stevenson Road
Fremont, CA 94538

Pro shop (510) 656-6862

- driving range
- ✓ **practice greens**
- power carts
- ✓ **pull carts**
- ✓ **golf club rental**
- locker rooms
- showers
- executive course
- accommodations
- ✓ **food and beverages**
- ✓ **clubhouse**

**Mike Pope**
Manager/Professional

**Paul Fudenna**
Superintendent

***Course information:*** This public course has nine holes and par is 27. The course is 2,048 yards and rated 49.0 for 18 holes from the regular tees. The slope rating is 67. Women's tees are 2,048 yards and rated 50.3. The slope rating is 70.

***Play policy and fees:*** Green fees are $5.50 for nine holes and $7.50 for 18 holes on weekdays, $7.50 for nine holes and $11.00 for 18 holes on weekends. Senior rates are $4.50 for nine holes and $6.50 for 18 holes on weekdays. Reserve tee times one week in advance. Proper golf etiquette must be followed.

***Location:*** From Interstate 880 in Fremont, take the Stevenson Boulevard exit east. Drive 1.5 miles east to the course.

***Course description:*** Condo development took over nine holes of this formerly 18-hole course in 1991. This is a short course with only par-3s. The longest hole is 165 yards. There are several water hazards and an abundance of trees, which demand accuracy and make the course a challenge for any level of player. Don't underestimate the dinky 67-yard number six. This is a hole that requires finesse. You must hit over water, which always means trouble, with the hazard just six feet from the green. Typically, players either fly the hole or dump it in the lake, although golf humor at the course has it that someone actually skipped the ball over the water and into the hole for an ace. But you can't believe everything you read—or hear—at a golf course. In any event, keep it low and under the wind. Annual tournaments include the TAK Ladies Invitational (May), the St. Patrick's Day Tournament (March), Christmas Tournament (December) and the Thanksgiving Tournament (November). Host pro Mike Pope holds the men's course record at 49. There is no women's course record. A total of 50,000 rounds are played here each year.

# SUNOL VALLEY GOLF COURSE

**Course 61**
MAP E1 grid f9

NORTHERN E1

**Clark Glasson**

PO Box 609
Sunol, CA 94586

Interstate 680
at Andrade Road
Sunol, CA 94586

Pro shop (510) 862-2404

- driving range
- ✓ **practice greens**
- ✓ **power carts**
- pull carts
- ✓ **golf club rental**
- ✓ **locker rooms**
- ✓ **showers**
- executive course
- accommodations
- ✓ **food and beverages**
- ✓ **clubhouse**

**Jerry Thormann**
Professional

**Bill Andrade**
Superintendent

***Course information:*** This public facility has 36 holes. Par is 72 on both courses.

The Palm Course is detailed below.

The Cypress Course is 6,195 yards and rated 69.1 from the championship tees, and 5,801 yards and rated 67.2 from the regular tees. The slope ratings are 115 championship and 112 regular. Women's tees are 6,083 yards and rated 74.4 from the championship tees, and 5,479 yards and rated 70.1 from the forward tees. The slope ratings are 124 championship and 115 forward.

***Play policy and fees:*** Green fees are $20 to walk weekdays, or $30 with a cart. Weekends are $45; carts are mandatory and included. Reserve tee times seven days in advance. This course is available for outside tournaments.

***Location:*** From Interstate 680 in Sunol, exit on Andrade Road North. The course is located adjacent to the freeway.

***Course description:*** Nestled in the Mission Hills, the Palm Course is aptly named, with palm trees lining the wide fairways. There's plenty to worry about on both courses: tight, rolling hills, lots of trees, water hazards and bunkers. The greens are true but tricky. An estimated 500 tournaments were played on these two courses last year. Sunol Valley was the site of the Alameda County Open back in the early 1970s.

Palm Course

| Hole | 1 | 2 | 3 | 4 | 5 | 6 | 7 | 8 | 9 | Out | BLUE | Rating: 72.2 |
|---|---|---|---|---|---|---|---|---|---|---|---|---|
| BLUE | 375 | 343 | 525 | 420 | 195 | 305 | 333 | 231 | 584 | 3321 | | Slope: 118 |
| WHITE | 350 | 324 | 485 | 383 | 175 | 284 | 319 | 217 | 547 | 3084 | | |
| Par | 4 | 4 | 5 | 4 | 3 | 4 | 4 | 3 | 5 | 36 | WHITE | Rating: 70.3 |
| Handicap | 3 | 7 | 9 | 1 | 13 | 17 | 11 | 15 | 5 | x | | Slope: 114 |
| RED | 313 | 292 | 473 | 410 | 150 | 269 | 300 | 195 | 527 | 2929 | | |
| Par | 4 | 4 | 5 | 5 | 3 | 4 | 4 | 3 | 5 | 37 | RED | Rating: 74.4 |
| Handicap | 7 | 11 | 3 | 9 | 17 | 15 | 5 | 13 | 1 | x | | Slope: 124 |

| Hole | 10 | 11 | 12 | 13 | 14 | 15 | 16 | 17 | 18 | In | Totals | |
|---|---|---|---|---|---|---|---|---|---|---|---|---|
| BLUE | 561 | 369 | 409 | 197 | 369 | 207 | 540 | 434 | 433 | 3522 | BLUE | 6843 |
| WHITE | 537 | 329 | 385 | 177 | 356 | 193 | 519 | 401 | 425 | 3325 | WHITE | 6409 |
| Par | 5 | 4 | 4 | 3 | 4 | 3 | 5 | 4 | 4 | 36 | Par | 72 |
| Handicap | 6 | 14 | 2 | 18 | 12 | 16 | 8 | 10 | 4 | x | | |
| RED | 495 | 260 | 357 | 155 | 335 | 172 | 508 | 368 | 418 | 3068 | RED | 5997 |
| Par | 5 | 4 | 4 | 3 | 4 | 3 | 5 | 4 | 5 | 37 | Par | 74 |
| Handicap | 4 | 12 | 6 | 16 | 8 | 14 | 2 | 10 | 18 | x | | |

# CASTLEWOOD COUNTRY CLUB

**Course 62**
MAP E1 grid f9

**1923**
**William Park Bell**

707 Country Club Circle
Pleasanton, CA 94566

Pro shop (510) 846-5151
Clubhouse (510) 846-2871

- ✓ **driving range**
- ✓ **practice greens**
- ✓ **power carts**
- ✓ **pull carts**
- ✓ **golf club rental**
- ✓ **locker rooms**
- ✓ **showers**
- executive course
- accommodations
- ✓ **food and beverages**
- ✓ **clubhouse**

**Ernie Barbour**
Professional

**Larry O'Leary**
Director of Golf

**Bob Dalton**
Superintendent

***Course information:*** This private club has 36 holes. The Valley Course is 6,669 yards and rated 72.2 with a slope of 126 from the championship tees, and 6,371 yards and rated 70.9 with a slope of 123 from the regular tees. Women's tees are 5,900 yards and rated 73.8 with a slope of 129 from the forward tees.

The Hill Course is detailed below.

***Play policy and fees:*** Reciprocal play is accepted with members of other private clubs. Have your club pro call for arrangements. Green fees are $45 Mon.-Thur., and $55 on Fridays, weekends, and holidays, plus $10 for a cart when accompanied by a member. Fees are $82 plus $12 for a cart when unaccompanied by a member. Shirts with collars and golf shoes are required. Shorts must have a five-inch inseam. No jeans may be worn. Closed Mondays.

***Location:*** From Interstate 680 in Pleasanton, take the Sunol-Castlewood Drive exit. Drive straight for one block. The Valley Course is on the right side of the road and the Hill Course is further up the hill.

***Course description:*** The recently remodeled Valley Course is now one of the best in the East Bay. Designer Robert Muir Graves added contours and mounds to define the fairways, and also re-did all of the greens. It's a tough, demanding test. Phoebe Atherton Hearst originally owned all of the property here. Luther Burbank planted exotic trees and palms. The 1981 Sectional U.S. Open Qualifying was held at Castlewood. This club is host each August to the Wilson Pro-Junior Golf Tournament. Hole 18 affords a spectacular view of the valley. The men's course record is held by former PGA Tour winner Ron Cerrudo, who scored 62 on both courses in 1962. Don't expect to see anyone break that record; the course has changed considerably in the last 30 years. It's five shots tougher now because the trees are taller and the fairways aren't hard rock like they were in '62.

| Hole | 1 | 2 | 3 | 4 | 5 | 6 | 7 | 8 | 9 | Out | BLUE | Rating: 70.7 |
|---|---|---|---|---|---|---|---|---|---|---|---|---|
| BLUE | 424 | 472 | 396 | 186 | 421 | 141 | 482 | 406 | 335 | 3263 | | Slope: 124 |
| WHITE | 424 | 457 | 388 | 172 | 412 | 130 | 457 | 389 | 325 | 3154 | | |
| Par | 4 | 5 | 4 | 3 | 4 | 3 | 4 | 4 | 4 | 35 | WHITE | Rating: 69.8 |
| Handicap | 3 | 13 | 15 | 11 | 5 | 17 | 7 | 1 | 9 | x | | Slope: 123 |
| RED | 408 | 390 | 360 | 117 | 397 | 107 | 454 | 382 | 313 | 2928 | | |
| Par | 5 | 5 | 4 | 3 | 5 | 3 | 5 | 4 | 4 | 38 | RED | Rating: 72.0 |
| Handicap | 9 | 5 | 13 | 15 | 3 | 17 | 11 | 1 | 7 | x | | Slope: 129 |

| Hole | 10 | 11 | 12 | 13 | 14 | 15 | 16 | 17 | 18 | In | Totals | |
|---|---|---|---|---|---|---|---|---|---|---|---|---|
| BLUE | 276 | 479 | 139 | 326 | 360 | 404 | 397 | 211 | 413 | 3005 | BLUE | 6268 |
| WHITE | 264 | 463 | 139 | 316 | 348 | 394 | 354 | 201 | 370 | 2849 | WHITE | 6003 |
| Par | 4 | 5 | 3 | 4 | 4 | 4 | 4 | 3 | 4 | 35 | Par | 70 |
| Handicap | 12 | 14 | 16 | 10 | 4 | 2 | 6 | 8 | 18 | x | | |
| RED | 239 | 426 | 114 | 301 | 297 | 381 | 338 | 183 | 316 | 2595 | RED | 5523 |
| Par | 4 | 5 | 3 | 4 | 4 | 4 | 4 | 3 | 4 | 35 | Par | 73 |
| Handicap | 12 | 6 | 18 | 10 | 8 | 2 | 4 | 16 | 14 | x | | |

# SHARON HEIGHTS GOLF AND COUNTRY CLUB

**Course 63**
MAP E1 grid g4



**1962**
**Jack Fleming**

2900 Sand Hill Road
Menlo Park, CA 94025

Pro shop (415) 854-6429
Clubhouse (415) 854-6422

✓ **driving range**
✓ **practice greens**
✓ **power carts**
✓ **pull carts**
✓ **golf club rental**
✓ **locker rooms**
✓ **showers**
executive course
accommodations
✓ **food and beverages**
✓ **clubhouse**

**Robert E. Lee**
Manager

**James Knipp**
Professional

**Ross Brownlie**
Superintendent

***Course information:*** This private course has 18 holes and par is 72. The course is 6,872 yards and rated 73.5 from the championship tees, and 6,520 yards and rated 71.8 from the regular tees. The slope ratings are 132 championship and 129 regular. Women's tees are a long 6,185 yards and rated 76.4 from the forward tees. The slope rating is 141.

***Play policy and fees:*** Reciprocal play is accepted with members of other private clubs upon approval of the head pro. Guests must be sponsored by a member. Guest fees are $35 weekdays and $50 weekends when accompanied by a member, and $75 if unaccompanied on weekdays, and $100 if unaccompanied on weekends. Carts are $18. Fees and ratings could change by summer '93.

***Location:*** From Interstate 280 in Menlo Park, take Sand Hill Road exit toward Stanford University. The course is located on the left, less than a quarter mile off Sand Hill Road.

***Course description:*** This course is long and challenging. Some work will be done to improve tees, bunkers and fairways in the winter of 1993, but the course should be even better, if not a little longer, by summer '93. Redwoods, ranging in height from 40 to 80 feet, often come into play. They seemingly just jump right out into the fairway at times. The course boasts some of the best greens between San Francisco and Monterey. They're large, smooth and fast. The course is hilly, but walkable. Members include 49er greats Randy Cross and Bill Walsh and baseball superstar Willie Mays.

MAP ON PAGE 184

## MENLO PARK VETERANS GOLF COURSES

**Course 64**
MAP E1 grid f9

**1923**
**William Park Bell**

795 Willow Road
Menlo Park, CA 94025

Pro Shop (415) 493-5000

- ✓ **driving range**
- ✓ **practice greens**
- ✓ **power carts**
- ✓ **pull carts**
- ✓ **golf club rental**
- ✓ **locker rooms**
- ✓ **showers**
- executive course
- accommodations
- ✓ **food and beverages**
- ✓ **clubhouse**

*Course information:* This private facility is short, but no yardage or rating information was available.

*Play policy and fees:* Free to patients of Palo Alto or Menlo Park VA Hospitals. Must have a doctor's order. Course has special hours and requirements. It is not open to the public.

*Location:* From Highway 101 in Palo Alto/Menlo Park, take the Menlo Park or Willow Road exit. Follow it to the hospital. The courses are on hospital grounds.

*Course description:* The course serves patients of the Veteran's Administration Hospitals in Palo Alto and Menlo Park. It's free to all patients, but not open to the public.

## STANFORD GOLF COURSE

**Course 65**
MAP E1 grid g5

198 Junipero Serra Blvd.
Stanford, CA 94305

Pro shop (415)323-0944

- ✓ **driving range**
- ✓ **practice greens**
- ✓ **power carts**
- ✓ **pull carts**
- golf club rental
- ✓ **locker rooms**
- ✓ **showers**
- executive course
- accommodations
- ✓ **food and beverages**
- ✓ **clubhouse**

**Larry O'Neill**
Professional/ Dir. of Golf

**Tom Thatcher**
Superintendent

*Course information:* This private course has 18 holes and par is 71. The course is 6,770 yards and rated 72.9 from the tournament tees, 6,346 yards and rated 70.9 from the championship tees. Slope ratings are 131 championship and 127 forward. Women's tees are 5,890 yards and rated 74.2. The slope is rated 135.

*Play policy and fees:* Members and guests only. Guests must be accompanied by a member. Guest fees are $33 weekdays and $38 weekends. Carts are $21.

*Location:* From Interstate 280, take the Sand Hill Road exit in Menlo Park. Drive east toward Stanford University. Turn right on Junipero Serra Boulevard and continue to the course. From Highway 101, take the University Avenue exit, which turns into Palm Drive. Turn right on West Campus Drive, right again on Junipero Serra Boulevard and continue to the course.

*Course description:* This sprawling layout is dotted with towering eucalyptus and oak trees and is characterized by large, contoured greens and lots of bunkers. There are no breathers, especially on the nerve-wracking, infamous, 474-yard par-4 12th hole. It's extremely long with one big oak positioned in the middle of the fairway. The 439-yard second, a dogleg left, and the 435-yard 10th are cast-iron tests. Rated among the top courses in the state, it was host to the 1946, 1966, 1981 and 1989 NCAA Men's Championships; the 1981 and 1988 NCAA Women's Championships; the 1959 USGA Junior Championship and the Western Amateur. It offers far-reaching views of San Francisco and, weather permitting, the entire bay. Students can play this course, so it can get very crowded, but it's worth the wait.

# PALO ALTO GOLF COURSE

**Course 66**
MAP E1 grid g5

**1956**
**William Francis Bell**

1875 Embarcadero Road
Palo Alto, CA 94303

Pro shop (415) 856-0881

- ✓ **driving range**
- ✓ **practice greens**
- ✓ **power carts**
- ✓ **pull carts**
- ✓ **golf club rental**
- locker rooms
- showers
- executive course
- accommodations
- ✓ **food and beverages**
- clubhouse

**Brad Lozares**
Professional

**Paul Dias**
Superintendent

NORTHERN E1

***Course information:*** This public course has 18 holes. See card below for yardage and rating information.

***Play policy and fees:*** Green fees are $16 weekdays and $20 weekends. Twilight rates are $9 weekdays and $12 weekends. Carts are $18. Call for reservations. On weekdays a seven-day lead time is recommended and on weekends by the Tuesday preceding. Shirts must be worn at all times.

***Location:*** From Highway 101 in Palo Alto, take the Embarcadero Road exit east. The course is located on the left about a half mile from the highway. It's just before the airport.

***Course description:*** This is a long and often windy course. The greens are large. Trees and straight fairways are characteristic. Hole four is the most difficult. It's a 435-yard par-4, usually into the wind. Hole 14, a 229-yard par-3, also plays into the wind and is a good test for the driver. Annual tournaments include: Palo Alto City Women's Amateur (April), Santa Clara Valley Best-Ball (May), Palo Alto City Men's Amateur (September), Palo Alto City Seniors Amateur (October), Times-Tribune Junior Tournament, and Town & Country Women's Golf Tournament. The course record of 64 is held by Brad Henninger. A total of 102,000 rounds are played here each year.

| Hole | 1 | 2 | 3 | 4 | 5 | 6 | 7 | 8 | 9 | Out | | |
|---|---|---|---|---|---|---|---|---|---|---|---|---|
| BLUE | 546 | 411 | 200 | 435 | 395 | 445 | 362 | 194 | 537 | 3525 | BLUE | Rating: 72.1 |
| WHITE | 519 | 394 | 140 | 423 | 375 | 430 | 344 | 179 | 520 | 3324 | | Slope: 116 |
| Par | 5 | 4 | 3 | 4 | 4 | 4 | 4 | 3 | 5 | 36 | WHITE | Rating: 70.4 |
| Handicap | 5 | 7 | 13 | 1 | 9 | 3 | 11 | 17 | 15 | x | | Slope: 113 |
| RED | 489 | 369 | 101 | 399 | 358 | 386 | 309 | 142 | 502 | 3055 | | |
| Par | 5 | 4 | 3 | 5 | 4 | 4 | 4 | 3 | 5 | 37 | RED | Rating: 74.0 |
| Handicap | 1 | 9 | 17 | 7 | 11 | 5 | 13 | 15 | 3 | x | | Slope: 122 |

| Hole | 10 | 11 | 12 | 13 | 14 | 15 | 16 | 17 | 18 | In | Totals | |
|---|---|---|---|---|---|---|---|---|---|---|---|---|
| BLUE | 313 | 162 | 492 | 383 | 229 | 481 | 427 | 447 | 402 | 3336 | BLUE | 6861 |
| WHITE | 290 | 152 | 475 | 362 | 213 | 466 | 414 | 425 | 373 | 3170 | WHITE | 6494 |
| Par | 4 | 3 | 5 | 4 | 3 | 5 | 4 | 4 | 4 | 36 | Par | 72 |
| Handicap | 18 | 12 | 14 | 8 | 4 | 16 | 6 | 2 | 10 | x | | |
| RED | 283 | 106 | 460 | 362 | 175 | 440 | 378 | 387 | 335 | 2926 | RED | 5981 |
| Par | 4 | 3 | 5 | 4 | 3 | 5 | 4 | 4 | 4 | 36 | Par | 73 |
| Handicap | 14 | 18 | 2 | 10 | 16 | 4 | 8 | 6 | 12 | x | | |

# MOFFETT FIELD GOLF COURSE

**Course 67**
MAP E1 grid g6

**1968**
**Robert Muir Graves**

MWR Fund, Building 25
NAS Moffett Field,
CA 94035

Pro shop (415) 404-4702
Clubhouse (415) 404-4705

- ✓ **driving range**
- ✓ **practice greens**
- ✓ **power carts**
- ✓ **pull carts**
- ✓ **golf club rental**
- ✓ **locker rooms**
- ✓ **showers**
- executive course
- accommodations
- ✓ **food and beverages**
- ✓ **clubhouse**

**Lee Henderson**
Manager

**Bobby Bihl**
Professional

**Jeff Hardy**
Superintendent

*Course information:* This military course has 18 holes and par is 72. The course is 6,491 yards and rated 70.0 from the championship tees, and 6,329 yards and rated 69.3 from the regular tees. The slope ratings are 111 championship and 109 regular. Women's tees are 6,003 yards and rated 72.9 from the championship tees, and 5,976 yards and rated 72.7 from the forward tees. The slope ratings are 116 championship and 116 forward.

*Play policy and fees:* Active and retired military personnel and guests only. Guest fees are $11 for nine holes and $16 for 18 holes. Carts are $10 for nine holes and $14 for 18 holes. Weekday play is on a first-come first-served basis. Reservations are required for weekends and holidays.

*Location:* From Highway 101 in Mountain View, take the Moffett Boulevard exit. Drive north to the main gate of Moffett Field Naval Air Station for instructions.

*Course description:* This course is mostly flat and open with more than 7,000 pine, poplar and cedar trees. Three lakes come into play, and it is easily walkable. Kikuyu grass makes the course distinctive. It tends to create flyer lies, requiring the golfer to 'pick' the ball for best results. This isn't a demanding course, but the fact that out-of-bounds comes into play on several holes does keep your attention. A total of 45,000 rounds are played here each year.

# SUNNYVALE GOLF COURSE

**Course 68**
MAP E1 grid g6

***Course information:*** This public course has 18 holes. See card below for yardage and rating information.

***Play policy and fees:*** Sunnyvale resident green fees are $14 weekdays and $20 weekends. Non-resident green fees are $18 weekdays and $23 weekends. Twilight rates for residents are $10 weekdays and $12 weekends. Non-residents twilight rates are $11 weekdays and $14 weekends. Carts are $20. Play is first-come first-served weekdays, and the Monday prior for residents reserving weekend play, and the Tuesday prior for non-residents reserving weekend play.

***Location:*** From Highway 101 in northern Sunnyvale, exit onto Mathilda Avenue south. Turn right on Maude Avenue and right again on Macara Avenue.

***Course description:*** The short, flat course boasts several long par-3s. Conspiring trees, wind, lakes and doglegs all demand good positioning. Beware of the 358-yard 18th hole, a par-4 over water with a three-tiered green guarded by bunkers. Extensive remodeling of the course was completed in early 1991. This public course has one of the largest pro shops in the country, offering full-service sales and repairs. A total of 105,000 rounds are played here each year.

**1968**
**Clark Glasson**

605 Macara Lane
Sunnyvale, CA 94086

Pro shop (408) 738-3666
Clubhouse (408) 739-8900

- driving range
- ✓ **practice greens**
- ✓ **power carts**
- ✓ **pull carts**
- ✓ **golf club rental**
- locker rooms
- showers
- executive course
- accommodations
- ✓ **food and beverages**
- ✓ **clubhouse**

**Art Wilson**
Professional

**Mark Petersen**
Manager

**Curtis Black**
Superintendent

| Hole | 1 | 2 | 3 | 4 | 5 | 6 | 7 | 8 | 9 | Out | | |
|---|---|---|---|---|---|---|---|---|---|---|---|---|
| BLUE | 381 | 401 | 500 | 175 | 296 | 389 | 161 | 341 | 432 | 3088 | BLUE | Rating: 69.7 |
| WHITE | 365 | 368 | 404 | 149 | 286 | 341 | 136 | 322 | 402 | 2853 | | Slope: 119 |
| Par | 4 | 4 | 5 | 3 | 4 | 4 | 3 | 4 | 4 | 35 | WHITE | Rating: 67.6 |
| Handicap | 7 | 3 | 11 | 17 | 15 | 13 | 9 | 1 | 5 | x | | Slope: 114 |
| RED | 346 | 294 | 464 | 126 | 274 | 320 | 117 | 298 | 380 | 2619 | | |
| Par | 4 | 4 | 5 | 3 | 4 | 4 | 3 | 4 | 5 | 36 | RED | Rating: 70.2 |
| Handicap | 7 | 3 | 11 | 17 | 15 | 13 | 9 | 1 | 5 | x | | Slope: 120 |

| Hole | 10 | 11 | 12 | 13 | 14 | 15 | 16 | 17 | 18 | In | Totals | |
|---|---|---|---|---|---|---|---|---|---|---|---|---|
| BLUE | 529 | 417 | 381 | 198 | 368 | 201 | 323 | 386 | 358 | 3161 | BLUE | 6249 |
| WHITE | 499 | 392 | 339 | 161 | 340 | 178 | 303 | 353 | 333 | 2898 | WHITE | 5751 |
| Par | 5 | 4 | 4 | 3 | 4 | 3 | 4 | 4 | 4 | 35 | Par | 70 |
| Handicap | 18 | 8 | 16 | 6 | 12 | 14 | 4 | 10 | 2 | x | | |
| RED | 481 | 369 | 313 | 126 | 323 | 161 | 290 | 322 | 301 | 2686 | RED | 5305 |
| Par | 5 | 4 | 4 | 3 | 4 | 3 | 4 | 4 | 4 | 35 | Par | 71 |
| Handicap | 18 | 8 | 16 | 6 | 12 | 14 | 4 | 10 | 2 | x | | |

# SHORELINE GOLF LINKS

**Course 69**
MAP E1 grid g6

***Course information:*** This public course has 18 holes and par is 72. The course is 6,735 yards and rated 72.5 from the championship tees, and 6,143 yards and rated 70.1 from the regular tees. The slope ratings are 125 championship and 121 regular. Women's tees are 5,516 yards and rated 71.7. The slope rating is 121.

***Play policy and fees:*** Green fees are $29 weekdays and $38 weekends. Twilight rates are $17 every day. Carts are $22. Reservations are recommended. You may reserve a tee time six days in advance.

***Location:*** From Highway 101 in Mountain View, take the Shoreline Boulevard exit north. Follow it to the 2600 block.

***Course description:*** This sprawling, flat, links-style course demands accuracy with the long irons. The greens are large and undulating, the fairways are narrow and there are more than 80 bunkers. It's very easy to land a ball in the long grass or the water (and there's plenty of water). Hole four is a short par, but look out because it's over water and between bunkers. You're also shooting across water on the 11th and 17th holes. The wind can blow here, but it's a fun course. The course record is 64. The city has approved a new clubhouse, but it remains to be built. The grass driving range is one of the busiest on the peninsula. The Player's West Women's Tournament is played here every fall. A total of 70,000 rounds are played here each year.

**1983**
**Robert Trent Jones, Jr.**

PO Box 1206
Mountain View, CA 94043

2600 North Shoreline Blvd.
Mountain View, CA 94043

Pro shop (415) 969-2041

- ✓ **driving range**
- ✓ **practice greens**
- ✓ **power carts**
- ✓ **pull carts**
- ✓ **golf club rental**
- locker rooms
- showers
- executive course
- accommodations
- ✓ **food and beverages**
- clubhouse

**Scott Kramer**
Manager/Professional

**Al Rafalski**
Superintendent

# SUMMIT POINTE GOLF COURSE

**Course 70**
MAP E1 grid g8

**1978**

1500 Country Club Drive
Milpitas, CA 95035

Pro shop (408) 262-8813
Clubhouse (408) 262-2500

- driving range
- ✓ **practice greens**
- ✓ **power carts**
- ✓ **pull carts**
- ✓ **golf club rental**
- locker rooms
- showers
- executive course
- accommodations
- ✓ **food and beverages**
- ✓ **clubhouse**

**Bob Christian**
Manager

**Jeff Yeager**
Professional

**Paul Gillis**
Superintendent

NORTHERN E1

***Course information:*** This public course has 18 holes. See card below for yardage and rating information.

***Play policy and fees:*** Green fees are $20 weekdays and $31 weekends. Carts are $22. Twilight rates are $15 weekdays and $20 weekends. Reservations are recommended one week in advance. This course is available for outside tournaments.

***Location:*** From Interstate 680 in Milpitas, take the Jacklin Road exit east to Evans Road. Turn left and then right on Country Club Drive.

***Course description:*** The front nine is mostly open and hilly, while the back nine is flat and tight. Almost every hole on the back nine has water. The greens are tough and fast with tricky breaks. Hole 16, a par-3, is 199 yards over water, and was once described as one of the best holes in Northern California. Annual tournaments include the Milpitas/Berryessa YMCA (April), 100 Club (May), and the Chamber of Commerce (August). The course record of 64 is held by Estaban Toledo, who is currently on the Nike tour. A total of 75,000 rounds are played here each year.

| Hole | 1 | 2 | 3 | 4 | 5 | 6 | 7 | 8 | 9 | Out | BLUE | Rating: 70.0 |
|---|---|---|---|---|---|---|---|---|---|---|---|---|
| BLUE | 322 | 528 | 122 | 362 | 183 | 384 | 338 | 401 | 515 | 3155 | | Slope: 121 |
| WHITE | 300 | 483 | 117 | 351 | 175 | 375 | 329 | 393 | 505 | 3028 | | |
| Par | 4 | 5 | 3 | 4 | 3 | 4 | 4 | 4 | 5 | 36 | WHITE | Rating: 68.7 |
| Handicap | 15 | 3 | 17 | 5 | 9 | 13 | 7 | 1 | 11 | x | | Slope: 117 |
| RED | 273 | 448 | 107 | 342 | 169 | 274 | 326 | 383 | 462 | 2784 | | |
| Par | 4 | 5 | 3 | 4 | 3 | 4 | 4 | 4 | 5 | 36 | RED | Rating: 70.6 |
| Handicap | 15 | 3 | 17 | 7 | 11 | 13 | 9 | 1 | 5 | x | | Slope: 121 |

| Hole | 10 | 11 | 12 | 13 | 14 | 15 | 16 | 17 | 18 | In | Totals | |
|---|---|---|---|---|---|---|---|---|---|---|---|---|
| BLUE | 358 | 329 | 364 | 154 | 488 | 498 | 199 | 388 | 398 | 3176 | BLUE | 6331 |
| WHITE | 346 | 322 | 352 | 143 | 473 | 492 | 178 | 381 | 348 | 3035 | WHITE | 6063 |
| Par | 4 | 4 | 4 | 3 | 5 | 5 | 3 | 4 | 4 | 36 | Par | 72 |
| Handicap | 16 | 12 | 4 | 18 | 8 | 2 | 14 | 10 | 6 | x | | |
| RED | 330 | 310 | 329 | 112 | 458 | 438 | 122 | 291 | 322 | 2712 | RED | 5496 |
| Par | 4 | 4 | 4 | 3 | 5 | 5 | 3 | 4 | 4 | 36 | Par | 72 |
| Handicap | 14 | 16 | 6 | 18 | 2 | 4 | 12 | 10 | 8 | x | | |

# SPRING VALLEY GOLF COURSE

**Course 71**
MAP E1 grid g9

PO Box 360050
Milpitas, CA 95035

3441 East Calaveras
Boulevard
Milpitas, CA 95035

Pro shop (408) 262-1722

- ✓ **driving range**
- ✓ **practice greens**
- ✓ **power carts**
- ✓ **pull carts**
- ✓ **golf club rental**
- locker rooms
- showers
- executive course
- accommodations
- ✓ **food and beverages**
- ✓ **clubhouse**

**Richard Stewart**
Professional

**Rick Jetter**
Director of Golf

**Greg Jetter**
Superintendent

***Course information:*** This public course has 18 holes and par is 70. The course is 6,099 yards and rated 68.8 from the championship tees, and 5,866 yards and rated 67.8 from the regular tees. The slope ratings are 114 championship and 111 regular. Women's tees are 5,513 yards and rated 69.2. The slope rating is 109.

***Play policy and fees:*** Green fees are $18 weekdays and $26 weekends. Twilight rates are $13 weekdays and $15 weekends. Carts are $20. Reservations recommended.

***Location:*** From Interstate 880 or Interstate 680 in Milpitas, exit on 237/Calaveras and drive east to the course.

***Course description:*** Holes are being remodeled so look for a possible change in par and ratings. This rolling course is set in the foothills outside Milpitas. It's a gambler's paradise. Doglegs and water, plus cypress, pine and elm trees all come into play. There aren't many bunkers, but as a consolation they made the bunkers extra tricky. Stay below the pin. Improved course condition has made this a good test. There are three holes over water, including the 185-yard 11th. The course record of 61 is held by Joe Tamburino. A total of 85,000 rounds are played here each year.

# LOS ALTOS GOLF AND COUNTRY CLUB

**Course 72**
MAP E1 grid h5

**1923**
**Tom Nicoll**

1560 Country Club Drive
Los Altos, CA 94024

Pro shop (415) 948-2146
Clubhouse (415) 948-1024

- driving range
- ✓ **practice greens**
- ✓ **power carts**
- ✓ **pull carts**
- ✓ **golf club rental**
- ✓ **locker rooms**
- ✓ **showers**
- executive course
- accommodations
- ✓ **food and beverages**
- ✓ **clubhouse**

**Brian Inkster**
Professional

**Kenneth Kelley**
Manager

**Mike Simpson**
Superintendent

NORTHERN E1

***Course information:*** This private course has 18 holes. See card below for yardage and rating information.

***Play policy and fees:*** Reciprocal play is accepted with members of other selected private clubs. Have your club pro call for arrangements. Members and guests only. Green fees for reciprcators are $80, plus $20 for a cart. Guests fees are $40 when accompanied by a member. Carts are $20. Reservations required two weeks in advance.

***Location:*** From Interstate 280 in Los Altos, take the Magdelena Avenue exit northeast. Turn right on the Foothill Expressway and continue to Loyola Drive. Flip a right and another right onto Country Club Drive.

***Course description:*** It's pretty out here. The course is tight, tree-lined and has undulating greens. The par-3 third hole requires a 231-yard carry over a barranca from an elevated tee. It'll test you. Three-time U.S. Amateur Champion and LPGA standout Julie Inkster holds the women's record of 68; head pro Brian Inkster grew up on the course. The men's course record is 64, set by Jeff Brehaut in 1989. Dan Forsman, three-time PGA tour winner, is also from here. The clubhouse underwent renovation and re-opened in late summer of 1992. Come and enjoy the scenery. A total of 40,000 rounds are played here each year.

| Hole | 1 | 2 | 3 | 4 | 5 | 6 | 7 | 8 | 9 | Out | BLUE | Rating: 71.4 |
|---|---|---|---|---|---|---|---|---|---|---|---|---|
| BLUE | 519 | 390 | 231 | 347 | 349 | 143 | 388 | 424 | 412 | 3203 | | Slope: 126 |
| WHITE | 507 | 366 | 221 | 332 | 329 | 133 | 378 | 412 | 412 | 3090 | | |
| Par | 5 | 4 | 3 | 4 | 4 | 3 | 4 | 4 | 4 | 35 | WHITE | Rating: 70.5 |
| Handicap | 11 | 7 | 3 | 13 | 15 | 17 | 9 | 1 | 5 | x | | Slope: 123 |
| RED | 492 | 347 | 189 | 315 | 314 | 113 | 364 | 398 | 403 | 2935 | | |
| Par | 5 | 4 | 3 | 4 | 4 | 3 | 4 | 5 | 5 | 37 | RED | Rating: 75.0 |
| Handicap | 1 | 7 | 13 | 5 | 9 | 17 | 3 | 15 | 11 | x | | Slope: 134 |

| Hole | 10 | 11 | 12 | 13 | 14 | 15 | 16 | 17 | 18 | In | Totals | |
|---|---|---|---|---|---|---|---|---|---|---|---|---|
| BLUE | 412 | 340 | 385 | 333 | 429 | 155 | 344 | 545 | 388 | 3331 | BLUE | 6534 |
| WHITE | 387 | 315 | 366 | 322 | 413 | 145 | 334 | 490 | 388 | 3160 | WHITE | 6250 |
| Par | 4 | 4 | 4 | 4 | 4 | 3 | 4 | 5 | 4 | 36 | Par | 71 |
| Handicap | 6 | 10 | 14 | 16 | 2 | 18 | 12 | 8 | 4 | x | | |
| RED | 338 | 309 | 352 | 299 | 406 | 115 | 328 | 459 | 370 | 2976 | RED | 5911 |
| Par | 4 | 4 | 4 | 4 | 5 | 3 | 4 | 5 | 4 | 37 | Par | 74 |
| Handicap | 12 | 6 | 10 | 14 | 16 | 18 | 8 | 4 | 2 | x | | |

# DEEP CLIFF GOLF COURSE

**Course 73**
MAP E1 grid h5

*Course information:* This public course has 18 holes and par is 60. The course is 3,164 yards and rated 55.2 for 18 holes from the weekend tees, and 3,260 yards and rated 55.6 from the regular tees. The slope ratings are 84 weekend and 85 regular. Women's yardage and ratings were unavailable.

*Play policy and fees:* Green fees are $18 weekdays and $24 weekends. Reservations are recommended one week in advance. This course is available for tournaments.

*Location:* From Interstate 280 in Sunnyvale, take the Foothill Expressway exit south to McClellan Road. Turn left and then turn right onto Clubhouse Lane.

*Course description:* This executive course has three par-4s on the front nine and three par-4s on the back nine. It requires good placement shots because of the narrow corridor-type fairways. A creek feeding into Saratoga Creek bisects the course and comes into play on several holes. A total of 90,000 rounds are played here each year.

**1965**
**Clark Glasson**

PO Box 60302
Cupertino, CA 95014

10700 Clubhouse Lane
Cupertino, CA 95014

Pro shop (408) 253-5357
Clubhouse (408) 253-5359

- driving range
- ✓ **practice greens**
- power carts
- ✓ **pull carts**
- ✓ **golf club rental**
- locker rooms
- showers
- ✓ **executive course**
- accommodations
- ✓ **food and beverages**
- ✓ **clubhouse**

**Steve Schwartz**
Manager

**Mark Francetic**
Superintendent

# PALO ALTO HILLS GOLF AND COUNTRY CLUB

**Course 74**
MAP E1 grid h5

**1962**
**Clark Glasson**

3000 Alexis Drive
Palo Alto, CA 94304

Pro shop (415) 948-2320
Clubhouse (415) 948-1800

- ✓ **driving range**
- ✓ **practice greens**
- ✓ **power carts**
- ✓ **pull carts**
- ✓ **golf club rental**
- ✓ **locker rooms**
- ✓ **showers**
- executive course
- accommodations
- ✓ **food and beverages**
- ✓ **clubhouse**

**Lyn Nelson**
Manager

**Mike Garvale**
Superintendent

*Course information:* This private course has 18 holes and par is 71. The course is 6,249 yards and rated 71.2 from the championship tees, and 6,036 yards and rated 70.2 from the regular tees. The slope ratings are 130 championship and 128 regular. Women's tees are 5,703 yards and rated 73.7. The slope rating is 135.

*Play policy and fees:* Reciprocal play is accepted with members of other private clubs. Have your pro call to set up a time. Green fees for reciprocators are $55 weekdays and $100 weekends. Carts are additional. Guest fees are $35 weekdays and $45 weekends when accompanied by a member. Carts are $18. Reservations are recommended. Proper golf attire required.

*Location:* From Interstate 280 or Highway 101, take the Page Mill Expressway exit south. Drive one mile to Alexis Drive and continue a half mile to the course.

*Course description:* Although this sporty course is short, it plays considerably longer than the yardage indicates. It's a defensive course, tight with undulating fairways and elevated greens. Water comes into play on five holes. Low-handicappers shouldn't be overly confident (unless you're naturally that way) and first-timers should beware. Watch out for the par-4 third hole, a nasty, downhill tester. Situated in the hills, the course offers picturesque views of the bay, so don't forget to look up. The Tall Tree Invitational Tournament plays here at the end of May. Course records are owned by John Test with a 62 and Shirley Cerrudo who shot a 72. A total of 40,000 rounds are played here each year.

## BLACKBERRY FARM GOLF COURSE

**Course 75**
MAP E1 grid h5

**1962**
**Robert Muir Graves**

22100 Stevens Creek Blvd.
Cupertino, CA 95014

Pro shop (408) 253-9200
Clubhouse (408) 255-3300

- driving range
- ✓ **practice greens**
- power carts
- ✓ **pull carts**
- ✓ **golf club rental**
- locker rooms
- showers
- executive course
- accommodations
- ✓ **food and beverages**
- ✓ **clubhouse**

**Jeff Piserchio**
Manager/Professional

**Ernie Alvarez**
Superintendent

***Course information:*** This public course has nine holes. Par is 58 for 18 holes. The course is 3,182 yards and rated 55.9 for 18 holes from the regular tees. The slope rating is 78. Women's tees are 3,182 and rated 58.5 for 18 holes. The slope rating is 83.

***Play policy and fees:*** Green fees for residents of Cupertino are $6.50 weekdays and $8.25 weekends. Nonresident green fees are $7.50 weekdays and $9.25 weekends. Reservations are accepted one week in advance. This course is available for outside tournaments.

***Location:*** From Interstate 280 in Cupertino, take the Foothill Expressway exit south. Continue to Stevens Creek Boulevard, turn left and drive one-half mile up to the course on the left.

***Course description:*** This flat, narrow course has lots of water and trees. It's relatively short with dome shaped greens. The 120-yard, par-3 eighth hole is over water. Short and sweet, but you can work on your putting. A total of 80,000 rounds are played here each year.

## SUNKEN GARDENS GOLF COURSE

**Course 76**
MAP E1 grid h6

**1959**
**Robert Dean Putman**

1010 South Wolfe Road
Sunnyvale, CA 94086

Pro shop (408) 739-6588
Clubhouse (408) 732-4980

- ✓ **driving range**
- ✓ **practice greens**
- ✓ **power carts**
- ✓ **pull carts**
- ✓ **golf club rental**
- locker rooms
- showers
- ✓ **executive course**
- accommodations
- ✓ **food and beverages**
- ✓ **clubhouse**

**Bill Condaxis**
Manager

***Course information:*** This public course has nine holes. Par is 58 for 18 holes. The course is 2,876 yards. It is not rated.

***Play policy and fees:*** Green fees are $7 weekdays and $9 weekends. To reserve a tee time you must pre-pay each day for a tee time that day. Weekend reservations are made the Tuesday prior to the weekend. This course is available for outside tournaments.

***Location:*** This course is located between Highway 101 and Interstate 280 in Sunnyvale. Exit off on Wolfe Road toward El Camino Real. The course is on the east side of the street.

***Course description:*** This mostly flat course borders a former quarry and is somewhat tight. There are two par-4s and the rest are par-3s. The course is an excellent layout for beginners, juniors and seniors.

# SAN JOSE MUNICIPAL GOLF COURSE

**Course 77**
MAP E1 grid h7

**1968**
**Robert Muir Graves**

1560 Oakland Road
San Jose, CA 95131

Pro shop (408) 441-4653

- ✓ **driving range**
- ✓ **practice greens**
- ✓ **power carts**
- ✓ **pull carts**
- ✓ **golf club rental**
- locker rooms
- showers
- executive course
- accommodations
- ✓ **food and beverages**
- ✓ **clubhouse**

**Mike Rawitser**
Director of Golf

**Bob McGrath**
Professional

**John Martin**
Superintendent

***Course information:*** This public course has 18 holes. See card below for yardage and rating information.

***Play policy and fees:*** Green fees are $20 weekdays and $27 weekends. Twilight rates are $12 weekdays and $15 weekends. There is a special $15 rate for the first 40 players each day for the first hour the course is open on weekends, which applies to nine holes only. You play the back nine. Carts are $12 for nine holes and $22 for 18 holes. Reservations are recommended one week in advance and there is a standby list each day.

***Location:*** From Highway 101 heading south in San Jose, take the 13th Street exit and cross back over the freeway on Oakland Road. Follow it for one mile to the course on your right.

***Course description:*** This course averages from 400 to 450 players a day, depending on the season. The course is relatively flat and undemanding, and makes a good intermediate test of golf. There are a few long par-4s. The fairways are wide and the water hazards have lost some of their zip due to the drought, including two lakes which are dry. Watch for lots of doglegs and large, undulating greens. The course itself is in excellent condition, and is one of the busiest in Northern California, with 108,000 rounds played here each year.

| Hole | 1 | 2 | 3 | 4 | 5 | 6 | 7 | 8 | 9 | Out | | |
|---|---|---|---|---|---|---|---|---|---|---|---|---|
| BLUE | 492 | 403 | 402 | 201 | 364 | 383 | 184 | 418 | 502 | 3349 | BLUE | Rating: 70.1 |
| WHITE | 478 | 390 | 381 | 184 | 349 | 373 | 159 | 403 | 478 | 3195 | | Slope: 108 |
| Par | 5 | 4 | 4 | 3 | 4 | 4 | 3 | 4 | 5 | 36 | WHITE | Rating: 68.7 |
| Handicap | 11 | 3 | 9 | 5 | 17 | 7 | 15 | 1 | 13 | x | | Slope: 105 |
| RED | 429 | 318 | 311 | 147 | 305 | 340 | 122 | 371 | 436 | 2779 | | |
| Par | 5 | 4 | 4 | 3 | 4 | 4 | 3 | 4 | 5 | 36 | RED | Rating: 69.7 |
| Handicap | 17 | 11 | 9 | 5 | 7 | 3 | 13 | 1 | 15 | x | | Slope: 112 |

| Hole | 10 | 11 | 12 | 13 | 14 | 15 | 16 | 17 | 18 | In | Totals | |
|---|---|---|---|---|---|---|---|---|---|---|---|---|
| BLUE | 377 | 543 | 147 | 394 | 361 | 415 | 381 | 194 | 498 | 3310 | BLUE | 6659 |
| WHITE | 361 | 530 | 139 | 379 | 350 | 404 | 361 | 165 | 478 | 3167 | WHITE | 6362 |
| Par | 4 | 5 | 3 | 4 | 4 | 4 | 4 | 3 | 5 | 36 | Par | 72 |
| Handicap | 12 | 4 | 18 | 6 | 16 | 2 | 8 | 10 | 14 | x | | |
| RED | 328 | 461 | 121 | 321 | 317 | 346 | 338 | 153 | 468 | 2853 | RED | 5632 |
| Par | 4 | 5 | 3 | 4 | 4 | 4 | 4 | 3 | 5 | 36 | Par | 72 |
| Handicap | 12 | 16 | 14 | 6 | 10 | 2 | 4 | 8 | 18 | x | | |

# SANTA CLARA GOLF AND TENNIS CLUB

**Course 78**
MAP E1 grid h7

**1986**
**Robert Muir Graves**

5155 Stars & Stripes
Santa Clara, CA 95054

Pro shop (408) 980-9515
Clubhouse (408) 986-1666

- ✓ **driving range**
- ✓ **practice greens**
- ✓ **power carts**
- ✓ **pull carts**
- ✓ **golf club rental**
- ✓ **locker rooms**
- ✓ **showers**
- executive course
- ✓ **accommodations**
- ✓ **food and beverages**
- ✓ **clubhouse**

**Tim Walsh**
Manager

**Mike Paul**
Professional

**Allan Schlothauer**
Superintendent

***Course information:*** This public course has 18 holes. Women's tees are 6,020 yards and rated 73.8 with a slope of 118 from the gold tees. See card below for additonal yardage and rating information.

***Play policy and fees:*** Green fees for residents of the city of Santa Clara are $11 weekdays and $16 weekends. Non-resident green fees are $18 weekdays and $24 weekends. Twilight rates for residents are $6 weekdays and $10 weekends. Twilight rates for non-residents are $12 weekdays and $15 weekends. Carts are $10 for nine holes and $20 for 18 holes. A single-rider cart is $12. Residents must reserve tee times eight days in advance, and non-residents must reserve tee times seven days in advance. Residents must have an ID card issued by the pro shop. This course is available for outside tournaments.

***Location:*** From Highway 101 north in Sunnyvale or Highway 237 south, take the Great America Parkway exit. Go east on Tasman Drive to Centennial Boulevard. Turn left and drive to Stars & Stripes Avenue.

***Course description:*** This course has rolling hills and is long and open with a links-style rough on the fairway. It's walkable. There are doglegs and blind shots, and the wind can blow. The par-4 15th, at 440-yards, is brutal in the afternoon wind. Water comes into play on two par-4s on the front. The course is located across the street from the San Francisco 49ers' training facilities. The course record of 66 is held by Ed Perkins. A total of 110,000 rounds are played here each year.

| Hole | 1 | 2 | 3 | 4 | 5 | 6 | 7 | 8 | 9 | Out | BLUE | Rating: 73.0 |
|---|---|---|---|---|---|---|---|---|---|---|---|---|
| BLUE | 539 | 387 | 370 | 397 | 421 | 232 | 557 | 146 | 372 | 3421 | | Slope: 126 |
| WHITE | 511 | 366 | 338 | 378 | 400 | 205 | 541 | 131 | 351 | 3221 | | |
| Par | 5 | 4 | 4 | 4 | 4 | 3 | 5 | 3 | 4 | 36 | WHITE | Rating: 71.4 |
| Handicap | 9 | 11 | 13 | 7 | 1 | 5 | 3 | 17 | 15 | x | | Slope: 122 |
| RED | 475 | 330 | 290 | 347 | 363 | 174 | 486 | 100 | 318 | 2883 | | |
| Par | 5 | 4 | 4 | 4 | 4 | 3 | 5 | 3 | 4 | 36 | RED | Rating: 71.5 |
| Handicap | 3 | 9 | 13 | 7 | 5 | 15 | 1 | 17 | 11 | x | | Slope: 115 |

| Hole | 10 | 11 | 12 | 13 | 14 | 15 | 16 | 17 | 18 | In | Totals | |
|---|---|---|---|---|---|---|---|---|---|---|---|---|
| BLUE | 382 | 362 | 398 | 186 | 524 | 440 | 425 | 189 | 495 | 3401 | BLUE | 6822 |
| WHITE | 358 | 335 | 382 | 168 | 503 | 430 | 404 | 172 | 484 | 3236 | WHITE | 6457 |
| Par | 4 | 4 | 4 | 3 | 5 | 4 | 4 | 3 | 5 | 36 | Par | 72 |
| Handicap | 14 | 10 | 8 | 16 | 12 | 2 | 4 | 6 | 18 | x | | |
| RED | 316 | 292 | 302 | 116 | 441 | 361 | 366 | 123 | 439 | 2756 | RED | 5639 |
| Par | 4 | 4 | 4 | 3 | 5 | 4 | 4 | 3 | 5 | 36 | Par | 72 |
| Handicap | 10 | 14 | 12 | 18 | 2 | 6 | 8 | 16 | 4 | x | | |

# PRUNERIDGE GOLF COURSE

**Course 79**
MAP E1 grid h7

*Course information:* This public course has nine holes. Par is 62 for 18 holes. The course is 3,720 yards and rated 56.3 for 18 holes from the regular tees. The slope rating is 73. Women's tees are 3,408 yards and rated 60.0. The slope rating is 75.

*Play policy and fees:* Green fees are $8 weekdays and $9.50 weekends. The course is very busy. Call well ahead for a tee time.

*Location:* The course is located between Highway 101 and Interstate 280 in Santa Clara on Saratoga Avenue, which is off the San Tomas Expressway. From Interstate 280, take the Saratoga Avenue exit north.

*Course description:* This short, flat and walkable course was redesigned in 1977 by Robert Trent Jones, Jr. Watch out for ducks on the lake at the ninth hole. They can get aggressive if they aren't fed on the spot. This is a very tight, high-quality executive course featuring four par-4s in the 280-340 range. The 340-yard third has a 25-yard-wide fairway. A total of 100,000 rounds are played here each year.

**Jack Fleming**

400 North Saratoga Avenue
Santa Clara, CA 95050

Pro shop (408) 248-4424

- ✓ **driving range**
- ✓ **practice greens**
- power carts
- ✓ **pull carts**
- ✓ **golf club rental**
- locker rooms
- showers
- ✓ **executive course**
- accommodations
- ✓ **food and beverages**
- ✓ **clubhouse**

**Wayne Wallick**
Director of Golf

**Tom Wallick**
Superintendent

# THUNDERBIRD GOLF COURSE

**Course 80**
MAP E1 grid h8

*Course information:* This public course has 18 holes and par is 64. The course is 4,700 yards and rated 56.6 from the regular tees. The slope rating is 81. Women's tees are 4,700 yards and unrated.

*Play policy and fees:* Green fees are $14 weekdays and $17 weekends. Twilight rates are $11 after 3 p.m. weekdays and $14 weekends and holidays. Seniors' (over 65) rate is $12 weekdays. Carts are $15. Play is on a first-come first-served basis.

*Location:* The course is located on King Road in San Jose where Interstate 680, Interstate 280 and Highway 101 meet. From Interstate 680, take the King Road exit and head north to the course.

*Course description:* This mostly flat executive course is short with lots of trees and mostly par-3s. There's one par-5 on each end of the course. A total of 80,000 rounds are played here each year.

221 South King Road
San Jose, CA 95116

Pro shop (408) 259-3355

- ✓ **driving range**
- ✓ **practice greens**
- ✓ **power carts**
- ✓ **pull carts**
- ✓ **golf club rental**
- locker rooms
- showers
- ✓ **executive course**
- accommodations
- food and beverages
- clubhouse

**Brigid Moreton**
Professional

**Paul Lopez**
Manager/Superintendent

# SAN JOSE COUNTRY CLUB

**Course 81**
MAP E1 grid h9

**1912**
**Tom Nicoll**

15571 Alum Rock Avenue
San Jose, CA 95127

Pro shop (408) 258-3636
Clubhouse (408) 258-4901

- ✓ **driving range**
- ✓ **practice greens**
- ✓ **power carts**
- ✓ **pull carts**
- ✓ **golf club rental**
- ✓ **locker rooms**
- ✓ **showers**
- executive course
- accommodations
- ✓ **food and beverages**
- ✓ **clubhouse**

**Howard Blethen**
Manager

**Barry Brumfield**
Professional

***Course information:*** This private course has 18 holes. See card below for yardage and rating information.

***Play policy and fees:*** Reciprocal play is accepted with members of other private clubs. Have your professional call in advance for arrangements. Guest fees are $35 everyday when accompanied by a member and $75 without a member. Carts are mandatory and included in the fees. The dress code is strictly enforced.

***Location:*** From Interstate 680 in San Jose, take the Alum Rock Avenue exit east. Drive 2.5 miles to 15571 Alum Rock Avenue.

***Course description:*** Situated in the foothills overlooking the Santa Clara Valley, this course is one of the oldest in California with a history that extends back to 1896. The course is short, hilly and tight. The small greens require accurate iron play and a deft short game. From the tee on the 4th hole, you can see much of the course. On a clear day, you can see San Francisco. The Santa Clara County Championship has been held here for 67 years. The course has two of the finest finishing holes in the region: number 17, a par-5 across a ravine, at 516 yards; and number 18, at 367 yards, which requires a layup shot off the tee. Both greens are well-bunkered. Precise approach shots are needed. The men's record is 59 and the women's is 69.

| Hole | 1 | 2 | 3 | 4 | 5 | 6 | 7 | 8 | 9 | Out | BLUE | Rating: 69.9 |
|---|---|---|---|---|---|---|---|---|---|---|---|---|
| BLUE | 303 | 316 | 174 | 432 | 145 | 392 | 156 | 436 | 353 | 2707 | | Slope: 118 |
| WHITE | 293 | 301 | 159 | 420 | 145 | 381 | 125 | 421 | 353 | 2598 | | |
| Par | 4 | 4 | 3 | 4 | 3 | 4 | 3 | 4 | 4 | 33 | WHITE | Rating: 68.6 |
| Handicap | 14 | 10 | 12 | 2 | 18 | 6 | 16 | 4 | 8 | x | | Slope: 115 |
| RED | 274 | 250 | 149 | 347 | 132 | 362 | 106 | 421 | 343 | 2384 | | |
| Par | 4 | 4 | 3 | 5/4 | 3 | 4 | 3 | 5 | 4 | 35/34 | RED | Rating: 71.2 |
| Handicap | 10 | 8 | 12 | 6 | 16 | 2 | 18 | 14 | 4 | x | | Slope: 125 |

| Hole | 10 | 11 | 12 | 13 | 14 | 15 | 16 | 17 | 18 | In | Totals | |
|---|---|---|---|---|---|---|---|---|---|---|---|---|
| BLUE | 209 | 477 | 439 | 404 | 158 | 366 | 536 | 516 | 367 | 3472 | BLUE | 6179 |
| WHITE | 190 | 454 | 429 | 392 | 142 | 357 | 516 | 496 | 349 | 3325 | WHITE | 5923 |
| Par | 3 | 5 | 4 | 4 | 3 | 4 | 5 | 5 | 4 | 37 | Par | 70 |
| Handicap | 13 | 15 | 1 | 9 | 17 | 11 | 5 | 3 | 7 | x | | |
| RED | 178 | 443 | 418 | 373 | 123 | 282 | 467 | 470 | 336 | 3090 | RED | 5474 |
| Par | 3 | 5 | 5 | 4 | 3 | 4 | 5 | 5 | 4 | 38 | Par | 73/72 |
| Handicap | 15 | 11 | 13 | 7 | 17 | 9 | 5 | 1 | 3 | x | | |

# SARATOGA COUNTRY CLUB

**Course 82**
MAP E1 grid i5

*Course information:* This private course has nine holes. Par is 68 for 18 holes. The course is 4,770 yards and rated 65.0 for 18 holes from the regular tees. The slope rating is 119. Women's tees are the same. The women's rating is 69.5, with a slope of 121.

*Play policy and fees:* Reciprocal play is accepted with members of other private clubs. Guest fees are $10 for nine holes and $15 for 18 holes weekdays, and $18 for nine holes and $25 for 18 holes weekends. Carts are $7 for nine holes and $14 for 18 holes.

*Location:* From Interstate 280 in Cupertino, take the Highway 85/Sunnyvale Road exit south to the Saratoga city line. Turn right on Prospect Road to the course.

*Course description:* Two holes have been added to lengthen the course, and a driving range opened in 1992. This hilly course has extremely narrow, tree-lined fairways. The 7th, 8th and 9th are good holes, the last a 199-yard par-3.

PO Box 2759
Saratoga, CA 95070

21990 Prospect Road
Saratoga, CA 95070

Pro shop (408) 253-5494
Clubhouse (408) 253-0340

driving range
✓ **practice greens**
✓ **power carts**
✓ **pull carts**
✓ **golf club rental**
✓ **locker rooms**
✓ **showers**
✓ **executive course**
accommodations
✓ **food and beverages**
✓ **clubhouse**

**Mike Fish**
Professional

**Leon Snethen**
Superintendent

# LA RINCONADA COUNTRY CLUB

**Course 83**
MAP E1 grid i6

**1929**

14597 Clearview Drive
Los Gatos, CA 95030

Pro shop (408) 395-4220
Clubhouse (408) 395-4181

- ✓ **driving range**
- ✓ **practice greens**
- ✓ **power carts**
- ✓ **pull carts**
- ✓ **golf club rental**
- ✓ **locker rooms**
- ✓ **showers**
- executive course
- accommodations
- ✓ **food and beverages**
- ✓ **clubhouse**

**Charlie Eddie**
Professional

**Bob Painter**
Superintendent

***Course information:*** This private course has 18 holes and par is 70. The course is 6,028 yards and rated 69.5 from the regular tees. The slope rating is 120. Women's tees are 5,713 yards and rated 73.7 from the forward tees. The slope rating is 130 forward.

***Play policy and fees:*** Reciprocal play is accepted with members of other private clubs Tuesdays, Thursdays and Fridays. Advance arrangements are required. Green fees for reciprocators are $50 when unaccompanied by a member, plus cart. Guest fees are $40 with a member. Carts are $10 for nine holes and $18 for 18 holes.

***Location:*** From Highway 17 in San Jose, take the Lark Avenue exit. Turn left on Winchester Boulevard. Turn right on La Rinconada Drive and follow it to Clearview Drive. Turn left to the course.

***Course description:*** Robert Dean Putman redesigned this course in 1960. Club records credit pro Phil Jefferson with grooming this course during its youth. The course is on the site of the former Puccinelli vineyard. A major remodeling project of the greens will last until fall of 1993. The course will probably be re-rated afterwards. Temporary greens now serve the course, whose mature layout is short and narrow with tree-lined fairways and undulating greens. There is a lake that comes into play on the 14th and 15th holes. Located in the foothills of Los Gatos, this course offers a scenic view of the southern Santa Clara Valley. The best hole is the 414-yard 9th; it's uphill, and, when the new green is in, will require high-quality shots to score. It is walkable. In case you're wondering about the club's logo, it's shaped like a cat, which seems logical for a Los Gatos golf course. A total of 50,000 rounds are played here each year.

# PLEASANT HILLS GOLF COURSE

**Course 84**
MAP E1 grid i9

2050 South White Road
San Jose, CA 95152-1386

Pro shop (408) 238-3485
Clubhouse (408) 243-7533

- driving range
- ✓ **practice greens**
- ✓ **power carts**
- ✓ **pull carts**
- ✓ **golf club rental**
- locker rooms
- showers
- ✓ **executive course**
- accommodations
- ✓ **food and beverages**
- ✓ **clubhouse**

**Francis Duino**
Manager

**Forrest Fezlar**
Head Professional

**Henry Duino, Jr.**
Superintendent

***Course information:*** This public course has 18 holes and par is 72. There is also an 18-hole, par-3 course. The course is 6,478 yards and rated 71.0 from the championship tees, and 6,125 yards and rated 69.5 from the regular tees. The slope ratings are: 122 championship and 119 regular. Women's tees are 5,754 yards and rated 70.9. The slope rating is 114.

***Play policy and fees:*** Green fees are $18 weekdays and $23 weekends. Twilight rates are $12 weekdays and $14 weekends. Carts are $11 for nine holes and $19 for 18 holes. Green fees for the executive course are $8 weekdays and $10 weekends. Reservations are recommended one week in advance for the regulation course, and are first-come first-served for the executive course.

***Location:*** From Highway 101 in San Jose, take the Tully Road East exit. Drive northeast past Capitol Expressway and turn left on South White Road to the course.

***Course description:*** Situated at the base of the foothills, this course has a half million trees (or so it seems), including fig, apple and eucalyptus, that all come into play. A flat course dominated by trees, it's always in good shape. Not many bunkers mark the course, which is green and straight ahead. Of note: Forrest Fezler finished second to Hale Irwin in the U.S Open at Winged Foot. A total of 70,000 rounds are played here per year.

# THE VILLAGES GOLF AND COUNTRY CLUB

**Course 85**
MAP E1 grid i9

**1970**
**Robert Muir Graves**

5000 Cribari Lane
San Jose, CA 95135

Pro shop (408) 274-3220
Clubhouse (408) 272-4400

- ✓ **driving range**
- ✓ **practice greens**
- ✓ **power carts**
- pull carts
- golf club rental
- locker rooms
- showers
- ✓ **executive course**
- accommodations
- ✓ **food and beverages**
- ✓ **clubhouse**

**Al Braga**
Professional

**Brian Bagley**
Superintendent

***Course information:*** This private course has 27 holes and par is 72. The Villages Course is 6,707 yards and rated 71.5 from the championship tees, and 6,338 yards and rated 69.8 from the regular tees. The slope ratings are 119 championship, 115 regular. Women's tees are 5,851 yards and rated 72.4. The slope rating is 123. The executive nine is 730 yards and par is 27.

***Play policy and fees:*** Reciprocal play is accepted with members of other private clubs. Green fees for reciprocators are $38 weekday, $45 weekend. With a member, guest fees are $23 weekdays and $28 weekends. Carts are $12 for nine holes and $18 for 18 holes.

***Location:*** From Highway 101 in eastern San Jose, take the Capitol Expressway northeast. Turn right on Aborn Road and drive one mile. Turn right on San Felipe Road and drive 2.5 miles to the Villages Parkway. Turn left and drive to Cribari Lane and the course.

***Course description:*** This retirement-community course doesn't have a lot of hazards. The bunkers come into play for the longer hitters. The 17th and 18th are long par-4s, with out-of-bounds on the left. The 17th has water on the right. On the 18th, there's an out-of-bounds left and a long carry over a creek to make this into-the-wind par-4 a challenge. A total of 86,000 rounds are played here per year.

# SILVER CREEK VALLEY COUNTRY CLUB

**Course 86**
MAP E1 grid j9

*Course information:* This new private course opened nine holes in the fall of 1992, with the full 18 slated to be ready in summer 1993. From the gold tees, it measures 6,842 yards. No ratings were available. See card below for additional information.

*Play policy and fees:* No reciprocation with other clubs. Guests with a member pay $35 on weekdays, $45 on weekends. Rates could change. Carts are $10.

*Location:* Take 101 in San Jose to the Silver Valley Creek Road exit. Head east over the hills about 1.3 miles. Pass the Information Pavillion, then proceed under the bridge. The course is on the right.

*Course description:* Designer Robinson left his trademark of "water, water and more water" on this sprawling , hilly course. Several holes have steep drops, and some fairways slant severely. Carts are mandatory. There are dramatic holes: the 367-yard 14th, called "Wetlands," is fun. Watch out for the huge hazard in front of the green. The 524-yard 16th is almost unfair, due to long carry and the huge oak on the left. The 17th has a huge fountain left of the green, and the 18th is marked by a cascading waterfall, which is quite dramatic.

**1992**
**Ted Robinson**

5106 Silver Creek Valley Road
San Jose, CA 95138

Pro shop (408) 239-5775

- ✓ **driving range**
- ✓ **practice greens**
- ✓ **power carts**
- pull carts
- ✓ **golf club rental**
- ✓ **locker rooms**
- ✓ **showers**
- executive course
- accommodations
- ✓ **food and beverages**
- ✓ **clubhouse**

**Jay Jackson**
Professional

**Nick Checklenis**
Superintendent

NORTHERN E1

| Hole | 1 | 2 | 3 | 4 | 5 | 6 | 7 | 8 | 9 | Out | | |
|---|---|---|---|---|---|---|---|---|---|---|---|---|
| BLUE | 483 | 204 | 373 | 328 | 170 | 496 | 354 | 385 | 413 | 3206 | BLUE | Rating: -- |
| WHITE | 458 | 176 | 349 | 314 | 156 | 467 | 331 | 370 | 393 | 3014 | | Slope: -- |
| Par | 5 | 3 | 4 | 4 | 3 | 5 | 4 | 4 | 4 | 36 | WHITE | Rating: -- |
| Handicap | 9 | 7 | 3 | 13 | 15 | 1 | 17 | 5 | 11 | x | | Slope: -- |
| RED | 405 | 148 | 306 | 271 | 103 | 432 | 287 | 344 | 370 | 2666 | | |
| Par | 5 | 3 | 4 | 4 | 3 | 5 | 4 | 4 | 4 | 36 | RED | Rating: -- |
| Handicap | 3 | 15 | 7 | 11 | 17 | 1 | 13 | 5 | 9 | x | | Slope: -- |

| Hole | 10 | 11 | 12 | 13 | 14 | 15 | 16 | 17 | 18 | In | Totals | |
|---|---|---|---|---|---|---|---|---|---|---|---|---|
| BLUE | 413 | 483 | 204 | 373 | 328 | 170 | 496 | 354 | 385 | 3206 | BLUE | 6412 |
| WHITE | 393 | 458 | 176 | 349 | 314 | 156 | 467 | 331 | 370 | 3014 | WHITE | 6028 |
| Par | 4 | 5 | 3 | 4 | 4 | 3 | 5 | 4 | 4 | 36 | Par | 72 |
| Handicap | 11 | 9 | 7 | 3 | 13 | 15 | 1 | 17 | 5 | x | | |
| RED | 370 | 405 | 148 | 306 | 271 | 103 | 432 | 287 | 344 | 2666 | RED | 5332 |
| Par | 4 | 5 | 3 | 4 | 4 | 3 | 5 | 4 | 4 | 36 | Par | 72 |
| Handicap | 9 | 3 | 15 | 7 | 11 | 17 | 1 | 13 | 5 | x | | |

# BOULDER CREEK GOLF AND COUNTRY CLUB

**Course 87**
MAP E1 grid j4

**1963**
**Jack Fleming**

16901 Big Basin Highway
Boulder Creek, CA

Pro shop (408) 338-2121
Clubhouse (408) 338-2111

driving range
✓ **practice greens**
✓ **power carts**
pull carts
✓ **golf club rental**
locker rooms
showers
✓ **executive course**
✓ **accommodations**
✓ **food and beverages**
✓ **clubhouse**

**Hal Wells**
Professional

**Leonard A. Walsh**
Superintendent

***Course information:*** This resort course has 18 holes. See card below for yardage and rating information.

***Play policy and fees:*** Green fees are $17 weekdays and $26 weekends. Special discount rates are available. Carts are $16. Call ahead to secure a tee time.

***Location:*** From Santa Cruz, drive 12 miles north on Highway 9 to Boulder Creek. In Boulder Creek, take Highway 236 three miles northwest to the course on the left.

***Course description:*** This scenic course is situated in the midst of the redwoods and is well maintained. It's short, slightly rolling and tight. The immaculate greens are the great neutralizer for the lack of length. A new sprinkler system will make the course better. There are 10 par-3s—all tight and demanding. Packages are available in which two-night, three-day stays include green fees, food coupons, and lodging for $118 per person. The course is the home of the Boulder Creek Pro Am, and the Northern California Junior 13-And-Under Championships (August). A total of 65,000 rounds are played here per year.

| Hole | 1 | 2 | 3 | 4 | 5 | 6 | 7 | 8 | 9 | Out | BLUE | Rating: -- |
|---|---|---|---|---|---|---|---|---|---|---|---|---|
| BLUE | - | - | - | - | - | - | - | - | - | - | | Slope: -- |
| WHITE | 225 | 177 | 310 | 387 | 139 | 189 | 159 | 157 | 265 | 2008 | | |
| Par | 4 | 3 | 4 | 4 | 3 | 3 | 3 | 3 | 4 | 31 | WHITE | Rating: 61.5 |
| Handicap | 17 | 7 | 5 | 1 | 13 | 3 | 9 | 15 | 11 | x | | Slope: 98 |
| RED | 225 | 177 | 310 | 387 | 139 | 189 | 159 | 157 | 207 | 1950 | | |
| Par | 4 | 3 | 4 | 5 | 3 | 3 | 3 | 3 | 4 | 32 | RED | Rating: 63.3 |
| Handicap | 15 | 5 | 1 | 17 | 9 | 3 | 13 | 7 | 11 | x | | Slope: 98 |

| Hole | 10 | 11 | 12 | 13 | 14 | 15 | 16 | 17 | 18 | In | Totals | |
|---|---|---|---|---|---|---|---|---|---|---|---|---|
| BLUE | - | - | - | - | - | - | - | - | - | - | BLUE | -- |
| WHITE | 182 | 168 | 440 | 325 | 138 | 410 | 169 | 436 | 120 | 2388 | WHITE | 4396 |
| Par | 3 | 3 | 5 | 4 | 3 | 5 | 3 | 5 | 3 | 34 | Par | 65 |
| Handicap | 2 | 4 | 8 | 14 | 18 | 10 | 6 | 12 | 16 | x | | |
| RED | 182 | 125 | 355 | 325 | 96 | 410 | 169 | 325 | 90 | 2077 | RED | 4027 |
| Par | 4 | 3 | 5 | 4 | 3 | 5 | 3 | 5 | 3 | 35 | Par | 67 |
| Handicap | 8 | 4 | 14 | 12 | 16 | 2 | 6 | 18 | 10 | x | | |

# ALMADEN GOLF AND COUNTRY CLUB

**Course 88**
MAP E1 grid j7

**1955**
**Jack Fleming**

6663 Hampton Drive
San Jose, CA 95120

Pro shop (408) 268-3959
Clubhouse (408) 268-4653

- ✓ **driving range**
- ✓ **practice greens**
- ✓ **power carts**
- ✓ **pull carts**
- ✓ **golf club rental**
- ✓ **locker rooms**
- ✓ **showers**
- executive course
- accommodations
- ✓ **food and beverages**
- ✓ **clubhouse**

**D. Scott Hoyt**
Professional

**Mike Basile**
Superintendent

***Course information:*** This private course has 18 holes. See card below for yardage and rating information.

***Play policy and fees:*** Reciprocal play is accepted with members of other private clubs Tuesdays, Thursdays and Fridays. Green fees for reciprocators are $40 with a member and $75 unaccompanied. Carts are $10 for nine holes and $20 for 18 holes.

***Location:*** From Highway 101 in San Jose, exit on Capitol Expressway west to the Almaden Expressway. Turn left and drive 4.5 miles to Crown Boulevard. Turn right and continue to Hampton Drive.

***Course description:*** This scenic, demanding course set in the Silicon Valley has a tree-lined, rolling terrain. The greens are undulating. It was the site of the annual San Jose LPGA Classic. On the 185-yard 13th, a huge oak tree and out-of-bounds on the left make most bail out on the right. The 430-yard 16th requires a good tee shot. Trees on the right guard a heavy slope down to 'Death Valley.' The 370-yard dogleg 17th forces most players to bail out again into 'Chicken Alley' on the right. The women's course record is 62, set by Palo Alto native Vicki Fergon during the 1984 San Jose Classic. (As a result, she entered the LPGA all-time record books by tying Mickey Wright's 18-hole scoring record of 62, posting another all-time record of 11 birdies in one round.) The men's course record is 64. A total of 54,000 rounds are played here per year.

| Hole | 1 | 2 | 3 | 4 | 5 | 6 | 7 | 8 | 9 | Out | BLUE | Rating: 72.5 |
|---|---|---|---|---|---|---|---|---|---|---|---|---|
| BLUE | 489 | 369 | 354 | 423 | 444 | 153 | 514 | 177 | [illegible] | 3340 | | Slope: 128 |
| WHITE | 477 | 351 | 343 | 412 | 398 | 146 | 492 | 162 | 412 | 3193 | | |
| Par | 5 | 4 | 4 | 4 | 4 | 3 | 5 | 3 | 4 | 36 | WHITE | Rating: 71.0 |
| Handicap | 9 | 13 | 11 | 1 | 3 | 17 | 7 | 15 | 5 | x | | Slope: 125 |
| RED | 412 | 340 | 338 | 424 | 378 | 117 | 480 | 152 | 364 | 3005 | | |
| Par | 5 | 4 | 4 | 5 | 4 | 3 | 5 | 3 | 4 | 37 | RED | Rating: 74.3 |
| Handicap | 13 | 7 | 9 | 11 | 5 | 17 | 1 | 15 | 3 | x | | Slope: 130 |

| Hole | 10 | 11 | 12 | 13 | 14 | 15 | 16 | 17 | 18 | In | Totals | |
|---|---|---|---|---|---|---|---|---|---|---|---|---|
| BLUE | 541 | 421 | 412 | 187 | 352 | 191 | 449 | 416 | 509 | 3478 | BLUE | 6824 |
| WHITE | 520 | 402 | 400 | 164 | 336 | 166 | 416 | 395 | 502 | 3301 | WHITE | 6494 |
| Par | 5 | 4 | 4 | 3 | 4 | 3 | 4 | 4 | 5 | 36 | Par | 72 |
| Handicap | 12 | 4 | 6 | 10 | 16 | 18 | 2 | 8 | 14 | x | | |
| RED | 486 | 374 | 383 | 129 | 314 | 137 | 410 | 357 | 465 | 3055 | RED | 6060 |
| Par | 5 | 4 | 4 | 3 | 4 | 3 | 5 | 4 | 5 | 37 | Par | 74 |
| Handicap | 4 | 6 | 2 | 18 | 12 | 16 | 14 | 8 | 10 | x | | |

# SANTA TERESA GOLF CLUB

**Course 89**
**MAP E1 grid j8**

***Course information:*** This public course has 18 holes. See card below for yardage and rating information.

***Play policy and fees:*** Green fees are $22 weekdays and $30 weekends. Twilight rates are $13 weekdays and $16 weekends and holidays. Carts are $11 for nine holes and $20 for 18 holes. Reserve a tee time one week in advance.

***Location:*** From Highway 101 in San Jose, take the Bernal Road exit west. Drive two miles to the course.

***Course description:*** This challenging course, the pride of the South Bay public courses, is long with tree-lined fairways. The front nine is flat, and the back nine is hilly. This course was voted the best municipal course in Santa Clara Valley. The testy 16th hole is one reason why: it's a tough par-3 of 220 yards, into a strong prevailing wind. A tough hole. Assistant Pro John Snopkowski holds the men's course record at 65, set in mid-1991. The women's course record was unavailable. The winds make various holes more difficult. The dogleg left first stretches 416 yards into the wind. The bunkering can be deceptive, for they are set about 10 yards short of greens. The Norcal PGA Jr./Sr. Tournament was played here in 1991. A total of 99,000 rounds are played here each year.

**1963**
**George Santana**

260 Bernal Road
San Jose, CA 95119

Pro shop (408) 225-2650
Restaurant (408) 226-3170

- ✓ **driving range**
- ✓ **practice greens**
- ✓ **power carts**
- ✓ **pull carts**
- ✓ **golf club rental**
- locker rooms
- showers
- executive course
- accommodations
- ✓ **food and beverages**
- ✓ **clubhouse**

**Bob Mejias**
Professional

**John Snopkowski**
Assistant Professional

**Jim Ross**
Superintendent

| Hole | 1 | 2 | 3 | 4 | 5 | 6 | 7 | 8 | 9 | Out | BLUE | Rating: 71.1 |
|---|---|---|---|---|---|---|---|---|---|---|---|---|
| BLUE | 416 | 512 | 351 | 384 | 166 | 409 | 190 | 408 | 436 | 3272 | | Slope: 121 |
| WHITE | 404 | 492 | 343 | 368 | 151 | 396 | 162 | 400 | 426 | 3142 | | |
| Par | 4 | 5 | 4 | 4 | 3 | 4 | 3 | 4 | 4 | 35 | WHITE | Rating: 70.0 |
| Handicap | 1 | 13 | 15 | 11 | 17 | 5 | 9 | 3 | 7 | x | | Slope: 119 |
| RED | 380 | 482 | 324 | 359 | 142 | 385 | 145 | 350 | 420 | 2987 | | |
| Par | 4 | 5 | 4 | 4 | 3 | 4 | 3 | 4 | 5 | 36 | RED | Rating: 73.5 |
| Handicap | 5 | 1 | 11 | 7 | 17 | 3 | 15 | 13 | 9 | x | | Slope: 125 |

| Hole | 10 | 11 | 12 | 13 | 14 | 15 | 16 | 17 | 18 | In | Totals | |
|---|---|---|---|---|---|---|---|---|---|---|---|---|
| BLUE | 383 | 498 | 417 | 405 | 184 | 371 | 220 | 571 | 421 | 3470 | BLUE | 6742 |
| WHITE | 373 | 479 | 397 | 393 | 171 | 349 | 190 | 529 | 407 | 3288 | WHITE | 6430 |
| Par | 4 | 5 | 4 | 4 | 3 | 4 | 3 | 5 | 4 | 36 | Par | 71 |
| Handicap | 10 | 16 | 8 | 4 | 18 | 14 | 12 | 6 | 2 | x | | |
| RED | 352 | 434 | 361 | 384 | 161 | 334 | 148 | 471 | 400 | 3045 | RED | 6032 |
| Par | 4 | 5 | 4 | 4 | 3 | 4 | 3 | 5 | 5 | 37 | Par | 73 |
| Handicap | 12 | 2 | 6 | 8 | 16 | 14 | 18 | 4 | 10 | x | | |

# RIVERSIDE GOLF COURSE

**Course 90**
MAP E1 grid j9

***Course information:*** This public course has 18 holes. See card below for yardage and rating information.

***Play policy and fees:*** Green fees are $19 weekdays and $25 weekends. Carts are $24. Reservations are recommended one week in advance. Shirts and shoes are required at all times. This course is available for outside tournaments.

***Location:*** From Highway 101 in Morgan Hill, take the Cochrane Road exit. From Highway 101 in Coyote, exit at Bernal Road. Turn onto the Monterey Road heading south toward Morgan Hill. Turn at Palm Avenue and look for the signs.

***Course description:*** This long, rolling course rewards good positioning. There are a lot of trees, and the greens are among the best in Santa Clara Valley. All the par-3s are over 200 yards from the back tees. When the wind is blowing, the 459-yard 10th becomes a bear, and the green is an easy place to four-putt. Many tournaments are held here, and it's fairly busy, so call ahead for tee times. A total of 80,000 rounds are played here each year.

**1967**
**Jack Fleming**

P.O. Box 13128
Coyote, CA 95013

Monterey Road at
Palm Avenue
Coyote, CA 95013-1328

Pro shop (408) 463-0622

- ✓ **driving range**
- ✓ **practice greens**
- ✓ **power carts**
- ✓ **pull carts**
- ✓ **golf club rental**
- locker rooms
- ✓ **showers**
- executive course
- accommodations
- ✓ **food and beverages**
- ✓ **clubhouse**

**Tom Smith**
Professional

**Cliff Rourke**
Superintendent

| Hole | 1 | 2 | 3 | 4 | 5 | 6 | 7 | 8 | 9 | Out | | |
|---|---|---|---|---|---|---|---|---|---|---|---|---|
| BLUE | 511 | 204 | 514 | 364 | 328 | 204 | 479 | 370 | 439 | 3413 | BLUE | Rating: 70.8 |
| WHITE | 501 | [illegible] | 181 | 333 | 320 | 195 | 417 | 361 | 429 | 3220 | | Slope: 116 |
| Par | 5 | 3 | 5 | 4 | 4 | 3 | 4 | 4 | 4 | 36 | WHITE | Rating: 69.4 |
| Handicap | 13 | 15 | 11 | 7 | 9 | 17 | 1 | 5 | 3 | x | | Slope: 113 |
| RED | 479 | 145 | 443 | 316 | 293 | 164 | 374 | 330 | 429 | 2973 | | |
| Par | 5 | 3 | 5 | 4 | 4 | 3 | 4 | 4 | 5 | 37 | RED | Rating: 72.5 |
| Handicap | 3 | 17 | 7 | 11 | 13 | 15 | 1 | 9 | 5 | x | | Slope: 118 |

| Hole | 10 | 11 | 12 | 13 | 14 | 15 | 16 | 17 | 18 | In | Totals | |
|---|---|---|---|---|---|---|---|---|---|---|---|---|
| BLUE | 459 | 378 | 200 | 369 | 530 | 204 | 371 | 408 | 493 | 3412 | BLUE | 6825 |
| WHITE | 426 | 367 | 187 | 361 | 521 | 172 | 362 | 405 | 483 | 3284 | WHITE | 6504 |
| Par | 4 | 4 | 3 | 4 | 5 | 3 | 4 | 4 | 5 | 36 | Par | 72 |
| Handicap | 2 | 8 | 18 | 14 | 10 | 6 | 12 | 4 | 16 | x | | |
| RED | 377 | 335 | 154 | 340 | 483 | 157 | 346 | 357 | 447 | 2996 | RED | 5969 |
| Par | 4 | 4 | 3 | 4 | 5 | 3 | 4 | 4 | 5 | 36 | Par | 73 |
| Handicap | 6 | 14 | 16 | 10 | 2 | 18 | 12 | 8 | 4 | x | | |

# MAP E2

(26 COURSES)

PAGES.. 268-291

NOR-CAL MAP.....see page 30
adjoining maps
NORTH (D2).......see page 126
EAST (E3)..........see page 292
SOUTH (F2) .......see page 344
WEST (E1).........see page 184

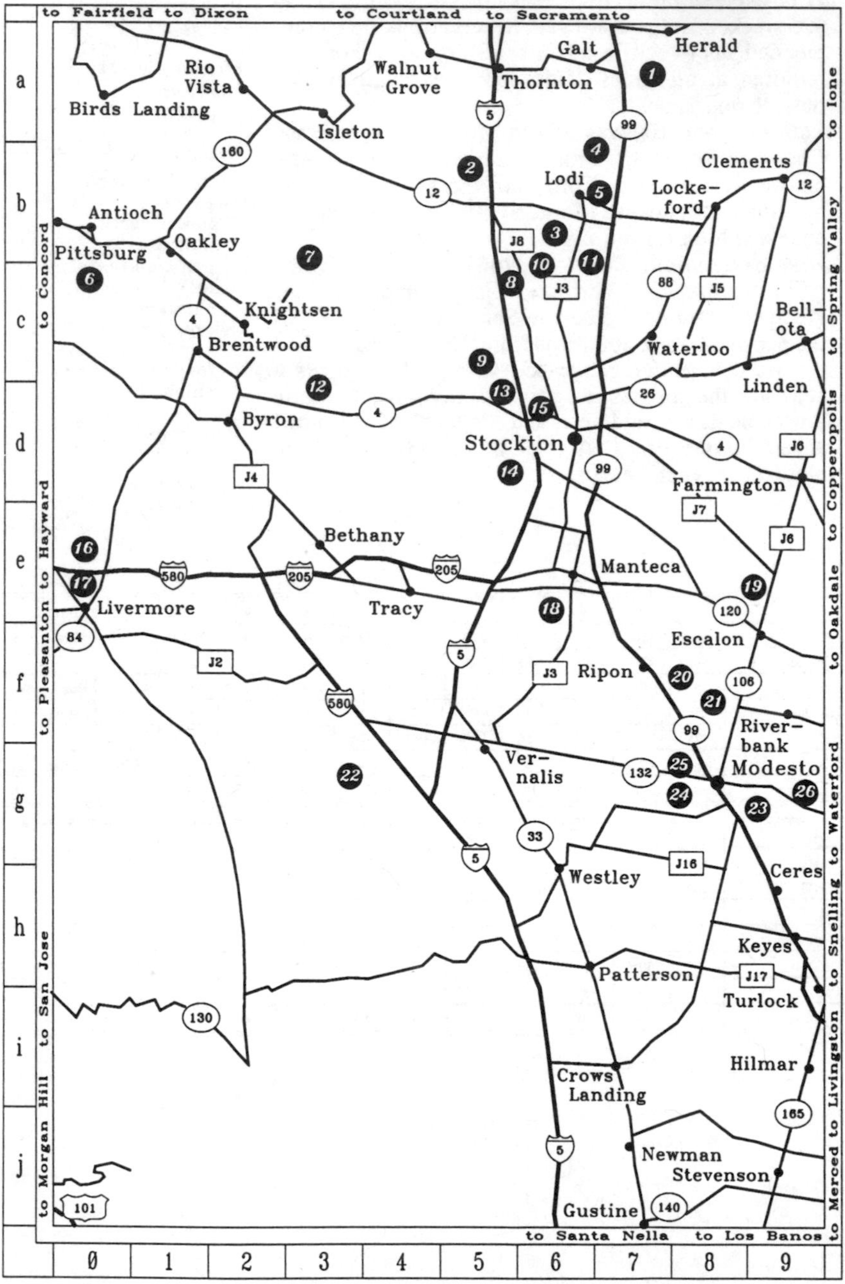

to Fairfield to Dixon
to Courtland
to Sacramento
to Ione
to Spring Valley
to Copperopolis
to Oakdale
to Waterford
to Snelling
to Livingston
to Merced
to Santa Nella
to Los Banos
to Concord
to Hayward
to Pleasanton
to San Jose
to Morgan Hill

Rio Vista
Birds Landing
Walnut Grove
Isleton
Thornton
Galt
Herald
Lodi
Clements
Lockeford
Antioch
Pittsburg
Oakley
Knightsen
Brentwood
Bellota
Waterloo
Linden
Byron
Stockton
Farmington
Bethany
Manteca
Tracy
Livermore
Escalon
Ripon
Riverbank
Modesto
Vernalis
Westley
Ceres
Keyes
Patterson
Turlock
Hilmar
Crows Landing
Newman
Stevenson
Gustine

5
99
160
12
J8
J3
88
J5
4
26
J6
J4
J7
580
205
120
84
J2
106
132
33
J16
J17
130
165
140
101

1 2 3 4 5 6 7 8 9 10 11 12 13 14 15 16 17 18 19 20 21 22 23 24 25 26

a b c d e f g h i j

0 1 2 3 4 5 6 7 8 9

# DRY CREEK RANCH GOLF COURSE

**Course 1**
MAP E2 grid a7

**1962**
**Jack Fleming**

809 Crystal Way
Galt, CA 95632

Pro shop (209) 745-2330
Clubhouse (209) 745-4653

- ✓ **driving range**
- ✓ **practice greens**
- ✓ **power carts**
- ✓ **pull carts**
- ✓ **golf club rental**
- ✓ **locker rooms**
- ✓ **showers**
- executive course
- accommodations
- ✓ **food and beverages**
- ✓ **clubhouse**

**Rod Sims**
Professional

**Dave Davies**
Superintendent

NORTHERN E2

***Course information:*** This public course has 18 holes. See card below for yardage and rating information.

***Play policy and fees:*** Green fees Monday through Thursday are $16, $20 Fridays and $26 weekends and holidays. Carts are $18.

***Location:*** From Sacramento, drive 24 miles south on Highway 99 to Galt. Take the Central Galt exit onto "C" Street and drive east. Turn right on Crystal Way and drive to the course.

***Course description:*** This challenging, tree-lined course has been rated among the top public courses in the state. It has a difficult combination of first and last holes. The first hole tees off into a narrow chute with a grove of oaks as out-of-bounds. The 18th hole doglegs to the left with oak trees and a creek bed that provide headaches. Rounds are made or ruined on either hole. There are numerous other outstanding holes: the par-4 sixth, a monster of 424 yards from the back tees; number 13, a par-4 of moderate length (397 yards) that due to placement of the trees leaves little room for error on either the drive on the appraoch; and number 15, a dogleg of 434 yards. PGA Tour pro Bob Eastwood assisted in the design of the back nine. Few public courses are in consistently better shape.

| Hole | 1 | 2 | 3 | 4 | 5 | 6 | 7 | 8 | 9 | Out | | |
|---|---|---|---|---|---|---|---|---|---|---|---|---|
| BLUE | 421 | 365 | 552 | 358 | 161 | 442 | 207 | 495 | 331 | 3327 | BLUE | Rating: 72.7 |
| | | | | | | | | | | | | Slope: 129 |
| WHITE | 409 | 352 | 533 | 350 | 151 | 424 | 192 | 480 | 319 | 3210 | | |
| Par | 4 | 4 | 5 | 4 | 3 | 4 | 3 | 5 | 4 | 36 | WHITE | Rating: 71.3 |
| Handicap | 3 | 11 | 7 | 13 | 17 | 1 | 9 | 5 | 15 | x | | Slope: 126 |
| RED | 291 | 333 | 524 | 337 | 138 | 408 | 170 | 383 | 306 | 2890 | | |
| Par | 4 | 4 | 5 | 4 | 3 | 5 | 3 | 4 | 4 | 36 | RED | Rating: 73.9 |
| Handicap | 11 | 7 | 1 | 9 | 17 | 5 | 15 | 3 | 13 | x | | Slope: 128 |

| Hole | 10 | 11 | 12 | 13 | 14 | 15 | 16 | 17 | 18 | In | Totals | |
|---|---|---|---|---|---|---|---|---|---|---|---|---|
| BLUE | 551 | 159 | 531 | 431 | 322 | 467 | 358 | 190 | 437 | 3446 | BLUE | 6773 |
| WHITE | 539 | 142 | 521 | 397 | 302 | 434 | 350 | 180 | 427 | 3292 | WHITE | 6502 |
| Par | 5 | 3 | 5 | 4 | 4 | 4 | 4 | 3 | 4 | 36 | Par | 72 |
| Handicap | 8 | 18 | 6 | 10 | 14 | 2 | 12 | 16 | 4 | x | | |
| RED | 532 | 128 | 435 | 373 | 278 | 423 | 335 | 161 | 397 | 3062 | RED | 5952 |
| Par | 5 | 3 | 5 | 4 | 4 | 5 | 4 | 3 | 5 | 38 | Par | 74 |
| Handicap | 2 | 18 | 4 | 10 | 14 | 6 | 12 | 16 | 8 | x | | |

# WOODBRIDGE GOLF AND COUNTRY CLUB

**Course 2**
**MAP E2 grid b5**

***Course information:*** This private course has 27 holes and par is 71. The three nine-hole course combinations are Lake Middle, River Lake and Middle River.

The Lake Middle Course is 6,489 yards for 18 holes from the regular tees. The slope rating is 125. The rating is 70.9. Women's tees are 6,168 yards and rated 76.2. The slope rating is 134.

The River Lake Course is 6,394 yards and rated 70.8 from the regular tees. The slope rating is 122 Women's tees are 6,009 yards and rated 75.0. The slope rating is 127.

The Middle River Course is detailed below.

***Play policy and fees:*** No outside play accepted. Reciprocal play is accepted on a limited basis with members of other private clubs. The green fee for reciprocators is $45. Guest rates are $25. Members and guests only. Carts are $14. Reservations are required one week in advance. Closed Mondays.

***Location:*** Located between Interstate 5 and Highway 99 in Woodbridge on Woodbridge Road.

***Course description:*** Built in 1923, the greens are small and traditional. Of the three nines, the River Course is the oldest. The Middle Course has rolling terrain, and the Lake Course is the youngest and boasts lots of water. All three reward accuracy over distance. Of the 18-hole setups, the Middle River is the oldest and best-regarded, playing host to the University of Pacific Invitational every other year.

**1923**

PO Box 806
Woodbridge, CA 95258

800 East Woodbridge Road
Woodbridge, CA 95258

Pro shop (209) 369-2371
Clubhouse (209) 334-5454

- ✓ **driving range**
- ✓ **practice greens**
- ✓ **power carts**
- ✓ **pull carts**
- ✓ **golf club rental**
- ✓ **locker rooms**
- ✓ **showers**
- executive course
- accommodations
- ✓ **food and beverages**
- ✓ **clubhouse**

**Robert E. Vocker**
Professional

**Ron Kateen**
Manager

**Jim Husting**
Superintendent

Middle River Course

| Hole | 1 | 2 | 3 | 4 | 5 | 6 | 7 | 8 | 9 | Out | | |
|---|---|---|---|---|---|---|---|---|---|---|---|---|
| BLUE | - | - | - | - | - | - | - | - | - | - | BLUE | Rating: -- |
| | | | | | | | | | | | | Slope: -- |
| WHITE | 504 | 363 | 177 | 365 | 404 | 380 | 355 | 165 | 494 | 3207 | | |
| Par | 5 | 4 | 3 | 4 | 4 | 4 | 4 | 3 | 5 | 36 | WHITE | Rating: 70.1 |
| Handicap | 7 | 3 | 6 | 4 | 1 | 2 | 5 | 8 | 9 | x | | Slope: 121 |
| RED | 500 | 345 | 166 | 348 | 392 | 373 | 346 | 129 | 490 | 3089 | | |
| Pa | 5 | 4 | 3 | 4 | 4 | 4 | 4 | 3 | 5 | 36 | RED | Rating: 75.4 |
| Handicap | 1 | 7 | 8 | 5 | 2 | 4 | 6 | 9 | 3 | x | | Slope: 131 |

| Hole | 10 | 11 | 12 | 13 | 14 | 15 | 16 | 17 | 18 | In | Totals | |
|---|---|---|---|---|---|---|---|---|---|---|---|---|
| BLUE | - | - | - | - | - | - | - | - | - | - | BLUE | -- |
| WHITE | 482 | 170 | 418 | 202 | 345 | 518 | 215 | 364 | 398 | 3112 | WHITE | 6319 |
| Par | 5 | 3 | 4 | 3 | 4 | 5 | 3 | 4 | 4 | 35 | Par | 71 |
| Handicap | 9 | 8 | 1 | 5 | 6 | 2 | 4 | 7 | 3 | x | | |
| RED | 474 | 144 | 415 | 184 | 335 | 478 | 184 | 340 | 383 | 2937 | RED | 6026 |
| Par | 5 | 3 | 5 | 3 | 4 | 5 | 3 | 4 | 4 | 36 | Par | 72 |
| Handicap | 3 | 9 | 5 | 7 | 4 | 1 | 8 | 6 | 2 | x | | |

# VENETIAN GARDENS GOLF COURSE

**Course**
MAP E2 grid b6

1555 Mosaic Way
Stockton, CA 95207

Pro shop (209) 447-3871

- ✓ **driving range**
- ✓ **practice greens**
- power carts
- pull carts
- golf club rental
- locker rooms
- showers
- executive course
- accommodations
- food and beverages
- clubhouse

***Course information:*** This private course has 18 holes and par is 54. The yards and ratings were unavailable.

***Play policy and fees:*** The course is private. No outside or reciprocal play is accepted.

***Location:*** From Interstate 5 in Stockton, turn onto March Lane and drive one mile east to Venetian Drive North. Turn right on Mosaic Way to the Venetian Gardens Community golf course.

***Course description:*** This course is located in Venetian Gardens, a private residential community.

# FOREST LAKE GOLF COURSE

**Course**
MAP E2 grid b7

**1957**
2450 East Woodson Road
Acampo, CA 95220

Pro shop (209) 369-5451

- ✓ **driving range**
- ✓ **practice greens**
- ✓ **power carts**
- ✓ **pull carts**
- ✓ **golf club rental**
- locker rooms
- showers
- ✓ **executive course**
- accommodations
- ✓ **food and beverages**
- ✓ **clubhouse**

**David Ring**
Manager/Professional

**Jerry Bodenhorn**
Superintendent

***Course information:*** This public course has 18 holes and par is 60 on Mondays, Tuesday and Thursdays, and par is 66 on Fridays, Saturdays and Sundays.

There are actually 24 holes consisting of two different (white and alternate white) 18-hole layouts for men and women. The white course is par 60 (4,005 yards, 56.0 rating, 83 slope). The alternate white men's course is par 66 (4,915 yards, 61.3 rating, 90 slope). For women, the white course plays to a par of 64 (3,685 yards, 58.4 rating, 83 slope) and the alternate white has a par of 72 (4,915 yards, 64.0 rating, 95 slope).

***Play policy and fees:*** Green fees are $5 for nine holes and $8 for 18 holes weekdays, and $7 for nine holes and $11 for 18 holes weekends and holidays. Carts are $7 for nine holes and $14 for 18 holes. Reservations required one week in advance. This course is available for outside tournaments.

***Location:*** From Highway 99 in Acampo (just north of Lodi), take the Jahant Road exit west, which turns into Woodson Road. Take Woodson Road one mile to the course on the left.

***Course description:*** This short course offers tight fairways and a variety of mature trees and some water. The new front nine, with some elevated greens and tees, is slightly tougher than the back nine. The alternate white (also called the blue) course is the newer of the two combinations. Mitch Harrison's 52 is the course record on the white course; Bob Van Dyke and Ray Madrid share the alternate white record at 63.

# MICKE GROVE GOLF LINKS

**Course 5**
MAP E2 grid b7

***Course information:*** This public course has 18 holes. Par is 72 for men and women. The course is 6,566 yards from the championship tees with a rating of 71.1 and 118 slope. The regular tees are 6,026 yards with a 68.7 rating and 112 slope. Women's tees are 5,286 yards. The rating is 69.7 with a 111 slope.

***Play policy and fees:*** Green fees are $13 weekdays and $20 weekends. Carts are $10 per rider.

***Location:*** Take Highway 99 south from Sacramento and north from Modesto to Armstrong Road. Take Armstrong about a half mile east, then turn left on Micke Grove Road. The course is on your right.

***Course description:*** This new and highly acclaimed links-style course is set among the vineyards. The greens are large and there is plenty of water. The signature hole is number 14, a par-3 of 180 yards over water. Beware of the strong winds that often blow. Mike Lane's 65 is the course record.

**1990**
**American Golf**

11401 N. Micke Grove Rd.
Lodi, CA 95240

Pro shop (209) 369-4410

- ✓ **driving range**
- ✓ **practice greens**
- ✓ **power carts**
- ✓ **pull carts**
- ✓ **golf club rental**
- locker rooms
- showers
- executive course
- accommodations
- ✓ **food and beverages**
- ✓ **clubhouse**

**Rob Billings**
Manager

**Bob Billings**
Professional

**Pete Bowman**
Superintendent

# LONE TREE GOLF COURSE

**Course 6**
MAP E2 grid c0

PO Box 2115
Antioch, CA 94531

4800 Golf Course Road
Antioch, CA 94509

Pro shop (510) 757-5200

- ✓ **driving range**
- ✓ **practice greens**
- ✓ **power carts**
- ✓ **pull carts**
- ✓ **golf club rental**
- locker rooms
- showers
- executive course
- accommodations
- ✓ **food and beverages**
- ✓ **clubhouse**

**Pat Cain**
Manager/Professional

**Wayne Lindelof**
Superintendent

***Course information:*** This public course has 18 holes. See card below for yardage and rating information. Ratings and slope are expected to change in 1993, however; the 1992 numbers are listed here.

***Play policy and fees:*** Green fees for residents of the city of Antioch are $9 for nine holes weekdays, $18 for 18 holes weekdays and $14 for 18 holes weekends. Nonresident green fees are $11 for nine holes weekdays, $13 for 18 holes weekdays and $16 for 18 holes weekends. Carts are $11 for nine holes and $16 for 18 holes.

***Location:*** From Highway 4 in Antioch, take the Lone Tree Way exit south. Bend to the right and go five lights. Turn right onto Golf Course Road.

***Course description:*** This hilly yet open course has a unique par of 73. In spite of its name, there are lots of trees and it's walkable. The best hole is probably number five, 392 yards from the back tees. To have any shot at a good number, a golfer must carry a creek 185 yards off the tee. The green is the biggest on the course. Robert Muir Graves is heading a renovation of the front side.

| Hole | 1 | 2 | 3 | 4 | 5 | 6 | 7 | 8 | 9 | Out | | |
|---|---|---|---|---|---|---|---|---|---|---|---|---|
| BLUE | 471 | 167 | 291 | 521 | 392 | 379 | 426 | 165 | 362 | 3174 | BLUE | Rating: 69.8 |
| WHITE | 458 | 133 | 275 | 496 | 360 | 370 | 405 | 145 | 348 | 2990 | | Slope: 116 |
| Par | [illegible] | [illegible] | [illegible] | [illegible] | 4 | 4 | 4 | 3 | 4 | 36 | WHITE | Rating: 67.8 |
| Handicap | 9 | 11 | 17 | 5 | 7 | 15 | 1 | 13 | 3 | x | | Slope: 112 |
| RED | 454 | 121 | 271 | 446 | 330 | 338 | 373 | 122 | 341 | 2796 | | |
| Par | 5 | 3 | 4 | 5 | 4 | 4 | 4 | 3 | 4 | 36 | RED | Rating: 71.8 |
| Handicap | 3 | 17 | 15 | 1 | 11 | 9 | 7 | 13 | 5 | x | | Slope: 119 |

| Hole | 10 | 11 | 12 | 13 | 14 | 15 | 16 | 17 | 18 | In | Totals | |
|---|---|---|---|---|---|---|---|---|---|---|---|---|
| BLUE | 428 | 166 | 514 | 382 | 129 | 355 | 496 | 486 | 303 | 3259 | BLUE | 6433 |
| WHITE | 417 | 151 | 505 | 373 | 83 | 330 | 476 | 464 | 284 | 3083 | WHITE | 6073 |
| Par | 4 | 3 | 5 | 4 | 3 | 4 | 5 | 5 | 4 | 37 | Par | 73 |
| Handicap | 2 | 16 | 6 | 12 | 18 | 4 | 8 | 10 | 14 | x | | |
| RED | 399 | 135 | 500 | 368 | 73 | 307 | 459 | 451 | 281 | 2973 | RED | 5769 |
| Par | 5 | 3 | 5 | 4 | 3 | 4 | 5 | 5 | 4 | 38 | Par | 74 |
| Handicap | 8 | 16 | 2 | 10 | 18 | 12 | 4 | 6 | 14 | x | | |

# THE ISLAND GOLF CLUB



**1966**
**R.E. Baldock**

PO Box 27
Bethel Island, CA 94511

3303 Gateway Road
Bethel Island, CA 94511

Pro shop (510) 684-2654
Clubhouse (510) 684-2775

- ✓ **driving range**
- ✓ **practice greens**
- ✓ **power carts**
- ✓ **pull carts**
- ✓ **golf club rental**
- locker rooms
- showers
- executive course
- accommodations
- ✓ **food and beverages**
- ✓ **clubhouse**

**Ed Rawlings**
Director of Golf

**John Oderda**
Head Professional

**Jim Adams**
Superintendent

***Course information:*** This public course has 18 holes. See card below for yardage and rating information.

***Play policy and fees:*** Green fees are $8.50 for nine holes, and $11 for 18 holes weekdays and $17 for 18 holes weekends. There is no weekend rate for nine holes. Carts are $11 for nine holes and $18 for 18 holes.

***Location:*** Take Highway 4 toward Oakley and exit at Cypress Road east. Turn left at Bethel Island Road and then right at Gateway Road to the course.

***Course description:*** Formerly known as the Bethel Island Golf Course, this links-style layout has been around for more than 25 years. It is flat and windy with lots of trees, water and bunkers. The average golfer will be at home. It's challenging, but a fair test. The number one handicap hole is the par-5 sixth, 468 yards into the delta breeze. The 18th hole is a good one as well, measuring 417 yards from the blues and 395 yards from the whites.

| Hole | 1 | 2 | 3 | 4 | 5 | 6 | 7 | 8 | 9 | Out | | |
|---|---|---|---|---|---|---|---|---|---|---|---|---|
| BLUE | 332 | 533 | 175 | 390 | 416 | 468 | 418 | 190 | 300 | 3222 | BLUE | Rating: -- |
| WHITE | 321 | 520 | 167 | 380 | 400 | 456 | 403 | 176 | 290 | 3113 | | Slope: -- |
| Par | 4 | 5 | 3 | 4 | 4 | 5 | 4 | 3 | 4 | 36 | WHITE | Rating: 69.2 |
| Handicap | 13 | 5 | 15 | 7 | 1 | 11 | 3 | 9 | 17 | x | | Slope: 114 |
| RED | 295 | 491 | 147 | 362 | 370 | 433 | 381 | 149 | 280 | 2908 | | |
| Par | 4 | 5 | 3 | 4 | 4 | 5 | 4 | 3 | 4 | 36 | RED | Rating: 71.9 |
| Handicap | 11 | 1 | 17 | 9 | 7 | 3 | 5 | 15 | 13 | x | | Slope: 113 |

| Hole | 10 | 11 | 12 | 13 | 14 | 15 | 16 | 17 | 18 | In | Totals | |
|---|---|---|---|---|---|---|---|---|---|---|---|---|
| BLUE | 308 | 347 | 437 | 272 | 164 | 498 | 158 | 510 | 417 | 3111 | BLUE | 6333 |
| WHITE | 298 | 332 | 417 | 267 | 161 | 493 | 142 | 502 | 395 | 3007 | WHITE | 6120 |
| Par | 4 | 4 | 4 | 4 | 3 | 5 | 3 | 5 | 4 | 36 | Par | 72 |
| Handicap | 14 | 8 | 2 | 16 | 10 | 6 | 18 | 12 | 4 | x | | |
| RED | 266 | 312 | 402 | 242 | 128 | 462 | 112 | 470 | 411 | 2805 | RED | 5713 |
| Par | 4 | 4 | 5 | 4 | 3 | 5 | 3 | 5 | 5 | 38 | Par | 74 |
| Handicap | 14 | 10 | 6 | 12 | 16 | 2 | 18 | 4 | 8 | x | | |

# SWENSON PARK GOLF COURSE

**Course 8**
**MAP E2 grid c5**

**1952**
**Jack Fleming**

6803 Alexandria Place
Stockton, CA 95207

Pro shop (209)477-0774

- ✓ **driving range**
- ✓ **practice greens**
- ✓ **power carts**
- ✓ **pull carts**
- ✓ **golf club rental**
- locker rooms
- showers
- ✓ **executive course**
- accommodations
- ✓ **food and beverages**
- ✓ **clubhouse**

**Ernie George**
Manager/Professional

**Tom Nowak**
Superintendent

NORTHERN E2

***Course information:*** This public course has 18 holes and par is 72. A par-3 executive course is also available. The course is 6,407 yards and rated 70.1 from the white tees. The slope rating is 110. Women's tees are 6,266 yards and rated 73.8 from the forward tees, with a par of 74. The slope rating for women is 114. The par-27 executive course measures 2,760 yards and is not rated.

***Play policy and fees:*** Green fees are $9 weekdays and $10 weekends for 18 holes. The executive course is $6 weekdays and $6.50 weekends. Carts are $12 for nine holes and $20 for 18 holes. Reservations should be made one week in advance and then there is a $1 reservation fee.

***Location:*** Heading north on Interstate 5 on the north side of Stockton, take the Benjamin Holt Drive exit east. Turn left on Alexandria Place and drive to the course on the left.

***Course description:*** Swenson Park offers some of the lowest green fees in Northern California for a regulation track. It is a wide-open layout with fewer than a dozen traps and just two water holes. The 15th and 16th holes, however, feature extremely demanding tee shots through narrow chutes. Rick Burgess holds the course record at 62. The executive course is dotted with water hazards, though only two holes are longer than 150 yards.

# STOCKTON GOLF AND COUNTRY CLUB

**Course 9**
MAP E2 grid c5

**1914**
**Alister MacKenzie**

PO Box 336
Stockton, CA 95204

West End of Country
Club Boulevard
Stockton, CA 95204

Pro shop (209) 466-6221
Clubhouse (209) 466-4313

- ✓ **driving range**
- ✓ **practice greens**
- ✓ **power carts**
- ✓ **pull carts**
- ✓ **golf club rental**
- ✓ **locker rooms**
- ✓ **showers**
- executive course
- accommodations
- ✓ **food and beverages**
- ✓ **clubhouse**

**Alan Reed**
Manager

**Jim Kane**
Professional

**Bill Fountain**
Superintendent

***Course information:*** This private course has 18 holes and par is 71. The course is 6,426 yards and rated 70.3 from the championship tees, and 6,275 yards and rated 69.6 from the regular tees. The slope ratings are 125 championship and 123 regular. Women's tees are 6,023 yards and rated 74.8. The slope rating is 126 and par is 71.

***Play policy and fees:*** Reciprocal play is accepted with members of other private clubs. Guest fees are $20 when accompanied by a member and the reciprocal fee is $50. Carts are $8 for nine holes and $15 for 18 holes. Closed Mondays.

***Location:*** From Interstate 5 in Stockton, take the Country Club Boulevard exit west and drive 1.5 miles to the course.

***Course description:*** The flavor of Alister MacKenzie's original design remains nearly 80 years later on this course bordered by Stockton's deep-water channel. The fairways are primarily bermuda grass and the greens are bent. It is a tight course with countless eucalyptus trees. The par-3s are outstanding, three of them measuring from 188 to 212 yards. The first hole is bordered by the channel. The new head pro is Jim Kane, the former Olympic Club pro who played in 1992 U.S. Open at Pebble Beach.

# ELKHORN COUNTRY CLUB

**Course 10**
MAP E2 grid c6

*Course information:* This private course has 18 holes. See card below for yardage and rating information.

*Play policy and fees:* Reciprocal play is accepted with members of other private clubs. Bring your credentials. Members and guests only. Guest fees are $20 on weekdays and $30 on weekends. Guest fees after 2 p.m. are $10. Fees for reciprocal players are $29 on weekdays and $39 on weekends. Carts are $20. Reservations are recommended one week in advance. This course is available for outside tournaments.

*Location:* From Interstate 5, take the Eight Mile Road exit and drive three miles east. Turn right on Davis Road and drive one-quarter mile. Turn left on Elkhorn drive.

*Course description:* This tough course rewards accuracy over distance. It has mostly short par-4s. Over 63 bunkers guard the fairways and the elevated greens. Trees abound. Every year the Oldsmobile Scramble Sectionals and the NCPGA Junior Championships are held here. Don Blake, Jeff Wilson and Rod Souza share the men's course record of 63. The women's mark is 69 by Dana Arnold.

**Bert Stamps**

1050 Elkhorn Drive
Stockton, CA 95209

Pro shop (209) 477-0252
Clubhouse (209) 477-8896

- ✓ **driving range**
- ✓ **practice greens**
- ✓ **power carts**
- ✓ **pull carts**
- golf club rental
- ✓ **locker rooms**
- ✓ **showers**
- executive course
- accommodations
- ✓ **food and beverages**
- ✓ **clubhouse**

**Bob Young**
General Manager

**Ty Caplin**
Director of Golf

**Ron Cropley**
Professional

**Del Burgess**
Superintendent

| Hole | 1 | 2 | 3 | 4 | 5 | 6 | 7 | 8 | 9 | Out | | |
|---|---|---|---|---|---|---|---|---|---|---|---|---|
| BLUE | 404 | 155 | 449 | 419 | 301 | 476 | 416 | 526 | 163 | 3309 | BLUE | Rating: 70.9 |
| | | | | | | | | | | | | Slope: 124 |
| WHITE | 391 | 152 | 430 | 395 | 271 | 471 | 358 | 472 | 140 | 3080 | | |
| Par | 4 | 3 | 4 | 4 | 4 | 5 | 4 | 5 | 3 | 36 | WHITE | Rating: 69.0 |
| Handicap | 7 | 17 | 5 | 9 | 11 | 13 | 3 | 1 | 15 | x | | Slope: 120 |
| RED | 373 | 137 | 418 | 377 | 251 | 449 | 342 | 452 | 122 | 2921 | | |
| Par | 4 | 3 | 5 | 4 | 4 | 5 | 4 | 5 | 3 | 37 | RED | Rating: 73.1 |
| Handicap | 15 | 17 | 7 | 5 | 11 | 3 | 13 | 1 | 9 | x | | Slope: 124 |

| Hole | 10 | 11 | 12 | 13 | 14 | 15 | 16 | 17 | 18 | In | Totals | |
|---|---|---|---|---|---|---|---|---|---|---|---|---|
| BLUE | 430 | 507 | 361 | 171 | 414 | 336 | 213 | 395 | 418 | 3245 | BLUE | 6554 |
| WHITE | 426 | 483 | 356 | 140 | 393 | 275 | 188 | 362 | 381 | 3004 | WHITE | 6084 |
| Par | 4 | 5 | 4 | 3 | 4 | 4 | 3 | 4 | 4 | 35 | Par | 71 |
| Handicap | 2 | 4 | 6 | 16 | 14 | 8 | 18 | 10 | 12 | x | | |
| RED | 418 | 473 | 341 | 76 | 389 | 262 | 157 | 353 | 377 | 2846 | RED | 5767 |
| Par | 5 | 5 | 4 | 3 | 4 | 4 | 3 | 4 | 4 | 36 | Par | 73 |
| Handicap | 10 | 8 | 14 | 18 | 4 | 6 | 16 | 12 | 2 | x | | |

# OAKMOORE GOLF COURSE

**Course 11**
MAP E2 grid c6

*Course information:* This private course has nine holes. Par is 72 for 18 holes. The course is 6,517 yards and rated 71.6. Women's yardage is 5,600 yards. There is no women's course rating.

*Play policy and fees:* This course is reserved exclusively for tournament groups. Call for reservations.

*Location:* From Highway 99 in Stockton, exit at Business 99/Wilson Way south and follow to the course.

*Course description:* This is a most unusual course in that it is soley used for outside tournaments. The approximate cost to each member of a visiting group is $24, which includes golf, cart and use of clubhouse. The course itself is wooded with three lakes and mostly elevated greens.

**1959**

3737 North Wilson Way
Stockton, CA 95205

Pro shop (209) 462-6712
Reservations (209) 943-1983
Clubhouse (209) 462-6712

driving range
✓ **practice greens**
✓ **power carts**
pull carts
golf club rental
✓ **locker rooms**
✓ **showers**
executive course
accommodations
food and beverages
✓ **clubhouse**

**Tony Garcia**
Manager

# DISCOVERY BAY

**Course 12**
MAP E2 grid d3

*Course information:* This private course has 18 holes and par is 71. The course is 6,554 yards and rated 72.1 from the championship tees, and 6,173 yards and rated 69.8 from the regular tees. The slope ratings are 128 championship and 123 regular. Women's tees are 5,249 yards and rated 70.2. The slope rating is 123.

*Play policy and fees:* Reciprocal play is accepted with members of other private clubs. Have your club pro call to make arrangements. Members and guests only. Green fees for reciprocators are $55 weekdays and $65 weekends. Guest fees are $28 weekdays and $42 weekends. Guests must be accompanied by a member. Carts are $20.

*Location:* From Highway 4, take the Discovery Bay Boulevard exit. Take the second right onto Clubhouse Drive.

*Course description:* Water can be—and often is—found on 16 of 18 holes. Set in rolling terrain, Discovery Bay is wide open with undulated greens. The par-3 17th hole features what amounts to an island green, though there is room to bail out left on the 178-yard (blue tees) hole. The course record of 65 belongs to Joey Ferrari, one of Northern California's most accomplished amateurs.

**1986**
**Ted Robinson**

1475 Clubhouse Drive
Byron, CA 94514

Pro shop (510) 634-0705

✓ **driving range**
✓ **practice greens**
✓ **power carts**
✓ **pull carts**
✓ **golf club rental**
✓ **locker rooms**
✓ **showers**
executive course
accommodations
✓ **food and beverages**
✓ **clubhouse**

**Abdul Majzoub**
Manager

**Tony Troncale**
Professional

**Rich Eichner**
Superintendent

# LYONS GOLF COURSE

**Course 13**
MAP E2 grid d5
61

*Course information:* This military course has nine holes. Par is 64 for 18 holes. The course is 4,090 yards and rated 58.5 from the regular tees. The slope rating is 89. Women's yardage is 3,726 yards, though ratings are not available.

*Play policy and fees:* Public play is not accepted: federal government employees, military and guests only. Green fees vary according to military status, ranging from $4 to $6.50. Guest fees are $8.50. Everyone pays $8.50 on weekends.

*Location:* From Interstate 5 in Stockton, take the Highway 4/Charter Way exit west. Turn right on Navy Drive and drive to Washington Street. Cross the bridge over the river onto Rough and Ready Island and onto the course.

*Course description:* This course has ponds that come into play on five of the nine holes. The greens are well bunkered. Lyons Golf Course is located on Rough and Ready Island in the heart of the Delta.

Rough and Ready Island
Stockton, CA 95203

Pro shop (209) 944-0442

- driving range
- ✓ **practice greens**
- power carts
- ✓ **pull carts**
- ✓ **golf club rental**
- locker rooms
- showers
- executive course
- accommodations
- food and beverages
- clubhouse

**Kermit Hagan**
Professional

**Richard Laird**
Recreation Director

# VAN BUSKIRK GOLF COURSE

**Course 14**
MAP E2 grid d6

***Course information:*** This public course has 18 holes. See card below for yardage and rating information.

***Play policy and fees:*** Green fees are $10 weekdays and $11 weekends. Carts are $20 for 18 holes.

***Location:*** From Interstate 5 in Stockton, exit at Eighth Street West. Drive along the freeway south on Manthey Road to Houston Avenue and drive to the course.

***Course description:*** This flat, open course has three ponds with water coming into play on nearly every hole in the front nine. Notable is the seventh hole, a long par-5 with out-of-bounds on the left and water on the right. On the back nine, the greens are somewhat elevated. The Stockton City Championship is held here each August.

**1961**
**Larry Norstrom**

1740 Houston Avenue
Stockton, CA 95206

Pro shop (209) 464-5629
Clubhouse (209) 463-0653

- ✓ **driving range**
- ✓ **practice greens**
- ✓ **power carts**
- pull carts
- ✓ **golf club rental**
- locker rooms
- ✓ **showers**
- executive course
- accommodations
- ✓ **food and beverages**
- ✓ **clubhouse**

**Jose Santiago**
Manager/Professional

**Tom Nowak**
Superintendent

| Hole | 1 | 2 | 3 | 4 | 5 | 6 | 7 | 8 | 9 | Out | BLUE | Rating: -- |
|---|---|---|---|---|---|---|---|---|---|---|---|---|
| BLUE | - | - | - | - | - | - | - | - | - | - | | Slope: -- |
| WHITE | 379 | 519 | 345 | 384 | 180 | 334 | 580 | 145 | 350 | 3216 | | |
| Par | 4 | 5 | 4 | 4 | 3 | 4 | 5 | 3 | 4 | 36 | WHITE | Rating: 69.3 |
| Handicap | 5 | 7 | 15 | 3 | 9 | 11 | 1 | 17 | 13 | x | | Slope: 110 |
| RED | 363 | 491 | 326 | 360 | 169 | 334 | 566 | 128 | 280 | 3017 | | |
| Par | 4 | 5 | 4 | 4 | 3 | 4 | 6 | 3 | 4 | 37 | RED | Rating: 73.5 |
| Handicap | 7 | 3 | 9 | 5 | 15 | 11 | 1 | 17 | 13 | x | | Slope: 114 |

| Hole | 10 | 11 | 12 | 13 | 14 | 15 | 16 | 17 | 18 | In | Totals | |
|---|---|---|---|---|---|---|---|---|---|---|---|---|
| BLUE | - | - | - | - | - | - | - | - | - | - | BLUE | -- |
| WHITE | 456 | 183 | 551 | 510 | 243 | 370 | 379 | 224 | 440 | 3356 | WHITE | 6572 |
| Par | 4 | 3 | 5 | 5 | 4 | 4 | 4 | 3 | 4 | 36 | Par | 72 |
| Handicap | 2 | 14 | 8 | 16 | 18 | 12 | 10 | 6 | 4 | x | | |
| RED | 367 | 156 | 456 | 464 | 218 | 357 | 327 | 165 | 400 | 2910 | RED | 5927 |
| Par | 4 | 3 | 5 | 5 | 4 | 4 | 4 | 3 | 5 | 37 | Par | 74 |
| Handicap | 10 | 18 | 2 | 4 | 14 | 8 | 12 | 16 | 6 | x | | |

# BROOKSIDE COUNTRY CLUB

**Course 15**
MAP E2 grid d6



*Course information:* Par is 72 for men and women. There are two tees for men and women. The blues, 6,720 yards, are rated 72.6 with a slope of 125. The whites, 6,244 yards, are 69.8 and 118. The golds, 5,681 yards, are rated 72.2 with a 121 slope, and the reds measure 5,022 yards with a 68.2 rating and 112 slope.

*Play policy and fees:* This 18-hole private course accepts reciprocal play with members of other clubs. The reciprocal fee of $60 includes cart. The rate for guests accompanied by a member is $30 weekdays, $40 weekends. Carts are $20.

*Location:* Take I-5 to March Lane exit on the north end of Stockton. Follow March Lane west until it runs into the course.

*Course description:* Destined to become one of the Valley's best courses, Brookside is a links-style lay-out that offers a spellbinding view of ocean freighters floating down the inland channel to the Port of Stock-ton. Water comes into play on 10 of 18 holes, the most notorious being number 16, a double dogleg of 559 yards. Its holes offer a nice change of pace, from the 450-yard uphill ninth to the chip-shot 12th of 131 yards. The course opened in October, 1991 and the course records are held by Mike Baty, 64 on the white tees, and Mike Omlansky, 66 on the blues.

**Robert Trent Jones, Jr.**

3603 St. Andrews Drive
Stockton, CA 95219

Pro shop (209) 956-6200

- ✓ **driving range**
- ✓ **practice greens**
- ✓ **power carts**
- ✓ **pull carts**
- ✓ **golf club rental**
- ✓ **locker rooms**
- ✓ **showers**
- executive course
- accommodations
- ✓ **food and beverages**
- ✓ **clubhouse**

**Bob Johnson**
Manager

**Jay Walkinshaw**
Professional

**Jim Ferrin**
Superintendent

# SPRINGTOWN GOLF COURSE

**Course 16**
MAP E2 grid e0

***Course information:*** This public course has nine holes. See card below for yardage and rating information.

***Play policy and fees:*** Green fees are $11 for nine holes and $16 for 18 holes on weekdays, $13 for nine holes and $19 for 18 holes on weekends. Carts are $20 for each 18 holes. Reservations are recommended seven days in advance. This course is available for outside tournaments.

***Location:*** From Interstate 580 in Livermore, take the Springtown Boulevard exit north. Turn right on Bluebell, which turns into Larkspur Drive.

***Course description:*** This short course is well maintained with water on two holes, undulating greens, and two long par-3s of 190 and 202 yards. This is a test for golfers of all abilities. The third hole is perhaps the most memorable, with a large palm tree and bunker next to the par-4 green.

**1961**
939 Larkspur Drive
Livermore, CA 94550

Pro shop (510) 455-5695

- ✓ **driving range**
- ✓ **practice greens**
- ✓ **power carts**
- ✓ **pull carts**
- ✓ **golf club rental**
- locker rooms
- showers
- executive course
- accommodations
- ✓ **food and beverages**
- ✓ **clubhouse**

**Keith Boam**
Manager

**Mike Orlando**
Professional

**Mulkh Raj**
Superintendent

| Hole | 1 | 2 | 3 | 4 | 5 | 6 | 7 | 8 | 9 | Out | BLUE | Rating: -- |
|---|---|---|---|---|---|---|---|---|---|---|---|---|
| BLUE | - | - | - | - | - | - | - | - | - | - | | Slope: -- |
| WHITE | 472 | 190 | 355 | 202 | 353 | 90 | 285 | 355 | 467 | 2769 | | |
| Par | 5 | 3 | 4 | 3 | 4 | 3 | 4 | 4 | 5 | 35 | WHITE | Rating:65.9 |
| Handicap | 5 | 7 | 1 | 3 | 11 | 17 | 15 | 9 | 13 | x | | Slope: 104 |
| RED | 411 | 149 | 318 | 190 | 343 | 76 | 276 | 343 | 457 | 2563 | | |
| Par | 5 | 3 | 4 | 3 | 4 | 3 | 4 | 4 | 5 | 35 | RED | Rating: 69.1 |
| Handicap | 10 | 16 | 8 | 12 | 4 | 18 | 14 | 6 | 2 | x | | Slope: 108 |

| Hole | 10 | 11 | 12 | 13 | 14 | 15 | 16 | 17 | 18 | In | Totals | |
|---|---|---|---|---|---|---|---|---|---|---|---|---|
| BLUE | - | - | - | - | - | - | - | - | - | - | BLUE | -- |
| WHITE | 473 | 209 | 428 | 202 | 365 | 122 | 298 | 364 | 480 | 2941 | WHITE | 5710 |
| Par | 5 | 3 | 4 | 3 | 4 | 3 | 4 | 4 | 5 | 35 | Par | 70 |
| Handicap | 6 | 8 | 2 | 4 | 12 | 18 | 16 | 10 | 14 | x | | |
| RED | 472 | 190 | 355 | 202 | 353 | 90 | 285 | 355 | 467 | 2769 | RED | 5332 |
| Par | 5 | 3 | 4 | 3 | 4 | 3 | 4 | 4 | 5 | 35 | Par | 70 |
| Handicap | 1 | 15 | 7 | 11 | 3 | 17 | 13 | 5 | 9 | x | | |

# LAS POSITAS GOLF COURSE

**Course 17**
MAP E2 grid e0



*Course information:* This public course has 18 holes and par is 72. There is also a nine-hole executive course. The course is 6,725 yards and rated 72.0 from the tournament tees, 6,377 yards and rated 70.5 from the championship tees, and 5,719 yards and rated 68.2 from the regular tees. The slope ratings are 126 tournament, 122 championship and 113 regular. Women's tees are 5,270 yards and rated 70.1. The slope rating is 120.

*Play policy and fees:* Green fees for residents of Livermore are $10 for nine holes and $18 for 18 holes weekdays, and $14 for nine holes and $22 for 18 holes weekends. Non-resident green fees are $12 for nine holes and $18 for 18 holes weekdays, and $15 for nine holes and $26 for 18 holes weekends. Carts are $26. This course is available for outside tournaments. Closed Christmas.

*Location:* From Interstate 580 East, exit on Airway Boulevard. This course is located near the Livermore Airport on the south side.

*Course description:* This flat, tree-lined course has four lakes and a creek that come into play on seven holes. The greens are large and some are clevated. The fairways are wide and lush. This is a fly-in course with overnight accommodations nearby. The back nine is just two years old because it had to be shortened to accommodate the adjacent airport. The 14th hole (334 yards, par-4) doglegs around a lake and tempts long hitters to go for the green on the tee shot. But with a carry of at least 235 yards—good luck. Doug Brooke's 66 is the lowest score ever shot here.

PO Box 1048
Livermore, CA 94550

909 Clubhouse Drive
Livermore, CA 94550

Pro shop (510) 443-3122

- ✓ **driving range**
- ✓ **practice greens**
- ✓ **power carts**
- ✓ **pull carts**
- ✓ **golf club rental**
- locker rooms
- showers
- ✓ **executive course**
- accommodations
- ✓ **food and beverages**
- ✓ **clubhouse**

**Dan Lippstreu**
Professional

**Mulkh Raj**
Superintendent

# MANTECA GOLF COURSE

**Course 18**
MAP E2 grid e6

***Course information:*** This public course has 18 holes. See card below for yardage and rating information.

***Play policy and fees:*** Green fees are $10.75 weekdays and $14.25 weekends. Carts are $16 weekdays and $18 weekends. Nine-hole rates are $7 weekdays and $8 weekends.

***Location:*** Located in Manteca off Highway 120 between Interstate 5 and Highway 99. From Highway 120, take the Union Road exit heading north. The course is on the left, past Center Street.

***Course description:*** A magnificent new clubhouse makes this municipal course seem like a country club. The golf course is both fun and demanding. Number 11 is probably the most difficult hole, a 430-yard par-4 that used to be a par-5. The 18th hole is an excellent finisher, a long dogleg of 413 yards, and the par-3s offer variety. Number 17 is a tough 168-yarder to a sloping, bunkered green. Pat Biocini and Kevin Wentworth share the course record with 65s.

**1967**

PO Box 611
Manteca, CA 95336

305 North Union Road
Manteca, CA 95336

Pro shop (209) 825-2500

✓ **driving range**
✓ **practice greens**
✓ **power carts**
✓ **pull carts**
✓ **golf club rental**
✓ **locker rooms**
showers
executive course
accommodations
✓ **food and beverages**
✓ **clubhouse**

**Alan Thomas**
Professional

**Allen Mooser**
Manager/Superintendent

| Hole | 1 | 2 | 3 | 4 | 5 | 6 | 7 | 8 | 9 | Out | BLUE | Rating: 70.7 |
|---|---|---|---|---|---|---|---|---|---|---|---|---|
| BLUE | 528 | 283 | 442 | 504 | 177 | 346 | 339 | 145 | 522 | 3286 | | Slope: 119 |
| WHITE | 519 | 276 | 414 | 485 | 174 | 336 | 324 | 129 | 513 | 3170 | | |
| Par | 5 | 4 | 4 | 5 | 3 | 4 | 4 | 3 | 5 | 37 | WHITE | Rating: 69.9 |
| Handicap | 5 | 15 | 1 | 17 | 3 | 9 | 11 | 13 | 7 | x | | Slope: 117 |
| RED | 512 | 262 | 393 | 457 | 165 | 312 | 299 | 101 | 480 | 2981 | | |
| Par | 5 | 4 | 4 | 5 | 3 | 4 | 4 | 3 | 5 | 37 | RED | Rating: 72.1 |
| Handicap | 1 | 13 | 7 | 5 | 15 | 9 | 11 | 17 | 3 | x | | Slope: 115 |

| Hole | 10 | 11 | 12 | 13 | 14 | 15 | 16 | 17 | 18 | In | Totals | |
|---|---|---|---|---|---|---|---|---|---|---|---|---|
| BLUE | 394 | 433 | 297 | 484 | 176 | 407 | 394 | 174 | 421 | 3180 | BLUE | 6466 |
| WHITE | 384 | 430 | 294 | 477 | 170 | 402 | 389 | 168 | 413 | 3127 | WHITE | 6297 |
| Par | 4 | 4 | 4 | 5 | 3 | 4 | 4 | 3 | 4 | 35 | Par | 72 |
| Handicap | 12 | 2 | 10 | 18 | 16 | 8 | 6 | 14 | 4 | x | | |
| RED | 309 | 377 | 287 | 451 | 136 | 366 | 327 | 132 | 373 | 2758 | RED | 5739 |
| Par | 4 | 4 | 4 | 5 | 3 | 4 | 4 | 3 | 4 | 35 | Par | 72 |
| Handicap | 12 | 4 | 14 | 2 | 16 | 8 | 10 | 18 | 6 | x | | |

# ESCALON GOLF COURSE

**Course 19**
MAP E2 grid e9

***Course information:*** This public course has nine holes. See card below for yardage and rating information.

***Play policy and fees:*** Green fees are $4.75 for nine holes and $8.50 for 18 holes weekdays, and $5.25 for nine holes and $9.50 for 18 holes weekends. Reservations are taken anytime.

***Location:*** Driving south on Highway 99, take the Manteca exit heading toward Escalon. Turn left on Escalon Bellota Road and drive to the course.

***Course description:*** This short course is flat with one pond with four par-4s and five par-3s. It is easy to walk and is particularly popular among seniors. The course record is 25 for nine holes.

**1985**
**Ken Roberts**

17051 South Escalon
Bellota Road
Escalon, CA 95320

Pro shop (209) 838-1277

- ✓ **driving range**
- ✓ **practice greens**
- power carts
- ✓ **pull carts**
- ✓ **golf club rental**
- locker rooms
- showers
- ✓ **executive course**
- accommodations
- ✓ **food and beverages**
- ✓ **clubhouse**

**Lorie Wann**
Manager

**John DeFilippi**
Professional

**Tom Hagan**
Superintendent

| Hole | 1 | 2 | 3 | 4 | 5 | 6 | 7 | 8 | 9 | Totals | BLUE | Rating: -- |
|---|---|---|---|---|---|---|---|---|---|---|---|---|
| BLUE | - | | - | - | - | - | - | - | - | - | | Slope: -- |
| WHITE | 185 | 80 | 70 | 190 | 195 | 175 | 250 | 220 | 165 | 1520 | | |
| Par | 4 | 3 | 3 | 4 | 3 | 3 | 4 | 4 | 3 | 31 | WHITE | Rating: 59.6 |
| Handicap | - | - | | - | - | - | - | - | - | x | | Slope: 67 |
| RED | 185 | 80 | 70 | 190 | 195 | 175 | 250 | 220 | 165 | 1520 | | |
| Par | 4 | 3 | 3 | 4 | 3 | 3 | 4 | 4 | 3 | 31 | RED | Rating: 59.6 |
| Handicap | - | - | - | - | - | - | - | - | - | x | | Slope: 67 |

| Hole | 10 | 11 | 12 | 13 | 14 | 15 | 16 | 17 | 18 | In | Totals | |
|---|---|---|---|---|---|---|---|---|---|---|---|---|
| BLUE | - | - | - | - | - | - | - | - | - | - | BLUE | -- |
| WHITE | 185 | 80 | 70 | 190 | 195 | 175 | 250 | 220 | 165 | 1520 | WHITE | 3040 |
| Par | 4 | 3 | 3 | 4 | 3 | 3 | 4 | 4 | 3 | 31 | Par | 62 |
| Handicap | | | | | | | | | | x | | |
| RED | - | - | - | - | - | - | - | - | - | - | RED | -- |
| Par | | | | | | | | | | | Par | |
| Handicap | | | | | | | | | | x | | |

# SPRING CREEK GOLF AND COUNTRY CLUB

**Course 20**
MAP E2 grid f7

**1976**
**Jack Fleming**

PO Box 535
Ripon, CA 95366

16436 East Spring Creek Dr.
Ripon, CA 95366

Pro shop (209) 599-3630
Clubhouse (209) 599-3258

- ✓ **driving range**
- ✓ **practice greens**
- ✓ **power carts**
- pull carts
- golf club rental
- ✓ **locker rooms**
- ✓ **showers**
- executive course
- accommodations
- ✓ **food and beverages**
- ✓ **clubhouse**

**Peter Hand**
General Manager

**Steve Brown**
Professional

**Cal Shipman**
Superintendent

***Course information:*** This private course has 18 holes and par is 72. The course is 6,380 yards and rated 70.7 from the championship tees, and 6,144 yards and rated 69.6 from the regular tees. The slope ratings are 124 championship and 121 regular. Women's tees are 5,626 yards and rated 72.4. The slope rating for women is 128.

***Play policy and fees:*** Reciprocal play is accepted with members of other private clubs. Have your club pro call for arrangements after 2 p.m. Guest fees are $20 when accompanied by a member and $35 when unaccompanied. Mandatory carts are $16. Appropriate dress is required. Reciprocal fees match those of the visitor's home club.

***Location:*** From Highway 99 in Ripon (north of Modesto), take the Ripon exit to the east side of the freeway. Drive two miles to Spring Creek Drive and the course.

***Course description:*** This flat course is tight with lots of oak trees, two of which are stationed in the middle of narrow fairways. The ninth hole is a notable par-4 that crosses water. At 432 yards, it places a premium on accuracy. Annual tournaments include the JGANC Spring Creek Classic, Seniors Invitational, Men's Invitational, Ladies Invitational, and Couples Invitational. The NCGA Qualifying and CGA Qualifying have been held here. The men's course record is 64, held jointly by Ron Brown and Robert Warren. The women's course record is 68, held by Keri Arnold-Cusenza.

# DEL RIO COUNTRY CLUB

**Course 21**
MAP E2 grid f8

**1926**
**William Park Bell**

801 Stewart Road
Modesto, CA 95356

Pro shop (209) 545-0013
Clubhouse (209) 545-0723

- ✓ **driving range**
- ✓ **practice greens**
- ✓ **power carts**
- ✓ **pull carts**
- ✓ **golf club rental**
- ✓ **locker rooms**
- ✓ **showers**
- executive course
- accommodations
- ✓ **food and beverages**
- ✓ **clubhouse**

**Duncan Reno**
Manager

**Bill Womeldorf**
Professional

**Steve Smith**
Superintendent

***Course information:*** This private course has 18 holes and par is 72. The course is 6,875 yards and rated 72.8 from the championship tees, and 6,650 yards and rated 71.7 from the regular tees. The slope ratings are 126 championship and 122 regular. Women's tees are 6,345 yards and rated 76.2 from the championship tees, and 5,986 yards and rated 75.0 from the forward tees. The slope ratings are 131 championship and 130 forward.

***Play policy and fees:*** Reciprocal play with members of other private clubs is accepted on Tuesdays, Thursdays and Fridays. Guest fees are $25 with a member and $50 without weekdays, and $35 with a member weekends. No play is allowed without a member on weekends. Carts are $16. This course is available for limited outside tournaments. Closed Mondays.

***Location:*** From Highway 99 in Modesto, take the Salida exit onto Kerinin Avenue North. Turn left at Dale Road and follow it to the "T." Turn right on Ladd and drive one mile to Saint John and go left up to the club.

***Course description:*** This course was designed in 1926 by William Park Bell. It's a challenging, rolling country course that demands good shot placement. The greens are fast, undulating, and have subtle breaks. Nine additional holes are on the design boards. It hosted the 1990 U.S. Senior Women's Amateur Championship, and annually hosts the Bumgartner Junior Championships in July. Del Rio is generally acknowledged to be one of the top 15-20 courses in northern California, a classic layout from the old school of golf course architecture.

# TRACY GOLF AND COUNTRY CLUB

**Course 22**
MAP E2 grid g4

**1956**
**Robert Trent Jones, Sr.**

35200 South Chrisman Road
Tracy, CA 95376

Pro shop (209) 835-9463

- ✓ **driving range**
- ✓ **practice greens**
- ✓ **power carts**
- ✓ **pull carts**
- ✓ **golf club rental**
- ✓ **locker rooms**
- ✓ **showers**
- executive course
- accommodations
- ✓ **food and beverages**
- ✓ **clubhouse**

**Steve Moreland**
Manager/Professional

**George Murakami**
Superintendent

***Course information:*** This private course has 18 holes. See card below for yardage and rating information.

***Play policy and fees:*** Reciprocal play is accepted with members of other private clubs. Have your club pro call ahead for arrangements. Reciprocal rates are $32 weekdays, $40 weekends. Guest fees are $18 on weekdays and $25 on weekends when accompanied by a member, $25 weekdays and $32 on weekends without a member. Carts are $16.

***Location:*** From Interstate 580, take the Chrisman Road exit. The course is located next to the highway.

***Course description:*** This flat course has rolling terrain, fast, elevated greens, four ponds and numerous bunkers. The original nine holes were designed by Robert Trent Jones, Sr. The front nine is tight while the newer back side is more wide-open. The first hole is a monster, 429 yards into the wind. The par-5 fifth hole (497 yards) is an excellent hole as well. All out-of-bounds on the course is left, so big hooks are deadly. Host pro Steve Moreland holds the course record at 63.

| Hole | 1 | 2 | 3 | 4 | 5 | 6 | 7 | 8 | 9 | Out | BLUE | Rating: 70.7 |
|---|---|---|---|---|---|---|---|---|---|---|---|---|
| BLUE | 429 | 330 | 305 | 200 | 497 | 174 | 406 | 526 | 454 | 3321 | | Slope: 118 |
| WHITE | 413 | 319 | 297 | 185 | 485 | 160 | 374 | 482 | 409 | 3124 | | |
| Par | 4 | 4 | 4 | 3 | 5 | 3 | 4 | 5 | 4 | 36 | WHITE | Rating: 69.5 |
| Handicap | 1 | 9 | 17 | 5 | 15 | 13 | 7 | 11 | 3 | x | | Slope: 115 |
| RED | 406 | 259 | 275 | 148 | 485 | 113 | 369 | 435 | 394 | 2884 | | |
| Par | 5 | 4 | 4 | 3 | 5 | 3 | 4 | 5 | 4 | 37 | RED | Rating: 72.7 |
| Handicap | 9 | 13 | 11 | 15 | 1 | 17 | 3 | 5 | 7 | x | | Slope: 125 |

| Hole | 10 | 11 | 12 | 13 | 14 | 15 | 16 | 17 | 18 | In | Totals | |
|---|---|---|---|---|---|---|---|---|---|---|---|---|
| BLUE | 353 | 140 | 386 | 156 | 551 | 465 | 321 | 394 | 532 | 3298 | BLUE | 6619 |
| WHITE | 339 | 134 | 378 | 146 | 523 | 441 | 304 | 323 | 515 | 3103 | WHITE | 6227 |
| Par | 4 | 3 | 4 | 3 | 5 | 4 | 4 | 4 | 5 | 36 | Par | 72 |
| Handicap | 14 | 16 | 4 | 12 | 8 | 2 | 18 | 6 | 10 | x | | |
| RED | 322 | 128 | 360 | 130 | 472 | 404 | 298 | 282 | 492 | 2892 | RED | 5776 |
| Par | 4 | 3 | 4 | 3 | 5 | 5 | 4 | 4 | 5 | 37 | Par | 74 |
| Handicap | 8 | 16 | 4 | 18 | 6 | 14 | 12 | 10 | 2 | x | | |

# RIVER OAKS GOLF COURSE

**Course 23**
MAP E2 grid g8

*Course information:* This public course has 18 holes and par is 58. The course is 2,885 yards and rated 52.7 from the regular tees. The slope rating is 74. Women's tees are 2,640 yards with a rating of 54.3. The slope rating is 75.

*Play policy and fees:* Green fees are $8 weekdays and $10 weekends and holidays. Reservations are recommended one week in advance. Nine-hole rates are $4 wekdays, $6 weekends. All players must wear proper golf attire. Only golf or tennis shoes may be worn on the course.

*Location:* From Modesto, drive south on Highway 99. Take the Hatch Road exit east. The course is located on the left past Mitchell Road.

*Course description:* This tree-lined course runs along the Tuolumne River. It has some ponds and no bunkers. It doesn't take much time to get through this course. The men's record, 52, is held by Rob Phipps, and Evelyn Phillips holds the record for women at 65.

**1979**
**Jim D. Phipps**

PO Box 97
Ceres, CA 95307

3441 East Hatch Road
Hughson, CA 95362

Pro shop (209) 537-4653

- ✓ **driving range**
- ✓ **practice greens**
- power carts
- ✓ **pull carts**
- ✓ **golf club rental**
- locker rooms
- showers
- ✓ **executive course**
- accommodations
- ✓ **food and beverages**
- clubhouse

**Robert Phipps**
Manager

**Linda Collins–Maurer**
Professional

**Mike Phipps**
Superintendent

# DRYDEN PARK GOLF COURSE

**Course 24**
MAP E2 grid g8

***Course information:*** This public course has 27 holes. Par is 72 for the Dryden Course and 70 for the Modesto Municipal Course at 18 holes.

The Dryden Course is 6,514 yards and rated 69.3 from the championship tees, and 6,140 yards and rated 67.9 from the regular tees. The slope ratings are 119 championship and 116 regular. Women's tees are 5,910 yards and rated 73.3. The slope rating is 115.

***Play policy and fees:*** Green fees are $13 weekdays and $15 weekends. Twilight rate is $11. Carts are $16. Reservations are recommended one week in advance. This course is available for outside tournaments.

***Location:*** This course is located right off Highway 99 in Modesto. Take the Tuolumne Boulevard/B Street exit and make a right on Tuolumne.

***Course description:*** The Tuolumne River runs along side this course. The front nine is flat, and the back nine is somewhat hilly. Numerous pine trees make Dryden a nice test despite its relatively modest length. (See the following listing for Modesto Municipal Course for additional information.)

**1959**
920 South Sunset Boulevard
Modesto, CA 95351

Pro shop (209) 577-5359
Muni Course (209) 577-5360
Clubhouse (209) 529-5530

✓ **driving range**
✓ **practice greens**
✓ **power carts**
✓ **pull carts**
✓ **golf club rental**
locker rooms
showers
executive course
accommodations
✓ **food and beverages**
✓ **clubhouse**

**Sue Fiscoe**
Professional

**Leonard Theis**
Superintendent

# MODESTO MUNICIPAL GOLF COURSE

**Course 25**
MAP E2 grid g8

921 Sunset
Modesto, CA 95351

Pro shop (209) 577-5360

- driving range
- ✓ practice greens
- ✓ power carts
- ✓ pull carts
- ✓ golf club rental
- locker rooms
- showers
- executive course
- accommodations
- ✓ food and beverages
- ✓ clubhouse

**Sue Fiscoe**
Professional

**Leonard Theis**
Superintendent

*Course information:* This public course has nine holes and par is 70 for 18 holes. The course is 6,074 yards and rated 68.2 with a slope of 113 for 18 holes from the regular tees. Women's tees are 5,868 yards and rated 72.0 with a slope of 112 for 18 holes.

*Play policy and fees:* Green fees are $9 for nine holes and $13 for 18 holes weekdays, and $11 for nine holes and $15 for 18 holes weekends and holidays. The weekday late-play green fee after 3 p.m. during the summer season is $7. The weekend late-play green fee after 3 p.m. is $9. Wednesdays are senior (65 and over) days and the green fee is $5 for nine holes between 9 a.m. and 3 p.m. Carts are $8 for nine holes and $16 for 18 holes. Reservations are recommended.

*Location:* On Highway 99 off Toulumne Boulevard, take the "B" Street off-ramp and make a right at the stop sign. Drive one-half block on Neece Drive, and stay left along the river to the course.

*Course description:* This course is walkable and fairly flat. The fairways are narrow and the trees are mature. The ninth is considered one of the top 18 holes in the area. At 424 yards, it's a par-4 dogleg right with out-of-bounds on the right and trees on both sides. You can't see the green from the tee, but there is a bunker to the left front and a cart path to the right. The green holds if the shot is well executed. This is one of the best nine-hole layouts around.

# MODESTO CREEKSIDE GOLF COURSE

**Course 26**
MAP E2 grid g9

**1991**
**Steve Halsey**

701 Lincoln
Modesto, CA 95353

Pro shop (209) 571-5123

- ✓ driving range
- ✓ practice greens
- ✓ power carts
- ✓ pull carts
- ✓ golf club rental
- locker rooms
- showers
- executive course
- accommodations
- ✓ food and beverages
- ✓ clubhouse

**Sue Fiscoe**
Manager/Professional

**Leonard Theis**
Superintendent

*Course information:* This public course has 18 holes. Par is 72. The course is 6,610 yards and rated 70.3 with a 115 slope from the blue tees. The course is 6,021 yards and rated 67.8 from the regular tees. The slope rating is 109. Women's tees are 5,496 yards and rated 69.5 with a 108 slope.

*Play policy and fees:* Green fees are $13 weekdays and $15 weekends. Carts are $17. This course is available for outside tournaments. Weekday reservations are recommended one week in advance, and weekend reservations are taken the prior Monday.

*Location:* From Highway 99 in Modesto, take Highway 132 to Lincoln. Turn left on Lincoln and follow it to the deadline at the course.

*Course description:* This course opened in late 1991. It is relatively flat with two holes playing into the creekside. There are three ponds which come into play on six holes. There are some two-tiered greens, but they're large. Once the trees mature, this course will be demonstrably tougher. The par-4 18th hole is 392 yards from the white tees with water on both sides of the fairway.

# MAP E3

(14 COURSES)

PAGES.. 292-305


NOR-CAL MAP.....see page 30
adjoining maps
NORTH (D3).......see page 158
EAST (E4)..........see page 306
SOUTH (F3) .......see page 352
WEST (E2)..........see page268

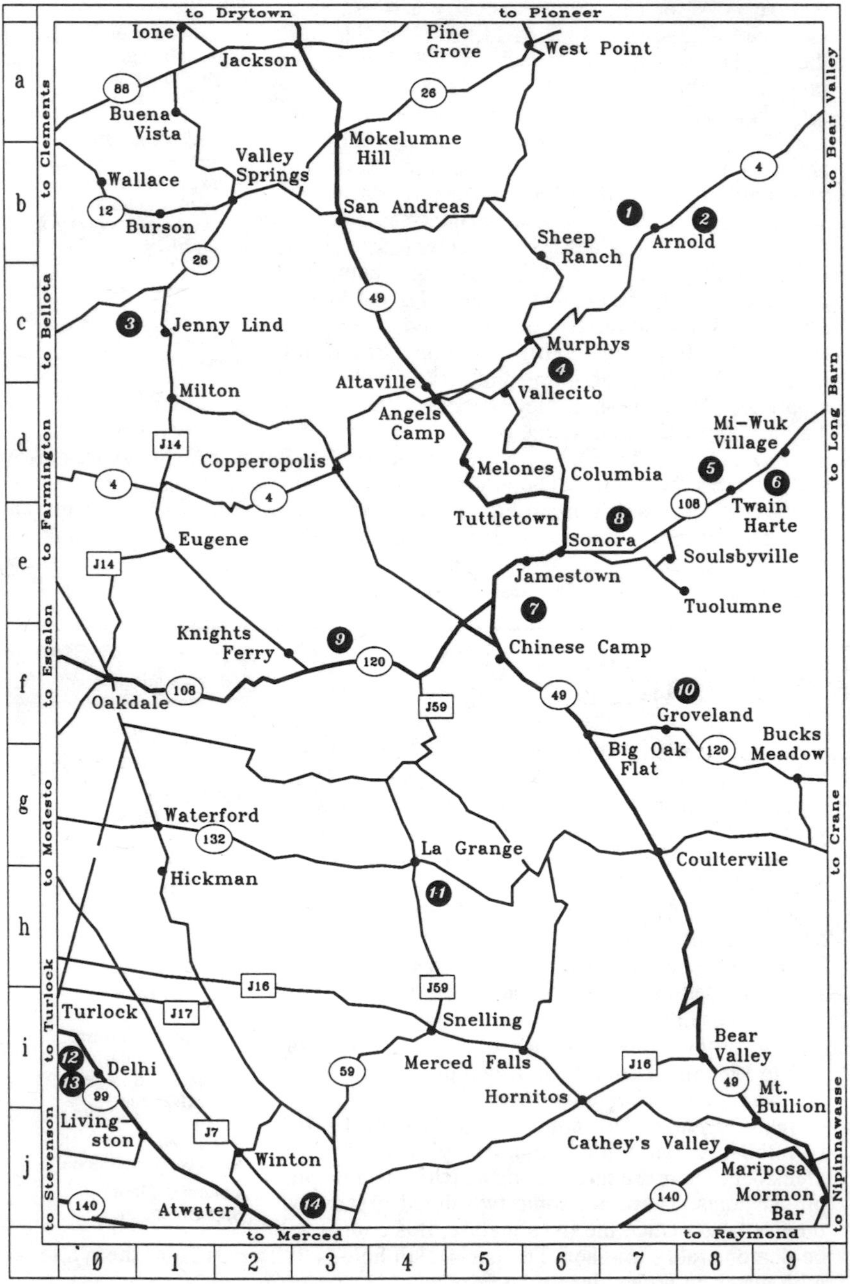

to Drytown
to Pioneer
to Clements
to Bellota
to Farmington
to Escalon
to Modesto
to Turlock
to Stevenson
to Bear Valley
to Long Barn
to Crane
to Nipinnawasse
to Merced
to Raymond

Ione
Jackson
Pine Grove
West Point
88
26
Buena Vista
Mokelumne Hill
Valley Springs
Wallace
12
Burson
San Andreas
4
1
2
Arnold
Sheep Ranch
26
49
3
Jenny Lind
Murphys
4
Milton
Altaville
Vallecito
Angels Camp
Mi-Wuk Village
J14
Copperopolis
Melones
Columbia
5
6
4
4
108
Twain Harte
Tuttletown
8
Eugene
Sonora
J14
Soulsbyville
Jamestown
Tuolumne
7
Knights Ferry
9
Chinese Camp
120
108
Oakdale
J59
49
10
Groveland
Bucks Meadow
Big Oak Flat
120
Waterford
132
La Grange
Coulterville
Hickman
11
J16
J59
Turlock
J17
Snelling
12
Delhi
13
99
59
Merced Falls
Bear Valley
J16
49
Mt. Bullion
Hornitos
Living-ston
J7
Cathey's Valley
Winton
Mariposa
14
140
Atwater
140
Mormon Bar

a b c d e f g h i j

0 1 2 3 4 5 6 7 8 9

# MEADOWMOUNT GOLF COURSE

**Course 1**
MAP E3 grid b7

**1962**
PO Box 586
Arnold, CA 95223

Highway 4 and
Country Club Drive
Arnold, CA 95223

Pro shop (209) 795-1313
Clubhouse (209) 795-3585

- driving range
- ✓ **practice greens**
- ✓ **power carts**
- ✓ **pull carts**
- ✓ **golf club rental**
- locker rooms
- showers
- executive course
- accommodations
- ✓ **food and beverages**
- ✓ **clubhouse**

**Jeff Christensen**
Manager/Head Professional/
Superintendent

*Course information:* This public course has nine holes. Par is 72 for 18 holes. The course is 6,000 yards and rated 67.6 for 18 holes from the regular tees. The slope rating is 113. Women's tees are 5,565 yards and rated 71.0. The slope rating is 114.

*Play policy and fees:* Green fees are $9 for nine holes and $13.75 for 18 holes weekdays, and $10.50 for nine holes and $15 for 18 holes weekends. Carts are $10.25 for nine holes and $19 for 18 holes.

*Location:* From Highway 99, drive 70 miles east on Highway 4, past Murphys to Arnold. The course is on the left.

*Course description:* This flat course is narrow thanks to the forest of pine trees lining each fairway. The greens are small and Rae's Creek—no relation to the more famous Rae's Creek of Augusta National fame—runs through the entire course. The fifth hole (354 yards) is an absolute beauty with out-of-bounds left and a lake right. The green is tucked into the pines. Meadowmount is generally open from March through November. Head pro Jeff Christiansen has the course record at 64.

# SEQUOIA WOODS COUNTRY CLUB

**Course 2**
MAP E3 grid b8

**1976**

***Course information:*** This private course has 18 holes. See card below for yardage and rating information.

***Play policy and fees:*** Reciprocal play is accepted with members of other private clubs at $30 for 18 holes and $16 for nine holes. Guest fees are $20 when accompanied by a member and $30 without. Carts are $18 when accompanied by a member and $20 without. Reservations are recommended two weeks in advance. This course is available for outside tournaments.

***Location:*** From Highway 99, drive east on Highway 4 to Arnold. Exit right on Blue Lake Springs and follow the signs to the club. The course is a 90-minute drive from Stockton.

***Course description:*** This sprawling, mountain course is tougher than the rating indicates. The front nine is situated in a spacious meadow. Trade in the woods for irons on the back nine, because it gets narrow and steep. Out-of-bounds run along both sides of the fairways. Par is 38 on the front side, with the par-5 sixth hole measuring 531 yards uphill. Number six doglegs right around a creek and offers no room for error off the tee. Club member John Trench shot a record 62 in 1984.

PO Box 748
Arnold, CA 95223

1000 Cypress Point Drive
Arnold, CA 95223

Pro shop (209) 795-2141
Clubhouse (209) 795-1378

- driving range
- ✓ **practice greens**
- ✓ **power carts**
- ✓ **pull carts**
- ✓ **golf club rental**
- ✓ **locker rooms**
- ✓ **showers**
- executive course
- accommodations
- ✓ **food and beverages**
- ✓ **clubhouse**

**John Eckland**
Manager

**Larry Babica**
Professional

**John Castillo**
Superintendent

| Hole | 1 | 2 | 3 | 4 | 5 | 6 | 7 | 8 | 9 | Out | | |
|---|---|---|---|---|---|---|---|---|---|---|---|---|
| BLUE | 404 | 405 | 260 | 484 | 386 | 531 | 164 | 308 | 530 | 3472 | BLUE | Rating: 67.3 |
| WHITE | 386 | 396 | 248 | 478 | 380 | 427 | 147 | 293 | 521 | 3277 | | Slope: 114 |
| Par | 4 | 4 | 4 | 5 | 4 | 5 | 3 | 4 | 5 | 38 | WHITE | Rating: 65.8 |
| Handicap | 3 | 7 | 17 | 9 | 11 | 1 | 13 | 15 | 5 | x | | Slope: 111 |
| RED | 379 | 388 | 231 | 394 | 353 | 416 | 126 | 273 | 496 | 3056 | | |
| Par | 4 | 4 | 4 | 5 | 4 | 5 | 3 | 4 | 5 | 38 | RED | Rating: 67.8 |
| Handicap | 7 | 5 | 15 | 9 | 11 | 3 | 17 | 13 | 1 | x | | Slope: 111 |

| Hole | 10 | 11 | 12 | 13 | 14 | 15 | 16 | 17 | 18 | In | Totals | |
|---|---|---|---|---|---|---|---|---|---|---|---|---|
| BLUE | 161 | 198 | 309 | 305 | 263 | 199 | 235 | 80 | 400 | 2150 | BLUE | 5622 |
| WHITE | 126 | 184 | 290 | 290 | 260 | 181 | 223 | 77 | 381 | 2017 | WHITE | 5294 |
| Par | 3 | 3 | 4 | 4 | 4 | 3 | 4 | 3 | 4 | 32 | Par | 70 |
| Handicap | 16 | 6 | 10 | 8 | 12 | 4 | 14 | 18 | 2 | x | | |
| RED | 121 | 118 | 281 | 280 | 246 | 160 | 198 | 72 | 356 | 1187 | RED | 4943 |
| Par | 3 | 3 | 4 | 4 | 4 | 3 | 4 | 3 | 4 | 32 | Par | 70 |
| Handicap | 16 | 14 | 4 | 6 | 8 | 12 | 10 | 18 | 2 | x | | |

# LA CONTENTA GOLF CLUB

**Course 3**
MAP E3 grid c1

**1974**

1653 Highway 26
Valley Springs, CA 95252

Pro shop (209) 772-1081
Clubhouse (209) 772-1082

- driving range
- ✓ **practice greens**
- ✓ **power carts**
- ✓ **pull carts**
- ✓ **golf club rental**
- locker rooms
- showers
- executive course
- accommodations
- ✓ **food and beverages**
- ✓ **clubhouse**

**Rod Metzler**
Director of Golf

**Curt Hammond**
Director of Golf

**Glen Reynolds**
Professional

**Rod Butler**
Superintendent

NORTHERN E3

***Course information:*** This semi-private course has 18 holes. See card below for yardage and rating information.

***Play policy and fees:*** Green fees are $16 Monday through Thursday, $21 Friday and $26 weekends. Carts are $18. Reservations are recommended two weeks in advance. This course is available for outside tournaments.

***Location:*** From Highway 99 in Stockton, take the Fremont (Highway 26) exit east. Drive 28 miles on Highway 26 to the course.

***Course description:*** Set in the rolling foothills 35 miles east of Stockton, this tight, hilly course challenges you with out-of-bounds on 14 holes and water on nine holes. The trademark hole is the 13th, a par-3 that drops 100 feet from the tee to an "L" shaped green almost completely surrounded by water. Be ready to hit plenty of blind shots as well as approaches from sidehill lies, but La Contenta is in excellent shape and affords outstanding vistas on virtually every hole.

| Hole | 1 | 2 | 3 | 4 | 5 | 6 | 7 | 8 | 9 | Out | BLUE | Rating: 71.3 |
|---|---|---|---|---|---|---|---|---|---|---|---|---|
| BLUE | 430 | 165 | 490 | 360 | 305 | 342 | 466 | 200 | 477 | 3230 | | Slope: 127 |
| WHITE | 369 | 120 | 465 | 340 | 285 | 302 | 453 | 164 | 409 | 2907 | | |
| Par | 4 | 3 | 5 | 4 | 4 | 4 | 5 | 3 | 4 | 36 | WHITE | Rating: 69.4 |
| Handicap | 7 | 17 | 3 | 9 | 15 | 11 | 5 | 13 | 1 | x | | Slope: 124 |
| RED | 331 | 101 | 439 | 300 | 232 | 252 | 420 | 109 | 333 | 2517 | | |
| Par | 4 | 3 | 5 | 4 | 4 | 4 | 5 | 3 | 4 | 36 | RED | Rating: 70.8 |
| Handicap | 5 | 15 | 1 | 13 | 11 | 9 | 3 | 17 | 7 | x | | Slope: 120 |

| Hole | 10 | 11 | 12 | 13 | 14 | 15 | 16 | 17 | 18 | In | Totals | |
|---|---|---|---|---|---|---|---|---|---|---|---|---|
| BLUE | 410 | 400 | 332 | 177 | 451 | 340 | 403 | 311 | 447 | 3271 | BLUE | 6501 |
| WHITE | 377 | 375 | 313 | 166 | 438 | 325 | 389 | 300 | 435 | 3118 | WHITE | 6025 |
| Par | 4 | 4 | 4 | 3 | 5 | 4 | 4 | 4 | 4 | 36 | Par | 72 |
| Handicap | 8 | 14 | 10 | 12 | 6 | 16 | 4 | 18 | 2 | x | | |
| RED | 364 | 313 | 265 | 102 | 410 | 259 | 385 | 250 | 402 | 2740 | RED | 5257 |
| Par | 4 | 4 | 4 | 3 | 5 | 4 | 4 | 4 | 5 | 37 | Par | 73 |
| Handicap | 8 | 10 | 12 | 18 | 2 | 14 | 6 | 16 | 4 | x | | |

# FOREST MEADOWS GOLF COURSE

**Course 4**
MAP E3 grid c6

**1971**
**Robert Trent Jones, Jr.**

Highway 4 Box 70
Murphys, CA 95247

Pro shop (209) 728-3439
Clubhouse (209) 728-3440

driving range
practice greens
✓ **power carts**
✓ **pull carts**
✓ **golf club rental**
locker rooms
showers
✓ **executive course**
✓ **accommodations**
✓ **food and beverages**
✓ **clubhouse**

**Debbie Lagomarsino**
Manager

**Norby Wilson**
Professional

**Ward Souza**
Superintendent

***Course information:*** This public course has 18 holes. Women's tees are rated 62.2 with a slope of 95 from the white tees. See card below for additional yardage and rating information.

***Play policy and fees:*** From October 1 through April 30, green fees are $14. From May 1 through September 30, green fees are $12 for nine holes and $20 for 18 holes. Carts are $20 for 18 holes. Reservations are recommended two weeks in advance. Shirts and shoes are required. No short shorts may be worn. This course is available for outside tournaments. Winter play is subject to weather conditions.

***Location:*** From Highway 99, drive east on Highway 4 to Murphys. The course is about 3.5 miles east of Murphys on Highway 4.

***Course description:*** This is a beautiful Sierra Nevada course traversed by the Stanislaus River Canyon. Situated at 3,500 feet, its panoramic layout mixes aesthetics and serious play and offers a challenge to low- and high-handicappers alike. Known for its excellent, fast greens, the course places a premium on putting. Mike Lane, a Northern California Gulf Association points champion, holds the course record with a 51.

| Hole | 1 | 2 | 3 | 4 | 5 | 6 | 7 | 8 | 9 | Out | BLUE | Rating: 58.3 |
|---|---|---|---|---|---|---|---|---|---|---|---|---|
| BLUE | 509 | 139 | 184 | 333 | 191 | 157 | 132 | 172 | 207 | 2024 | | Slope: 95 |
| WHITE | - | - | - | - | - | - | - | - | - | - | | |
| Par | 5 | 3 | 3 | 4 | 3 | 3 | 3 | 3 | 3 | 30 | WHITE | Rating: -- |
| Handicap | 1 | 15 | 11 | 3 | 5 | 13 | 17 | 9 | 7 | x | | Slope: -- |
| RED | 485 | 107 | 151 | 305 | 144 | 125 | 92 | 118 | 151 | 1678 | | |
| Par | 5 | 3 | 3 | 4 | 3 | 3 | 3 | 3 | 3 | 30 | RED | Rating: 58.0 |
| Handicap | 1 | 15 | 5 | 3 | 7 | 11 | 17 | 13 | 9 | x | | Slope: 90 |

| Hole | 10 | 11 | 12 | 13 | 14 | 15 | 16 | 17 | 18 | In | Totals | |
|---|---|---|---|---|---|---|---|---|---|---|---|---|
| BLUE | 351 | 119 | 120 | 130 | 102 | 195 | 366 | 149 | 330 | 1862 | BLUE | 3886 |
| WHITE | - | - | - | - | - | - | - | - | - | - | WHITE | -- |
| Par | 4 | 3 | 3 | 3 | 3 | 3 | 4 | 3 | 4 | 30 | Par | 60 |
| Handicap | 4 | 12 | 18 | 14 | 16 | 8 | 2 | 10 | 6 | x | | |
| RED | 318 | 90 | 84 | 108 | 77 | 141 | 318 | 112 | 295 | 1543 | RED | 3221 |
| Par | 4 | 3 | 3 | 3 | 3 | 3 | 4 | 3 | 4 | 30 | Par | 60 |
| Handicap | 4 | 14 | 16 | 12 | 18 | 8 | 2 | 10 | 6 | x | | |

# TWAIN HARTE GOLF AND COUNTRY CLUB

**Course 5**
MAP E3 grid d8

**1961**
**R.E. Baldock**
**Robert Dean Putman**

PO Box 333
Twain Harte, CA 95383

22909 Meadow Lane
Twain Harte, CA 95383

Pro shop (209) 586-3131

- driving range
- ✓ **practice greens**
- power carts
- ✓ **pull carts**
- ✓ **golf club rental**
- ✓ **locker rooms**
- showers
- ✓ **executive course**
- accommodations
- ✓ **food and beverages**
- ✓ **clubhouse**

**Tim Huber**
Manager/Professional

**Curtis Johnson**
Superintendent

*Course information:* This short semi-private course has nine holes. Par is 58 for 18 holes. The course is 3,436 yards and rated 57.1 for 18 holes from the championship tees, and 3,326 yards and rated 56.4 from the regular tees. The slope ratings are 88 championship and 87 regular. Women's tees are 3,514 yards and rated 61.0 for 18 holes from the championship tees, and 3,433 yards and rated 59.7 from the forward tees. The slope ratings are 98 championship and 92 forward.

*Play policy and fees:* Green fees are $10 for nine holes and $15 for 18 holes. Senior rates are $6 for nine holes and $10 for 18 holes Mondays only, and junior rates (under 16) are $5 and $8.

*Location:* From Highway 108 in Twain Harte (10 miles east of Sonora), turn left on Meadow Lane.

*Course description:* Plenty of trees make this executive course a challenge. There are two ponds. The best hole is number seven, a par-3 of 170 yards (it is a par-4 of 201 yards for women) into an elevated green with a large bunker in front. This is an excellent course for beginners in a setting all players can enjoy.

# SIERRA PINES GOLF COURSE

**Course 6**
MAP E3 grid d9

**1967**

PO Box 1013
Twain Harte, CA 95383

23736 South Fork Road
Twain Harte, CA 95383

Pro shop (209) 586-2118

- ✓ **driving range**
- ✓ **practice greens**
- ✓ **power carts**
- ✓ **pull carts**
- ✓ **golf club rental**
- locker rooms
- showers
- executive course
- accommodations
- ✓ **food and beverages**
- ✓ **clubhouse**

**MaryBeth Ryan**
Manager

*Course information:* This public course has nine holes. Par is 62 for 18 holes. The course is 4,400 yards and rated 61.1 for 18 holes from the regular tees. The slope rating is 94. Women's tees are 4,200 yards and rated 63.9. The slope rating is 104.

*Play policy and fees:* Green fees are $9 for nine holes and $12 for 18 holes weekdays, and $10 for nine holes and $14 for 18 holes weekends. Carts are $12 for nine holes and $16 for 18 holes. Reservations are recommended. This course is available for outside tournaments.

*Location:* From Highway 108, take the Twain Harte Drive exit and drive into Twain Harte. Drive one mile, making sure you pass under the arch. Drive straight through town and take the left fork in the road, which is South Fork Road. Follow South Fork to the course.

*Course description:* This is a challenging, but friendly course with a barbecue picnic area. Some of the greens are sloped, so study the course carefully. This hilly, mountain course is nestled in a valley with lots of trees. It's cool in the summer months. There is no charge for non-players.

# MOUNTAIN SPRINGS GOLF COURSE

**Course 7**
MAP E3 grid e6

**1990**
**Robert Muir Graves**

1000 Championship Drive
Sonora, CA 95370

Pro shop (209) 532-1000

- ✓ **driving range**
- ✓ **practice greens**
- ✓ **power carts**
- pull carts
- ✓ **golf club rental**
- ✓ **locker rooms**
- showers
- executive course
- accommodations
- ✓ **food and beverages**
- ✓ **clubhouse**

**Doug Wayne**
Professional

**Jim Smith**
Superintendent

***Course information:*** This semi-private course has 18 holes. The men's tees are 5760 yards and are rated 67.7 with a slope of 119 from the gold tees. See card below for additional yardage and rating information.

***Play policy and fees:*** Outside play is accepted. Green fees are $10 Mondays and Tuesdays, $15 Wednesday through Friday, and $24 weekends. There is a weekday senior citizen fee of $11. Carts are $18. Reservations are accepted one week in advance. This course is available for outside tournaments.

***Location:*** From Highway 108 in Sonora, turn right on Lime Kiln Road. Drive two and a half miles to the course entrance on the right.

***Course description:*** This rolling layout is located in the heart of the Gold Country and offers sweeping views. Six lakes and 70 bunkers come into play. Scenic vistas are afforded on the first, fifth, 10th, 15th and 17th holes. The pride of the course is the 200-yard, par-3 eighth hole across water, hitting to a narrow green with bunkers in the back with water up to the apron. This new course is maturing well.

| Hole | 1 | 2 | 3 | 4 | 5 | 6 | 7 | 8 | 9 | Out | BLUE | Rating: 71.9 |
|---|---|---|---|---|---|---|---|---|---|---|---|---|
| BLUE | 380 | 340 | 160 | 420 | 575 | 370 | 390 | 200 | 540 | 3375 | | Slope: 128 |
| WHITE | 365 | 320 | 135 | 400 | 550 | 360 | 370 | 170 | 520 | 3190 | | |
| Par | 4 | 4 | 3 | 4 | 5 | 4 | 4 | 3 | 5 | 36 | WHITE | Rating: 70.2 |
| Handicap | 13 | 17 | 15 | 1 | 3 | 5 | 11 | 7 | 9 | x | | Slope: 124 |
| RED | 320 | 280 | 105 | 320 | 475 | 310 | 300 | 105 | 475 | 2690 | | |
| Par | 4 | 4 | 3 | 4 | 5 | 4 | 4 | 3 | 5 | 36 | RED | Rating: 68.8 |
| Handicap | 5 | 9 | 17 | 7 | 3 | 11 | 13 | 15 | 1 | x | | Slope: 112 |

| Hole | 10 | 11 | 12 | 13 | 14 | 15 | 16 | 17 | 18 | In | Totals | |
|---|---|---|---|---|---|---|---|---|---|---|---|---|
| BLUE | 360 | 370 | 330 | 380 | 180 | 515 | 185 | 425 | 545 | 3290 | BLUE | 6665 |
| WHITE | 350 | 355 | 320 | 360 | 160 | 500 | 165 | 400 | 525 | 3135 | WHITE | 6325 |
| Par | 4 | 4 | 4 | 4 | 3 | 5 | 3 | 4 | 5 | 36 | Par | 72 |
| Handicap | 14 | 10 | 18 | 8 | 16 | 4 | 12 | 2 | 6 | x | | |
| RED | 270 | 310 | 300 | 305 | 100 | 335 | 110 | 330 | 445 | 2505 | RED | 5195 |
| Par | 4 | 4 | 4 | 4 | 3 | 4 | 3 | 4 | 5 | 35 | Par | 71 |
| Handicap | 10 | 8 | 14 | 12 | 18 | 4 | 16 | 6 | 2 | x | | |

## PHOENIX LAKE GOLF COURSE

Course 8
MAP E3 grid e7

1968
Bert Stamps

21448 Paseo de Los Portales
Sonora, CA 95370

Pro shop (209) 532-0111

- ✓ **driving range**
- ✓ **practice greens**
- ✓ **power carts**
- ✓ **pull carts**
- ✓ **golf club rental**
- locker rooms
- showers
- executive course
- accommodations
- ✓ **food and beverages**
- ✓ **clubhouse**

**Chris Bitticks**
Professional

**George Graul**
Superintendent

***Course information:*** This public facility has nine holes. Par is 70 for 18 holes. The course is 5,400 yards and rated 66.4 from the regular tees (18 holes). The slope rating is 115. Women's tees are 4,944 yards and rated 67.8. The slope rating is 114.

***Play policy and fees:*** Green fees are $9 for nine holes and $13 for 18 holes weekdays, and $9 for nine holes and $13 for 18 holes weekends. Carts are $9 for nine holes and $16 for 18 holes.

***Location:*** From Highway 108 in Sonora, take the Phoenix Lake Road exit left. The course is on the left on Paseo de Los Portales. The course is about three miles from Highway 108.

***Course description:*** The relatively short yardage of this course is deceptive since Phoenix Lake Golf Course is extremely narrow with pines and oaks lining the fairways. Only two holes run parallel to one another. Sullivan's Creek come into play on five holes. The second hole (par-4, 361 yards) requires a tee shot that carries 180 yards over the creek down a narrow fairway. The par-3 sixth hole is a bear, measuring 231 yards downhill.

## OAKDALE GOLF AND COUNTRY CLUB

Course 9
MAP E3 grid f3

1961
R. E. Baldock

243 North Stearns Road
Oakdale, CA 95361

Pro shop (209) 847-2924
Clubhouse (209) 847-2984

- ✓ **driving range**
- ✓ **practice greens**
- ✓ **power carts**
- ✓ **pull carts**
- ✓ **golf club rental**
- ✓ **locker rooms**
- ✓ **showers**
- executive course
- accommodations
- ✓ **food and beverages**
- ✓ **clubhouse**

**Jay D. Ward**
Professional

**Jack Darrow**
Superintendent

***Course information:*** This private course has 18 holes and par is 72. The course is 6,717 yards and rated 71.8 from the championship tees, and 6,445 yards and rated 70.6 from the regular tees. The slope ratings are 122 championship and 120 regular. Women's tees are 5,765 yards and rated 73.7. The slope rating is 125.

***Play policy and fees:*** Reciprocal play is accepted with members of other private clubs. Have your club pro call in advance for arrangements. Guest fees are $20 weekdays and $25 weekends when accompanied by a member. Guests must be accompanied by a member. Green fee for reciprocators is $40. Carts are $9 for nine holes and $16 for 18 holes.

***Location:*** Driving east on Highway 108, turn left on Stearns Road. The course is located north of Oakdale.

***Course description:*** Long and rolling, Oakdale Country Club is medium tight with average-sized greens. A number of the tee boxes and greens are elevated. The par-3 ninth is 200 yards downhill to a well-bunkered green with water on the right. Number five is a 600-yard par-5 that doglegs left with a large elevated green.

# PINE MOUNTAIN LAKE GOLF COURSE

**Course 10**
MAP E3 grid f8

**1969**
**William Francis Bell**

PO Box PMLA
Groveland, CA 95321

Mueller Drive
Groveland, CA 95321

Pro shop (209) 962-7471
Clubhouse (209) 962-7866

- ✓ **driving range**
- ✓ **practice greens**
- ✓ **power carts**
- pull carts
- ✓ **golf club rental**
- ✓ **locker rooms**
- showers
- executive course
- ✓ **accommodations**
- ✓ **food and beverages**
- ✓ **clubhouse**

**John Gray**
Manager

**Steve Caulkins**
Professional

**Kirk Golden**
Superintendent

***Course information:*** This private course has 18 holes. Women's tees are 5,355 yards and rated 70.8 with a slope of 128 from the gold tees. See card below for additional yardage and rating information.

***Play policy and fees:*** Reciprocal play is accepted with members of other private clubs. Property owners and their guests only. Green fees for reciprocators is $50. Guest green fees are $30. Carts are $22. Reservations should be made two weeks in advance.

***Location:*** From Interstate 5 in Manteca, take Highway 120 east to Groveland. The course is located north of Groveland on Mueller Drive.

***Course description:*** Pine Mountain Lake is a hilly course set at 3,500 feet. The fairways are outlined by trees and the greens are large with pronounced undulation. Hitting the driver straight is the key to scoring well here. The par-4 11th hole measures an outrageous 475 yards. It plays shorter, however, due to a 75-foot drop in elevation. Head pro Steve Caulkins holds the course record at 62.

| Hole | 1 | 2 | 3 | 4 | 5 | 6 | 7 | 8 | 9 | Out | | |
|---|---|---|---|---|---|---|---|---|---|---|---|---|
| BLUE | 406 | 325 | 189 | 471 | 430 | 406 | 189 | 360 | 310 | 3086 | BLUE | Rating: 70.6 |
| WHITE | 378 | 317 | 184 | 466 | 408 | 403 | 169 | 342 | 302 | 2969 | | Slope: 125 |
| Par | 4 | 4 | 3 | 5 | 4 | 4 | 3 | 4 | 4 | 35 | WHITE | Rating: 69.5 |
| Handicap | 11 | 13 | 15 | 5 | 3 | 1 | 9 | 7 | 17 | x | | Slope: 122 |
| RED | 364 | 315 | 173 | 450 | 391 | 398 | 144 | 346 | 295 | 2876 | | |
| Par | 4 | 4 | 3 | 5 | 4 | 5 | 3 | 4 | 4 | 35 | RED | Rating: 73.6 |
| Handicap | 9 | 5 | 17 | 1 | 3 | 7 | 15 | 11 | 13 | x | | Slope: 130 |

| Hole | 10 | 11 | 12 | 13 | 14 | 15 | 16 | 17 | 18 | In | Totals | |
|---|---|---|---|---|---|---|---|---|---|---|---|---|
| BLUE | 429 | 489 | 396 | 372 | 168 | 320 | 525 | 185 | 381 | 3265 | BLUE | 6351 |
| WHITE | 419 | 475 | 370 | 367 | 136 | 317 | 525 | 172 | 366 | 3147 | WHITE | 6116 |
| Par | 4 | 4 | 4 | 4 | 3 | 4 | 5 | 3 | 4 | 35 | Par | 70 |
| Handicap | 8 | 2 | 12 | 10 | 18 | 14 | 4 | 16 | 6 | x | | |
| RED | 417 | 410 | 364 | 331 | 127 | 305 | 439 | 158 | 343 | 2894 | RED | 5770 |
| Par | 4 | 4 | 4 | 4 | 3 | 4 | 5 | 3 | 4 | 35 | Par | 71 |
| Handicap | 8 | 10 | 4 | 12 | 18 | 14 | 2 | 16 | 6 | x | | |

# LAKE DON PEDRO GOLF AND COUNTRY CLUB

**Course 11**
MAP E3 grid h4

NORTHERN E3

**1970**
**William Francis Bell**

PO Box 193
La Grange, CA 95329

Ranchito Drive at Fachada
La Grange, CA 95329

Pro shop (209) 852-2242

- driving range
- ✓ **practice greens**
- ✓ **power carts**
- pull carts
- golf club rental
- ✓ **locker rooms**
- ✓ **showers**
- executive course
- accommodations
- ✓ **food and beverages**
- ✓ **clubhouse**

**Ray Claveran**
Manager/Professional

**John Michels**
Superintendent

***Course information:*** This semi-private course has 18 holes. See card below for yardage and rating information.

***Play policy and fees:*** Outside play is accepted. Green fees are $10 weekdays and $15 weekends. Carts are $18. Reservations are recommended one week in advance. This course is available for outside tournaments.

***Location:*** From Highway 99 in Modesto, drive 30 miles east on Highway 132 to La Grange. In six miles, exit on Hayward Road south and follow to the course to Fachada/Ranchito.

***Course description:*** Ninety nine percent of the players here ride carts since the course is quite hilly. There are a lot of semi-blind shots and even more sidehill, uphill and downhill lies. The eighth hole is a par-5 that measures 533 yards from the blues and 480 from the reds with two lakes to negotiate.

| Hole | 1 | 2 | 3 | 4 | 5 | 6 | 7 | 8 | 9 | Out | | |
|---|---|---|---|---|---|---|---|---|---|---|---|---|
| BLUE | 367 | 470 | 365 | 351 | 185 | 343 | 246 | 533 | 315 | 3175 | BLUE | Rating: 68.6 |
| WHITE | 361 | 457 | 358 | 340 | 176 | 335 | 207 | 501 | 305 | 3040 | | Slope: 112 |
| Par | 4 | 5 | 4 | 4 | 3 | 4 | 3 | 5 | 4 | 36 | WHITE | Rating: 67.4 |
| Handicap | 7 | 17 | 5 | 11 | 13 | 9 | 3 | 1 | 15 | x | | Slope: 110 |
| RED | 311 | 450 | 325 | 326 | 145 | 321 | 154 | 480 | 300 | 2812 | | |
| Par | 4 | 5 | 4 | 4 | 3 | 4 | 3 | 5 | 4 | 36 | RED | Rating: 70.7 |
| Handicap | 11 | 3 | 7 | 9 | 17 | 5 | 15 | 1 | 13 | x | | Slope: 112 |

| Hole | 10 | 11 | 12 | 13 | 14 | 15 | 16 | 17 | 18 | In | Totals | |
|---|---|---|---|---|---|---|---|---|---|---|---|---|
| BLUE | 206 | 472 | 365 | 391 | 402 | 190 | 402 | 533 | 175 | 3156 | BLUE | 6311 |
| WHITE | 194 | 462 | 350 | 384 | 392 | 176 | 393 | 522 | 156 | 3092 | WHITE | 6069 |
| Par | 3 | 5 | 4 | 4 | 4 | 3 | 4 | 5 | 3 | 35 | Par | 71 |
| Handicap | 2 | 4 | 12 | 10 | 6 | 16 | 8 | 14 | 18 | x | | |
| RED | 168 | 412 | 315 | 346 | 375 | 126 | 411 | 482 | 121 | 2756 | RED | 5568 |
| Par | 3 | 5 | 4 | 4 | 4 | 3 | 5 | 5 | 3 | 36 | Par | 72 |
| Handicap | 14 | 8 | 12 | 10 | 6 | 16 | 4 | 2 | 18 | x | | |

# TURLOCK GOLF AND COUNTRY CLUB

**Course 12**
MAP E3 grid i0

**1959**
**Robert Dean Putman**

PO Box X
Turlock, CA 95381

10532 North Golf Links Rd.
Turlock, CA 95380

Pro shop (209) 634-4976
Clubhouse (209) 634-5471

- ✓ **driving range**
- ✓ **practice greens**
- ✓ **power carts**
- ✓ **pull carts**
- golf club rental
- ✓ **locker rooms**
- ✓ **showers**
- executive course
- accommodations
- ✓ **food and beverages**
- ✓ **clubhouse**

**Barry Bremmer**
Manager

**Shane Balfour**
Professional

**Dave Rodriguez**
Superintendent

***Course information:*** This private course has 18 holes. See card below for yardage and rating information.

***Play policy and fees:*** Reciprocal play is accepted with members of other private clubs. Reciprocal fees are $40. Guest fees are $30. Carts are $20.

***Location:*** From Highway 99 south in Turlock, exit on Lander Avenue south and turn left on Bradbury. Turn right onto Golf Links Road and drive to the course.

***Course description:*** This flat course is deceiving. It's tight and the rough is difficult. The 14th hole is a rugged test. At 365 yards, this par-4 requires a carry over water and then doglegs 90 degrees. It's primarily a placement course with tricky greens. The California State Amateur Qualifying was held here in 1991.

| Hole | 1 | 2 | 3 | 4 | 5 | 6 | 7 | 8 | 9 | Out | BLUE | Rating: 71.9 |
|---|---|---|---|---|---|---|---|---|---|---|---|---|
| BLUE | 424 | 492 | 431 | 202 | 509 | 436 | 179 | 379 | 286 | 3338 | | Slope: 123 |
| WHITE | 407 | 482 | 420 | 184 | 495 | 422 | 152 | 368 | 260 | 3190 | | |
| Par | 4 | 5 | 4 | 3 | 5 | 4 | 3 | 4 | 4 | 36 | WHITE | Rating: 70.6 |
| Handicap | 3 | 9 | 1 | 13 | 11 | 5 | 15 | 7 | 17 | x | | Slope: 121 |
| RED | 385 | 449 | 409 | 171 | 483 | 358 | 124 | 311 | 228 | 2918 | | |
| Par | 4 | 5 | 5 | 3 | 5 | 4 | 3 | 4 | 4 | 37 | RED | Rating: 73.4 |
| Handicap | 3 | 5 | 9 | 13 | 1 | 7 | 17 | 11 | 15 | x | | Slope: 129 |

| Hole | 10 | 11 | 12 | 13 | 14 | 15 | 16 | 17 | 18 | In | Totals | |
|---|---|---|---|---|---|---|---|---|---|---|---|---|
| BLUE | 368 | 191 | 382 | 480 | 365 | 219 | 479 | 432 | 400 | 3316 | BLUE | 6654 |
| WHITE | 356 | 158 | 354 | 471 | 347 | 204 | 475 | 424 | 389 | 3178 | WHITE | 6368 |
| Par | 4 | 3 | 4 | 5 | 4 | 3 | 5 | 4 | 4 | 36 | Par | 72 |
| Handicap | 10 | 18 | 4 | 16 | 6 | 12 | 14 | 2 | 8 | x | | |
| RED | 324 | 142 | 334 | 450 | 297 | 184 | 426 | 412 | 319 | 2888 | RED | 5806 |
| Par | 4 | 3 | 4 | 5 | 4 | 3 | 5 | 5 | 4 | 37 | Par | 74 |
| Handicap | 10 | 18 | 8 | 4 | 6 | 16 | 2 | 12 | 14 | x | | |

# POQUITO LAKE GOLF AND COUNTRY CLUB

**Course 13**
MAP E3 grid i0

**1978**

PO Box 268
Hilmar, CA 95324

19920 West First Street
Hilmar, CA 95324

Pro shop (209) 668-2255
Lounge (209) 668-3825

- driving range
- ✓ **practice greens**
- ✓ **power carts**
- ✓ **pull carts**
- ✓ **golf club rental**
- locker rooms
- showers
- ✓ **executive course**
- accommodations
- ✓ **food and beverages**
- ✓ **clubhouse**

**Bill Garcia**
President

**Ralph Garcia**
Manager/Professional
Superintendent

*Course information:* This public course has nine holes. Par is 58 for 18 holes. The course is 3,000 yards for nine holes from the regular tees with a 55.0 rating and 82 slope. Women's yardages are the same..

*Play policy and fees:* Green fees are $5 for nine holes and $8 for 18 holes weekdays, and $7 for nine holes and $10 for 18 holes weekends. Green fees for seniors and juniors are $5 for nine holes and $9 for 18 holes weekdays, and $6 for nine holes and $11 for 18 holes weekends. Reservations are recommended. This course is available for tournaments.

*Location:* From Highway 99 south of Turlock, take the Lander Avenue exit. Turn on First Street and drive to the course. It's right next door to the Hilmar Post Office.

*Course description:* This course reopened August 15, 1991 after a two-year closure. It was formerly known as Golden Valley Golf Course. It has undergone a complete renovation of greens and fairways. New bunkers have been added. There are 12 different species of mature trees, including coast redwoods, Italian stonepine, Canary Island pine and, of course, Monterey pine. This course is flat, tight and narrow. There are two par-4s and lots of water. It's tough to shoot par here. The course records of 25 for nine holes and 54 for 18 holes are held by George Buzzini. Several local tournaments are held at this course annually. This course is considered one of best maintained courses in the San Joaquin Valley.

# RANCHO DEL REY GOLF COURSE

**Course 14**
MAP E3 grid j3

**1963**
5250 Green Sands Avenue
Atwater, CA 95301

Pro shop (209) 358-7131
Clubhouse (209) 358-0024

- ✓ **driving range**
- ✓ **practice greens**
- ✓ **power carts**
- ✓ **pull carts**
- ✓ **golf club rental**
- locker rooms
- showers
- executive course
- accommodations
- ✓ **food and beverages**
- ✓ **clubhouse**

**Bob Riechel**
Manager

**Jack Brink**
Superintendent

***Course information:*** This public course has 18 holes and par is 72. The course is 6,712 yards and rated 71.8 from the championship tees, and 6,262 yards and rated 69.7 from the regular tees. The slope ratings are 119 championship and 115 regular. Women's tees are 5,856 yards and rated 71.9. The slope rating is 125. Par for women is 75.

***Play policy and fees:*** Green fees are $9 for nine holes and $16 for 18 holes weekdays, and $11 for nine holes and $20 for 18 holes weekends. Twilight rates begin at noon and are $7 for nine holes and $11 for 18 holes weekdays, and $8 nine holes and $13 for 18 holes weekends. Carts are $10 for nine holes and $18 for 18 holes. Tee times are made Monday to Monday. Shirts must be worn at all times. This course is available for outside tournaments.

***Location:*** From Highway 99 in Atwater, exit north onto Bucharch Road. Then turn left on Green Sands Avenue and follow it to the course.

***Course description:*** This course is mostly flat lots of trees and water. The signature hole is number 17, a par-3 of 160 yards from the white tees with two willows and large bunkers framing the green. The course record of 63 is held by Pete Culver.

MAP ON PAGE 292

# MAP E4
(1 COURSE)

PAGES.. 306-307

NOR-CAL MAP.....see page 30
adjoining maps
NORTH (D4).......see page 174
EAST (E5)..........see page 308
SOUTH (F4) .......see page 358
WEST (E3)..........see page 292

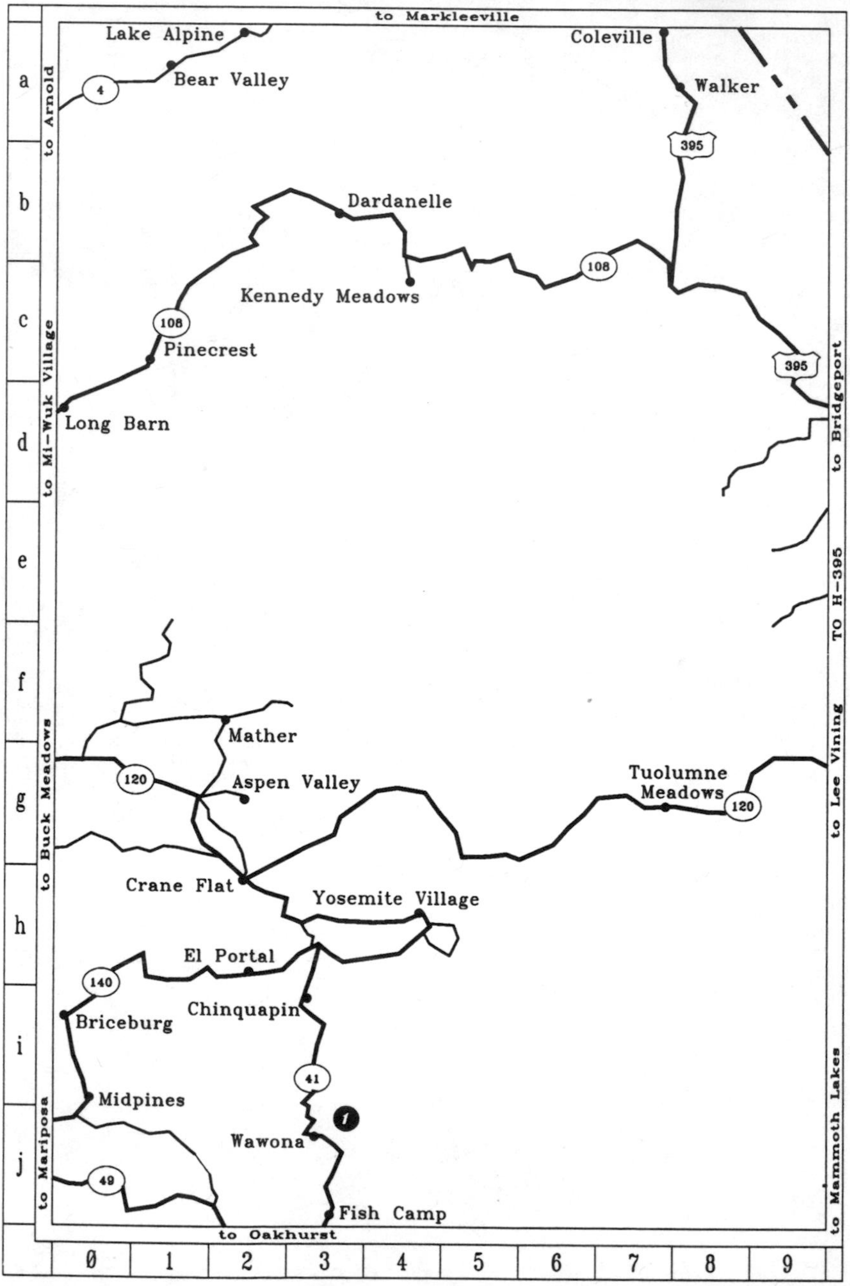

to Markleeville
Lake Alpine
Bear Valley
4
to Arnold
Coleville
Walker
395
Dardanelle
108
Kennedy Meadows
108
Pinecrest
Long Barn
to Mi-Wuk Village
395
to Bridgeport
TO H-395
Mather
120
Aspen Valley
Tuolumne Meadows
120
to Lee Vining
to Buck Meadows
Crane Flat
Yosemite Village
El Portal
140
Briceburg
Chinquapin
41
Midpines
1
Wawona
49
to Mariposa
Fish Camp
to Oakhurst
to Mammoth Lakes

a b c d e f g h i j

0 1 2 3 4 5 6 7 8 9

# WAWONA HOTEL GOLF COURSE

**Course 1**
MAP E4 grid j3

**1918**
**Alister MacKenzie**

PO Box 2005
Yosemite National Park
CA 95389

Highway 41
Yosemite National Park
CA 95389

Pro shop (209) 375-6572

- driving range
- ✓ **practice greens**
- ✓ **power carts**
- ✓ **pull carts**
- ✓ **golf club rental**
- ✓ **locker rooms**
- ✓ **showers**
- executive course
- ✓ **accommodations**
- ✓ **food and beverages**
- clubhouse

**Sam Winstead**
Manager

**Kim Porter**
Superintendent

***Course information:*** This public course has nine holes. See card below for yardage and rating information.

***Play policy and fees:*** Green fees are $12 for nine holes and $17.25 for 18 holes. Carts are $10 for nine holes and $15 for 18 holes. Reservations are recommended during the entire season. Guests of the Wawona Hotel should make golf reservations at the same time they make room reservations. The course is open April 1 to November 1.

***Location:*** This course is located between Oakhurst and Yosemite on Highway 41 on the south end of the park.

***Course description:*** This is a short, scenic course in Yosemite National Park. There are lots of redwood trees, and the course is well maintained. Deer and other wildlife abound. The adjacent Wawona Hotel is a wonderful place to stay and dine. Wawona Golf Course is one of numerous Northern California courses designed by Scottish architectural giant Alister MacKenzie.

| Hole | 1 | 2 | 3 | 4 | 5 | 6 | 7 | 8 | 9 | Out | BLUE | Rating: -- |
|---|---|---|---|---|---|---|---|---|---|---|---|---|
| BLUE | - | - | - | - | - | - | - | - | - | | | Slope: -- |
| WHITE | 464 | 229 | 470 | 393 | 349 | 185 | 402 | 167 | 358 | 3017 | | |
| Par | 5 | 3 | 5 | 4 | 4 | 3 | 4 | 3 | 4 | 35 | WHITE | Rating: 69.1 |
| Handicap | 11 | 5 | 15 | 7 | 3 | 13 | 1 | 17 | 9 | x | | Slope: 117 |
| RED | 394 | 183 | 457 | 366 | 339 | 157 | 385 | 113 | 329 | 2723 | | |
| Par | 5 | 3 | 5 | 4 | 4 | 3 | 4 | 3 | 4 | 35 | RED | Rating: 70.9 |
| Handicap | 3 | 13 | 1 | 9 | 7 | 15 | 5 | 17 | 11 | x | | Slope: 119 |

| Hole | 10 | 11 | 12 | 13 | 14 | 15 | 16 | 17 | 18 | In | Totals | |
|---|---|---|---|---|---|---|---|---|---|---|---|---|
| BLUE | - | - | - | - | - | - | - | - | - | - | BLUE | -- |
| WHITE | 474 | 217 | 479 | 380 | 353 | 154 | 417 | 153 | 371 | 2998 | WHITE | 6015 |
| Par | 5 | 3 | 5 | 4 | 4 | 3 | 4 | 3 | 4 | 35 | Par | 70 |
| Handicap | 12 | 8 | 14 | 6 | 4 | 16 | 2 | 18 | 10 | x | | |
| RED | 429 | 223 | 444 | 375 | 350 | 154 | 355 | 135 | 318 | 2783 | RED | 5506 |
| Par | 5 | 4 | 5 | 4 | 4 | 3 | 4 | 3 | 4 | 36 | Par | 71 |
| Handicap | 4 | 14 | 2 | 10 | 8 | 16 | 6 | 18 | 12 | x | | |

# MAP E5

(1 COURSE)

PAGES.. 308-309

NOR-CAL MAP.....see page 30
adjoining maps
NORTH ..........................no map
EAST ............................no map
SOUTH (F5) .......see page 372
WEST (E4).........see page 306

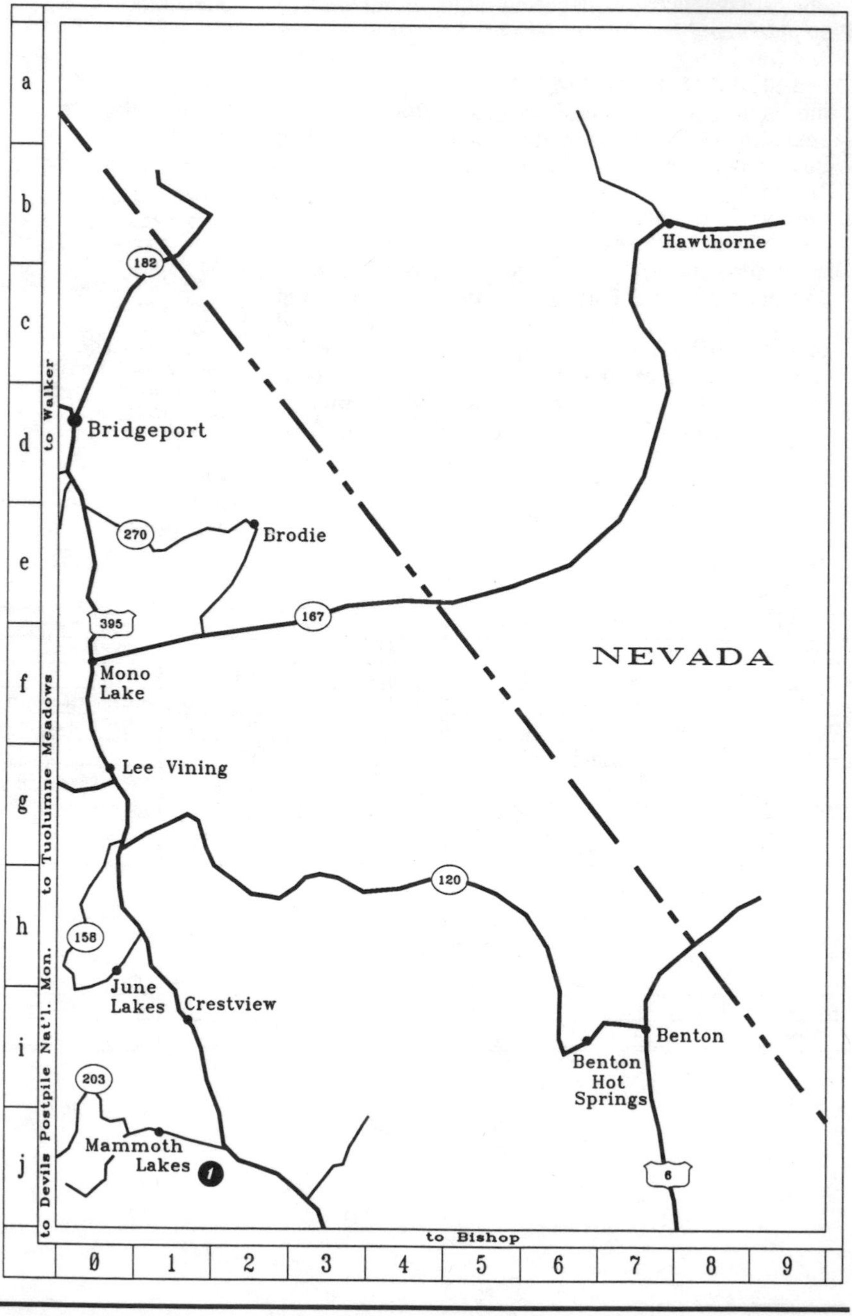

# SNOWCREEK GOLF COURSE

**Course 1**
MAP E5 grid j1

*Course information:* This semi-private facility is nine holes. Men's tees are 6,510 yards and are rated 70.5 with a slope of 118 from the black tees. See card below for additonal yardage and rating information.

*Play policy and fees:* Green fees are $20 for nine holes and $30 for 18 holes weekdays, and $25 for nine holes and $35 for 18 holes weekends. Carts are $7 per person for nine holes and $10 per person for 18 holes. Reservations are recommended one week in advance. This course is available for outside tournaments. The course is open from Memorial Day Weekend through mid-October.

*Location:* From Highway 395, take Highway 203 west to Old Mammoth Road. Turn left on Old Mammoth Road and drive about one mile to the course. The course is on the left side.

*Course description:* Golfers tend to be overcome by the scenery, but the course itself is also an eyeful. The fairways are narrow and water comes into play on nearly every hole. The greens are relatively large for a course of this distance, which is a plus factor. There are plans to expand the course to 18 holes, and with the expansion the course will balloon to over 7,000 yards from the back tees. At an elevation of 7,800 feet, it promises to be one incredible challenge. Of course, at that elevation there is a one to one-and-a-half club difference over the typical Greater Los Angeles course. There are plenty of condos at Mammonth Lakes, including some which overlook the course.

**1991**
**Ted Robinson**

PO Box 569
Mammoth Lakes, CA 93546

Old Mammoth Road
Mammoth Lakes, CA 93546

Pro shop (619) 934-6633

- ✓ **driving range**
- ✓ **practice greens**
- ✓ **power carts**
- ✓ **pull carts**
- ✓ **golf club rental**
- locker rooms
- showers
- executive course
- accommodations
- ✓ **food and beverages**
- ✓ **clubhouse**

**Tim Standifer**
General Manager

**Kristine McCue**
Head Professional

| Hole | 1 | 2 | 3 | 4 | 5 | 6 | 7 | 8 | 9 | Out | | |
|---|---|---|---|---|---|---|---|---|---|---|---|---|
| BLUE | 538 | 397 | 173 | 350 | 330 | 430 | 155 | 391 | 334 | 3098 | BLUE | Rating: 69.1 |
| WHITE | 515 | 370 | 149 | 335 | 320 | 401 | 145 | 375 | 315 | 2925 | | Slope: 115 |
| Par | 5 | 4 | 3 | 4 | 4 | 4 | 3 | 4 | 4 | 35 | WHITE | Rating: 67.5 |
| Handicap | 4 | 1 | 3 | 6 | 9 | 5 | 8 | 2 | 7 | x | | Slope: 112 |
| RED | 480 | 293 | 128 | 323 | 310 | 344 | 131 | 328 | 285 | 2622 | | |
| Par | 5 | 4 | 3 | 4 | 4 | 4 | 3 | 4 | 4 | 35 | RED | Rating: 69.2 |
| Handicap | 4 | 1 | 3 | 6 | 9 | 5 | 8 | 2 | 7 | x | | Slope: 114 |

| Hole | 10 | 11 | 12 | 13 | 14 | 15 | 16 | 17 | 18 | In | Totals | |
|---|---|---|---|---|---|---|---|---|---|---|---|---|
| BLUE | 538 | 397 | 173 | 350 | 330 | 430 | 155 | 391 | 334 | 3098 | BLUE | 6196 |
| WHITE | 515 | 370 | 149 | 335 | 320 | 401 | 145 | 375 | 315 | 2925 | WHITE | 5850 |
| Par | 5 | 4 | 3 | 4 | 4 | 4 | 3 | 4 | 4 | 35 | Par | 70 |
| Handicap | 4 | 1 | 3 | 6 | 9 | 5 | 8 | 2 | 7 | x | | |
| RED | 480 | 293 | 128 | 323 | 310 | 344 | 131 | 328 | 285 | 2622 | RED | 5244 |
| Par | 5 | 4 | 3 | 4 | 4 | 4 | 3 | 4 | 4 | 35 | Par | 70 |
| Handicap | 4 | 1 | 3 | 6 | 9 | 5 | 8 | 2 | 7 | x | | |

# Central California Golf Courses

# CENTRAL CALIFORNIA COURSES

As soon as you declare that within the boundaries of Central California is Monterey Bay, it immediately becomes tempting to lump the entire region under one big golf heading: Pebble Beach.

True, Pebble Beach and her golf courses are the best-known of the region. And it's hard to argue against the supremacy of her tracts. Between Pebble Beach, Cypress Point, Spanish Bay and Poppy Hills, you get just about everything you could ask for: magnificent, challenging, well-maintained courses which fall into everybody's playing category—public, private and resort.

You want diversity of style? From the slick thumbnails that Pebble Beach has for greens to the rolling Scottish links of Spanish Bay, to the more open, free swinging American styling of Poppy Hills, you get extreme diversity. And all in top-notch condition.

But by no means is Pebble all that Central California has to offer. Because as you look inland, at the burgeoning Fresno area—and in fact much of the San Joaquin Valley—new courses are beginning to sprout up. This growth spurt in the central valley of the state can be fairly easily attributed to the favorable climate, availability of land at reasonable prices, and relative ease of permitting.

If crowds don't scare you away, try Morro Bay Golf Course. Called "the Poor Man's Pebble Beach," this delightful tract features ocean views on almost every hole—for only $15 per round! No wonder it's also one of the busiest courses in the state.

Santa Barbara offers classic courses such as the private 1929 Alister MacKenzie layout at The Valley Club of Montecito, as well as an abundance of public courses such as the scenic and popular La Purisima Golf Course, a 1986 Robert Muir Graves design.

Add to the mix the unusual Furnace Creek Golf Course in Death Valley—one of the lowest courses in the world at 214 feet below sea level—and it becomes abundantly clear that Central California provides golf courses of all ilk and trial.

# CEN-CAL BY AREA

**(MAP, COURSES, PAGE)**



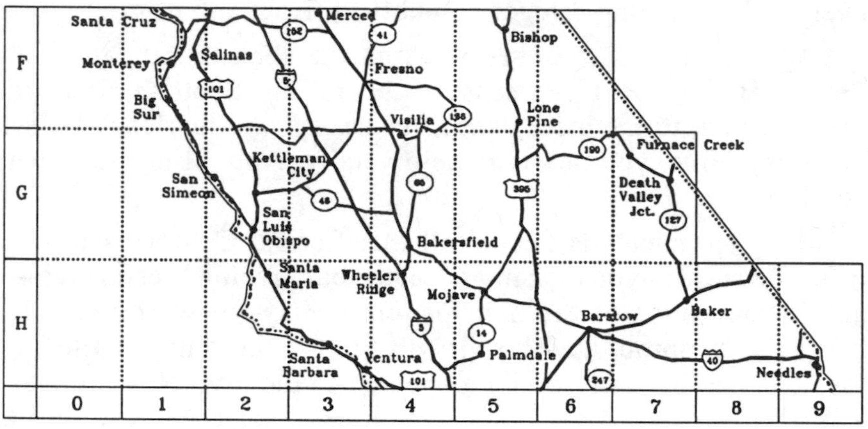

# CEN-CAL BY CITY
## (CITY and MAP PAGE)



CENTRAL

# MAP F1

(28 COURSES)

PAGES.. 316-343

CEN-CAL MAP...see page 256
adjoining maps
NORTH (E1).......see page 184
EAST (F2)..........see page 344
SOUTH.........................no map
WEST...........................no map

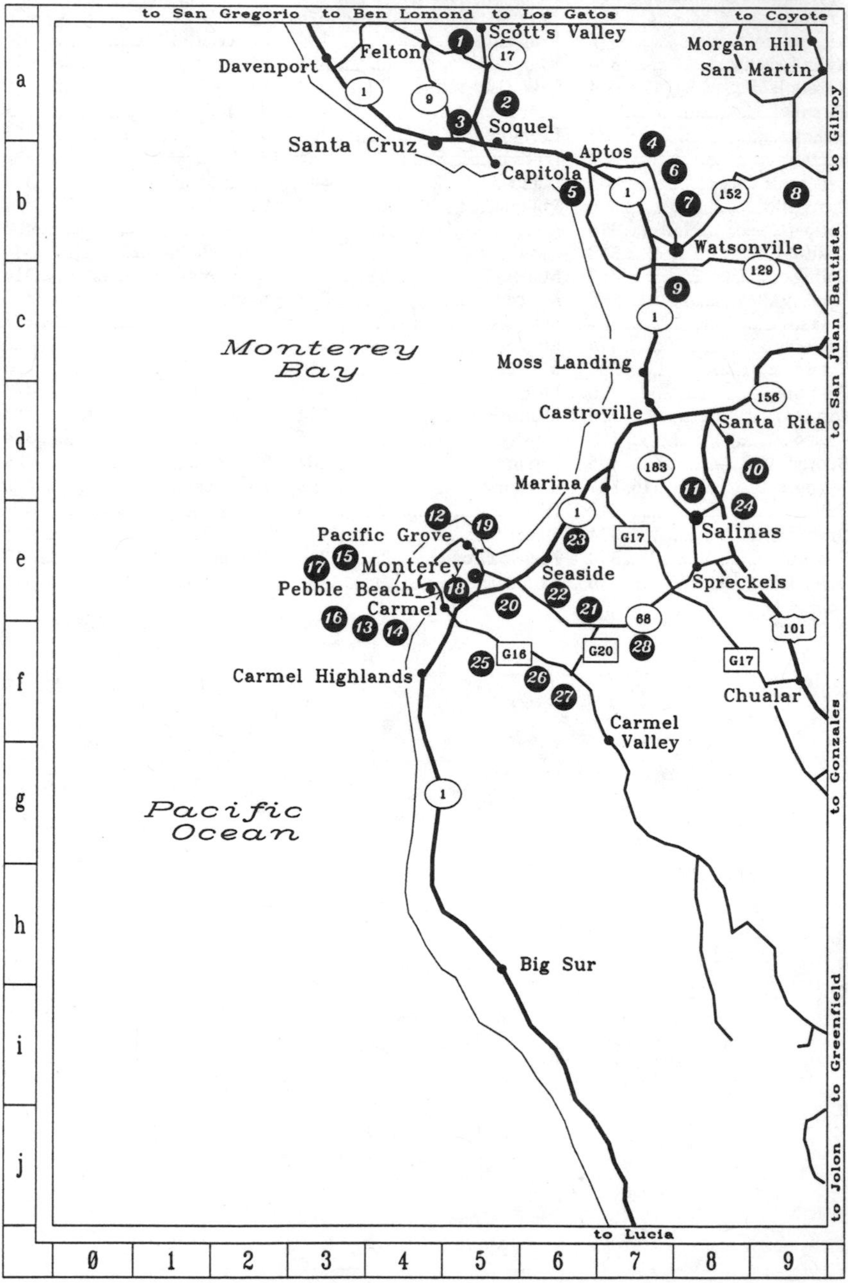

to San Gregorio to Ben Lomond to Los Gatos

to Coyote

Scott's Valley

Felton

Davenport

Morgan Hill

San Martin

to Gilroy

Soquel

Santa Cruz

Aptos

Capitola

Watsonville

to San Juan Bautista

Monterey Bay

Moss Landing

Castroville

Santa Rita

Marina

Pacific Grove

Monterey

Pebble Beach

Carmel

Seaside

Salinas

Spreckels

Carmel Highlands

Chualar

Carmel Valley

to Gonzales

Pacific Ocean

Big Sur

to Greenfield

to Jolon

to Lucia

1 9 17 1 152 129 1 156 183 1 G17 68 101 G16 G20 G17 1

1 2 3 4 5 6 7 8 9 10 11 12 13 14 15 16 17 18 19 20 21 22 23 24 25 26 27 28

a b c d e f g h i j

0 1 2 3 4 5 6 7 8 9

# VALLEY GARDENS GOLF COURSE

**Course 1**
MAP F1 grid a5

**1971**
**R.E. Baldock**

263 Mount Hermon Road
Scotts Valley, CA 95066

Pro shop (408) 438-3058

- driving range
- ✓ **practice greens**
- power carts
- ✓ **pull carts**
- ✓ **golf club rental**
- locker rooms
- showers
- ✓ **executive course**
- accommodations
- ✓ **food and beverages**
- ✓ **clubhouse**

**Jerry Imel**
Director of Golf/Pro

**Sandy Woodruff**
Owner

**Pat Voeks**
Superintendent

*Course information:* This public course has nine holes. Par is 62 for 18 holes. The course is 3,530 yards and rated 54.1 for 18 holes from the regular tees. The slope rating is 82. Women's tees are 3,114 yards and rated 57.4 for 18 holes. The slope rating is 85.

*Play policy and fees:* Green fees are $8 weekdays and $9 weekends for nine holes. Reservations are recommended one week in advance.

*Location:* From Highway 17 in Scotts Valley, drive one mile west on Mount Hermon Road.

*Course description:* This course is short, tight and flat. There are 27 different varieties of trees that come into play, which adds up to a lot of trees. Beginners, juniors and seniors will find it an excellent layout. The layout is in super shape. Jerry Imel holds the course record with a 26.



# DE LAVEAGA GOLF COURSE

**Course 2**
MAP F1 grid a5

**1970**
**Bert Stamps**

401 Upper Park Road, Box A
Santa Cruz, CA 95065

Pro shop (408) 423-7212

- ✓ **driving range**
- ✓ **practice greens**
- ✓ **power carts**
- ✓ **pull carts**
- ✓ **golf club rental**
- locker rooms
- showers
- executive course
- accommodations
- ✓ **food and beverages**
- ✓ **clubhouse**

**Gary Loustalot**
Professional

**Don Paul**
Superintendent

*Course information:* This public layout has 18 holes and par is 72. The course is 6,010 yards and rated 70.1 from the regular tees. The slope rating is 130. Women's tees are 5,331 yards and rated 70.6 from the forward tees. The slope rating is 125.

*Play policy and fees:* Green fees are $22 weekdays and $30 weekends. Twilight rates are $14 weekdays and $18.50 weekends. Carts are $22 with a $3 deposit.

*Location:* From San Francisco, take Interstate 280 to Highway 17 toward Santa Cruz. Take Highway 1 south to the Morrisey exit. Turn right on Fairmount and right on Branciforte Drive. Turn right again on Upper Park Road and proceed to the course.

*Course description:* This tight, rolling course in the Santa Cruz mountains has lateral hazards on nearly every hole. Staying on the fairways off the tee is vital. The course may give the appearance of birdie opportunities, but they don't come easily. The Santa Cruz City Championships were held here in 1992. The men's course record of 64 is held jointly by brothers Tim and Michael Loustalot, sons of host pro, Gary.

# PASATIEMPO GOLF COURSE

**Course 3**
MAP F1 grid a5

***Course information:*** This semi-private course has 18 holes. See card below for yardage and rating information.

***Play policy and fees:*** Outside play is accepted. Green fees are $75 Monday through Thursday, and $85 Friday through Sunday and holidays. Optional carts are $27. Reservations are recommended. To reserve a weekday tee time call one week before, and call on Monday at 10 a.m. for the coming weekend. Appropriate golf attire required. Rubber studded shoes are not allowed. This course is available for outside tournaments.

***Location:*** From San Francisco, drive south on Interstate 280. Take Highway 17 toward Santa Cruz. Exit on Pasatiempo and follow the signs to the course.

***Course description:*** This course was designed by Alister MacKenzie, creator of Cypress Point and Augusta National. It opened in 1929 and still ranks as one of the best in the nation. The par-4, 395-yard number 16 was Alister MacKenzie's "favorite hole in golf." It's a blind driving hole, hitting across a creek to a three-tiered green. There are hazards and out-of-bounds on both sides of the fairway, which doglegs to the left. There's not much choice of route on this hole. Play it right-center on the drive to take advantage of a fairway that breaks back to the left. This was the site of the 1986 U.S. Women's Amateur and the annual Western Intercollegiate. The course overlooks the Pacific Ocean and Monterey Bay. The men's course record of 63 is held by Ken Venturi, Brian Pini, and Forrest Fezler. The women's record is 70, held by Sandy Woodruff.

**1929**
**Alister MacKenzie**

PO Box 535
Santa Cruz, CA 95060

18 Clubhouse Road
Santa Cruz, CA 95060

Pro shop (408) 459-9155

- ✓ **driving range**
- ✓ **practice greens**
- ✓ **power carts**
- ✓ **pull carts**
- ✓ **golf club rental**
- ✓ **locker rooms**
- ✓ **showers**
- executive course
- accommodations
- ✓ **food and beverages**
- ✓ **clubhouse**

**Shawn McEntee**
Professional

**Dean Gump**
Superintendent

| Hole | 1 | 2 | 3 | 4 | 5 | 6 | 7 | 8 | 9 | Out | BLUE | Rating: 72.9 |
|---|---|---|---|---|---|---|---|---|---|---|---|---|
| BLUE | 504 | 442 | 217 | 395 | 191 | 521 | 346 | 177 | 489 | 3282 | | Slope: 138 |
| WHITE | 466 | 417 | 203 | 362 | 177 | 502 | 335 | 163 | 466 | 3091 | | |
| Par | 5 | 4 | 3 | 4 | 3 | 5 | 4 | 3 | 5 | 36 | WHITE | Rating: 71.4 |
| Handicap | 18 | 8 | 2 | 12 | 6 | 14 | 4 | 10 | 16 | x | | Slope: 134 |
| RED | 458 | 378 | 175 | 320 | 156 | 486 | 327 | 150 | 415 | 2865 | | |
| Par | 5 | 4 | 3 | 4 | 3 | 5 | 4 | 3 | 5 | 36 | RED | Rating: 72.9 |
| Handicap | 8 | 10 | 14 | 12 | 16 | 2 | 6 | 18 | 4 | x | | Slope: 133 |

| Hole | 10 | 11 | 12 | 13 | 14 | 15 | 16 | 17 | 18 | In | Totals | |
|---|---|---|---|---|---|---|---|---|---|---|---|---|
| BLUE | 444 | 384 | 376 | 492 | 426 | 145 | 395 | 366 | 173 | 3201 | BLUE | 6483 |
| WHITE | 440 | 375 | 372 | 478 | 390 | 125 | 372 | 354 | 157 | 3063 | WHITE | 6154 |
| Par | 4 | 4 | 4 | 5 | 4 | 3 | 4 | 4 | 3 | 35 | Par | 71 |
| Handicap | 5 | 3 | 13 | 17 | 9 | 15 | 1 | 7 | 11 | x | | |
| RED | 440 | 331 | 371 | 447 | 331 | 96 | 353 | 345 | 88 | 2782 | RED | 5647 |
| Par | 5 | 4 | 4 | 5 | 4 | 3 | 4 | 4 | 3 | 36 | Par | 72 |
| Handicap | 5 | 1 | 11 | 7 | 13 | 17 | 3 | 9 | 15 | x | | |

# APTOS PAR-3 GOLF COURSE

**Course 4**
MAP F1 grid b6

***Course information:*** This public course has nine holes. Par is 27. The course is 1,044 yards for nine holes. All play is from the same tees. The course is unrated.

***Play policy and fees:*** Green fees are $5 for nine holes. Reservations are recommended one day in advance.

***Location:*** This course is located off Highway 1 in Aptos. Take the Park Avenue exit and drive under the freeway toward the hills. Turn right at the first stop sign at Soquel Drive. Drive past the fire station and proceed to the telephone pole which is handily marked "golf." Turn right and continue to the course.

***Course description:*** This short, par-3 course is flat and open. It's excellent for beginners or players trying to sharpen their iron play. It takes about an hour and a half to get nine holes in. The men's record is 22.

**1962**
2600 Mar Vista Drive
Aptos, CA 95003

Pro shop (408) 688-5000

- ✓ **driving range**
- ✓ **practice greens**
- power carts
- ✓ **pull carts**
- ✓ **golf club rental**
- locker rooms
- showers
- executive course
- accommodations
- ✓ **food and beverages**
- clubhouse

## APTOS SEASCAPE GOLF COURSE

**Course 5**
MAP F1 grid b6

**1927**
610 Clubhouse Drive
Aptos, CA 95003

Pro shop (408) 688-3214
Clubhouse (408) 688-3254

- ✓ **driving range**
- ✓ **practice greens**
- ✓ **power carts**
- ✓ **pull carts**
- ✓ **golf club rental**
- ✓ **locker rooms**
- ✓ **showers**
- executive course
- accommodations
- ✓ **food and beverages**
- ✓ **clubhouse**

**Bruce Pluim**
General Manager

**Don Elser**
Professional

**Mike McCraw**
Superintendent

***Course information:*** This public course has 18 holes. See card below for yardage and rating information.

***Play policy and fees:*** Green fees November through March are $27 weekdays and $45 weekends and holidays. Rates after 1 p.m. are $20 weekdays and $30 weekends and holidays. Super twilight rates after 3 p.m. are $12 weekdays and $17 weekends. Green fees October through April are $32 weekdays and $30 weekends and holidays. Twilight rates after 3 p.m. are $22 weekdays and $33 weekends and holidays. Twilight rates after 5 p.m. are $14 weekdays and $20 weekends and holidays. Rates are subject to change April 1, 1993. Carts are $14 for nine holes and $23 for 18 holes. Reservations are recommended one week in advance for weekday play and the Monday prior at 10 a.m. for weekend and holiday play. This course is available for outside tournaments.

***Location:*** From Santa Cruz, drive seven miles south on Highway 1. Exit on Rio Del Mar and go right. Turn left on Clubhouse Drive.

***Course description:*** This scenic course has rolling, oceanside character, although you can't actually see the ocean. Cypress trees and bunkers border every hole. The course is tight and accuracy is vital. Par-3s are the key to success here. The 180-yard driving range is for iron practice only. The course record of 62 is held by Jeff McMillen.

| Hole | 1 | 2 | 3 | 4 | 5 | 6 | 7 | 8 | 9 | Out | BLUE | Rating: -- |
|---|---|---|---|---|---|---|---|---|---|---|---|---|
| BLUE | - | - | - | - | - | - | - | - | - | - | | Slope: -- |
| WHITE | 526 | 362 | 132 | 449 | 201 | 345 | 197 | 406 | 435 | 3053 | | |
| Par | 5 | 4 | 3 | 5 | 3 | 4 | 3 | 4 | 5 | 36 | WHITE | Rating: 69.6 |
| Handicap | 15 | 7 | 17 | 11 | 5 | 9 | 3 | 1 | 13 | x | | Slope: 124 |
| RED | 480 | 346 | 110 | 431 | 138 | 316 | 152 | 356 | 414 | 2743 | | |
| Par | 5 | 4 | 3 | 5 | 3 | 4 | 3 | 4 | 5 | 36 | RED | Rating: 71.8 |
| Handicap | 5 | 7 | 17 | 1 | 15 | 11 | 13 | 9 | 3 | x | | Slope: 120 |

| Hole | 10 | 11 | 12 | 13 | 14 | 15 | 16 | 17 | 18 | In | Totals | |
|---|---|---|---|---|---|---|---|---|---|---|---|---|
| BLUE | - | - | - | - | - | - | - | - | - | - | BLUE | -- |
| WHITE | 407 | 441 | 437 | 373 | 359 | 210 | 344 | 126 | 366 | 3063 | WHITE | 6116 |
| Par | 4 | 5 | 5 | 4 | 4 | 3 | 4 | 3 | 4 | 36 | Par | 72 |
| Handicap | 4 | 14 | 16 | 2 | 12 | 8 | 6 | 18 | 10 | x | | |
| RED | 390 | 425 | 419 | 355 | 306 | 183 | 313 | 107 | 335 | 2833 | RED | 5576 |
| Par | 4 | 5 | 5 | 4 | 4 | 3 | 4 | 3 | 4 | 36 | Par | 72 |
| Handicap | 2 | 10 | 14 | 4 | 16 | 12 | 6 | 18 | 8 | x | | |

## CASSERLY PAR-3 GOLF COURSE

**Course 6**
MAP F1 grid b7

**1966**
**Robert Sanford**

626 Casserly Road
Watsonville, CA 95076

Pro shop (408) 724-1654

- driving range
- ✓ **practice greens**
- power carts
- ✓ **pull carts**
- ✓ **golf club rental**
- locker rooms
- showers
- executive course
- accommodations
- food and beverages
- clubhouse

**Robert Sanford**
Manager

**Jean Sanford**
Manager

**George Sanford**
Superintendent

*Course information:* This public course has nine holes. Par is 54 for 18 holes. The course is 2,422 yards for 18 holes. All play is from the same tees. The course is unrated.

*Play policy and fees:* Green fees are $4 for nine holes. Pull carts only. Pull carts are 50 cents. Play is on a first-come first-served basis.

*Location:* This course is located between Highway 101 and Highway 1. From Highway 1 heading east toward Watsonville, take the Airport Boulevard exit and follow it to Green Valley Road. Turn left and follow Green Valley Road 1.5 miles to Casserly Road.

*Course description:* This all par-3 course has two water hazards as well as hills that come into play. It's a good beginners course. You can play nine holes in an hour during your lunch break. The course record of 22 is held by Ed Rhodes.



## SPRING HILLS GOLF COURSE

**Course 7**
MAP F1 grid b8

**1963**
**Hank Schimpeler**

31 Smith Road
Watsonville, CA 95076

Pro shop (408) 724-1404

- ✓ **driving range**
- ✓ **practice greens**
- ✓ **power carts**
- ✓ **pull carts**
- golf club rental
- locker rooms
- showers
- executive course
- accommodations
- ✓ **food and beverages**
- ✓ **clubhouse**

**Hank Schimpeler**
Owner

**Willie Barber**
Professional

*Course information:* This public course has 18 holes and par is 71.The course is 6,218 yards and rated 68.4 from the regular tees. The slope rating is 114. Women's tees are 5,784 yards and rated 73.3 from the championship tees, and 5,428 yards and rated 71.1 from the forward tees. The slope ratings are 121 championship and 117 forward.

*Play policy and fees:* Green fees are $20 weekdays and $25 weekends. Carts are $10 for nine holes and $20 for 18 holes. Reservations are recommended one week in advance. This course is available for outside tournaments. A pull-cart costs $2.

*Location:* From Highway 1 in Watsonville, take Green Valley Road north to Casserly Road. Turn right and then left on Smith Road to the course. From Highway 152, take Carlton Road north to Casserly and then Smith Road.

*Course description:* The back nine opened for play in 1963 and the front nine opened for play in 1969. Situated in the foothills, this short course is tight with lots of trees. The many doglegs make placement important. The back nine is rolling and scenic. Don White holds the course record with a 63.

# GAVILAN GOLF COURSE

**Course 8**
MAP F1 grid b9

***Course information:*** This public course, owned by Gavilan College, has nine holes. See card below for yardage and rating information.

***Play policy and fees:*** Green fees are $8 weekdays and $10 weekends for all-day play. Senior rates are $6 on weekdays. Carts are $6 for nine holes and $10 for 18 holes. Play is on a first-come, first-served basis.

***Location:*** From Highway 101 in Gilroy, take the Castro Valley exit and follow it until it dead ends. Turn right on Santa Teresa Boulevard. Go to the south gate at the Gavilan Community College Campus.

***Course description:*** This course dates back to the 1960s. It is a short, mostly flat course and excellent for beginners. The greens are small and tricky and offer a challenge. Don Leienzo holds the course record with 54.

5055 Santa Teresa Boulevard
Gilroy, CA 95020

Pro shop (408) 848-1363

- ✓ **driving range**
- ✓ **practice greens**
- ✓ **power carts**
- ✓ **pull carts**
- ✓ **golf club rental**
- locker rooms
- showers
- ✓ **executive course**
- accommodations
- ✓ **food and beverages**
- ✓ **clubhouse**

**Ted Hernandez**
Superintendent

**Joe Simonds**
Professional

| Hole | 1 | 2 | 3 | 4 | 5 | 6 | 7 | 8 | 9 | Out | | |
|---|---|---|---|---|---|---|---|---|---|---|---|---|
| BLUE | - | - | - | - | - | - | - | - | - | - | BLUE | Rating: -- |
| | | | | | | | | | | | | Slope: -- |
| WHITE | 117 | 276 | 356 | 227 | 145 | 166 | 266 | 87 | 159 | 1799 | | |
| Par | 3 | 4 | 4 | 4 | 3 | 3 | 4 | 3 | 3 | 31 | WHITE | Rating: 55.6 |
| Handicap | 18 | 2 | 6 | 12 | 16 | 4 | 14 | 10 | 8 | x | | Slope: 73 |
| RED | 117 | 276 | 356 | 227 | 145 | 166 | 266 | 87 | 159 | 1799 | | |
| Par | 3 | 4 | 4 | 4 | 3 | 3 | 4 | 3 | 3 | 31 | RED | Rating: 55.6 |
| Handicap | 18 | 2 | 6 | 12 | 16 | 4 | 14 | 10 | 8 | x | | Slope: 73 |

| Hole | 10 | 11 | 12 | 13 | 14 | 15 | 16 | 17 | 18 | In | Totals | |
|---|---|---|---|---|---|---|---|---|---|---|---|---|
| BLUE | - | - | - | - | - | - | - | - | - | - | BLUE | -- |
| WHITE | 127 | 286 | 366 | 215 | 190 | 170 | 256 | 92 | 137 | 1839 | WHITE | 3638 |
| Par | 3 | 4 | 4 | 4 | 3 | 3 | 4 | 3 | 3 | 31 | Par | 62 |
| Handicap | 17 | 3 | 7 | 13 | 1 | 5 | 15 | 11 | 9 | x | | |
| RED | 127 | 286 | 366 | 215 | 190 | 170 | 256 | 92 | 137 | 1839 | RED | 3638 |
| Par | 3 | 4 | 4 | 4 | 4 | 3 | 4 | 3 | 3 | 32 | Par | 63 |
| Handicap | 17 | 3 | 7 | 13 | 1 | 5 | 15 | 11 | 9 | x | | |

# PAJARO VALLEY GOLF COURSE

**Course 9**
**MAP F1 grid c7**

**1926**
**Floyd McFarlen**

PO Box 133
Watsonville, CA 95076

967 Salinas Road
Watsonville, CA 95076

Pro shop (408) 724-3851

- ✓ **driving range**
- ✓ **practice greens**
- ✓ **power carts**
- ✓ **pull carts**
- ✓ **golf club rental**
- ✓ **locker rooms**
- ✓ **showers**
- executive course
- accommodations
- ✓ **food and beverages**
- ✓ **clubhouse**

**Gary Cursio**
Manager

**Nick Lombardo**
Professional

**Gary Feliciano**
Superintendent

***Course information:*** This public course has 18 holes. See card below for yardage and rating information.

***Play policy and fees:*** Green fees are $34 weekdays and $45 weekends and holidays. Twilight rates after 3 p.m. are $22. Carts are $23 and optional. Reservations recommended the last Friday of each month at 7 a.m. for weekdays, and the Monday prior at 12:30 p.m. for weekends and holidays. This course is available for outside tournaments.

***Location:*** Take Highway 1 south past Watsonville. After the Riverside Drive exit, head to the top of the hill where the lanes merge. Turn left at the flashing yellow lights on Salinas Road and proceed three-fourths of a mile to the course on the right.

***Course description:*** Dating back to the late 1920s, this course is short and wide with rolling fairways. The 12th hole, a long par-4, features a three-tiered green surrounded by bunkers. The Little Helpers Golf Tournament is held here annually.

| Hole | 1 | 2 | 3 | 4 | 5 | 6 | 7 | 8 | 9 | Out | | |
|---|---|---|---|---|---|---|---|---|---|---|---|---|
| BLUE | 455 | 389 | 189 | 504 | 286 | 360 | 103 | 393 | 355 | 3034 | BLUE | Rating: 69.0 |
| WHITE | 440 | 378 | 179 | 481 | 282 | 348 | 98 | 392 | 348 | 2946 | | Slope: 122 |
| Par | 5 | 4 | 3 | 5 | 4 | 4 | 3 | 4 | 4 | 36 | WHITE | Rating: 68.2 |
| Handicap | 8 | 4 | 14 | 10 | 16 | 6 | 18 | 2 | 12 | x | | Slope: 119 |
| RED | 443 | 354 | 130 | 401 | 272 | 339 | 96 | 379 | 337 | 2751 | | |
| Par | 5 | 4 | 3 | 4 | 4 | 4 | 3 | 4 | 4 | 35 | RED | Rating: 71.5 |
| Handicap | 6 | 8 | 16 | 4 | 14 | 10 | 18 | 2 | 12 | x | | Slope: 121 |

| Hole | 10 | 11 | 12 | 13 | 14 | 15 | 16 | 17 | 18 | In | Totals | |
|---|---|---|---|---|---|---|---|---|---|---|---|---|
| BLUE | 345 | 171 | 417 | 376 | 160 | 468 | 393 | 515 | 355 | 3200 | BLUE | 6234 |
| WHITE | 341 | 171 | 412 | 370 | 146 | 459 | 375 | 505 | 340 | 3119 | WHITE | 6065 |
| Par | 4 | 3 | 4 | 4 | 3 | 5 | 4 | 5 | 4 | 36 | Par | 72 |
| Handicap | 15 | 7 | 1 | 13 | 17 | 9 | 3 | 5 | 11 | x | | |
| RED | 345 | 151 | 404 | 312 | 149 | 428 | 352 | 487 | 322 | 2950 | RED | 5701 |
| Par | 4 | 3 | 5 | 4 | 3 | 5 | 4 | 5 | 4 | 37 | Par | 72 |
| Handicap | 9 | 15 | 7 | 13 | 17 | 3 | 5 | 1 | 11 | x | | |

# SHERWOOD GREENS GOLF COURSE

**Course 10**
MAP F1 grid d8

1050 North Main Street
Salinas, CA 93906

Pro shop (408) 758-7333

✓ **driving range**
✓ **practice greens**
✓ **power carts**
✓ **pull carts**
✓ **golf club rental**
locker rooms
showers
executive course
accommodations
food and beverages
✓ **clubhouse**

**Glen Stubblefield**
Professional

**E.L. "Cotton" Kaiser**
Professional

**Tony Silvera**
Superintendent

*Course information:* This public course has nine holes. See card below for yardage and rating information.

*Play policy and fees:* Green fees are $4.50 for nine holes and $7 for 18 holes for Salinas residents, and $6 for nine holes and $9 for 18 holes for non-residents. Special discount rates are available for juniors 17 years and under. Pull carts are available for $1 for nine holes.

*Location:* From Highway 101 in Salinas driving south, take the Boronda Road exit. Driving north exit on Laurel Drive. Both Boronda and Laurel lead to North Main Street and the course, which is located next to the Salinas Rodeo stadium.

*Course description:* This short, flat course is tight and is a good test for beginners. It places a premium on iron play. Some trees will keep you honest off the tee.

| Hole | 1 | 2 | 3 | 4 | 5 | 6 | 7 | 8 | 9 | Out | BLUE | Rating: -- |
|---|---|---|---|---|---|---|---|---|---|---|---|---|
| BLUE | - | - | - | - | - | - | - | - | - | - | | Slope: -- |
| WHITE | 125 | 187 | 131 | 111 | 77 | 120 | 228 | 135 | 127 | 1241 | | |
| Par | 3 | 3 | 3 | 3 | 3 | 3 | 4 | 3 | 3 | 28 | WHITE | Rating: 53.7 |
| Handicap | 16 | 4 | 6 | 14 | 18 | 12 | 2 | 8 | 10 | x | | Slope: 73 |
| RED | 125 | 187 | 131 | 111 | 77 | 120 | 228 | 135 | 127 | 1241 | | |
| Par | 3 | 3 | 3 | 3 | 3 | 3 | 4 | 3 | 3 | 28 | RED | Rating: 53.7 |
| Handicap | 16 | 4 | 6 | 14 | 18 | 12 | 2 | 8 | 10 | x | | Slope: 73 |

| Hole | 10 | 11 | 12 | 13 | 14 | 15 | 16 | 17 | 18 | In | Totals | |
|---|---|---|---|---|---|---|---|---|---|---|---|---|
| BLUE | - | - | - | - | - | - | - | - | - | - | BLUE | -- |
| WHITE | 144 | 197 | 142 | 150 | 100 | 151 | 250 | 138 | 160 | 1432 | WHITE | 2673 |
| Par | 3 | 3 | 3 | 3 | 3 | 3 | 4 | 3 | 3 | 28 | Par | 56 |
| Handicap | 11 | 3 | 15 | 9 | 17 | 7 | 1 | 13 | 5 | x | | |
| RED | 144 | 197 | 142 | 150 | 100 | 151 | 250 | 138 | 160 | 1432 | RED | 2673 |
| Par | 3 | 3 | 3 | 3 | 3 | 3 | 4 | 3 | 3 | 28 | Par | 56 |
| Handicap | 11 | 3 | 15 | 9 | 17 | 7 | 1 | 13 | 5 | x | | |

# SALINAS GOLF AND COUNTRY CLUB

**Course 11**
MAP F1 grid d8

PO Box 4277
Salinas, CA 93912

475 San Juan Grade Road
Salinas, CA 93906

Pro shop (408) 449-1526
Clubhouse (408) 449-1527
Office (408) 449-6617

- ✓ **driving range**
- ✓ **practice greens**
- ✓ **power carts**
- ✓ **pull carts**
- ✓ **golf club rental**
- ✓ **locker rooms**
- ✓ **showers**
- executive course
- accommodations
- ✓ **food and beverages**
- ✓ **clubhouse**

**Gregg St. Germain**
Professional

**Bill Kissick**
Superintendent

**Ted Watson**
Manager

***Course information:*** This private course has 18 holes and par is 72. The course is 5,887 yards and rated 68.6 from the regular tees. The slope rating is 119. Women's tees are 5,620 yards and rated 72.8. The slope rating is 125.

***Play policy and fees:*** Reciprocal play is accepted with members of other private clubs, after 1 p.m. Weekdays, guest fees are $20 when accompanied by a member and $40 when unaccompanied. Weekends, guest fees are $25 when accompanied and $50 when unaccompanied. Carts are $15. Tee times should be reserved one week in advance. Proper golf attire required. Closed Mondays.

***Location:*** From Highway 101 in Salinas, take the Boronda Road exit. Turn right on Main Street (the first stoplight) and follow it to San Juan Grade Road. Turn right on San Juan Grade Road and drive 2.5 miles to the course.

***Course description:*** This short course is tight and hilly with small, tricky greens. It has lots of trees. Many up and down holes require finesse shots from the sidehill lies. It's a good test for the irons and the short game. This course was the site of a battle fought by General Fremont during the Mexican-American War. The men's course record of 60 is held by Kurt Dillard, and the women's by Pat Cornett, at 67.

# THE LINKS AT SPANISH BAY

**Course 12**
MAP F1 grid e4

*Course information:* This resort course has 18 holes. See card below for yardage and rating information.

*Play policy and fees:* Green fees are $110 for Pebble Beach Resort guests, and $135 for the public. Carts are included. Caddies are $35 per bag. Players may carry their own bag. Golf club rental is $35. Resort guests may make tee time reservations with their room reservations 18 months in advance. Outside players (two or more) may make reservations 60 days in advance.

*Location:* From Highway 1 in Monterey, exit at Highway 68/W.R. Holman (Pacific Grove Carmel Highway) north. The highway becomes Forest Avenue. Turn left at Sunset Drive and take it to 17 Mile Drive in Pacific Grove. Turn left onto 17 Mile Drive and drive a one-quarter mile to the entrance gate of the 17 Mile Drive. The course is 500 yards past the gate.

*Course description:* This fast-rolling course, designed by Robert Trent Jones, Jr., Tom Watson and Frank "Sandy" Tatum in 1987, is tailored in the pure Scottish fashion, complete with fescue grass fairways and greens, pot bunkers and mounds. Unlike traditional layouts, the architects want golfers to hit run-up shots and keep the ball low. Considering that all but four holes flank the ocean, this strategy is especially advantageous when the wind kicks up, which it often does. Most of the holes are flanked by sand and natural vegetation indigenous to the area, making accuracy a must. Large expanses of sand dunes, up to 24 feet in height, covered with native grasses and plants, characterize the course. The back nine is particularly enjoyable. It features a par-4 12th, a short par-3 13th and a difficult par-4 17th. In 1991, its first year of eligiblity, it was named one of the top 100 courses in the United States.

**1987**
**Robert Trent Jones, Jr.**
**Tom Watson**
**Frank "Sandy" Tatum**

PO Box 658
Pebble Beach, CA 93953

2700 17 Mile Drive
Pebble Beach, CA 93953

Pro shop (408) 647-7495

driving range
✓ **practice greens**
✓ **power carts**
pull carts
✓ **golf club rental**
locker rooms
showers
executive course
✓ **accommodations**
✓ **food and beverages**
✓ **clubhouse**

**Rich Cosand**
Manager/Professional

**Jess Pifferinni**
Superintendent

| Hole | 1 | 2 | 3 | 4 | 5 | 6 | 7 | 8 | 9 | Out | BLUE | Rating: 74.6 |
|---|---|---|---|---|---|---|---|---|---|---|---|---|
| BLUE | 500 | 307 | 405 | 190 | 459 | 395 | 418 | 163 | 394 | 3231 | | Slope: 142 |
| WHITE | 461 | 265 | 334 | 176 | 405 | 345 | 382 | 148 | 357 | 2873 | | |
| Par | 5 | 4 | 4 | 3 | 4 | 4 | 4 | 3 | 4 | 35 | WHITE | Rating: 72.1 |
| Handicap | 9 | 13 | 5 | 15 | 1 | 11 | 3 | 17 | 7 | x | | Slope: 133 |
| RED | 434 | 224 | 285 | 127 | 349 | 301 | 342 | 120 | 326 | 2508 | | |
| Par | 5 | 4 | 4 | 3 | 4 | 4 | 4 | 3 | 4 | 35 | RED | Rating: 70.6 |
| Handicap | 9 | 13 | 5 | 15 | 1 | 11 | 3 | 17 | 7 | x | | Slope: 129 |

| Hole | 10 | 11 | 12 | 13 | 14 | 15 | 16 | 17 | 18 | In | Totals | |
|---|---|---|---|---|---|---|---|---|---|---|---|---|
| BLUE | 520 | 365 | 432 | 126 | 571 | 390 | 200 | 414 | 571 | 3589 | BLUE | 6820 |
| WHITE | 464 | 318 | 406 | 99 | 535 | 342 | 157 | 369 | 515 | 3205 | WHITE | 6078 |
| Par | 5 | 4 | 4 | 3 | 5 | 4 | 3 | 4 | 5 | 37 | Par | 72 |
| Handicap | 8 | 14 | 6 | 18 | 2 | 12 | 16 | 4 | 10 | x | | |
| RED | 401 | 285 | 341 | 76 | 475 | 296 | 130 | 321 | 476 | 2801 | RED | 5309 |
| Par | 5 | 4 | 4 | 3 | 5 | 4 | 3 | 4 | 5 | 37 | Par | 72 |
| Handicap | 8 | 14 | 6 | 18 | 2 | 12 | 16 | 4 | 10 | x | | |

# PETER HAY GOLF COURSE

**Course 13**
MAP F1 grid e4

*Course information:* This public layout has nine holes and par is 54 for 18 holes. The course is 1,570 yards at 18 holes.

*Play policy and fees:* Green fees are $7 for all day, and juniors under 16 are free when accompanied by an adult. No reservations are taken.

*Location:* From Highway 1, take the Pebble Beach gate. The guard will give you instructions and a map. The course is next to Pebble Beach Golf Links.

*Course description:* This par-3 course provides an excellent opportunity to tune-up your short game. The course has been replanted with rye grass. Additional tees allow playing the holes from a different location on a second round. This par-3 course is short and tight, with some hills and lots of trees; the longest hole is 110 yards. It is named for the late Peter Hay, the designer and longtime pro at Pebble Beach.

**1957**
**Peter Hay**

PO Box 658
Pebble Beach, CA 93953

17 Mile Drive
Pebble Beach, CA 93953

Pro shop (408) 625-8518

- ✓ **driving range**
- ✓ **practice greens**
- power carts
- pull carts
- ✓ **golf club rental**
- locker rooms
- showers
- ✓ **executive course**
- ✓ **accommodations**
- ✓ **food and beverages**
- clubhouse

**R.J. Harper**
Professional

**Randy Damon**
Superintendent



MAP ON PAGE 316

# PEBBLE BEACH GOLF LINKS

**Course 14**
MAP F1 grid e4

***Course information:*** This resort course has 18 holes. See card below for yardage and rating information.

***Play policy and fees:*** Green fees for Pebble Beach Resort guests are $150. For other players, the fee is $200, including carts. Carts are $18 per rider for spectators. Players now have the option of carrying their own bag. Caddies are available.

***Location:*** From Highway 1, take the Pebble Beach exit and drive to the Pebble Beach Resort gate for instructions and a map.

***Course description:*** Designed by Jack Neville in 1919, this is one of the most scenic and demanding courses in the world. Eight holes flank the ocean, placing the entire course under the influence of fog, mist and wind. The par-5 18th hole is considered by many to be the finest finishing hole in golf. Used regularly for the AT&T Pebble Beach Pro-Am (formerly the Bing Crosby Pro-Am), the course was the site of the 1972, 1982, and 1992 U.S. Opens; the 1977 PGA Championship; and the 1929, 1947 and 1961 U.S. Amateur. The course is best remembered for Tom Watson's dramatic victory in the 1982 Open. Tied with Jack Nicklaus, Watson holed a chip shot for a birdie at the par-3 17th hole ("the shot that was heard around the world"), then birdied the picturesque but demanding 18th.

**1919**
**Jack Neville**

PO Box 658
Pebble Beach, CA 93953

17 Mile Drive
Pebble Beach, CA 93953

Pro shop (408) 625-8518
Reservation (408) 624-6611

- ✓ **driving range**
- ✓ **practice greens**
- ✓ **power carts**
- pull carts
- ✓ **golf club rental**
- ✓ **locker rooms**
- showers
- ✓ **executive course**
- ✓ **accommodations**
- ✓ **food and beverages**
- ✓ **clubhouse**

**R. J. Harper**
Professional

**Ed Miller**
Director of Golf Operations

**Randy Damon**
Superintendent

| Hole | 1 | 2 | 3 | 4 | 5 | 6 | 7 | 8 | 9 | Out | | |
|---|---|---|---|---|---|---|---|---|---|---|---|---|
| BLUE | 373 | 502 | 388 | 327 | 166 | 516 | 107 | 431 | 464 | 3274 | BLUE | Rating: 75 |
| WHITE | 338 | 439 | 341 | 303 | 156 | 487 | 103 | 405 | 439 | 3011 | | Slope: 144 |
| Par | 4 | 5 | 4 | 4 | 3 | 5 | 3 | 4 | 4 | 36 | WHITE | Rating: 72.7 |
| Handicap | 8 | 10 | 12 | 16 | 14 | 2 | 18 | 6 | 4 | x | | Slope: 139 |
| RED | 322 | 363 | 275 | 256 | 140 | 385 | 88 | 350 | 330 | 2509 | | |
| Par | 4 | 5 | 4 | 4 | 3 | 5 | 3 | 4 | 4 | 36 | RED | Rating: 71.9 |
| Handicap | 8 | 10 | 12 | 16 | 14 | 2 | 18 | 6 | 4 | x | | Slope: 130 |

| Hole | 10 | 11 | 12 | 13 | 14 | 15 | 16 | 17 | 18 | In | Totals | |
|---|---|---|---|---|---|---|---|---|---|---|---|---|
| BLUE | 426 | 384 | 202 | 392 | 565 | 397 | 402 | 209 | 548 | 3525 | BLUE | 6799 |
| WHITE | 395 | 374 | 184 | 373 | 553 | 366 | 388 | 175 | 538 | 3346 | WHITE | 6357 |
| Par | 4 | 4 | 3 | 4 | 5 | 4 | 4 | 3 | 5 | 36 | Par | 72 |
| Handicap | 7 | 5 | 17 | 9 | 1 | 13 | 11 | 15 | 3 | x | | |
| RED | 296 | 316 | 166 | 285 | 420 | 308 | 307 | 164 | 426 | 2688 | RED | 5197 |
| Par | 4 | 4 | 3 | 4 | 5 | 4 | 4 | 3 | 5 | 36 | Par | 72 |
| Handicap | 7 | 5 | 17 | 9 | 1 | 13 | 11 | 15 | 3 | x | | |

# MONTEREY PENINSULA COUNTRY CLUB

**Course 15**
MAP F1 grid e4

**1926**
**R.E. Baldock**

PO Box 2090
Pebble Beach, CA 93953

3000 Club Road
Pebble Beach, CA 93953

Pro shop (408) 372-8141

- ✓ **driving range**
- ✓ **practice greens**
- ✓ **power carts**
- ✓ **pull carts**
- ✓ **golf club rental**
- ✓ **locker rooms**
- ✓ **showers**
- executive course
- ✓ **accommodations**
- ✓ **food and beverages**
- ✓ **clubhouse**

**Mike Chapman**
Professional

**Bob Holmes**
Operations Manager

**Bob Zoller**
Superintendent

***Course information:*** This private facility has 36 holes. Par is 72 on the Dunes Course. Par is 71 on the Shore Course.

The Dunes Course is 6,505 yards and rated 70.9 from the championship tees, and 6,167 yards and rated 69.4 from the regular tees. The slope ratings are 123 championship and 120 regular. Women's tees are 5,966 yards and rated 74.7. The slope rating is 129.

The Shore Course is 6,361 yards and rated 70.6 from the championship tees, and 6,173 yards and rated 69.7 from the regular tees. The slope ratings are 125 championship and 123 regular. Women's tees are 5,935 yards and rated 74.4. The slope rating is 130.

***Play policy and fees:*** Reciprocal play is accepted and fees are $80. Guest fees are $65 when accompanied by a member and $70 as a guest. Carts are $30. Reservations are recommended 24 hours in advance. The dress code includes: no denims, no shorts, and skirts must be at least mid-knee in length.

***Location:*** From Highway 1 in Monterey, take Highway 68/W.R. Holman (Pacific Grove exit). Take Highway 68/W.R. Holman to David Avenue. Turn left on David Avenue and drive less than a one-quarter of a mile. Turn right on Congress Avenue. Turn left at Forest Lodge Road and drive to the entrance gate of the 17 Mile Drive. Head south on Sloat Road and turn right on Club Road.

***Course description:*** These meandering, scenic courses are flanked by pine trees and sand dunes. There are also several waterfalls. The greens are tricky and immaculate with a lot of undulation. Keep the ball below the hole. The picturesque Dunes Course is longer and situated farther inland. It was used for the Bing Crosby Pro-Am for 18 years. The Shore Course is shorter and tighter. Designed by R. E. Baldock, it flanks the ocean and is more exposed to the elements. The short par-5s are reachable in two for the long hitters.

# CYPRESS POINT CLUB

Course 16
MAP F1 grid e4

*Course information:* This private course has 18 holes. See card below for yardage and rating information.

*Play policy and fees:* Reciprocal play is not accepted. Members and guests only. Guest fees are $35 when accompanied by a member and $175 unaccompanied. Carts are $20.

*Location:* From Highway 1, take the Pacific Grove exit. At the first stop sign, drive to the Carmel Hill gate leading into Pebble Beach. Instructions and a map are given at the gate.

*Course description:* This spectacular course is the best-known work of the Scottish architect Alister MacKenzie, who designed it in 1928. Flanked by sand and sea, the course makes the most of its natural resources. The greens are fast and undulating. The famous par-3 16th hole requires a 200-yard carry over the ocean and usually produces the highest per-hole stroke average on the PGA Tour. The shorter par-3 15th hole flanks the ocean and is one of the prettiest in the world. The club is exclusive. Members include Clint Eastwood and George Schultz. The course was used for the AT&T Pebble Beach National Pro-Am (formerly the Bing Crosby National Pro-Am) from 1947 to 1990. Gabe Breur holds the course record with a 62.

**1928**
**Alister MacKenzie**

PO Box 466
Pebble Beach, CA 93953

17 Mile Drive
Pebble Beach, CA 93953

Pro shop (408) 624-2223

- ✓ **driving range**
- ✓ **practice greens**
- ✓ **power carts**
- pull carts
- ✓ **golf club rental**
- ✓ **locker rooms**
- ✓ **showers**
- executive course
- ✓ **accommodations**
- ✓ **food and beverages**
- ✓ **clubhouse**

**Jim Langley**
Professional

| Hole | 1 | 2 | 3 | 4 | 5 | 6 | 7 | 8 | 9 | Out | | |
|---|---|---|---|---|---|---|---|---|---|---|---|---|
| BLUE | 421 | 548 | 162 | 384 | 493 | 518 | 168 | 363 | 292 | 3349 | BLUE | Rating: 72.3 |
| WHITE | 409 | 538 | 155 | 373 | 471 | 509 | 161 | 347 | 282 | 3245 | | Slope: 134 |
| Par | 4 | 5 | 3 | 4 | 5 | 5 | 3 | 4 | 4 | 37 | WHITE | Rating: 71.2 |
| Handicap | 5 | 1 | 17 | 7 | 11 | 3 | 15 | 9 | 13 | x | | Slope: 130 |
| RED | 409 | 510 | 142 | 366 | 416 | 475 | 155 | 319 | 247 | 3039 | | |
| Par | 5 | 5 | 3 | 4 | 5 | 5 | 3 | 4 | 4 | 38 | RED | Rating: 74.1 |
| Handicap | 11 | 1 | 17 | 7 | 5 | 3 | 13 | 9 | 15 | x | | Slope: 139 |

| Hole | 10 | 11 | 12 | 13 | 14 | 15 | 16 | 17 | 18 | In | Totals | |
|---|---|---|---|---|---|---|---|---|---|---|---|---|
| BLUE | 480 | 437 | 404 | 365 | 388 | 143 | 231 | 393 | 346 | 3187 | BLUE | 6536 |
| WHITE | 480 | 428 | 397 | 343 | 382 | 127 | 219 | 382 | 329 | 3087 | WHITE | 6332 |
| Par | 5 | 4 | 4 | 4 | 4 | 3 | 3 | 4 | 4 | 35 | Par | 72 |
| Handicap | 16 | 4 | 2 | 14 | 8 | 18 | 6 | 10 | 12 | x | | |
| RED | 480 | 401 | 310 | 285 | 323 | 119 | 208 | 355 | 296 | 2777 | RED | 5816 |
| Par | 5 | 5 | 4 | 4 | 4 | 3 | 4 | 4 | 4 | 37 | Par | 75 |
| Handicap | 2 | 10 | 8 | 14 | 6 | 18 | 16 | 4 | 12 | x | | |

# SPYGLASS HILL GOLF COURSE

**Course 17**
MAP F1 grid e4

**1966**
**Robert Trent Jones, Sr.**

PO Box 658
Pebble Beach, CA 93953

Stevenson Drive and
Spyglass Hill
Pebble Beach, CA 93953

Pro shop (408) 625-8563
Reservation (408) 647-7500

- ✓ **driving range**
- ✓ **practice greens**
- ✓ **power carts**
- pull carts
- ✓ **golf club rental**
- locker rooms
- showers
- executive course
- ✓ **accommodations**
- ✓ **food and beverages**
- ✓ **clubhouse**

**Laird Small**
Professional

**Jeff Graham**
Superintendent

***Course information:*** This semi-private course has 18 holes. See card below for yardage and rating information.

***Play policy and fees:*** Outside play is accepted. Green fees are $145 for NCGA members, $150 for non-members and $125 for Pebble Beach Resort guests (The Inn at Spanish Bay Inn or the Lodge at Pebble Beach). Carts are included in the fees. Resort guests may book 18 months ahead with the room reservations, and non-guests 60 days ahead.

***Location:*** From Highway 1, take the Pebble Beach exit and drive to the Pebble Beach gate for instructions and a map.

***Course description:*** This long, demanding course, designed by Robert Trent Jones, Sr. in 1966, can be unforgiving. Used annually for the AT&T Pebble Beach National Pro-Am, it almost always produces the highest scoring average. The first five holes wind through sand dunes and offer magnificent ocean views. It's surrounded by Monterey pines. The large, undulating greens are protected by ponds on three par-5s. The names given to each of the holes were derived from Robert Louis Stevenson's classic, *Treasure Island.* You'll find Treasure Island on the first hole (it's actually an island in the sand), Long John Silver on the 14th (a double dogleg par-5) and Black Dog on the 16th (an infamous par-4).

| Hole | 1 | 2 | 3 | 4 | 5 | 6 | 7 | 8 | 9 | Out | BLUE | Rating: 76.1 |
|---|---|---|---|---|---|---|---|---|---|---|---|---|
| BLUE | 600 | 350 | 150 | 365 | 180 | 415 | 515 | 395 | 425 | 3395 | | Slope: 141 |
| WHITE | 551 | 325 | 125 | 347 | 138 | 377 | 474 | 367 | 408 | 3112 | | |
| Par | 5 | 4 | 3 | 4 | 3 | 4 | 5 | 4 | 4 | 36 | WHITE | Rating: 73.1 |
| Handicap | 3 | 13 | 17 | 9 | 15 | 7 | 11 | 1 | 5 | x | | Slope: 135 |
| RED | 488 | 254 | 89 | 298 | 111 | 369 | 466 | 305 | 407 | 2787 | | |
| Par | 5 | 4 | 3 | 4 | 3 | 4 | 5 | 4 | 5 | 37 | RED | Rating: 73.7 |
| Handicap | 1 | 13 | 17 | 11 | 15 | 7 | 3 | 9 | 5 | x | | Slope: 133 |

| Hole | 10 | 11 | 12 | 13 | 14 | 15 | 16 | 17 | 18 | In | Totals | |
|---|---|---|---|---|---|---|---|---|---|---|---|---|
| BLUE | 400 | 520 | 180 | 440 | 555 | 130 | 465 | 320 | 405 | 3415 | BLUE | 6810 |
| WHITE | 371 | 485 | 148 | 418 | 514 | 104 | 434 | 308 | 383 | 3165 | WHITE | 6277 |
| Par | 4 | 5 | 3 | 4 | 5 | 3 | 4 | 4 | 4 | 36 | Par | 72 |
| Handicap | 12 | 10 | 16 | 4 | 6 | 18 | 2 | 14 | 8 | x | | |
| RED | 364 | 421 | 102 | 390 | 483 | 79 | 406 | 301 | 362 | 2908 | RED | 5695 |
| Par | 4 | 5 | 3 | 4 | 5 | 3 | 5 | 4 | 4 | 37 | Par | 74 |
| Handicap | 10 | 4 | 18 | 8 | 2 | 16 | 6 | 14 | 12 | x | | |

# POPPY HILLS GOLF COURSE

**Course 18**
MAP F1 grid e5

**1986**
**Robert Trent Jones, Jr.**

PO Box 1157
Pebble Beach, CA 93953

3200 Lopez on 17 Mile Drive
Pebble Beach, CA 93953

Pro shop (408) 625-2154
Reservation (408) 625-2035

- ✓ **driving range**
- ✓ **practice greens**
- ✓ **power carts**
- pull carts
- ✓ **golf club rental**
- ✓ **locker rooms**
- ✓ **showers**
- executive course
- accommodations
- ✓ **food and beverages**
- ✓ **clubhouse**

**John Geertsen, Jr.**
Professional

**Kevin Orona**
Manager

**Manuel Sousa**
Superintendent

***Course information:*** This public course has 18 holes. See card below for yardage and rating information.

***Play policy and fees:*** Green fees are $40 for NCGA members and $65 for NCGA guests (limited to three per day), and $90 for nonmembers. Carts are $28. Reservations are recommended one month in advance on the corresponding date.

***Location:*** From Highway 1, take the Pebble Beach exit and proceed to the Pebble Beach gate for instructions and a map.

***Course description:*** Designed by Robert Trent Jones, Jr. in 1986, this course is long and tight with lots of trees, water and sand. The large, undulating greens are well guarded by bunkers and pot bunkers. Many of the greens are flanked by chipping areas, which give the player an option to chip or putt. On most holes, the option also exists to either play it safe or go for broke, especially on the par-5 ninth and 18th holes. This is the home of the Northern California Golf Association. There are numerous NCGA events held here throughout the year. This course became one of three in rotation for the annual AT&T Pebble Beach National Pro-Am in 1991. The other two courses are Pebble Beach Golf Links and Spyglass Hill Golf Course. The Men's NCAA Division I Championships were held here in 1991. It was also the site of the 1990 Spalding Invitation Pro-Am. The men's record of 66 is held jointly by John Cook and Larry Mize. Julie Inkster holds the women's course record of 67, set during the 1990 Spalding Invitational Pro-Am.

| Hole | 1 | 2 | 3 | 4 | 5 | 6 | 7 | 8 | 9 | Out | BLUE | Rating: 74.6 |
|---|---|---|---|---|---|---|---|---|---|---|---|---|
| BLUE | 413 | 162 | 406 | 560 | 426 | 181 | 388 | 390 | 557 | 3483 | | Slope: 141 |
| WHITE | 396 | 128 | 369 | 524 | 381 | 141 | 351 | 370 | 508 | 3168 | | |
| Par | 4 | 3 | 4 | 5 | 4 | 3 | 4 | 4 | 5 | 36 | WHITE | Rating: 71.7 |
| Handicap | 7 | 15 | 5 | 1 | 9 | 17 | 11 | 13 | 3 | x | | Slope: 134 |
| RED | 316 | 100 | 262 | 498 | 343 | 120 | 313 | 330 | 461 | 2743 | | |
| Par | 4 | 3 | 4 | 5 | 4 | 3 | 4 | 4 | 5 | 36 | RED | Rating: 71.8 |
| Handicap | 7 | 15 | 5 | 1 | 8 | 17 | 11 | 13 | 3 | x | | Slope: 125 |

| Hole | 10 | 11 | 12 | 13 | 14 | 15 | 16 | 17 | 18 | In | Totals | |
|---|---|---|---|---|---|---|---|---|---|---|---|---|
| BLUE | 515 | 214 | 531 | 393 | 417 | 210 | 439 | 163 | 500 | 3382 | BLUE | 6865 |
| WHITE | 500 | 174 | 502 | 368 | 392 | 175 | 409 | 126 | 474 | 3120 | WHITE | 6288 |
| Par | 5 | 3 | 5 | 4 | 4 | 3 | 4 | 3 | 5 | 36 | Par | 72 |
| Handicap | 4 | 16 | 2 | 10 | 12 | 14 | 6 | 18 | 8 | x | | |
| RED | 402 | 151 | 479 | 343 | 360 | 148 | 272 | 115 | 420 | 2690 | RED | 5433 |
| Par | 5 | 3 | 5 | 4 | 4 | 3 | 4 | 3 | 5 | 36 | Par | 72 |
| Handicap | 7 | 15 | 5 | 1 | 9 | 17 | 11 | 13 | 3 | x | | |

# PACIFIC GROVE GOLF COURSE

**Course 19**
MAP F1 grid e5

**1932**
**Jack Neville**

77 Asilomar Boulevard
Pacific Grove, CA 93950

Pro shop (408) 648-3177
Clubhouse (408) 648-3175

- ✓ **driving range**
- ✓ **practice greens**
- ✓ **power carts**
- ✓ **pull carts**
- ✓ **golf club rental**
- locker rooms
- showers
- executive course
- accommodations
- ✓ **food and beverages**
- ✓ **clubhouse**

**Peter Vitarisi**
Professional

**Dave Griffiths**
Superintendent

***Course information:*** This public course has 18 holes and par is 70. The course is 5,533 yards and rated 66.3 from the regular tees. The slope rating is 115. Women's tees are 5,553 yards and rated 71.8 from the championship tees, and 5,324 yards and rated 70.5 from the forward tees. The slope ratings are 117 championship and 114 forward.

***Play policy and fees:*** Green fees are $20 Monday through Thursday, and $23 Friday through Sundays and holidays. Twilight rates after 4 p.m. are $11. Carts are $20; pull-carts are $1.50 for nine holes, and $2.50 for 18. Reservations are recommended seven days in advance.

***Location:*** From Highway 1 in Monterey, take Highway 68/W.R. Holman (Pacific Grove Highway) west. Turn right at Asilomar Avenue and follow it to the cemetery and lighthouse.

***Course description:*** This tight, scenic oceanside course has a Scottish links-style flavor and is fun to play. The front nine weaves through the forest and is flanked by trees, while the back nine is bordered by sand dunes and ice plants. An old lighthouse stands guard over the course. Pacific Grove Golf Course used to be one of Monterey Peninsula's best kept secrets, but with an estimated 160,000 rounds nowadays played each year, you may want to make reservations. The men's course record of 62 is held by numerous people, among them head pro Peter Vitarisi.

# OLD DEL MONTE GOLF COURSE

**Course 20**
MAP F1 grid e5

**1897**
**Charles Maud**

1300 Sylvan Road
Monterey, CA 93940

Pro shop (408) 373-2436

- driving range
- ✓ **practice greens**
- ✓ **power carts**
- ✓ **pull carts**
- ✓ **golf club rental**
- locker rooms
- showers
- executive course
- ✓ **accommodations**
- ✓ **food and beverages**
- ✓ **clubhouse**

**Joe Holdridge**
Professional

**Pete Bibber**
Superintendent

***Course information:*** This public course has 18 holes. See card below for yardage and rating information.

***Play policy and fees:*** Hotel guest green fees are $35, Monday through Thursday, and $40 Friday through Sunday. Outside green fees are $40 Monday through Thursday and $45 Friday through Saturday. The course has special arrangements with hotels in the area and guests of those hotels (such as the adjacent Hyatt) get courtesy discount rates. Special discounts are available for residents also. Carts are $10 per rider Monday through Thursday, and $12 per rider Friday through Saturday.

***Location:*** In Monterey heading south on Highway 1, take the central Monterey exit. At the first stoplight, go left on Camino Aguajito Road and go back under the highway. Turn left at Mark Thomas Drive which runs parallel to Highway 1 and turn right at Sylvan Road to the course. It's next to the Hyatt.

***Course description:*** The oldest course west of the Mississippi in continuous use, this course was built in 1897 as a nine-hole layout and expanded to 18 holes in 1901. It was reported in those early days of golf to be the first course in the world to have green fairways throughout the seasons. Old Del Monte hosted the first state amateur in 1912, and continues to hold flights of the annual tournament each year. It was also host to the Western Amateur in 1916. This inland course offers a meandering, hilly layout with lots of trees and tight doglegs. The short, but infuriating par-4, 18th hole looks simple to birdie, but will drive you crazy. This course plays host to the California State Amateur.

| Hole | 1 | 2 | 3 | 4 | 5 | 6 | 7 | 8 | 9 | Out | | |
|---|---|---|---|---|---|---|---|---|---|---|---|---|
| BLUE | 499 | 321 | 373 | 188 | 318 | 193 | 374 | 381 | 514 | 3161 | BLUE | Rating: 70.8 |
| WHITE | 484 | 307 | 363 | 162 | 291 | 185 | 362 | 366 | 504 | 3024 | | Slope: 122 |
| Par | 5 | 4 | 4 | 3 | 4 | 3 | 4 | 4 | 5 | 36 | WHITE | Rating: 69.5 |
| Handicap | 9 | 17 | 5 | 15 | 13 | 3 | 1 | 11 | 7 | x | | Slope: 119 |
| RED | 414 | 302 | 355 | 140 | 273 | 177 | 302 | 303 | 413 | 2679 | | |
| Par | 5 | 4 | 4 | 3 | 4 | 3 | 4 | 4 | 5 | 36 | RED | Rating: 71.1 |
| Handicap | 1 | 11 | 5 | 17 | 13 | 15 | 9 | 7 | 3 | x | | Slope: 118 |

| Hole | 10 | 11 | 12 | 13 | 14 | 15 | 16 | 17 | 18 | In | Totals | |
|---|---|---|---|---|---|---|---|---|---|---|---|---|
| BLUE | 287 | 323 | 161 | 529 | 217 | 344 | 413 | 473 | 370 | 3117 | BLUE | 6278 |
| WHITE | 280 | 315 | 145 | 514 | 209 | 318 | 413 | 459 | 330 | 2983 | WHITE | 6007 |
| Par | 4 | 4 | 3 | 5 | 3 | 4 | 4 | 5 | 4 | 36 | Par | 72 |
| Handicap | 16 | 14 | 12 | 10 | 4 | 8 | 2 | 18 | 6 | x | | |
| RED | 275 | 308 | 122 | 403 | 202 | 297 | 407 | 428 | 310 | 2752 | RED | 5431 |
| Par | 4 | 4 | 3 | 5 | 4 | 4 | 5 | 5 | 4 | 38 | Par | 74 |
| Handicap | 14 | 12 | 18 | 4 | 16 | 10 | 6 | 2 | 8 | x | | |

# LAGUNA SECA GOLF COURSE

**Course 21**
MAP F1 grid e6

*Course information:* This public course has 18 holes. See card below for yardage and rating information.

*Play policy and fees:* Green fees are $45 everyday. Twilight rates are $22 after 3 p.m. Carts are $23. Reservations are recommended.

*Location:* On the east side of Monterey on Highway 68, exit north on York Road and drive to the end.

*Course description:* Designed by Robert Trent Jones, Sr., this challenging course has a number of elevated tees and greens. It's a sprawling course bordered by oak trees. There are lots of bunkers. It's known as "The Sunshine Golf Course" because it has some of the best weather in the area. Johnny Miller holds the course record with a 64.

**1970**
**Robert Trent Jones, Sr.**

10520 York Road
Monterey, CA 93940

Pro shop (408) 373-3701

- driving range
- ✓ **practice greens**
- ✓ **power carts**
- ✓ **pull carts**
- ✓ **golf club rental**
- ✓ **locker rooms**
- ✓ **showers**
- executive course
- accommodations
- ✓ **food and beverages**
- ✓ **clubhouse**

**Nancy Lewis**
Professional

**Bob Costa**
Executive Superintendent

**Jeff Hardy**
Superintendent

CENTRAL F1

| Hole | 1 | 2 | 3 | 4 | 5 | 6 | 7 | 8 | 9 | Out | | |
|---|---|---|---|---|---|---|---|---|---|---|---|---|
| BLUE | 343 | 151 | 500 | 379 | 504 | 318 | 355 | 157 | 404 | 3111 | BLUE | Rating: 70.4 |
| | | | | | | | | | | | | Slope: 123 |
| WHITE | [illegible] | [illegible] | 407 | 378 | 479 | 293 | 324 | 132 | 385 | 2959 | | |
| Par | 4 | 3 | 5 | 4 | 5 | 4 | 4 | 3 | 4 | 36 | WHITE | Rating: 68.5 |
| Handicap | 13 | 15 | 7 | 3 | 9 | 11 | 5 | 17 | 1 | x | | Slope: 119 |
| RED | 302 | 134 | 479 | 369 | 474 | 280 | 305 | 99 | 374 | 2816 | | |
| Par | 4 | 3 | 5 | 4 | 5 | 4 | 4 | 3 | 5 | 37 | RED | Rating: 70.2 |
| Handicap | 11 | 15 | 1 | 7 | 3 | 13 | 9 | 17 | 5 | x | | Slope: 119 |

| Hole | 10 | 11 | 12 | 13 | 14 | 15 | 16 | 17 | 18 | In | Totals | |
|---|---|---|---|---|---|---|---|---|---|---|---|---|
| BLUE | 420 | 324 | 173 | 540 | 154 | 542 | 393 | 127 | 341 | 3014 | BLUE | 6125 |
| WHITE | 380 | 282 | 164 | 502 | 137 | 502 | 361 | 112 | 312 | 2752 | WHITE | 5711 |
| Par | 4 | 4 | 3 | 5 | 3 | 5 | 4 | 3 | 4 | 35 | Par | 71 |
| Handicap | 6 | 12 | 14 | 8 | 16 | 2 | 4 | 18 | 10 | x | | |
| RED | 341 | 245 | 117 | 481 | 117 | 410 | 265 | 94 | 300 | 2370 | RED | 5186 |
| Par | 4 | 4 | 3 | 5 | 3 | 5 | 4 | 3 | 4 | 35 | Par | 72 |
| Handicap | 6 | 12 | 14 | 4 | 16 | 2 | 10 | 18 | 8 | x | | |

# U.S. NAVY GOLF COURSE

**Course 22**
MAP F1 grid e6

***Course information:*** This military course has 18 holes. Women's championship tees are 5,449 yards, rated 67.4, and have a slope rating of 117. See card below for additional yardage and rating information.

***Play policy and fees:*** You must be accompanied by a member of the military to play. Green fees are $7 weekdays and $9 weekends. Guest green fees are $12 weekdays and $15 weekends. Carts are $6.50 for nine holes and $12.50 for 18 holes. Reservations are recommended 48 hours in advance for play on Fridays, Saturdays and Sundays. There is a dress code. No children under eight years of age are permitted.

***Location:*** From Highway 1 in Monterey, take the Casa Verde Way exit south to Fairgrounds Road.

***Course description:*** This short, flat course has narrow fairways and lots of trees. Four lakes come into play. It has some of the best greens on the Monterey Peninsula. The men's course record here is 63, held by assistant professional Peter Niles. The women's course record is 70.

**1962**
**Robert Muir Graves**

MWR Dept., Code 456
NPS Monterey, CA 93943

Mark Thomas Drive
and Garden Road
Monterey, CA 93943

Pro shop (408) 656-2167
Clubhouse (408) 373-8118

- ✓ **driving range**
- ✓ **practice greens**
- ✓ **power carts**
- ✓ **pull carts**
- ✓ **golf club rental**
- locker rooms
- showers
- executive course
- accommodations
- ✓ **food and beverages**
- ✓ **clubhouse**

**Gene Newton**
Manager/Professional

**Daniel R. Tracy**
Superintendent

| Hole | 1 | 2 | 3 | 4 | 5 | 6 | 7 | 8 | 9 | Out | BLUE | Rating: -- |
|---|---|---|---|---|---|---|---|---|---|---|---|---|
| BLUE | - | - | - | - | - | - | - | - | - | - | | Slope: -- |
| WHITE | 350 | 153 | 344 | 193 | 361 | 335 | 496 | 320 | 400 | 2952 | | |
| Par | 4 | 3 | 4 | 3 | 4 | 4 | 5 | 4 | 4 | 35 | WHITE | Rating: 67.4 |
| Handicap | 5 | 17 | 9 | 11 | 7 | 13 | 3 | 15 | 1 | x | | Slope: 116 |
| RED | 337 | 122 | 325 | 180 | 323 | 317 | 464 | 310 | 402 | 2780 | | |
| Par | 4 | 3 | 4 | 3 | 4 | 4 | 5 | 4 | 5 | 36 | RED | Rating: 69.3 |
| Handicap | 11 | 17 | 9 | 15 | 13 | 7 | 1 | 5 | 3 | x | | Slope: 115 |

| Hole | 10 | 11 | 12 | 13 | 14 | 15 | 16 | 17 | 18 | In | Totals | |
|---|---|---|---|---|---|---|---|---|---|---|---|---|
| BLUE | - | - | - | - | - | - | - | - | - | - | BLUE | -- |
| WHITE | 433 | 122 | 154 | 458 | 361 | 251 | 136 | 168 | 539 | 2622 | WHITE | 5574 |
| Par | 4 | 3 | 3 | 5 | 4 | 4 | 3 | 3 | 5 | 34 | Par | 69 |
| Handicap | 2 | 16 | 10 | 8 | 6 | 18 | 14 | 12 | 4 | x | | |
| RED | 410 | 102 | 140 | 442 | 347 | 239 | 127 | 164 | 444 | 2415 | RED | 5195 |
| Par | 5 | 3 | 3 | 5 | 4 | 4 | 3 | 3 | 5 | 35 | Par | 71 |
| Handicap | 8 | 14 | 10 | 4 | 2 | 16 | 18 | 12 | 6 | x | | |

# FORT ORD GOLF COURSE

**Course 23**
MAP F1 grid e6

**1953**
**Gen. Robert McClure**

Box 40, McClure Way
Fort Ord, CA 93941

McClure Way
Fort Ord, CA 93941

Pro shop (408) 242-3268

- ✓ **driving range**
- ✓ **practice greens**
- ✓ **power carts**
- ✓ **pull carts**
- ✓ **golf club rental**
- ✓ **locker rooms**
- ✓ **showers**
- executive course
- accommodations
- ✓ **food and beverages**
- ✓ **clubhouse**

**Doug Parker**
Manager/Professional

**Donald Frazier**
Superintendent

***Course information:*** This military facility has 36 holes.

The Black Horse Course is a par 72, and is 6,396 yards and rated 69.8 with a slope of 120 from the championship tees, and 6,059 yards and rated 68.4 with a slope of 116 from the regular tees. Women's tees are 5,613 yards and are rated 72.5 with a slope of 129.

The Bayonet Course is is detailed below.

***Play policy and fees:*** Guest fees are $25 weekdays and $30 weekends and holidays if sponsored by retired or active duty military personnel. Guest fees for non-sponsored guests are $40 weekdays and $60 weekends and holidays. The club is reciprocal with other Army facilities. Carts are $12 for military and $20 for civilians. Reservations are recommended seven days in advance for active duty personnel, six days for retirees, five days for DOD employees, and 48 hours for other guests. No short shorts, rubber cleats or tank tops for men allowed.

***Location:*** The main gate of Fort Ord is off Highway 1 at Light Fighter Drive. Ask for directions at the gate. The course is on McClure Way off North-South Road. You must show current drivers license and vehicle insurance and registration to be admitted through the gate.

***Course description:*** The Bayonet Course is long and difficult. The front nine is longer and more open and the back nine has several tight doglegs and tricky greens. It's used regularly for the PGA Tour qualifying school. The Black Horse Course is shorter and more forgiving. It has a meandering layout bordered by tall trees and bunkers. Both courses are located near the ocean and offer scenic views. They also can be foggy and windy. Nathaniel Crosby holds the Bayonet Course record for men with 66 and Julie Inkster holds the women's with 68. It's the site of the annual Josten's Invitational, hosted by San Jose State. The course record at Black Horse is 65.

Bayonet Course

| Hole | 1 | 2 | 3 | 4 | 5 | 6 | 7 | 8 | 9 | Out | BLUE | Rating: 74.0 |
|---|---|---|---|---|---|---|---|---|---|---|---|---|
| BLUE | 514 | 441 | 362 | 631 | 462 | 185 | 346 | 210 | 344 | 3495 | | Slope: 132 |
| WHITE | 480 | 422 | 348 | 609 | 419 | 167 | 329 | 193 | 331 | 3298 | | |
| Par | 5 | 4 | 4 | 5 | 4 | 3 | 4 | 3 | 4 | 36 | WHITE | Rating: 72.1 |
| Handicap | 7 | 5 | 9 | 3 | 1 | 17 | 11 | 15 | 13 | x | | Slope: 127 |
| RED | 398 | 315 | 300 | 507 | 393 | 150 | 303 | 162 | 306 | 2834 | | |
| Par | 5 | 4 | 4 | 5 | 5 | 3 | 4 | 3 | 4 | 37 | RED | Rating: 73.7 |
| Handicap | 11 | 13 | 5 | 1 | 3 | 17 | 7 | 15 | 9 | x | | Slope: 134 |

| Hole | 10 | 11 | 12 | 13 | 14 | 15 | 16 | 17 | 18 | In | Totals | |
|---|---|---|---|---|---|---|---|---|---|---|---|---|
| BLUE | 503 | 427 | 396 | 449 | 216 | 411 | 351 | 183 | 551 | 3487 | BLUE | 6982 |
| WHITE | 480 | 407 | 381 | 436 | 164 | 389 | 337 | 166 | 519 | 3279 | WHITE | 6577 |
| Par | 5 | 4 | 4 | 4 | 3 | 4 | 4 | 3 | 5 | 36 | Par | 72 |
| Handicap | 12 | 10 | 2 | 4 | 16 | 6 | 14 | 18 | 8 | x | | |
| RED | 455 | 397 | 316 | 342 | 136 | 290 | 323 | 160 | 427 | 2846 | RED | 5680 |
| Par | 5 | 5 | 4 | 4 | 3 | 4 | 4 | 3 | 5 | 37 | Par | 74 |
| Handicap | 6 | 12 | 2 | 10 | 18 | 14 | 4 | 16 | 8 | x | | |



MAP ON PAGE 316

# SALINAS FAIRWAYS GOLF COURSE

**Course 24**
MAP F1 grid e8

**1961**

PO Box 1201
Salinas, CA 93902

45 Skyway Boulevard
Salinas, CA 93905

Pro shop (408) 758-7300

- ✓ **driving range**
- ✓ **practice greens**
- ✓ **power carts**
- ✓ **pull carts**
- ✓ **golf club rental**
- locker rooms
- showers
- executive course
- accommodations
- ✓ **food and beverages**
- ✓ **clubhouse**

**E.L. "Cotton" Kaiser**
Professional

**Glen Stubblefield**
Professional

**Roger Martinez**
Superintendent

***Course information:*** This public links has 18 holes. See card below for yardage and rating information.

***Play policy and fees:*** Green fees are $9 weekdays and $12 weekends for Salinas residents, and $13 weekdays and $16 weekends for non-residents. Twilight rates after 2:30 p.m. in the summer and 3:30 p.m. in the winter are $7 for residents and $9 for non-residents any day. Carts are $17. Reservations are recommended. This course has limited availability for tournaments.

***Location:*** From Highway 101 in Salinas, exit on Airport Boulevard east and follow it until it dead ends at the airport. Turn left on Skyway Boulevard to the course.

***Course description:*** This flat, tight course is well maintained, has lots of trees and is often windy. You can salvage par on this course because the greens are large and fair. The course is located next to the Salinas Airport. The men's course record is 64, held by Glen Stubblefield.

| Hole | 1 | 2 | 3 | 4 | 5 | 6 | 7 | 8 | 9 | Out | | |
|---|---|---|---|---|---|---|---|---|---|---|---|---|
| BLUE | 380 | 342 | 166 | 465 | 418 | 550 | 404 | 189 | 353 | 3267 | BLUE | Rating: 70.4 |
| WHITE | 369 | 342 | 142 | 458 | 404 | 536 | 394 | 160 | 343 | 3148 | | Slope: 114 |
| Par | 4 | 4 | 3 | 5 | 4 | 5 | 4 | 3 | 4 | 36 | WHITE | Rating: 69.3 |
| Handicap | 6 | 10 | 14 | 16 | 2 | 4 | 12 | 18 | 8 | x | | Slope: 111 |
| RED | 323 | 328 | 128 | 443 | 326 | 451 | 329 | 156 | 328 | 2812 | | |
| Par | 4 | 4 | 3 | 5 | 4 | 5 | 4 | 3 | 4 | 36 | RED | Rating: 71.0 |
| Handicap | 10 | 16 | 16 | 2 | 8 | 4 | 6 | 14 | 12 | x | | Slope: 115 |

| Hole | 10 | 11 | 12 | 13 | 14 | 15 | 16 | 17 | 18 | In | Totals | |
|---|---|---|---|---|---|---|---|---|---|---|---|---|
| BLUE | 433 | 550 | 341 | 192 | 388 | 415 | 411 | 137 | 533 | 3400 | BLUE | 6667 |
| WHITE | 415 | 529 | 331 | 163 | 378 | 400 | 398 | 130 | 519 | 3263 | WHITE | 6411 |
| Par | 4 | 5 | 4 | 3 | 4 | 4 | 4 | 3 | 5 | 36 | Par | 72 |
| Handicap | 3 | 1 | 11 | 17 | 7 | 9 | 13 | 15 | 5 | x | | |
| RED | 406 | 464 | 319 | 165 | 304 | 332 | 321 | 125 | 426 | 2862 | RED | 5674 |
| Par | 5 | 5 | 4 | 3 | 4 | 4 | 4 | 3 | 5 | 37 | Par | 73 |
| Handicap | 5 | 1 | 11 | 13 | 7 | 15 | 9 | 17 | 3 | x | | |

# RANCHO CANADA GOLF COURSE

**Course 25**
MAP F1 grid f5

**1971**
**Robert Dean Putman**

PO Box 22590
Carmel, CA 93922

Carmel Valley Road
Carmel, CA 93922

Pro shop (408) 624-0111

- ✓ **driving range**
- ✓ **practice greens**
- ✓ **power carts**
- ✓ **pull carts**
- ✓ **golf club rental**
- locker rooms
- showers
- executive course
- accommodations
- ✓ **food and beverages**
- ✓ **clubhouse**

**Dave Lewis**
Professional

**Tim Greenwald**
Superintendent

***Course information:*** This public facility has 36 holes. Par is 71 on the East Course and 72 on the West Course.

The East Course is 6,113 yards and rated 68.9 from the championship tees, and 5,822 yards and rated 67.3 from the regular tees. The slope ratings are 114 championship and 111 regular. Women's tees are 5,279 yards and rated 69.5. The slope rating is 118.

The West Course is 6,306 yards and rated 70.6 from the championship tees, and 6,078 yards and rated 69.6 from the regular tees. The slope ratings are 122 championship and 120 regular. Women's tees are 5,574 yards and rated 71.6. The slope rating is 121.

***Play policy and fees:*** Green fees are $50 until 3 p.m. and $25 after 3 p.m. There is a late twilight green fee of $12 after 5 p.m. during the summer season. Carts are $25. Reservations are recommended seven days in advance weekends and holidays, and up to 30 days in advance for weekdays. This course is available for outside tournaments.

***Location:*** From Highway 1 in Carmel, take the Carmel Valley Road exit. Drive 1.5 miles east to the course.

***Course description:*** These courses are short and tight with lots of trees. They offer excellent par-3 holes. The West Course is tougher with lots of mature pine trees. The Carmel River, although it does not always have water in it in dry years, comes into play on both courses. There are four lakes on the East Course. The 15th hole on the West Course may be the tightest par-4 you'll ever play. There's no shortage of conversation about this hole. This course hosted the 1991 Western Intercollegiate Championships, and annually hosts the Herman Edwards Benefit Tournament. The East Course record is 63. The West Course record is also 63, held by John Kennaday.

# THE GOLF CLUB AT QUAIL LODGE

**Course 26**
MAP F1 grid f6

**1964**
**Robert Muir Graves**

8000 Valley Greens Drive
Carmel, CA 93923

Pro shop (408) 624-2770
Clubhouse (408) 624-1581

- ✓ **driving range**
- ✓ **practice greens**
- ✓ **power carts**
- pull carts
- ✓ **golf club rental**
- ✓ **locker rooms**
- ✓ **showers**
- executive course
- ✓ **accommodations**
- ✓ **food and beverages**
- ✓ **clubhouse**

**Dan Weiss**
Director of Golf/Pro

**Denis Kerr**
Superintendent

***Course information:*** This private course has 18 holes. See card below for yardage and rating information.

***Play policy and fees:*** Reciprocal play is accepted with members of other private clubs. Have your club pro call for arrangements. Guest fees are $95. Carts are included. Tee time reservations should be made six weeks in advance. Shirts with collars are required. Walking shorts are permitted, but no jeans, tank tops or hard rubber golf shoes may be worn.

***Location:*** From Highway 1 in Carmel, take the Carmel Valley Road exit. Drive three miles to Valley Greens Drive. Turn right on Valley Greens Road and follow it to the course.

***Course description:*** This is a five-star resort located in the beautiful Carmel Valley and flanked by ragged mountain vistas. Doris Day has a home overlooking this course. This scenic, hilly layout is notable for its fast greens, bunkers and water. A premium is placed on accuracy and shot placement. This course hosted the U.S. Golf Association Senior Amateur Championship in 1975, and the California Golf Association's 75th Amateur Championship in 1986. The men's course record is held by Lennie Clements, who shot 62 in the Spalding Pro-Am in 1988. The California State Women's Amateur is held here each December.

| Hole | 1 | 2 | 3 | 4 | 5 | 6 | 7 | 8 | 9 | Out | | |
|---|---|---|---|---|---|---|---|---|---|---|---|---|
| BLUE | 549 | 209 | 401 | 407 | 197 | 352 | 371 | 219 | 537 | 3242 | BLUE | Rating: 71.7 |
| WHITE | 536 | 196 | 387 | 330 | 189 | 337 | 362 | 208 | 525 | 3070 | | Slope: 126 |
| Par | 5 | 3 | 4 | 4 | 3 | 4 | 4 | 3 | 5 | 35 | WHITE | Rating: 70.2 |
| Handicap | 5b/5w | 13/17 | 3/11 | 1/7 | 15/13 | 11/3 | 17/9 | 9/15 | 7/1 | x | | Slope: 122 |
| RED | 455 | 156 | 338 | 320 | 171 | 311 | 357 | 178 | 450 | 2736 | | |
| Par | 5 | 3 | 4 | 4 | 3 | 4 | 4 | 3 | 5 | 35 | RED | Rating: 71.6 |
| Handicap | 3 | 17 | 11 | 5 | 15 | 7 | 9 | 13 | 1 | x | | Slope: 122 |

| Hole | 10 | 11 | 12 | 13 | 14 | 15 | 16 | 17 | 18 | In | Totals | |
|---|---|---|---|---|---|---|---|---|---|---|---|---|
| BLUE | 345 | 346 | 223 | 385 | 507 | 522 | 411 | 161 | 373 | 3273 | BLUE | 6515 |
| WHITE | 321 | 333 | 135 | 375 | 494 | 509 | 399 | 149 | 356 | 3071 | WHITE | 6141 |
| Par | 4 | 4 | 3 | 4 | 5 | 5 | 4 | 3 | 4 | 36 | Par | 71 |
| Handicap | 12/12 | 16/14 | 4/18 | 6/10 | 14/8 | 8/2 | 2/4 | 18/16 | 10/6 | x | | |
| RED | 294 | 323 | 125 | 319 | 437 | 418 | 348 | 92/110 | 343 | 2717 | RED | 5453 |
| Par | 4 | 4 | 3 | 4 | 5 | 5 | 4 | 3 | 4 | 36 | Par | 71 |
| Handicap | 14 | 10 | 16 | 12 | 2 | 4 | 8 | 18 | 6 | x | | |

# CARMEL VALLEY RANCH RESORT

**Course 27**
MAP F1 grid f6

**1981**
**Pete Dye**

1 Old Ranch Road
Carmel, CA 93923

Pro shop (408) 626-2510

✓ **driving range**
✓ **practice greens**
✓ **power carts**
pull carts
✓ **golf club rental**
✓ **locker rooms**
✓ **showers**
executive course
✓ **accommodations**
✓ **food and beverages**
✓ **clubhouse**

**Ted Goln**
Director of Golf/Pro

**Mike Higuera**
Superintendent

***Course information:*** This private resort course has 18 holes. Women's championship tees are 5,582 yards and rated 72.0, with a slope rating of 132. See card below for additional yardage and rating information.

***Play policy and fees:*** Reciprocal play is accepted with members of other private clubs. The golf professional from the reciprocal course must call to make arrangements. Guest fees are $50 when accompanied by a member, $80 for hotel guests and $95 for unaccompanied guests (includes carts and range balls). Carts are mandatory. Golf attire is the only acceptable dress on the golf course. No blue jeans, tank tops or short shorts may be worn.

***Location:*** From Highway 1 in Carmel, take the Carmel Valley Road exit and drive seven miles. Turn right on Robinson Canyon Road and left on Old Ranch Road.

***Course description:*** This imaginative Pete Dye design features large greens, railroad ties and deep bunkers. Most holes arc tight and unforgiving. The back nine is especially hilly and creative. The 14th hole is 90 yards wide with five distinct levels and an elevation change of at least 150 feet from top to bottom. Other elevation differences of up to 350 feet create interesting golf shots and spectacular views. The men's course record is 62, held by Tim Morris and Lennie Clements, in the Spalding Pro-Am in 1987.

| Hole | 1 | 2 | 3 | 4 | 5 | 6 | 7 | 8 | 9 | Out | BLUE | Rating: 70.1 |
|---|---|---|---|---|---|---|---|---|---|---|---|---|
| BLUE | 380 | 350 | 330 | 420 | 172 | 560 | 126 | 450 | 400 | 3188 | | Slope: 124 |
| WHITE | 365 | 314 | 315 | 340 | 147 | 515 | 114 | 430 | 385 | 2925 | | |
| Par | 4 | 4 | 4 | 4 | 3 | 5 | 3 | 4 | 4 | 35 | WHITE | Rating: 67.8 |
| Handicap | 7 | 13 | 15 | 5 | 11 | 1 | 17 | 3 | 9 | x | | Slope: 119 |
| RED | 319 | 284 | 285 | 298 | 109 | 461 | 105 | 370 | 326 | 2557 | | |
| Par | 4 | 4 | 4 | 4 | 3 | 5 | 3 | 4 | 4 | 35 | RED | Rating: 69.1 |
| Handicap | 7 | 15 | 13 | 11 | 9 | 1 | 17 | 3 | 5 | x | | Slope: 121 |

| Hole | 10 | 11 | 12 | 13 | 14 | 15 | 16 | 17 | 18 | In | Totals | |
|---|---|---|---|---|---|---|---|---|---|---|---|---|
| BLUE | 520 | 430 | 407 | 164 | 330 | 420 | 231 | 410 | 415 | 3327 | BLUE | 6515 |
| WHITE | 500 | 395 | 400 | 140 | 300 | 405 | 211 | 389 | 390 | 3130 | WHITE | 6055 |
| Par | 5 | 4 | 4 | 3 | 4 | 4 | 3 | 4 | 4 | 35 | Par | 70 |
| Handicap | 12 | 2 | 4 | 18 | 16 | 8 | 14 | 6 | 10 | x | | |
| RED | 389 | 353 | 351 | 114 | 264 | 316 | 142 | 296 | 306 | 2531 | RED | 5088 |
| Par | 5 | 4 | 4 | 3 | 4 | 4 | 3 | 4 | 4 | 35 | Par | 70 |
| Handicap | 6 | 4 | 2 | 18 | 14 | 8 | 16 | 12 | 10 | x | | |

# CORRAL DE TIERRA COUNTRY CLUB

**Course 28**
MAP F1 grid f7

**1959**
**R. E. Baldock**

81 Corral de Tierra Road
Salinas, CA 93908

Pro shop (408) 484-1325
Clubhouse (408) 484-1112

- ✓ **driving range**
- ✓ **practice greens**
- ✓ **power carts**
- ✓ **pull carts**
- ✓ **golf club rental**
- ✓ **locker rooms**
- ✓ **showers**
- executive course
- accommodations
- ✓ **food and beverages**
- ✓ **clubhouse**

**Gerry Greenfield**
Professional

**Scott Domnkie**
Superintendent

***Course information:*** This private course has 18 holes and par is 72. The course is 6,536 yards and rated 71.4 from the tournament tees, 6,231 yards and rated 70.2 from the championship tees, and 6,072 yards and rated 68.7 from the regular tees. The slope ratings are 123 tournament, 120 championship and 115 regular. Women's tees are 6,263 yards and rated 75.5 from the championship tees, and 6,072 yards and rated 74.3 from the forward tees. The slope ratings are 129 championship and 127 forward.

***Play policy and fees:*** Reciprocal play is accepted with members of other private clubs on Thursdays and Fridays only. Guest fees are $30 when accompanied by a member and $60 when unaccompanied. Carts are $20. Reservations recommended one week in advance. No blue jeans may be worn. Closed Mondays.

***Location:*** From Highway 68 between Salinas and Monterey, take the Corral de Tierra Road exit south. Drive three-fourths of a mile to the course.

***Course description:*** This rolling, tree-lined course has undulating greens. Water comes into play on several holes. The par-4 first hole starts from a scenic, elevated tee. The par-5s are tight, but reachable in two for long hitters. The men's course record is 63, by Mike Evans, and the women's is 70.

# MAP F2
(6 COURSES)

PAGES.. 344-351

CEN-CAL MAP...see page 314
adjoining maps
NORTH (E2).......see page 268
EAST (F3)...........see page 352
SOUTH (G2).......see page 374
WEST (F1)..........see page 316

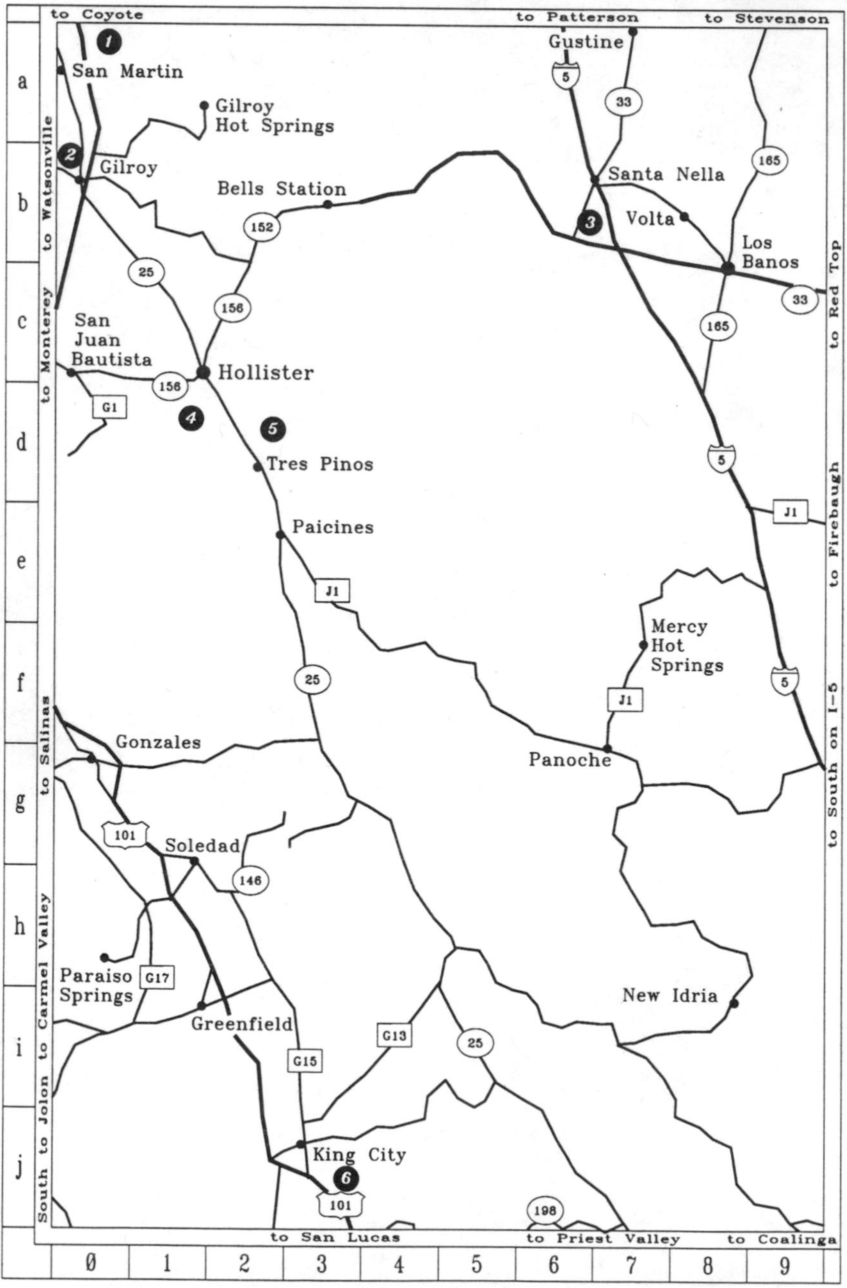

to Coyote
to Patterson
to Stevenson
to Watsonville
to Monterey
to Red Top
to Firebaugh
to South on I-5
to Salinas
South to Jolon to Carmel Valley
to San Lucas
to Priest Valley
to Coalinga
San Martin
Gilroy Hot Springs
Gilroy
Bells Station
Gustine
Santa Nella
Volta
Los Banos
San Juan Bautista
Hollister
Tres Pinos
Paicines
Mercy Hot Springs
Panoche
Gonzales
Soledad
Paraiso Springs
Greenfield
New Idria
King City
1
2
3
4
5
6
5
33
165
152
25
156
156
G1
J1
J1
J1
25
101
146
G17
G13
25
G15
101
198

a
b
c
d
e
f
g
h
i
j

0 1 2 3 4 5 6 7 8 9

# HILL COUNTRY GOLF COURSE

**Course 1**
MAP F2 grid a0

***Course information:*** This public course has 18 holes. See card below for yardage and rating information.

***Play policy and fees:*** Green fees are $10 weekdays and $13 weekends and holidays. The seniors rate is $8 weekdays. Carts are $12. The pro shop closes daily at 2:30 p.m. weekdays, but the course is open. Check in at the restaurant bar. Play is first come, first-served. Reservations are recommended one week in advance for weekend play. This course is available for outside tournaments.

***Location:*** From Highway 101 in Morgan Hill, exit at Tennant Avenue east. Drive to Foothill Avenue and turn right. The course is on the left.

***Course description:*** Home of the "Flying Lady," this hilly course is mostly par-3s and a good test of the short game. The longest hole is the first one, a 368-yard par-4. This course can be played in under four hours. Water comes into play on half the holes at the green. There are two steep hills too, so stretch it out and enjoy yourself. Players only on the course.

**1972**

PO Box 999
Morgan Hill, CA 95037

15060 Foothill Avenue
Morgan Hill, CA 95037

Pro shop (408) 779-4136
(408) 227-4607

- driving range
- ✓ **practice greens**
- ✓ **power carts**
- ✓ **pull carts**
- golf club rental
- locker rooms
- showers
- ✓ **executive course**
- accommodations
- ✓ **food and beverages**
- ✓ **clubhouse**

**Jeannine Parshall**
Manager

**Irv Perch**
Owner

**Nick Altermirano**
Superintendent

CENTRAL F2

| Hole | 1 | 2 | 3 | 4 | 5 | 6 | 7 | 8 | 9 | Out | BLUE | Rating: |
|---|---|---|---|---|---|---|---|---|---|---|---|---|
| BLUE | - | - | - | - | - | - | - | - | - | - | | Slope: -- |
| WHITE | 368 | 171 | 156 | 124 | 107 | 177 | 96 | 121 | 142 | 1464 | | |
| Par | 4 | 3 | 3 | 3 | 3 | 3 | 3 | 3 | 3 | 28 | WHITE | Rating: 59.3 |
| Handicap | 1 | 5 | 3 | 7 | 17 | 11 | 15 | 13 | 9 | x | | Slope: 81 |
| RED | 310 | 137 | 156 | 124 | 102 | 177 | 90 | 121 | 138 | 1355 | | |
| Par | 4 | 3 | 3 | 3 | 3 | 3 | 3 | 3 | 3 | 28 | RED | Rating: 55.8 |
| Handicap | 1 | 5 | 3 | 7 | 17 | 11 | 15 | 13 | 9 | x | | Slope: 81 |

| Hole | 10 | 11 | 12 | 13 | 14 | 15 | 16 | 17 | 18 | In | Totals | |
|---|---|---|---|---|---|---|---|---|---|---|---|---|
| BLUE | - | - | - | - | - | - | - | - | - | - | BLUE | - |
| WHITE | 180 | 301 | 266 | 137 | 140 | 112 | 105 | 127 | 278 | 1646 | WHITE | 3110 |
| Par | 3 | 4 | 4 | 3 | 3 | 3 | 3 | 3 | 4 | 30 | Par | 58 |
| Handicap | 8 | 2 | 10 | 14 | 6 | 18 | 12 | 18 | 4 | x | | |
| RED | 176 | 211 | 196 | 136 | 133 | 101 | 105 | 115 | 225 | 1398 | RED | 2753 |
| Par | 3 | 4 | 4 | 3 | 3 | 3 | 3 | 3 | 4 | 28 | Par | 58 |
| Handicap | 8 | 2 | 10 | 14 | 6 | 18 | 12 | 18 | 4 | x | | |

# GILROY GOLF COURSE

**Course 2**
**MAP F2 grid b0**

***Course information:*** This public course has nine holes. See card below for yardage and rating information.

***Play policy and fees:*** Green fees are $12 weekdays and $16 weekends and holidays. Twilight senior and junior rates are available. Reservations may be made seven days in advance. This course is available for outside tournaments.

***Location:*** From Highway 101, drive two miles west on Hecker Pass Highway (Highway 152) in Gilroy. The course is on the right.

***Course description:*** There are actually 11 holes on this course, changing the back nine into a different layout. This mature course is situated in oak-studded foothills. The terrain is rolling and hilly with tricky small greens. Panoramic views of the valley are available on the eighth and 17th holes. The course record is 60, held by George Archer.

**1920**
2695 Hecker Pass Highway
Gilroy, CA 95020

Pro shop (408) 848-0490

- ✓ **driving range**
- ✓ **practice greens**
- ✓ **power carts**
- ✓ **pull carts**
- ✓ **golf club rental**
- locker rooms
- showers
- executive course
- accommodations
- ✓ **food and beverages**
- ✓ **clubhouse**

**Don DeLorenzo**
Manager/Professional

**Darren Marcus**
Superintendent

| Hole | 1 | 2 | 3 | 4 | 5 | 6 | 7 | 8 | 9 | Out | BLUE | Rating: -- |
|---|---|---|---|---|---|---|---|---|---|---|---|---|
| BLUE | - | - | - | - | - | - | - | - | - | - | | Slope: -- |
| WHITE | 394 | 343 | 374 | 520 | 151 | 374 | 393 | 261 | 169 | 2979 | | |
| Par | 4 | 4 | 4 | 5 | 3 | 4 | 4 | 3 | 3 | 34 | WHITE | Rating: 67.8 |
| Handicap | 3 | 11 | 5 | 13 | 15 | 9 | 1 | 7 | 17 | x | | Slope: 109 |
| RED | 380 | 330 | 369 | 474 | 123 | 370 | 373 | 225 | 142 | 2786 | | |
| Par | 5 | 4 | 4 | 5 | 3 | 4 | 5 | 4 | 3 | 37 | RED | Rating: 70.5 |
| Handicap | 9 | 11 | 3 | 7 | 13 | 5 | 1 | 15 | 17 | x | | Slope: 112 |

| Hole | 10 | 11 | 12 | 13 | 14 | 15 | 16 | 17 | 18 | In | Totals | |
|---|---|---|---|---|---|---|---|---|---|---|---|---|
| BLUE | - | - | - | - | - | - | - | - | - | - | BLUE | -- |
| WHITE | 371 | 366 | 352 | 500 | 128 | 388 | 350 | 345 | 168 | 2968 | WHITE | 5947 |
| Par | 4 | 4 | 4 | 5 | 3 | 4 | 4 | 4 | 3 | 35 | Par | 69 |
| Handicap | 2 | 10 | 8 | 16 | 12 | 6 | 4 | 18 | 14 | x | | |
| RED | 365 | 360 | 341 | 450 | 95 | 365 | 342 | 240 | 157 | 2715 | RED | 5501 |
| Par | 4 | 4 | 4 | 5 | 3 | 4 | 4 | 4 | 3 | 35 | Par | 72 |
| Handicap | 4 | 12 | 10 | 8 | 18 | 2 | 6 | 14 | 16 | x | | |

# FOREBAY GOLF COURSE

**Course 3**
MAP F2 grid b6

***Course information:*** This public course has nine holes. See card below for yardage and rating information.

***Play policy and fees:*** Green fees are $8.50 for nine holes and $12.50 for 18 holes weekdays, and $10 for nine holes and $15 for 18 holes weekends. The senior rate is $7.50 for nine holes and $10 for 18 holes. Each Thursday is senior day and there is a special rate of $6.50 for nine holes and $8.50 for 18 holes. Carts are $8 for nine holes and $16 for 18 holes. Reservations are recommended one week in advance. This course is available for outside tournaments.

***Location:*** In Santa Nella on Interstate 5, exit onto Highway 33 south. Turn right on Bayview Road and follow to the course.

***Course description:*** This is a flat course with new trees and a creek. The testy, 424-yard, par-4 ninth hole requires a second shot carry over the creek.

**1964**
**Joe Sontor**

PO Box 703
Santa Nella, CA 95322

29500 Bayview Road
Santa Nella, CA 95322

Pro shop (209) 826-3637

- ✓ **driving range**
- ✓ **practice greens**
- ✓ **power carts**
- ✓ **pull carts**
- ✓ **golf club rental**
- locker rooms
- showers
- executive course
- accommodations
- ✓ **food and beverages**
- clubhouse

**Greg Arnaudo**
Owner

**"Titi" Willington**
Manager

**P.R. Carpentier**
Professional

CENTRAL F2

| Hole | 1 | 2 | 3 | 4 | 5 | 6 | 7 | 8 | 9 | Out | BLUE | Rating: -- |
|---|---|---|---|---|---|---|---|---|---|---|---|---|
| BLUE | - | - | - | - | - | - | - | - | - | - | | Slope: -- |
| WHITE | 353 | 392 | 193 | 513 | 341 | 178 | 461 | 393 | 424 | 3248 | | |
| Par | 4 | 4 | 3 | 5 | 4 | 3 | 5 | 4 | 4 | 36 | WHITE | Rating: 69.7 |
| Handicap | 13 | 3 | 11 | 7 | 15 | 17 | 9 | 5 | 1 | x | | Slope: 105 |
| RED | 330 | 250 | 167 | 480 | 340 | 160 | 450 | 365 | 375 | 2917 | | |
| Par | 4 | 4 | 3 | 5 | 4 | 3 | 5 | 4 | 5 | 37 | RED | Rating: 68.7 |
| Handicap | 11 | 13 | 15 | 1 | 9 | 17 | 3 | 7 | 5 | x | | Slope: 109 |

| Hole | 10 | 11 | 12 | 13 | 14 | 15 | 16 | 17 | 18 | In | Totals | |
|---|---|---|---|---|---|---|---|---|---|---|---|---|
| BLUE | - | - | - | - | - | - | - | - | - | - | BLUE | -- |
| WHITE | 368 | 402 | 198 | 525 | 350 | 185 | 407 | 405 | 501 | 3341 | WHITE | 6589 |
| Par | 4 | 4 | 3 | 5 | 4 | 3 | 4 | 4 | 5 | 36 | Par | 72 |
| Handicap | 14 | 4 | 12 | 10 | 16 | 18 | 2 | 6 | 8 | x | | |
| RED | 340 | 240 | 150 | 470 | 330 | 140 | 460 | 350 | 390 | 2870 | RED | 5787 |
| Par | 4 | 4 | 3 | 5 | 4 | 3 | 5 | 4 | 5 | 37 | Par | 74 |
| Handicap | 12 | 14 | 16 | 2 | 10 | 18 | 4 | 8 | 6 | x | | |

# RIDGEMARK GOLF AND COUNTRY CLUB

**Course 4**
MAP F2 grid d1

**1972**
**Richard Bigler**

3800 Airline Highway
Hollister, CA 95023

Pro shop (408) 637-1010
Clubhouse (408) 637-8151

- ✓ **driving range**
- ✓ **practice greens**
- ✓ **power carts**
- ✓ **pull carts**
- ✓ **golf club rental**
- locker rooms
- showers
- executive course
- ✓ **accommodations**
- ✓ **food and beverages**
- ✓ **clubhouse**

**Jim Prusa**
General Manager

**Kathy Wake**
Professional

**Rick Key**
Superintendent

***Course information:*** This semi-private facility has 36 holes. Par is 72 on both courses.

The Diablo Course is 6,603 yards and rated 71.9 from the championship tees, and 6,066 yards and rated 69.3 from the regular tees. The slope ratings are 123 championship and 118 regular. Women's tees are 5,475 yards and rated 72.5. The slope rating is 125. Women's tees on the Galiban Course are rated 76.3 with a slope of 133 from the white tees. See card below for additional yardage and rating information.

***Play policy and fees:*** Outside play is accepted. Green fees are $25 Monday through Thursday, and $40 Fridays, weekends and holidays. Twilight rates are available. Carts are $24 and mandatory until 3 p.m. Tee time reservations should be made one week in advance. Every other day one of the two courses is open to public play. These courses are available for outside tournaments.

***Location:*** From Highway 101 south, take the Highway 25 exit south of Gilroy and drive 13 miles on Highway 25 to Hollister. The course is located five miles south of Hollister.

***Course description:*** These rolling, hilly courses have large, contoured greens. The Diablo Course is steeper and requires more placement. It's slightly shorter than the Gabilan Course and also has many more water hazards. The Gabilan Course is flatter and less deceptive. Wind is often a factor, as is frequent out-of-bounds. The Diablo course record is 63, held by Greg Beaulieu, and the Gabilan course record is 63, held by John Bedell.

## Gabilan Course

| Hole | 1 | 2 | 3 | 4 | 5 | 6 | 7 | 8 | 9 | Out | BLUE | Rating: 72.0 |
|---|---|---|---|---|---|---|---|---|---|---|---|---|
| BLUE | 412 | 500 | 537 | 200 | 385 | 385 | 386 | 384 | 191 | 3380 | | Slope: 124 |
| WHITE | 369 | 482 | 513 | 187 | 345 | 369 | 386 | 361 | 173 | 3185 | | |
| Par | 4 | 5 | 5 | 3 | 4 | 4 | 4 | 4 | 3 | 36 | WHITE | Rating: 69.9 |
| Handicap | 10 | 14 | 7 | 15 | 11 | 4 | 2 | 6 | 12 | x | | Slope: 120 |
| RED | 332 | 435 | 476 | 168 | 302 | 346 | 373 | 332 | 131 | 2885 | | |
| Par | 4 | 5 | 5 | 3 | 4 | 4 | 4 | 4 | 3 | 36 | RED | Rating: 72.7 |
| Handicap | 10 | 13 | 1 | 17 | 11 | 5 | 2 | 7 | 18 | x | | Slope: 124 |

| Hole | 10 | 11 | 12 | 13 | 14 | 15 | 16 | 17 | 18 | In | Totals | |
|---|---|---|---|---|---|---|---|---|---|---|---|---|
| BLUE | 350 | 396 | 240 | 476 | 437 | 212 | 341 | 399 | 540 | 3391 | BLUE | 6771 |
| WHITE | 331 | 365 | 190 | 453 | 402 | 181 | 301 | 350 | 519 | 3092 | WHITE | 6277 |
| Par | 4 | 4 | 3 | 5 | 4 | 3 | 4 | 4 | 5 | 36 | Par | 72 |
| Handicap | 16 | 1 | 8 | 17 | 3 | 13 | 18 | 5 | 9 | x | | |
| RED | 313 | 323 | 181 | 415 | 349 | 160 | 273 | 324 | 460 | 2798 | RED | 5683 |
| Par | 4 | 4 | 3 | 5 | 4 | 3 | 4 | 4 | 5 | 36 | Par | 72 |
| Handicap | 14 | 3 | 9 | 12 | 6 | 16 | 15 | 8 | 4 | x | | |

# BOLADO PARK GOLF COURSE

**Course 5**
MAP F2 grid d2

*Course information:* This public course has nine holes and par is 70 for 18 holes. The course is 5,986 yards and rated 67.6 for 18 holes from the regular tees. The slope rating is 110. Women's tees are 5,636 yards and rated 71.6. The slope rating is 114.

*Play policy and fees:* Green fees are $12 weekdays and $16 weekends. Carts are $10 for nine holes and $20 for $18 holes. Play is on a first-come first-served basis.

*Location:* This course is located five miles south of Hollister on Highway 25/Airline Highway in Tres Pinos.

*Course description:* This flat course has well-maintained greens. In fact, Senior PGA Tour pro George Archer uses these greens for practice. The course was rebuilt in 1958 in its present location by George Santana. The course record is 63, held by General M.I. Moncado.

**1928**
**W.I. Hawkins**
**Col. George E. Sikes**

PO Box 419
Tres Pinos, CA 95075

7777 Airline Highway 25
Tres Pinos, CA 95075

Pro shop (408) 628-9995

- ✓ **driving range**
- ✓ **practice greens**
- ✓ **power carts**
- ✓ **pull carts**
- golf club rental
- ✓ **locker rooms**
- showers
- executive course
- accommodations
- ✓ **food and beverages**
- ✓ **clubhouse**

**Bob Trevino**
Manager

**Sal Hernandez**
Superintendent



MAP ON PAGE 344

# KING CITY GOLF COURSE

**Course 6**
**MAP F2 grid j3**

***Course information:*** This public course has nine holes. See card below for yardage and rating information.

***Play policy and fees:*** Green fees are $8 for nine holes and $12 for 18 holes on weekdays, and $9 for nine holes and $14 for 18 holes on weekends and holidays. Twilight rates are $5 for nine holes and $8 for 18 holes after 2 p.m. Tee time reservations should be made one week in advance. This course is available for outside tournaments.

***Location:*** From Highway 101 in King City, take the Canal Street exit. Turn right on Division Street. At the second stop sign, turn right on South Vanderhurst and drive to the course.

***Course description:*** Robert Dean Putman redesigned this course in 1976. This flat, short course has small, tricky greens and tree-lined fairways. A creek meanders through the terrain and comes into play on four holes. It's well-conditioned. The men's course record is 62, set in 1984 by then-amateur Mark Pumphrey. The women's course record is 72.

**1953**

613 South Vanderhurst
King City, CA 93930

Pro shop (408) 385-4546

- ✓ **driving range**
- ✓ **practice greens**
- ✓ **power carts**
- ✓ **pull carts**
- ✓ **golf club rental**
- locker rooms
- showers
- executive course
- accommodations
- ✓ **food and beverages**
- ✓ **clubhouse**

**Jon Olson**
Professional/Superintendent

**Mark Pumphrey**
Professional

| Hole | 1 | 2 | 3 | 4 | 5 | 6 | 7 | 8 | 9 | Out | BLUE | Rating: -- |
|---|---|---|---|---|---|---|---|---|---|---|---|---|
| BLUE | - | - | - | - | - | - | - | - | - | - | | Slope: -- |
| WHITE | 199 | 259 | 404 | 161 | 501 | 532 | 361 | 169 | 231 | 2817 | | |
| Par | 3 | 4 | 4 | 3 | 5 | 5 | 4 | 3 | 4 | 35 | WHITE | Rating: 66.4 |
| Handicap | 11 | 15 | 1 | 13 | 7 | 5 | 3 | 9 | 17 | x | | Slope: 107 |
| RED | 199 | 259 | 350 | 161 | 465 | 480 | 361 | 169 | 231 | 2675 | | |
| Par | 3 | 4 | 4 | 3 | 5 | 5 | 4 | 3 | 4 | 35 | RED | Rating: 68.3 |
| Handicap | 11 | 15 | 5 | 17 | 7 | 3 | 1 | 13 | 9 | x | | Slope: 110 |

| Hole | 10 | 11 | 12 | 13 | 14 | 15 | 16 | 17 | 18 | In | Totals | |
|---|---|---|---|---|---|---|---|---|---|---|---|---|
| BLUE | - | - | - | - | - | - | - | - | - | - | BLUE | -- |
| WHITE | 199 | 259 | 404 | 161 | 501 | 532 | 361 | 169 | 231 | 2817 | WHITE | 5634 |
| Par | 3 | 4 | 4 | 3 | 5 | 5 | 4 | 3 | 4 | 35 | Par | 70 |
| Handicap | 12 | 16 | 2 | 14 | 8 | 6 | 4 | 10 | 18 | x | | |
| RED | 199 | 259 | 350 | 161 | 465 | 480 | 361 | 169 | 231 | 2675 | RED | 5350 |
| Par | 3 | 4 | 4 | 3 | 5 | 5 | 4 | 3 | 4 | 35 | Par | 70 |
| Handicap | 12 | 16 | 6 | 18 | 8 | 4 | 2 | 14 | 10 | x | | |

# MAP F3
(6 COURSES)

PAGES.. 352-357

CEN-CAL MAP...see page 314
adjoining maps
NORTH (E3).......see page 292
EAST (F4)..........see page 358
SOUTH (G3).......see page 382
WEST (F2).........see page 344

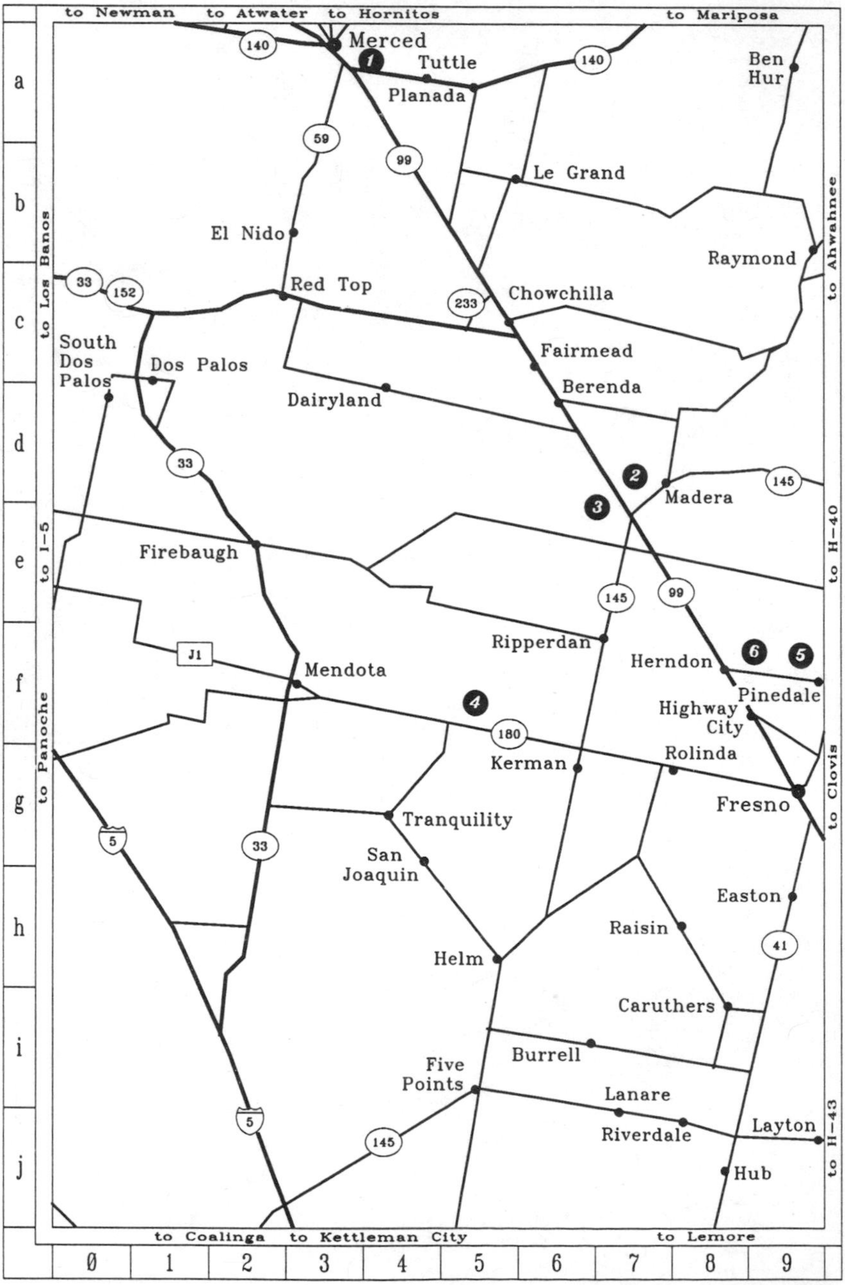

to Newman to Atwater to Hornitos to Mariposa

Merced
Tuttle
Planada
Ben Hur
Le Grand
El Nido
Raymond
Red Top
Chowchilla
South Dos Palos
Dos Palos
Fairmead
Dairyland
Berenda
Madera
Firebaugh
Ripperdan
Herndon
Mendota
Pinedale
Highway City
Kerman
Rolinda
Fresno
Tranquility
San Joaquin
Easton
Raisin
Helm
Caruthers
Burrell
Five Points
Lanare
Riverdale
Layton
Hub

to Los Banos
to I-5
to Panoche
to Ahwahnee
to H-40
to Clovis
to H-43

140 59 99 233 33 152 145 J1 180 5 41

to Coalinga to Kettleman City to Lemore

| a | b | c | d | e | f | g | h | i | j |
|---|---|---|---|---|---|---|---|---|---|

| 0 | 1 | 2 | 3 | 4 | 5 | 6 | 7 | 8 | 9 |
|---|---|---|---|---|---|---|---|---|---|

# MERCED GOLF AND COUNTRY CLUB

**Course 1**
**MAP F3 grid a3**

**1961**
**R.E. Baldock**

6333 North Golf Road
Merced, CA 95340

Pro shop (209) 722-3357
Clubhouse (209) 722-6268

- ✓ **driving range**
- ✓ **practice greens**
- ✓ **power carts**
- ✓ **pull carts**
- ✓ **golf club rental**
- ✓ **locker rooms**
- ✓ **showers**
- executive course
- accommodations
- ✓ **food and beverages**
- ✓ **clubhouse**

**Ed Leinenkugel**
Professional

**Harold Stone**
Superintendent

*Course information:* This private club has 18 holes and par is 72. The course is 6,423 yards and rated 70.4 from the championship tees, and 6,145 yards and rated 69.1 from the regular tees. The slope ratings are 119 championship and 117 regular. Women's tees are 6,139 yards and rated 75.7 from the championship tees, and 5,722 yards and rated 73.0 from the forward tees. The slope ratings are 132 championship and 124 forward.

*Play policy and fees:* Reciprocal play is accepted with members of other private clubs. Green fees for reciprocators are $35. Guest fees are $25 accompanied by a member and $35 unaccompanied. Carts are $7 for nine holes and $14 for 18 holes.

*Location:* From Highway 99 in Merced, take "G" Street north. Follow it to Bellevue Road, turn right and then turn left onto North Golf Road.

*Course description:* Redesigned by Robert Dean Putman, this quiet valley course is short with rolling hills and lots of trees.



# MADERA GOLF AND COUNTRY CLUB

**Course 2**
**MAP F3 grid d7**

**1955**
**R.E. Baldock**

Road 26 at Avenue 19
Madera, CA 93638

Pro shop (209) 674-2682
Clubhouse (209) 674-9132

- ✓ **driving range**
- ✓ **practice greens**
- ✓ **power carts**
- ✓ **pull carts**
- ✓ **golf club rental**
- ✓ **locker rooms**
- ✓ **showers**
- executive course
- accommodations
- ✓ **food and beverages**
- ✓ **clubhouse**

**Howard Roseen**
Professional

**Bob Stucky**
Superintendent

*Course information:* This private course has 18 holes and par is 72. The course is 6,774 yards and rated 70.7 from the championship tees, and 6,555 yards and rated 69.8 from the regular tees. The slope ratings are 119 championship and 117 regular. Women's tees are 5,900 yards and rated 74.3. The slope rating is 128.

*Play policy and fees:* Reciprocal play is accepted with members of other private clubs. Green fees for reciprocators are $30. Guest fees are $15 accompanied by a member and $30 unaccompanied. Carts are $14.

*Location:* From Highway 99 in Madera, north of downtown, take the Avenue 17 exit east. Turn left onto County Road 26. The course is at Avenue 19.

*Course description:* This sporty course has lots of rolling hills. Tall eucalyptus trees come into play on the front nine, and maturing pine trees on the back nine. It's easily walkable. Howard Roseen holds the course record of 64, set in 1967.

# MADERA MUNICIPAL GOLF COURSE

**Course 3**
MAP F3 grid d6

**1991**
**Robert Dean Putman**

23200 Avenue 17
Madera, CA 93637

Pro shop (209) 675-3504
Clubhouse (209) 675-3533

- ✓ **driving range**
- ✓ **practice greens**
- ✓ **power carts**
- ✓ **pull carts**
- ✓ **golf club rental**
- locker rooms
- showers
- executive course
- accommodations
- ✓ **food and beverages**
- ✓ **clubhouse**

**Dean Rollins**
Professional

**Mark Goodmanson**
Superintendent

***Course information:*** This public course has 18 holes. See card below for yardage and rating information.

***Play policy and fees:*** Green fees are $4.50 for nine holes and $9 for 18 holes weekdays, and $6 for nine holes and $12 for 18 holes weekends. The twilight rate is $6 weekdays and $8 weekends. Senior green fees are $6 and carts are reduced $3 weekdays only with the purchase of an annual discount card. Carts are $16. Reservations are recommended seven days in advance.

***Location:*** From Highway 99 north of Madera, take the Avenue 17 exit and follow it west one mile to the course.

***Course description:*** Robert Dean Putman tested his course on opening day, June 8, 1991, and shot a 68. Graciously, Putman has designed a course with wide appeal. Both low and high handicappers will enjoy this course. The greens are large and undulating, and well bunkered. "Getting down in two on some holes will be a major accomplishment and three or four putt greens may not be that rare for some," reported Paul Bittick, *Madera Tribune* sports editor. The fairways are bunkered, too, and four lakes come into play on eight holes. Bob Silva holds the course record at 66.

| Hole | 1 | 2 | 3 | 4 | 5 | 6 | 7 | 8 | 9 | Out | | |
|---|---|---|---|---|---|---|---|---|---|---|---|---|
| BLUE | 425 | 398 | 191 | 534 | 401 | 171 | 416 | 522 | 379 | 3437 | BLUE | Rating: 71.3 |
| WHITE | 404 | 342 | 158 | 496 | 389 | 150 | 378 | 493 | 359 | 3169 | | Slope: 119 |
| Par | 4 | 4 | 3 | 5 | 4 | 3 | 4 | 5 | 4 | 36 | WHITE | Rating: 69.1 |
| Handicap | 1 | 13 | 5 | 9 | 7 | 15 | 3 | 11 | 17 | x | | Slope: 115 |
| RED | 353 | 307 | 130 | 410 | 346 | 114 | 340 | 452 | 312 | 2764 | | |
| Par | 4 | 4 | 3 | 5 | 4 | 3 | 4 | 5 | 4 | 36 | RED | Rating: 70.3 |
| Handicap | 1 | 13 | 5 | 9 | 7 | 15 | 3 | 11 | 17 | x | | Slope: 112 |

| Hole | 10 | 11 | 12 | 13 | 14 | 15 | 16 | 17 | 18 | In | Totals | |
|---|---|---|---|---|---|---|---|---|---|---|---|---|
| BLUE | 417 | 187 | 529 | 406 | 381 | 188 | 343 | 387 | 541 | 3379 | BLUE | 6816 |
| WHITE | 390 | 167 | 512 | 392 | 365 | 147 | 329 | 356 | 523 | 3181 | WHITE | 6350 |
| Par | 4 | 3 | 5 | 4 | 4 | 3 | 4 | 4 | 5 | 36 | Par | 72 |
| Handicap | 2 | 14 | 8 | 4 | 6 | 12 | 18 | 16 | 10 | x | | |
| RED | 342 | 110 | 393 | 346 | 321 | 112 | 296 | 331 | 456 | 2707 | RED | 5471 |
| Par | 4 | 3 | 5 | 4 | 4 | 3 | 4 | 4 | 5 | 36 | Par | 72 |
| Handicap | 2 | 14 | 8 | 4 | 6 | 12 | 18 | 16 | 10 | x | | |

# FRESNO WEST GOLF COURSE

**Course 4**
MAP F3 grid f5

**1966**
**R.E. Baldock**

23986 West Whitesbridge Rd.
Kerman, CA 93630

Pro shop (209) 846-8655

- ✓ **driving range**
- ✓ **practice greens**
- ✓ **power carts**
- ✓ **pull carts**
- ✓ **golf club rental**
- locker rooms
- showers
- executive course
- accommodations
- ✓ **food and beverages**
- ✓ **clubhouse**

**Ron Goering**
Manager/Professional

**Carlos Rodriguez**
Superintendent

***Course information:*** This public course has 18 holes and par is 72. The course is 6,959 yards and rated 72.4 from the championship tees, and 6,607 yards and rated 70.6 from the regular tees. The slope ratings are 118 championship and 114 regular. Women's tees are 6,000 yards and rated 74.1. The slope rating is 122.

***Play policy and fees:*** Green fees are $12 weekdays and $15 weekends. Carts are $10 for nine holes and $20 for 18 holes. Reservations are recommended one week in advance. This course is available for outside tournaments.

***Location:*** From Highway 99 in Fresno, take the Highway 180/Whitesbridge Road exit. Drive past Kerman to the course.

***Course description:*** This is a very quiet, championship golf course. It's long, flat and often windy. There's water on eight holes. If you want to prove yourself a golfer, make par on the eighth. It's a 174-yard par-3 with water to the left and behind the green. Harold Chuhlantseff holds the course record with a 65.



MAP ON PAGE 352

# FIG GARDEN GOLF COURSE

**Course 5**
MAP F3 grid f9

***Course information:*** This semi-private course has 18 holes. See card below for yardage and rating information.

***Play policy and fees:*** Outside play is accepted. Green fees are $25 every day. Twilight rates after 12 noon summer season and 1 p.m. winter season are $13. Carts are $14 for nine holes, and $23 for 18 holes. Reservations are recommended. This course is available for outside tournaments. Call a year ahead.

***Location:*** Heading south toward Fresno on Highway 99, take the Herndon exit east. Turn left on North Van Ness Boulevard and drive to the course.

***Course description:*** Robert Dean Putman redesigned this course in 1973. It's a tight course and has two lakes and a river for a bonus. The greens are small and fast. The 465-yard, par-4 16th hole is a monster with the river flanking the left side. Gary Bauer holds the men's course record with a 61. Shelly Hammond holds the women's record with a 68.

**1958**
**Nick Lombardo**

7700 North Van Ness
Boulevard
Fresno, CA 93711

Pro shop (209) 439-2928

- ✓ **driving range**
- ✓ **practice greens**
- ✓ **power carts**
- pull carts
- ✓ **golf club rental**
- ✓ **locker rooms**
- showers
- executive course
- accommodations
- ✓ **food and beverages**
- ✓ **clubhouse**

**Gary Bauer**
Professional

**Dave Knott**
Superintendent

| Hole | 1 | 2 | 3 | 4 | 5 | 6 | 7 | 8 | 9 | Out | BLUE | Rating: 70.5 |
|---|---|---|---|---|---|---|---|---|---|---|---|---|
| BLUE | 342 | 390 | 170 | 560 | 445 | 588 | 205 | 365 | 311 | 3376 | | Slope: 122 |
| WHITE | 342 | 379 | 140 | 500 | 445 | 552 | 169 | 360 | 301 | 3188 | | |
| Par | 4 | 4 | 3 | 5 | 4 | 5 | 3 | 4 | 4 | 36 | WHITE | Rating: 68.7 |
| Handicap | 15 | 9 | 13 | 5 | 1 | 3 | 7 | 11 | 17 | x | | Slope: 112 |
| RED | 323 | 355 | 83 | 486 | 385 | 474 | 159 | 339 | 279 | 2883 | | |
| Par | 4 | 4 | 3 | 5 | 4 | 5 | 3 | 4 | 4 | 36 | RED | Rating: 72.2 |
| Handicap | 11 | 5 | 17 | 1 | 7 | 3 | 15 | 9 | 13 | x | | Slope: 127 |

| Hole | 10 | 11 | 12 | 13 | 14 | 15 | 16 | 17 | 18 | In | Totals | |
|---|---|---|---|---|---|---|---|---|---|---|---|---|
| BLUE | 410 | 175 | 354 | 335 | 385 | 477 | 440 | 189 | 480 | 3245 | BLUE | 6621 |
| WHITE | 375 | 165 | 330 | 325 | 362 | 471 | 406 | 178 | 472 | 3084 | WHITE | 6272 |
| Par | 4 | 3 | 4 | 4 | 4 | 5 | 4 | 3 | 5 | 36 | Par | 72 |
| Handicap | 4 | 10 | 18 | 16 | 8 | 12 | 2 | 6 | 14 | x | | |
| RED | 334 | 154 | 301 | 290 | 334 | 403 | 375 | 123 | 408 | 2722 | RED | 5605 |
| Par | 4 | 3 | 4 | 4 | 4 | 5 | 4 | 3 | 5 | 36 | Par | 72 |
| Handicap | 6 | 18 | 12 | 10 | 14 | 4 | 8 | 16 | 2 | x | | |

# SAN JOAQUIN VALLEY COUNTRY CLUB

**Course 6**
**MAP F3 grid f9**

**1961**
**Robert Dean Putman**

3484 West Bluff Avenue
Fresno, CA 93711

Pro shop (209) 439-3359
Clubhouse (209) 439-3483

- ✓ **driving range**
- ✓ **practice greens**
- ✓ **power carts**
- ✓ **pull carts**
- golf club rental
- ✓ **locker rooms**
- ✓ **showers**
- executive course
- accommodations
- ✓ **food and beverages**
- ✓ **clubhouse**

**Terry Treece**
Professional

**Mike Paniccia**
Director of Golf

**Owen Stone**
Superintendent

***Course information:*** This private course has 18 holes and par is 72. The course is 6,970 yards and rated 73.3 from the tournament tees, 6,438 yards and rated 71.6 from the championship tees, and 6,126 yards and rated 70.0 from the regular tees. The slope ratings are 128 tournament, 125 championship and 120 regular. Women's tees are 5,760 yards and rated 72.9. The slope rating is 128.

***Play policy and fees:*** Reciprocal play is accepted with members of other private clubs. Guest fees are $25 with a member and $50 for reciprocal players. Carts are $9 per person.

***Location:*** From Highway 99 in Herndon, take the West Herndon Avenue exit. Drive East to North Marks Avenue and turn left. Then turn right on West Bluff and continue to the course.

***Course description:*** This is a long, rolling course with lots of trees. The San Joaquin River comes into play on the north side on three holes. The highlight here is the well-maintained greens, which are fast and tricky. The men's course record is 63, held by Mike Barr, and the women's course record is 67, held by Kathleen Scrivner.

# MAP F4
(17 COURSES)

PAGES. 358 -371

CEN-CAL MAP...see page 314
adjoining maps
NORTH (E4).......see page 306
EAST (F5)..........see page 372
SOUTH (G4).......see page 384
WEST (F3).........see page 352

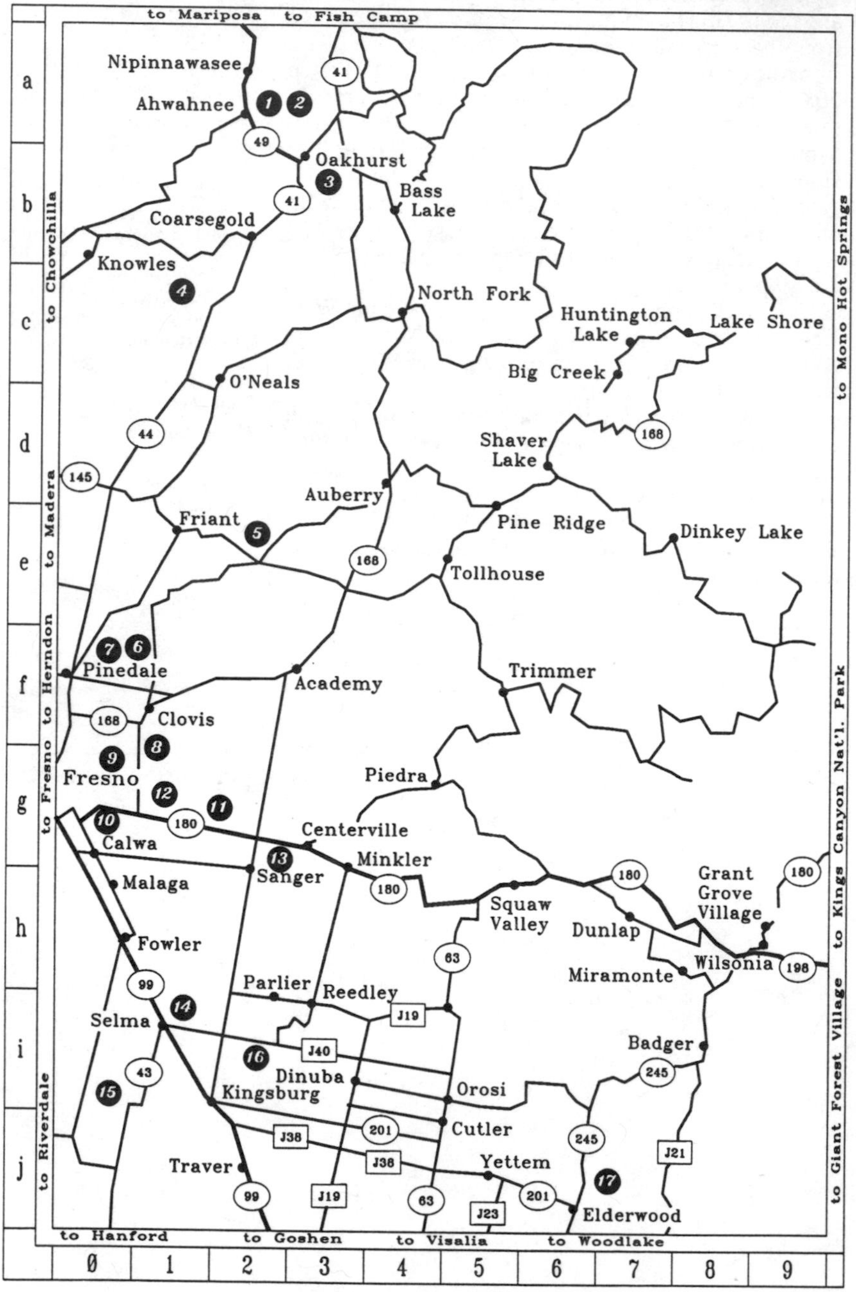

to Mariposa to Fish Camp
to Chowchilla
to Madera
to Fresno to Herndon
to Riverdale
to Mono Hot Springs
to Giant Forest Village to Kings Canyon Nat'l. Park
to Hanford to Goshen to Visalia to Woodlake

a b c d e f g h i j
0 1 2 3 4 5 6 7 8 9

Nipinnawasee
Ahwahnee 1 2
41
49
Oakhurst
3
Bass Lake
41
Coarsegold
Knowles
4
North Fork
Huntington Lake
Lake Shore
Big Creek
O'Neals
44
168
Shaver Lake
145
Auberry
Pine Ridge
Friant
5
Dinkey Lake
168
Tollhouse
7 6
Pinedale
Academy
Trimmer
168
Clovis
8
9
Fresno
Piedra
12
11
10
180
Centerville
Calwa
13
Sanger
Minkler
Malaga
180
180
Grant Grove Village
180
Squaw Valley
Dunlap
Fowler
63
Wilsonia
198
99
Miramonte
Parlier
Reedley
14
J19
Selma
Badger
16
J40
43
Dinuba
245
15
Kingsburg
Orosi
201
Cutler
J38
245
J21
J38
Yettem
Traver
17
99
J19
63
J23
201
Elderwood

# RIVER CREEK GOLF COURSE

**Course 1**
MAP F4 grid a2

*Course information:* This public course has nine holes. Par is 72 for 18. The course is 6,232 yards and rated 69.3 from the championship tees, and 5,986 yards and rated 68.2 from the regular tees. The slope ratings are 120 championship and 117 regular. Women's tees are 5,568 yards and rated 66.3 from the regular tees. The slope ratings are 110 championship and 106 regular.

*Play policy and fees:* Green fees are $7 for nine and $13 for 18 holes weekdays, and $10 for nine and $18 for 18 holes weekends. Carts are $10 for nine and $18 for 18 holes.

*Location:* Take Highway 49 to Road 600 in Ahwahnee.

*Course description:* There are lots of trees that guard many holes on this course. Water comes into play on three holes. The par-4, 4th hole is a 372-yard monster. The course record of 67 is held by Ron Winsell.

**1991**
**John Hillborn**

41709 Road 600
Ahwahnee, CA 93601

Pro shop (209) 683-3388

- ✓ **driving range**
- ✓ **practice greens**
- ✓ **power carts**
- pull carts
- ✓ **golf club rental**
- ✓ **locker rooms**
- ✓ **showers**
- executive course
- accommodations
- ✓ **food and beverages**
- ✓ **clubhouse**

**Jerry Nikkel**
Professional

**Tom Hillborn**
Superintendent

**John Hillborn**
Owner

CENTRAL F4

# AHWAHNEE COUNRY CLUB

**Course 2**
MAP F4 grid a2

*Course information:* This semi-private course has 18 holes and par is 72. This course is 6,232 yards and rated 70.5 from the championship tees, and 5,721 yards and rated 68.4 from the regular tees. The slope ratings are 126 championship and 122 regular. Women's tees are 4,860 yards and rated 68.5. The slope rating is 116.

*Play policy and fees:* Outside play is accepted. Green fees are $10 for nine and $17 for 18 holes. Carts are $4 for nine and $8 for 18 holes.

*Location:* Going towards Yosemite, take Highway 49 north to Oakhurst. Go three miles then east to Harmony Lane.

*Course description:* This is a mountain course with stress being put on accuracy. Good iron play is essential for a successful round. It has small greens, but they are fast and interesting. Note: the clubhouse is scheduled to be completed in January 1993.

**1988**
**Alan Thomas**

46785 Road 621
Ahwahnee, CA 93601

Pro shop (209) 683-6620

- ✓ **driving range**
- ✓ **practice greens**
- ✓ **power carts**
- ✓ **pull carts**
- ✓ **golf club rental**
- locker rooms
- showers
- executive course
- accommodations
- ✓ **food and beverages**
- ✓ **clubhouse**

**Jerry Nikkel**
Professional

**Tom Hillborn**
Superintendent

**John Hillborn**
Owner

## SIERRA SKY RANCH GOLF COURSE

**Course 3**
MAP F4 grid c1

***Course information:*** This course has been closed.

## YOSEMITE LAKES PARK GOLF COURSE

**Course 4**
MAP F4 grid c1

***Course information:*** This private course has nine holes. Par is 62 for 18 holes. The course is 3,534 yards and rated 57.9 from the regular tees. The slope rating is 98. Women's tees are 3,069 yards and rated 57.1. The slope rating is 85.

***Play policy and fees:*** Reciprocal play is accepted with members of other private clubs. Guest fees are $10. Carts are $10. Play is on a first-come first-served basis weekdays. Reservations are required on Fridays and weekends.

***Location:*** Driving toward Yosemite National Park on Highway 41 before Coarsegold, turn left on Yosemite Springs Parkway. Drive four miles to the course.

***Course description:*** This is a fun, short course. Hills and water come into play on five holes. The fairways are narrow and the course can be unforgiving unless the ball is kept in the air. Don't expect this to be an easy stroll in the park. Diane Staurum holds the women's course record with a 64 and Gene Templeton holds the men's record with 59.

**1970**
**Buck Noonkester**

30250 Yosemite Springs Parkway
Coarsegold, CA 93614

Pro shop (209) 658-7468
Clubhouse (209) 658-7466

- driving range
- ✓ **practice greens**
- ✓ **power carts**
- ✓ **pull carts**
- ✓ **golf club rental**
- locker rooms
- showers
- ✓ **executive course**
- accommodations
- ✓ **food and beverages**
- ✓ **clubhouse**

**Karen Swagger**
Manager

**Buck Noonkester**
Superintendent

# BRIGHTON CREST COUNTRY CLUB

**Course 5**
MAP F4 grid e2

**1990**
**Johnny Miller**

PO Box 25281
Fresno, CA 93729-5281

21722 Fairway Oaks Lane
Friant, CA 93626

Pro shop (209) 299-8586
Office (209) 323-8076

- ✓ **driving range**
- ✓ **practice greens**
- ✓ **power carts**
- pull carts
- ✓ **golf club rental**
- locker rooms
- showers
- executive course
- accommodations
- ✓ **food and beverages**
- ✓ **clubhouse**

**Ron Winsell**
Professional

**Keith Justesen**
Superintendent

***Course information:*** This private course has 18 holes. Par is 72. The course is 6,831 yards and rated 73.5 from the tournament tees, and 6,363 yards and rated 71.4 from the championship tees, and 5,917 yards and rated 69.4 from the regular tees. The slope ratings are 135 tournament, 131 championship and 126 regular. Women's tees are 5,195 yards, a rating of 71.2, and 124 slope.

***Play policy and fees:*** Outside play is accepted. Members and guests only. Reciprocal play is accepted with members of other private clubs at a reduced rate. Have your club pro call for arrangements. Outside green fees are $50 weekdays, and $60 weekends. Green fees for guests accompanied by a member are $35 and $50 when unaccompanied. Carts are $10 per person for 18 holes. Reservations are recommended. This course is available for outside tournaments.

***Location:*** From Fresno take Highway 41 north to the Friant Road/Millerton Lake exit. Drive east on Friant Road for 15 miles to Friant and the course.

***Course description:*** This is the first Johnny Miller-designed course in California. It opened for play in September, 1990. The course features bent grass tees and greens. The fairways are rye and the roughs are fescue. At the 800-foot elevation the course is normally above the winter fog level and is also somewhat cooler during the summer months. The terrain is rolling and the course is dotted with native blue and valley oaks. *Golf Digest* has rated this course one of the top 25 new courses in the country. The greens, which Miller has sized to fit the difficulty of the hole, are subtle but undulating. Miller has humanely left ample room for pin placement. When you reach the green you should still be able to survive the hole. One of Miller's favorite holes is the par-5, 505-yard number three. There is a slight dogleg right and the second shot must go between two oaks. There is a lateral hazard on the entire left side, but until homes are built, the right side is clear. Water runs in front of the two-tiered small green. Watch out for native grasses off the fairway and the fescue rough. At 18 months old, the course looked like it had already been there for 50 years because of the terrain and large oaks. The unofficial men's course record is 66, held by host pro Ron Winsell.

# RIVERSIDE OF FRESNO GOLF COURSE

**Course 6**
MAP F4 grid f0

**1939**
7672 N. Josephine Avenue
Fresno, CA 93711

Pro shop (209) 275-5900
Clubhouse (209) 275-6515

- ✓ **driving range**
- ✓ **practice greens**
- ✓ **power carts**
- ✓ **pull carts**
- ✓ **golf club rental**
- locker rooms
- showers
- executive course
- accommodations
- ✓ **food and beverages**
- ✓ **clubhouse**

**Mike Catanesi**
Professional

**Gary Rogers**
Superintendent

***Course information:*** This public course has 18 holes and par is 72. The course is 6,621 yards and rated 71.2 from the championship tees, and 6,395 yards and rated 70.2 from the regular tees. The slope ratings are 122 championship and 120 regular. Women's tees are 6,008 yards and rated 74.4. The slope rating is 129.

***Play policy and fees:*** Green fees are $11 weekdays and $13 weekends and holidays. Carts are $10 for nine holes and $18 for 18 holes. Reservations are recommended one week in advance. This course is available for outside tournaments.

***Location:*** From Highway 99 in Fresno, exit onto Herndon Avenue east. Cross the railroad tracks and turn left on Van Buren, then turn right on Josephine and follow it to the course.

***Course description:*** This rolling course is long and well guarded by trees. It's testy with a number of sidehill lies to medium-sized greens. Bring every club. Notable is the 10th hole, which tees off from a bluff, hitting to a green guarded on the right by an overhanging tree. The hole is 423 yards and par-4. Bruce Sanders and Harold Chuhlantseff hold the course record with a 63.

| Hole | 1 | 2 | 3 | 4 | 5 | 6 | 7 | 8 | 9 | Out | | |
|---|---|---|---|---|---|---|---|---|---|---|---|---|
| BLUE | 380 | 174 | 377 | 424 | 159 | 567 | 357 | 179 | 555 | 3172 | BLUE | Rating: 71.2 |
| WHITE | 365 | 153 | 368 | 412 | 149 | 556 | 349 | 169 | 548 | 3069 | | Slope: 122 |
| Par | 4 | 3 | 4 | 4 | 3 | 5 | 4 | 3 | 5 | 35 | WHITE | Rating: 70.2 |
| Handicap | 17 | 9 | 7 | 1 | 15 | 5 | 11 | 13 | 3 | x | | Slope: 120 |
| RED | 328 | 136 | 300 | 405 | 138 | 509 | 341 | 160 | 528 | 2845 | | |
| Par | 4 | 3 | 4 | 5 | 3 | 5 | 4 | 3 | 5 | 36 | RED | Rating: 74.4 |
| Handicap | 7 | 17 | 9 | 11 | 15 | 3 | 5 | 13 | 1 | x | | Slope: 129 |

| Hole | 10 | 11 | 12 | 13 | 14 | 15 | 16 | 17 | 18 | In | Totals | |
|---|---|---|---|---|---|---|---|---|---|---|---|---|
| BLUE | 423 | 149 | 361 | 437 | 505 | 203 | 519 | 385 | 467 | 3449 | BLUE | 6621 |
| WHITE | 412 | 140 | 349 | 409 | 495 | 185 | 504 | 376 | 456 | 3326 | WHITE | 6395 |
| Par | 4 | 3 | 4 | 4 | 5 | 3 | 5 | 4 | 5 | 37 | Par | 72 |
| Handicap | 6 | 18 | 14 | 2 | 12 | 4 | 10 | 8 | 16 | x | | |
| RED | 401 | 128 | 300 | 400 | 484 | 156 | 488 | 366 | 440 | 3163 | RED | 6008 |
| Par | 5 | 3 | 4 | 5 | 5 | 3 | 5 | 4 | 5 | 39 | Par | 75 |
| Handicap | 14 | 18 | 8 | 4 | 10 | 16 | 2 | 6 | 12 | x | | |

# FORT WASHINGTON GOLF AND COUNTRY CLUB

**Course 7**
MAP F4 grid f0

**1925**
**William "Willie" Watson**

10272 North Millbrook Avenue
Fresno, CA 93720

Pro shop (209) 434-9120
Clubhouse (209) 434-1702

- ✓ **driving range**
- ✓ **practice greens**
- ✓ **power carts**
- pull carts
- golf club rental
- ✓ **locker rooms**
- ✓ **showers**
- executive course
- accommodations
- ✓ **food and beverages**
- ✓ **clubhouse**

**Michael S. Mattingly**
Professional

**Paul Ludington**
Superintendent

*Course information:* This private course has 18 holes and par is 72. The course is 6,635 yards and rated 71.6 from the championship tees, and 6,446 yards and rated 70.4 from the regular tees. The slope ratings are 124 championship and 121 regular. Women's tees are 6,091 yards and 74.7. The slope rating is 129.

*Play policy and fees:* Reciprocal play is accepted with members of other private clubs. Guest fees are $20 with a member and $35 without, and $75 if you are from out of the area. Carts are $8.

*Location:* From Highway 99 in Fresno, take the Herndon Avenue exit east. Turn left on Blackstone Avenue. Turn right on Friant Road and then turn right again on Fort Washington which leads to the course.

*Course description:* This is a classic valley course. It was rated among the top 20 courses in Northern California in 1989. There are rolling hills, tree-lined fairways and fast, undulating greens. It's walkable. The Pro-Scratch is played here annually in May.

# VILLAGE GREEN GOLF COURSE

**Course 8**
MAP F4 grid f1

**1959**
**Robert Dean Putman**

222 South Clovis Avenue
Fresno, CA 93727

Pro shop (209) 255-2786
Clubhouse (209) 255-9030

- driving range
- ✓ **practice greens**
- ✓ **power carts**
- ✓ **pull carts**
- ✓ **golf club rental**
- locker rooms
- showers
- executive course
- ✓ **accommodations**
- ✓ **food and beverages**
- ✓ **clubhouse**

**Gordon Israelsky, Jr.**
Professional

**Anthony Westcott**
Superintendent

***Course information:*** This public course has nine holes and par is 60 for 18 holes. The course is 3,429 yards and rated 56.8 from the regular tees. The slope rating is 91. All play is from the same tees.

***Play policy and fees:*** Green fees are $5 for nine holes and $8 for 18 holes weekdays, and $6 for nine holes and $9 for 18 holes weekends. Carts are $7 for nine holes and $12 for 18 holes. Reservations are recommended. This course is available for outside tournaments.

***Location:*** From Highway 99 in Fresno, take the Tulare Avenue exit east to Clovis Avenue. The course is in the Village Green Country Club apartment complex.

***Course description:*** There are three par-4s and six par-3s on this course. All holes are well bunkered from tee to green and well maintained, with lots of trees. On hole seven, the ball carries over trees and a duck pond to the green. You can barely see the green. Try a five iron on this 157-yard, par-3 hole. Richard Ellis and Gordon Isrealsky, Jr. hold the course record of 56.

# PALM LAKES GOLF COURSE

**Course 9**
MAP F4 grid g0

***Course information:*** This public course has 18 holes. See card below for yardage and rating information.

***Play policy and fees:*** Green fees are $8 weekdays and $9 weekends and holidays. The rate for seniors is $5.50 and students are $4.50. Carts are $7.50 for nine holes and $15 for 18 holes. Reservations are recommended. This course is available for outside tournaments.

***Location:*** Driving south on Highway 99 from Madera, take the Shaw exit east past California State University Fresno. Turn right on Willow and then left at Dakota Avenue. The course is located across from the airport.

***Course description:*** This short executive course has one large lake which comes into play on four holes. The course is about 20 years old, but was remodeled six years ago. It is walkable.

5025 East Dakota
Fresno, CA 93727

Pro shop (209) 292-1144

- driving range
- ✓ **practice greens**
- ✓ **power carts**
- ✓ **pull carts**
- ✓ **golf club rental**
- locker rooms
- showers
- ✓ **executive course**
- accommodations
- ✓ **food and beverages**
- ✓ **clubhouse**

**Jim Moore**
Manager/Professional

**Joe Woods**
Superintendent

CENTRAL F4

| Hole | 1 | 2 | 3 | 4 | 5 | 6 | 7 | 8 | 9 | Out | | |
|---|---|---|---|---|---|---|---|---|---|---|---|---|
| BLUE | - | - | - | - | - | - | - | - | - | - | BLUE | Rating: -- |
| | | | | | | | | | | | | Slope: -- |
| WHITE | 318 | 386 | 159 | 121 | 172 | 180 | 249 | 165 | 328 | 2078 | | |
| Par | 4 | 4 | 3 | 3 | 3 | 3 | 3 | 3 | 4 | 30 | WHITE | Rating: 60.7 |
| Handicap | 13 | 1 | 7 | 18 | 12 | 9 | 2 | 14 | 13 | x | | Slope: 100 |
| RED | 318 | 386 | 159 | 121 | 172 | 180 | 249 | 165 | 328 | 2078 | | |
| Par | 4 | 4 | 3 | 3 | 3 | 3 | 4 | 3 | 4 | 31 | RED | Rating: 60.7 |
| Handicap | 5 | 1 | 15 | 17 | 11 | 13 | 7 | 9 | 3 | x | | Slope: 100 |

| Hole | 10 | 11 | 12 | 13 | 14 | 15 | 16 | 17 | 18 | In | Totals | |
|---|---|---|---|---|---|---|---|---|---|---|---|---|
| BLUE | - | - | - | - | - | - | - | - | - | - | BLUE | -- |
| WHITE | 313 | 161 | 182 | 211 | 381 | 358 | 260 | 195 | 323 | 2384 | WHITE | 4462 |
| Par | 4 | 3 | 3 | 3 | 4 | 4 | 4 | 3 | 4 | 32 | Par | 62 |
| Handicap | 8 | 17 | 5 | 6 | 10 | 11 | 4 | 3 | 16 | x | | |
| RED | 313 | 161 | 182 | 211 | 381 | 358 | 260 | 195 | 323 | 2384 | RED | 4462 |
| Par | 4 | 3 | 3 | 4 | 4 | 4 | 4 | 3 | 4 | 33 | Par | 64 |
| Handicap | 10 | 18 | 16 | 12 | 2 | 4 | 8 | 14 | 6 | x | | |

# SUNNYSIDE COUNTRY CLUB

**Course 10**
MAP F4 grid g0

***Course information:*** This private club has 18 holes. The men's gold tees are 6,099 yards, rated 69.1, and have a slope rating of 116. The women's gold tees are 6,094 yards, rated 74.8, and have a slope rating of 130. See card below for additional yardage and rating information.

***Play policy and fees:*** Reciprocal play is accepted with members of other private clubs. Have your club pro call for arrangements. Guest fees are $25 when accompanied by a member, and $50 when unaccompanied. Carts are $9 per person. No denim of any kind may be worn. Shorts must have a six-inch seam, and shirts must have collars.

***Location:*** From Highway 99 in Fresno, take the Ventura Avenue/Kings Canyon Road exit east for seven miles to Clovis Avenue and turn left on East Butler to the course.

***Course description:*** This long, demanding course has tight fairways and lots of sand and trees. Be careful of the greens: they look innocent enough, but they're small, fast and quite tricky. Originally built in 1906, William Park Bell redesigned the course in the 1940s. Kevin Sutherland holds the course record at 61. The women's record is owned by LPGA golfer Shelley Hamlin at 67. The USGA Junior Championship was played here in August 1992. The United Express Pro-Scratch is an annual tournament played in early May. The California State Junior was played here in 1992.

**1906**

5704 East Butler
Fresno, CA 93727

Pro shop (209) 255-6871
Clubhouse (209) 251-6011

- ✓ **driving range**
- ✓ **practice greens**
- ✓ **power carts**
- ✓ **pull carts**
- ✓ **golf club rental**
- ✓ **locker rooms**
- ✓ **showers**
- executive course
- accommodations
- ✓ **food and beverages**
- ✓ **clubhouse**

**Steve Menchinella**
Professional

**Al Korpak**
Manager

**Joe Tompkins**
Superintendent

| Hole | 1 | 2 | 3 | 4 | 5 | 6 | 7 | 8 | 9 | Out | | |
|---|---|---|---|---|---|---|---|---|---|---|---|---|
| BLUE | 415 | 387 | 441 | 200 | 527 | 135 | 404 | 421 | 548 | 3478 | BLUE | Rating: 72.3 |
| WHITE | 404 | 367 | 427 | 186 | 511 | 122 | 383 | 402 | 534 | 3336 | | Slope: 126 |
| Par | 4 | 4 | 4 | 3 | 5 | 3 | 4 | 4 | 5 | 36 | WHITE | Rating: 70.4 |
| Handicap | 3 | 7 | 1 | 11 | 15 | 17 | 9 | 5 | 13 | x | | Slope: 121 |
| RED | 354 | 302 | 405 | 160 | 452 | 93 | 335 | 347 | 457 | 2905 | | |
| Par | 4 | 4 | 5 | 3 | 5 | 3 | 4 | 4 | 5 | 37 | RED | Rating: 71.8 |
| Handicap | 7 | 11 | 15 | 13 | 1 | 17 | 9 | 5 | 3 | x | | Slope: 124 |

| Hole | 10 | 11 | 12 | 13 | 14 | 15 | 16 | 17 | 18 | In | Totals | |
|---|---|---|---|---|---|---|---|---|---|---|---|---|
| BLUE | 344 | 436 | 340 | 158 | 385 | 548 | 352 | 188 | 551 | 3302 | BLUE | 6780 |
| WHITE | 323 | 419 | 325 | 149 | 373 | 527 | 322 | 159 | 511 | 3108 | WHITE | 6444 |
| Par | 4 | 4 | 4 | 3 | 4 | 5 | 4 | 3 | 5 | 36 | Par | 72 |
| Handicap | 16 | 2 | 8 | 14 | 6 | 4 | 12 | 18 | 10 | x | | |
| RED | 295 | 371 | 252 | 137 | 330 | 440 | 265 | 120 | 424 | 2634 | RED | 5539 |
| Par | 4 | 4 | 4 | 3 | 4 | 5 | 4 | 3 | 5 | 36 | Par | 73 |
| Handicap | 16 | 2 | 10 | 14 | 8 | 4 | 12 | 18 | 6 | x | | |

# BELMONT COUNTRY CLUB

**Course 11**
MAP F4 grid g1

***Course information:*** This private course has 18 holes and par is 72. The course is 6,397 yards and rated 70.7 from the championship tees, and 6,234 yards and rated 69.7 from the regular tees. The slope ratings are 119 championship and 117 regular. Women's tees are 6,248 yards and rated 75.3 from the championship tees, and 5,989 yards and rated 73.8 from the forward tees. The slope ratings are 131 tournament, 130 championship and 127 forward.

***Play policy and fees:*** Reciprocal play is accepted with members of other private clubs. Have your club pro call for arrangements. Guest fees are $20 when accompanied by a member and $50 unaccompanied weekdays, and $35 when accompanied by a member and $50 unaccompanied weekends. Carts are $8 for one person and $16 for two people. This course has limited availability for outside tournaments.

***Location:*** In Fresno on Highway 99, take the Belmont Avenue exit east. Drive 13.5 miles to the course on the right.

***Course description:*** This course was redesigned by Robert Dean Putman in 1985. It is a well-maintained course, short and tight with big greens and lots of trees. It's a good test of irons and short game. Gary Rever holds the course record with a 62.

**1957**
**Bert Stamps**

8253 East Belmont
Fresno, CA 93727

Pro shop (209) 251-5076
Clubhouse (209) 251-5078

- ✓ **driving range**
- ✓ **practice greens**
- ✓ **power carts**
- ✓ **pull carts**
- ✓ **golf club rental**
- ✓ **locker rooms**
- ✓ **showers**
- executive course
- accommodations
- ✓ **food and beverages**
- ✓ **clubhouse**

**Mike Schy**
Professional

**Bill Griffith**
Superintendent

# FRESNO AIRWAYS GOLF COURSE

**Course 12**
MAP F4 grid g1

***Course information:*** This public course has 18 holes and par is 68. The course is 5,194 yards and rated 63.7 from the regular tees. The slope rating is 104. Women's tees are 5,740 yards and rated 67.9. The slope rating is 110.

***Play policy and fees:*** Green fees are $9 weekdays and $10 weekends. Carts are $17. Reservations are recommended. This course is available for outside tournaments.

***Location:*** From Highway 99 in Fresno, exit on Belmont Avenue east and turn right on Clovis Avenue. Drive to East Shields Avenue and the course.

***Course description:*** This flat, tree-lined course is short and sporty. It's a mature course and excellent for beginners and intermediate players. The course record is 58.

**1952**

5440 East Shields Avenue
Fresno, CA 93727

Pro shop (209) 291-6254
Clubhouse (209) 291-3162

- ✓ **driving range**
- ✓ **practice greens**
- ✓ **power carts**
- ✓ **pull carts**
- ✓ **golf club rental**
- locker rooms
- showers
- executive course
- accommodations
- ✓ **food and beverages**
- ✓ **clubhouse**

**Eric Thurston**
Professional

# SHERWOOD FOREST GOLF COURSE

**Course 13**
**MAP F4 grid g3**

*Course information:* This public course has 18 holes and par is 71. The course is 6,205 yards and rated 67.5 from the regular tees. The slope rating is 110. Women's tees are 5,605 yards and rated 70.5. The slope rating is 114.

*Play policy and fees:* Green fees are $13 Monday through Thursday, and $16 Fridays, weekends and holidays. Carts are $20. Reservations are recommended one week in advance. This course is available for outside tournaments.

*Location:* In Fresno on Highway 99, take Highway 180/Kings Canyon Road east 19 miles. Turn left on Frankwood Avenue. The course is on the left.

*Course description:* This scenic course runs along the Kings River and offers a view of the mountains on every hole. The course has trees on every hole. Only five holes are fairly open. Thom Rose holds the course record with 62.

**1968**
**R.E. Baldock**

79 North Frankwood Avenue
Sanger, CA 93657

Pro shop (209) 787-2611

- ✓ **driving range**
- ✓ **practice greens**
- ✓ **power carts**
- ✓ **pull carts**
- ✓ **golf club rental**
- locker rooms
- ✓ **showers**
- executive course
- accommodations
- ✓ **food and beverages**
- ✓ **clubhouse**

**Randy Hansen**
Professional

**Robert Tillema**
Superintendent

# SELMA VALLEY GOLF

**Course 14**
**MAP F4 grid i1**

***Course information:*** This public course has 18 holes. Women's championship tees are 5,280 yards, rated 69.6, and have a slope rating of 119. See card below for additional yardage and rating information.

***Play policy and fees:*** Green fees are $10 weekdays and $14 weekends. Carts are $10 for nine holes and $18 for 18 holes. Reservations are recommended one week in advance. This course is available for outside tournaments. Dates are booked the second week in January for 1992.

***Location:*** From Highway 99 in Selma (20 miles south of Fresno), exit onto Rose Avenue east. The course is 2.5 miles on the right.

***Course description:*** This mostly flat course is short with many doglegs. Particularly good for beginning and intermediate players. It's a fast course to play. A round can be played in less than four hours on a weekend.

**1956**
**Robert Dean Putman**

12389 East Rose Avenue
Selma, CA 93662

Pro shop (209) 896-2424

- ✓ **driving range**
- ✓ **practice greens**
- ✓ **power carts**
- ✓ **pull carts**
- ✓ **golf club rental**
- locker rooms
- showers
- executive course
- accommodations
- ✓ **food and beverages**
- ✓ **clubhouse**

**Walt Short**
Manager/Professional

**Jack Lopez**
Superintendent

**Duffy Allison**
Director of Golf

| Hole | 1 | 2 | 3 | 4 | 5 | 6 | 7 | 8 | 9 | Out | BLUE | Rating: -- |
|---|---|---|---|---|---|---|---|---|---|---|---|---|
| BLUE | - | - | - | - | - | - | - | - | - | - | | Slope: -- |
| WHITE | 405 | 370 | 165 | 375 | 280 | 305 | 150 | 478 | 300 | 2828 | | |
| Par | 4 | 4 | 3 | 4 | 4 | 4 | 3 | 5 | 4 | 35 | WHITE | Rating: 64.6 |
| Handicap | 1 | 3 | 9 | 5 | 15 | 17 | 13 | 7 | 11 | x | | Slope: 107 |
| RED | 399 | 367 | 142 | 370 | 277 | 304 | 136 | 416 | 300 | 2711 | | |
| Par | 5 | 4 | 3 | 4 | 4 | 4 | 3 | 5 | 4 | 36 | RED | Rating: 68.9 |
| Handicap | 3 | 5 | 15 | 7 | 13 | 11 | 17 | 1 | 9 | x | | Slope: 117 |

| Hole | 10 | 11 | 12 | 13 | 14 | 15 | 16 | 17 | 18 | In | Totals | |
|---|---|---|---|---|---|---|---|---|---|---|---|---|
| BLUE | | | | | | | | | | | BLUE | |
| WHITE | 270 | 259 | 385 | 355 | 362 | 105 | 392 | 119 | 252 | 2499 | WHITE | 5327 |
| Par | 4 | 4 | 4 | 4 | 4 | 3 | 4 | 3 | 4 | 34 | Par | 69 |
| Handicap | 12 | 10 | 4 | 8 | 6 | 14 | 2 | 16 | 18 | x | | |
| RED | 270 | 259 | 385 | 353 | 362 | 80 | 379 | 119 | 252 | 2459 | RED | 5170 |
| Par | 4 | 4 | 4 | 4 | 4 | 3 | 4 | 3 | 4 | 34 | Par | 70 |
| Handicap | 10 | 12 | 2 | 8 | 6 | 18 | 4 | 16 | 14 | x | | |

# KINGS COUNTRY CLUB

**Course 15**
MAP F4 grid i0

***Course information:*** This private course has 18 holes. See card below for yardage and rating information.

***Play policy and fees:*** Reciprocal play is accepted with members of other private clubs. Green fees for reciprocators are $35 any day. Guest fees are $15 when accompanied by a member weekdays and $25 unaccompanied weekends. Carts are $14.

***Location:*** Driving south on Highway 99 from Fresno, take the Highway 43 exit south and turn right at Dover Avenue. Drive two miles to 12th Avenue and turn right and follow it to the end.

***Course description:*** This tough course plays longer than the yardage suggests. Towering oak trees and two lakes conspire against the golfer. Don't take the 623-yard, par-5 15th for granted. It may appear to be a dull straight-away stretch, but figure on using all the wood in your bag to eventually arrive at the green. Fortunately, it's a welcoming green. For those familiar with Fort Ord's Bayonet Course, this hole is reported to be reminiscent of the 13th there. Craig Statler holds the course record of 63.

3529 12th Avenue
Hanford, CA 93230

Pro shop (209) 582-0740
Clubhouse (209) 582-2264

- ✓ **driving range**
- ✓ **practice greens**
- ✓ **power carts**
- ✓ **pull carts**
- ✓ **golf club rental**
- ✓ **locker rooms**
- ✓ **showers**
- executive course
- accommodations
- ✓ **food and beverages**
- ✓ **clubhouse**

**John Echols**
Professional

**Bob Dalton**
Superintendent

| Hole | 1 | 2 | 3 | 4 | 5 | 6 | 7 | 8 | 9 | Out | | |
|---|---|---|---|---|---|---|---|---|---|---|---|---|
| BLUE | 477 | 394 | 505 | 205 | 291 | 439 | 173 | 419 | 421 | 3324 | BLUE | Rating: 71.5 |
| WHITE | 473 | 377 | 471 | 192 | 286 | 421 | 155 | 399 | 403 | 3177 | | Slope: 115 |
| Par | 5 | 4 | 5 | 3 | 4 | 4 | 3 | 4 | 4 | 36 | WHITE | Rating: 70.1 |
| Handicap | 17 | 7 | 15 | 5 | 13 | 1 | 11 | 9 | 3 | x | | Slope: 112 |
| RED | 451 | 363 | 467 | 170 | 259 | 370 | 134 | 397 | 383 | 2994 | | |
| Par | 5 | 4 | 5 | 3 | 4 | 4 | 3 | 4 | 4 | 36 | RED | Rating: 74.2 |
| Handicap | 5 | 11 | 3 | 15 | 13 | 9 | 17 | 1 | 7 | x | | Slope: 126 |

| Hole | 10 | 11 | 12 | 13 | 14 | 15 | 16 | 17 | 18 | In | Totals | |
|---|---|---|---|---|---|---|---|---|---|---|---|---|
| BLUE | 192 | 407 | 331 | 474 | 368 | 623 | 436 | 140 | 426 | 3397 | BLUE | 6721 |
| WHITE | 178 | 394 | 320 | 463 | 355 | 580 | 428 | 118 | 416 | 3252 | WHITE | 6429 |
| Par | 3 | 4 | 4 | 5 | 4 | 5 | 4 | 3 | 4 | 36 | Par | 72 |
| Handicap | 10 | 8 | 14 | 12 | 16 | 2 | 4 | 18 | 6 | x | | |
| RED | 167 | 363 | 302 | 443 | 315 | 514 | 380 | 98 | 412 | 2994 | RED | 5988 |
| Par | 3 | 4 | 4 | 5 | 4 | 5 | 4 | 3 | 5 | 37 | Par | 73 |
| Handicap | 14 | 8 | 10 | 4 | 12 | 2 | 6 | 18 | 16 | x | | |

## KINGS RIVER GOLF AND COUNTRY CLUB

**Course 16**
MAP F4 grid i2

3100 Avenue 400
Kingsburg, CA 93631

Pro shop (209) 897-2077
Clubhouse (209) 897-5661

- ✓ **driving range**
- ✓ **practice greens**
- ✓ **power carts**
- ✓ **pull carts**
- ✓ **golf club rental**
- ✓ **locker rooms**
- ✓ **showers**
- executive course
- accommodations
- ✓ **food and beverages**
- ✓ **clubhouse**

**Charles Blanks**
Professional

**David Stone**
Superintendent

***Course information:*** This private course has 18 holes and par is 72. The course is 6,678 yards and rated 71.5 from the championship tees, and 6,396 yards and rated 70.2 from the regular tees. The slope ratings are 122 championship and 119 regular. Women's tees are 6,431 yards and rated 76.4 from the championship tees, and 6,014 yards and rated 74.3 from the forward tees. The slope ratings are 135 championship and 130 forward.

***Play policy and fees:*** Reciprocal play is accepted with members of other private clubs. Guest fees are $20 with a member and whatever your club charges guests without. Carts are $12. Closed Mondays.

***Location:*** Located between Fresno and Visalia on Highway 99, take the Highway 201/Avenue 400 exit east over the Kings River to the course on the left.

***Course description:*** This course is mostly flat and walkable. The Kings River borders the course. Robert Dean Putman redesigned the back nine of this course in 1957.



## OAK PATCH GOLF COURSE

**Course 17**
MAP F4 grid j6

30400 Road 158
Visalia, CA 93291

Pro shop (209) 733-5000

- driving range
- ✓ **practice greens**
- power carts
- ✓ **pull carts**
- ✓ **golf club rental**
- locker rooms
- showers
- ✓ **executive course**
- accommodations
- ✓ **food and beverages**
- ✓ **clubhouse**

**Harry Harrison**
Professional

***Course information:*** This public course has nine holes and par is 56 for 18 holes. The course is 5,400 yards for 18 holes.

***Play policy and fees:*** Green fees are $3.50 for nine holes and $7 for 18 holes, and $4 for nine holes and $8 for 18 holes weekends. Carts are $1.50

***Location:*** From Visalia, drive seven miles east on Highway 198 to Ivanhoe. Turn off on County Road 156. Follow signs under the bridge, turning right after the bridge, and continue on to the course.

***Course description:*** This course has one par-4, the "toughest hole in the Valley," according to pro Harry Harrison, who gets the Nicest Pro Award. This hole is 240 yards and runs along the Kaweah River. Tournaments are now being accepted.

# MAP F5

(1 COURSE)

PAGES.. 372-373

CEN-CAL MAP...see page 314
adjoining maps
NORTH (E5).......see page 308
EAST............................no map
SOUTH (G5).......see page 398
WEST (F4).........see page 358

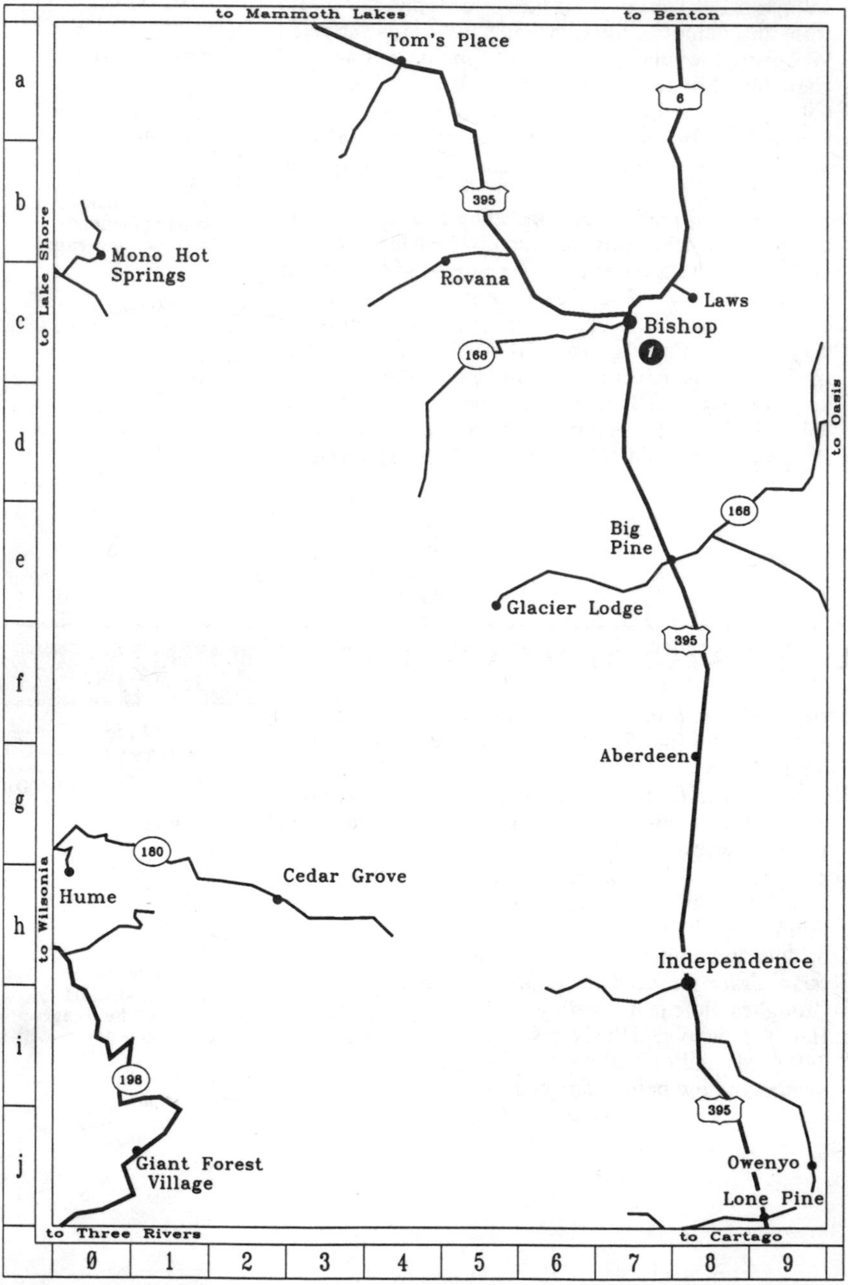

to Mammoth Lakes
to Benton
Tom's Place
6
395
Mono Hot Springs
to Lake Shore
Rovana
Laws
Bishop
1
168
to Oasis
168
Big Pine
Glacier Lodge
395
Aberdeen
180
Cedar Grove
Hume
to Wilsonia
Independence
198
395
Giant Forest Village
Owenyo
Lone Pine
to Three Rivers
to Cartago

a b c d e f g h i j

0 1 2 3 4 5 6 7 8 9

# BISHOP COUNTRY CLUB

**Course 1**
MAP F5 grid c7

*Course information:* This semi-private course has 18 holes. See card below for yardage and rating information.

*Play policy and fees:* Outside play is accepted. Reservations are recommended one week in advance. Green fees are $20 weekdays and $25 weekends. Carts are $18.

*Location:* Drive one mile south of Bishop on Highway 395.

*Course description:* The first nine opened for play in 1952, and the second nine opened in 1984. This difficult course has lots of trees and bunkers. Water hazards spice up every hole. Keep the ball out of the rough. This is a course that challenges accuracy.

**1952**

PO Box 1586
Bishop, CA 93514

Highway 395 South
Bishop, CA 93514

Pro shop (619) 873-5828

- ✓ **driving range**
- ✓ **practice greens**
- ✓ **power carts**
- ✓ **pull carts**
- ✓ **golf club rental**
- ✓ **locker rooms**
- showers
- executive course
- accommodations
- ✓ **food and beverages**
- ✓ **clubhouse**

**John Theilade, Jr.**
Manager/Professional

**Reuben Lorgoria**
Superintendent

CENTRAL F5

| Hole | 1 | 2 | 3 | 4 | 5 | 6 | 7 | 8 | 9 | Out | BLUE | Rating: 70.9 |
|---|---|---|---|---|---|---|---|---|---|---|---|---|
| BLUE | 381 | 531 | 385 | 196 | 488 | 424 | 422 | 207 | 417 | 3451 | | Slope: 122 |
| WHITE | 361 | 479 | 360 | 181 | 473 | 406 | 386 | 179 | 390 | 3215 | | |
| Par | 4 | 5 | 4 | 3 | 5 | 4 | 4 | 3 | 4 | 36 | WHITE | Rating: 68.5 |
| Handicap | 5 | 13 | 9 | 15 | 17 | 3 | 1 | 11 | 7 | x | | Slope: 118 |
| RED | 352 | 424 | 309 | 150 | 420 | 330 | 329 | 166 | 329 | 2809 | | |
| Par | 4 | 5 | 4 | 3 | 5 | 4 | 4 | 3 | 4 | 36 | RED | Rating: 70.8 |
| Handicap | 1 | 5 | 7 | 17 | 9 | 13 | 3 | 15 | 11 | x | | Slope: 119 |

| Hole | 10 | 11 | 12 | 13 | 14 | 15 | 16 | 17 | 18 | In | Totals | |
|---|---|---|---|---|---|---|---|---|---|---|---|---|
| BLUE | 562 | 403 | 401 | 208 | 322 | 196 | 527 | 169 | 422 | 3210 | BLUE | 6661 |
| WHITE | 527 | 367 | 360 | 189 | 268 | 179 | 506 | 130 | 397 | 2923 | WHITE | 6138 |
| Par | 5 | 4 | 4 | 3 | 4 | 3 | 5 | 3 | 4 | 35 | Par | 71 |
| Handicap | 8 | 6 | 4 | 12 | 14 | 10 | 16 | 18 | 2 | x | | |
| RED | 485 | 401 | 348 | 166 | 259 | 124 | 445 | 113 | 403 | 2744 | RED | 5553 |
| Par | 5 | 5 | 4 | 3 | 4 | 3 | 5 | 3 | 5 | 37 | Par | 73 |
| Handicap | 6 | 2 | 10 | 16 | 14 | 18 | 8 | 12 | 4 | x | | |

# MAP G2
(7 COURSES)

PAGES.. 374-381

CEN-CAL MAP...see page 314
adjoining maps
NORTH (F2) .......see page 344
EAST (G3) ..........see page 382
SOUTH (H2) .......see page 404
WEST ..........................no map

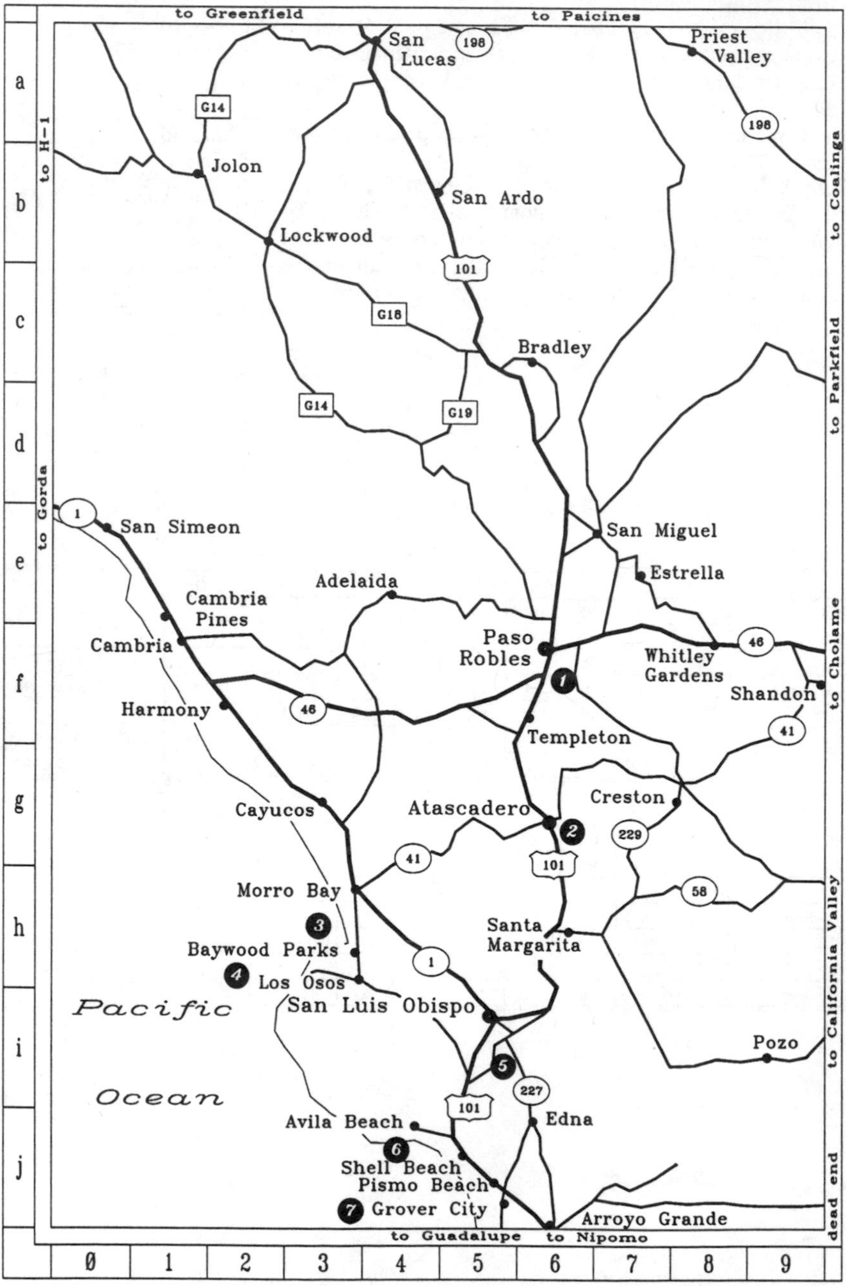

to Greenfield
to Paicines
to H-1
to Gorda
to Coalinga
to Parkfield
to Cholame
to California Valley
dead end
to Guadalupe
to Nipomo

San Lucas
198
Priest Valley
G14
Jolon
San Ardo
Lockwood
101
G18
Bradley
G14
G19
1
San Simeon
San Miguel
Estrella
Adelaida
Cambria Pines
Cambria
Paso Robles
Whitley Gardens
46
Shandon
1
Harmony
46
Templeton
41
Creston
Cayucos
Atascadero
2
229
41
101
Morro Bay
58
3
Santa Margarita
Baywood Parks
4
Los Osos
1
Pacific
San Luis Obispo
Ocean
Pozo
5
227
101
Avila Beach
Edna
6
Shell Beach
Pismo Beach
7
Grover City
Arroyo Grande

a b c d e f g h i j

0 1 2 3 4 5 6 7 8 9

# PASO ROBLES GOLF AND COUNTRY CLUB

**Course 1**
MAP G2 grid f6

**1960**
**Bert Stamps**

PO Box 2120
Paso Robles, CA 93447

1600 Country Club Drive
Paso Robles, CA 93447

Pro shop (805) 238-4722
Clubhouse (805) 238-4710

- ✓ **driving range**
- ✓ **practice greens**
- ✓ **power carts**
- pull carts
- golf club rental
- ✓ **locker rooms**
- showers
- executive course
- accommodations
- ✓ **food and beverages**
- ✓ **clubhouse**

**Jim Crotz**
Professional

**Ben H. Swinney**
Superintendent

***Course information:*** This private course has 18 holes and par is 71. The course is 6,195 yards and rated 70.0 from the championship tees, and 6,015 yards and rated 69.2 from the regular tees. The slope ratings are 122 championship, 118 regular and 124 women. Women's tees are 5,714 yards and rated 73.6.

***Play policy and fees:*** Reciprocal play is accepted with members of other private clubs. Guest fees are $20. Carts are $20. Reservations are recommended. This course is available for outside tournaments. Men must wear shirts with collars. No tank tops, cut-offs or short shorts allowed. Bermuda length shorts are permitted.

***Location:*** Travel 27 miles north of San Luis Obispo on Highway 101 to the Spring Street exit in Paso Robles. Turn right onto Niblick Bridge and drive to Country Club Drive.

***Course description:*** This short, walkable course is very sporty and tight with seven lakes and lots of doglegs. It is a shot-maker's course. It takes a round or two to learn where to lay-up and where to go for it. Among the holes to watch for is number five, which is a sharp dogleg requiring a near perfect tee shot. The green is guarded by trees. The par-4 seventh hole is also a challenge with its huge tree in the center of the fairway. Former baseball great Sandy Koufax was a long-time club member. Annual tournaments include the Jack and Jill Invitational in June and the Member-Guest September Tournament. The Almond Blossom Ladies Invitational is held in February. The course record is 64.

# CHALK MOUNTAIN GOLF COURSE

**Course 2**
MAP G2 grid g6

10,000 El Bordo Road
Atascadero, CA 93422

Pro shop (805) 466-8848

- ✓ **driving range**
- ✓ **practice greens**
- ✓ **power carts**
- ✓ **pull carts**
- ✓ **golf club rental**
- locker rooms
- showers
- executive course
- accommodations
- ✓ **food and beverages**
- ✓ **clubhouse**

**Gary Wishon**
Professional

**Bob Schneiderhan**
Superintendent

*Course information:* This public course has 18 holes. See card below for yardage and rating information.

*Play policy and fees:* Green fees are $8 for nine holes and $13.50 for 18 holes weekdays, and $9.25 for nine holes and $15.50 for 18 holes weekends. Senior rates are $3.75 weekdays and $7.50 weekends. Carts are $16. Reservations are recommended one day in advance weekdays, and three days in advance weekends.

*Location:* Off Highway 101 at the south end of Atascadero, exit at Santa Rosa Avenue heading east. Follow the Heilman Regional Park signs out El Camino Real and El Bordo Road to the course.

*Course description:* This is a short, narrow course set in the mountains among groves of oak trees. It's the kind of course you have to play a few times before you can actually play it. Don't expect to score well on the first time out. A hole to watch: number four, 404 yards, par-4. Known as "Cardiac Hill," it plays straight up. You can see the green from the tee, which isn't much help. The hole is deceptive in its distance and the tendency is to hit too short. Be straight off the tee or you're in the woods looking for a path through the trees. Dean Greene holds the men's course record with 64. Lorraine Doherty holds the women's record with 71.

| Hole | 1 | 2 | 3 | 4 | 5 | 6 | 7 | 8 | 9 | Out | BLUE | Rating: 70.6 |
|---|---|---|---|---|---|---|---|---|---|---|---|---|
| BLUE | 510 | 319 | 334 | 404 | 140 | 467 | 232 | 580 | 359 | 3345 | | Slope: 121 |
| WHITE | 495 | 311 | 324 | 379 | 123 | 455 | 200 | 557 | 341 | 3185 | | |
| Par | 5 | 4 | 4 | 4 | 3 | 5 | 3 | 5 | 4 | 37 | WHITE | Rating: 68.6 |
| Handicap | 5 | 13 | 7 | 1 | 17 | 15 | 11 | 3 | 9 | x | | Slope: 118 |
| RED | 453 | 262 | 282 | 328 | 107 | 409 | 188 | 523 | 289 | 2841 | | |
| Par | 5 | 4 | 4 | 4 | 3 | 5 | 3 | 5 | 4 | 37 | RED | Rating: 65.4 |
| Handicap | 5 | 13 | 7 | 3 | 17 | 9 | 15 | 1 | 11 | x | | Slope: 107 |

| Hole | 10 | 11 | 12 | 13 | 14 | 15 | 16 | 17 | 18 | In | Totals | |
|---|---|---|---|---|---|---|---|---|---|---|---|---|
| BLUE | 533 | 355 | 192 | 353 | 175 | 474 | 152 | 340 | 414 | 2988 | BLUE | 6333 |
| WHITE | 515 | 348 | 179 | 310 | 164 | 461 | 129 | 329 | 406 | 2841 | WHITE | 6026 |
| Par | 5 | 4 | 3 | 4 | 3 | 5 | 3 | 4 | 4 | 35 | Par | 72 |
| Handicap | 8 | 6 | 12 | 14 | 10 | 2 | 18 | 16 | 4 | x | | |
| RED | 469 | 278 | 162 | 274 | 135 | 415 | 104 | 299 | 349 | 2485 | RED | 5326 |
| Par | 5 | 4 | 3 | 4 | 3 | 5 | 3 | 4 | 4 | 35 | Par | 72 |
| Handicap | 6 | 8 | 16 | 12 | 10 | 2 | 18 | 14 | 4 | x | | |

## MORRO BAY GOLF COURSE

**Course 3**
MAP G2 grid h3

***Course information:*** This public course has 18 holes and par is 71. The course is 6,113 yards and rated 69.1 from the regular tees. Women's tees are 5,727 yards and rated 72.3. The slope ratings are 116 regular and 118 women.

***Play policy and fees:*** Green fees are $15 weekdays and $17.50 weekends. Senior rates are $7 Monday through Friday. Junior rates are $6.50 any day. Call for other special rates. Carts are $18. Reservations must be made the preceeding week of play.

***Location:*** North from San Luis Obispo, take Highway 101 and exit on Highway 1 to Morro Bay. Follow the Morro Bay State Park signs to the course.

***Course description:*** This picturesque layout is located in the Morro Bay State Park and has ocean views from almost every hole. It's slightly hilly with tree-lined fairways. It is one of the busiest courses in the state and is referred to as "The Poor Man's Pebble Beach." Tricky greens are compared to Poppy Hills or Spyglass. To speed up play, most of the bunkers were removed in the 1960s. There are only four traps on the course.

**1926**
201 State Park Road
Morro Bay, CA 93442

Pro shop (805) 772-4341
Starter (805) 772-4560

✓ **driving range**
✓ **practice greens**
✓ **power carts**
✓ **pull carts**
✓ **golf club rental**
locker rooms
showers
executive course
accommodations
✓ **food and beverages**
✓ **clubhouse**

**Lori Murry**
Professional

**Ray Festa**
Superintendent

# BEST WESTERN SEA PINES GOLF RESORT

**Course 4**
MAP G2 grid h3

**1954**
250 Howard Street
Los Osos, CA 93402

Pro shop (805) 528-1788

- ✓ **driving range**
- ✓ **practice greens**
- ✓ **power carts**
- ✓ **pull carts**
- ✓ **golf club rental**
- ✓ **locker rooms**
- showers
- ✓ **executive course**
- ✓ **accommodations**
- ✓ **food and beverages**
- clubhouse

**Tauna Matheny**
Professional

**Gary Setting**
Superintendent

***Course information:*** This public course has nine holes. See card below for yardage information.

***Play policy and fees:*** Green fees are $6.50 weekdays and $7.50 weekends.

***Location:*** Off Highway 101 in Los Osos, take the Los Osos Valley Road exit and drive west to the course which is about 11 miles from the highway. Take the entrance to Montana de Oro State Park.

***Course description:*** This well-maintained course has more than 200 trees lining the narrow fairways. Most are pine trees over 25 years old. The first fairway has been removed and relocated to make way for a parking lot so watch out for the new row of small connecting ponds along the left side of the fairway.

| Hole | 1 | 2 | 3 | 4 | 5 | 6 | 7 | 8 | 9 | Out | BLUE | Rating: -- |
|---|---|---|---|---|---|---|---|---|---|---|---|---|
| BLUE | - | - | - | - | - | - | - | - | - | - | | Slope: -- |
| WHITE | 145 | 200 | 120 | 110 | 141 | 250 | 125 | 97 | 176 | 1364 | | |
| Par | 3 | 3 | 3 | 3 | 3 | 4 | 3 | 3 | 3 | 28 | WHITE | Rating: -- |
| Handicap | 9 | 15 | 7 | 1 | 5 | 13 | 11 | 17 | 3 | x | | Slope: -- |
| RED | 145 | 200 | 120 | 110 | 141 | 250 | 125 | 97 | 176 | 1364 | | |
| Par | 3 | 4 | 3 | 3 | 3 | 4 | 3 | 3 | 4 | 30 | RED | Rating: -- |
| Handicap | 7 | 13 | 5 | 15 | 3 | 1 | 9 | 11 | 17 | x | | Slope: -- |

| Hole | 10 | 11 | 12 | 13 | 14 | 15 | 16 | 17 | 18 | In | Totals | |
|---|---|---|---|---|---|---|---|---|---|---|---|---|
| BLUE | - | - | - | - | - | - | - | - | - | - | BLUE | -- |
| WHITE | 145 | 200 | 120 | 110 | 141 | 250 | 125 | 97 | 176 | 1364 | WHITE | 2728 |
| Par | 3 | 3 | 3 | 3 | 3 | 4 | 3 | 3 | 3 | 28 | Par | 56 |
| Handicap | 10 | 16 | 8 | 2 | 6 | 14 | 12 | 18 | 4 | x | | |
| RED | 145 | 200 | 120 | 110 | 141 | 250 | 125 | 97 | 176 | 1364 | RED | 2728 |
| Par | 3 | 4 | 3 | 3 | 3 | 4 | 3 | 3 | 4 | 30 | Par | 60 |
| Handicap | 8 | 14 | 6 | 16 | 4 | 2 | 10 | 12 | 18 | x | | |

# SAN LUIS OBISPO GOLF AND COUNTRY CLUB

**Course 5**
MAP G2 grid i5

**1957**
255 Country Club Drive
San Luis Obispo, CA 93401

Pro shop (805) 543-4035
Clubhouse (805) 543-3400

- ✓ **driving range**
- ✓ **practice greens**
- ✓ **power carts**
- ✓ **pull carts**
- ✓ **golf club rental**
- ✓ **locker rooms**
- ✓ **showers**
- executive course
- accommodations
- ✓ **food and beverages**
- ✓ **clubhouse**

**Scott Cartwright**
Professional

**Ron Armstrong**
Superintendent.

***Course information:*** This private course has 18 holes and par is 72. The course is 6,858 yards and rated 74.2 from the tournament tees, 6,614 yards and rated 72.5 from the championship tees, and 6,390 yards and rated 70.5 from the regular tees. The slope ratings are 135 tournament, 129 championship and 124 regular. Women's tees are 5,919 yards with a rating of 73.6. The slope rating is 124.

***Play policy and fees:*** Reciprocal play is accepted with members of other private clubs. Members and guests only. Fees for reciprocators are $55. Carts are $10. Reservations for morning tee times are recommended.

***Location:*** Take the Marsh Street exit off Highway 101 in San Luis Obispo and turn right. Travel to Broad Street (Highway 227) and turn right. Drive 4.5 miles to Los Ranchos Road, then right to Country Club Drive and right again to the club.

***Course description:*** This rolling course along the central coast plays longer than it looks because of the lush fairways that provide little roll. Thick stands of pine trees line the fairways waiting for errant tee shots. The greens are protected by strategically placed bunkers. The back nine has completely new greens which are much faster and don't hold quite as well as the front nine. Play short onto the green to avoid overrunning. The greens are fairly flat. The course record is 64, held by Loren Roberts.

# SAN LUIS BAY RESORT

**Course 6**
MAP G2 grid j4

*Course information:* This public course has 18 holes. See card below for yardage and rating information.

*Play policy and fees:* Green fees are $20 weekdays and $25 weekends. Carts are $22. Reservations are recommended.

*Location:* Take the Avila Beach exit off Highway 101 north of Pismo Beach, and drive west for three miles to the entrance of the San Luis Bay Inn. Turn right and follow the signs to the club.

*Course description:* Situated in the heart of California's central coast, this course is both beautiful and challenging. The front nine is nestled in an oak-lined canyon bisected by a gentle flowing creek. Accuracy and club selection are important. The back nine calls for distance and placement as it traverses back and forth across San Luis Creek and a tidal lagoon. Some holes have been reworked, resulting in overall shorter, but insignificantly so, yardage. The course record is 65, held by S. Scott Sickich.

**1968**
**Desmond Muirhead**

PO Box 2140
Avila Beach, CA 93424

Pro shop (805) 595-2307

- ✓ **driving range**
- ✓ **practice greens**
- ✓ **power carts**
- ✓ **pull carts**
- ✓ **golf club rental**
- locker rooms
- showers
- executive course
- accommodations
- ✓ **food and beverages**
- ✓ **clubhouse**

**S. Scott Sickich**
Professional

**John Emerson**
Superintendent

| Hole | 1 | 2 | 3 | 4 | 5 | 6 | 7 | 8 | 9 | Out | | |
|---|---|---|---|---|---|---|---|---|---|---|---|---|
| BLUE | 415 | 234 | 470 | 363 | 373 | 188 | 376 | 171 | 540 | 3130 | BLUE | Rating: 70.9 |
| WHITE | 397 | 200 | 446 | 327 | 359 | 159 | 327 | 144 | 523 | 2882 | | Slope: 122 |
| Par | 4 | 3 | 5 | 4 | 4 | 3 | 4 | 3 | 5 | 35 | WHITE | Rating: 69.0 |
| Handicap | 3 | 5 | 13 | 7 | 15 | 9 | 1 | 17 | 11 | x | | Slope: 116 |
| RED | 370 | 133 | 433 | 282 | 336 | 133 | 263 | 102 | 410 | 2462 | | |
| Par | 4 | 3 | 5 | 4 | 4 | 3 | 4 | 3 | 5 | 35 | RED | Rating: 68.2 |
| Handicap | 3 | 17 | 1 | 11 | 5 | 13 | 7 | 15 | 9 | x | | Slope: 121 |

| Hole | 10 | 11 | 12 | 13 | 14 | 15 | 16 | 17 | 18 | In | Totals | |
|---|---|---|---|---|---|---|---|---|---|---|---|---|
| BLUE | 434 | 502 | 388 | 529 | 326 | 207 | 389 | 185 | 353 | 3313 | BLUE | 6443 |
| WHITE | 419 | 495 | 375 | 504 | 318 | 178 | 383 | 169 | 325 | 3166 | WHITE | 6048 |
| Par | 4 | 5 | 4 | 5 | 4 | 3 | 4 | 3 | 4 | 36 | Par | 71 |
| Handicap | 6 | 12 | 2 | 14 | 18 | 15 | 4 | 10 | 8 | x | | |
| RED | 338 | 437 | 293 | 408 | 279 | 140 | 318 | 157 | 284 | 2654 | RED | 5116 |
| Par | 4 | 5 | 4 | 5 | 4 | 3 | 4 | 3 | 4 | 36 | Par | 71 |
| Handicap | 4 | 6 | 2 | 16 | 12 | 18 | 8 | 14 | 10 | x | | |

# PISMO STATE BEACH GOLF COURSE

**Course 7**
MAP G2 grid j5

**1967**
25 Grand Beach Ave.
Grover Beach, CA 93433

Pro shop (805) 481-5215

- driving range
- ✓ **practice greens**
- power carts
- ✓ **pull carts**
- ✓ **golf club rental**
- locker rooms
- showers
- executive course
- ✓ **accommodations**
- ✓ **food and beverages**
- ✓ **clubhouse**

**Floyd Hord**
Professional

**Jay Lowe**
Superintendent

***Course information:*** This public course has nine holes and par is 54 for 18 holes. The course is 2,795 yards for 18 holes.

***Play policy and fees:*** Green fees are $5.25 weekdays and $6 weekends for nine holes. Weekday twilight rates after 4 p.m. are $5 and weekend twilight rates are $5.50. Call for special senior rates.

***Location:*** On Highway 1 in Grover City, turn right on Grand Avenue toward the beach and follow to the course.

***Course description:*** This flat course has water on seven holes, plus excellent ocean views. There are no sand traps. Monterey pines line the fairways, which play tough when the wind blows in March. This is a good course for beginners.



MAP ON PAGE 374

# MAP G3

(2 COURSES)

PAGES.. 382-383

CEN-CAL MAP...see page 314
adjoining maps
NORTH (F3) .......see page 352
EAST (G4) ..........see page 384
SOUTH (H3) .......see page 412
WEST ((G2) ........see page 374

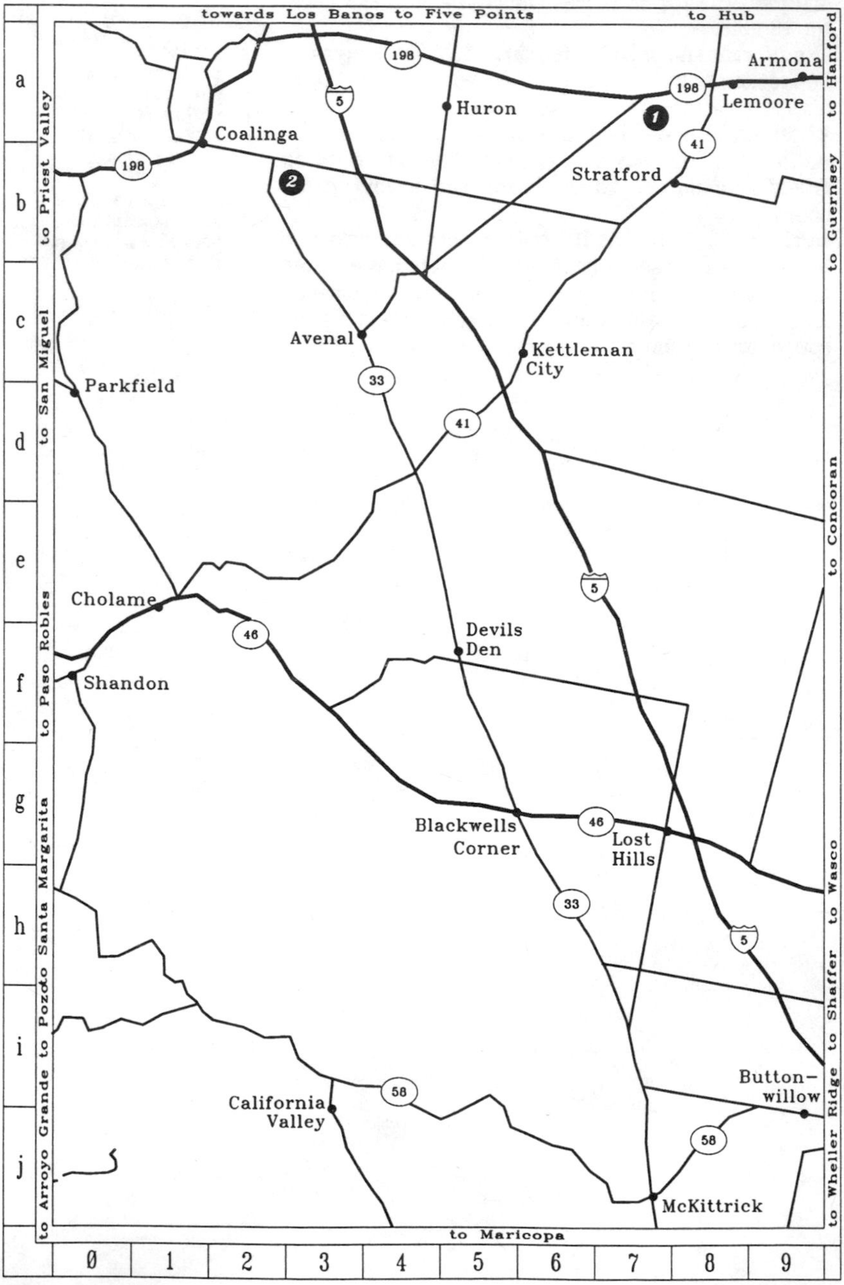

towards Los Banos to Five Points
to Hub
to Hanford
to Guernsey
to Concoran
to Wasco
to Shaffer
to Wheller Ridge
to Maricopa
to Arroyo Grande to Pozo
to Santa Margarita
to Paso Robles
to San Miguel
to Priest Valley

Armona
Lemoore
Huron
Coalinga
Stratford
Avenal
Kettleman City
Parkfield
Cholame
Shandon
Devils Den
Blackwells Corner
Lost Hills
California Valley
Button-willow
McKittrick

198
5
41
33
46
58
1
2

a
b
c
d
e
f
g
h
i
j

0 1 2 3 4 5 6 7 8 9

## LEMOORE GOLF COURSE

**Course 1**
MAP G3 grid a7

*Course information:* This public course has 18 holes. Par is 72 for 18 holes. From the blue tees, the course is 6,431 yards and rated 69.8, with a slope rating of 118. From the white tees, the course is 5,978 yards and rated 67.8 with a slope rating of 112. Women's tees are 5,126 yards and rated 67.9. The slope rating is 115. The course is expected to expand to a full 18 holes in April, 1992. The yardage will then increase to 6,472 yards and the course will be re-rated.

*Play policy and fees:* Green fees are $8 weekdays for nine holes and and $11 for 18 holes. It is $10 for nine holes and 13.50 for 18 holes on weekends. Carts are $10 for nine holes and $16 for 18.

*Location:* From Highway 198 in Visalia, drive west to the Lemoore Naval Air Station/Lemoore Airport. The course is on the left.

*Course description:* This flat course is walkable with lots of trees. There are lakes and four par-5s. There is a new clubhouse and an enlarged pro shop. The course record is 68, held by Mike Moreland.

**1930**
350 West Ione
Lemoore, CA 93245

Pro shop (209) 924-9658

- ✓ **driving range**
- ✓ **practice greens**
- ✓ **power carts**
- ✓ **pull carts**
- ✓ **golf club rental**
- locker rooms
- showers
- executive course
- accommodations
- ✓ **food and beverages**
- ✓ **clubhouse**

**Rich Rhoadas**
Manager/Professional

**Dick McAllister**
Superintendent

## POLVADERO GOLF AND COUNTRY CLUB

**Course 2**
MAP G3 grid b3

*Course information:* This public course has nine holes. Par is 72 for 18 holes. The course is 6,526 yards and rated 70.2 from the regular tees (18 holes). The slope rating is 115. Women's tees are 5,825 yards and rated 72.8. The slope rating is 122.

*Play policy and fees:* Green fees are $8 for nine holes and $10 for 18 holes weekdays, and $9 and $11 weekends. Carts are $7 for nine holes and $14 for 18 holes. Play is on a first-come first-served basis.

*Location:* From Interstate 5 by Coalinga, take the Jayne Avenue exit west to Sutter Avenue. Turn left and the course is on the right.

*Course description:* This hilly course is walkable. There are mature trees and two lakes coming into play on two holes. The course is a good exercise for players of all abilities.

**1989**
41605 Sutter Avenue
Coalinga, CA 93210

Pro shop (209) 935-3578

- ✓ **driving range**
- ✓ **practice greens**
- ✓ **power carts**
- ✓ **pull carts**
- ✓ **golf club rental**
- locker rooms
- showers
- executive course
- accommodations
- ✓ **food and beverages**
- clubhouse

**Charles Hudson**
Manager/Professional

**Jeff Neal**
Superintendent

# MAP G4
(14 COURSES)

PAGES.. 384-397

CEN-CAL MAP...see page 314
adjoining maps
NORTH (F4) .......see page 358
EAST (G5) .........see page 398
SOUTH (H4) .......see page 426
WEST (G3) .........see page 382

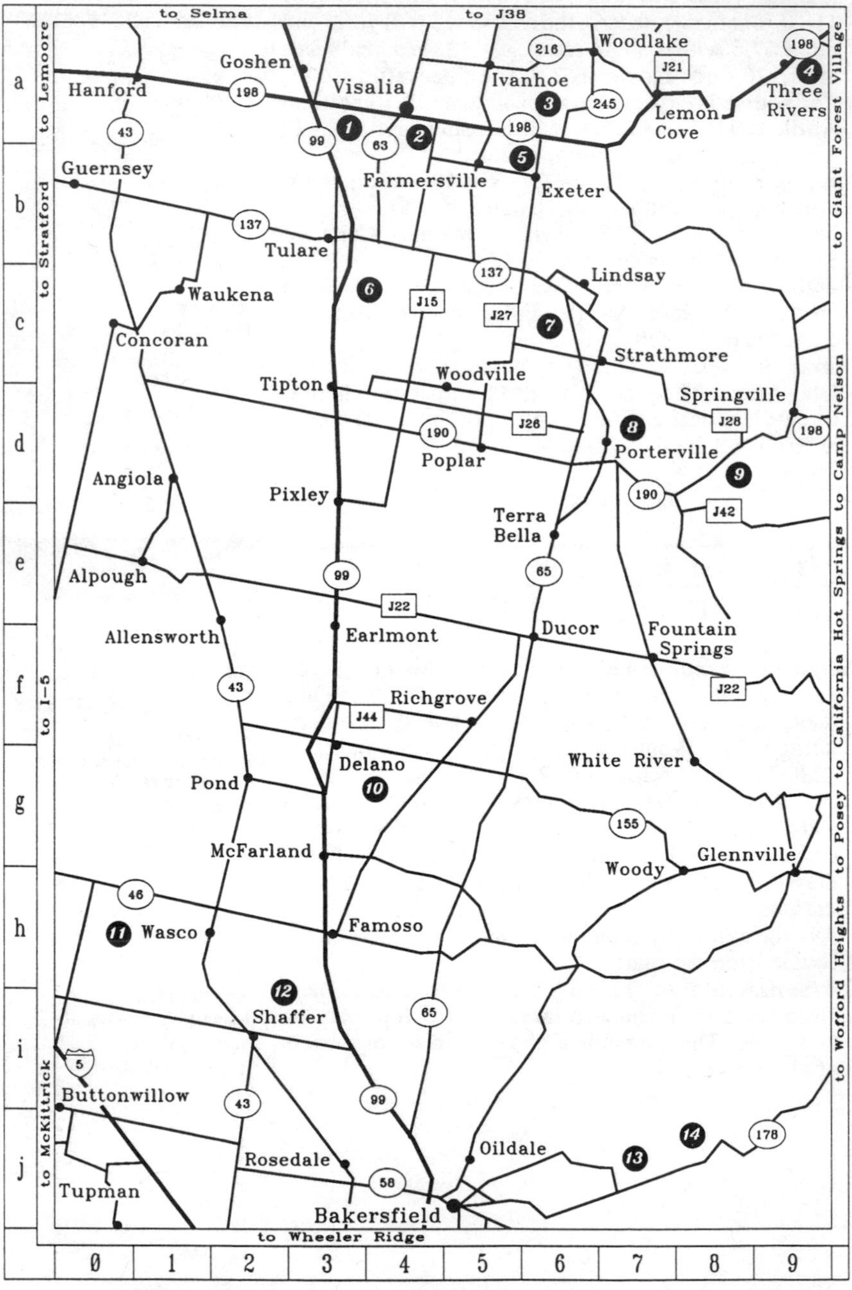

to Selma
to J38
to Lemoore
to Stratford
to I-5
to McKittrick
to Wheeler Ridge
to Giant Forest Village
to Camp Nelson
to California Hot Springs
to Posey
to Wofford Heights

Goshen
Hanford
Visalia
Ivanhoe
Woodlake
Three Rivers
Lemon Cove
Farmersville
Exeter
Guernsey
Tulare
Lindsay
Waukena
Concoran
Strathmore
Tipton
Woodville
Springville
Poplar
Porterville
Angiola
Pixley
Terra Bella
Alpough
Allensworth
Earlmont
Ducor
Fountain Springs
Richgrove
Delano
White River
Pond
McFarland
Woody
Glennville
Wasco
Famoso
Shaffer
Buttonwillow
Rosedale
Oildale
Tupman
Bakersfield

198, 43, 99, 63, 216, 245, 137, 190, 65, 155, 46, 58, 178, 5, J21, J15, J27, J26, J28, J42, J22, J44

1 2 3 4 5 6 7 8 9 10 11 12 13 14

a b c d e f g h i j

0 1 2 3 4 5 6 7 8 9

The Olympic Club Golf Course in San Francisco

**Above:** *The 5th green and clubhouse at Carmel Valley Ranch Resort*
**Below:** *The north course at Rancho Murieta Country Club near Sacramento*

**Above:** *Hole 9 at Brighton Crest Golf Course near Fresno*
**Below:** *The Stadium Course at PGA West*

The 16th hole at Incline Village, Lake Tahoe

**Above:** *The 18th tees at Pelican Hill Golf Club on the Newport Coast*

**Below:** *Silverado Country Club*

**Above:** *The 18th hole at Half Moon Bay Golf Course*

**Below:** *Autumn golfing at Northstar at Tahoe*

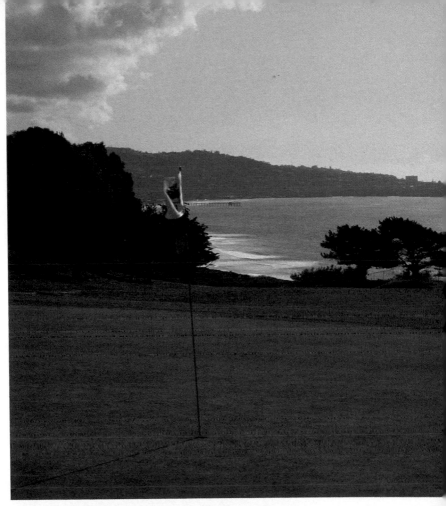

***Above:*** *Torrey Pines Golf Course in San Diego*
***Below:*** *Hole 11 at Ojai Valley Country Club*
***Following page:*** *The 16th at Cypress in Monterey*

# VALLEY OAKS GOLF COURSE

**Course 1**
MAP G4 grid a3

***Course information:*** This public course has 18 holes. Women's championship tees are 6,269 yards and rated 76.2, and have a slope rating of 130. See card below for additional yardage and rating information.

***Play policy and fees:*** Green fees are $8 for nine holes and $10 for 18 holes weekdays, and $9 for nine holes and $12 for 18 holes weekends. Carts are $10 for nine holes and $16 for 18 holes. Weekday play is on a first-come first-served basis. Weekend reservations are taken the prior Thursday morning. This course is available for outside tournaments.

***Location:*** In Visalia on Highway 99, take the Highway 198 turnoff east. Drive one mile and exit at the Holiday Inn. Continue to the course, located next to the airport.

***Course description:*** Robert Dean Putman re-designed this layout in 1972. It is a flat course with trees and water, and features fast, large, well-maintained greens. Good putting is essential to scoring well. Course records are 61 at the regular tees, 63 (Ted Keanery) at the championship tees and 74 for women.

**Richard Bigler**

1800 South Plaza Drive
Visalia, CA 93277

Pro shop (209) 651-1441
Clubhouse (209) 651-0840

- ✓ **driving range**
- ✓ **practice greens**
- ✓ **power carts**
- ✓ **pull carts**
- ✓ **golf club rental**
- locker rooms
- showers
- executive course
- accommodations
- ✓ **food and beverages**
- ✓ **clubhouse**

**Ryan Wiezycki**
Professional

**Bill Rodriguez**
Superintendent

CENTRAL G4

| Hole | 1 | 2 | 3 | 4 | 5 | 6 | 7 | 8 | 9 | Out | | |
|---|---|---|---|---|---|---|---|---|---|---|---|---|
| BLUE | 476 | 374 | 361 | 396 | 168 | 354 | 209 | 402 | 490 | 3230 | BLUE | Rating: 70.7 |
| | | | | | | | | | | | | Slope: 119 |
| WHITE | 468 | 359 | 335 | 386 | 152 | 341 | 200 | 389 | 482 | 3112 | | |
| Par | 5 | 4 | 4 | 4 | 3 | 4 | 3 | 4 | 5 | 36 | WHITE | Rating: 69.4 |
| Handicap | 15 | 7 | 9 | 1 | 13 | 11 | 3 | 5 | 17 | x | | Slope: 116 |
| RED | 422 | 343 | 307 | 373 | 139 | 323 | 174 | 369 | 465 | 2915 | | |
| Par | 5 | 4 | 4 | 4 | 3 | 4 | 3 | 4 | 5 | 36 | RED | Rating: 73.0 |
| Handicap | 3 | 9 | 15 | 5 | 17 | 13 | 11 | 7 | 1 | x | | Slope: 122 |

| Hole | 10 | 11 | 12 | 13 | 14 | 15 | 16 | 17 | 18 | In | Totals | |
|---|---|---|---|---|---|---|---|---|---|---|---|---|
| BLUE | 369 | 376 | 517 | 509 | 151 | 381 | 395 | 204 | 432 | 3334 | BLUE | 6564 |
| WHITE | 351 | 331 | 492 | 501 | 140 | 369 | 385 | 189 | 408 | 3166 | WHITE | 6278 |
| Par | 4 | 4 | 5 | 5 | 3 | 4 | 4 | 3 | 4 | 36 | Par | 72 |
| Handicap | 10 | 6 | 14 | 12 | 18 | 16 | 8 | 2 | 4 | x | | |
| RED | 336 | 321 | 385 | 476 | 109 | 316 | 363 | 174 | 400 | 2880 | RED | 5795 |
| Par | 4 | 4 | 5 | 5 | 3 | 4 | 4 | 3 | 5 | 37 | Par | 73 |
| Handicap | 8 | 12 | 4 | 2 | 18 | 16 | 10 | 14 | 6 | x | | |

## SIERRA VIEW GOLF COURSE OF VISALIA

**Course 2**
MAP G4 grid a4

**1959**
**Robert Dean Putman**

12608 Avenue 264
Visalia, CA 93277

Pro shop (209) 732-2078

- ✓ **driving range**
- ✓ **practice greens**
- ✓ **power carts**
- ✓ **pull carts**
- ✓ **golf club rental**
- ✓ **locker rooms**
- showers
- executive course
- accommodations
- ✓ **food and beverages**
- ✓ **clubhouse**

**Darrell Klassen**
Professional

**Gary McIntosh**
Superintendent

*Course information:* This public course has 18 holes and par is 72. The course is 6,388 yards and rated 68.9 from the championship tees, and 6,169 yards and rated 67.8 from the regular tees. The slope ratings are 107 championship and 105 regular. Women's tees are 5,892 yards and rated 71.6. The slope rating is 114.

*Play policy and fees:* Green fees are $7.50 for nine holes and $11 for 18 holes weekdays, and $9 and $12 weekends. Carts are $9 for nine holes and $16 for 18 holes. If you want a spot during the weekend, call at least a week in advance. This course is available for tournaments.

*Location:* On Highway 99 in south Visalia, take the Avenue 264 exit (Tagus exit) east. Continue down four miles to the course.

*Course description:* Situated in the San Joaquin Valley, this course has fast greens and lots of trees and bunkers. Mostly flat, the four par-5s measure under 500 yards and are easily reachable for long hitters. The course record is 61, held by Jerry Heard.

## VISALIA COUNTRY CLUB

**Course 3**
MAP G4 grid a6

**1910**
625 Ranch Road
Visalia, CA 93291

Pro shop (209) 734-1458
Clubhouse (209) 734-5871

- ✓ **driving range**
- ✓ **practice greens**
- ✓ **power carts**
- ✓ **pull carts**
- ✓ **golf club rental**
- ✓ **locker rooms**
- ✓ **showers**
- executive course
- accommodations
- ✓ **food and beverages**
- ✓ **clubhouse**

**Mike Robertson**
Professional

**Rick West**
Superintendent

*Course information:* This private course has 18 holes and par is 72. The course is 6,673 yards and rated 72.0 from the tournament tees, 6,307 yards and rated 69.9 from the championship tees, and 5,438 yards and rated 67.2 from the regular tees. The slope ratings are 122 tournament, 119 championship and 112 regular. Women's tees are 5,829 yards and rated 73.3 from the championship tees, and 5,438 yards and rated 70.8 from the forward tees. The slope ratings are 130 championship and 122 forward.

*Play policy and fees:* Reciprocal play is accepted with members of other private clubs. Green fees are $15 with a member and $30 without, and $50 if you are from out of the area. Carts are $8 per rider for nine holes and $14 per rider for 18 holes. Reservations are recommended. Closed Mondays.

*Location:* From Highway 99, take the Visalia exit. Go three stoplights and turn left onto West Main and then left again on Ranch Road and follow it to the end.

*Course description:* The original nine holes were built in 1910 and Robert Dean Putman redesigned this course in 1960. This flat, open course has lots of trees and bunkers. There's water on eight holes. The greens are large and tricky. The course record is 66, held by Brad Stovall.

# THREE RIVERS GOLF COURSE

**Course 4**
MAP G4 grid a9

***Course information:*** This public course has nine holes. Par is 70 for 18 holes. The course is 5,504 yards and rated 65.7 for 18 holes from the championship tees, and 5,262 yards and rated 64.6 from the regular tees. The slope ratings are 107 championship and 106 regular. Women's tees are 4,082 yards and rated 63.6 for 18 holes. The slope rating is 97.

***Play policy and fees:*** Green fees are $7 for nine holes and $10 for 18 holes weekdays, and $9 for nine holes and $12 for 18 holes weekends and holidays. Carts are $9 for nine holes and $15 for 18 holes.

***Location:*** From Highway 99 in Tulare take Highway 198 east through Visalia to Three Rivers. The course is next to the highway.

***Course description:*** This course is semi-flat with sloping fairways and there are two ponds.

**1962**
**Robert Dean Putman**

PO Box 202
Three Rivers, CA 93271

41117 Sierra Drive
Three Rivers, CA 93271

Pro shop (209) 561-3133

- driving range
- practice greens
- ✓ **power carts**
- ✓ **pull carts**
- ✓ **golf club rental**
- locker rooms
- showers
- executive course
- accommodations
- ✓ **food and beverages**
- ✓ **clubhouse**

**Ken Pilcher**
Manager

**Kurt Gardiner**
Superintendent

# EXETER PUBLIC GOLF COURSE

**Course 5**
MAP G4 grid b6

**1963**
**R.E. Baldock**

510 West Visalia
Exeter, CA 93221

Pro shop (209) 592-4783

- ✓ **driving range**
- ✓ **practice greens**
- ✓ **power carts**
- ✓ **pull carts**
- ✓ **golf club rental**
- locker rooms
- showers
- ✓ **executive course**
- accommodations
- ✓ **food and beverages**
- ✓ **clubhouse**

**Bart Taylor**
Manager

**Dan and Pam Diel**
Owners

***Course information:*** This public course has nine holes. The course is in the process of being rated. See card below for yardage information.

***Play policy and fees:*** Green fees are $5 for nine holes and $10 for 18 holes weekdays, and $6 and $11 weekends. Pull carts are $1.50. Power carts are $7 for nine holes and $11 for 18 holes. Reservations are recommended. This course is available for outside tournaments.

***Location:*** From Highway 99 in Visalia, drive east on Highway 198 (toward Three Rivers). Turn right on Anderson Road (Highway 180). Follow it to Visalia Road and turn left to the course.

***Course description:*** A lot of water comes into play on this tree-lined, mature course. Three of the holes are par-4s. The course is in excellent condition.

| Hole | 1 | 2 | 3 | 4 | 5 | 6 | 7 | 8 | 9 | Out | BLUE | Rating: -- |
|---|---|---|---|---|---|---|---|---|---|---|---|---|
| BLUE | - | - | - | - | - | - | - | - | - | - | | Slope: -- |
| WHITE | 300 | 165 | 108 | 100 | 400 | 85 | 110 | 105 | 270 | 1643 | | |
| Par | 4 | 3 | 3 | 3 | 4 | 3 | 3 | 3 | 4 | 30 | WHITE | Rating: -- |
| Handicap | 7 | 3 | 9 | 13 | 1 | 15 | 5 | 11 | 17 | x | | Slope: -- |
| RED | 300 | 165 | 108 | 100 | 400 | 85 | 110 | 105 | 270 | 1643 | | |
| Par | 4 | 3 | 3 | 3 | 5 | 3 | 3 | 3 | 4 | 31 | RED | Rating: -- |
| Handicap | 7 | 3 | 9 | 13 | 1 | 15 | 5 | 11 | 17 | x | | Slope: -- |

| Hole | 10 | 11 | 12 | 13 | 14 | 15 | 16 | 17 | 18 | In | Totals | |
|---|---|---|---|---|---|---|---|---|---|---|---|---|
| BLUE | - | - | - | - | - | - | - | - | - | - | BLUE | -- |
| WHITE | 300 | 165 | 108 | 100 | 400 | 85 | 110 | 105 | 270 | 1643 | WHITE | 3286 |
| Par | 4 | 3 | 3 | 3 | 4 | 3 | 3 | 3 | 4 | 30 | Par | 60 |
| Handicap | 8 | 4 | 10 | 14 | 2 | 16 | 6 | 12 | 18 | x | | |
| RED | 300 | 165 | 108 | 100 | 400 | 85 | 110 | 105 | 270 | 1643 | RED | 3286 |
| Par | 4 | 3 | 3 | 3 | 5 | 3 | 3 | 3 | 4 | 31 | Par | 62 |
| Handicap | 8 | 4 | 10 | 14 | 2 | 16 | 6 | 12 | 18 | x | | |

# TULARE GOLF COURSE

Course 6
MAP G4 grid c3

***Course information:*** This public course has 18 holes. Women's championship tees are 5,975 yards, rated 72.9, and have a slope rating of 116. See card below for additional yardage and rating information.

***Play policy and fees:*** Green fees are $9 for nine holes and $13 for 18 holes weekdays, and $11 for nine holes and $17 for 18 holes weekends. Carts are $9 for nine holes and $16 for 18 holes. Weekend reservations are recommended the prior Tuesday morning. This course is available for tournaments.

***Location:*** From Highway 99 in Tulare, head east on Avenue 200. Turn left on South Laspina. The course is on the right.

***Course description:*** This course is mostly flat and open with several lakes. This is a course that plows its money back into the greens, fairways and irrigation system, and it shows in the yearly improvements. An estimated $500,000 was spent in the last two years on improvements. The course record is 61, held by Jimmy Hill.

**1956**
**R.E. Baldock**

5310 South Laspina
Tulare, CA 93274

Pro shop (209) 686-5300
Clubhouse (209) 686-0270

- ✓ **driving range**
- ✓ **practice greens**
- ✓ **power carts**
- ✓ **pull carts**
- ✓ **golf club rental**
- ✓ **locker rooms**
- ✓ **showers**
- executive course
- accommodations
- ✓ **food and beverages**
- ✓ **clubhouse**

**Dave Vogt**
Professional

**Kevin Friesen**
Superintendent

CENTRAL G4

| Hole | 1 | 2 | 3 | 4 | 5 | 6 | 7 | 8 | 9 | Out | BLUE | Rating: 71.3 |
|---|---|---|---|---|---|---|---|---|---|---|---|---|
| BLUE | 375 | 489 | 367 | 210 | 410 | 530 | 158 | 414 | 411 | 3364 | | Slope: 118 |
| WHITE | 367 | 471 | 358 | 197 | 394 | 515 | 148 | 396 | 397 | 3243 | | |
| Par | 4 | 5 | 4 | 3 | 4 | 5 | 3 | 4 | 4 | 36 | WHITE | Rating: 70.4 |
| Handicap | 13 | 17 | 7 | 9 | 5 | 15 | 11 | 3 | 1 | x | | Slope: 116 |
| RED | 355 | 432 | 334 | 162 | 293 | 449 | 131 | 267 | 296 | 2719 | | |
| Par | 4 | 5 | 4 | 3 | 4 | 5 | 3 | 4 | 4 | 36 | RED | Rating: 70.8 |
| Handicap | 3 | 7 | 5 | 15 | 11 | 1 | 17 | 13 | 9 | x | | Slope: 112 |

| Hole | 10 | 11 | 12 | 13 | 14 | 15 | 16 | 17 | 18 | In | Totals | |
|---|---|---|---|---|---|---|---|---|---|---|---|---|
| BLUE | 382 | 517 | 386 | 142 | 354 | 405 | 202 | 467 | 515 | 3370 | BLUE | 6734 |
| WHITE | 376 | 510 | 377 | 134 | 346 | 398 | 192 | 453 | 505 | 3291 | WHITE | 6534 |
| Par | 4 | 5 | 4 | 3 | 4 | 4 | 3 | 4 | 5 | 36 | Par | 72 |
| Handicap | 6 | 14 | 10 | 18 | 12 | 4 | 8 | 2 | 16 | x | | |
| RED | 364 | 436 | 373 | 125 | 337 | 289 | 174 | 380 | 429 | 2907 | RED | 5626 |
| Par | 4 | 5 | 4 | 3 | 4 | 4 | 3 | 4 | 5 | 36 | Par | 72 |
| Handicap | 12 | 2 | 6 | 18 | 10 | 14 | 16 | 8 | 4 | x | | |

# LINDSAY MUNICIPAL GOLF COURSE

**Course 7**
MAP G4 grid c6

**1961**
Tulare and Elmwood
Lindsay, CA 93221

Pro shop (209) 562-1144

- ✓ **driving range**
- practice greens
- power carts
- ✓ **pull carts**
- ✓ **golf club rental**
- locker rooms
- showers
- ✓ **executive course**
- accommodations
- food and beverages
- clubhouse

**Bill Maaske**
Manager/Superintendent

***Course information:*** This public course has nine holes. Par is 54 for 18 holes. The course is 2,180 yards for 18 holes.

***Play policy and fees:*** Green fees are $2.75 for nine and $5 for 18 holes weekdays and $3 for nine holes and $5.50 for 18 holes weekends. Pull carts are $1.

***Location:*** This course is located in the city park, eight blocks east of Highway 65 between Exeter and Porterville.

***Course description:*** This is a short course that you can play twice. It's located in the Lindsay City Park. It's flat with lots of trees and small greens. It's a good course for beginners, seniors and players wanting to work on their irons. The driving range is for irons only.

# PORTERVILLE GOLF COURSE

**Course 8**
MAP G4 grid d7

*Course information:* This public course has nine holes. See card below for yardage and rating information.

*Play policy and fees:* Green fees are $7 for nine holes and $11 for 18 holes weekdays, and $8 for nine holes and $15 for 18 holes weekends. Carts are $7.50 for nine holes and $15 for 18 holes. Play is on a first-come first-served basis. Closed Mondays.

*Location:* From Highway 99 south of Fresno, take the Highway 196 exit east. Then take Highway 65 into Porterville. Take Olive east and then a right on Piano. Take the first left and continue over the hill to the course.

*Course description:* This course is mostly flat and narrow with out-of-bounds on every hole. The greens are quite small. The course record is 61, set by Arlie Morris.

**1920**
702 East Isham Avenue
Porterville, CA 93257

Pro shop (209) 784-9468

- ✓ **driving range**
- ✓ **practice greens**
- ✓ **power carts**
- ✓ **pull carts**
- ✓ **golf club rental**
- ✓ **locker rooms**
- showers
- executive course
- accommodations
- ✓ **food and beverages**
- ✓ **clubhouse**

**Arlie Morris**
Professional

**John Wilson**
Superintendent

CENTRAL G4

| Hole | 1 | 2 | 3 | 4 | 5 | 6 | 7 | 8 | 9 | Out | | |
|---|---|---|---|---|---|---|---|---|---|---|---|---|
| BLUE | - | - | - | - | - | - | - | - | - | - | BLUE | Rating: -- |
| | | | | | | | | | | | | Slope: -- |
| WHITE | 350 | 184 | 385 | 260 | 400 | 140 | 345 | 450 | 380 | 2849 | | |
| Par | 4 | 3 | 4 | 4 | 4 | 3 | 4 | 5 | 4 | 35 | WHITE | Rating: 65.6 |
| Handicap | 9 | 3 | 13 | 17 | 1 | 15 | 5 | 11 | 7 | x | | Slope: 103 |
| RED | 350 | 184 | 385 | 232 | 400 | 140 | 280 | 450 | 380 | 2756 | | |
| Par | 4 | 3 | 4 | 4 | 5 | 3 | 4 | 5 | 4 | 36 | RED | Rating: 69.8 |
| Handicap | 7 | 15 | 9 | 13 | 3 | 17 | 11 | 1 | 5 | x | | Slope: 117 |

| Hole | 10 | 11 | 12 | 13 | 14 | 15 | 16 | 17 | 18 | In | Totals | |
|---|---|---|---|---|---|---|---|---|---|---|---|---|
| BLUE | - | - | - | - | - | - | - | - | - | - | BLUE | -- |
| WHITE | 350 | 184 | 385 | 260 | 400 | 140 | 345 | 450 | 380 | 2849 | WHITE | 5698 |
| Par | 4 | 3 | 4 | 4 | 4 | 3 | 4 | 5 | 4 | 35 | Par | 70 |
| Handicap | 10 | 4 | 14 | 18 | 2 | 16 | 6 | 12 | 8 | x | | |
| RED | 350 | 184 | 385 | 232 | 400 | 140 | 280 | 450 | 380 | 2756 | RED | 5512 |
| Par | 4 | 3 | 4 | 4 | 5 | 3 | 4 | 5 | 4 | 36 | Par | 72 |
| Handicap | 8 | 16 | 10 | 14 | 4 | 18 | 12 | 2 | 6 | x | | |

## RIVER ISLAND COUNTRY CLUB

**Course 9**
MAP G4 grid d8

***Course information:*** This private course has 18 holes and par is 72. The course is 7,025 yards and rated 72.8 from the championship tees, and 6,433 yards and rated 69.9 from the regular tees. The slope ratings are 127 championship and 119 regular. Women's tees are 5,780 yards and rated 72.8. The slope rating is 128.

***Play policy and fees:*** Reciprocal play is accepted with members of other private clubs. Guest fees are $25 with a member and $40 without. Carts are $10 per person. Reservations are recommended two weeks in advance.

***Location:*** Take Highway 190 and drive past Porterville for 15 minutes. The entrance to this private country club resort course is on the right.

***Course description:*** This long, sprawling course wanders through old oak trees and offers a variety of holes. The Tule River flows through the terrain. You cross the river 11 times, and it comes into play on nine holes. The course is walkable, but there is a lot of distance between holes. The former head-pro, Julius Aquino, set the course record, a 64.

**1964**
**Robert Dean Putman**

31989 River Island Drive
Porterville, CA 93257

Pro shop (209) 784-9425
Clubhouse (209) 781-2917

- ✓ **driving range**
- ✓ **practice greens**
- ✓ **power carts**
- pull carts
- ✓ **golf club rental**
- ✓ **locker rooms**
- ✓ **showers**
- executive course
- ✓ **accommodations**
- ✓ **food and beverages**
- ✓ **clubhouse**

**Terry Treece**
Professional

**Bill Trask**
Superintendent

## DELANO PUBLIC GOLF COURSE

**Course 10**
MAP G4 grid g4

***Course information:*** This public course has nine holes. Par is 64 for 18 holes. The course is 4,384 yards and rated 60.8. The slope rating is 94.

***Play policy and fees:*** Green fees are $6.50 weekdays and $8.50 weekends and holidays.

***Location:*** Take Highway 99 north to Woodlands Avenue exit, head east to Lexington and take a left. Course is on the right.

***Course description:*** This flat course offers undulating fairways. Ponds come into play on the first, eighth and ninth holes. Number three is a 219 yards par-3 with trees on left and right, making for tight play. Number four is a par-5, 501-yard challenge. This traditional course boasts numerous and huge eucalyptus trees along the fairways. The course record is 56, held by Jerry Perez.

**1962**

PO Box 608 Memorial Park
Delano, CA 93216

Pro shop (805) 725-7527

- ✓ **driving range**
- ✓ **practice greens**
- ✓ **power carts**
- ✓ **pull carts**
- ✓ **golf club rental**
- locker rooms
- showers
- executive course
- accommodations
- ✓ **food and beverages**
- ✓ **clubhouse**

**Jerry Perez**
Professional/Manager

**Richard Felix**

# WASCO VALLEY ROSE GOLF COURSE

**Course 11**
MAP G4 grid h1

***Course information:*** This public course has 18 holes. See card below for yardage and rating information.

***Play policy and fees:*** Green fees are $8.50 weekdays and $10.50 weekends. Carts are $15 with a $5 key deposit. Reservations are recommended. This course is available for outside tournaments.

***Location:*** From Highway 99 take the Highway 46 exit west. Drive two miles west of Wasco and take the Leonard Avenue exit to the course. The course is about 20 miles northwest of Bakersfield.

***Course description:*** Six lakes come into play on this course. There are several undulating fairways and elevated tees and greens. The 18th provides an exciting finish, particularly if you survive the undulating fairway, a large lake and bunker, all of which come into play off the tee. The men's course record is 67.

**1991**
**Robert Dean Putman**

301 North Leonard Avenue
Wasco, CA 93280

Pro shop (805) 758-8301

- ✓ **driving range**
- ✓ **practice greens**
- ✓ **power carts**
- ✓ **pull carts**
- ✓ **golf club rental**
- locker rooms
- showers
- executive course
- accommodations
- ✓ **food and beverages**
- ✓ **clubhouse**

**Joe Haggerty**
Professional

**William Stone**
Superintendent



| Hole | 1 | 2 | 3 | 4 | 5 | 6 | 7 | 8 | 9 | Out | | |
|---|---|---|---|---|---|---|---|---|---|---|---|---|
| BLUE | 436 | 188 | 361 | 522 | 155 | 416 | 413 | 403 | 551 | 3445 | BLUE | Rating: 72.5 |
| WHITE | 380 | 163 | 325 | 468 | 118 | 392 | 381 | 375 | 484 | 3086 | | Slope: 121 |
| Par | 4 | 3 | 4 | 5 | 3 | 4 | 4 | 4 | 5 | 36 | WHITE | Rating: 69.4 |
| Handicap | 3 | 1 | 13 | 11 | 17 | 9 | 5 | 7 | 15 | x | | Slope: 115 |
| RED | 352 | 96 | 285 | 422 | 102 | 334 | 305 | 341 | 432 | 2669 | | |
| Par | 4 | 3 | 4 | 5 | 3 | 4 | 4 | 4 | 5 | 36 | RED | Rating: 72.0 |
| Handicap | 4 | 2 | 6 | 16 | 18 | 14 | 12 | 10 | 8 | x | | Slope: 116 |

| Hole | 10 | 11 | 12 | 13 | 14 | 15 | 16 | 17 | 18 | In | Totals | |
|---|---|---|---|---|---|---|---|---|---|---|---|---|
| BLUE | 401 | 363 | 500 | 160 | 437 | 410 | 162 | 414 | 570 | 3417 | BLUE | 6862 |
| WHITE | 370 | 332 | 482 | 135 | 403 | 378 | 137 | 387 | 520 | 3144 | WHITE | 6230 |
| Par | 4 | 4 | 5 | 3 | 4 | 4 | 3 | 4 | 5 | 36 | Par | 72 |
| Handicap | 4 | 18 | 10 | 16 | 6 | 2 | 12 | 14 | 8 | x | | |
| RED | 325 | 293 | 423 | 84 | 355 | 325 | 108 | 325 | 449 | 2687 | RED | 5356 |
| Par | 4 | 4 | 5 | 3 | 4 | 4 | 3 | 4 | 5 | 36 | Par | 72 |
| Handicap | 3 | 15 | 7 | 17 | 5 | 1 | 11 | 13 | 9 | x | | |

MAP ON PAGE 384

# NORTH KERN GOLF COURSE

**Course 12**
MAP G4 grid i3

***Course information:*** This public course has 18 holes. See card below for yardage and rating information.

***Play policy and fees:*** Green fees are $7.75 weekdays and $10.25 weekends. Call for special rates. Carts are $15. Reservations are recommended weekends and holidays.

***Location:*** From Bakersfield, travel north on Highway 99 for 12 miles to the Shafter exit. Head east for 2.5 miles to the course.

***Course description:*** This course is packed with trees and bunkers. Nevertheless, the fairways are wide and level, leading to small greens. The sixth hole is a devil. It's a 442-yard, par-4 that plays uphill and into the wind. The green is heavily bunkered in front, leaving only a narrow opening. Pin placement on this hole can add more yardage to an already long hole. The Kern County Amateur Championships are held here each October and the Kern County Two-Man, Best Ball Tournament is held each April. The course record is 63, set in 1985 by former head pro Bill McKinley.

**1953**
**Kermit Styber**

PO Box 80545
Bakersfield, CA 93380

17412 Quality Road
Bakersfield, CA 93380

Pro shop (805) 399-0347

- ✓ **driving range**
- ✓ **practice greens**
- ✓ **power carts**
- ✓ **pull carts**
- ✓ **golf club rental**
- ✓ **locker rooms**
- ✓ **showers**
- executive course
- accommodations
- ✓ **food and beverages**
- ✓ **clubhouse**

**Keith Perkins**
Professional

**Jack Agar**
Professional

**Richard Koop**
Superintendent

| Hole | 1 | 2 | 3 | 4 | 5 | 6 | 7 | 8 | 9 | Out | BLUE | Rating: 71.4 |
|---|---|---|---|---|---|---|---|---|---|---|---|---|
| BLUE | 500 | 355 | 345 | 545 | 213 | 442 | 178 | 429 | 390 | 3397 | | Slope: 115 |
| WHITE | 480 | 333 | 336 | 525 | 198 | 428 | 156 | 408 | 373 | 3237 | | |
| Par | 5 | 4 | 4 | 5 | 3 | 4 | 3 | 4 | 4 | 36 | WHITE | Rating: 69.9 |
| Handicap | 17 | 13 | 9 | 15 | 5 | 1 | 11 | 3 | 7 | x | | Slope: 109 |
| RED | 451 | 326 | 318 | 508 | 184 | 422 | 134 | 385 | 365 | 3093 | | |
| Par | 5 | 4 | 4 | 5 | 3 | 5 | 3 | 5 | 4 | 38 | RED | Rating: 72.7 |
| Handicap | 3 | 13 | 9 | 1 | 15 | 5 | 17 | 7 | 11 | x | | Slope: 116 |

| Hole | 10 | 11 | 12 | 13 | 14 | 15 | 16 | 17 | 18 | In | Totals | |
|---|---|---|---|---|---|---|---|---|---|---|---|---|
| BLUE | 375 | 193 | 390 | 435 | 395 | 490 | 454 | 165 | 475 | 3372 | BLUE | 6769 |
| WHITE | 356 | 181 | 374 | 411 | 384 | 469 | 440 | 151 | 458 | 3224 | WHITE | 6461 |
| Par | 4 | 3 | 4 | 4 | 4 | 5 | 4 | 3 | 5 | 36 | Par | 72 |
| Handicap | 6 | 12 | 8 | 4 | 10 | 16 | 2 | 14 | 18 | x | | |
| RED | 344 | 168 | 362 | 400 | 374 | 459 | 437 | 139 | 406 | 3089 | RED | 6182 |
| Par | 4 | 3 | 4 | 5 | 4 | 5 | 5 | 3 | 5 | 38 | Par | 76 |
| Handicap | 14 | 16 | 10 | 8 | 12 | 4 | 6 | 18 | 2 | x | | |

# KERN RIVER GOLF COURSE

**Course 13**
MAP G4 grid j7

***Course information:*** This public course has 18 holes. See card below for yardage and rating information.

***Play policy and fees:*** Green fees are $7.75 weekdays and $10.25 weekends. Call for special rates. Carts are $16. Reservations are recommended. Make reservations the prior Wednesday.

***Location:*** From Highway 99 in Bakersfield, take Highway 178 east to Alfred Herrall Highway. Follow the signs to Lake Ming.

***Course description:*** This public facility will test your golf skill. It is one of two courses in the area that is rated over par. It was originally designed in the 1920s as a nine-hole course. Nine more holes were added in the 1950s. The course features rolling terrain and an abundance of mature trees. One word of caution. There are two long par-3 holes on the back nine that can ruin your day. A hole to remember is number 11. It is 235 yards from the back. If you miss the green to the right you're stymied behind trees. The green is sharply sloped downhill and difficult to putt. Don't leave the ball above the hole. The course record is 62 for men, by Ron Baker, and 71 for women.

**1953**
**William Park Bell**

PO Box 6339
Bakersfield, CA 93386

Pro shop (805) 872-5128

- ✓ **driving range**
- ✓ **practice greens**
- ✓ **power carts**
- ✓ **pull carts**
- ✓ **golf club rental**
- ✓ **locker rooms**
- ✓ **showers**
- executive course
- accommodations
- ✓ **food and beverages**
- ✓ **clubhouse**

**Ruby Foss**
President

**Jim Foss**
Professional

**Ron Baker**
Superintendent

| Hole | 1 | 2 | 3 | 4 | 5 | 6 | 7 | 8 | 9 | Out | BLUE | Rating: 70.3 |
|---|---|---|---|---|---|---|---|---|---|---|---|---|
| BLUE | 529 | 138 | 465 | 453 | 293 | 163 | 395 | 543 | 200 | 3179 | | Slope: 119 |
| WHITE | 516 | 129 | 454 | 436 | 282 | 152 | 388 | 534 | 180 | 3071 | | |
| Par | 5 | 3 | 4 | 4 | 4 | 3 | 4 | 5 | 3 | 35 | WHITE | Rating: 68.7 |
| Handicap | 9 | 17 | 1 | 3 | 15 | 13 | 5 | 7 | 11 | x | | Slope: 113 |
| RED | 492 | 118 | 435 | 400 | 267 | 135 | 376 | 519 | 165 | 2907 | | |
| Par | 5 | 3 | 5 | 4 | 4 | 3 | 4 | 5 | 3 | 36 | RED | Rating: 72.3 |
| Handicap | 7 | 17 | 11 | 5 | 13 | 15 | 3 | 1 | 9 | x | | Slope: 116 |

| Hole | 10 | 11 | 12 | 13 | 14 | 15 | 16 | 17 | 18 | In | Totals | |
|---|---|---|---|---|---|---|---|---|---|---|---|---|
| BLUE | 381 | 235 | 365 | 339 | 459 | 366 | 382 | 222 | 530 | 3279 | BLUE | 6458 |
| WHITE | 376 | 225 | 358 | 332 | 436 | 359 | 373 | 218 | 510 | 3187 | WHITE | 6258 |
| Par | 4 | 3 | 4 | 4 | 4 | 4 | 4 | 3 | 5 | 35 | Par | 70 |
| Handicap | 10 | 4 | 8 | 18 | 2 | 12 | 14 | 6 | 16 | x | | |
| RED | 361 | 211 | 344 | 320 | 424 | 346 | 357 | 205 | 496 | 3064 | RED | 5971 |
| Par | 4 | 3 | 4 | 4 | 5 | 4 | 4 | 4 | 5 | 37 | Par | 73 |
| Handicap | 10 | 6 | 14 | 12 | 16 | 8 | 4 | 18 | 2 | x | | |



MAP ON PAGE 384

# RIO BRAVO COUNTRY CLUB

Course 14
MAP G4 grid j8

***Course information:*** This private course has 18 holes. See card below for yardage and rating information.

***Play policy and fees:*** Members and guests only. Green fees are $25 when accompanied by a member, and $50 unaccompanied. $50 for reciprocators, including carts. Carts are $16. Reservations are required.

***Location:*** From Highway 99 in Bakersfield, take Highway 178 east and drive about 12 miles to the Rio Bravo Resort area. Continue past the airport and turn right to the course.

***Course description:*** This is a private resort course with a beautiful championship layout set in the foothills of the Tehachapi Mountains. It plays long and has excellent greens. It is the site of the PGA tour qualifying school and the Southern California Open. The hole to watch out for is number 11, affectionately known as Big Bertha. It's par-5 and 616 yards uphill to a difficult green. You never have a flat lie on this hole. The green, the most difficult on the course, is severely sloped left-to-right and tough to read. The course record is 64, held by Sam Randolph.

**1975**
**Robert Muir Graves**

15200 Casa Club Road
Bakersfield, CA 93306

Pro shop (805) 871-4653

- ✓ **driving range**
- ✓ **practice greens**
- ✓ **power carts**
- pull carts
- golf club rental
- ✓ **locker rooms**
- ✓ **showers**
- executive course
- ✓ **accommodations**
- ✓ **food and beverages**
- ✓ **clubhouse**

**Bruce Burroughs**
Professional

**Rick Stone**
Superintendent

| Hole | 1 | 2 | 3 | 4 | 5 | 6 | 7 | 8 | 9 | Out | | |
|---|---|---|---|---|---|---|---|---|---|---|---|---|
| BLUE | 406 | 387 | 568 | 426 | 223 | 552 | 410 | 192 | 372 | 3536 | BLUE | Rating: 74.4 |
| WHITE | 373 | 370 | 548 | 406 | 191 | 529 | 388 | 162 | 354 | 3321 | | Slope: 138 |
| Par | 4 | 4 | 5 | 4 | 3 | 5 | 4 | 3 | 4 | 36 | WHITE | Rating: 70.9 |
| Handicap | 8 | 10 | 14 | 2 | 16 | 6 | 4 | 18 | 12 | x | | Slope: 122 |
| RED | 322 | 319 | 498 | 352 | 160 | 473 | 345 | 137 | 303 | 2909 | | |
| Par | 4 | 4 | 5 | 4 | 3 | 5 | 4 | 3 | 4 | 36 | RED | Rating: 72.5 |
| Handicap | 14 | 12 | 4 | 8 | 16 | 2 | 6 | 18 | 10 | x | | Slope: 120 |

| Hole | 10 | 11 | 12 | 13 | 14 | 15 | 16 | 17 | 18 | In | Totals | |
|---|---|---|---|---|---|---|---|---|---|---|---|---|
| BLUE | 405 | 616 | 392 | 244 | 446 | 345 | 155 | 358 | 521 | 3482 | BLUE | 7018 |
| WHITE | 365 | 596 | 336 | 219 | 419 | 326 | 144 | 331 | 498 | 3234 | WHITE | 6555 |
| Par | 4 | 5 | 4 | 3 | 4 | 4 | 3 | 4 | 5 | 36 | Par | 72 |
| Handicap | 17 | 1 | 11 | 5 | 3 | 13 | 15 | 7 | 9 | x | | |
| RED | 313 | 526 | 302 | 157 | 370 | 278 | 109 | 289 | 451 | 2795 | RED | 5704 |
| Par | 4 | 5 | 4 | 3 | 4 | 4 | 3 | 4 | 5 | 36 | Par | 72 |
| Handicap | 15 | 1 | 11 | 13 | 5 | 9 | 17 | 7 | 3 | x | | |

MAP ON PAGE 384

# MAP G5

(2 COURSES)

PAGES.. 398-399

CEN-CAL MAP...see page 314
adjoining maps
NORTH (F5) .......see page 372
EAST (G6) .........see page 400
SOUTH (H5) .......see page 444
WEST (G4) .........see page 384

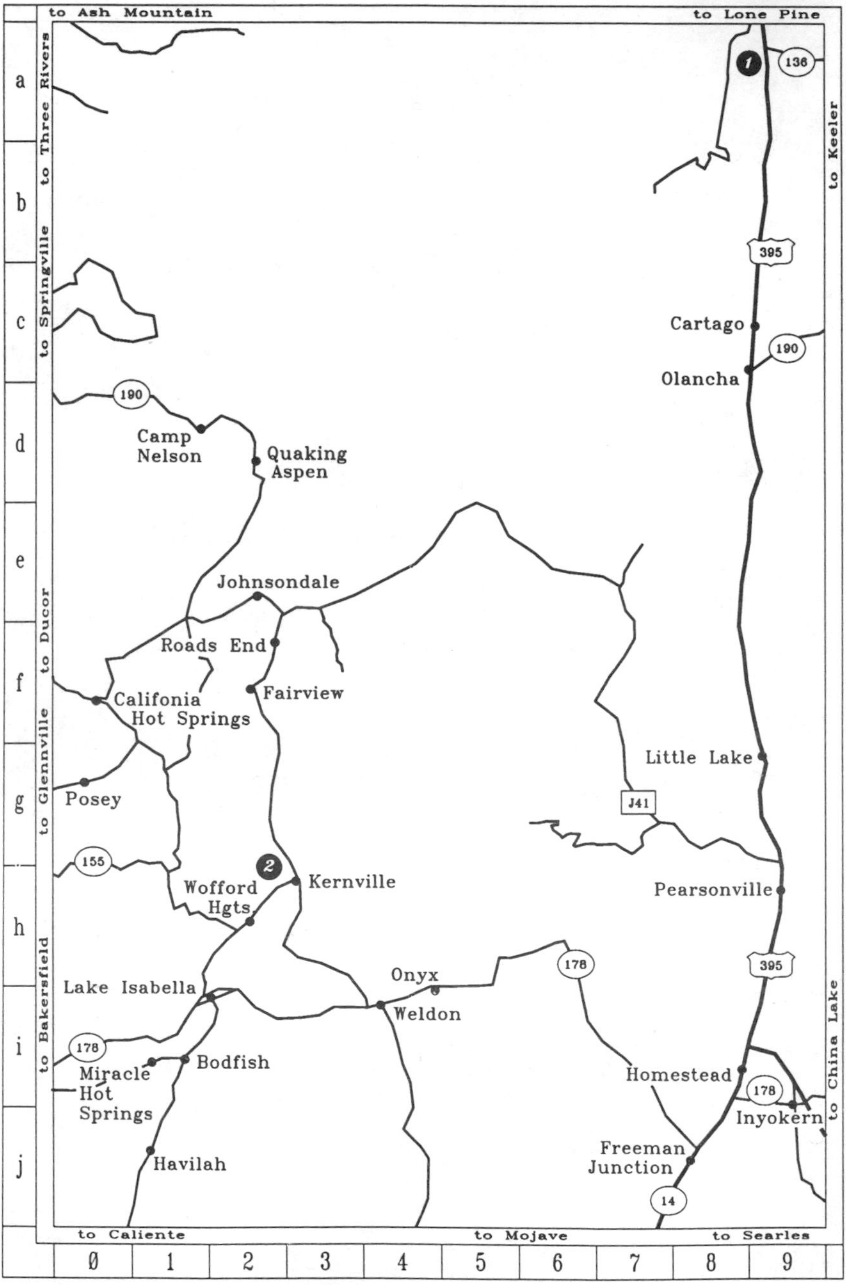

to Ash Mountain
to Lone Pine
to Three Rivers
to Springville
to Keeler
to Ducor
to Glennville
to Bakersfield
to China Lake
to Caliente
to Mojave
to Searles

a
b
c
d
e
f
g
h
i
j

0 1 2 3 4 5 6 7 8 9

1
2
136
395
190
178
155
14
J41

Cartago
Olancha
Camp Nelson
Quaking Aspen
Johnsondale
Roads End
Fairview
California Hot Springs
Posey
Little Lake
Pearsonville
Kernville
Wofford Hgts
Lake Isabella
Onyx
Weldon
Bodfish
Miracle Hot Springs
Havilah
Homestead
Inyokern
Freeman Junction

## MOUNT WHITNEY GOLF COURSE

**Course 1**
MAP G5 grid a9

**1958**
PO Box O
Lone Pine, CA 93545

Highway 395
Lone Pine, CA 93545

Pro shop (619) 876-5795

✓ **driving range**
✓ **practice greens**
✓ **power carts**
✓ **pull carts**
✓ **golf club rental**
✓ **locker rooms**
showers
executive course
accommodations
✓ **food and beverages**
✓ **clubhouse**

**Brad Taylor**
Manager/Pro/Superintendent

***Course information:*** This public course has nine holes. Par is 72 for 18 holes. The course is 6,624 yards and rated 70.1 from the championship tees, and 6,376 yards and rated 69.3 from the regular tees (18 holes). The slope ratings are 116 championship and 114 regular. Women's tees are 5,692 yards and rated 71.0. The slope rating is 112.

***Play policy and fees:*** Green fees are $8 weekdays and $10 weekends. Carts are $8.50 for nine holes and $17 for 18 holes.

***Location:*** Drive on Highway 395 to Lone Pine.

***Course description:*** This scenic course is situated in the foothills of Mount Whitney. It's flat with some water, bunkers, trees and narrow fairways. Accurate iron play is essential. The course record is 64, held by Mike Sullivan.



## KERN VALLEY GOLF COURSE COUNTRY CLUB

**Course 2**
MAP G5 grid h2

**1957**
**Jack Ewing**

PO Box 888
Kernville, CA 93238

9472 Burlando Road
Kernville, CA 93238

Pro shop (619) 376-2828

✓ **driving range**
✓ **practice greens**
✓ **power carts**
✓ **pull carts**
✓ **golf club rental**
locker rooms
showers
executive course
accommodations
✓ **food and beverages**
✓ **clubhouse**

**Rick Eaton**
Professional

**James Downard**
Superintendent

**Bob Talbot**
Manager

***Course information:*** This semi-private course has nine holes. Par is 72 for 18 holes. The course is 6,282 yards and rated 68.2 from the regular tees for 18 holes. The slope rating is 101.

***Play policy and fees:*** Outside play is accepted. Green fees are $7 for nine holes and $12 for 18 holes weekdays. On weekends it's $8 for nine holes and $15 for 18 holes. Call for special rates. Carts are $8 for nine and $15 for 18 holes. This course is available for outside tournaments by appointment.

***Location:*** From Bakersfield travel northeast on Highway 178 for 50 miles. The course is located one-half mile south of Kernville on Highway 155.

***Course description:*** This is a well-maintained, fairly flat, short course. Trees line the narrow fairways demanding accuracy off the tees and a good short game. The course record is 64, held by former pro Alan Jones.

# MAP G6

(1 COURSE)

PAGES.. 400-401

CEN-CAL MAP...see page 314
adjoining maps
NORTH ........................no map
EAST (G7) .........see page 402
SOUTH (H6) .......see page 456
WEST (G5) ........see page 398

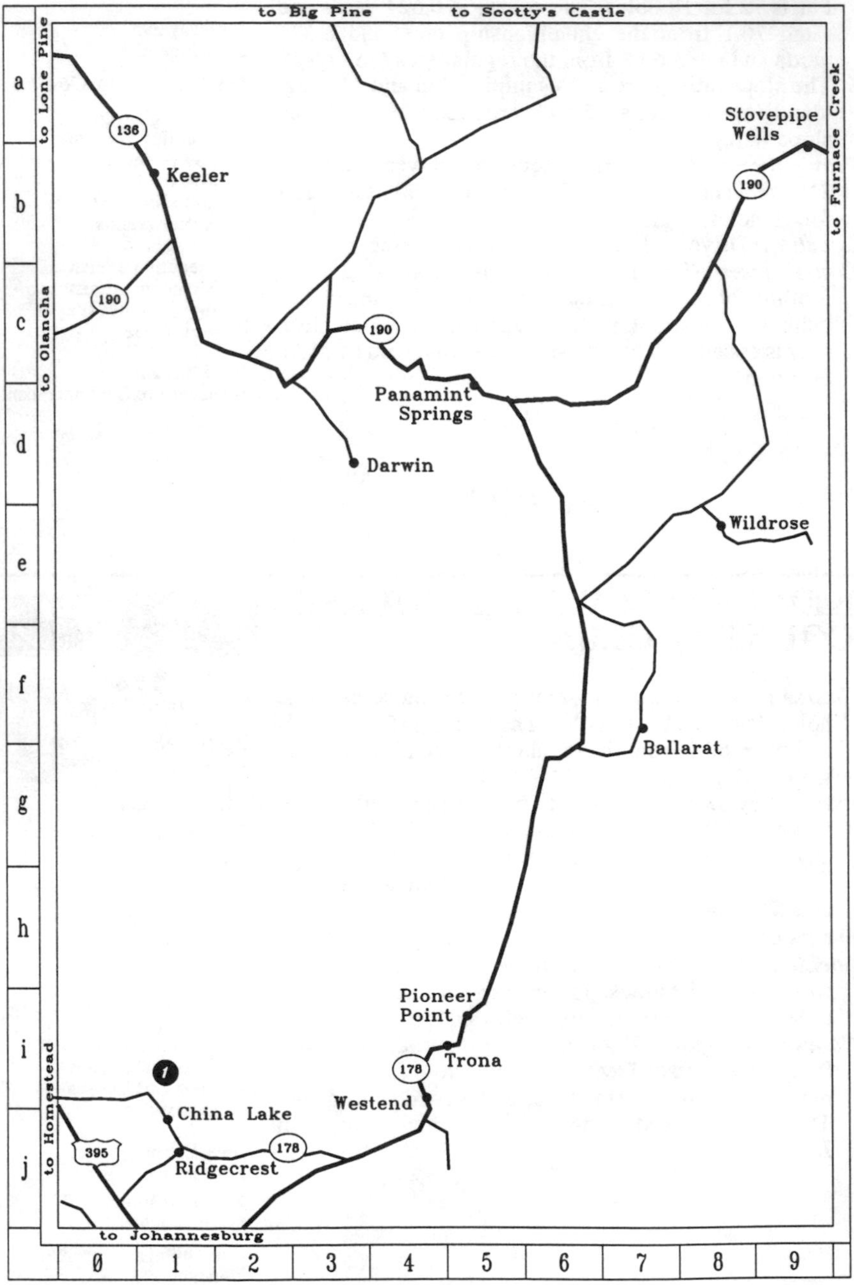

# CHINA LAKE GOLF COURSE

**Course 1**
MAP G6 grid i1

***Course information:*** This military course has 18 holes. Women's championship tees are 5,914 yards, rated 71.2, and have a slope rating of 112. See card below for additional yardage and rating information.

***Play policy and fees:*** Outside play is accepted. Green fees are $14.50 weekdays and $20 weekends for outside play. Other fees vary according to military or civilian status. Call for special rates. Carts are $14. Reservations are recommended.

***Location:*** From the town of Mojave, travel north on Highway 14 for approximately 40 miles to Highway 178. Turn right and drive east for about 13 miles to the entrance of China Lake Naval Weapons Station. Obtain a pass at the gate and continue to the course on Midway Drive.

***Course description:*** This is a flat, desert course with lots of bunkers and trees. There are no water hazards. Beware of the 10th hole, a 568-yard, par-5. It is an uphill, dogleg right with two fairway traps. The two-tiered green has made more than one military commander wave the white flag and surrender. China Lake hosts a men's and women's club championship each year. Drew Martin and John Hemond share the men's course record with a 65, and Jane Nechero holds the women's record with a 76.

**1957**
**George Bell**

PO Box 507
Ridgecrest, CA 93555

411 Midway Drive
Ridgecrest, CA 93555

Pro shop (619) 939-2990

- ✓ **driving range**
- ✓ **practice greens**
- ✓ **power carts**
- ✓ **pull carts**
- ✓ **golf club rental**
- ✓ **locker rooms**
- ✓ **showers**
- executive course
- accommodations
- ✓ **food and beverages**
- ✓ **clubhouse**

**Tom Page**
Manager/Pro/Superintendent

CENTRAL G6

| Hole | 1 | 2 | 3 | 4 | 5 | 6 | 7 | 8 | 9 | Out | | |
|---|---|---|---|---|---|---|---|---|---|---|---|---|
| BLUE | 489 | 365 | 404 | 335 | 444 | 191 | 537 | 182 | 420 | 3367 | BLUE | Rating: 72.4 |
| | | | | | | | | | | | | Slope: 119 |
| WHITE | 461 | 347 | 388 | 322 | 434 | 168 | 518 | 151 | 411 | 3200 | | |
| Par | 5 | 4 | 4 | 4 | 4 | 3 | 5 | 3 | 4 | 36 | WHITE | Rating: 70.9 |
| Handicap | 17 | 7 | 5 | 16 | 1 | 11 | 9 | 13 | 3 | x | | Slope: 114 |
| RED | 417 | 302 | 320 | 289 | 324 | 110 | 442 | 139 | 346 | 2689 | | |
| Par | 5 | 4 | 4 | 4 | 4 | 3 | 5 | 3 | 4 | 36 | RED | Rating: 68.7 |
| Handicap | 5 | 11 | 7 | 13 | 9 | 17 | 3 | 15 | 1 | x | | Slope: 109 |

| Hole | 10 | 11 | 12 | 13 | 14 | 15 | 16 | 17 | 18 | In | Totals | |
|---|---|---|---|---|---|---|---|---|---|---|---|---|
| BLUE | 548 | 235 | 398 | 418 | 431 | 347 | 393 | 175 | 539 | 3484 | BLUE | 6851 |
| WHITE | 533 | 216 | 381 | 408 | 413 | 340 | 380 | 164 | 516 | 3351 | WHITE | 6551 |
| Par | 5 | 3 | 4 | 4 | 4 | 4 | 4 | 3 | 5 | 36 | Par | 72 |
| Handicap | 8 | 6 | 12 | 4 | 2 | 16 | 10 | 14 | 18 | x | | |
| RED | 474 | 148 | 307 | 291 | 342 | 329 | 320 | 160 | 432 | 2803 | RED | 5492 |
| Par | 5 | 3 | 4 | 4 | 4 | 4 | 4 | 3 | 5 | 36 | Par | 72 |
| Handicap | 2 | 18 | 8 | 12 | 6 | 4 | 14 | 16 | 10 | x | | |

# MAP G7
(1 COURSE)

PAGES.. 402-403

CEN-CAL MAP...see page 314
adjoining maps
NORTH ........................no map
EAST ............................no map
SOUTH..........................no map
WEST (G6) .........see page 400

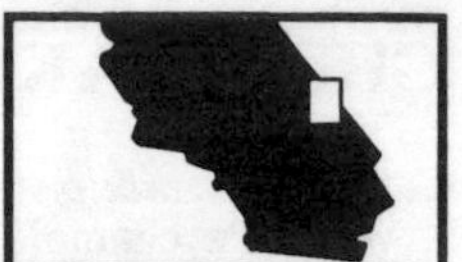

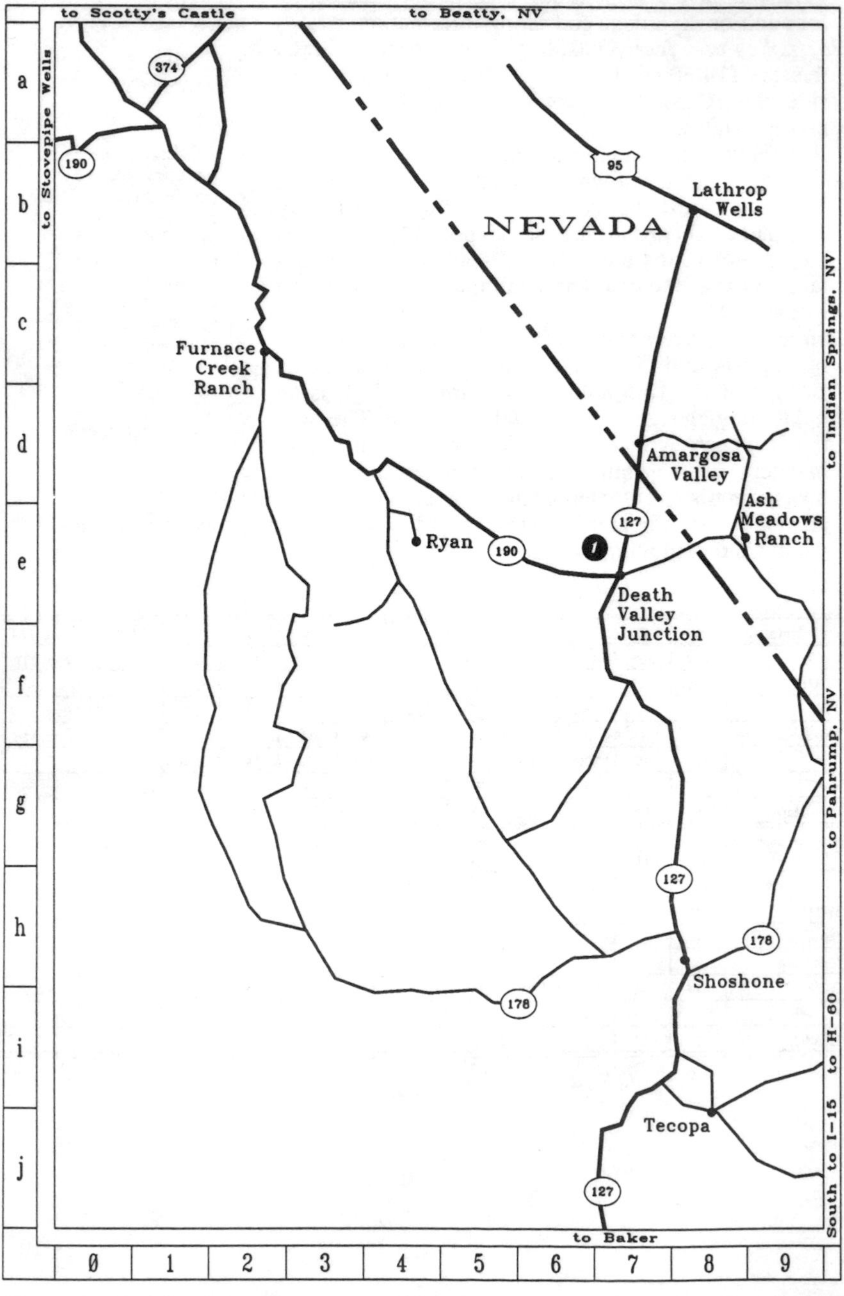

to Scotty's Castle
to Beatty, NV
to Stovepipe Wells
to Indian Springs, NV
to Pahrump, NV
South to I-15 to H-60
to Baker

374
190
95
127
178

NEVADA
Lathrop Wells
Furnace Creek Ranch
Amargosa Valley
Ash Meadows Ranch
Ryan
1
Death Valley Junction
Shoshone
Tecopa

a
b
c
d
e
f
g
h
i
j

0 1 2 3 4 5 6 7 8 9

# FURNACE CREEK GOLF COURSE

Course 1
MAP G7 grid e7

**1930**

PO Box 187
Death Valley, CA 92328

Furnace Creek Ranch
Death Valley, CA 92328

Pro shop (619) 786-2301
Clubhouse (619) 786-2345

- ✓ **driving range**
- ✓ **practice greens**
- ✓ **power carts**
- ✓ **pull carts**
- ✓ **golf club rental**
- ✓ **locker rooms**
- ✓ **showers**
- ✓ **executive course**
- ✓ **accommodations**
- ✓ **food and beverages**
- ✓ **clubhouse**

**Rick Hertzwig**
Director of Golf

**Bill Hindmin**
Superintendent

***Course information:*** This resort course has 18 holes and par is 70. The course is 5,750 yards and rated 66.3 from the regular tees. The slope rating is 96. Women's tees are 4,977 yards and rated 68.1. The slope rating is 99.

***Play policy and fees:*** Green fees are $13 for nine holes and $25 for 18 holes. Outside play is accepted. Carts are $18 for 18 holes. Pro shop closes from May 15 to November 1, but tee times are still sold from the 19th Hole during those months.

***Location:*** Located in Death Valley, west of Highway 127 on Highway 190.

***Course description:*** This is the world's lowest golf course at 214 feet below sea level. Built in 1930, it was one of the first all-grass courses in Southern California, and the bunkers today remain grass rather than sand. There is water on nine holes. Wildlife abounds on this desert course and ranges from coyotes to Canada geese. From the 12th hole there is a spectacular view of the towering Panamint Mountains. The course record is 62.

# MAP H2
(7 COURSES)

PAGES.. 404-411

CEN-CAL MAP...see page 314
adjoining maps
NORTH (G2).......see page 374
EAST (H3) ..........see page 412
SOUTH..........................no map
WEST............................no map

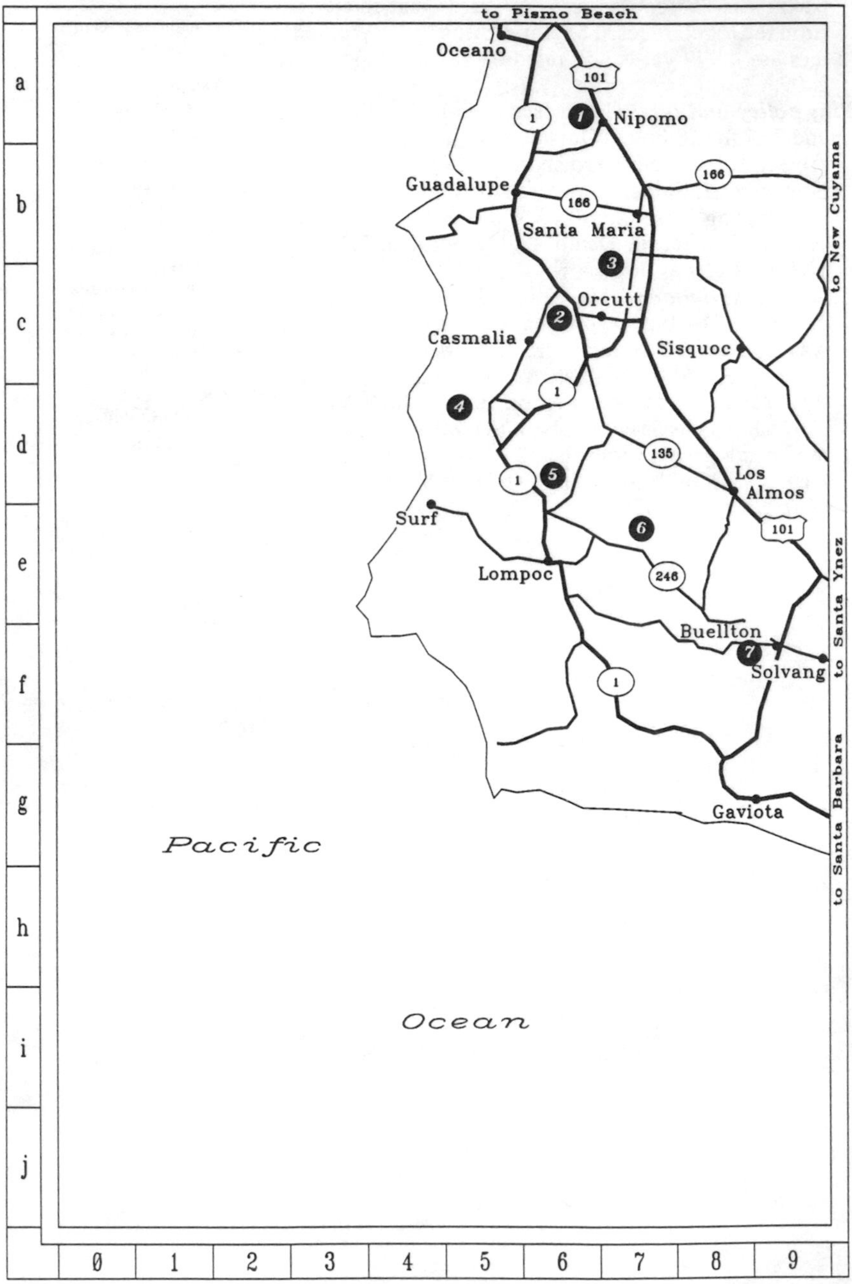

to Pismo Beach
Oceano
101
1
Nipomo
166
Guadalupe
166
Santa Maria
Orcutt
Casmalia
Sisquoc
1
to New Cuyama
135
Los Almos
1
Surf
101
Lompoc
246
Buellton
Solvang
to Santa Ynez
1
Gaviota
to Santa Barbara
Pacific
Ocean

a b c d e f g h i j

0 1 2 3 4 5 6 7 8 9

# BLACK LAKE GOLF RESORT

**Course 1**
MAP H2 grid a6

***Course information:*** This resort course has 18 holes. See card below for yardage and rating information.

***Play policy and fees:*** Green fees are $23 weekdays and $34 on weekends. Call for special rates. Carts are $22 and mandatory until 4 p.m. Reservations are recommended. Give one week lead time for reservations.

***Location:*** Travel north on Highway 101 from Los Angeles past Santa Maria to the Tefft Street exit in Nipomo. Turn left over the highway to Pomeroy, then turn left to Willow and right to the golf course.

***Course description:*** This well-designed course offers tree-lined fairways, several lakes and a rolling terrain. Among the holes to watch for are the par-5 11th, 502 yards with a narrow fairway, left lateral water hazard and bunkered right side. Several annual tournaments are held here including the John Madden Celebrity Golf Classic in June, and the Burton Gilliam Celebrity Golf Classic in March. The course record is 65.

**1965**
**Ted Robinson (1986)**

1490 Golf Course Lane
Nipomo, CA 93444

Pro shop (805) 481-4204
Starter (805) 343-1214

- ✓ **driving range**
- ✓ **practice greens**
- ✓ **power carts**
- ✓ **pull carts**
- ✓ **golf club rental**
- locker rooms
- showers
- executive course
- ✓ **accommodations**
- ✓ **food and beverages**
- ✓ **clubhouse**

**Dan Stills**
Professional

**Berne Finch**
PGA Apprentice

**Phil Sheridan**
Superintendent

CENTRAL H2

| Hole | 1 | 2 | 3 | 4 | 5 | 6 | 7 | 8 | 9 | Out | BLUE | Rating: 70.4 |
|---|---|---|---|---|---|---|---|---|---|---|---|---|
| BLUE | 145 | 398 | 342 | 396 | 404 | 527 | 330 | 160 | 573 | 3275 | | Slope: 121 |
| WHITE | 127 | 359 | 322 | 378 | 396 | 517 | 315 | 134 | 527 | 3075 | | |
| Par | 3 | 4 | 4 | 4 | 4 | 5 | 4 | 3 | 5 | 36 | WHITE | Rating: 68.8 |
| Handicap | 17 | 11 | 9 | 3 | 5 | 7 | 15 | 13 | 1 | x | | Slope: 114 |
| RED | 121 | 343 | 310 | 359 | 381 | 501 | 294 | 109 | 471 | 2889 | | |
| Par | 3 | 4 | 4 | 4 | 4 | 5 | 4 | 3 | 5 | 36 | RED | Rating: 71.8 |
| Handicap | 17 | 11 | 9 | 7 | 5 | 3 | 13 | 15 | 1 | x | | Slope: 122 |

| Hole | 10 | 11 | 12 | 13 | 14 | 15 | 16 | 17 | 18 | In | Totals | |
|---|---|---|---|---|---|---|---|---|---|---|---|---|
| BLUE | 380 | 506 | 369 | 442 | 173 | 408 | 334 | 159 | 366 | 3137 | BLUE | 6412 |
| WHITE | 365 | 493 | 352 | 434 | 148 | 394 | 314 | 145 | 348 | 2993 | WHITE | 6068 |
| Par | 4 | 5 | 4 | 5 | 3 | 4 | 4 | 3 | 4 | 36 | Par | 72 |
| Handicap | 6 | 4 | 10 | 12 | 14 | 2 | 16 | 18 | 8 | x | | |
| RED | 345 | 445 | 332 | 420 | 122 | 376 | 271 | 123 | 291 | 2725 | RED | 5614 |
| Par | 4 | 5 | 4 | 5 | 3 | 4 | 4 | 3 | 4 | 36 | Par | 72 |
| Handicap | 8 | 2 | 10 | 6 | 18 | 4 | 14 | 16 | 12 | x | | |

# RANCHO MARIA GOLF COURSE

**Course 2**
MAP H2 grid c6

**1965**
**R. E. Baldock**

1950 Casmalia Road
Santa Maria, CA 93455

Pro shop (805) 937-2019

- ✓ **driving range**
- ✓ **practice greens**
- ✓ **power carts**
- ✓ **pull carts**
- ✓ **golf club rental**
- locker rooms
- showers
- executive course
- accommodations
- ✓ **food and beverages**
- ✓ **clubhouse**

**Jack O'Keefe**
Professional

**Don Jones**
Superintendent

**Course information:** This public course has 18 holes. See card below for yardage and rating information.

***Play policy and fees:*** Green fees are $18 weekdays and $24 weekends. Carts are $18. Reservations are recommended. Make reservations two days in advance during the week and a week in advance for weekends.

***Location:*** Take the Orcutt/Clark Avenue exit off Highway 101 in Santa Maria, and drive west on Clark Avenue for 2.5 miles to Highway 1. Turn right and drive one mile to the course.

***Course description:*** This course is located in the foothills southwest of Santa Maria. There are no parallel fairways and the rolling greens can be very fast. Watch for number 13 in the afternoon. This par-4, 438-yard hole is dangerous in a confronting wind. The wind has been known to blow the ball out-of-bounds into the trees off the tee, but the real challenge is getting home in two with a long iron from a downhill lie. The green, which slopes to the right, is also well-bunkered on that side. If you miss to the left, it's hard to stop the ball. The course record is 60, held by John McComish.

| Hole | 1 | 2 | 3 | 4 | 5 | 6 | 7 | 8 | 9 | Out | | |
|---|---|---|---|---|---|---|---|---|---|---|---|---|
| BLUE | 341 | 533 | 164 | 374 | 347 | 205 | 513 | 307 | 176 | 2960 | BLUE | Rating: 70.0 |
| WHITE | 329 | 498 | 155 | 363 | 338 | 197 | 499 | 297 | 158 | 2834 | | Slope: 114 |
| Par | 4 | 5 | 3 | 4 | 4 | 3 | 5 | 4 | 3 | 35 | WHITE | Rating: 68.7 |
| Handicap | 13 | 7 | 15 | 1 | 9 | 5 | 3 | 17 | 11 | x | | Slope: 109 |
| RED | 301 | 461 | 138 | 247 | 320 | 181 | 476 | 276 | 130 | 2533 | | |
| Par | 4 | 5 | 3 | 4 | 4 | 3 | 5 | 4 | 3 | 35 | RED | Rating: 70.3 |
| Handicap | 11 | 3 | 15 | 13 | 5 | 9 | 1 | 7 | 17 | x | | Slope: 113 |

| Hole | 10 | 11 | 12 | 13 | 14 | 15 | 16 | 17 | 18 | In | Totals | |
|---|---|---|---|---|---|---|---|---|---|---|---|---|
| BLUE | 348 | 358 | 191 | 438 | 488 | 163 | 424 | 498 | 522 | 3430 | BLUE | 6390 |
| WHITE | 338 | 347 | 181 | 432 | 471 | 151 | 408 | 473 | 513 | 3314 | WHITE | 6148 |
| Par | 4 | 4 | 3 | 4 | 5 | 3 | 4 | 5 | 5 | 37 | Par | 72 |
| Handicap | 10 | 14 | 6 | 2 | 16 | 18 | 4 | 12 | 8 | x | | |
| RED | 237 | 326 | 166 | 415 | 418 | 132 | 378 | 411 | 488 | 2971 | RED | 5504 |
| Par | 4 | 4 | 3 | 5 | 5 | 3 | 4 | 5 | 5 | 38 | Par | 73 |
| Handicap | 16 | 8 | 14 | 12 | 10 | 18 | 2 | 6 | 4 | x | | |

# SANTA MARIA COUNTRY CLUB

**Course 3**
MAP H2 grid c7

**1920**
505 West Waller Lane
Santa Maria, CA 93455

Pro shop (805) 937-7872
Clubhouse (805) 937-2025
Supt. (805) 937-4945

- ✓ **driving range**
- ✓ **practice greens**
- ✓ **power carts**
- ✓ **pull carts**
- golf club rental
- ✓ **locker rooms**
- ✓ **showers**
- executive course
- accommodations
- ✓ **food and beverages**
- ✓ **clubhouse**

**Gary Quigley**
Professional

**Dale Foster**
Superintendent

***Course information:*** This private course has 18 holes and par is 72. The course is 6,495 yards and rated 71.4 from the championship tees, and 6,270 yards and rated 69.8 from the regular tees. The slope ratings are 128 championship and 122 regular.

***Play policy and fees:*** Reciprocal play is accepted with members of other private clubs. But aside from that, members and guests only. Guest fees are $35 weekdays and $50 weekends. Carts are $16. Reservations are recommended. Closed Mondays.

***Location:*** Travel south of Santa Maria on Highway 101 to the Betteravia exit. Turn west and drive to Broadway, then south to Waller Lane. From there go right to the club.

***Course description:*** This is a fairly level course, but don't let that fool you. It is heavily wooded and more than one golfer has claimed to have lost a ball to a hungry chipmunk. The original nine holes were built in the 1920s; the second nine were built in the 1950s.



MAP ON PAGE 404

# VANDENBERG AFB GOLF COURSE

**Course 4**
MAP H2 grid d5

**1965**
**Robert Dean Putman**

Vandenberg AFB,
CA 93437

Pro shop (805) 734-8232
Starter (805) 734-1333

- ✓ **driving range**
- ✓ **practice greens**
- ✓ **power carts**
- ✓ **pull carts**
- ✓ **golf club rental**
- ✓ **locker rooms**
- ✓ **showers**
- executive course
- accommodations
- ✓ **food & beverages**
- ✓ **clubhouse**

**Rick Vigil**
Manager

**John Belt**
Superintendent

***Course information:*** This military course has 18 holes. See card below for yardage and rating information.

***Play policy and fees:*** Members and guests only. Green fees range from $7 to $30 depending on personnel status. Reservations are recommended. Outside guest fees are $40 weekdays, $50 weekends. Carts are $14.

***Location:*** Highway 101 north to Highway 1 take the Lompoc-Vandenberg exit (just beyond Gaviota coming from the south) north to Vandenberg AFB. Drive past the main gate about four miles to the exit for Marshallia Ranch, left to the course.

***Course description:*** Set three miles from the ocean, this tight and heavily-wooded course becomes increasingly difficult as the prevailing winds pick up. Each hole is separated by dense stands of trees which line the fairways and are behind all the greens. The course is fairly flat and walkable. Number nine and number 16 holes are rated among the best in Santa Barbara County. Number nine is par-4, 434 yards through a chute to a narrow landing area and onto a green with two large bunkers front left and right. Warning: the green is surrounded by ice plant. Number 16 is a par-4 playing 416 yards straight uphill and into the wind. For most golfers it's unreachable in two. Pros play a driver and two iron or a three wood to reach in two. An average of 245 rounds a day are played on this course. First tee time is not until 7 a.m. Morning and evening fog can cut short a day's play. Closed Mondays. The course record is 67, set by Rex Coldwell.

| Hole | 1 | 2 | 3 | 4 | 5 | 6 | 7 | 8 | 9 | Out | | |
|---|---|---|---|---|---|---|---|---|---|---|---|---|
| BLUE | 406 | 387 | 160 | 569 | 386 | 375 | 194 | 367 | 434 | 3278 | BLUE | Rating: 74.1 |
| WHITE | 385 | 366 | 140 | 526 | 351 | 361 | 174 | 332 | 403 | 3038 | | Slope: 130 |
| Par | 4 | 4 | 3 | 5 | 4 | 4 | 3 | 4 | 4 | 35 | WHITE | Rating: 71.1 |
| Handicap | 1 | 9 | 17 | 13 | 11 | 5 | 15 | 7 | 3 | x | | Slope: 122 |
| RED | 308 | 360 | 130 | 436 | 343 | 251 | 169 | 302 | 317 | 2616 | | |
| Par | 4 | 4 | 3 | 5 | 4 | 4 | 3 | 4 | 4 | 35 | RED | Rating: 71.4 |
| Handicap | 9 | 3 | 17 | 5 | 1 | 15 | 13 | 11 | 7 | x | | Slope: 117 |

| Hole | 10 | 11 | 12 | 13 | 14 | 15 | 16 | 17 | 18 | In | Totals | |
|---|---|---|---|---|---|---|---|---|---|---|---|---|
| BLUE | 366 | 359 | 489 | 217 | 436 | 586 | 416 | 206 | 492 | 3567 | BLUE | 6388 |
| WHITE | 348 | 346 | 447 | 181 | 415 | 571 | 402 | 190 | 450 | 3350 | WHITE | 6845 |
| Par | 4 | 4 | 5 | 3 | 4 | 5 | 4 | 3 | 5 | 37 | Par | 72 |
| Handicap | 10 | 8 | 18 | 12 | 4 | 6 | 2 | 14 | 16 | x | | |
| RED | 245 | 304 | 345 | 171 | 315 | 465 | 379 | 181 | 383 | 2788 | RED | 5404 |
| Par | 4 | 4 | 4 | 3 | 4 | 5 | 5 | 3 | 5 | 37 | Par | 72 |
| Handicap | 12 | 10 | 4 | 6 | 18 | 2 | 8 | 14 | 16 | x | | |

# THE VILLAGE COUNTRY CLUB

**Course 5**
MAP H2 grid d6

**1964**
**Ted Robinson**

4300 Clubhouse Road
Lompoc, CA 93436

Pro shop (805) 733-3537
Clubhouse (805) 733-3535

- ✓ **driving range**
- ✓ **practice greens**
- ✓ **power carts**
- ✓ **pull carts**
- ✓ **golf club rental**
- ✓ **locker rooms**
- ✓ **showers**
- executive course
- accommodations
- ✓ **food and beverages**
- ✓ **clubhouse**

**Dan Unrue**
Professional

**Phil Brown**
Superintendent

***Course information:*** This private course has 18 holes and par is 72. The course is 6,564 yards and rated 71.6 from the championship tees, and 6,269 yards and rated 69.6 from the regular tees. The slope ratings are 125 championship and 115 regular.

***Play policy and fees:*** Reciprocal play is accepted with members of other private clubs. The fees for reciprocators are $30 weekdays and $40 weekends. Carts are $18. Reservations are recommended.

***Location:*** Travel north from Lompoc on Highway 1 to Burton Mesa Boulevard and turn left. At Clubhouse Road, turn right.

***Course description:*** Gently rolling terrain and fairways lined with mature pine and oak trees mark this interesting course. Driving accuracy is rewarded. The par-4 and par-5 holes are doglegs. The greens are mostly contoured and they can be challenging. At par-4 and 370 yards, number 15 is a tough water hazard hole. Water is on the left within the landing zone. Be straight down the fairway; if you get too far to the right you're in the creek. Your second shot should be 130 yards to 140 yards uphill to a two-tiered green. Pin placement makes all the difference here. The green is fast and will hold if you hit the top tier; if you hit the lower tier your ball will roll back.

# LA PURISIMA GOLF COURSE

Course 6
MAP H2 grid e7

**1986**
**Robert Muir Graves**

3455 State Highway 246
Lompoc, CA 93436

Pro shop (805) 735-8395

- ✓ **driving range**
- ✓ **practice greens**
- ✓ **power carts**
- ✓ **pull carts**
- ✓ **golf club rental**
- locker rooms
- showers
- executive course
- accommodations
- ✓ **food and beverages**
- ✓ **clubhouse**

**Jim De Laby**
Professional

**John Canny**
Superintendent

**Mike McGinnis**
Director of Golf

***Course information:*** This long public course has 18 holes. See card below for yardage and rating information.

***Play policy and fees:*** Green fees are $40 weekdays and $50 on the weekends. Twilight fees after 2 p.m. are $20 weekdays and $25 weekends. Carts are $11. Reservations are recommended especially on weekends and should be made seven days in advance. The course is available for outside tournaments.

***Location:*** The course is 12 miles west of Buellton on Highway 246. It is four miles east of Lompoc.

***Course description:*** This is a highly rated public course. Overlooking Lompoc Valley, this scenic course meanders among the oak groves over rolling terrain. Three lakes come into play here, not to mention the wind, which can pick up in the afternoon. John McComish holds the course record with a 65. Among the tournaments played here are the Lompoc City Championship in April, the California Stroke Play Championship in July, the La Purisima Invitational in June, and the Santa Barbara County Championship in October. The course record is 66, set by Dave Garrell.

| Hole | 1 | 2 | 3 | 4 | 5 | 6 | 7 | 8 | 9 | Out | BLUE | Rating: 75.5 |
|---|---|---|---|---|---|---|---|---|---|---|---|---|
| BLUE | 542 | 432 | 158 | 340 | 433 | 566 | 427 | 437 | 227 | 3562 | | Slope: 142 |
| WHITE | 529 | 403 | 130 | 321 | 400 | 527 | 400 | 405 | 201 | 3316 | | |
| Par | 5 | 4 | 3 | 4 | 4 | 5 | 4 | 4 | 3 | 36 | WHITE | Rating: 72.8 |
| Handicap | 9 | 3 | 17 | 13 | 1 | 7 | 5 | 11 | 15 | x | | Slope: 132 |
| RED | 447 | 337 | 98 | 274 | 344 | 457 | 353 | 353 | 165 | 2828 | | |
| Par | 5 | 4 | 3 | 4 | 4 | 5 | 4 | 4 | 3 | 36 | RED | Rating: 73.3 |
| Handicap | 5 | 7 | 17 | 11 | 9 | 1 | 3 | 13 | 15 | x | | Slope: 131 |

| Hole | 10 | 11 | 12 | 13 | 14 | 15 | 16 | 17 | 18 | In | Totals | |
|---|---|---|---|---|---|---|---|---|---|---|---|---|
| BLUE | 465 | 389 | 609 | 169 | 366 | 532 | 436 | 167 | 410 | 3543 | BLUE | 7105 |
| WHITE | 438 | 371 | 587 | 149 | 366 | 503 | 395 | 145 | 387 | 3341 | WHITE | 6657 |
| Par | 4 | 4 | 5 | 3 | 4 | 5 | 4 | 3 | 4 | 36 | Par | 72 |
| Handicap | 4 | 16 | 2 | 18 | 10 | 6 | 8 | 14 | 12 | x | | |
| RED | 365 | 329 | 558 | 123 | 304 | 458 | 340 | 118 | 340 | 2935 | RED | 5763 |
| Par | 4 | 4 | 5 | 3 | 4 | 5 | 4 | 3 | 4 | 36 | Par | 72 |
| Handicap | 10 | 16 | 4 | 18 | 12 | 6 | 8 | 14 | 2 | x | | |

# ZACA CREEK GOLF COURSE

**Course 7**
MAP H2 grid f9

***Course information:*** This public course has nine holes. Par is 58 for 18 holes. The course is 3,088 yards and rated 54.5 from the regular tees. The slope rating is 76.

***Play policy and fees:*** Green fees are $5 weekdays and $6 weekends for nine holes, and $4 for a replay. Pull carts are $1.50. Reservations are recommended. This course is available for outside tournaments.

***Location:*** Travel 37 miles northwest of Santa Barbara on Highway 101 to the Highway 246 exit and turn west. Drive to the Avenue of Flags and go left. Continue to Shadow Mountain Drive and turn right to the course.

***Course description:*** Nestled in the Santa Ynez Valley, this flat course offers seven par-3s and two par-4s that will test every club in your bag. The holes range from 90 to 310 yards. The men's record is 54.

**1985**

223 Shadow Mountain Drive
Buellton, CA 93427

Pro shop (805) 688-2575

- ✓ **driving range**
- ✓ **practice greens**
- ✓ **power carts**
- ✓ **pull carts**
- ✓ **golf club rental**
- locker rooms
- showers
- executive course
- accommodations
- ✓ **food and beverages**
- clubhouse

**Bob Kotowski**
Professional

**Jeff Young**
Superintendent

# MAP H3
(14 COURSES)

PAGES.. 412-425

CEN-CAL MAP...see page 314
adjoining maps
NORTH (G3).......see page 382
EAST (H4) .........see page 426
SOUTH (I3).........see page 468
WEST (H2) .........see page 404

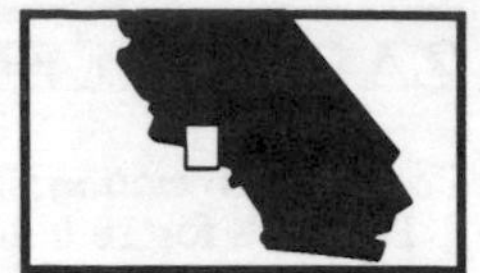

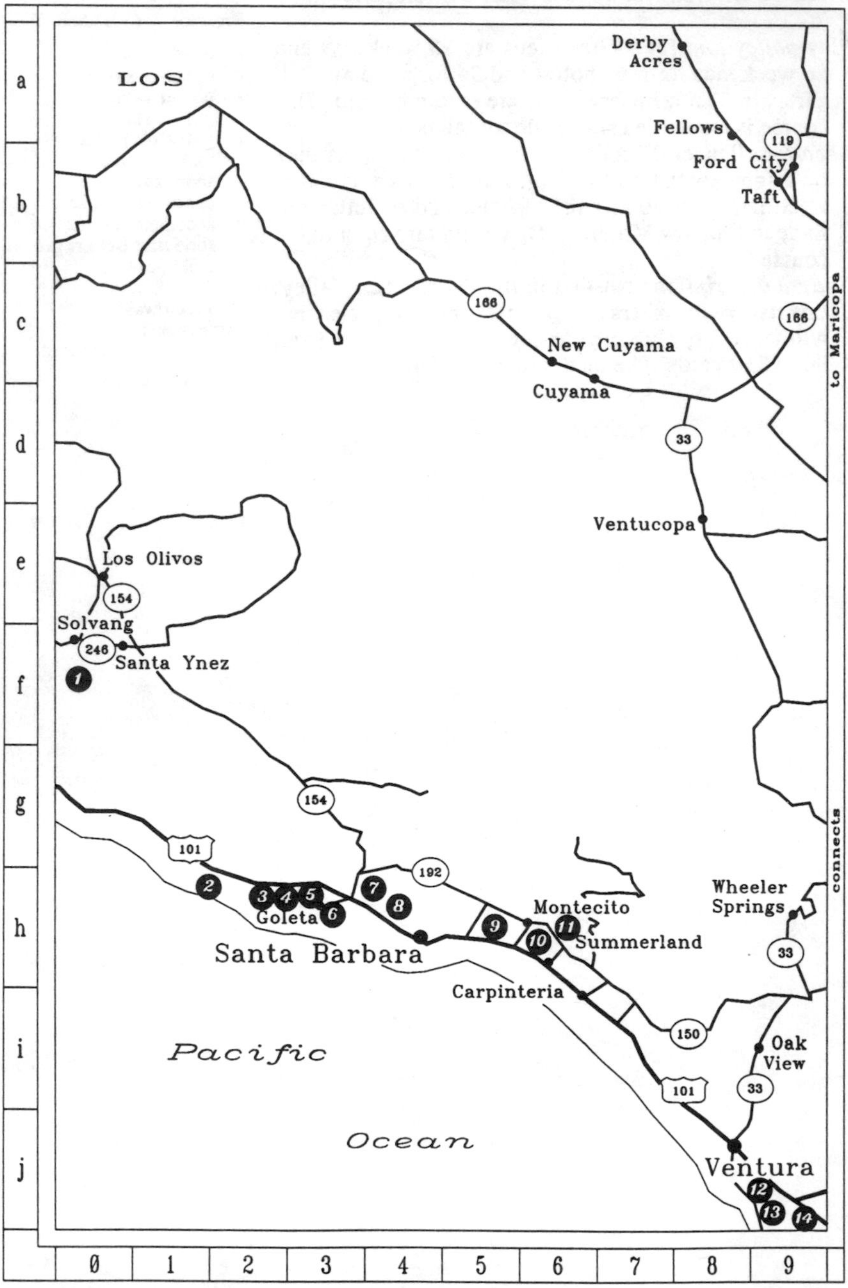

# ALISAL GUEST RANCH AND GOLF COURSE

**Course 1**
MAP H3 grid f0

*Course information:* This resort course has 18 holes. See card below for yardage and rating information.

*Play policy and fees:* Reciprocal play is accepted with members of private clubs. Members and guests only. Alisal Guest Ranch guests are welcome. Fee for reciprocators is $65. Play/stay packages can be arranged by Alisal Guest Ranch. Carts are $22. Reservations are recommended.

*Location:* Off of Highway 101, in Solvang, take Mission Drive (in downtown Solvang) and turn south on Alisal Road and drive 1.75 miles to the course.

*Course description:* Located on the 10,000-acre Alisal Ranch, a working cattle ranch, the scenic course is set in a valley. When you're not watching for native birds and deer, keep an eye for number five, a par-3 175-yard hole that gives a view of Solvang and the Santa Ynez Valley from its elevated tee. Players hit across Alisal Creek to a green guarded by bunkers on both sides and the creek 60 feet below. The tight fairways of the course are lined with mature oaks and sycamores. The course is well maintained and usually uncrowded. An early morning round offers the chance to see numerous birds and other wildlife on this pleasant and walkable course.

PO Box 26
Solvang, CA 93463

1054 Alisal Road
Solvang, CA 93463

Pro shop (805) 688-4215
Clubhouse (805) 688-6411

- ✓ **driving range**
- ✓ **practice greens**
- ✓ **power carts**
- ✓ **pull carts**
- ✓ **golf club rental**
- ✓ **locker rooms**
- ✓ **showers**
- executive course
- ✓ **accommodations**
- ✓ **food and beverages**
- ✓ **clubhouse**

**John Hardy**
Professional

**Scott Buley**
Superintendent

CENTRAL H3

| Hole | 1 | 2 | 3 | 4 | 5 | 6 | 7 | 8 | 9 | Out | | |
|---|---|---|---|---|---|---|---|---|---|---|---|---|
| BLUE | 518 | 165 | 384 | 485 | 160 | 481 | 337 | 414 | 199 | 3143 | BLUE | Rating: 70.7 |
| WHITE | 495 | 152 | 377 | 458 | 151 | 453 | 306 | 403 | 145 | 2940 | | Slope: 121 |
| Par | 5 | 3 | 4 | 5 | 3 | 5 | 4 | 4 | 3 | 36 | WHITE | Rating: 68.3 |
| Handicap | 5 | 15 | 3 | 13 | 17 | 9 | 11 | 1 | 7 | x | | Slope: 114 |
| RED | 420 | 143 | 372 | 451 | 131 | 411 | 301 | 383 | 135 | 2747 | | |
| Par | 5 | 3 | 4 | 5 | 3 | 5 | 4 | 4 | 3 | 36 | RED | Rating: 73.5 |
| Handicap | 9 | 13 | 3 | 7 | 17 | 5 | 11 | 1 | 15 | x | | Slope: 127 |

| Hole | 10 | 11 | 12 | 13 | 14 | 15 | 16 | 17 | 18 | In | Totals | |
|---|---|---|---|---|---|---|---|---|---|---|---|---|
| BLUE | 486 | 441 | 320 | 523 | 165 | 330 | 379 | 410 | 199 | 3253 | BLUE | 6396 |
| WHITE | 468 | 417 | 305 | 491 | 153 | 310 | 372 | 386 | 184 | 3086 | WHITE | 6026 |
| Par | 5 | 4 | 4 | 5 | 3 | 4 | 4 | 4 | 3 | 36 | Par | 72 |
| Handicap | 12 | 2 | 18 | 6 | 16 | 10 | 8 | 4 | 14 | x | | |
| RED | 448 | 407 | 296 | 480 | 135 | 304 | 365 | 377 | 150 | 2962 | RED | 5709 |
| Par | 5 | 5 | 4 | 5 | 3 | 4 | 4 | 4 | 3 | 37 | Par | 73 |
| Handicap | 10 | 16 | 12 | 4 | 18 | 8 | 6 | 2 | 14 | x | | |

# SANDPIPER GOLF COURSE

**Course 2**
**MAP H3 grid h2**

***Course information:*** This public course has 18 holes. The men's tees are rated 67.4 with a slope of 108 from the red tees. See card below for additional yardage and rating information.

***Play policy and fees:*** Green fees are $45 weekdays and $65 weekends. Carts are $22. Reservations are recommended. Collared shirts must be worn on the golf course and golf shoes. Long shorts are permitted.

***Location:*** Travel 12 miles north of Santa Barbara on Highway 101, and turn off at the Winchester Canyon Road/Hollister Avenue exit. Turn left at the stop sign, and drive one-quarter mile on Hollister Avenue to the course.

***Course description:*** This is a wonderful course. It's rated among the top 25 public courses in the nation. It is set along the ocean and offers breathtaking views from just about every hole. It offers rolling fairways and a long, wide-open, links-style layout. The back nine is well bunkered and hilly. The beautiful 510-yard, par-5 13th hole is often used as a backdrop for commercials. For the average golfer, though, it is extremely strategic. The hole is perched on a cliff and there are two chasms to traverse. The first one, off the tee, is unavoidable. The second chasm stands in front of the approach shot and can be avoided by going around it, but it will cost you a stroke. It's a strategic hole because of the choice between a longer, but safer, route or the short way with the most risk involved. The course record of 64 was set in 1977 by Mike McGinnis and tied in 1990 by Don Parsons, former California State Amateur champion. Owen Brown, Mike Gorton, and Kevin Marsh also tied the record with 64.

**1971**
**William Francis Bell**

7925 Hollister Avenue
Goleta, CA 93117

Pro shop (805) 968-1541

- ✓ **driving range**
- ✓ **practice greens**
- ✓ **power carts**
- ✓ **pull carts**
- ✓ **golf club rental**
- locker rooms
- showers
- executive course
- accommodations
- ✓ **food and beverages**
- ✓ **clubhouse**

**John Hughes**
Professional

**Mike McGinnis**
Director of Golf

**Goyo Santa Maria**
Superintendent

**Paul Casas**
Director of Maintenance

| Hole | 1 | 2 | 3 | 4 | 5 | 6 | 7 | 8 | 9 | Out | BLUE | Rating: 75.0 |
|---|---|---|---|---|---|---|---|---|---|---|---|---|
| BLUE | 524 | 471 | 424 | 232 | 507 | 195 | 391 | 396 | 418 | 3558 | | Slope: 135 |
| WHITE | 505 | 429 | 395 | 205 | 489 | 171 | 363 | 366 | 398 | 3321 | | |
| Par | 5 | 4 | 4 | 3 | 5 | 3 | 4 | 4 | 4 | 36 | WHITE | Rating: 72.5 |
| Handicap | 9 | 1 | 3 | 5 | 13 | 17 | 15 | 11 | 7 | x | | Slope: 126 |
| RED | 454 | 376 | 353 | 171 | 428 | 132 | 336 | 359 | 372 | 2981 | | |
| Par | 5 | 4 | 4 | 3 | 5 | 3 | 4 | 4 | 4 | 36 | RED | Rating: 72.6 |
| Handicap | 5 | 1 | 13 | 15 | 7 | 17 | 9 | 11 | 3 | x | | Slope: 117 |

| Hole | 10 | 11 | 12 | 13 | 14 | 15 | 16 | 17 | 18 | In | Totals | |
|---|---|---|---|---|---|---|---|---|---|---|---|---|
| BLUE | 381 | 224 | 356 | 516 | 446 | 599 | 392 | 421 | 174 | 3509 | BLUE | 7067 |
| WHITE | 381 | 201 | 338 | 516 | 425 | 578 | 373 | 367 | 170 | 3349 | WHITE | 6670 |
| Par | 4 | 3 | 4 | 5 | 4 | 5 | 4 | 4 | 3 | 36 | Par | 72 |
| Handicap | 4 | 14 | 18 | 6 | 2 | 8 | 10 | 16 | 12 | x | | |
| RED | 315 | 148 | 252 | 399 | 413 | 471 | 341 | 304 | 99 | 2742 | RED | 5723 |
| Par | 4 | 3 | 4 | 5 | 5 | 5 | 4 | 4 | 3 | 37 | Par | 73 |
| Handicap | 8 | 16 | 14 | 2 | 10 | 4 | 6 | 12 | 18 | x | | |

# OCEAN MEADOWS GOLF CLUB

**Course 3**
MAP H3 grid h2

***Course information:*** This public course has nine holes. See card below for yardage and rating information.

***Play policy and fees:*** Green fees are $11 for nine holes, $15 for 18 weekdays and $12 for nine holes and $20 for 18 holes weekends and holidays. Call for special rates. Carts are $14. This course is available for outside tournaments. Reservations recommended for weekends one week ahead.

***Location:*** Go north of Santa Barbara on Highway 101 to Storke-Glen Annie exit, then drive south one mile to Whittier Drive.

***Course description:*** This relatively flat course has tree-lined fairways and mountain views. It is built within the boundaries of an ecologically rich ocean slough and consequently has numerous lateral water hazards. Bird watchers (not to be confused with birdie watchers) might want to bring binoculars to view the beautiful and abundant wildlife in the area which includes blue herons and white egrets. It'll take more than binoculars to see an eagle. Mike McGinnis and Don Parson tied the course record with 64.

**1964**
6925 Whittier Drive
Goleta, CA 93117

Pro shop (805) 968-6814

- ✓ **driving range**
- ✓ **practice greens**
- ✓ **power carts**
- ✓ **pull carts**
- ✓ **golf club rental**
- locker rooms
- showers
- executive course
- accommodations
- ✓ **food and beverages**
- ✓ **clubhouse**

**Terry Afflack**
PGA Apprentice

**Simon Herrera**
Superintendent

CENTRAL H3

| Hole | 1 | 2 | 3 | 4 | 5 | 6 | 7 | 8 | 9 | Out | | |
|---|---|---|---|---|---|---|---|---|---|---|---|---|
| BLUE | 328 | 196 | 394 | 489 | 359 | 199 | 345 | 377 | 509 | 3196 | BLUE | Rating: 70.0 |
| WHITE | 320 | 163 | 372 | 474 | 339 | 170 | 329 | 354 | 480 | 3001 | | Slope: 115 |
| Par | 4 | 3 | 4 | 5 | 4 | 3 | 4 | 4 | 5 | 36 | WHITE | Rating: 68.2 |
| Handicap | 7 | 17 | 5 | 3 | 11 | 15 | 13 | 9 | 1 | x | | Slope: 108 |
| RED | 311 | 112 | 319 | 437 | 299 | 125 | 295 | 308 | 451 | 2657 | | |
| Par | 4 | 3 | 4 | 5 | 4 | 3 | 4 | 4 | 5 | 36 | RED | Rating: 65.1 |
| Handicap | 5 | 17 | 7 | 3 | 11 | 15 | 13 | 9 | 1 | x | | Slope: 102 |

| Hole | 10 | 11 | 12 | 13 | 14 | 15 | 16 | 17 | 18 | In | Totals | |
|---|---|---|---|---|---|---|---|---|---|---|---|---|
| BLUE | 328 | 196 | 394 | 489 | 359 | 199 | 345 | 377 | 509 | 3196 | BLUE | 6392 |
| WHITE | 320 | 163 | 372 | 474 | 339 | 170 | 329 | 354 | 480 | 3001 | WHITE | 6002 |
| Par | 4 | 3 | 4 | 5 | 4 | 3 | 4 | 4 | 5 | 36 | Par | 72 |
| Handicap | 10 | 14 | 6 | 4 | 12 | 16 | 18 | 8 | 2 | x | | |
| RED | 311 | 112 | 319 | 437 | 299 | 125 | 295 | 308 | 451 | 2657 | RED | 5314 |
| Par | 4 | 3 | 4 | 5 | 4 | 3 | 4 | 4 | 5 | 36 | Par | 72 |
| Handicap | 10 | 18 | 6 | 4 | 14 | 16 | 12 | 8 | 2 | x | | |

# TWIN LAKES GOLF COURSE

**Course 4**
MAP H3 grid h3

***Course information:*** This public course has nine holes. See card below for yardage and rating information.

***Play policy and fees:*** Green fees are $6.50 weekdays and $7.50 weekends. Replays are $4 during the week and $4.50 on weekends. Ask for senior and junior discounts. Hand carts are $1.50.

***Location:*** Take the Fairview exit off Highway 101 north of Santa Barbara and drive west to the course.

***Course description:*** As its name implies, the course has two lakes, but five years of drought have left them high and dry most of the time. No water hazard here. Players can play out of dry lake bed. This is a short yet tight course that tests iron play. Added attractions: lighted driving range and practice bunkers. Don Parsons holds the course record with 23, for nine holes.

6034 Hollister Avenue
Goleta, CA 93117

Pro shop (805) 964-1414

- ✓ **driving range**
- ✓ **practice greens**
- power carts
- ✓ **pull carts**
- ✓ **golf club rental**
- locker rooms
- showers
- executive course
- accommodations
- food and beverages
- clubhouse

**Jim Ley**
Professional

**Luciano Nungaray**
Superintendent

| Hole | 1 | 2 | 3 | 4 | 5 | 6 | 7 | 8 | 9 | Totals | | |
|---|---|---|---|---|---|---|---|---|---|---|---|---|
| BLUE | 95 | 134 | 94 | 335 | 126 | 109 | 360 | 89 | 132 | 1504 | BLUE | Rating: -- |
| WHITE | 75 | 121 | 76 | 285 | 109 | 92 | 335 | 79 | 120 | 1292 | | Slope: -- |
| Par | 3 | 3 | 3 | 4 | 3 | 3 | 4 | 3 | 3 | 29 | WHITE | Rating: 53.6 |
| Handicap | 9 | 3 | 7 | 2 | 5 | 6 | 1 | 8 | 4 | x | | Slope: 73 |
| RED | - | - | - | - | - | - | - | - | - | - | | |
| Par | - | - | - | - | - | - | - | - | - | - | RED | Rating: -- |
| Handicap | - | - | - | - | - | - | - | - | - | x | | Slope: -- |

| Hole | 10 | 11 | 12 | 13 | 14 | 15 | 16 | 17 | 18 | In | Totals | |
|---|---|---|---|---|---|---|---|---|---|---|---|---|
| BLUE | 95 | 134 | 94 | 335 | 126 | 109 | 360 | 89 | 132 | 1504 | BLUE | 3008 |
| WHITE | 75 | 121 | 76 | 285 | 109 | 92 | 335 | 79 | 120 | 1292 | WHITE | 2584 |
| Par | 3 | 3 | 3 | 4 | 3 | 3 | 4 | 3 | 3 | 29 | Par | 58 |
| Handicap | 9 | 3 | 7 | 2 | 5 | 6 | 1 | 8 | 4 | x | | |
| RED | - | - | - | - | - | - | - | - | - | - | RED | -- |
| Par | - | - | - | - | - | - | - | - | - | - | Par | -- |
| Handicap | - | - | - | - | - | - | - | - | - | x | | |

## NEW HORIZONS GOLF COURSE

**Course 5**
MAP H3 grid h3

250 Moreton Bay Lane
Goleta, CA 93117
Clubhouse (805) 964-4797

- driving range
- practice greens
- power carts
- pull carts
- golf club rental
- locker rooms
- showers
- executive course
- accommodations
- food and beverages
- clubhouse

**Gary Gruetzmacher**
Superintendent

***Course information:*** This private course has nine holes. The course is a pitch and putt.

***Play policy and fees:*** Members and guests only. Open 8 a.m. to 4:30 p.m.

***Location:*** From Santa Barbara on Highway 101, take the Fairview exit and turn right. At the second light, turn right on Encina and drive one block to the course.

***Course description:*** This pitch-and-putt course has no holes over 100 yards. It's situated in a condominium complex in a mountain setting.

CENTRAL H3

## HIDDEN OAKS COUNTRY CLUB

**Course 6**
MAP H3 grid h3

**1975**
4760 Calle Camarade
Santa Barbara, CA 93110
Pro shop (805) 967-3493

- driving range
- ✓ **practice greens**
- power carts
- ✓ **pull carts**
- golf club rental
- locker rooms
- showers
- ✓ **executive course**
- accommodations
- food and beverages
- clubhouse

**Greg Holland**
Owner

***Course information:*** This public course has nine holes and par is 27. The course is 1,118 yards for nine holes and is not rated.

***Play policy and fees:*** Green fees are $7 weekdays and $9 weekends and holidays.

***Location:*** Off Highway 101 heading south to Santa Barbara, take the Turnpike exit and turn left on Hollister. On Puente turn right, which takes you to Calle Camarade and the course. The course is located on the oceanside.

***Course description:*** This short course is all par-3s. The course has undergone extensive work in the last five years. There are bent greens and lush, narrow fairways. A well on the course provides year-round water and in the drought years the course was the only green spot in the Santa Barbara area. The longest hole is number nine at 175 yards. Number six is tricky shooting down from an elevated tee 122 yards to the green. Don't miss your first shot on any hole or you're in trouble.

MAP ON PAGE 412

# LA CUMBRE GOLF AND COUNTRY CLUB

**Course 7**
MAP H3 grid h4

***Course information:*** This private course has 18 holes and par is 71. The course is 6,363 yards and rated 70.8 from the championship tees, and 6,122 yards and rated 69.4 from the regular tees. The slope ratings are 128 championship and 121 regular.

***Play policy and fees:*** Reciprocal play is accepted with members of other private clubs. Members and guests only. Green fees for reciprocators are $75. Carts are $22. Reservations are recommended.

***Location:*** Turn off Hope Avenue/LaCumbre Road, turn left on Frontage Road and then left on LaCumbre Road and continue one-quarter mile past the arched entrance to Hope Ranch Park to Via Laguna, then go left to the club.

***Course description:*** This is a well-maintained flat course with a 30-acre lake coming into play on the back nine. Five holes border the lake. The course pre-dates the surrounding homes of the Hope Ranch residential development. Al Geiberger holds the course record with a 61. The course is under construction, to be completed in the spring of 1993.

**1957**
**William Park Bell**

PO Box 3158
Santa Barbara, CA 93110

4015 Via Laguna
Santa Barbara, CA 93110

Pro shop (805) 682-3131
Clubhouse (805) 687-2421

- ✓ **driving range**
- ✓ **practice greens**
- ✓ **power carts**
- ✓ **pull carts**
- ✓ **golf club rental**
- ✓ **locker rooms**
- ✓ **showers**
- executive course
- accommodations
- ✓ **food and beverages**
- ✓ **clubhouse**

**Sam Randolph**
Professional

**Doug Weddle**
Superintendent

# SANTA BARBARA COMMUNITY GOLF COURSE

**Course 8**
MAP H3 grid h4

**1958**

PO Box 3033
Santa Barbara, CA 93130

3500 McCaw Avenue
Santa Barbara, CA 93105

Pro shop (805) 687-7087

- ✓ **driving range**
- ✓ **practice greens**
- ✓ **power carts**
- ✓ **pull carts**
- ✓ **golf club rental**
- locker rooms
- showers
- executive course
- accommodations
- ✓ **food and beverages**
- ✓ **clubhouse**

**Richard Chavez**
Professional

**David Smoot**
Superintendent

***Course information:*** This public course has 18 holes. See card below for yardage and rating information.

***Play policy and fees:*** Green fees are $17 weekdays and $19 weekends. Tournament rate is $22 for weekdays and $24 weekends. Carts are $18. Pull carts are $2.

***Location:*** Turn off Highway 101 at Las Positas Road in Santa Barbara and drive east for three-quarters of a mile to McCaw Avenue. Turn left and continue one-quarter mile to the course.

***Course description:*** This course is set in the foothills above Santa Barbara and offers a nice view of the Channel Islands. Trees border the fairways, which are made up of Kikuyu grass and limit roll. Among the tournaments held here are the Santa Barbara City Championship held over Memorial Day Weekend, the Santa Barbara Classic during the first weekend in August and the Santa Barbara City Seniors held in mid-September. Jeff Hewes holds the men's course record with a 59, and Peggy Hogan's 65 is the women's record. This is a busy golf course, especially when the grass is green following the drought period. Play has returned to more than 300 rounds a day. The Santa Barbara Women's Open is held here each August.

| Hole | 1 | 2 | 3 | 4 | 5 | 6 | 7 | 8 | 9 | Out | | |
|---|---|---|---|---|---|---|---|---|---|---|---|---|
| BLUE | 346 | 290 | 112 | 362 | 368 | 481 | 435 | 193 | 511 | 3098 | BLUE | Rating: 67.2 |
| WHITE | 334 | 277 | 100 | 351 | 355 | 473 | 425 | 165 | 495 | 2975 | | Slope: 103 |
| Par | 4 | 4 | 3 | 4 | 4 | 5 | 4 | 3 | 5 | 36 | WHITE | Rating: 66.1 |
| Handicap | 9 | 15 | 17 | 3 | 7 | 11 | 1 | 13 | 5 | x | | Slope: 101 |
| RED | 318 | 260 | 86 | 341 | 349 | 466 | 416 | 143 | 479 | 2858 | | |
| Par | 4 | 4 | 3 | 4 | 4 | 5 | 5 | 3 | 5 | 37 | RED | Rating: 64.9 |
| Handicap | 9 | 15 | 17 | 5 | 3 | 7 | 11 | 13 | 1 | x | | Slope: 99 |

| Hole | 10 | 11 | 12 | 13 | 14 | 15 | 16 | 17 | 18 | In | Totals | |
|---|---|---|---|---|---|---|---|---|---|---|---|---|
| BLUE | 138 | 387 | 455 | 96 | 398 | 381 | 176 | 398 | 482 | 2911 | BLUE | 6009 |
| WHITE | 128 | 370 | 440 | 86 | 386 | 373 | 167 | 385 | 467 | 2802 | WHITE | 5777 |
| Par | 3 | 4 | 4 | 3 | 4 | 4 | 3 | 4 | 5 | 34 | Par | 70 |
| Handicap | 16 | 8 | 2 | 18 | 6 | 14 | 12 | 4 | 10 | x | | |
| RED | 121 | 360 | 427 | 80 | 377 | 366 | 158 | 374 | 415 | 2678 | RED | 5536 |
| Par | 3 | 4 | 5 | 3 | 4 | 4 | 3 | 4 | 5 | 35 | Par | 72 |
| Handicap | 14 | 10 | 16 | 18 | 4 | 12 | 8 | 2 | 6 | x | | |

# MONTECITO COUNTRY CLUB

**Course 9**
MAP H3 grid h5

**1922**
**Max Behr**

PO Box 1170
Santa Barbara, CA 93108

920 Summit Road
Santa Barbara, CA 93108

Pro shop (805) 969-0800
Clubhouse (805) 969-3216

- driving range
- ✓ **practice greens**
- ✓ **power carts**
- pull carts
- ✓ **golf club rental**
- ✓ **locker rooms**
- ✓ **showers**
- executive course
- accommodations
- ✓ **food and beverages**
- ✓ **clubhouse**

**Larry Talkington**
Professional

**Vincente Ramirez**
Superintendent

***Course information:*** This private course has 18 holes and par is 71. The course is 6,184 yards and rated 69.9 from the regular tees. The slope rating is 122. The women's tees are 5,597 yards and rated 74.0. The slope rating is 128.

***Play policy and fees:*** Reciprocal play is accepted with members of other private clubs. The guest fee is $60. Guests should have their club professional make reservations with the Montecito pro shop. Guest rate for carts is $24. Guests of the Santa Barbara Biltmore, San Ysidro Ranch, Red Lion and Montecito Inn may also play the course. Reservations are recommended.

***Location:*** Take Hermosillo exit off Highway 101 south of Santa Barbara. Hermosillo merges with Hot Springs. Turn left on Hot Springs and then take the next left onto Summit Road, which leads into the club.

***Course description:*** Although short, this is a challenging course that emphasizes shot-making. Ocean and mountain views are abundant from the rolling, tree-lined fairways and well-kept, undulating greens. The course plays much longer than yardage indicates. Accuracy and the ability to make good shots from troublesome lies are needed to score well here. Among the holes to watch for are the par-4, 455-yard third hole and the 18th, which is a top-notch 545-yard par-5. On almost every lie the ball is either above or below your feet, which adds to the challenge. There is a practice range under construction.

# BIRNAM WOOD GOLF CLUB

**Course 10**
**MAP H3 grid h6**

***Course information:*** This private course has 18 holes. See card below for yardage and rating information.

***Play policy and fees:*** Members and guests only. The green fee is $75 or $30 when guest plays with member. Carts are $25.

***Location:*** Take the Sheffield Drive exit off Highway 101 in Santa Barbara and drive to the end. Turn left on East Valley Road and drive up the hill to the club entrance.

***Course description:*** This is a short course that demands accurate shot-making skills. There are numerous out-of-bounds markers to the left and right. Barrancas are found in front of the greens making it impossible to roll the ball on. Sharpen up your iron play before tackling this well-maintained, Robert Trent Jones, Sr. beauty. New placement of the tee on par-4 number seven extends the length of this hole to 375 yards. The hole was proving too easy and to add to the difficulty a tree was planted to the left side of the fairway. Diane Wootton holds the women's record with a 68, and Jimmy Allen holds the men's record with a 63.

**1966**
**Robert Trent Jones, Sr.**

2031 Packing House Road
Santa Barbara, CA 93108

Pro shop (805) 969-0919
Clubhouse (805) 969-2223

- ✓ **driving range**
- ✓ **practice greens**
- ✓ **power carts**
- ✓ **pull carts**
- golf club rental
- ✓ **locker rooms**
- ✓ **showers**
- executive course
- ✓ **accommodations**
- ✓ **food and beverages**
- ✓ **clubhouse**

**Bob Roux**
Professional

**Martin Moore**
Superintendent

CENTRAL H3

| Hole | 1 | 2 | 3 | 4 | 5 | 6 | 7 | 8 | 9 | Out | BLUE | Rating: -- |
|---|---|---|---|---|---|---|---|---|---|---|---|---|
| BLUE | - | - | - | - | - | - | - | - | - | - | | Slope: - |
| WHITE | 405 | 155 | 382 | 334 | 149 | 360 | [illegible] | [illegible] | 430 | 2924 | | |
| Par | 4 | 3 | 4 | 4 | 3 | 4 | 4 | 4 | 5 | 35 | WHITE | Rating: 68.7 |
| Handicap | 1 | 11 | 3 | 7 | 17 | 5 | 13 | 9 | 15 | x | | Slope: 121 |
| RED | 387 | 115 | 347 | 295 | 123 | 306 | 299 | 284 | 427 | 2583 | | |
| Par | 5 | 3 | 4 | 4 | 3 | 4 | 4 | 4 | 5 | 36 | RED | Rating: 71.4 |
| Handicap | 3 | 17 | 9 | 5 | 15 | 13 | 11 | 7 | 1 | x | | Slope: 123 |

| Hole | 10 | 11 | 12 | 13 | 14 | 15 | 16 | 17 | 18 | In | Totals | |
|---|---|---|---|---|---|---|---|---|---|---|---|---|
| BLUE | - | - | - | - | - | - | - | - | - | - | BLUE | -- |
| WHITE | 374 | 400 | 135 | 350 | 470 | 179 | 405 | 165 | 488 | 2966 | WHITE | 5890 |
| Par | 4 | 4 | 3 | 4 | 5 | 3 | 4 | 3 | 5 | 35 | Par | 70 |
| Handicap | 6 | 2 | 18 | 8 | 12 | 14 | 4 | 10 | 16 | x | | |
| RED | 339 | 370 | 100 | 317 | 432 | 157 | 357 | 119 | 453 | 2644 | RED | 5227 |
| Par | 4 | 4 | 3 | 4 | 5 | 3 | 4 | 3 | 5 | 35 | Par | 71 |
| Handicap | 10 | 4 | 18 | 12 | 2 | 16 | 6 | 14 | 8 | x | | |

MAP ON PAGE 412

# THE VALLEY CLUB OF MONTECITO

**Course 11**
MAP H3 grid h6

**1929**
**Alister MacKenzie**

PO Box 5640
Santa Barbara, CA 93150

1901 East Valley Road
Santa Barbara, CA 93108

Pro shop (805) 969-4681
Clubhouse (805) 969-2215

- ✓ **driving range**
- ✓ **practice greens**
- ✓ **power carts**
- pull carts
- golf club rental
- ✓ **locker rooms**
- ✓ **showers**
- executive course
- ✓ **accommodations**
- ✓ **food and beverages**
- ✓ **clubhouse**

**Scott Puailoa**
Professional

**Scott Jorgenson**
Superintendent

**Barton Clapp**
Manager

***Course information:*** This private course has 18 holes and par is 72. The course is 6,608 yards and rated 72.1 from the championship tees, and 6,333 yards and rated 70.0 from the regular tees. The slope ratings are 133 championship and 122 regular. Women's tees are 5,813 yards and rated 73.5. The slope rating is 127.

***Play policy and fees:*** Members and guests only. Green fees are $100 for guests unaccompanied by a member. With a member it is $30. Carts are $20.

***Location:*** Take the San Ysidro Road exit off Highway 101 and travel north to East Valley Road. Turn right and drive one mile to Valley Club Road, then turn right to the club.

***Course description:*** The course features small greens and a natural setting. A creek runs through about half the holes and the narrow fairways are bordered by large cypress and pine trees. The ocean is visible from many holes. The course is very exclusive. Less than 100 members use it regularly. It is rated among the top 20 courses in the state. There have been no modifications to the course since it opened in 1929. The course record of 61 is held by John Pate.

# OLIVAS PARK GOLF COURSE

**Course 12**
MAP H3 grid j9

***Course information:*** This public course has 18 holes. See card below for yardage and rating information.

***Play policy and fees:*** Green fees are $14 weekdays and $19 weekends. Call for special rates. Carts are $18. Reservations are recommended.

***Location:*** From Pierpoint Bay in Ventura, take Harbor Boulevard to Olivas Park Drive. Drive three-fourths of a mile to the course.

***Course description:*** This beautiful and flat course is less than one-half mile from Ventura Harbor. Cool ocean breezes can play havoc with shots, but the view is worth the trouble. In about 1969 the Santa Clara River flooded the course and it had to be reconstructed. This is one of the courses that hosts the Ventura County Championships each August. The San Buena Ventura Pro-Am Classic is played here each May. Matt Eilson holds the course record of 62.

**1969**
3750 Olivas Park Drive
Ventura, CA 93003

Pro shop (805) 485-5712

- ✓ **driving range**
- ✓ **practice greens**
- ✓ **power carts**
- ✓ **pull carts**
- ✓ **golf club rental**
- locker rooms
- showers
- executive course
- accommodations
- ✓ **food and beverages**
- ✓ **clubhouse**

**Lee Harlow**
Professional

**Bob Jenkins**
Superintendent

| Hole | 1 | 2 | 3 | 4 | 5 | 6 | 7 | 8 | 9 | Out | BLUE | Rating: 71.3 |
|---|---|---|---|---|---|---|---|---|---|---|---|---|
| BLUE | 535 | 359 | 142 | 531 | 194 | 397 | 372 | 389 | 405 | 3314 | | Slope: 119 |
| WHITE | 516 | 334 | 133 | 499 | 183 | 361 | 359 | 377 | 390 | 3152 | | |
| Par | 5 | 4 | 3 | 5 | 3 | 4 | 4 | 4 | 4 | 36 | WHITE | Rating: 69.5 |
| Handicap | 11 | 15 | 17 | 9 | 7 | 5 | 13 | 3 | 1 | x | | Slope: 115 |
| RED | 435 | 330 | 112 | 449 | 153 | 303 | 349 | 302 | 330 | 2763 | | |
| Par | 5 | 4 | 3 | 5 | 3 | 4 | 4 | 4 | 4 | 36 | RED | Rating: 71.3 |
| Handicap | 5 | 9 | 15 | 1 | 17 | 13 | 7 | 11 | 3 | x | | Slope: 117 |

| Hole | 10 | 11 | 12 | 13 | 14 | 15 | 16 | 17 | 18 | In | Totals | |
|---|---|---|---|---|---|---|---|---|---|---|---|---|
| BLUE | 535 | 357 | 458 | 191 | 429 | 341 | 396 | 183 | 544 | 3436 | BLUE | 6750 |
| WHITE | 506 | 328 | 425 | 174 | 404 | 313 | 384 | 162 | 505 | 3201 | WHITE | 6353 |
| Par | 5 | 4 | 4 | 3 | 4 | 4 | 4 | 3 | 5 | 36 | Par | 72 |
| Handicap | 16 | 10 | 4 | 14 | 2 | 18 | 6 | 12 | 8 | x | | |
| RED | 476 | 242 | 359 | 136 | 376 | 254 | 337 | 151 | 407 | 2738 | RED | 5501 |
| Par | 5 | 4 | 4 | 3 | 4 | 4 | 4 | 3 | 5 | 36 | Par | 72 |
| Handicap | 10 | 12 | 8 | 18 | 4 | 16 | 2 | 14 | 6 | x | | |

# BUENA VENTURA GOLF COURSE

**Course 13**
MAP H3 grid j9

5882 Olivas Park Drive
Ventura, CA 93003

Pro shop (805) 642-2231

driving range
✓ **practice greens**
✓ **power carts**
✓ **pull carts**
✓ **golf club rental**
✓ **locker rooms**
✓ **showers**
executive course
accommodations
✓ **food and beverages**
✓ **clubhouse**

**Mark Wipf**
Professional

**Ed Naylor**
Superintendent

*Course information:* This public course has 18 holes. Women's tees are rated 74.9 with a slope of 121 from the white tees. See card below for additional yardage and rating information.

*Play policy and fees:* Green fees are $14 weekdays and $17 weekends. Call for special rates. Carts are $18. Reservations are recommended.

*Location:* From Highway 101 (Ventura Freeway) in Ventura, take Victoria Boulevard to Olivas Park Drive, turn left and go about three miles to the course.

*Course description:* An excellent course for golfers with a good short game. Tight fairways and quick greens make this a challenge. The number 14 hole is the one to watch on this course. It's a par-3, 130-yard nightmare that requires a straight iron over two legs of a lake that loops through the fairway. (Try saying that fast 10 times in a row.) There is also water on the back side of the medium-sized green. Miss the green to the left and you're in a bunker. A good 7-iron usually does it. Proper clubbing is obviously important on this hole. Brad Sherfy holds the course record of 62.

| Hole | 1 | 2 | 3 | 4 | 5 | 6 | 7 | 8 | 9 | Out | | |
|---|---|---|---|---|---|---|---|---|---|---|---|---|
| BLUE | 393 | 207 | 306 | 318 | 378 | 548 | 535 | 162 | 349 | 3196 | BLUE | Rating: 70.5 |
| WHITE | 383 | 191 | 294 | 309 | 367 | 537 | 527 | 149 | 330 | 3087 | | Slope: 119 |
| Par | 4 | 3 | 4 | 4 | 4 | 5 | 5 | 3 | 4 | 36 | WHITE | Rating: 69.2 |
| Handicap | 1 | 9 | 13 | 15 | 5 | 7 | 3 | 17 | 11 | x | | Slope: 116 |
| RED | 366 | 128 | 240 | 294 | 320 | 479 | 450 | 128 | 297 | 2702 | | |
| Par | 4 | 3 | 4 | 4 | 4 | 5 | 5 | 3 | 4 | 36 | RED | Rating: 71.3 |
| Handicap | 5 | 17 | 13 | 11 | 7 | 3 | 1 | 15 | 9 | x | | Slope: 115 |

| Hole | 10 | 11 | 12 | 13 | 14 | 15 | 16 | 17 | 18 | In | Totals | |
|---|---|---|---|---|---|---|---|---|---|---|---|---|
| BLUE | 397 | 225 | 341 | 378 | 144 | 293 | 529 | 483 | 426 | 3216 | BLUE | 6412 |
| WHITE | 387 | 212 | 324 | 333 | 130 | 281 | 512 | 464 | 416 | 3059 | WHITE | 6146 |
| Par | 4 | 3 | 4 | 4 | 3 | 4 | 5 | 5 | 4 | 36 | Par | 72 |
| Handicap | 8 | 4 | 14 | 12 | 16 | 18 | 6 | 10 | 2 | x | | |
| RED | 359 | 171 | 309 | 314 | 89 | 262 | 417 | 439 | 381 | 2741 | RED | 5443 |
| Par | 4 | 3 | 4 | 4 | 3 | 4 | 5 | 5 | 5 | 37 | Par | 73 |
| Handicap | 8 | 16 | 10 | 12 | 18 | 14 | 2 | 4 | 6 | x | | |

# RIVER RIDGE GOLF CLUB

**Course 14**
MAP H3 grid j9

***Course information:*** This public course has 18 holes. See card below for yardage and rating information.

***Play policy and fees:*** Green fees are $14 weekdays and $20 weekends. Call for special rates. Carts are $18.

***Location:*** Take the Vineyard exit off Highway 101 in Oxnard and drive west for three miles to the course.

***Course description:*** This is a rolling, links-style course with lots of water. One par-3 features an island green. That's the 191-yard number 14, a pivotal hole in a tight match. If you're in the water on your first effort, you still have to make the green from the drop area, which is 70 yards out and that's a tough shot to make if you're trying to close with a bogey. This is another course that hosts the Ventura County Championships each August. The Oxnard City Championships are played here each July and the Strawberry Classic is played here in April. When the SCGA qualifier was played here in 1991, the low qualifier was a 71, which says a lot about the course. You'll need every club in the bag because of the wind and hills and you must pay attention all day. Whew. The course record from the blue tees is 63, held by Mark Rapko. From the white tees, Carol Hogan holds the record with 67.

**1985**
**William Francis Bell**

2401 West Vineyard Avenue
Oxnard, CA 93030

Pro shop (805) 983-4653

- ✓ **driving range**
- ✓ **practice greens**
- ✓ **power carts**
- ✓ **pull carts**
- ✓ **golf club rental**
- locker rooms
- showers
- executive course
- ✓ **accommodations**
- ✓ **food and beverages**
- ✓ **clubhouse**

**Marc Sipes**
Professional

**Kyle Kanny**
Superintendent

CENTRAL H3

| Hole | 1 | 2 | 3 | 4 | 5 | 6 | 7 | 8 | 9 | Out | | |
|---|---|---|---|---|---|---|---|---|---|---|---|---|
| BLUE | 395 | 337 | 163 | 586 | 146 | 494 | 403 | 215 | 518 | 3257 | BLUE | Rating: 70.7 |
| | | | | | | | | | | | | Slope: 118 |
| WHITE | 378 | 319 | 127 | 559 | 135 | 461 | 388 | 192 | 503 | 3062 | | |
| Par | 4 | 4 | 3 | 5 | 3 | 5 | 4 | 3 | 5 | 36 | WHITE | Rating: 68.7 |
| Handicap | 5 | 13 | 15 | 1 | 17 | 11 | 7 | 9 | 3 | x | | Slope: 109 |
| RED | 358 | 313 | 102 | 541 | 107 | 414 | 204 | 180 | 458 | 2737 | | |
| Par | 4 | 4 | 3 | 5 | 3 | 5 | 4 | 3 | 5 | 36 | RED | Rating: 72.0 |
| Handicap | 3 | 7 | 17 | 1 | 15 | 13 | 11 | 9 | 5 | x | | Slope: 120 |

| Hole | 10 | 11 | 12 | 13 | 14 | 15 | 16 | 17 | 18 | In | Totals | |
|---|---|---|---|---|---|---|---|---|---|---|---|---|
| BLUE | 445 | 506 | 383 | 386 | 191 | 388 | 351 | 139 | 497 | 3286 | BLUE | 6543 |
| WHITE | 413 | 467 | 353 | 361 | 158 | 368 | 323 | 133 | 473 | 3049 | WHITE | 6111 |
| Par | 4 | 5 | 4 | 4 | 3 | 4 | 4 | 3 | 5 | 36 | Par | 72 |
| Handicap | 2 | 14 | 8 | 12 | 6 | 4 | 10 | 18 | 16 | x | | |
| RED | 382 | 420 | 324 | 346 | 122 | 328 | 296 | 119 | 451 | 2788 | RED | 5525 |
| Par | 4 | 5 | 4 | 4 | 3 | 4 | 4 | 3 | 5 | 36 | Par | 72 |
| Handicap | 4 | 2 | 8 | 6 | 14 | 10 | 16 | 18 | 12 | x | | |

# MAP H4

**(19 COURSES)**

**PAGES.. 426-443**

CEN-CAL MAP...see page 314
adjoining maps
NORTH (G4)........see page 384
EAST (H5) ..........see page 444
SOUTH (I4).........see page 470
WEST (H3) .........see page 412

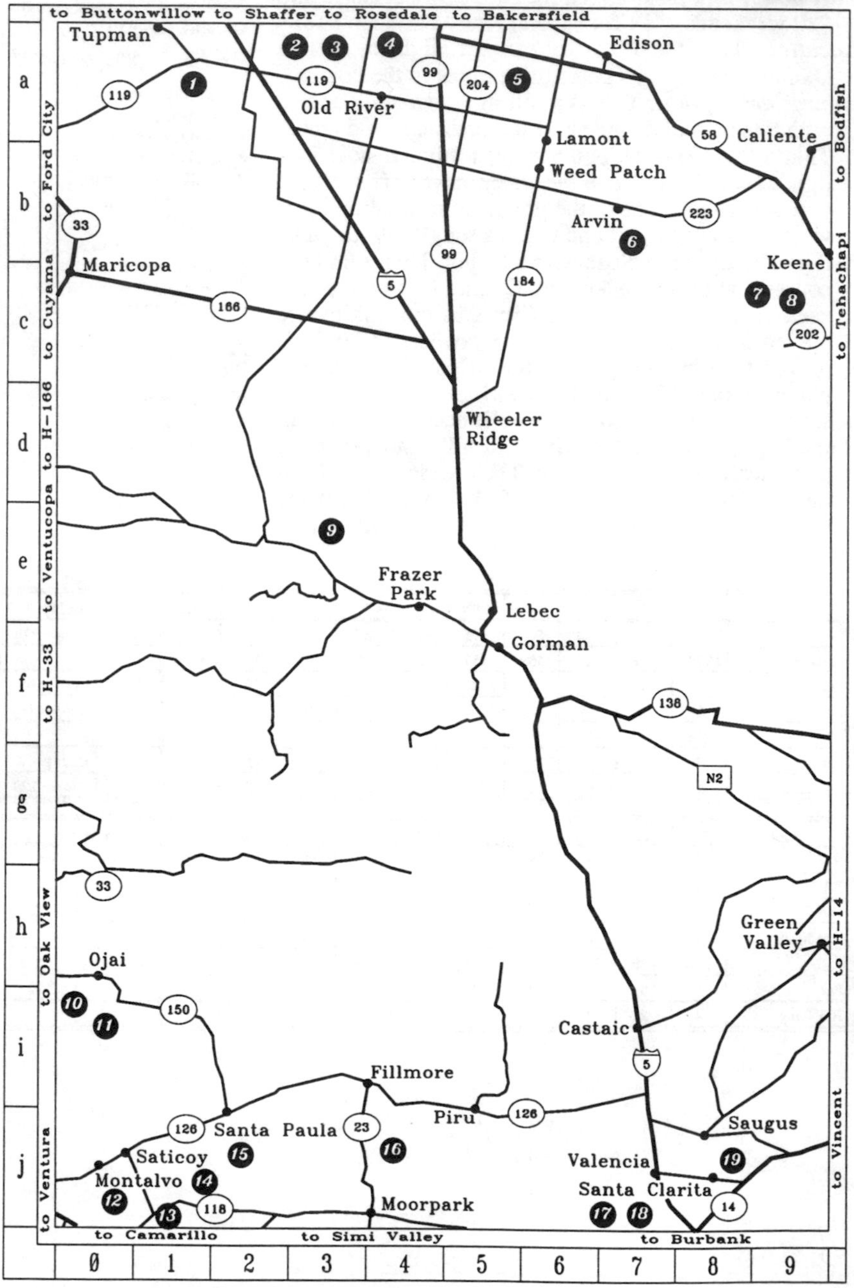

to Buttonwillow to Shaffer to Rosedale to Bakersfield

to Ford City to Cuyama to H-166 to Ventucopa to H-33 to Oak View

to Bodfish to Tehachapi to H-14 to Vincent

to Ventura to Camarillo to Simi Valley to Burbank

Tupman 2 3 4 Edison

1 119 119 99 204 5

Old River

Lamont 58 Caliente

Weed Patch

33 Arvin 223

6

Maricopa 99 184 Keene

5

166 7 8

202

Wheeler Ridge

9

Frazer Park Lebec

Gorman

138

N2

33

Green Valley

Ojai

10 150

11 Castaic

5

Fillmore

Piru 126 Saugus

126 Santa Paula 23 16

Saticoy 15 Valencia 19

Montalvo 14 Santa Clarita

12 Moorpark

13 118 17 18 14

a b c d e f g h i j

0 1 2 3 4 5 6 7 8 9

# BUENA VISTA GOLF COURSE

**Course 1**
MAP H4 grid a1

***Course information:*** This public course has 18 holes. The gold tees are 5,833 yards, rated 66.9, and have a slope rating of 110. See card below for additional yardage and rating information.

***Play policy and fees:*** Green fees are $7.75 weekdays and $10.25 weekends. Call for special rates. Carts are $16.

***Location:*** Take the Highway 119 exit off Interstate 5 and travel west for about five miles to the golf course.

***Course description:*** Originally a nine-hole layout, this course is the only green spot in the whole desert, thanks to irrigation from an on-site well. An introduction to this course begins with the first hole, a 355-yard par-4. This is not a mirage. The green sits on top of a hill 100 yards in the air and is the highest point on the golf course. Hit your tee shot to the flat area of the fairway in order to avoid an uphill lie, and then go for the large, flat green at the top. Overall, the course offers a rolling layout dotted with many palm trees. Chris Zumbro holds the course record of 63.

**1953**
**George Mifflin**

10256 Golf Course Road
Taft, CA 93268

Pro shop (805) 763-5124

- ✓ **driving range**
- ✓ **practice greens**
- ✓ **power carts**
- ✓ **pull carts**
- ✓ **golf club rental**
- locker rooms
- ✓ **showers**
- executive course
- accommodations
- ✓ **food and beverages**
- ✓ **clubhouse**

**David James**
Director of Golf

**Ray George**
Superintendent/Professional

CENTRAL H4

| Hole | 1 | 2 | 3 | 4 | 5 | 6 | 7 | 8 | 9 | Out | BLUE | Rating: 72.1 |
|---|---|---|---|---|---|---|---|---|---|---|---|---|
| BLUE | 363 | 214 | 409 | 513 | 525 | 120 | 440 | 420 | 425 | 3429 | | Slope: 124 |
| WHITE | 355 | 180 | 391 | 500 | 487 | 116 | 420 | 405 | 392 | 3246 | | |
| Par | 4 | 3 | 4 | 5 | 5 | 3 | 4 | 4 | 4 | 36 | WHITE | Rating: 69.9 |
| Handicap | 15 | 9 | 3 | 11 | 13 | 17 | 5 | 1 | 7 | x | | Slope: 118 |
| RED | 328 | 156 | 324 | 467 | 425 | 99 | 358 | 366 | 375 | 2898 | | |
| Par | 4 | 3 | 4 | 5 | 5 | 3 | 4 | 5 | 4 | 37 | RED | Rating: 72.0 |
| Handicap | 5 | 15 | 11 | 1 | 7 | 17 | 9 | 13 | 3 | x | | Slope: 117 |

| Hole | 10 | 11 | 12 | 13 | 14 | 15 | 16 | 17 | 18 | In | Totals | |
|---|---|---|---|---|---|---|---|---|---|---|---|---|
| BLUE | 410 | 518 | 340 | 184 | 400 | 560 | 320 | 151 | 373 | 3256 | BLUE | 6685 |
| WHITE | 363 | 488 | 330 | 151 | 387 | 536 | 307 | 143 | 362 | 3067 | WHITE | 6313 |
| Par | 4 | 5 | 4 | 3 | 4 | 5 | 4 | 3 | 4 | 36 | Par | 72 |
| Handicap | 12 | 6 | 10 | 16 | 4 | 2 | 14 | 18 | 8 | x | | |
| RED | 330 | 408 | 323 | 125 | 328 | 433 | 281 | 120 | 305 | 2653 | RED | 5551 |
| Par | 4 | 5 | 4 | 3 | 4 | 5 | 4 | 3 | 4 | 36 | Par | 73 |
| Handicap | 12 | 6 | 14 | 16 | 2 | 4 | 10 | 18 | 8 | x | | |

# STOCKDALE COUNTRY CLUB

**Course 2**
**MAP H4 grid a3**

*Course information:* This private course has 18 holes. See card below for yardage and rating information.

*Play policy and fees:* Reciprocal play is accepted with members of other private clubs. Have your club pro call for arrangements. It costs $50 for reciprocal play. Call for special rates. Carts are $18. Reservations are recommended.

*Location:* From the north take the Stockdale exit off Highway 99 in Bakersfield. Travel west to the Stockdale Highway. Turn right and drive one-half mile to the club entrance.

*Course description:* This 82-year-old course was re-designed in 1978 by Robert Dean Putman. It has numerous trees and few water hazards on a traditional layout. It hosts the Men's Silver Invitational in October and the Mr. and Mrs. Invitational each June.

**1909**
**1978**
**Robert Dean Putman**

PO Box 9457
Bakersfield, CA 93309

7001 Stockdale Highway
Bakersfield, CA 93309

Pro shop (805) 832-0587
Clubhouse (805) 832-0310

- ✓ **driving range**
- ✓ **practice greens**
- ✓ **power carts**
- ✓ **pull carts**
- golf club rental
- ✓ **locker rooms**
- ✓ **showers**
- executive course
- accommodations
- ✓ **food and beverages**
- ✓ **clubhouse**

**Rolly Allen**
Professional

**Cory Edgewood**
Superintendent

| Hole | 1 | 2 | 3 | 4 | 5 | 6 | 7 | 8 | 9 | Out | | |
|---|---|---|---|---|---|---|---|---|---|---|---|---|
| BLUE | 341 | 400 | 365 | 341 | 414 | 407 | 168 | 506 | 337 | 3279 | BLUE | Rating: 70.4 |
| WHITE | 324 | 385 | 345 | 341 | 393 | 394 | 149 | 494 | 337 | 3162 | | Slope: 120 |
| Par | 4 | 4 | 4 | 4 | 4 | 4 | 3 | 5 | 4 | 36 | WHITE | Rating: 69.2 |
| Handicap | 11 | 1 | 7 | 13 | 3 | 5 | 9 | 17 | 15 | x | | Slope: 116 |
| RED | 291 | 344 | 335 | 329 | 382 | 382 | 138 | 484 | 323 | 3008 | | |
| Par | 4 | 4 | 4 | 4 | 4 | 4 | 3 | 5 | 4 | 36 | RED | Rating: 74.0 |
| Handicap | 13 | 5 | 7 | 15 | 1 | 3 | 17 | 9 | 11 | x | | Slope: 124 |

| Hole | 10 | 11 | 12 | 13 | 14 | 15 | 16 | 17 | 18 | In | Totals | |
|---|---|---|---|---|---|---|---|---|---|---|---|---|
| BLUE | 119 | 391 | 496 | 297 | 450 | 169 | 533 | 372 | 221 | 3048 | BLUE | 6327 |
| WHITE | 119 | 377 | 476 | 290 | 426 | 137 | 513 | 372 | 209 | 2919 | WHITE | 6081 |
| Par | 3 | 4 | 5 | 4 | 4 | 3 | 5 | 4 | 3 | 35 | Par | 71 |
| Handicap | 18 | 4 | 14 | 16 | 2 | 12 | 10 | 8 | 6 | x | | |
| RED | 108 | 361 | 465 | 273 | 386 | 122 | 483 | 363 | 195 | 2756 | RED | 5764 |
| Par | 3 | 4 | 5 | 4 | 4 | 3 | 5 | 4 | 3 | 35 | Par | 71 |
| Handicap | 18 | 4 | 10 | 12 | 2 | 16 | 6 | 8 | 14 | x | | |

# SUNDALE COUNTRY CLUB

**Course 3**
MAP H4 grid a3

***Course information:*** This private course has 18 holes. See card below for yardage and rating information.

***Play policy and fees:*** Reciprocal play is accepted with members of other private clubs. Otherwise, members and guests only. Closed Mondays. Green fees are $30. Carts are $16. This course is available for outside tournaments. Shorts must come to mid-thigh, shirts must have collars and no T-shirts are allowed. Reservations should be made a week in advance.

***Location:*** Take the Ming Avenue exit off Highway 99 in Bakersfield, and travel west to New Stine Road. Turn right and drive one-quarter mile to Sundale Avenue. Turn left and drive one-half mile to the club.

***Course description:*** Formerly a public course known as Kern City, this layout is mostly flat with water and mature trees. The front ninc has no parallel holes. Water can be found on six holes and there is one long par-3. The course is deceptively difficult because the par-4 holes are long and the par-3 holes are tough. The course looks extremely simple but it just doesn't play that way. Club pro James Kiger holds the men's course record with a 64. Val Skinner fired a 68 for the women's course record during a mini-tour event. The Bakersfield City Championship has been held at Sundale since 1980. In addition, the Sundale Invitational is held each summer.

**1964**
6218 Sundale Avenue
Bakersfield, CA 93309

Pro shop (805) 831-5224
Clubhouse (805) 831-4200

- ✓ **driving range**
- ✓ **practice greens**
- ✓ **power carts**
- ✓ **pull carts**
- golf club rental
- ✓ **locker rooms**
- ✓ **showers**
- executive course
- accommodations
- ✓ **food and beverages**
- ✓ **clubhouse**

**James Kiger**
Professional

**Mike Greer**
Superintendent

CENTRAL H4

| Hole | 1 | 2 | 3 | 4 | 5 | 6 | 7 | 8 | 9 | Out | BLUE | Rating: 72.3 |
|---|---|---|---|---|---|---|---|---|---|---|---|---|
| BLUE | 397 | 510 | 395 | 363 | 544 | 225 | 412 | 195 | 390 | 3431 | | Slope: 122 |
| WHITE | 386 | 496 | 383 | 349 | 534 | 212 | 392 | 185 | 380 | 3317 | | |
| Par | 4 | 5 | 4 | 4 | 5 | 3 | 4 | 3 | 4 | 36 | WHITE | Rating: 70.5 |
| Handicap | 5 | 17 | 7 | 15 | 13 | 3 | 1 | 9 | 11 | x | | Slope: 116 |
| RED | 363 | 487 | 370 | 338 | 518 | 179 | 366 | 136 | 370 | 3127 | | |
| Par | 4 | 5 | 4 | 4 | 5 | 3 | 4 | 3 | 4 | 36 | RED | Rating: 74.7 |
| Handicap | 9 | 5 | 7 | 13 | 1 | 15 | 3 | 17 | 11 | x | | Slope: 124 |

| Hole | 10 | 11 | 12 | 13 | 14 | 15 | 16 | 17 | 18 | In | Totals | |
|---|---|---|---|---|---|---|---|---|---|---|---|---|
| BLUE | 471 | 197 | 388 | 380 | 523 | 362 | 384 | 164 | 484 | 3353 | BLUE | 6784 |
| WHITE | 460 | 190 | 379 | 372 | 504 | 340 | 379 | 155 | 474 | 3253 | WHITE | 6570 |
| Par | 4 | 3 | 4 | 4 | 5 | 4 | 4 | 3 | 5 | 36 | Par | 72 |
| Handicap | 2 | 6 | 10 | 8 | 18 | 14 | 4 | 16 | 12 | x | | |
| RED | 448 | 177 | 372 | 359 | 482 | 289 | 370 | 105 | 437 | 3039 | RED | 6166 |
| Par | 5 | 3 | 4 | 4 | 5 | 4 | 4 | 3 | 5 | 37 | Par | 73 |
| Handicap | 12 | 14 | 10 | 6 | 8 | 16 | 4 | 18 | 2 | x | | |

# SEVEN OAKS COUNTRY CLUB

**Course 4**
MAP H4 grid a4

***Course information:*** This private course has 18 holes. The gold tees are 5,970 yards, rated 67.5, and have a slope rating of 108. See card below for additional yardage and rating information.

***Play policy and fees:*** Reciprocal play is not accepted. Members and guests only. Guest fees are $50. Carts are $10.

***Location:*** From Highway 99 in Bakersfield, take the Ming Avenue exit west. The course is on the left.

***Course description:*** The course has mounded flat land. It is well bunkered, with lots of water. The Hogan Tour stops here in October.

**1992**
**Robert Muir Graves**

PO Box 1165
Bakersfield, CA 93389

10,000 Ming Avenue
Bakersfield, CA 93311

Pro shop (805) 665-4653

✓ **driving range**
✓ **practice greens**
✓ **power carts**
✓ **pull carts**
✓ **golf club rental**
✓ **locker rooms**
✓ **showers**
executive course
accommodations
✓ **food and beverages**
✓ **clubhouse**

**Steve Jessup**
Superintendent

**Bill Tape**
Director of Golf

**Tony Murray**
Professional

| Hole | 1 | 2 | 3 | 4 | 5 | 6 | 7 | 8 | 9 | Out | | |
|---|---|---|---|---|---|---|---|---|---|---|---|---|
| BLUE | 414 | 376 | 385 | 175 | 540 | 456 | 384 | 219 | 620 | 3569 | BLUE | Rating: 74.5 |
| WHITE | 385 | 348 | 351 | 155 | 498 | 430 | 349 | 195 | 581 | 3292 | | Slope: 128 |
| Par | 4 | 4 | 4 | 3 | 5 | 4 | 4 | 3 | 5 | 36 | WHITE | Rating: 71.2 |
| Handicap | 9 | 11 | 15 | 17 | 7 | 3 | 13 | 5 | 1 | x | | Slope: 120 |
| RED | 319 | 287 | 293 | 113 | 425 | 370 | 286 | 141 | 507 | 2741 | | |
| Par | 4 | 4 | 4 | 3 | 5 | 4 | 4 | 3 | 5 | 36 | RED | Rating: 71.6 |
| Handicap | - | - | - | - | - | - | - | - | - | x | | Slope: 122 |

| Hole | 10 | 11 | 12 | 13 | 14 | 15 | 16 | 17 | 18 | In | Totals | |
|---|---|---|---|---|---|---|---|---|---|---|---|---|
| BLUE | 384 | 425 | 155 | 518 | 416 | 228 | 476 | 567 | 381 | 3550 | BLUE | 7119 |
| WHITE | 359 | 397 | 132 | 490 | 391 | 200 | 429 | 537 | 351 | 3286 | WHITE | 6578 |
| Par | 4 | 4 | 3 | 5 | 4 | 3 | 4 | 5 | 4 | 36 | Par | 72 |
| Handicap | 14 | 6 | 18 | 16 | 10 | 4 | 2 | 8 | 12 | x | | |
| RED | 295 | 333 | 95 | 415 | 324 | 151 | 363 | 464 | 282 | 2722 | RED | 5463 |
| Par | 4 | 4 | 3 | 5 | 4 | 3 | 4 | 5 | 4 | 36 | Par | 72 |
| Handicap | - | - | - | - | - | - | - | - | - | x | | |

# VALLE GRANDE GOLF COURSE

**Course 5**
MAP H4 grid a5

**1952**
1119 Watts Drive
Bakersfield, CA 93307

Pro shop (805) 832-2259

- ✓ **driving range**
- ✓ **practice greens**
- ✓ **power carts**
- ✓ **pull carts**
- golf club rental
- locker rooms
- showers
- executive course
- accommodations
- ✓ **food and beverages**
- ✓ **clubhouse**

**Roland Reese**
Professional

**Corky Nena**
Superintendent

*Course information:* This public course has 18 holes and par is 72. The course is 6,066 yards and rated 68.4 from the regular tees. The slope rating is 108. The women's course is 5,531 yards and rated 68.9.

*Play policy and fees:* Green fees are $9 on weekdays and $12 on weekends. Call for special rates. Carts are $16. Reservations are accepted. This course is available for tournaments.

*Location:* Travel east on Highway 58 from Bakersfield and turn right on Cottonwood Road and drive 1.25 miles. Turn left on Watts Drive to the club.

*Course description:* This course is level and appears simple to play, but don't be fooled. Out-of-bounds markers and an abundance of trees make this a tight course. There are also two water channels running through the fairways, which add to its charm and difficulty.



# SYCAMORE CANYON GOLF CLUB

**Course 6**
MAP H4 grid b7

**1989**
**Robert Dean Putman**

500 Kenmar Lane
Arvin, CA 93203

Pro shop (805) 854-3163

- ✓ **driving range**
- ✓ **practice greens**
- ✓ **power carts**
- ✓ **pull carts**
- ✓ **golf club rental**
- locker rooms
- showers
- executive course
- accommodations
- ✓ **food and beverages**
- ✓ **clubhouse**

**Paul Fakundiny**
Professional/Manager

**Steve Smith**
Superintendent

*Course information:* This public course has 18 holes and par is 72. The course is 7,100 yards and rated 73.0 from the championship tees, and 6,644 yards and rated 70.9 from the regular tees. The slope ratings are 122 championship and 118 regular. Women's tees are 5,744 yards and rated 71.6. The course is being re-rated.

*Play policy and fees:* Green fees are $9 weekdays and $11 weekends. The twilight rates are $5.50 weekdays and $7.50 weekends. Senior rates are $5. Carts are $15. Reservations are recommended.

*Location:* Take Highway 99 south of Bakersfield to Bear Mountain/Arvin exit, then go 10 miles east to South Derby Street, then south 3.5 miles to the course.

*Course description:* Twenty acres of water come into play on 14 holes. Beware of the 602-yard ninth hole. It doglegs around a lake that runs 300 yards parallel to the hole. This par-5 is the number-one handicap hole on this course. You may not want to see the rest of the back nine after this monster. The course is made up of long par-4 and par-3 holes and every green has at least two bunkers.

# HORSE THIEF GOLF AND COUNTRY CLUB

**Course 7**
MAP H4 grid c8

PO Box 2931
Tehachapi, CA 93561

Star Route 1
Tehachapi, CA 93561

Pro shop (805) 822-6114

- ✓ **driving range**
- ✓ **practice greens**
- ✓ **power carts**
- ✓ **pull carts**
- ✓ **golf club rental**
- locker rooms
- ✓ **showers**
- executive course
- ✓ **accommodations**
- ✓ **food and beverages**
- ✓ **clubhouse**

**Mike Iyoki**
Professional

**Tim Kelly**
Superintendent

**Pete Snider**
Director of Golf

***Course information:*** This resort course has 18 holes. The gold tees are rated 66.9 and have a slope rating of 106 for men, and the white tees are rated 74.1 and have a slope rating of 122 for women. See card below for additional yardage and rating information.

***Play policy and fees:*** This course is affiliated with Sky Mountain Lodge at Stallion Springs Resort. Outside play is also accepted. Green fees are $18 weekdays and $28 weekends. Call for special rates. Carts are $19. Reservations are recommended. This course is available for tournaments.

***Location:*** From Bakersfield, travel east on Highway 58 for 38 miles to Tehachapi, and take the Highway 202 exit. Follow the signs for 16 miles to the Stallion Springs Resort.

***Course description:*** This course is set in the mountains, and although not particularly long, it requires accuracy. The most prominent features are the oak trees and rocks that come into play. Water also is a factor on four of the holes.

| Hole | 1 | 2 | 3 | 4 | 5 | 6 | 7 | 8 | 9 | Out | | |
|---|---|---|---|---|---|---|---|---|---|---|---|---|
| BLUE | 378 | 405 | 562 | 416 | 194 | 563 | 145 | 365 | 385 | 3413 | BLUE | Rating: 72.1 |
| WHITE | 353 | 370 | 540 | 406 | 185 | 541 | 131 | 351 | 329 | 3206 | | Slope: 129 |
| Par | 4 | 4 | 5 | 4 | 3 | 5 | 3 | 4 | 4 | 36 | WHITE men | Rating: 70.1 |
| Handicap | 13 | 9 | 1 | 5 | 11 | 3 | 17 | 7 | 15 | x | | Slope: 121 |
| GOLD | 311 | 326 | 492 | 365 | 147 | 481 | 96 | 340 | 265 | 2823 | | |
| Par | 4 | 4 | 5 | 4 | 3 | 5 | 3 | 4 | 4 | 36 | GOLD women | Rating: 71.1 |
| Handicap | 11 | 9 | 1 | 5 | 15 | 3 | 17 | 7 | 13 | x | | Slope: 116 |

| Hole | 10 | 11 | 12 | 13 | 14 | 15 | 16 | 17 | 18 | In | Totals | |
|---|---|---|---|---|---|---|---|---|---|---|---|---|
| BLUE | 380 | 134 | 511 | 398 | 167 | 401 | 422 | 380 | 472 | 3265 | BLUE | 6678 |
| WHITE | 370 | 127 | 493 | 383 | 155 | 385 | 402 | 369 | 458 | 3142 | WHITE | 6348 |
| Par | 4 | 3 | 5 | 4 | 3 | 4 | 4 | 4 | 5 | 36 | Par | 72 |
| Handicap | 14 | 18 | 4 | 2 | 16 | 10 | 6 | 12 | 8 | x | | |
| GOLD | 342 | 119 | 460 | 344 | 132 | 357 | 362 | 300 | 438 | 2854 | GOLD | 5677 |
| Par | 4 | 3 | 5 | 4 | 3 | 4 | 4 | 4 | 5 | 36 | Par | 72 |
| Handicap | 10 | 18 | 4 | 6 | 16 | 12 | 8 | 14 | 2 | x | | |

# OAK TREE COUNTRY CLUB

**Course 8**
MAP H4 grid c9

**1972**
PO Box 4100
Tehachapi, CA 93561

29540 Rolling Oak
Tehachapi, CA 93561

Pro shop (805) 821-5144
Clubhouse (805) 821-5521

- ✓ **driving range**
- ✓ **practice greens**
- ✓ **power carts**
- ✓ **pull carts**
- ✓ **golf club rental**
- locker rooms
- showers
- executive course
- accommodations
- ✓ **food and beverages**
- ✓ **clubhouse**

**Don Moulton**
Professional

**Ralph Laughlin**
Superintendent

*Course information:* This private course has nine holes. Par is 72 for 18 holes. The course is 6,298 yards and rated 69.0 from the regular tees for 18 holes. The slope rating is 110. From the yellow tees, the course is 5,675 and rated 73.0. From the red tees, the course is 2,747 and rated 36.

*Play policy and fees:* Reciprocal play is accepted with members of other private clubs. Green fees are $10 weekdays and $15 weekends. Call for special rates. Carts are $14 for two people. Reservations are recommended one week in advance.

*Location:* From Bakersfield, travel east on Highway 58 for 38 miles to the town of Tehachapi and take the Highway 202 exit. Follow the signs for about 14 miles to Bear Valley Springs.

*Course description:* The course, set at 4,000 feet, is rimmed by mountains. It's a level layout set around a small lake. Trees dot the fairways and jutting rocks add to the mountainous look of the course, but they rarely come into play.

# PINE MOUNTAIN CLUB

**Course 9**
MAP H4 grid e3

**1972**
2524 Beechwood Way
Pine Mountain, CA 93222

Pro shop (805) 242-3734
Clubhouse (805) 242-3788

- ✓ **driving range**
- ✓ **practice greens**
- ✓ **power carts**
- ✓ **pull carts**
- ✓ **golf club rental**
- ✓ **locker rooms**
- showers
- ✓ **executive course**
- accommodations
- ✓ **food and beverages**
- ✓ **clubhouse**

**John Snabb**
Professional

**Jim Gordon**
Superintendent

*Course information:* This private course has nine holes. Par is 60 for 18 holes. The course is 3,610 yards and rated 58.8 from the regular tees for 18 holes. The slope rating is 100.

*Play policy and fees:* Guests may play with members only. Guest fees are $7 for nine holes and $11 for 18 holes weekdays, and $9 for nine holes and $13 for 18 holes weekends and holidays. Carts are $8 weekdays and $9 weekends.

*Location:* Travel 40 miles south of Bakersfield on Interstate 5 and take the Frazier Park exit to Frazier Mountain Road. Drive west five miles and continue west on Cuddly Valley Road for another six miles to the top of the mountain. Turn right on Mill Potrero Road and drive five miles to the course.

*Course description:* This is an interesting course set at 5,500 feet and nestled among the beautiful pine trees. You may want to pack mountaineering boots. The fifth hole is known as Cardiac Hill, obviously because of its steepness. This hole is one of the reasons why the club now has power carts. Tom Watkins holds the course record with a 55.

# OJAI VALLEY INN AND COUNTRY CLUB

**Course 10**
MAP H4 grid i0

**1923**
**George C. Thomas**

Country Club Road
Ojai, CA 93023

Pro shop (805) 646-5511

- ✓ **driving range**
- ✓ **practice greens**
- ✓ **power carts**
- pull carts
- ✓ **golf club rental**
- ✓ **locker rooms**
- ✓ **showers**
- executive course
- ✓ **accommodations**
- ✓ **food and beverages**
- ✓ **clubhouse**

**Scott Flynn**
Director of Golf

**Sam Williamson**
Superintendent

***Course information:*** This resort course has 18 holes. See card below for yardage and rating information.

***Play policy and fees:*** Outside play is accepted, with starting times arranged three days in advance. The green fees are $90 for those staying at the resort, which includes carts, range balls and club storage. Outsiders pay $100. Golf packages are also available. Reservations are recommended.

***Location:*** From Ventura, travel north 13 miles on Highway 33 to Ojai, and turn right on Country Club Drive.

***Course description:*** This beautiful, mountainside course was built in the 1920s by George C. Thomas and was improved by Jay Morrish during 1988. The Ojai Valley Inn has been a long time favorite of the Hollywood set and was once owned by Loretta Young and Hoagy Carmichael. Several films have used the Inn as a setting including *Lost Horizons, Pat and Mike* and *The Two Jakes* with Jack Nicholson. Among the holes to watch for are the par-4, 442-yard fourth, which is a beauty. The drive from the championship tee on this hole must carry up a barranca. Part of the hole is hidden by the barranca and large oak trees. If you're in the fairway you can play the hole; if you're not in the fairway, you're cooked. Number 11 is a 358 yard, par-4 that crosses a barranca not once but twice. The tee shot from the championship tee must carry 200 yards to a safe landing area. Everything kicks toward the barranca so you have to play down the left side. The second shot requires a mid to short iron that has to carry the barranca again. The green is surrounded by large oak trees and it's difficult to tell where the pin is. Obviously, distance is difficult to judge on this hole. This course is also the home of the Senior PGA Tour GTE West Classic and numerous Southern California PGA events. Chi Chi Rodriguez set the men's record in the 1992 Senior PGA Tour GTE West Classic with a 62.

| Hole | 1 | 2 | 3 | 4 | 5 | 6 | 7 | 8 | 9 | Out | BLUE | Rating: 70.6 |
|---|---|---|---|---|---|---|---|---|---|---|---|---|
| BLUE | 405 | 203 | 563 | 442 | 177 | 359 | 402 | 227 | 487 | 3264 | | Slope: 123 |
| WHITE | 399 | 186 | 546 | 397 | 167 | 327 | 387 | 181 | 458 | 3048 | | |
| Par | 4 | 3 | 5 | 4 | 3 | 4 | 4 | 3 | 5 | 35 | WHITE | Rating: 68.9 |
| Handicap | 7 | 13 | 9 | 1 | 17 | 3 | 5 | 15 | 11 | x | | Slope: 117 |
| RED | 364 | 152 | 471 | 359 | 145 | 300 | 350 | 133 | 435 | 2709 | | |
| Par | 4 | 3 | 5 | 4 | 3 | 4 | 4 | 3 | 5 | 35 | RED | Rating: 70.2 |
| Handicap | 7 | 13 | 1 | 5 | 15 | 11 | 9 | 17 | 3 | x | | Slope: 123 |

| Hole | 10 | 11 | 12 | 13 | 14 | 15 | 16 | 17 | 18 | In | Totals | |
|---|---|---|---|---|---|---|---|---|---|---|---|---|
| BLUE | 412 | 358 | 115 | 297 | 440 | 312 | 392 | 128 | 517 | 2971 | BLUE | 6235 |
| WHITE | 406 | 330 | 105 | 274 | 433 | 299 | 379 | 119 | 499 | 2844 | WHITE | 5892 |
| Par | 4 | 4 | 3 | 4 | 4 | 4 | 4 | 3 | 5 | 35 | Par | 70 |
| Handicap | 6 | 10 | 18 | 14 | 4 | 12 | 2 | 16 | 8 | x | | |
| RED | 404 | 297 | 98 | 128 | 416 | 283 | 352 | 103 | 435 | 2516 | RED | 5225 |
| Par | 5 | 4 | 3 | 3 | 5 | 4 | 4 | 3 | 5 | 36 | Par | 71 |
| Handicap | 8 | 6 | 16 | 14 | 10 | 12 | 2 | 18 | 4 | x | | |

# SOULE PARK GOLF COURSE

**Course 11**
MAP H4 grid i0

**1962**
**William Park Bell**

PO Box 758
Ojai, CA 93023

1033 East Ojai Avenue
Ojai, CA 93023

Pro shop (805) 646-5633
Clubhouse (805) 646-5685

- ✓ **driving range**
- ✓ **practice greens**
- ✓ **power carts**
- ✓ **pull carts**
- ✓ **golf club rental**
- locker rooms
- ✓ **showers**
- executive course
- accommodations
- ✓ **food and beverages**
- ✓ **clubhouse**

**Jim Allen**
Professional

**Roger Spector**
Superintendent

***Course information:*** This public course has 18 holes. See card below for additional yardage and rating information.

***Play policy and fees:*** Green fees are $16 weekdays and $20 weekends. Senior rates are $11 weekdays. Reservations are recommended. Call for a tee time. The twilight rate is $11 weekdays and $14 weekends. Carts are $20.

***Location:*** From Ventura, travel north 16 miles on Highway 33 to the town of Ojai. Turn right on East Ojai Avenue and drive one-half mile to the course.

***Course description:*** This course is set at the base of the mountains in the Ojai Valley and traverses a rolling terrain. A creek runs through the course. Mature trees line the fairways. A hole that will stagger many a golfer is the 568-yard, par-5 fifth. This is a three-shot hole with a creek running in front of the green, requiring a 120-yard carry over the creek for the third shot. The green is partially blocked by a huge oak tree. Number five is definitely a position hole. The course record is 62, held by Gary Hitch.

| Hole | 1 | 2 | 3 | 4 | 5 | 6 | 7 | 8 | 9 | Out | | |
|---|---|---|---|---|---|---|---|---|---|---|---|---|
| BLUE | - | - | - | - | - | - | - | - | - | - | BLUE | Rating: -- |
| | | | | | | | | | | | | Slope: -- |
| WHITE | 341 | 373 | 135 | 517 | 409 | 211 | 568 | 293 | 309 | 3156 | | |
| Par | 4 | 4 | 3 | 5 | 4 | 3 | 5 | 4 | 4 | 36 | WHITE | Rating: 69.1 |
| Handicap | 9 | 7 | 17 | 5 | 3 | 13 | 1 | 15 | 11 | x | | Slope: 107 |
| RED | 332 | 322 | 114 | 493 | 333 | 190 | 538 | 286 | 302 | 2910 | | |
| Par | 4 | 4 | 3 | 5 | 4 | 3 | 5 | 4 | 4 | 36 | RED | Rating: 71.0 |
| Handicap | 9 | 5 | 17 | 3 | 7 | 15 | 1 | 13 | 11 | x | | Slope: 115 |

| Hole | 10 | 11 | 12 | 13 | 14 | 15 | 16 | 17 | 18 | In | Totals | |
|---|---|---|---|---|---|---|---|---|---|---|---|---|
| BLUE | - | - | - | - | - | - | - | - | - | - | BLUE | -- |
| WHITE | 146 | 526 | 395 | 347 | 383 | 396 | 167 | 505 | 377 | 3242 | WHITE | 6398 |
| Par | 3 | 5 | 4 | 4 | 4 | 4 | 3 | 5 | 4 | 36 | Par | 72 |
| Handicap | 18 | 10 | 6 | 16 | 4 | 2 | 14 | 8 | 12 | x | | |
| RED | 132 | 461 | 374 | 277 | 374 | 377 | 154 | 496 | 339 | 2984 | RED | 5894 |
| Par | 3 | 5 | 4 | 4 | 4 | 4 | 3 | 5 | 4 | 36 | Par | 72 |
| Handicap | 16 | 4 | 10 | 14 | 8 | 6 | 18 | 2 | 12 | x | | |

# SATICOY REGIONAL GOLF COURSE

**Course 12**
MAP H4 grid j0

**1926**
1025 South Wells Road
Ventura, CA 93004

Pro shop (805) 647-6678

- ✓ **driving range**
- ✓ **practice greens**
- ✓ **power carts**
- ✓ **pull carts**
- ✓ **golf club rental**
- locker rooms
- showers
- executive course
- accommodations
- ✓ **food and beverages**
- clubhouse

**Palicka Gallagher**
Professional

**Matt Mulvany**
Superintendent

***Course information:*** This public course has nine holes. See card below for yardage and rating information.

***Play policy and fees:*** Green fees are $8 for nine holes weekdays and $10 for nine holes weekends, and $10 for 18 holes weekdays and $12 for 18 holes weekends. Call for special rates. Carts are $10 for nine holes and $16 for 18 holes. This course is available for outside tournaments. Seniors (over 62 years old) pay $9 for nine holes, and $14 for 18 holes.

***Location:*** Take the Central Avenue exit off Highway 101 south of Ventura and continue on Central for 1.5 miles. Turn right on Highway 118 and drive 1.5 miles to Los Angeles Avenue and turn left. Drive four miles to the course.

***Course description:*** This course was built in 1926 as the Saticoy Golf and Country Club. It has narrow fairways, gradual slopes and quick greens.

| Hole | 1 | 2 | 3 | 4 | 5 | 6 | 7 | 8 | 9 | Out | BLUE | Rating: -- |
|---|---|---|---|---|---|---|---|---|---|---|---|---|
| BLUE | - | - | - | - | - | - | - | - | - | - | | Slope: -- |
| WHITE | 315 | 333 | 466 | 432 | 171 | 159 | 417 | 165 | 323 | 2781 | | |
| Par | 4 | 4 | 5 | 4 | 3 | 3 | 4 | 3 | 4 | 34 | WHITE | Rating: 64.6 |
| Handicap | 11 | 9 | 7 | 3 | 13 | 17 | 1 | 15 | 5 | x | | Slope: 97 |
| RED | 310 | 333 | 466 | 395 | 165 | 154 | 417 | 158 | 323 | 2721 | | |
| Par | 4 | 4 | 5 | 4 | 3 | 3 | 5 | 3 | 4 | 35 | RED | Rating: 69.3 |
| Handicap | 7 | 9 | 11 | 1 | 15 | 13 | 5 | 17 | 3 | x | | Slope: 113 |

| Hole | 10 | 11 | 12 | 13 | 14 | 15 | 16 | 17 | 18 | In | Totals | |
|---|---|---|---|---|---|---|---|---|---|---|---|---|
| BLUE | - | - | - | - | - | - | - | - | - | - | BLUE | -- |
| WHITE | 349 | 333 | 351 | 432 | 145 | 141 | 401 | 146 | 341 | 2639 | WHITE | 5420 |
| Par | 4 | 4 | 4 | 4 | 3 | 3 | 4 | 3 | 4 | 33 | Par | 67 |
| Handicap | 6 | 12 | 8 | 4 | 16 | 18 | 2 | 14 | 10 | x | | |
| RED | 344 | 300 | 351 | 425 | 145 | 141 | 401 | 151 | 312 | 2560 | RED | 5281 |
| Par | 4 | 4 | 4 | 5 | 3 | 3 | 5 | 3 | 4 | 35 | Par | 70 |
| Handicap | 8 | 10 | 2 | 14 | 16 | 6 | 12 | 18 | 4 | x | | |

# SATICOY COUNTRY CLUB

Course 13
MAP H4 grid j1

***Course information:*** This private course has 18 holes. See card below for yardage and rating information.

***Play policy and fees:*** Reciprocal play is accepted with members of other private clubs. Guests must be accompanied by a member while playing. Green fees are $45 with a member and $85 without a member. Carts are $10. Reservations are recommended.

***Location:*** Take the Central Avenue exit off Highway 101 just south of Ventura and drive north for two miles to Santa Clara Avenue. Turn right and travel 1.25 miles to Los Angeles Avenue and turn left. Drive one-half mile to the club.

***Course description:*** Make sure your tee shots are accurate here or you will be in for a long day. The fairways are tight and demanding. Greens are large and undulating. Many greens are elevated. The par-3 number 10 is 178 yards from the back tees, shooting down about 100 feet, over water to the green. Placed on the side of a mountain, this is the course to play in Ventura County if you're looking for golf and not scenery. Plans call for an additional set of tee boxes to lengthen the course.

**1964**
**William Francis Bell**

4450 Clubhouse Drive
Camarillo, CA 93010

Pro shop (805) 485-5216
Clubhouse (805) 485-4956

- ✓ **driving range**
- ✓ **practice greens**
- ✓ **power carts**
- pull carts
- golf club rental
- ✓ **locker rooms**
- showers
- executive course
- accommodations
- ✓ **food and beverages**
- ✓ **clubhouse**

**Lee Martin**
Professional

**Rich Wagner**
Superintendent

CENTRAL H4

| Hole | 1 | 2 | 3 | 4 | 5 | 6 | 7 | 8 | 9 | Out | | |
|---|---|---|---|---|---|---|---|---|---|---|---|---|
| BLUE | 407 | 354 | 425 | 205 | 405 | 511 | 387 | 563 | 189 | 3446 | BLUE | Rating: 74.4 |
| | | | | | | | | | | | | Slope: 140 |
| WHITE | 376 | 325 | 401 | 172 | 376 | 480 | 375 | 528 | 162 | 3195 | | |
| Par | 4 | 4 | 4 | 3 | 4 | 5 | 4 | 5 | 3 | 36 | WHITE | Rating: 71.0 |
| Handicap | 7 | 9 | 1 | 13 | 5 | 15 | 3 | 11 | 17 | x | | Slope: 128 |
| RED | 361 | 272 | 394 | 122 | 340 | 468 | 335 | 473 | 137 | 2902 | | |
| Par | 4 | 4 | 4 | 3 | 4 | 5 | 4 | 5 | 3 | 36 | RED | Rating: 72.7 |
| Handicap | 7 | 13 | 1 | 17 | 5 | 3 | 9 | 11 | 15 | x | | Slope: 128 |

| Hole | 10 | 11 | 12 | 13 | 14 | 15 | 16 | 17 | 18 | In | Totals | |
|---|---|---|---|---|---|---|---|---|---|---|---|---|
| BLUE | 178 | 404 | 359 | 207 | 536 | 410 | 341 | 474 | 569 | 3478 | BLUE | 6924 |
| WHITE | 164 | 365 | 330 | 190 | 502 | 378 | 323 | 439 | 521 | 3212 | WHITE | 6407 |
| Par | 3 | 4 | 4 | 3 | 5 | 4 | 4 | 4 | 5 | 36 | Par | 72 |
| Handicap | 18 | 4 | 16 | 12 | 6 | 8 | 14 | 2 | 10 | x | | |
| RED | 137 | 355 | 289 | 186 | 464 | 345 | 309 | 428 | 440 | 2953 | RED | 5855 |
| Par | 3 | 4 | 4 | 3 | 5 | 4 | 4 | 5 | 5 | 37 | Par | 73 |
| Handicap | 18 | 4 | 16 | 12 | 2 | 10 | 6 | 14 | 8 | x | | |

## LAS POSAS COUNTRY CLUB

**Course 14**
MAP H4 grid j1

*Course information:* This private course has 18 holes and par is 71. The course is 6,211 yards and rated 70.1 from the regular tees. The slope rating is 124. Women's red tees are 5,642 yards and rated 72.1 from the regular tees. The slope rating is 118. From the gold tees, the course is 5,612 yards and rated 68.9; the slope rating is 122.

*Play policy and fees:* Reciprocal play is accepted with members of other private clubs, otherwise members and guests only. Green fees are $35 weekdays and $60 weekends for reciprocators. Carts are $9 per person. Reservations are recommended. This course is available for outside tournaments.

*Location:* Take the Las Posas Road exit off Highway 101 in Camarillo and drive north for one-half mile to Crestview Avenue. Turn left and drive one-quarter mile to Valley Vista Drive and turn right. Continue one mile to Fairview Drive and turn left to the club.

*Course description:* The front nine is hilly with narrow fairways. The back nine is flatter, but well bunkered. The greens are soft, but with good speed. You can count on true putts.

955 Fairway Drive
Camarillo, CA 93010

Pro shop (805) 482-4518
Clubhouse (805) 388-2901

- ✓ **driving range**
- ✓ **practice greens**
- ✓ **power carts**
- ✓ **pull carts**
- ✓ **golf club rental**
- ✓ **locker rooms**
- ✓ **showers**
- executive course
- accommodations
- ✓ **food and beverages**
- ✓ **clubhouse**

**Bruce Hamilton**
Professional

**Pete Hernandez**
Superintendent

## MOUNTAIN VIEW GOLF CLUB

**Course 15**
MAP H4 grid j2

*Course information:* This public course has 18 holes and par is 69. The course is 5,335 yards and rated 64.9 from the regular tees. The slope rating is 103. Women's tees are 5,305 yards and rated 67.9. Slope is 106.

*Play policy and fees:* Green fees are $12 weekdays and $16 weekends. Twilight fees after 3 p.m. are $8 weekdays and $10 weekends. Call for special rates. Carts are $14 weekdays and $16 weekends. Reservations are recommended.

*Location:* Take the Highway 126 exit off Highway 101 just south of Ventura and drive east to the 10th Street exit. Turn left under the freeway and drive to Harvard Boulevard and turn right. At 12th Street, turn right and drive one-half mile to South Mountain Road. Turn right to course.

*Course description:* This is a short course set in a narrow valley at the base of South Mountain. Mature trees border the fairways of this wandering course. Tee boxes have recently been moved back on some holes, adding another 100 yards to its length. The course may seem small, but it's difficult. Keep the ball straight.

16799 S. Mountain Road
Santa Paula, CA 93060

Pro shop (805) 525-1571

- driving range
- ✓ **practice greens**
- ✓ **power carts**
- ✓ **pull carts**
- ✓ **golf club rental**
- locker rooms
- showers
- executive course
- accommodations
- ✓ **food and beverages**
- ✓ **clubhouse**

**Debra Burhoe**
Manager

**Kelly Gratton**
Superintendent

# ELKINS RANCH GOLF COURSE

**Course 16**
MAP H4 grid j4

**1962**

PO Box 695
Fillmore, CA 93016-0695

1386 Chambersburg Road
Fillmore, CA 93015

Pro shop (805) 524-1440
Clubhouse (805) 524-1121

- ✓ **driving range**
- ✓ **practice greens**
- ✓ **power carts**
- ✓ **pull carts**
- ✓ **golf club rental**
- locker rooms
- showers
- executive course
- accommodations
- ✓ **food and beverages**
- ✓ **clubhouse**

**Terry Taylor**
Professional

**Daniel Hodapp**
Professional

**Robert Shipper**
Superintendent

***Course information:*** This public course has 18 holes. See card below for yardage and rating information.

***Play policy and fees:*** Green fees are $19 weekdays and $24 weekends. Call for special rates. Carts are $20. This course is available for outside tournaments. Golfers must wear collared shirts. Bermuda shorts are allowed, but no cut-offs. Reservations are recommended and should be made 10 days in advance.

***Location:*** Take Interstate 5 north to Highway 126, turn west and drive 19 miles to Fillmore. At Highway 23, the second stop light, turn left and the course is 1.5 miles on the left.

***Course description:*** This course is set in a canyon in the country. There are lots of water holes and few parallel fairways. It's a very challenging course with five lakes, elevated tees and demanding greens. Fun for all levels of play. It's quiet and scenic, a great getaway course that sees 60,000 rounds a year.

| Hole | 1 | 2 | 3 | 4 | 5 | 6 | 7 | 8 | 9 | Out | | |
|---|---|---|---|---|---|---|---|---|---|---|---|---|
| BLUE | 329 | 416 | 199 | 521 | 403 | 464 | 169 | 355 | 416 | 3272 | BLUE | Rating: 69.9 |
| WHITE | 318 | 388 | 187 | 507 | 392 | 447 | 162 | 345 | 395 | 3137 | | Slope: 115 |
| Par | 4 | 4 | 3 | 5 | 4 | 5 | 3 | 4 | 4 | 36 | WHITE | Rating: 60.3 |
| Handicap | 17 | 1 | 7 | 11 | 5 | 15 | 13 | 9 | 3 | x | | Slope: 110 |
| RED | 309 | 383 | 162 | 483 | 365 | 432 | 145 | 311 | 385 | 2975 | | |
| Par | 4 | 5 | 3 | 5 | 4 | 5 | 3 | 4 | 5 | 38 | RED | Rating: 72.6 |
| Handicap | 11 | 13 | 17 | 3 | 1 | 5 | 15 | 7 | 9 | x | | Slope: 118 |

| Hole | 10 | 11 | 12 | 13 | 14 | 15 | 16 | 17 | 18 | In | Totals | |
|---|---|---|---|---|---|---|---|---|---|---|---|---|
| BLUE | 363 | 190 | 394 | 381 | 298 | 374 | 127 | 430 | 473 | 3030 | BLUE | 6302 |
| WHITE | 355 | 166 | 371 | 355 | 280 | 361 | 116 | 423 | 447 | 2874 | WHITE | 6010 |
| Par | 4 | 3 | 4 | 4 | 4 | 4 | 3 | 4 | 5 | 35 | Par | 71 |
| Handicap | 10 | 12 | 2 | 4 | 16 | 8 | 18 | 6 | 14 | x | | |
| RED | 344 | 153 | 360 | 336 | 268 | 291 | 96 | 384 | 438 | 2670 | RED | 5650 |
| Par | 4 | 3 | 4 | 4 | 4 | 4 | 3 | 4 | 5 | 35 | Par | 73 |
| Handicap | 6 | 16 | 2 | 8 | 12 | 14 | 18 | 4 | 10 | x | | |

# VALENCIA COUNTRY CLUB

**Course 17**
MAP H4 grid j8

*Course information:* This private course has 18 holes. The gold tees are 7,105 yards, rated 76.2, and have a slope rating of 144. See card below for additional yardage and rating information.

*Play policy and fees:* Members and guests only. Guests must be accompanied by member while playing. Green fees are $50 weekdays and $75 weekends, carts included. Reservations are recommended. Closed Mondays.

*Location:* From San Fernando, travel north on Interstate 5 for 12 miles to Magic Mountain Parkway and turn east on Tourney Road to the club.

*Course description:* This Robert Trent Jones, Sr. design offers a scenic, natural layout with lots of trees. Water comes into play on eight holes. It's always a love-hate relationship with Jones, so take your pick on number three. This hole is 222 yards and par-3 from the back tees. There is no bail out. There's water and bunkers on the right and trees on the left. It's considered one of the toughest par-3 holes in Southern California. From the blue tees, the course record is 63, held by Bob Burns. From the gold tees, the course record is 67, held by Jeff Flesher.

**1965**
**Robert Trent Jones, Sr.**

27330 North Tourney Road
Valencia, CA 91355

Pro shop (805) 254-6200

- ✓ **driving range**
- ✓ **practice greens**
- ✓ **power carts**
- pull carts
- ✓ **golf club rental**
- ✓ **locker rooms**
- ✓ **showers**
- executive course
- accommodations
- ✓ **food and beverages**
- ✓ **clubhouse**

**Rick Smith**
Professional

**Wayne Mills**
Superintendent

| Hole | 1 | 2 | 3 | 4 | 5 | 6 | 7 | 8 | 9 | Out | BLUE | Rating: 73.7 |
|---|---|---|---|---|---|---|---|---|---|---|---|---|
| BLUE | 508 | 393 | 222 | 385 | 340 | 410 | 171 | 351 | 496 | 3276 | | Slope: 137 |
| WHITE | 490 | 380 | 144 | 351 | 316 | 389 | 151 | 334 | 465 | 3020 | | |
| Par | 5 | 4 | 3 | 4 | 4 | 4 | 3 | 4 | 5 | 36 | WHITE | Rating: 70.8 |
| Handicap | 7 | 3 | 5 | 11 | 15 | 1 | 13 | 9 | 17 | x | | Slope: 126 |
| RED | 478 | 356 | 101 | 335 | 246 | 371 | 134 | 306 | 418 | 2745 | | |
| Par | 5 | 4 | 3 | 4 | 4 | 4 | 3 | 4 | 5 | 36 | RED | Rating: 73.6 |
| Handicap | 5 | 3 | 17 | 11 | 13 | 1 | 15 | 7 | 9 | x | | Slope: 130 |

| Hole | 10 | 11 | 12 | 13 | 14 | 15 | 16 | 17 | 18 | In | Totals | |
|---|---|---|---|---|---|---|---|---|---|---|---|---|
| BLUE | 459 | 355 | 357 | 378 | 203 | 514 | 186 | 448 | 547 | 3447 | BLUE | 6723 |
| WHITE | 439 | 333 | 338 | 363 | 178 | 484 | 158 | 427 | 521 | 3241 | WHITE | 6261 |
| Par | 4 | 4 | 4 | 4 | 3 | 5 | 3 | 4 | 5 | 36 | Par | 72 |
| Handicap | 2 | 16 | 18 | 14 | 12 | 6 | 10 | 4 | 8 | x | | |
| RED | 408 | 308 | 319 | 327 | 159 | 454 | 127 | 401 | 485 | 2988 | RED | 5733 |
| Par | 5 | 4 | 4 | 4 | 3 | 5 | 3 | 5 | 5 | 38 | Par | 74 |
| Handicap | 10 | 12 | 6 | 8 | 16 | 4 | 18 | 14 | 2 | x | | |

# VISTA VALENCIA GOLF CLUB

**Course 18**
MAP H4 grid j8

24700 West Trevino Drive
Valencia, CA 91355

Pro shop (805 ) 253-1870
Clubhouse (805) 253-0781

- ✓ **driving range**
- ✓ **practice greens**
- ✓ **power carts**
- ✓ **pull carts**
- ✓ **golf club rental**
- locker rooms
- showers
- ✓ **executive course**
- accommodations
- ✓ **food and beverages**
- ✓ **clubhouse**

**Steve Montenez**
Superintendent

***Course information:*** This public course has 18 holes. There is also a nine hole par-3 course. See card below for additional yardage and rating information.

***Play policy and fees:*** Green fees are $14 weekdays and $22 weekends. Call for special rates. Carts are $18. This course is available for tournaments.

***Location:*** In Valencia, traveling north on Interstate 5, exit at Lyons Avenue. Drive east for one-half mile to Wiley Canyon Road. Turn left and then left again at Tournament Road. Drive one-half mile to Trevino Road, turn left again then drive one-half mile to the club.

***Course description:*** This is a short course that requires good iron play. Five lakes are found on the layout and there is one island green. The course is always in good condition. The course record is 52, held by Donny Hinson.

| Hole | 1 | 2 | 3 | 4 | 5 | 6 | 7 | 8 | 9 | Out | | |
|---|---|---|---|---|---|---|---|---|---|---|---|---|
| BLUE | - | - | - | - | - | - | - | - | - | - | BLUE | Rating: -- |
| | | | | | | | | | | | | Slope: -- |
| WHITE | 434 | 175 | 92 | 68 | 135 | 328 | 388 | 121 | 166 | 1907 | | |
| Par | 4 | 3 | 3 | 3 | 3 | 4 | 4 | 3 | 3 | 30 | WHITE | Rating: 60.6 |
| Handicap | 5 | 1 | 17 | 15 | 11 | 13 | 3 | 9 | 7 | x | | Slope: 97 |
| RED | 420 | 165 | 92 | 67 | 135 | 318 | 385 | 117 | 161 | 1860 | | |
| Par | 5 | 3 | 3 | 3 | 3 | 4 | 4 | 3 | 3 | 31 | RED | Rating: 62.0 |
| Handicap | 9 | 3 | 17 | 15 | 13 | 11 | 1 | 7 | 5 | x | | Slope: 101 |

| Hole | 10 | 11 | 12 | 13 | 14 | 15 | 16 | 17 | 18 | In | Totals | |
|---|---|---|---|---|---|---|---|---|---|---|---|---|
| BLUE | - | - | - | - | - | - | - | - | - | - | BLUE | -- |
| WHITE | 366 | 215 | 186 | 370 | 98 | 157 | 311 | 137 | 413 | 2253 | WHITE | 4160 |
| Par | 4 | 3 | 3 | 4 | 3 | 3 | 4 | 3 | 4 | 31 | Par | 61 |
| Handicap | 10 | 2 | 8 | 6 | 16 | 12 | 14 | 18 | 4 | x | | |
| RED | 342 | 208 | 178 | 364 | 94 | 147 | 304 | 129 | 395 | 2161 | RED | 4021 |
| Par | 4 | 4 | 3 | 4 | 3 | 3 | 4 | 3 | 5 | 33 | Par | 64 |
| Handicap | 6 | 18 | 4 | 2 | 16 | 12 | 8 | 10 | 14 | x | | |

# FRIENDLY VALLEY GOLF COURSE

**Course 19**
MAP H4 grid j8

19345 Avenue of the Oaks
Newhall, CA 91321

Pro shop (805) 252-9859

- driving range
- ✓ **practice greens**
- power carts
- ✓ **pull carts**
- ✓ **golf club rental**
- locker rooms
- showers
- ✓ **executive course**
- accommodations
- food and beverages
- ✓ **clubhouse**

**John Lindy**
Manager

***Course information:*** This private course is nine holes and par is 27. There is also a pitch-and-putt course. The course is 1,425 yards from the regular tees. Yardage for the women's tees was unavailable.

***Play policy and fees:*** Members and guests only. This is a private residential course.

***Location:*** Take Highway 126 off Interstate 5 and follow to San Fernando Road. From there travel 1.5 miles to Avenue of the Oaks, go left and look for the course.

***Course description:*** This is a good opportunity for members to practice up on their short, short game.

MAP ON PAGE 426

# MAP H5

(10 COURSES)

PAGES.. 444-455

CEN-CAL MAP...see page 314
adjoining maps
NORTH (G5).......see page 398
EAST (H6) .........see page 456
SOUTH (I5).........see page 506
WEST (H4) .........see page 426

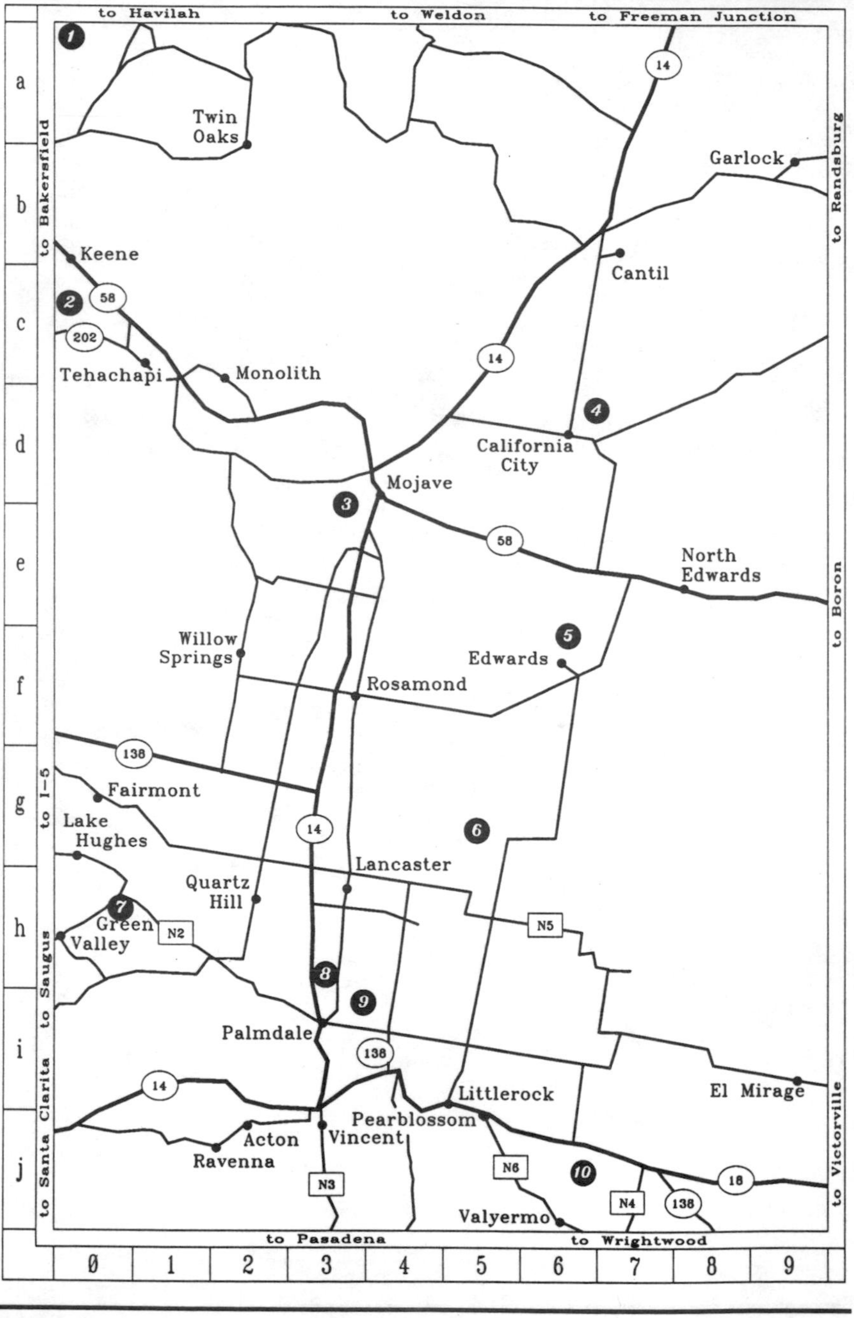

to Havilah
to Weldon
to Freeman Junction
to Bakersfield
to Randsburg
to Boron
to I-5
to Santa Clarita
to Saugus
to Victorville
to Pasadena
to Wrightwood

1
Twin Oaks
14
Garlock
Keene
Cantil
2
58
202
Tehachapi
Monolith
14
4
California City
Mojave
3
58
North Edwards
5
Willow Springs
Edwards
Rosamond
138
Fairmont
6
Lake Hughes
14
Lancaster
Quartz Hill
7
Green Valley
N2
N5
8
9
Palmdale
138
14
Littlerock
El Mirage
Pearblossom
Acton
Vincent
Ravenna
N6
10
18
N3
N4
138
Valyermo

a b c d e f g h i j

0 1 2 3 4 5 6 7 8 9

# BAKERSFIELD COUNTRY CLUB



**1950**
**William Francis Bell**

PO Box 6007
Bakersfield, CA 93306

4200 Country Club Drive
Bakersfield, CA 93306

Pro shop (805) 871-4121
Clubhouse (805) 871-4000

- ✓ **driving range**
- ✓ **practice greens**
- ✓ **power carts**
- pull carts
- golf club rental
- ✓ **locker rooms**
- ✓ **showers**
- executive course
- accommodations
- ✓ **food and beverages**
- ✓ **clubhouse**

**Dave Barber**
Professional

**Steve Scarbrough**
Superintendent

***Course information:*** This private course has 18 holes. See card below for yardage and rating information.

***Play policy and fees:*** Reciprocal play is accepted with members of other private clubs, otherwise members and guests only. Green fees for guests and reciprocators are $25 with a member and $50 without. Reservations for members only. Carts are $18. Reservations are recommended. Not open Mondays.

***Location:*** From Highway 99 at Bakersfield, go east on Highway 178 about six miles. Take the Oswell Street exit and turn right to Country Club Drive to the club.

***Course description:*** This is a nice, mature course situated on a hill. The layout requires excellent shot-making ability. Every club in the bag comes into play. Several long par-4s highlight the course. The course record is 63, held by Dave Barber.

| Hole | 1 | 2 | 3 | 4 | 5 | 6 | 7 | 8 | 9 | Out | | |
|---|---|---|---|---|---|---|---|---|---|---|---|---|
| BLUE | 375 | 529 | 177 | 454 | 455 | 597 | 342 | 184 | 348 | 3461 | BLUE | Rating: 72.9 |
| WHITE | 361 | 493 | 164 | 448 | 415 | 548 | 314 | 162 | 325 | 3230 | | Slope: 125 |
| Par | 4 | 5 | 3 | 4 | 4 | 5 | 4 | 3 | 4 | 36 | WHITE | Rating: 70.6 |
| Handicap | 5 | 9 | 13 | 1 | 3 | 7 | 15 | 11 | 17 | x | | Slope: 119 |
| RED | 352 | 485 | 156 | 443 | 400 | 473 | 306 | 132 | 302 | 3049 | | |
| Par | 4 | 5 | 3 | 5 | 4 | 5 | 4 | 3 | 4 | 37 | RED | Rating: 75.3 |
| Handicap | 5 | 3 | 15 | 11 | 1 | 7 | 9 | 17 | 13 | x | | Slope: 127 |

| Hole | 10 | 11 | 12 | 13 | 14 | 15 | 16 | 17 | 18 | In | Totals | |
|---|---|---|---|---|---|---|---|---|---|---|---|---|
| BLUE | 394 | 516 | 350 | 220 | 443 | 528 | 297 | 190 | 420 | 3358 | BLUE | 6819 |
| WHITE | 381 | 502 | 334 | 201 | 432 | 515 | 294 | 168 | 401 | 3228 | WHITE | 6458 |
| Par | 4 | 5 | 4 | 3 | 4 | 5 | 4 | 3 | 4 | 36 | Par | 72 |
| Handicap | 8 | 16 | 12 | 6 | 2 | 10 | 18 | 14 | 4 | x | | |
| RED | 371 | 496 | 328 | 198 | 429 | 511 | 294 | 154 | 326 | 3107 | RED | 6156 |
| Par | 4 | 5 | 4 | 3 | 5 | 5 | 4 | 3 | 4 | 37 | Par | 74 |
| Handicap | 6 | 4 | 12 | 8 | 14 | 2 | 16 | 18 | 10 | x | | |



MAP ON PAGE 444

# GOLDEN HILLS COUNTRY CLUB

Course 2
MAP H5 grid c0

**1963**
**Robert Trent Jones. Sr.**

22630 Woodford
Tehachapi Road
Tehachapi, CA 93561

Pro shop (805) 822-9118

- ✓ **driving range**
- ✓ **practice greens**
- ✓ **power carts**
- ✓ **pull carts**
- ✓ **golf club rental**
- ✓ **locker rooms**
- ✓ **showers**
- executive course
- accommodations
- ✓ **food and beverages**
- ✓ **clubhouse**

**Rick Dodd**
Professional

**Todd Paladini**
Superintendent

***Course information:*** This public course has 18 holes. Par is 72. The course is 6,284 yards and rated 70.6 from the regular tees. The slope rating is 118.

***Play policy and fees:*** Green fees are $7 weekdays and $8 weekends for nine holes, and $12 weekdays and $15 weekends for 18 holes. Call for special rates. Carts are $16.

***Location:*** From Bakersfield, travel east on Highway 58 for 38 miles to the town of Tehachapi, and turn right on Valley Road. Drive to Woodford-Tehachapi Road and turn right. Drive one mile to the course.

***Course description:*** This country course offers a hilly setting with lots of trees and some water. The layout is interesting with few parallel fairways. The addition of a second nine, expected to open in the fall of 1991, will increase the difficulty of this course besides merely making it longer. The new nine is hilly with valleys and big lakes. This course was formerly known as Deer Creek Country Club.

# CAMELOT GOLF COURSE

**Course 3**
MAP H5 grid d3

***Course information:*** This public course has nine holes. See card below for yardage and rating information.

***Play policy and fees:*** Senior monthly and yearly memberships are available for reduced green fees. Otherwise, green fees are $7 for nine holes and $11 for 18 holes weekdays, and $9 for nine holes and $14 for 18 holes weekends. Call for special rates. Carts are $14. Reservations are recommended. This course is available for tournaments. Shirts must be worn at all times on the golf course, as well as golf or tennis shoes.

***Location:*** Drive one mile south of the town of Mojave on Highway 14. Turn west on Camelot Boulevard and drive 1.5 miles to the course.

***Course description:*** This course features tree-lined, narrow fairways. The greens, which are in excellent shape, are extremely difficult to read and putt. The par-3 fifth hole offers a tough and humbling green. The course record is 63. Among the annual tournaments played here is the PGA-sponsored Pro-Am Tournament.

**1963**
3430 Camelot Boulevard
Mojave, CA 93501

Pro shop (805) 824-4107

- ✓ **driving range**
- ✓ **practice greens**
- ✓ **power carts**
- ✓ **pull carts**
- ✓ **golf club rental**
- locker rooms
- showers
- executive course
- accommodations
- ✓ **food and beverages**
- ✓ **clubhouse**

**Don Moulton**
Director of Golf

**Larry Jost**
Professional

**Mike Hill**
Superintendent

CENTRAL H5

| Hole | 1 | 2 | 3 | 4 | 5 | 6 | 7 | 8 | 9 | Out | BLUE | Rating: -- |
|---|---|---|---|---|---|---|---|---|---|---|---|---|
| BLUE | - | - | - | - | - | - | - | - | - | - | | Slope: -- |
| WHITE | 375 | 500 | 454 | 392 | 169 | 249 | 128 | 369 | 448 | 3084 | | |
| Par | 4 | 5 | 4 | 4 | 3 | 4 | 3 | 4 | 5 | 36 | WHITE | Rating: 70.2 |
| Handicap | 4 | 14 | 2 | 8 | 6 | 16 | 18 | 10 | 12 | x | | Slope: 120 |
| RED | 273 | 415 | 415 | 370 | 147 | 231 | 79 | 363 | 370 | 2663 | | |
| Par | 4 | 5 | 5 | 4 | 3 | 4 | 3 | 4 | 4 | 36 | RED | Rating: 72.5 |
| Handicap | 3 | 9 | 15 | 1 | 7 | 17 | 11 | 5 | 13 | x | | Slope: 111 |

| Hole | 10 | 11 | 12 | 13 | 14 | 15 | 16 | 17 | 18 | In | Totals | |
|---|---|---|---|---|---|---|---|---|---|---|---|---|
| BLUE | - | - | - | - | - | - | - | - | - | - | BLUE | -- |
| WHITE | 386 | 517 | 462 | 400 | 194 | 256 | 167 | 378 | 487 | 3247 | WHITE | 6331 |
| Par | 4 | 5 | 4 | 4 | 3 | 4 | 3 | 4 | 5 | 36 | Par | 72 |
| Handicap | 3 | 15 | 1 | 9 | 5 | 17 | 7 | 11 | 13 | x | | |
| RED | 361 | 417 | 400 | 389 | 170 | 248 | 100 | 265 | 381 | 2831 | RED | 5494 |
| Par | 4 | 5 | 5 | 4 | 3 | 4 | 3 | 4 | 4 | 36 | Par | 72 |
| Handicap | 4 | 10 | 12 | 2 | 8 | 16 | 18 | 6 | 14 | x | | |

# TIERRA DEL SOL

**Course 4**
**MAP H5 grid d6**

**1977**
**Devlin Von Hagge**

10300 North Loop Drive
California City, CA 93505

Clubhouse (619) 373-2384

- ✓ **driving range**
- ✓ **practice greens**
- ✓ **power carts**
- ✓ **pull carts**
- ✓ **golf club rental**
- ✓ **locker rooms**
- ✓ **showers**
- ✓ **executive course**
- ✓ **accommodations**
- ✓ **food and beverages**
- ✓ **clubhouse**

**Carroll Sharp**
Proessional

**Mark Cantrell**
Superintendent

***Course information:*** This public course has 18 holes and par is 72. The course is 6,908 yards and rated 74.1 from the championship tees, and 6,300 yards and rated 70.6 from the regular tees. The slope ratings are 137 championship and 129 regular. Women's tees are 5,227 yards and rated 68.4. The slope rating is 122.

***Play policy and fees:*** Green fees are $12 weekdays and $15 weekends. Call for special rates. Carts are $15. Reservations are recommended weekends and holidays one week in advance. Reserve a tee time a week in advance. Shirts must be worn in clubhouse area.

***Location:*** Drive north on Highway 14 from Lancaster to Mojave. Continue on 14 five more miles to California City Boulevard. Drive 8.5 miles to North Loop, turn left and continue two miles to the clubhouse.

***Course description:*** This 10-year-old, links-style course is level, long and open. There is water on 12 holes, there are 146 bunkers, and most of the greens are elevated. Hole five is the stickler: a 180-yard carry over water followed by a 240-yard drive leaves a 6-7-8 iron to an elevated green over water. The first Norm Crosby Tournaments were held here. Now the annual tournaments are the Gerry Kentner All Events and the High Desert Classic Pro-Am. The course record is 63, set by pro Dave Barber.

# MUROC LAKE GOLF COURSE

**Course 5**
MAP H5 grid f6

***Course information:*** This military course has 18 holes. See card below for yardage and rating information.

***Play policy and fees:*** Military personnel and guests only. Outside play accepted. Reciprocal play accepted with members of other Air Forces bases. Green fees are $7 to $15 depending on personnel status. Call for special rates. Carts are $14. Reservations are recommended.

***Location:*** Between the towns of Lancaster and Mojave on Highway 14, take the Rosamond exit and travel northeast for 15 miles to Lancaster Boulevard. Turn left and drive to Fitzgerald Boulevard. Turn left again and drive to Yucca Street and follow the signs.

***Course description:*** This is the greenest place in this part of the Mojave Desert, and it's not because of all the military uniforms. The course is well maintained and features a small lake and numerous mature trees that line the fairways. Tall trees, which offer a welcome relief from the afternoon sun, are spaced every 20 yards on both sides of the fairways. If you hit through the trees, you're at the mercy of the desert. There's very little out-of-bounds on this course.

PO Box 207,
Edwards AFB
Edwards, CA 93523

Pro shop (805) 277-3469
Clubhouse (805) 277-3467

- ✓ **driving range**
- ✓ **practice greens**
- ✓ **power carts**
- ✓ **pull carts**
- ✓ **golf club rental**
- locker rooms
- ✓ **showers**
- executive course
- accommodations
- ✓ **food &beverages**
- ✓ **clubhouse**

**Doug Carlton**
Professional/Manager

**Ralph Connors**
Superintendent

CENTRAL H5

| Hole | 1 | 2 | 3 | 4 | 5 | 6 | 7 | 8 | 9 | Out | | |
|---|---|---|---|---|---|---|---|---|---|---|---|---|
| BLUE | 326 | 407 | 530 | 456 | 376 | 231 | 557 | 216 | 404 | 3503 | BLUE | Rating: 73.5 |
| | | | | | | | | | | | | Slope: 128 |
| WHITE | 316 | 396 | 508 | 444 | 359 | 202 | 493 | 157 | 394 | 3269 | | |
| Par | 4 | 4 | 5 | 4 | 4 | 3 | 5 | 3 | 4 | 36 | WHITE | Rating: 71.5 |
| Handicap | 13 | 3 | 11 | 1 | 9 | 7 | 15 | 17 | 5 | x | | Slope: 120 |
| RED | 311 | 325 | 386 | 438 | 345 | 231 | 409 | 153 | 301 | 2899 | | |
| Par | 4 | 4 | 4 | 5 | 4 | 4 | 5 | 3 | 4 | 37 | RED | Rating: 72.3 |
| Handicap | 9 | 11 | 1 | 7 | 3 | 17 | 5 | 15 | 13 | x | | Slope: 115 |

| Hole | 10 | 11 | 12 | 13 | 14 | 15 | 16 | 17 | 18 | In | Totals | |
|---|---|---|---|---|---|---|---|---|---|---|---|---|
| BLUE | 571 | 374 | 222 | 435 | 347 | 498 | 437 | 199 | 368 | 3451 | BLUE | 6954 |
| WHITE | 539 | 365 | 180 | 425 | 338 | 478 | 427 | 158 | 361 | 3271 | WHITE | 6540 |
| Par | 5 | 4 | 3 | 4 | 4 | 5 | 4 | 3 | 4 | 36 | Par | 72 |
| Handicap | 8 | 6 | 10 | 4 | 14 | 18 | 2 | 16 | 12 | x | | |
| RED | 454 | 360 | 174 | 358 | 333 | 422 | 342 | 97 | 324 | 2864 | RED | 5763 |
| Par | 5 | 4 | 3 | 4 | 4 | 5 | 4 | 3 | 4 | 36 | Par | 73 |
| Handicap | 16 | 4 | 6 | 8 | 2 | 10 | 12 | 18 | 14 | x | | |

# RANCHO SIERRA

**Course 6**
MAP H5 grid g5

***Course information:*** This public course has nine holes. Par is 70 for 18 holes. The course is 4,904 yards and rated 62.3 from the regular tees. The slope rating is 91.

***Play policy and fees:*** Green fees are $7 for nine holes and $11 for 18 holes weekdays, and $9 for nine holes and $13 for 18 holes weekends. Call for special rates. Pull carts are $1.

***Location:*** Take the I exit off Highway 14 in the town of Lancaster, and travel east for about 10 miles to 60th Street. Turn left and drive 2.5 miles to the course.

***Course description:*** This a flat, short course with narrow fairways. Water comes into play on seven holes. Mature trees line the fairways, and the bunkers are all grass. Jack Roesinger and Sam Fogo designed this course.

**1963**
**Jack Roesinger**
**Sam Fogo**

47205 60th Street East
Lancaster, CA 93535

Pro shop (805) 946-1080

driving range
✓ **practice greens**
power carts
✓ **pull carts**
✓ **golf club rental**
locker rooms
showers
executive course
accommodations
✓ **food and beverages**
clubhouse

**Kevin Kretz**
Manager

**Kent Kretz**
Superintendent

# LAKE ELIZABETH GOLF CLUB

**Course 7**
**MAP H5 grid h0**

42532 Ranch Club Road
Lake Elizabeth, CA 93532

Pro shop (805) 724-1221

- ✓ **driving range**
- ✓ **practice greens**
- ✓ **power carts**
- pull carts
- ✓ **golf club rental**
- locker rooms
- showers
- exccutive course
- accommodations
- ✓ **food and beverages**
- ✓ **clubhouse**

**Brad Pierce**
Professional

**Jim Randall**
Superintendent

*Course information:* This public course has 18 holes. See card below for yardage and rating information.

*Play policy and fees:* Green fees are $20 weekdays and $26 weekends. Carts included. Call for special rates. Reservations are recommended. Shirts with collars required. No cut-offs or short shorts. This course is available for tournaments.

*Location:* Take the Palmdale Boulevard exit off Highway 14 and turn left onto Ranch Club Road. Go about 16 miles to the end of the road, turn left and follow signs to the clubhouse.

*Course description:* This medium-length course was expanded from nine to 18 holes nearly three years ago. It is fairly hilly with small greens. Seven lakes come into play. The par-4 fifth hole is 434 yards from the championship tees, which doesn't seem significant except for the fact that there is a 200-foot drop from tee to fairway. More than one golfer has been fooled into thinking the drive had more distance than it does.

CENTRAL H5

| Hole | 1 | 2 | 3 | 4 | 5 | 6 | 7 | 8 | 9 | Out | BLUE | Rating: 68.8 |
|---|---|---|---|---|---|---|---|---|---|---|---|---|
| BLUE | 364 | 183 | 326 | 199 | 434 | 224 | 503 | 391 | 509 | 3133 | | Slope: 118 |
| WHITE | 353 | 175 | 317 | 192 | 342 | 212 | 490 | 366 | 493 | 2940 | | |
| Par | 4 | 3 | 4 | 3 | 4 | 3 | 5 | 4 | 5 | 35 | WHITE | Rating: 67.1 |
| Handicap | 13 | 11 | 17 | 3 | 15 | 1 | 5 | 7 | 9 | x | | Slope: 114 |
| RED | 318 | 163 | 286 | 158 | 300 | 170 | 474 | 296 | 477 | 2642 | | |
| Par | 4 | 3 | 4 | 3 | 4 | 3 | 5 | 4 | 5 | 35 | RED | Rating: 72.9 |
| Handicap | 1 | 17 | 11 | 3 | 15 | 10 | 9 | 5 | 7 | x | | Slope: 115 |

| Hole | 10 | 11 | 12 | 13 | 14 | 15 | 16 | 17 | 18 | In | Totals | |
|---|---|---|---|---|---|---|---|---|---|---|---|---|
| BLUE | 175 | 405 | 481 | 166 | 474 | 135 | 366 | 171 | 479 | 2852 | BLUE | 5985 |
| WHITE | 139 | 393 | 474 | 149 | 463 | 122 | 351 | 164 | 463 | 2718 | WHITE | 5658 |
| Par | 3 | 4 | 5 | 3 | 5 | 3 | 4 | 3 | 5 | 35 | Par | 70 |
| Handicap | 14 | 8 | 2 | 16 | 4 | 18 | 6 | 12 | 10 | x | | |
| RED | 117 | 376 | 423 | 131 | 455 | 113 | 263 | 147 | 407 | 2432 | RED | 5074 |
| Par | 3 | 4 | 5 | 3 | 5 | 3 | 4 | 3 | 5 | 35 | Par | 70 |
| Handicap | 14 | 2 | 8 | 16 | 6 | 18 | 10 | 12 | 4 | x | | |

# ANTELOPE VALLEY COUNTRY CLUB

**Course 8**
MAP H5 grid h3

*Course information:* This private course has 18 holes. See card below for yardage and rating information.

*Play policy and fees:* Reciprocal play is accepted with members of other private clubs; otherwise members and guests only. Guest fees are $25 on weekdays and $35 weekends. Reciprocators are $35 weekdays and $45 weekends. Carts are $16.

*Location:* Take Avenue P east off Highway 14 in Palmdale and drive east for one block to Country Club Drive. Turn left and drive one-quarter mile to the club.

*Course description:* Don't forget to bring a sand wedge to this course. It is well bunkered but level, with many trees lining the fairways. Water can be found on several holes of this challenging course. The lake size has been enlarged on the par-3, 183-yard number 11. You must hit over the water to the large green, but don't hit short. The water comes to within five feet of the apron. Winds make every hole on this course different each day. The men's course record is a 64; the women's course record is a 66.

39800 Country Club Drive
Palmdale, CA 93550

Pro shop (805) 947-3400
Clubhouse (805) 947-3142

- ✓ **driving range**
- ✓ **practice greens**
- ✓ **power carts**
- ✓ **pull carts**
- golf club rental
- ✓ **locker rooms**
- ✓ **showers**
- executive course
- accommodations
- ✓ **food and beverages**
- ✓ **clubhouse**

**Steve Applegate**
Professional

**Dan McIntyre**
Superintendent

| Hole | 1 | 2 | 3 | 4 | 5 | 6 | 7 | 8 | 9 | Out | | |
|---|---|---|---|---|---|---|---|---|---|---|---|---|
| BLUE | 400 | 177 | 348 | 561 | 161 | 432 | 383 | 344 | 509 | 3315 | BLUE | Rating: 72.8 |
| WHITE | 382 | 167 | 332 | 539 | 149 | 400 | 366 | 321 | 487 | 3143 | | Slope: 129 |
| Par | 4 | 3 | 4 | 5 | 3 | 4 | 4 | 4 | 5 | 36 | WHITE | Rating: 70.6 |
| Handicap | 5 | 9 | 11 | 7 | 17 | 1 | 3 | 15 | 13 | x | | Slope: 122 |
| RED | 366 | 164 | 322 | 525 | 119 | 390 | 356 | 309 | 477 | 3028 | | |
| Par | 4 | 3 | 4 | 5 | 3 | 4 | 4 | 4 | 5 | 36 | RED | Rating: 74.3 |
| Handicap | 9 | 15 | 11 | 1 | 17 | 3 | 7 | 13 | 5 | x | | Slope: 118 |

| Hole | 10 | 11 | 12 | 13 | 14 | 15 | 16 | 17 | 18 | In | Totals | |
|---|---|---|---|---|---|---|---|---|---|---|---|---|
| BLUE | 467 | 183 | 393 | 353 | 502 | 414 | 434 | 179 | 500 | 3425 | BLUE | 6740 |
| WHITE | 443 | 171 | 378 | 325 | 478 | 394 | 425 | 167 | 484 | 3265 | WHITE | 6408 |
| Par | 4 | 3 | 4 | 4 | 5 | 4 | 4 | 3 | 5 | 36 | Par | 72 |
| Handicap | 2 | 12 | 6 | 10 | 18 | 8 | 4 | 14 | 16 | x | | |
| RED | 454 | 120 | 367 | 314 | 460 | 377 | 418 | 155 | 477 | 3129 | RED | 6157 |
| Par | 5 | 3 | 4 | 4 | 5 | 4 | 5 | 3 | 5 | 38 | Par | 74 |
| Handicap | 10 | 18 | 2 | 12 | 8 | 4 | 14 | 16 | 6 | x | | |

# DESERT AIRE GOLF COURSE

**Course 9**
MAP H5 grid i4

**1958**

3620 East Avenue "P"
Palmdale, CA 93550

Pro shop (805) 267-5666
Clubhouse (805) 266-3688

*Course information:* This public course has nine holes See card below for yardage and rating information.

*Play policy and fees:* Green fees are $7 weekdays and $10 weekends. Call for special rates. Carts are $8.50. This course is available for outside tournaments.

*Location:* Take Avenue P east off Highway 14 in Palmdale and drive four miles to the course.

*Course description:* This level, desert course is well bunkered with one lake. Mature trees line the fairways and offer welcome shade in the afternoon. The toughest hole is the 391-yard, par-4 eighth. It's straight and narrow with out-of-bounds to the right. Accuracy on a windy day is a must on this hole.

- ✓ **driving range**
- ✓ **practice greens**
- ✓ **power carts**
- ✓ **pull carts**
- ✓ **golf club rental**
- ✓ **locker rooms**
- showers
- executive course
- accommodations
- ✓ **food and beverages**
- ✓ **clubhouse**

**Gary Delano**
Professional

**Craig Graham**
Superintendent

CENTRAL H5

| Hole | 1 | 2 | 3 | 4 | 5 | 6 | 7 | 8 | 9 | Out | BLUE | Rating: -- |
|---|---|---|---|---|---|---|---|---|---|---|---|---|
| BLUE | - | - | - | - | - | - | - | - | - | - | | Slope: -- |
| WHITE | 481 | 372 | 356 | 141 | 352 | 136 | 376 | 391 | 457 | 3062 | | |
| Par | 5 | 4 | 4 | 3 | 4 | 3 | 4 | 4 | 5 | 36 | WHITE | Rating: 68.1 |
| Handicap | 10 | 4 | 16 | 18 | 6 | 12 | 8 | 2 | 14 | x | | Slope: 102 |
| RED | 432 | 358 | 351 | 136 | 339 | 130 | 325 | 342 | 386 | 2799 | | |
| Par | 5 | 4 | 4 | 3 | 4 | 3 | 4 | 4 | 4 | 35 | RED | Rating: 69.8 |
| Handicap | 12 | 4 | 8 | 10 | 2 | 16 | 10 | 6 | 14 | x | | Slope: -- |

| Hole | 10 | 11 | 12 | 13 | 14 | 15 | 16 | 17 | 18 | In | Totals | |
|---|---|---|---|---|---|---|---|---|---|---|---|---|
| BLUE | - | - | - | - | - | - | - | - | - | - | BLUE | -- |
| WHITE | 488 | 382 | 361 | 147 | 361 | 143 | 384 | 401 | 463 | 3133 | WHITE | 6195 |
| Par | 5 | 4 | 4 | 3 | 4 | 3 | 4 | 4 | 5 | 36 | Par | 72 |
| Handicap | 9 | 3 | 15 | 17 | 5 | 11 | 7 | 1 | 13 | x | | |
| RED | 481 | 372 | 356 | 141 | 352 | 136 | 376 | 391 | 457 | 3062 | RED | 5861 |
| Par | 5 | 4 | 4 | 3 | 4 | 3 | 4 | 4 | 5 | 36 | Par | 71 |
| Handicap | 11 | 3 | 7 | 17 | 1 | 15 | 9 | 5 | 13 | x | | |

# CRYSTALAIRE COUNTRY CLUB

**Course 10**
MAP H5 grid j6

**1956**
**William Francis Bell**

15701 Boca Raton
Llano, CA 93544

Pro shop (805) 944-2111

- ✓ **driving range**
- ✓ **practice greens**
- ✓ **power carts**
- ✓ **pull carts**
- golf club rental
- ✓ **locker rooms**
- ✓ **showers**
- executive course
- ✓ **accommodations**
- ✓ **food and beverages**
- ✓ **clubhouse**

**Allan Arvesen**
Professional

**Manuel Delgado**
Superintendent

***Course information:*** This private course has 18 holes. The women's tees are 5,311 yards, rated 69.7, and have a slope rating of 117 from the gold tees, and rated 77.6 with a slope of 132 from the white tees. See card below for additional yardage and rating information.

***Play policy and fees:*** Reciprocal play is accepted with members of other private clubs. Green fees are $35 weekdays and $40 weekends. Carts are $16 on weekdays, $18 weekends.

***Location:*** South of Lancaster take the Pearblossom exit off Highway 14 and travel about 16 miles east to the town of Llano. Turn south on 165th Street and drive to the club.

***Course description:*** This scenic country course is set in the high desert surrounded by mountains. The terrain is rolling to hilly with lots of mature trees and three lakes. Watch for the par-3, 150-yard sixth. Players must drive over the lake to reach the hole. This hole has been the downfall of many, but it has also recorded more holes-in-one then any other hole on the course. The course is at 3,500-foot elevation and is usually open in the winter. The course record is a 64.

| Hole | 1 | 2 | 3 | 4 | 5 | 6 | 7 | 8 | 9 | Out | BLUE | Rating: 73.8 |
|---|---|---|---|---|---|---|---|---|---|---|---|---|
| BLUE | 526 | 425 | 428 | 353 | 579 | 174 | 447 | 166 | 379 | 3477 | | Slope: 132 |
| WHITE | 505 | 415 | 411 | 339 | 561 | 150 | 437 | 152 | 366 | 3336 | | |
| Par | 5 | 4 | 4 | 4 | 5 | 3 | 4 | 3 | 4 | 36 | WHITE | Rating: 71.6 |
| Handicap | 9 | 7 | 5 | 17 | 1 | 13 | 3 | 15 | 11 | x | | Slope: 124 |
| RED | 497 | 370 | 407 | 332 | 506 | 113 | 435 | 145 | 360 | 3165 | | |
| Par | 4 | 4 | 4 | 4 | 5 | 3 | 5 | 3 | 4 | 36 | RED | Rating: 75.0 |
| Handicap | 3 | 13 | 9 | 11 | 1 | 15 | 7 | 17 | 5 | x | | Slope: 127 |

| Hole | 10 | 11 | 12 | 13 | 14 | 15 | 16 | 17 | 18 | In | Totals | |
|---|---|---|---|---|---|---|---|---|---|---|---|---|
| BLUE | 416 | 173 | 571 | 374 | 440 | 222 | 421 | 355 | 513 | 3485 | BLUE | 6962 |
| WHITE | 396 | 131 | 535 | 356 | 428 | 204 | 406 | 333 | 504 | 3293 | WHITE | 6629 |
| Par | 4 | 3 | 5 | 4 | 4 | 3 | 4 | 4 | 5 | 36 | Par | 72 |
| Handicap | 10 | 18 | 6 | 12 | 2 | 8 | 4 | 16 | 14 | x | | |
| RED | 375 | 115 | 490 | 325 | 389 | 178 | 356 | 326 | 496 | 3050 | RED | 6215 |
| Par | 4 | 3 | 5 | 4 | 4 | 3 | 4 | 4 | 5 | 36 | Par | 72 |
| Handicap | 14 | 18 | 4 | 12 | 6 | 16 | 10 | 8 | 2 | x | | |

# MAP H6
(5 COURSES)

PAGES.. 456-461

CEN-CAL MAP...see page 314
adjoining maps
NORTH (G6).......see page 400
EAST.............................no map
SOUTH (I6).........see page 584
WEST (H5) .........see page 444

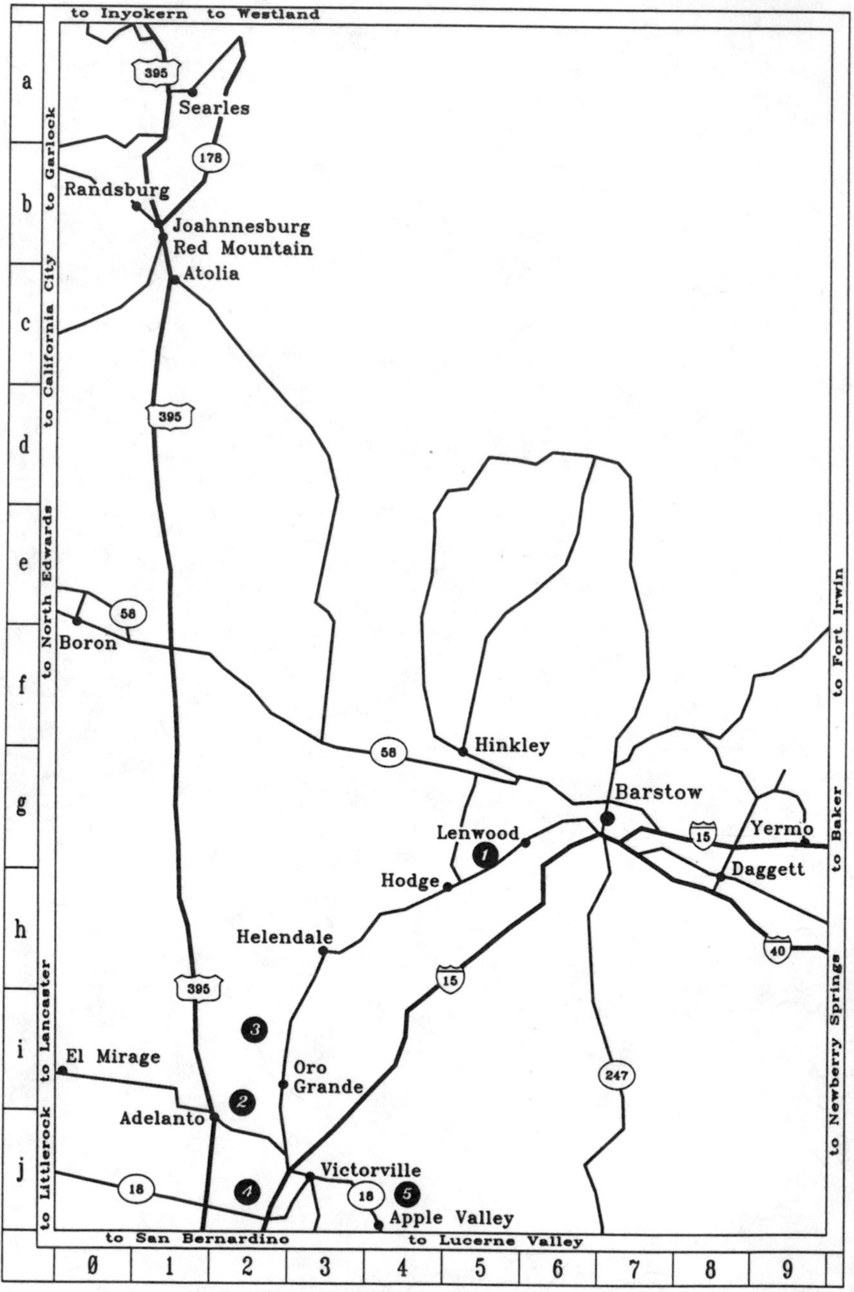

to Inyokern to Westland
to Garlock
to California City
to North Edwards
to Lancaster
to Littlerock
to Fort Irwin
to Baker
to Newberry Springs
to San Bernardino
to Lucerne Valley

a b c d e f g h i j

395
Searles
178
Randsburg
Joahnnesburg
Red Mountain
Atolia
395
58
Boron
58
Hinkley
Barstow
Lenwood
1
Hodge
15
Yermo
Daggett
40
Helendale
395
15
3
El Mirage
Oro
Grande
247
2
Adelanto
Victorville
18
4
18
5
Apple Valley

0 1 2 3 4 5 6 7 8 9

## SUN VALLEY COUNTRY CLUB

**Course 1**
MAP H6 grid g5

**1959**
**Ted Robinson**

2781 Country Club Drive
Barstow, CA 92311

Pro shop (619) 253-5201

- ✓ **driving range**
- ✓ **practice greens**
- ✓ **power carts**
- ✓ **pull carts**
- ✓ **golf club rental**
- ✓ **locker rooms**
- ✓ **showers**
- executive course
- accommodations
- ✓ **food and beverages**
- ✓ **clubhouse**

**Bill Sailors**
Manager

***Course information:*** This public course has nine holes. Par is 72 for 18 holes. The course is 6,381 yards and rated 69 for 18 holes from the regular tees. The slope rating is 114. Women's tees are 6,028 yards and rated 71.9. The slope rating is 112.

***Play policy and fees:*** Green fees are $8 for nine holes and $11 for 18 holes weekdays, and $10 for nine holes and $14 for 18 holes weekends. Carts are $8 for nine holes weekdays and $12 for 18 holes weekdays, and $10 for nine holes and $14 for 18 holes weekends. Play is on a first-come, first-served basis. This course is available for outside tournaments.

***Location:*** From Interstate 15, two miles west of Lenwood, take the Lenwood Road exit west. Drive to Main Street and turn west. Drive on Main Street to Country Club Drive and the course.

***Course description:*** Formerly known as the Sun and Sky Country Club, this is a straight and flat, tree-lined course that's perfect for beginners. The greens are small. The course is open year-round. The course record is 61, held by Mark Johnson.

## WEST WINDS GOLF COURSE

**Course 2**
MAP H6 grid j2

**1964**
Building 1140
George AFB, CA 92394

***Course information:*** This military course has closed.

# SILVER LAKES COUNTRY CLUB

**Course 3**
MAP H6 grid j2

**1974**
**Ted Robinson**

HC Box 2377
Helendale, CA 92342

14814 Club House Drive
Helendale, CA 92342

Pro shop (619) 245-7435

- ✓ **driving range**
- ✓ **practice greens**
- ✓ **power carts**
- pull carts
- ✓ **golf club rental**
- locker rooms
- showers
- executive course
- ✓ **accommodations**
- ✓ **food and beverages**
- ✓ **clubhouse**

**Eric Sletten**
Professional

**Mike Mggehee**
Superintendent

***Course information:*** This private facility has 27 holes and par is 72 for each of the 18-hole combinations. The North-South Course is detailed in the card below.

South-South Course:
Championship—6,924 yards, rated 73.4, slope 128;
Regular tees—6,516 yards, rated 70.7, slope 120;
Women's tees—5,732 yards, rated 71.7, slope 118.

The East-South Course:
Championship—6,709 yards, rated 72.3, slope 123;
Regular tees—6,395 yards, rated 69.9, slope 118;
Women's tees—5,635 yards, rated 71.1, slope 116.

The East-North Course:
Championship—6,697 yards, rated 71.8, slope 122;
Regular tees—6,341 yards, rated 69.5, slope 116;
Women's tees—5,467 yards, rated 70.4, slope 114.

The East-East Course:
Championship—6,614 yards, rated 71.2, slope 121;
Regular tees—6,274 yards, rated 69.2, slope 116;
Women's tees—5,538 yards, rated 70.7, slope 112.

***Play policy and fees:*** Reciprocal play accepted with members of private clubs; have your pro call ahead. Guests at the Inn at Silver Lakes are welcome. Green fees are $25 weekdays and $30 weekends. Carts are $18. Make reservations three days in advance.Available for outside tournaments.

***Location:*** Take Interstate 15 north from San Bernardino to the "D" Street/Apple Valley exit in Victorville. Turn left toward George Air Force Base and continue for 14 miles to Vista Road and turn left to the club.

***Course description:*** All combinations are very distinctive. The South Course has lots of water, the East Course has just one hole with water and the North Course has two holes with water. All three courses have good, long holes on them and they also have narrow holes.

North/South Course

| North Holes | 1 | 2 | 3 | 4 | 5 | 6 | 7 | 8 | 9 | Out | BLUE | Rating: 73.0 |
|---|---|---|---|---|---|---|---|---|---|---|---|---|
| BLUE | 416 | 483 | 364 | 345 | 171 | 417 | 578 | 216 | 400 | 3390 | | Slope: 125 |
| WHITE | 395 | 465 | 342 | 336 | 154 | 396 | 541 | 201 | 374 | 3204 | | |
| Par | 4 | 5 | 4 | 4 | 3 | 4 | 5 | 3 | 4 | 36 | WHITE | Rating: 70.5 |
| Handicap | 1 | 13 | 9 | 11 | 17 | 3 | 15 | 7 | 5 | x | | Slope: 120 |
| RED | 305 | 406 | 280 | 311 | 136 | 345 | 424 | 179 | 312 | 2698 | | |
| Par | 4 | 5 | 4 | 4 | 3 | 4 | 5 | 3 | 4 | 36 | RED | Rating: 70.9 |
| Handicap | 11 | 5 | 13 | 3 | 17 | 1 | 15 | 9 | 7 | x | | Slope: 118 |

| South Holes | 1 | 2 | 3 | 4 | 5 | 6 | 7 | 8 | 9 | In | Totals | |
|---|---|---|---|---|---|---|---|---|---|---|---|---|
| BLUE | 401 | 207 | 380 | 530 | 197 | 382 | 409 | 545 | 410 | 3462 | BLUE | 6852 |
| WHITE | 379 | 178 | 354 | 510 | 173 | 369 | 389 | 524 | 382 | 3258 | WHITE | 6462 |
| Par | 4 | 3 | 4 | 5 | 3 | 4 | 4 | 5 | 4 | 36 | Par | 72 |
| Handicap | 3 | 17 | 11 | 13 | 5 | 15 | 7 | 9 | 1 | x | | |
| RED | 340 | 151 | 318 | 456 | 146 | 337 | 324 | 442 | 352 | 2866 | RED | 5564 |
| Par | 4 | 3 | 4 | 5 | 3 | 4 | 4 | 5 | 4 | 36 | Par | 72 |
| Handicap | 5 | 17 | 7 | 3 | 15 | 11 | 13 | 9 | 1 | x | | |

# VICTORVILLE MUNICIPAL GOLF COURSE

**Course 4**
MAP H6 grid j2

**1962**
14144 Greentree Boulevard
Victorville, CA 92392

Pro shop (619) 245-4860

- driving range
- ✓ **practice greens**
- ✓ **power carts**
- ✓ **pull carts**
- ✓ **golf club rental**
- locker rooms
- showers
- executive course
- accommodations
- ✓ **food and beverages**
- clubhouse

**Ray Echols, Jr.**
Professional

**Ray Salberg**
Superintendent

***Course information:*** This public course has 18 holes. See card below for yardage and rating information.

***Play policy and fees:*** Green fees are $10 for nine holes and $14 for 18 holes weekdays and $12 for nine holes and $17 for 18 holes weekends. Carts are $12 for nine holes and $17 for 18 holes. Reservations are recommended. This course is available for tournaments. Dress code is enforced; no cut offs or short shorts for women, no tank tops for men.

***Location:*** From San Bernardino, drive north on Interstate 15 to Victorville. Exit at Palmdale Road and turn right. Drive to Greentree Boulevard and turn right. The course is 100 yards down the road.

***Course description:*** This is a hilly course but it is walkable. The course record for men is 65. The course record for women is 66.

| Hole | 1 | 2 | 3 | 4 | 5 | 6 | 7 | 8 | 9 | Out | BLUE | Rating: 71.2 |
|---|---|---|---|---|---|---|---|---|---|---|---|---|
| BLUE | 393 | 398 | 573 | 376 | 175 | 399 | 426 | 198 | 491 | 3429 | | Slope: 121 |
| WHITE | 376 | 362 | 535 | 356 | 154 | 386 | 414 | 175 | 477 | 3235 | | |
| Par | 4 | 4 | 5 | 4 | 3 | 4 | 4 | 3 | 5 | 36 | WHITE | Rating: 69.3 |
| Handicap | 9 | 5 | 3 | 13 | 17 | 11 | 1 | 7 | 13 | x | | Slope: 117 |
| RED | 365 | 330 | 470 | 345 | 133 | 374 | 367 | 153 | 467 | 3004 | | |
| Par | 4 | 4 | 5 | 4 | 3 | 4 | 4 | 3 | 5 | 36 | RED | Rating: 72.7 |
| Handicap | 7 | 13 | 3 | 11 | 17 | 9 | 1 | 15 | 5 | x | | Slope: 118 |

| Hole | 10 | 11 | 12 | 13 | 14 | 15 | 16 | 17 | 18 | In | Totals | |
|---|---|---|---|---|---|---|---|---|---|---|---|---|
| BLUE | 333 | 372 | 561 | 376 | 155 | 530 | 172 | 402 | 310 | 3211 | BLUE | 6640 |
| WHITE | 333 | 351 | 549 | 367 | 146 | 517 | 160 | 382 | 291 | 3096 | WHITE | 6331 |
| Par | 4 | 4 | 5 | 4 | 3 | 5 | 3 | 4 | 4 | 36 | Par | 72 |
| Handicap | 12 | 8 | 2 | 10 | 16 | 4 | 14 | 6 | 18 | x | | |
| RED | 313 | 339 | 482 | 317 | 137 | 460 | 147 | 360 | 276 | 2831 | RED | 5835 |
| Par | 4 | 4 | 5 | 4 | 3 | 5 | 3 | 4 | 4 | 36 | Par | 72 |
| Handicap | 12 | 6 | 2 | 14 | 18 | 4 | 16 | 8 | 10 | x | | |

# APPLE VALLEY COUNTRY CLUB

**Course 5**
MAP H6 grid j4

**1949**
**William Park Bell**

PO Box 1045
Apple Valley, CA 92307

15200 Rancherias Road
Apple Valley, CA 92307

Pro shop (619) 242-3125
Clubhouse (619) 242-3653

- ✓ **driving range**
- ✓ **practice greens**
- ✓ **power carts**
- ✓ **pull carts**
- ✓ **golf club rental**
- ✓ **locker rooms**
- ✓ **showers**
- executive course
- accommodations
- ✓ **food and beverages**
- ✓ **clubhouse**

**Clifford Moore**
Professional

**Jerry Moore**
Superintendent

***Course information:*** This private course has 18 holes. See card below for yardage and rating information.

***Play policy and fees:*** Reciprocal play is accepted with members of other private clubs, otherwise members and guests only. Green fees are $35 weekdays and $40 weekends. Carts are $18. Reservations are recommended. Dress code is enforced; no cut offs or short shorts for women, no tank tops for men.

***Location:*** From San Bernardino, drive north on Interstate 15 to the Apple Valley exit. Head east on Highway 18 to Rancherias Road and turn right. The course is on the right.

***Course description:*** This is a fairly level course with wide fairways, mature trees and some water. The greens can be hard and fast. The course plays much more difficult then it looks, especially when the wind is blowing, which may justify the high rating. The men's course record is 64.

| Hole | 1 | 2 | 3 | 4 | 5 | 6 | 7 | 8 | 9 | Out | BLUE | Rating: 73.2 |
|---|---|---|---|---|---|---|---|---|---|---|---|---|
| BLUE | 403 | 155 | 429 | 398 | 492 | 205 | 461 | 385 | 395 | 3323 | | Slope: 129 |
| WHITE | 385 | 141 | 397 | 358 | 486 | 171 | 426 | 381 | 379 | 3124 | | |
| Par | 4 | 3 | 4 | 4 | 5 | 3 | 4 | 4 | 4 | 35 | WHITE | Rating: 70.9 |
| Handicap | 5 | 17 | 3 | 13 | 7 | 15 | 1 | 9 | 11 | x | | Slope: 123 |
| RED | 365 | 113 | 267 | 321 | 475 | 146 | 420 | 372 | 327 | 2906 | | |
| Par | 4 | 3 | 4 | 4 | 5 | 3 | 5 | 4 | 4 | 36 | RED | Rating: 73.1 |
| Handicap | 5 | 15 | 3 | 13 | 1 | 17 | 7 | 9 | 11 | x | | Slope: 120 |

| Hole | 10 | 11 | 12 | 13 | 14 | 15 | 16 | 17 | 18 | In | Totals | |
|---|---|---|---|---|---|---|---|---|---|---|---|---|
| BLUE | 222 | 432 | 440 | 332 | 514 | 376 | 460 | 176 | 528 | 3482 | BLUE | 6805 |
| WHITE | 206 | 423 | 426 | 315 | 507 | 367 | 446 | 169 | 494 | 3353 | WHITE | 6477 |
| Par | 3 | 4 | 4 | 4 | 5 | 4 | 4 | 3 | 5 | 36 | Par | 71 |
| Handicap | 12 | 6 | 2 | 16 | 10 | 8 | 4 | 14 | 18 | x | | |
| RED | 187 | 359 | 415 | 307 | 474 | 326 | 365 | 125 | 465 | 3023 | RED | 5929 |
| Par | 3 | 4 | 5 | 4 | 5 | 4 | 4 | 3 | 5 | 37 | Par | 73 |
| Handicap | 16 | 8 | 4 | 14 | 2 | 12 | 10 | 18 | 6 | x | | |

MAP ON PAGE 456

# Southern California Golf Courses

# SOUTHERN CALIFORNIA COURSES

The golf urge is clearly present and accounted for in the southland, from the Mexican border to sprawling L.A., from the deserts and the mountains to the ocean. From one corner of the southland to the other, one thing is obvious: Southern California is golf crazy.

With almost half of the courses in the state located in the southern sector, you'll find every type of course imaginable. There are swanky private links with swanky celebrity members, oasis desert tracts, quaint nine-hole courses hidden within trailer parks, and deluxe seaside resort layouts.

In Los Angeles, clubs such as the Bel-Air Country Club, the Riviera Country Club, and the Los Angeles Country Club—all designed by the legendary George C. Thomas in the 1920s—boast some of the finest layouts in the state. If only you could get on them—they're also some of the most private clubs in the state.

Public courses also abound, although they're mostly pretty busy. If you live in Los Angeles, you already know this. But if you're visiting from Weaverville, get ready for some company on the links.

For one thing, the huge population base of Southern California creates greater demand for tee times. Consequently, play can be slower. But look at it this way: The weather is great! That's why everyone is on the golf course, anyway.

If you're looking for a refuge from the Los Angeles area, head to the desert, where some of the state's best resort courses rise out of the sand like brilliant green oases. They offer a unique brand of hazards, these desert tracts—mind numbing heat in the summer (you'll welcome water hazards, maybe jump in), tumbleweeds, jackrabbits, coyotes and that ubiquitous desert wind.

The San Diego area, too, and the scenic coastline just to its north, is a haven for public and resort golf. And so is the historic Ojai Valley Inn and Country Club just north of Los Angeles. The jury is in: Southern California offers some of the best and most unique golf experiences to be found in the Golden State.

# SO-CAL BY AREA
**(MAP, COURSES, PAGES)**



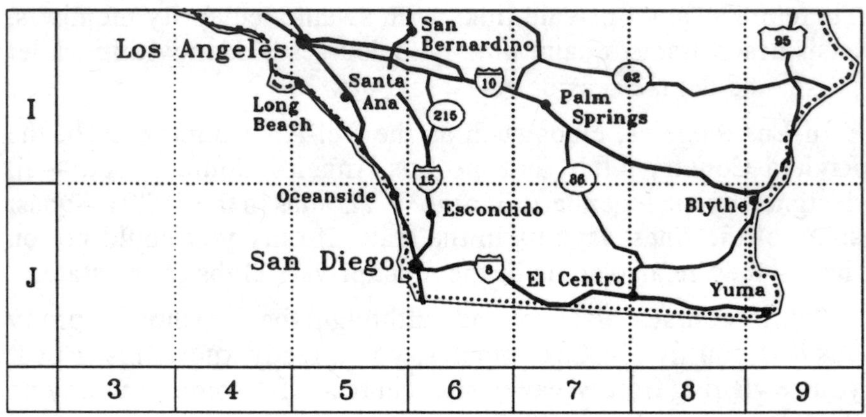

# SO-CAL BY CITY
## (CITY and MAP PAGE)

# MAP I3
(1 COURSE)

PAGES.. 468-469

SO-CAL MAP .....see page 466
adjoining maps
NORTH (H3).......see page 412
EAST (I4) ...........see page 470
SOUTH..........................no map
WEST ...........................no map

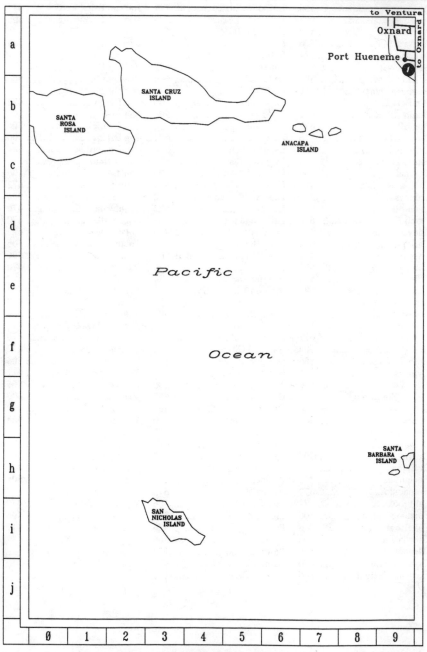

to Ventura

Oxnard

to Oxnard

Port Hueneme

1

SANTA CRUZ ISLAND

SANTA ROSA ISLAND

ANACAPA ISLAND

*Pacific*

*Ocean*

SANTA BARBARA ISLAND

SAN NICHOLAS ISLAND

a b c d e f g h i j

Ø 1 2 3 4 5 6 7 8 9

# CBC PORT HUENEME GOLF CLUB

**Course 1**
MAP 13 grid a9

**1957**
**Jack Daray**

Seabee Golf Course
Code 19
Port Hueneme, CA 93043

Pro shop (805) 982-2620

- ✓ **driving range**
- ✓ **practice greens**
- ✓ **power carts**
- ✓ **pull carts**
- ✓ **golf club rental**
- locker rooms
- showers
- executive course
- accommodations
- ✓ **food and beverages**
- ✓ **clubhouse**

**Chuck Green**
Professional/Manager

**George Garcia**
Superintendent

*Course information:* This military course has 18 holes. See card below for yardage and rating information.

*Play policy and fees:* Military personnel and guests only. Green fees vary according to military or civilian status. Reservations are recommended. Carts are $13. Closed Christmas.

*Location:* Take Ventura Road off Highway 101 in Oxnard and drive south on Ventura Road to Pleasant Valley Road. Turn right and travel to the Port Hueneme Naval Base.

*Course description:* This is a deceptive course. Although flat, it plays tough because of green and bunker placement. The prevailing west wind off the ocean and numerous trees add to the challenge. Jack Daray built the original nine holes here in 1957. In mid-1990, it was expanded to 18 holes. Give careful study to number 13. It's a par-3, 179 yards from the championship tee. The large green appears to be surrounded by water and it's tough getting there. The green is not only guarded by water, but there are also front bunkers left and right. Out-of-bounds is to the left and behind the green. Play is usually into a west wind. Aside from that, it's an easy hole!

| Hole | 1 | 2 | 3 | 4 | 5 | 6 | 7 | 8 | 9 | Out | | |
|---|---|---|---|---|---|---|---|---|---|---|---|---|
| BLUE | 365 | 222 | 326 | 423 | 360 | 180 | 356 | 505 | 300 | 3066 | BLUE | Rating: 69.1 |
| WHITE | 342 | 205 | 314 | 412 | 351 | 139 | 339 | 481 | 292 | 2875 | | Slope: 112 |
| Par | 4 | 3 | 4 | 4 | 4 | 3 | 4 | 5 | 4 | 35 | WHITE | Rating: 67.4 |
| Handicap | 11 | 13 | 15 | 3 | 5 | 7 | 9 | 1 | 17 | x | | Slope: 107 |
| RED | 317 | 150 | 303 | 402 | 339 | 110 | 321 | 388 | 284 | 2614 | | |
| Par | 4 | 3 | 4 | 5 | 4 | 3 | 4 | 5 | 4 | 36 | RED | Rating: 70.5 |
| Handicap | 11 | 13 | 9 | 3 | 5 | 17 | 7 | 1 | 15 | x | | Slope: 119 |

| Hole | 10 | 11 | 12 | 13 | 14 | 15 | 16 | 17 | 18 | In | Totals | |
|---|---|---|---|---|---|---|---|---|---|---|---|---|
| BLUE | 367 | 341 | 574 | 179 | 352 | 350 | 387 | 180 | 509 | 3209 | BLUE | 6275 |
| WHITE | 359 | 331 | 516 | 168 | 344 | 342 | 357 | 153 | 500 | 3070 | WHITE | 5495 |
| Par | 4 | 4 | 5 | 3 | 4 | 4 | 4 | 3 | 5 | 36 | Par | 71 |
| Handicap | 8 | 10 | 2 | 6 | 14 | 12 | 16 | 18 | 4 | x | | |
| RED | 352 | 321 | 508 | 158 | 336 | 334 | 301 | 123 | 406 | 2839 | RED | 5453 |
| Par | 4 | 4 | 5 | 3 | 4 | 4 | 4 | 3 | 5 | 36 | Par | 72 |
| Handicap | 6 | 10 | 2 | 8 | 14 | 12 | 16 | 18 | 4 | x | | |

# MAP I4

(48 COURSES)

PAGES.. 470-505

SO-CAL MAP .....see page 466
adjoining maps
NORTH (H4).......see page 426
EAST (I5) ...........see page 506
SOUTH.........................no map
WEST (I3) ..........see page 468

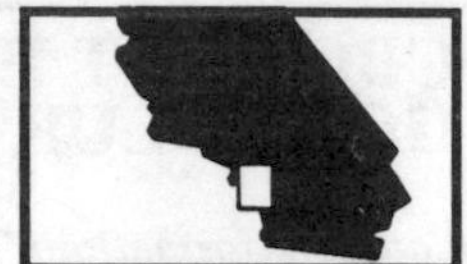

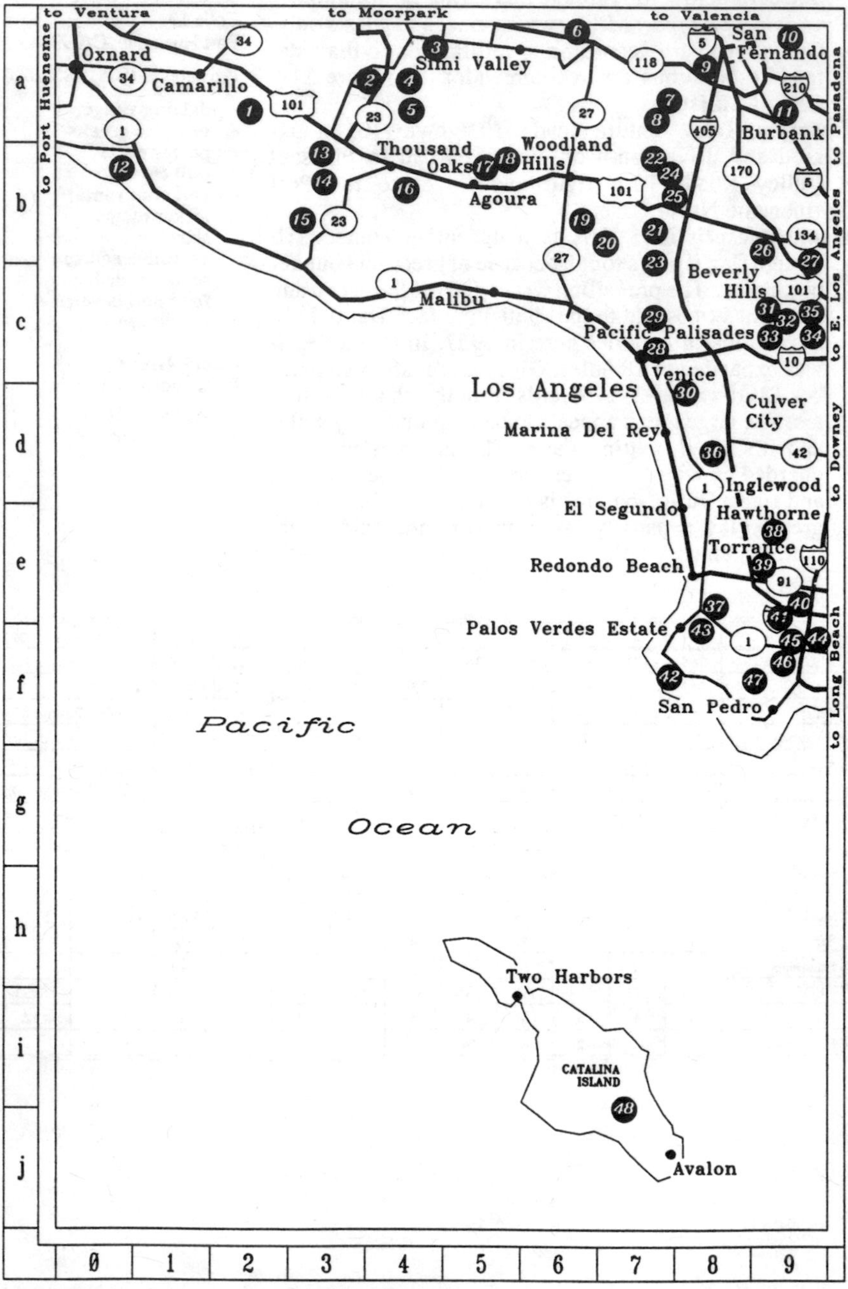

# CAMARILLO SPRINGS GOLF COURSE

**Course 1**
MAP I4 grid a2

**1972**
**Ted Robinson**

***Course information:*** This public course has 18 holes. See card below for yardage and rating information.

***Play policy and fees:*** Green fees are $20 weekdays and $40 weekends, including mandatory cart. Call for special rates. Reservations are required, and can be made 10 days in advance. Carts are $20.

***Location:*** Take the Camarillo Springs Road exit off Highway 101 in Camarillo, and drive south to the course.

***Course description:*** This is a well-maintained, easily walkable course with lots of trees. In 1989, the course underwent a complete reconfiguration. Even the hole sequence was changed. Three holes were altered and another two were changed. Water comes into play on 14 holes. Number six is a knockout. This par-5 is 512 yards from the championship tees and hits looking into a beautiful mountain range. Be straight on this hole, if no other. There are two lakes on the left and one is blind. Out-of-bounds is on the right and so are two fairway bunkers. The green is well trapped.

791 Camarillo Springs Road
Camarillo, CA 93012

Pro shop (805) 484-1075

- ✓ **driving range**
- ✓ **practice greens**
- ✓ **power carts**
- ✓ **pull carts**
- ✓ **golf club rental**
- ✓ **locker rooms**
- ✓ **showers**
- executive course
- accommodations
- ✓ **food and beverages**
- ✓ **clubhouse**

**Ron Stevens**
Manager

**Steve Andreason**
Professional

**Jesse Martinez**
Superintendent

| Hole | 1 | 2 | 3 | 4 | 5 | 6 | 7 | 8 | 9 | Out | BLUE | Rating: 70.2 |
|---|---|---|---|---|---|---|---|---|---|---|---|---|
| BLUE | 372 | 382 | 382 | 379 | 193 | 512 | 377 | 195 | 535 | 3327 | | Slope: 115 |
| WHITE | 345 | 357 | 358 | 352 | 169 | 464 | 331 | 161 | 518 | 3055 | | |
| Par | 4 | 4 | 4 | 4 | 3 | 5 | 4 | 3 | 5 | 36 | WHITE | Rating: 67.9 |
| Handicap | 11 | 9 | 1 | 5 | 15 | 3 | 13 | 7 | 17 | x | | Slope: 108 |
| RED | 322 | 319 | 305 | 330 | 141 | 406 | 286 | 108 | 467 | 2362 | | |
| Par | 4 | 4 | 4 | 4 | 3 | 5 | 4 | 3 | 5 | 36 | RED | Rating: 70.2 |
| Handicap | 9 | 5 | 11 | 7 | 13 | 1 | 15 | 17 | 3 | x | | Slope: 116 |

| Hole | 10 | 11 | 12 | 13 | 14 | 15 | 16 | 17 | 18 | In | Totals | |
|---|---|---|---|---|---|---|---|---|---|---|---|---|
| BLUE | 155 | 342 | 509 | 194 | 169 | 345 | 525 | 334 | 475 | 3048 | BLUE | 6375 |
| WHITE | 145 | 335 | 502 | 168 | 154 | 308 | 496 | 318 | 450 | 2876 | WHITE | 5931 |
| Par | 3 | 4 | 5 | 3 | 3 | 4 | 5 | 4 | 5 | 36 | Par | 72 |
| Handicap | 18 | 16 | 4 | 6 | 14 | 10 | 2 | 12 | 8 | x | | |
| RED | 135 | 329 | 484 | 147 | 115 | 264 | 410 | 299 | 430 | 2613 | RED | 4975 |
| Par | 3 | 4 | 5 | 3 | 3 | 4 | 5 | 4 | 5 | 36 | Par | 72 |
| Handicap | 16 | 8 | 4 | 14 | 18 | 12 | 6 | 10 | 2 | x | | |

## SUNSET HILLS COUNTRY CLUB

**Course 2**
MAP I4 grid a3

**1962**
4155 Erbes Road North
Thousand Oaks, CA 91360

Pro shop (805) 495-5407
Clubhouse (805) 495-6484

- driving range
- ✓ **practice greens**
- ✓ **power carts**
- pull carts
- golf club rental
- ✓ **locker rooms**
- ✓ **showers**
- executive course
- accommodations
- ✓ **food and beverages**
- ✓ **clubhouse**

**Michael Pease**
Manager

**David L.Foster**
Professional

**David Reich**
Superintendent

***Course information:*** This private course has 18 holes and par is 71. The course is 6,066 yards and rated 68.6 from the championship tees, and 5,769 yards and rated 67.4 from the regular tees. The slope ratings are 110 championship and 107 regular. Women's tees are 5,543 yards and rated 73.5. The slope rating is 124.

***Play policy and fees:*** Reciprocal play is accepted with members of other private clubs. Green fees are $35 weekdays and $50 weekends. Carts are $19. Reservations are recommended. This course is available for outside tournaments Mondays only. Tennis is also available. Golfers must wear collared shirts. No jeans allowed. Shorts must have a six-inch inseam.

***Location:*** From Highway 101 (Ventura Freeway), take the Fillmore exit (Highway 23) and drive north for 4.5 miles to Olsen Road. Turn left and drive one-half mile to Erbes Road. Turn left to the club.

***Course description:*** Narrow fairways, fast greens and blind tee shots are characteristic of this well-maintained course. All the holes are fun, but challenging. The course is consistently one of the best-kept in the area.

## SINALOA GOLF COURSE

**Course 3**
MAP I4 grid a4

**1958**
980 Madera Road
Simi, CA 93065

Pro shop (805)581-2662

- ✓ **driving range**
- ✓ **practice greens**
- power carts
- ✓ **pull carts**
- ✓ **golf club rental**
- locker rooms
- showers
- executive course
- accommodations
- food and beverages
- clubhouse

**Angel Lopez**
Professional/Manager

***Course information:*** This public course has nine holes. Par is 54 for 18 holes. The course is a very short 903 yards.

***Play policy and fees:*** Green fees are $4 for nine holes and $8 for 18 holes weekdays, and $4.75 for nine holes and $9.50 for 18 holes weekends. Call for special rates.

***Location:*** From Simi Valley, drive west on Highway 118 to the Madera Road exit, go left and follow the road to the course.

***Course description:*** In the mornings, this is where the area teaching pros come to sharpen their short games. Formerly a citrus ranch, this busy course is under the jurisdiction of the Rancho Simi Valley Recreation Park District.

# WOOD RANCH GOLF CLUB

**Course 4**
MAP 14 grid a4

**1985**
**Ted Robinson**

PO Box 1749
Simi Valley, CA 93065

301 Wood Ranch Parkway
Simi Valley, CA 93065

Pro shop (805) 522-7262
Clubhouse (805) 527-9663

- ✓ **driving range**
- ✓ **practice greens**
- ✓ **power carts**
- pull carts
- ✓ **golf club rental**
- ✓ **locker rooms**
- ✓ **showers**
- executive course
- accommodations
- ✓ **food and beverages**
- ✓ **clubhouse**

**Roger Rockefeller**
Professional

**Angus MacKenzie**
Director

**Gary Priday**
Superintendent

***Course information:*** This private club has 18 holes and par is 72. The course is 6,972 yards and rated 75.8 from the tournament tees, 6,536 yards and rated 72.1 from the championship tees, and 6,126 yards and rated 69.3 from the regular tees. The slope ratings are 151 tournament, 130 championship and 123 regular. Women's tees are 5,392 yards and rated 72.5. The slope rating is 129.

***Play policy and fees:*** No reciprocal play. Guests must be accompanied by a member. Guest fees are $35 weekdays and $75 weekends. Reciprocators are $45 weekdays and $85 weekends. Carts are included. Reservations are recommended. This course is available for outside tournaments on Mondays only.

***Location:*** From Los Angeles, travel north on Highway 101 to Highway 23. Head north to the Olsen Road exit and turn right. At Wood Ranch Parkway, turn right and drive to the club.

***Course description:*** This course is considered one of the toughest in the Los Angeles area. This is an excellent target golf course with water hazards on 11 holes, lots of deep pot bunkers, few trees and deep rough. It's long and demanding with a links-style flavor. The pride of the course is the 464-yard, par-4 16th hole. It drops 120 feet from the tee and requires a testy second shot to a severe, two-tiered green. Designed by Ted Robinson in 1985, the course is rated among the top 20 in the state. The course record from the gold tees is held by Rob Sullivan with a 65. Wood Ranch Golf Club was the site of the 1987 and 1988 GTE West Seniors Classic and the 1986 Pac 10 Golf Championship. A U.S. Amateur qualifier was played here in 1990.



MAP ON PAGE 470

# NORTH RANCH COUNTRY CLUB

**Course 5**
MAP 14 grid a4

4761 Valley Spring Drive
Westlake Village, CA 91362

Pro shop (818) 889-9421
Clubhouse (818) 889-3531

- ✓ **driving range**
- ✓ **practice greens**
- ✓ **power carts**
- pull carts
- ✓ **golf club rental**
- ✓ **locker rooms**
- ✓ **showers**
- executive course
- accommodations
- ✓ **food and beverages**
- ✓ **clubhouse**

**John Shuki**
Professional

**Duff Shaw**
Superintendent

*Course information:* This private club has 27 holes which break into three nines. Par is 72 on each of the 18-hole combinations.

The Valley-Oak Course is 6,678 yards and rated 73.0 from the championship tees, and 6,238 yards and rated 70.4 from the regular tees. The slope ratings are 133 championship and 124 regular. Women's tees are 5,447 yards and unrated.

The Valley-Lake Course is 6,879 yards and rated 72.8 from the championship tees, and 6,352 yards and rated 70.1 from the regular tees. The slope ratings are 124 championship and 117 regular. Women's tees are 5,328 yards and rated 73.4. The slope rating is 129.

The Lake-Oak Course is 6,886 yards and rated 72.4 from the championship tees, and 6,363 yards and rated 69.8 from the regular tees. The slope ratings are 124 championship and 117 regular. Women's tees are 5,379 yards and rated 73.5. The slope rating is 125.

*Play policy and fees:* Members and guests only. Green fees are $40 weekdays and $60 weekends. Carts are $16. Reservations are recommended. This course is available for outside tournaments on Mondays only.

*Location:* Travel north on Highway 101 to the Westlake Boulevard exit and drive north for two miles to Valley Spring Drive. Turn right and drive one mile to the club.

*Course description:* This course is known for its smooth, fast greens and tight fairways. Players who miss the fairway can find themselves in big trouble. The 1988 NCAA Championship was held here. The Southwest Intercollegiate Championships are held here each spring.

# SIMI HILLS GOLF COURSE

**Course 6**
MAP I4 grid a6

*Course information:* This public layout has 18 holes. The women's tees are rated 72.5 with a slope of 121 from the white tees. See card below for additional yardage and rating information.

*Play policy and fees:* Green fees are $13 weekdays and $20 weekends. Call for special rates. Carts are $20. Reservations are recommended and should be made one week in advance. Collared shirts must be worn on the course. Appropriate golf attire required.

*Location:* From Interstate 5 north of Los Angeles, travel west on Highway 118 for about 15 miles to the Stearns Street exit and turn right. Drive to Alamo Street and turn left to the course.

*Course description:* The course makes use of the natural terrain, once the site of a Chumash Indian Reservation. Many of the ancient trees were kept in place to enhance the beauty and increase the difficulty of the course, which winds its way through the hills and valleys. The Simi City Championship is held here in August. Several golf videos have been made at this course including Tom Sharp's *I Hate Golf.*

**1981**
5031 Alamo Street
Simi Valley, CA 93063

Pro shop (805) 991-5178
Clubhouse (805) 522-0813
Fax (805) 520-9379

- ✓ **driving range**
- ✓ **practice greens**
- ✓ **power carts**
- ✓ **pull carts**
- ✓ **golf club rental**
- locker rooms
- showers
- executive course
- accommodations
- ✓ **food and beverages**
- ✓ **clubhouse**

**Tom Szwedzinski**
Professional

**Kent Alkire**
Superintendent

| Hole | 1 | 2 | 3 | 4 | 5 | 6 | 7 | 8 | 9 | Out | | |
|---|---|---|---|---|---|---|---|---|---|---|---|---|
| BLUE | 515 | 391 | 396 | 366 | 362 | 193 | 407 | 180 | 544 | 3354 | BLUE | Rating: 70.5 |
| WHITE | 499 | 367 | 365 | 350 | 340 | 163 | 389 | 158 | 515 | 3146 | | Slope: 115 |
| Par | 5 | 4 | 4 | 4 | 4 | 3 | 4 | 3 | 5 | 36 | WHITE | Rating: 68.7 |
| Handicap | 17 | 3 | 15 | 9 | 5 | 13 | 7 | 11 | 1 | x | | Slope: 110 |
| RED | 462 | 327 | 333 | 313 | 297 | 137 | 349 | 140 | 464 | 2816 | | |
| Par | 5 | 4 | 4 | 4 | 4 | 3 | 4 | 3 | 5 | 36 | RED | Rating: 68.6 |
| Handicap | 13 | 5 | 11 | 9 | 7 | 15 | 1 | 17 | 3 | x | | Slope: 110 |

| Hole | 10 | 11 | 12 | 13 | 14 | 15 | 16 | 17 | 18 | In | Totals | |
|---|---|---|---|---|---|---|---|---|---|---|---|---|
| BLUE | 390 | 541 | 353 | 155 | 308 | 417 | 422 | 182 | 387 | 3155 | BLUE | 6509 |
| WHITE | 363 | 512 | 343 | 146 | 290 | 415 | 398 | 159 | 361 | 2987 | WHITE | 6133 |
| Par | 4 | 5 | 4 | 3 | 4 | 4 | 4 | 3 | 4 | 35 | Par | 71 |
| Handicap | 6 | 12 | 8 | 14 | 16 | 2 | 4 | 18 | 10 | x | | |
| RED | 336 | 467 | 295 | 138 | 260 | 357 | 353 | 137 | 340 | 2683 | RED | 2683 |
| Par | 4 | 5 | 4 | 3 | 4 | 4 | 4 | 3 | 4 | 35 | Par | 71 |
| Handicap | 10 | 2 | 14 | 18 | 16 | 6 | 4 | 12 | 8 | x | | |



MAP ON PAGE 470

# MISSION HILLS LITTLE LEAGUE GOLF COURSE

**Course 7**
MAP I4 grid a7

PO Box 2642
Sepulveda, CA 91343

Pro shop (818) 892-3019

- driving range
- ✓ **practice greens**
- power carts
- ✓ **pull carts**
- ✓ **golf club rental**
- locker rooms
- showers
- ✓ **executive course**
- accommodations
- food and beverages
- clubhouse

**Mike Mancini**
Manager

**Ed Cook**
Professional

*Course information:* This short public course has nine holes. It is 2,254 yards for 18 holes and par is 27.

*Play policy and fees:* Green fees are $3.75 weekdays and $4.75 weekends. Seniors' Day is Friday and Ladies' Day is Tuesday. Both days allow an additional 25-cent discount to these parties.

*Location:* Off Interstate 405, take the Nordoff exit west. Turn right on Woodley and you'll see the course on the hill by the Veteran's Administration Hospital.

*Course description:* This short flat course is good for beginners. A few trees dot the course, but there are no traps. All nine holes are par-3s.

# PORTER VALLEY COUNTRY CLUB

**Course 8**
MAP I4 grid a7

**1969**
19216 Singing Hills Drive
Northridge, CA 91326

Pro shop (818) 368-2919
Clubhouse (818) 360-1071

- ✓ **driving range**
- ✓ **practice greens**
- ✓ **power carts**
- pull carts
- ✓ **golf club rental**
- ✓ **locker rooms**
- ✓ **showers**
- executive course
- ✓ **accommodations**
- ✓ **food and beverages**
- ✓ **clubhouse**

**Ken Hazzard**
General Manager

**Ken Cherry**
Professional

**Kenneth Mentzer**
Superintendent

***Course information:*** This private course has 18 holes. See card below for yardage and rating information.

***Play policy and fees:*** Members and guests only. Green fees are $40 weekdays and $60 weekends. Carts are $19.

***Location:*** Take Interstate 405 to Highway 118 west. In Northridge, get off at Tampa Road and drive to the first light and take Porter Valley Drive to the club.

***Course description:*** This is a short course offering tight fairways and well-bunkered greens. There are a few water hazards. Golfers enjoy a beautiful view of the entire San Fernando Valley, as the course sits up in the hills. But the course itself is especially hilly. It is a fun little course that can be more difficult than it looks.

| Hole | 1 | 2 | 3 | 4 | 5 | 6 | 7 | 8 | 9 | Out | BLUE | Rating: 69.3 |
|---|---|---|---|---|---|---|---|---|---|---|---|---|
| BLUE | 337 | 412 | 139 | 352 | 366 | 391 | 570 | 193 | 395 | 3195 | | Slope: 116 |
| WHITE | 316 | 395 | 135 | 337 | 353 | 381 | 537 | 173 | 377 | 3004 | | |
| Par | 4 | 4 | 3 | 4 | 4 | 4 | 5 | 3 | 4 | 35 | WHITE | Rating: 67.5 |
| Handicap | 9 | 3 | 17 | 7 | 13 | 11 | 1 | 15 | 5 | x | | Slope: 113 |
| RED | 275 | 380 | 113 | 323 | 335 | 377 | 486 | 169 | 367 | 2825 | | |
| Par | 4 | 4 | 3 | 4 | 4 | 4 | 5 | 3 | 4 | 35 | RED | Rating: 69.1 |
| Handicap | 14 | 6 | 18 | 12 | 10 | 8 | 2 | 16 | 4 | x | | Slope: 115 |

| Hole | 10 | 11 | 12 | 13 | 14 | 15 | 16 | 17 | 18 | In | Totals | |
|---|---|---|---|---|---|---|---|---|---|---|---|---|
| BLUE | 504 | 277 | 200 | 455 | 217 | 377 | 176 | 328 | 401 | 2935 | BLUE | 6090 |
| WHITE | 488 | 260 | 176 | 433 | 200 | 341 | 160 | 321 | 386 | 2749 | WHITE | 5775 |
| Par | 5 | 4 | 3 | 5 | 3 | 4 | 3 | 4 | 4 | 35 | Par | 70 |
| Handicap | 2 | 18 | 14 | 10 | 4 | 8 | 16 | 12 | 6 | x | | |
| RED | 476 | 253 | 160 | 411 | 186 | 333 | 145 | 313 | 374 | 2651 | RED | 5476 |
| Par | 5 | 4 | 3 | 5 | 3 | 4 | 3 | 4 | 4 | 35 | Par | 70 |
| Handicap | 1 | 13 | 15 | 3 | 11 | 9 | 17 | 5 | 7 | x | | |

# KNOLLWOOD GOLF COURSE

**Course 9**
MAP I4 grid a8

***Course information:*** This public course has 18 holes and par is 72. The course is 6,597 yards and rated 70.7 from the championship tees, and 6,234 yards and rated 69.2 from the regular tees. The slope ratings are 155 championship and 112 regular. Women's tees are 5,838 yards and rated 72.3. The slope rating is 113.

***Play policy and fees:*** Green fees are $15.50 weekdays and $19.50 weekends for 18 holes. Carts are $18. Reservations are recommended.

***Location:*** From Los Angeles, take Interstate 5 north to Highway 118. Go west and exit at Balboa Boulevard, then go north three-fourths of a mile to the course.

***Course description:*** None of the holes on this course overlap. Instead they run single file through a string of homes. Many fairway shots will be uphill making it tough to judge distance. You might see a celebrity or two on this course. Among the notables who have made an appearance here are Bob Hope, Mickey Rooney, Claude Akins, Joe Don Baker, Omar Bradley and Bret Saberhagen. If you want to swap hole-in-one stories, ask for starter Ron Fitt. This 80-year-old has aced numbers eight, 13 and 17. He might even tell you about Roy Watts who hit his tee shot out-of-bounds at the 306-yard, par-4 14th hole, then teed up again and made a hole-in-one, giving him a birdie three on the hole. Dave Berganio holds the men's course record with a 64. Donna Caponi holds the women's record with a 70. Holes one and 10 were selected among the best 18 holes in the San Fernando Valley.

**1956**
**William Francis Bell**

12040 Balboa Boulevard
Granada Hills, CA 91344

Pro shop (818) 368-5709
Clubhouse (818) 363-8161
Starter (818) 363-8161

- ✓ **driving range**
- ✓ **practice greens**
- ✓ **power carts**
- ✓ **pull carts**
- ✓ **golf club rental**
- locker rooms
- showers
- executive course
- accommodations
- ✓ **food and beverages**
- ✓ **clubhouse**

**Rich Taylor**
Manager

**Brain Bode**
Professional

**Scott Williams**
Superintendent

## EL CARISO GOLF COURSE

**Course 10**
MAP I4 grid a9

**1975**
13100 Elridge Avenue
Sylmar, CA 91342

Pro shop (818) 367-6157
Clubhouse (818) 367-8742

- ✓ **driving range**
- ✓ **practice greens**
- ✓ **power carts**
- ✓ **pull carts**
- ✓ **golf club rental**
- locker rooms
- showers
- ✓ **executive course**
- accommodations
- ✓ **food and beverages**
- ✓ **clubhouse**

**Ed Anshem**
Professional/Manager

**Louie Acosta**
Superintendent

***Course information:*** This public course has 18 holes and par is 62. The course is 4,483 yards and rated 60.2 from the championship tees, and 4,065 yards and rated 58.3 from the regular tees. The slope ratings are 98 championship and 94 regular. Women's yardage is 3,557 and rated 58.9. The slope rating is 87.

***Play policy and fees:*** Green fees are $12 weekdays and $16 weekends. Call for special twilight and senior rates. Carts are $17. Reservations are recommended.

***Location:*** Take Interstate 210 to Hubbard exit and go east for one mile. At Elridge Avenue turn right and go three blocks to the course.

***Course description:*** A well-placed tee shot is important on this course. Five lakes come into play and each green is well-bunkered. Number five is a tough 389-yard par-4 that doglegs left and has water to the right. It is a fun little course where distance is not a factor.

## HANSEN DAM GOLF COURSE

**Course 11**
MAP I4 grid a9

10400 Glen Oaks Boulevard
Pacoima, CA 91331

Pro shop (818) 899-2200
Clubhouse (818) 899-7456

- ✓ **driving range**
- ✓ **practice greens**
- ✓ **power carts**
- ✓ **pull carts**
- ✓ **golf club rental**
- locker rooms
- showers
- executive course
- accommodations
- ✓ **food and beverages**
- ✓ **clubhouse**

**Jim Anderson**
Professional

**Tom Kornkben**
Superintendent

***Course information:*** This public course has 18 holes and par is 72. The course is 6,591 yards and rated 69.6 from the championship tees, and 6,266 yards and rated 68.1 from the regular tees. The slope ratings are 121 championship and 111 regular. Women's tees are 6,090 yards and rated 75.0. The slope rating is 121.

***Play policy and fees:*** Green fees are $12 weekdays and $16 weekends. Call for special rates. Carts are $17. Reservations are recommended. This course is available for outside tournaments.

***Location:*** From Interstate 5, take Osborne and go east 1.5 miles to Glen Oaks. Turn right to Montague and turn left to the course.

***Course description:*** This course plays longer than it looks. Big hitters must be careful about staying on the fairways. The greens tend to be small so chipping skills are important. The ninth hole is the number-one handicap hole on this course. It's a par-4, 450-yard stretch from the championship tee that requires the second shot to carry over a little dip and onto an elevated green.

## POINT MUGU GOLF CLUB

**Course 12**
MAP I4 grid b0

*Course information:* This military course has nine holes. Par is 70 for 18 holes. The course is 5,908 yards and rated 66.8 from the regular tees. The slope rating is 102.

*Play policy and fees:* Military personnel and guests only. Green fees vary according to military or civilian status.

*Location:* Take the Wood Road-USN Point Mugu exit off Highway 1 north of Camarillo Beach. Obtain a guest pass from the Visitor Information Center and enter the base at Mugu Road. Turn right at Third Street and drive to the course.

*Course description:* This course is wide open and flat for the most part. Four water hazards line the course, but the biggest obstacle is the sound of low-flying aircraft going to and from the nearby airstrip. Bring ear plugs. The course is neither long nor difficult.

PO Box 42287
NAS Point Mugu,
CA 93041

Pro shop (805) 989-7109

- ✓ **driving range**
- ✓ **practice greens**
- ✓ **power carts**
- ✓ **pull carts**
- ✓ **golf club rental**
- locker rooms
- showers
- executive course
- accommodations
- ✓ **food and beverages**
- ✓ **clubhouse**

**Gerry Garcia**
Professional/Manager/
Superintendent

## LOS ROBLES GOLF AND COUNTRY CLUB

**Course 13**
MAP I4 grid b3

**1965**
299 South Moorpark Road
Thousand Oaks, CA 91361

Pro shop (805) 495-6421

- ✓ **driving range**
- ✓ **practice greens**
- ✓ **power carts**
- ✓ **pull carts**
- ✓ **golf club rental**
- ✓ **locker rooms**
- ✓ **showers**
- executive course
- accommodations
- ✓ **food and beverages**
- ✓ **clubhouse**

**Bob Meyer**
Professional

**Alex Alvidrez**
Superintendent

*Course information:* This public course has 18 holes and par is 70. The course is 6,264 yards and rated 69.4 from the championship tees, and 5,868 yards and rated 67.0 from the regular tees. The slope ratings are 118 championship and 110 regular. Women's tees are 5,333 yards and rated 70.1. The slope rating is 117.

*Play policy and fees:* Green fees are $12 weekdays and $15 weekends, for Thosand Oaks residents, and $15 weekdays and $20 weekends for non-residents. Call for special rates. Carts are $16. Reservations are recommended. Golfers must wear appropriate golf attire.

*Location:* Travel north on Highway 101 (Ventura Freeway) to the Moorpark Road exit and turn left under the freeway. Drive one block and turn right to the club.

*Course description:* This is a moderately hilly course with three lakes and fairways flanked by trees. There are six par-3s. The Thousand Oaks City Championships is played here each August. The course features a variety of different holes, requiring players to both fade and draw the ball. It is a scenic course with many old oak trees. The course is in excellent condition considering the 120,000 rounds played here annually.

# SHERWOOD COUNTRY CLUB

**Course 14**
MAP I4 grid b3

**1989**
**Jack Nicklaus**

320 West Stafford Road
Thousand Oaks, CA 91361

Pro shop (805) 496-3036

- ✓ **driving range**
- ✓ **practice greens**
- ✓ **power carts**
- ✓ **pull carts**
- ✓ **golf club rental**
- ✓ **locker rooms**
- ✓ **showers**
- executive course
- accommodations
- ✓ **food and beverages**
- ✓ **clubhouse**

**Tom Barnard**
General Manager

**Ron Rhoads**
Professional

**Gary Davis**
Assistant Professional

***Course information:*** This private club has 18 holes and par is 72. The course is 7,025 yards from the tournament tees and rated 75.7, 6,594 yards from the championship tees and rated 72.9, and 6,003 from the regular tees and rated 69.5. The slope ratings are 146 tournament, 136 championship and 127 regular. Women's tees are 5,278 yards and rated at 65.5. The slope rating is 111.

***Play policy and fees:*** Members and guests only. Guests must be accompanied by a member. This club is not reciprocal. Guest fees are $40 weekdays and $60 weekends. Caddies are required. Closed Mondays.

***Location:*** Take Highway 101 to Westlake Boulevard, then drive south two miles to Potrero Road. Turn right and drive three miles to Stafford Road and left to the club.

***Course description:*** This course is the site of the annual Franklin Funds Shark Shootout hosted by Greg Norman, held in November. It was built on the site used for the original movie, "Robin Hood," a spectacular setting with huge oak trees that have been there for more than 100 years. Nicklaus designed the course so that it appears to have been there that long as well, though it opened in 1989. It is a typical Nicklaus layout, featuring flawless bent grass greens and fairways, several holes that favor the left-to-right player (of which Nickalus is one), and tiered greens surrounded by severe slopes and mounds certain to penalize those who miss them with approach shots. The course's signature hole is the 186-yard par-3 sixth. From an elevated tee, the tee shot must carry a series of seven ponds, pools and waterfalls and hold a wide, but shallow green. This course is one of Nicklaus' best creations. It features one of the poshest clubhouses in the country, constructed at a cost of $40 million.



MAP ON PAGE 470

## MALIBU COUNTRY CLUB

**Course 15**
MAP I4 grid b3

901 Encinal Canyon Road
Malibu, CA 90265

Pro shop (818) 889-6680

- driving range
- ✓ practice greens
- ✓ power carts
- pull carts
- ✓ golf club rental
- ✓ locker rooms
- ✓ showers
- executive course
- accommodations
- ✓ food and beverages
- ✓ clubhouse

**Ken Domino**
Professional

**Todd Matsumoto**
Superintendent

***Course information:*** This public course has 18 holes and par is 72. The course is 6,800 yards and rated 72.3 from the championship tees, and 6,282 yards and rated 69.3 from the regular tees. The slope ratings are 130 championship and 121 regular. Women's tees are 5,627 yards. Women's ratings were unavailable.

***Play policy and fees:*** Green fees are $45 weekdays and $65 weekends, carts included. No jeans or T-shirts.

***Location:*** Off Highway 101 in Malibu, exit on Kanan Road and drive 10 miles toward the beach. After the second tunnel, turn right on Mulholland Highway. When the road forks, stay left. You'll see the course in two miles on your right. It's on Encinal Canyon Road.

***Course description:*** Nestled in the Santa Monica Mountains, this hilly course can get warm since the hills block the ocean breezes. The ocean is not visible from this canyon course.

## WESTLAKE VILLAGE GOLF COURSE

**Course 16**
MAP I4 grid b4

PO Box 4216
Westlake Village, CA 91359

4812 Lakeview Canyon Road
Westlake Village, CA 91361

Pro shop (818) 889-0770
Pro shop (805) 495-8437

- ✓ driving range
- ✓ practice greens
- ✓ power carts
- ✓ pull carts
- ✓ golf club rental
- locker rooms
- showers
- ✓ executive course
- accommodations
- ✓ food and beverages
- ✓ clubhouse

**Ron Hinds**
Professional

**Rodolpho Ruiz**
Superintendent

***Course information:*** This public facility has 18 holes and par is 67. The course is a shortish 5,109 yards and rated 63.2 from the championship tees, and 4,668 yards and rated 61.1 from the regular tees. The slope ratings are 93 championship and 88 regular. Women's tees are 4,790 yards and rated 66.6. The slope rating is 113.

***Play policy and fees:*** Green fees are $14 weekdays and $22 weekends. Call for special rates. Carts are $17. Reservations are recommended.

***Location:*** Travel north on Highway 101 (Ventura Freeway) and take the Lindero Canyon Road exit. Drive south to Agoura Road and turn right. Continue three-fourths of a mile to Lakeview Canyon Road, and turn right to the course.

***Course description:*** This course offers well-kept greens, three lakes and scenic, tree-lined fairways, but it's the trees that make this course competitive and tough. Slice or hook and you're a dead golfer looking for a way to get back on the course. There are seven par-3s, nine par-4s and two par-5s. The par-5s, thankfully, are straight.

## LAKE LINDERO GOLF CLUB

**Course 17**
MAP I4 grid b5

5719 Lake Lindero Drive
Agoura, CA 91301

Pro shop (818) 889-1158

- driving range
- ✓ **practice greens**
- power carts
- ✓ **pull carts**
- ✓ **golf club rental**
- locker rooms
- showers
- executive course
- accommodations
- food and beverages
- ✓ **clubhouse**

**Tom Forman**
Professional

**Rafael Guillen**
Superintendent

***Course information:*** This semi-private course has nine holes. Par is 58 for 18 holes. The course is 3,338 yards and rated 52.9 from the regular tees. The slope rating is 90. Women's tees are 2,770 yards. There is no slope rating.

***Play policy and fees:*** Outside play is accepted. Green fees are $9.50 weekdays and $11.50 weekends. Call for special rates. This course is available for outside tournaments.

***Location:*** Travel north on Highway 101 (Ventura Freeway) to the Reyes Adobe exit. Turn right and drive to Thousand Oaks Boulevard. Turn left and continue to Lake Lindero Drive. The course will be on your left.

***Course description:*** This is a tight, but rolling course with lots of trees and relatively small greens. Don't expect to tear this course up with a big game. Accuracy counts. The toughest hole is the par-3, 178-yard number three. You must hit from a slightly elevated tee to a small green guarded on the right by a huge oak and bunker. To the left, there is an embankment that leads to a creek that flows through the course. Like all the holes on this course, if you're not where you should be with your tee shot, on or near the green, you're in trouble. There are two par-4s.

## CALABASAS PARK COUNTRY CLUB

**Course 18**
MAP I4 grid b6

4515 Park Entrada
Calabasas Park, CA 91302

Pro shop (818) 222-3222
Clubhouse (818) 222-3200

- ✓ **driving range**
- ✓ **practice greens**
- ✓ **power carts**
- ✓ **pull carts**
- ✓ **golf club rental**
- ✓ **locker rooms**
- ✓ **showers**
- executive course
- accommodations
- ✓ **food and beverages**
- ✓ **clubhouse**

**David Bartholomew**
Professional

**Ron Parker**
Superintendent

***Course information:*** This private course has 18 holes and par is 72. The course is 6,327 yards and rated 70.7 from the championship tees, and 6,082 yards and rated 69.6 from the regular tees. The slope ratings are 128 championship and 123 regular. Women's tees are 5,601 yards and rated 72.0. The slope rating is 122.

***Play policy and fees:*** Reciprocal play is accepted with members of other private clubs, otherwise members and guests only. Green fees are $39 weekdays and $70 weekends, cart included. Reservations are recommended. Closed Mondays.

***Location:*** Travel north on Highway 101 (Ventura Freeway) to Parkway Calabasas and turn at the first right and drive to the club.

***Course description:*** This 25-year-old layout is located in a rapidly developing residential area. It is well maintained with many trees, some lakes and rolling terrain, and though it isn't especially long, it can be difficult.

## WOODLAND HILLS COUNTRY CLUB

**Course 19**
MAP I4 grid b6

**1924**
**William Park Bell**

21150 Dumetz Road
Woodland Hills, CA 91364

Pro shop (818) 347-1476
Clubhouse: (818) 347-1511

- driving range
- ✓ **practice greens**
- ✓ **power carts**
- pull carts
- golf club rental
- ✓ **locker rooms**
- ✓ **showers**
- executive course
- accommodations
- ✓ **food and beverages**
- ✓ **clubhouse**

**Kerry Hopps**
Professional

**Vincent Vazquez**
Superintendent

*Course information:* This private club has 18 holes and par is 70. The course is 6,193 yards and rated 70.2 from the championship tees, and 5,954 yards and rated 68.8 from the regular tees. The slope ratings are 123 championship and 119 regular. Women's tees are 5,708 yards and rated 72.7. The slope rating is 124.

*Play policy and fees:* Members and guests only. Green fees are $30 weekdays and $45 weekends. Carts are $15. Closed Mondays.

*Location:* Travel north on Highway 101 (Ventura Freeway) in Woodland Hills to the DeSoto Avenue exit. Drive south past Ventura Boulevard three-fourths of a mile to Dumetz Road and turn right, then drive one-fourth of a mile to the club.

*Course description:* This course is located in a park-like setting with rolling hills and oak trees. The greens are among the most severe in Southern California; it is advisable to leave the ball below the hole, or you probably will pay a penalty of three putts.

## BRAEMAR COUNTRY CLUB

**Course 20**
MAP I4 grid b7

**1959**
**Ted Robinson**
**(West Course)**

PO Box 217
Tarzana, CA 91356

4001 Reseda Boulevard
Tarzana, CA 91356

Pro shop (818) 345-6520

- driving range
- ✓ **practice greens**
- ✓ **power carts**
- pull carts
- ✓ **golf club rental**
- ✓ **locker rooms**
- ✓ **showers**
- executive course
- accommodations
- ✓ **food and beverages**
- ✓ **clubhouse**

**Kevin Coombs**
Professional

**Richard Ray**
Superintendent

*Course information:* This private club has two 18-hole courses.

The East Course is par 70, 6,021 yards and rated 70.1 from the championship tees, and 5,776 yards and rated 68.7 from the regular tees. The slope ratings are 129 championship and 120 regular. Women's tees are 5,386 yards and rated 71.9. The slope rating is 127.

The West Course is par 71, 5,857 yards and rated 68.7 from the championship tees, and 5,593 yards and rated 67.3 from the regular tees. The slope ratings are 123 championship and 117 regular. Women's tees are 5,306 yards and rated 69.6, with a slope rating of 111.

*Play policy and fees:* Members and guests only. Green fees are $35 weekdays and $55 weekends. Carts are $19. This course is available for outside tournaments. No jeans or short shorts are allowed on the course. Men must wear collared shirts.

*Location:* Travel north on Highway 101 (Ventura Freeway) and take the Reseda Boulevard exit. Drive south for 2.5 miles to the end and turn right.

*Course description:* Both courses are short, tight and hilly. There are mature trees and a few parallel fairways. There is virtually no room for error because of a plethora of out-of-bounds, water hazards and other assorted obstacles.

# EL CABALLERO COUNTRY CLUB

**Course 21**
MAP I4 grid b7

***Course information:*** This private course has 18 holes. See card below for yardage and rating information.

***Play policy and fees:*** Members and guests only. Guests must be accompanied by a member. Green fees are $30 weekdays and $60 weekends. Carts are $16. Closed Mondays.

***Location:*** Traveling north on Highway 101 (Ventura Freeway) in Tarzana, exit on Reseda Boulevard south (it becomes Mecca Avenue). At Tarzana Drive, turn left to the club.

***Course description:*** This rolling course is challenging with large greens. It is one of the highest slope-rated courses in Southern California.

PO Box 570338
Tarzana, CA 91357-0338

18300 Tarzana Drive
Tarzana, CA 91356

Pro shop (818) 345-2770
Fax (818)345-3486

- ✓ **driving range**
- ✓ **practice greens**
- ✓ **power carts**
- ✓ **pull carts**
- golf club rental
- ✓ **locker rooms**
- ✓ **showers**
- executive course
- accommodations
- ✓ **food and beverages**
- ✓ **clubhouse**

**Terry Lange**
Professional

**John M. Pollok**
Superintendent

**Seymour Chernoy**
Manager

SOUTHERN I4

| Hole | 1 | 2 | 3 | 4 | 5 | 6 | 7 | 8 | 9 | Out | BLUE | Rating: 73.7 |
|---|---|---|---|---|---|---|---|---|---|---|---|---|
| BLUE | 510 | 434 | 383 | 407 | 361 | 216 | 514 | 212 | 456 | 3493 | | Slope: 139 |
| WHITE | 498 | 412 | 374 | 377 | 341 | 175 | 5002 | 181 | 425 | 3285 | | |
| Par | 5 | 4 | 4 | 4 | 4 | 3 | 5 | 3 | 4 | 36 | WHITE | Rating: 71.1 |
| Handicap (b/w) | 11/5 | 1/1 | 7/9 | 5/7 | 15/13 | 9/17 | 17/11 | 13/15 | 3/3 | x | | Slope: 128 |
| RED | 473 | 393 | 357 | 346 | 285 | 133 | 495 | 137 | 390 | 3009 | | |
| Par | 5 | 4 | 4 | 4 | 4 | 3 | 5 | 3 | 4 | 36 | RED | Rating: 74.8 |
| Handicap | 5 | 1 | 11 | 9 | 13 | 15 | 3 | 17 | 7 | x | | Slope: 130 |

| Hole | 10 | 11 | 12 | 13 | 14 | 15 | 16 | 17 | 18 | In | Totals | |
|---|---|---|---|---|---|---|---|---|---|---|---|---|
| BLUE | 167 | 402 | 528 | 381 | 386 | 419 | 173 | 458 | 423 | 3337 | BLUE | 6830 |
| WHITE | 143 | 383 | 503 | 364 | 363 | 397 | 151 | 425 | 404 | 3133 | WHITE | 6418 |
| Par | 3 | 4 | 5 | 4 | 4 | 4 | 3 | 4 | 4 | 35 | Par | 71 |
| Handicap (b/w) | 14/16 | 4/8 | 12/6 | 16/14 | 10/12 | 6/4 | 18/18 | 2/2 | 8/10 | x | | |
| RED | 121 | 337 | 468 | 333 | 348 | 369 | 124 | 415 | 379 | 2895 | RED | 5904 |
| Par | 3 | 4 | 5 | 4 | 4 | 4 | 3 | 5 | 4 | 36 | Par | 72 |
| Handicap | 16 | 12 | 2 | 14 | 4 | 8 | 18 | 10 | 6 | x | | |

# VAN NUYS GOLF COURSE

**Course 22**
MAP I4 grid b7

*Course information:* This public course has one nine-hole executive course and one 18-hole course. Par is 30 for nine holes and 54 for 18 holes. The 18-hole course is a short 2,181 yards and the nine-hole course is 1,691 yards.

*Play policy and fees:* Green fees are $5.50 weekdays and $6.50 weekends for nine holes; they are $8.50 weekdays and $9 weekends for 18 holes. Pull carts are $1. Call for special rates. Reservations may be made up to seven days in advance.

*Location:* Off Interstate 405 in Van Nuys, take the Sherman Way exit west. Turn left on Balboa and the course is on your left.

*Course description:* The executive course is one of the prominent par-3 courses in the area. The longest hole on this pitch-and-putt is 142 yards. Average playing time is under two hours. The 18-hole course is lined with trees and is relatively flat. There are lakes and ducks. The course is good for beginners.

6550 Odessa Avenue
Van Nuys, CA 91406

Pro shop (818) 785-8871

✓ **driving range**
✓ **practice greens**
power carts
✓ **pull carts**
✓ **golf club rental**
locker rooms
showers
✓ **executive course**
accommodations
✓ **food and beverages**
✓ **clubhouse**

**Chuck Piecha**
Professional

**Billy Feliz**
Superintendent

# MOUNTAINGATE COUNTRY CLUB

**Course 23**
MAP 14 grid b7

12445 Mountain Gate Dr.
Los Angeles, CA 90049

Pro shop (310) 476-2800
Clubhouse (310) 476-6215

- ✓ **driving range**
- ✓ **practice greens**
- ✓ **power carts**
- pull carts
- ✓ **golf club rental**
- ✓ **locker rooms**
- ✓ **showers**
- executive course
- accommodations
- ✓ **food and beverages**
- ✓ **clubhouse**

**Mike Miller**
Professional

**David Bermudez**
Superintendent

***Course information:*** This private course has 27 holes and par is 72 for each 18-hole combination.

The South/Lake Course is 6,770 yards and rated 72.9 from the championship tees, and 6,373 yards and rated 70.5 from the regular tees. The slope ratings are 129 championship and 122 regular. Women's tees are 5,698 yards and rated 73.3. The slope rating is 124.

The North/South Course is 6,694 yards and rated 72.0 from the championship tees, and 6,335 yards and rated 70.2 from the regular tees. The slope ratings are 128 championship and 121 regular. Women's tees are 5,711 yards and rated 73.2. The slope rating is 124.

The Lake/North Course is 6,410 yards and rated 70.4 from the championship tees, and 6,040 yards and rated 68.5 from the regular tees. The slope ratings are 118 championship and 110 regular. Women's tees are 5,517 yards and rated 71.8. The slope rating is 122.

***Play policy and fees:*** Reciprocal play is accepted with members of other private clubs (ask your pro to call), otherwise members and guests only. Green fees are $60 weekdays and $105 weekends. Carts are $12. Reservations are recommended. This course is available for outside tournaments on Mondays only.

***Location:*** Travel north on Interstate 405 to the Getty Center exit. Follow the exit to Sepulveda Boulevard and turn left, driving 1.5 miles to Mountain Gate Drive. From there, turn left to the club.

***Course description:*** This is a fairly new course with rolling fairways and difficult, undulating greens. The South in general is the most difficult of the courses to play. There are elevated greens and rolling hills. Don't expect to get a flat lie wherever you hit. The Senior PGA Tour has held tournaments here in the past few years, including the Johnny Mathis Classic and the GTE Senior Classic.

## WOODLEY LAKES GOLF COURSE

**Course 24**
MAP 14 grid b8

6331 Woodley Avenue
Van Nuys, CA 91406

Pro shop (818) 787-8163
Starter (818) 780-6886

- ✓ **driving range**
- ✓ **practice greens**
- ✓ **power carts**
- ✓ **pull carts**
- ✓ **golf club rental**
- locker rooms
- showers
- executive course
- accommodations
- ✓ **food and beverages**
- ✓ **clubhouse**

**John Perkins**
Professional

**Bob Davis**
Superintendent

***Course information:*** This public course has 18 holes and par is 72. The course is 6,782 yards and rated 70.9 from the championship tees, and 6,545 yards and rated 69.8 from the regular tees. The slope ratings are 111 championship and 109 regular. Women's tees are 6,242 yards and rated 74.3. The slope is 112.

***Play policy and fees:*** Green fees are $12 weekdays and $15 weekends. Carts are $16. Players must have a Los Angeles Parks and Recreation reservation card.

***Location:*** From Interstate 405 in Van Nuys, exit at Victory Boulevard and drive one-half mile to Woodley Avenue. From there, go left and drive to the course. The course is located about two miles from Van Nuys Airport.

***Course description:*** This is a relatively long and flat course with large greens. Many of the greens are elevated. The course is not too demanding unless you hit into one or more of its six lakes. The course record, 62, was set by former UCLA golfer, Duffy Waldorf, now a PGA Tour star.

## SEPULVEDA GOLF COURSE

**Course 25**
MAP 14 grid b8

**1953**
**William Park Bell**

16821 Burbank Boulevard
Encino, CA 91436

Pro shop (818) 986-4560
Starter (818) 995-1170

- ✓ **driving range**
- ✓ **practice greens**
- ✓ **power carts**
- ✓ **pull carts**
- ✓ **golf club rental**
- locker rooms
- ✓ **showers**
- executive course
- accommodations
- ✓ **food and beverages**
- ✓ **clubhouse**

**Dave Jenkins**
Professional

**Steve Ball**
Superintendent

***Course information:*** This public facility has two 18-hole courses.

The Balboa Course is par 70, 6,328 yards from the championship tees and rated 68.4, and 6,088 yards from the regular tees and rated 67.3. The slope ratings are 119 championship and 117 regular. Women's tees are 5,890 yards and rated 71.7. The slope rating is 117.

The Encino Course is par 72, 6,863 yards from the championship tees and rated 70.5, and 6,408 yards from the regular tees and rated 68.4. The slope ratings are 105 championship and 100 regular. Women's tees are 6,185 yards and rated 73.7. The slope rating is 119.

***Play policy and fees:*** Green fees are $12 weekdays and $16.50 weekends. Carts are $17. Reservations are recommended, but can only be made by holders of a Los Angeles Park and Recreation reservation card.

***Location:*** Take Highway 134 to the Burbank Boulevard exit in Encino, and go right about one-half mile.

***Course description:*** The Balboa course is long and demanding. Shot placement is crucial. The greens are bunkered. There are overhanging trees. It is a good test of golf skill for the intermediate player. The Encino Course, although longer, is much easier. It's wide open. However, it was closed for nine months in 1992, because of flooding during heavy rain storms in Southern California in February. The Balboa Course was not damaged.

## STUDIO CITY GOLF COURSE

**Course 26**
MAP I4 grid b9

*Course information:* This public track has nine holes. Par is 54 for 18 holes. The course is 975 yards for nine holes.

*Play policy and fees:* Green fees are $5.50 weekdays and $6.50 weekends and holidays.

*Location:* Take Highway 134 to Whitsett Avenue in Studio City and turn left and drive about two miles to the course.

*Course description:* This is a nine-hole, par-3 course with no hole longer than 135 yards. The adjoining driving range is open until 11 p.m. For those interested in a quick set of tennis, a tennis club is affiliated with the golf course.

4141 Whitsett Avenue
Studio City, CA 91604

Pro shop (818) 761-3250

- ✓ **driving range**
- ✓ **practice greens**
- power carts
- ✓ **pull carts**
- ✓ **golf club rental**
- locker rooms
- showers
- ✓ **executive course**
- accommodations
- ✓ **food and beverages**
- ✓ **clubhouse**

## LAKESIDE GOLF CLUB

**Course 27**
MAP I4 grid b9

**1926**
**Max Behr**

*Course information:* This private course has 18 holes and par is 70. The course is 6,534 yards and rated 71.9 from the championship tees, and 6,272 yards and rated 70.1 from the regular tees. The slope ratings are 129 championship and 121 regular. Women's tees are 5,949 yards and rated 74.3. The slope rating is 123.

*Play policy and fees:* Members and guests only. Guests must accompany a member. Guests fees are $35.

*Location:* Travel north on Highway 101 (Hollywood Freeway) to the Barham Boulevard exit, and drive north to Lakeside Drive. From there, turn left and drive to the club. Or, take Ventura Boulevard (Highway 134) to Pass Avenue south, crossing Riverside to Lakeside Drive. Turn right to the club.

*Course description:* Built in 1926, this rolling course has small undulating greens. It is a short-yardage course, but plays long. These fairways were once a haven for Hollywood's heroes and rogues: Bing Crosby, Dean Martin, Bob Hope and just about anybody else who ever had a golf tournament named for them played a round or two here. The Maury Luxford Pro-Am is held here each August. The Trans-Mississippi Mid-Amateur Championship was held here in 1991.

PO Box 2386
Toluca Lake Station
Toluca Lake, CA 91610

4500 Lakeside Drive
Burbank, CA 91602

Pro shop (818) 985-3335
Clubhouse (818) 984-0601

- ✓ **driving range**
- ✓ **practice greens**
- ✓ **power carts**
- pull carts
- ✓ **golf club rental**
- ✓ **locker rooms**
- ✓ **showers**
- executive course
- accommodations
- ✓ **food and beverages**
- ✓ **clubhouse**

**Dave Allaire**
Professional

**Brent Weston**
Superintendent

# THE RIVIERA COUNTRY CLUB

**Course 28**
MAP I4 grid c7

***Course information:*** This private course has 18 holes and par is 72. The course is 7,016 yards and rated 75.7 from the championship tees, and 6,522 yards and rated 72.4 from the regular tees. Women's yardage is 5,942 and rated 74.4. The slope ratings are 142 championship, 135 regular and 131 women.

***Play policy and fees:*** Limited reciprocal play is accepted with members of other private clubs. Hotel guests are welcome. Green fees for unattended guests are $150. The fee for hotel guests is $150. Green fees for guests playing with members is $75 weekdays and $90 weekends. Reservations are essential. This course is available for outside tournaments Mondays only.

***Location:*** Take the Sunset Boulevard exit off Interstate 405 and travel west for three miles to Capri Drive, then turn left to the club.

***Course description:*** This well-maintained course is more than 60 years old and has been played by scores of Hollywood's rich and famous. George C. Thomas designed the long and tough layout in 1926. The fairways and rough are planted with Kikuyu grass so there's not much roll. The 170-yard par-3 sixth hole features a bunker in the middle of the green. If that doesn't frighten you, maybe the par-4 18th will. It is considered one of the toughest holes in golf. The 1948 U.S. Open was played here and won by the great Ben Hogan, and Hal Sutton captured the 1983 PGA crown here. Hogan also won the LA Open here in 1947 and 1948, and the course became known as Hogan's Alley. The Los Angeles Open is played here annually. This course is rated among the top 20 in the state for good reason. The course record of 62 is jointly held by Larry Mize and Fred Couples. The 72-hole tournament record of 264 is held by Lanny Wadkins, set in the 1985 Los Angeles Open. It is the site of the 1995 PGA Championship.

**1926**
**George C. Thomas**

1250 Capri Drive
Pacific Palisades, CA 90272

Operations (310) 454-6591

- ✓ **driving range**
- ✓ **practice greens**
- ✓ **power carts**
- pull carts
- ✓ **golf club rental**
- ✓ **locker rooms**
- ✓ **showers**
- executive course
- ✓ **accommodations**
- ✓ **food and beverages**
- ✓ **clubhouse**

**Peter Oosterhuis**
Director of Golf

**Jim McPhilomy**
Superintendent

## BRENTWOOD COUNTRY CLUB

**Course 29**
MAP I4 grid c7

*Course information:* This private course has 18 holes and par is 72. The course is 6,734 yards and rated 72.3 from the championship tees, and 6,524 yards and rated 70.6 from the regular tees. Women's yardage is 6,035 and rated 68.1. The slope ratings are 124 championship, 117 regular and 110 women.

*Play policy and fees:* Members and guests only. Green fees are $35 weekdays and $50 weekends. Carts are $20.

*Location:* Travel west on Wilshire Boulevard to San Vincente Boulevard and bear right. At Burlingame Avenue, turn left to the club.

*Course description:* Accurate fairway play is important here. The course is fairly tight with lots of trees. The back nine is especially narrow and long. A small lake borders nine holes. The course also gets hilly in spots. What makes this a particularly good course are the greens: they are fast and true. So plan on putting accurately.

590 South Burlingame Avenue
Los Angeles, CA 90049

Pro shop (310) 451-8011

- ✓ **driving range**
- ✓ **practice greens**
- ✓ **power carts**
- ✓ **pull carts**
- golf club rental
- ✓ **locker rooms**
- ✓ **showers**
- executive course
- accommodations
- ✓ **food and beverages**
- ✓ **clubhouse**

**Bob Harrison**
Professional

**Bob O'Connell**
Superintendent

## PENMAR GOLF COURSE

**Course 30**
MAP I4 grid c7

*Course information:* This public course has nine holes. Par is 58 for 18 holes. The yards and rating were unavailable.

*Play policy and fees:* Green fees are $6.25 for nine holes weekdays, and $8.25 weekends. Call for special rates.

*Location:* In Venice, drive north on Lincoln Boulevard (Highway 1) to Rose Avenue, turn right and proceed two blocks to the course.

*Course description:* This nine-hole course offers an interesting and challenging layout in the heart of wild and wacky Venice.

1233 Rose Avenue
Venice, CA 90291

Pro shop (310) 396-6228

- driving range
- ✓ **practice greens**
- power carts
- ✓ **pull carts**
- ✓ **golf club rental**
- locker rooms
- showers
- executive course
- accommodations
- food and beverages
- clubhouse

**Randi Levenbaum**
Manager

# BEL-AIR COUNTRY CLUB

**Course 31**
MAP I4 grid c8

**1926**
**George C. Thomas**

10768 Bellagio Road
Los Angeles, CA 90077

Pro shop (310) 440-2423
Clubhouse (310) 476-9563

- driving range
- ✓ **practice greens**
- ✓ **power carts**
- pull carts
- ✓ **golf club rental**
- ✓ **locker rooms**
- ✓ **showers**
- executive course
- accommodations
- ✓ **food and beverages**
- ✓ **clubhouse**

**Ed Merrins**
Professional

**Steve Badger**
Superintendent

***Course information:*** This private course has 18 holes and par is 70. The course is 6,483 yards and rated 71.8 from the championship tees, and 6,212 yards and rated 70.3 from the regular tees. Women's yardage is 5,770 and rated 73.2. The slope ratings are 131 championship, 126 regular and 125 women.

***Play policy and fees:*** Green fees are $40 Monday through Thursday and $50 Friday through Sunday with a member. Green fees are $100 without a member. Carts are $18.

***Location:*** Take the Sunset Boulevard exit off Interstate 405 and travel east for three-fourths of a mile to Bellagio Road. Turn left and bear right. You'll shortly find the club entrance on your right.

***Course description:*** This austere, hilly course has narrow fairways and lots of trees. It's well bunkered with small greens and places a premium on accuracy. It was the site of the 1976 U.S. Amateur Championship and is the home course of the UCLA Bruins golf team. Designed by George C. Thomas in 1926, it rates among the top 20 in the state. One of the landmark holes is number 10, a par-3, 210-yard nerve-wracker, known as the ''Swinging Bridge.'' You park your cart on one side of a canyon, walk back to the tee box and hope your drive clears the canyon. The green is in sight, but that's no help. Talk about pressure. The tee is next to the club grill where there is always a critical gallery. Some golfers choose to hit from the women's tee which is out of sight from the grill. It's a no-win situation. Former Lakers star Jerry West is a member here.

# THE LOS ANGELES COUNTRY CLUB

Course 32
MAP 14 grid c8

**1921**
**George C. Thomas**

10101 Wilshire Boulevard
Los Angeles, CA 90024

Pro shop (310) 276-6104

- ✓ **driving range**
- ✓ **practice greens**
- ✓ **power carts**
- pull carts
- ✓ **golf club rental**
- ✓ **locker rooms**
- ✓ **showers**
- executive course
- ✓ **accommodations**
- ✓ **food and beverages**
- ✓ **clubhouse**

**Ed Oldfield Jr.**
Professional

**Mike Hathaway**
Superintendent

**James Brewer**
Manager

***Course information:*** This private club has two 18-hole courses. Par is 71 on the North Course and 70 on the South Course.

The North Course is 6,913 yards and rated 75.1 from the championship tees, and 6,610 yards and rated 72.9 from the regular tees. The slope ratings are 143 championship and 136 regular. Women's tees are 6,224 yards and rated 76.5. The slope rating is 143.

The South Course is 5,940 yards and rated 68.8 from the championship tees, and 5,638 yards and rated 67.1 from the regular tees. The slope ratings are 120 championship and 112 regular. Women's tees are 5,638 yards and rated 71.6. The slope rating is 112.

***Play policy and fees:*** Members and guests only. Guest fees are $15 Monday, $25 Tuesday through Friday, and $40 on weekends. Carts are $20. There are no tee times. No shorts are allowed on the golf course. Women must wear skirts.

***Location:*** Take the Wilshire Boulevard exit off Interstate 405, and drive east to the club.

***Course description:*** These are beautiful courses designed in 1921 by George C. Thomas. The North Course is ranked the number one course in Southern California and has been the home of five Los Angeles Open championships. It is regarded as among the best courses in the country. The USGA has repeatedly expressed an interest in playing the U.S. Open here. The membership is not interested. The North Course is the more difficult of the two. It features long, tight fairways and small greens with hilly terrain and lots of trees. The South Course is flatter and more open. The greens are tricky. They are small with subtle undulation. There is also a long par-5 at 565 yards. The North Course records are 64 for men and 68 for women.



MAP ON PAGE 470

# HILLCREST COUNTRY CLUB

**Course 33**

***Course information:*** This private course has 18 holes. See card below for yardage and rating information.

***Play policy and fees:*** Members and guests only. Guest fees are $25 weekdays and $50 weekends. Carts are $16.

***Location:*** Take the Pico Boulevard exit off Interstate 405 southbound, and travel east to the club. Northbound on Interstate 405 take the Venice Boulevard exit to Motor Street, which turns into Pico Boulevard and drive to the club.

***Course description:*** This is a relatively short and tree-lined course, and it can be testy. The fairways are lush and well-maintained. There is also a pitch-and-putt, six-hole, par-3 course. The 18-hole course record is 63 and is jointly held by Eric Monty and Greg Starkman. The Los Angeles Open qualifier was formerly held here.

10000 West Pico Boulevard
Los Angeles, CA 90064

Pro shop (310) 553-8911

- ✓ **driving range**
- ✓ **practice greens**
- ✓ **power carts**
- pull carts
- golf club rental
- locker rooms
- showers
- executive course
- accommodations
- food and beverages
- clubhouse

**Paul Wise**
Professional

**David Mastroleo**
Superintendent

**Leonard Fisher**
Manager

| Hole | 1 | 2 | 3 | 4 | 5 | 6 | 7 | 8 | 9 | Out | BLUE | Rating: 70.5 |
|---|---|---|---|---|---|---|---|---|---|---|---|---|
| BLUE | 384 | 169 | 338 | 548 | 431 | 174 | 317 | 490 | 377 | 3228 | | Slope: 122 |
| WHITE | 376 | 152 | 316 | 536 | 411 | 142 | 307 | 469 | 365 | 3074 | | |
| Par | 4 | 3 | 4 | 5 | 4 | 3 | 4 | 5 | 4 | 36 | WHITE | Rating: 68.7 |
| Handicap | 9 | 15 | 13 | 1 | 5 | 17 | 7 | 11 | 3 | x | | Slope: 115 |
| RED | 373 | 145 | 305 | 470 | 371 | 126 | 270 | 459 | 360 | 2879 | | |
| Par | 4 | 3 | 4 | 5 | 4 | 3 | 4 | 5 | 4 | 36 | RED | Rating: 73 |
| Handicap | 9 | 17 | 13 | 1 | 5 | 15 | 11 | 7 | 3 | x | | Slope: 122 |

| Hole | 10 | 11 | 12 | 13 | 14 | 15 | 16 | 17 | 18 | In | Totals | |
|---|---|---|---|---|---|---|---|---|---|---|---|---|
| BLUE | 298 | 441 | 189 | 422 | 534 | 384 | 150 | 311 | 416 | 3145 | BLUE | 6371 |
| WHITE | 288 | 436 | 172 | 406 | 509 | 367 | 129 | 299 | 389 | 2995 | WHITE | 6069 |
| Par | 4 | 4 | 3 | 4 | 5 | 4 | 3 | 4 | 4 | 35 | Par | 71 |
| Handicap | 12 | 2 | 16 | 4 | 10 | 8 | 18 | 14 | 6 | x | | |
| RED | 289 | 431 | 169 | 396 | 490 | 365 | 120 | 294 | 420 | 2974 | RED | 5853 |
| Par | 4 | 5 | 3 | 4 | 5 | 4 | 3 | 4 | 5 | 37 | Par | 73 |
| Handicap | 12 | 6 | 16 | 4 | 2 | 8 | 18 | 14 | 10 | x | | |

# RANCHO PARK GOLF COURSE

**Course 34**
MAP I4 grid c9

**1926**
10460 West Pico Boulevard.
Los Angeles, CA 90064

Pro shop (310) 839-4374
Coffee shop(310) 839-7750
Starter (310) 838-7373

- ✓ **driving range**
- ✓ **practice greens**
- ✓ **power carts**
- ✓ **pull carts**
- ✓ **golf club rental**
- ✓ **locker rooms**
- ✓ **showers**
- ✓ **executive course**
- **accommodations**
- ✓ **food and beverages**
- ✓ **clubhouse**

**Ron Weiner**
Professional

**Randy Haney**
Superintendent

**Clyde Blake**
Manager

***Course information:*** This public course has 18 holes and par is 71. There is also a nine-hole, par-3 course. The par is 27. The course is 6,585 yards and rated 71.7 from the championship tees, and 6,216 yards and rated 69.4 from the regular tees. The slope ratings are 124 championship and 117 regular. Women's tees are 6,003 and rated 73.4. The slope rating is 121.

***Play policy and fees:*** Green fees are $12 weekdays and $16 weekends. Carts are $18. Reservations are recommended, but can only be made by holders of a Los Angeles Park and Recreation reservation card. Standbys are welcome for non-card holders.

***Location:*** Take the Santa Monica Freeway to Overland exit. Travel north on Overland approximately three-fourths miles to Pico Boulevard. Turn right and drive one-half mile to the course.

***Course description:*** Arnold Palmer once made a 12 on the par-5 18th hole (No. 9 during professional events) during the Los Angeles Open here. Asked how he made 12, he replied, "I missed a three-footer for 11." A plaque has been placed near the tee at 18 to commemorate the event. The L.A. Open was played here 17 times, the last time in 1983 (won by Dr. Gil Morgan). Other winners here include Palmer (three times), Billy Casper (twice) and Ken Venturi. It is one of the most heavily played courses in the country, so expect slow play. The course features many trees and rolling terrain. It is the site of the Ralphs Senior Classic, an October stop on the Senior PGA Tour. The LPGA has held tournaments here as well.



MAP ON PAGE 470

# THE WILSHIRE COUNTRY CLUB

**Course 35**
MAP I4 grid c9

**1919**
301 North Rossmore Avenue
Los Angeles, CA 90004

Pro shop (213) 934-6050
Clubhouse (213) 934-1121

- ✓ **driving range**
- ✓ **practice greens**
- ✓ **power carts**
- pull carts
- golf club rental
- ✓ **locker rooms**
- ✓ **showers**
- executive course
- accommodations
- ✓ **food and beverages**
- ✓ **clubhouse**

**Roland Frenkel**
Manager

**Patrick Rielly Jr.**
Professional

**Alex Galaviz Jr.**
Superintendent

***Course information:*** This private club has 18 holes and par is 71. The course is 6,531 yards and rated 71.6 from the championship tees, and 6,295 yards and rated 70.2 from the regular tees. The slope ratings are 126 championship and 121 regular. Women's tees are 6,008 yards and rated 74.2. The slope rating is 127.

***Play policy and fees:*** Members and guests only. Fees are $35 weekdays and $50 on weekends for guests of members. Carts are $9.

***Location:*** Take the Santa Monica Boulevard exit off Highway 101 (Hollywood Freeway) and travel west for one mile to Vine Street. Turn left and drive one mile (becomes Rossmore Avenue) to the club on the right.

***Course description:*** Built in 1919, this course was used for the Los Angeles Open in 1926. The mostly level fairways are lined with mature trees and the greens are well maintained. A barranca runs through 14 of the 18 fairways.

# WESTCHESTER GOLF COURSE

**Course 36**
MAP I4 grid d8

***Course information:*** This public course has 15 holes and par is 53. The course is 3,470 yards.

***Play policy and fees:*** Green fees are $9 weekdays and $13 weekends. Carts are $14. Pull carts are $2.

***Location:*** Off of Interstate 405 in Westchester (near Inglewood), exit on Manchester Boulevard heading west and drive to the course on your left.

***Course description:*** There aren't many 15-hole executive courses, but this is one of them. The course lost three holes—numbers four, five and six—in 1990 to the Los Angeles International Airport for a road and is still looking for repayment. In the meantime, it has been reconfigured while it waits for overlapping governments to decide its fate. This executive course remains flat with one lake. It offers good practice for the irons. Jets taking off and landing can be bothersome.

**1967**
6900 West Manchester
Los Angeles, CA 90045

Pro shop (310) 649-9168
Starter (310) 649-9166

- ✓ **driving range**
- ✓ **practice greens**
- ✓ **power carts**
- ✓ **pull carts**
- ✓ **golf club rental**
- locker rooms
- showers
- ✓ **executive course**
- accommodations
- ✓ **food and beverages**
- clubhouse

**Michael Day**
Professional

**Robert Hall**
Manager

**Manuel Gutierrez**
Superintendent

# SEA AIRE PARK GOLF COURSE

**Course 37**
MAP I4 grid e8

***Course information:*** This public course has nine holes. Par is 27. The layout runs 618 yards.

***Play policy and fees:*** Green fees are $2.50 for Torrance residents and $3 for non-residents. Senior rates are $1 weekdays. Children are $1 any day.

***Location:*** In Torrance, drive west on Sepulveda. Cross Anza and turn left on Reynolds, then left on Lupine to the course.

***Course description:*** This is a short, par-3 course. The longest hole is 90 yards. It is a good practice course for your short iron game. Caters to a good number of beginners and it's cheap!

22730 Lupine Drive
Torrance, CA 90505

Pro shop (310) 316-9779

- driving range
- ✓ **practice greens**
- power carts
- pull carts
- ✓ **golf club rental**
- locker rooms
- showers
- executive course
- accommodations
- food and beverages
- clubhouse

# CHESTER WASHINGTON GOLF COURSE

**Course 38**
MAP I4 grid e9

1930 West 120th Street
Los Angeles, CA 90047

Pro shop (213) 756-6975

- ✓ **driving range**
- ✓ **practice greens**
- ✓ **power carts**
- ✓ **pull carts**
- ✓ **golf club rental**
- locker rooms
- showers
- executive course
- accommodations
- ✓ **food and beverages**
- ✓ **clubhouse**

**Mike Williams**
Professional

**Norm Wiens**
Superintendent

***Course information:*** This public course has 18 holes and par is 70. The course is 6,348 yards and rated 68.3 from its championship tees, and 6,002 yards and rated 66.7. The slope ratings are 107 championship and 104 regular. Women's tees are 5,646 yards and rated 71.8. The slope rating is 114.

***Play policy and fees:*** Green fees are $12.50 weekdays and $16.50 weekends. Carts are $18.

***Location:*** From Interstate 405 driving south (near Inglewood and Hawthorne), take the Imperial Highway exit and drive west. You'll see the Hawthorne Municipal Airport on your left. Turn right on Western Avenue to the course.

***Course description:*** This is a wide-open course for free swingers, and a confidence booster for everyone. There are few hazards to worry about.

# ALONDRA PARK GOLF COURSE

**Course 39**
MAP I4 grid e9

16400 South Prairie
Lawndale, CA 90260

Pro shop (310) 217-9915
Starter (310) 217-9919

- ✓ **driving range**
- ✓ **practice greens**
- ✓ **power carts**
- ✓ **pull carts**
- ✓ **golf club rental**
- locker rooms
- ✓ **showers**
- ✓ **executive course**
- accommodations
- ✓ **food and beverages**
- ✓ **clubhouse**

**Bruce Janke**
Professional

**Salvador Flores**
Superintendent

***Course information:*** This public facility has two 18-hole courses. The main course has a par of 72. The executive course has a par of 54. The main course is 6,500 yards and rated 69.4 from the championship tees, and 6,292 yards and rated 67.7 from the regular tees. The slope ratings are 106 championship and 104 regular. Women's tees are 6,100 yards and rated 73.0. The slope rating is 109. The executive course is 2,356 yards and rated 57.0.

***Play policy and fees:*** The green fees are $15.50 weekdays and $19.50 weekends for the main course, and $10 weekdays and $11 weekends for the executive course. Carts are $18.

***Location:*** Off Interstate 405 in Redondo Beach, take the Redondo Beach exit and drive northeast. The course is located on the corner of Prairie and Redondo Beach Boulevard.

***Course description:*** The main course is flat and open with ocean breezes from two miles away. It is not a difficult course, and there are very few places where golfers can get into trouble. The executive course is also flat and offers a good practice round. It is a good course for beginners and seniors.

# VICTORIA PARK GOLF COURSE

**Course 40**
MAP I4 grid e9

**1966**
**Edwin H. Ripperdan**

340 East 192nd Street
Carson, CA 90746

Pro shop (310) 323-6981
Reservation (310) 323-6981

- ✓ **driving range**
- ✓ **practice greens**
- ✓ **power carts**
- pull carts
- ✓ **golf club rental**
- locker rooms
- showers
- executive course
- accommodations
- ✓ **food and beverages**
- clubhouse

**Eugene Hardy**
Professional/Manager

**Jerry Wolfinden**
Superintendent

***Course information:*** This public course has 18 holes and par is 72. See card below for yardage and rating information.

***Play policy and fees:*** Green fees are $11 weekdays and $15 weekends. The twilight rate is $7 weekdays and $9 weekends. Senior citizens play for $5.50 and students are $4.50 during the week. Carts are $17. Two players and a cart are $125 on weekdays from noon to three p.m. Reservations are recommended.

***Location:*** Take Interstate 405 to the Avalon exit, then go north on Avalon to 192nd Street. Turn left on 192nd Street to the course.

***Course description:*** Most greens are protected by sand at this course. There are no water holes. The 515-yard first hole may put you in a sour mood right off the bat, if you're not aware of the fairway sand traps. It is an easy course to walk. The course features large greens and wide fairways. The wind usually comes up in the afternoon. Former Dodgers Maury Wills and Don Newcombe play here regularly. The course record is 64.

| Hole | 1 | 2 | 3 | 4 | 5 | 6 | 7 | 8 | 9 | Out | | |
|---|---|---|---|---|---|---|---|---|---|---|---|---|
| BLUE | 515 | 406 | 368 | 381 | 156 | 547 | 448 | 199 | 392 | 3412 | BLUE | Rating: 70.7 |
| WHITE | 500 | 394 | 358 | 368 | 144 | 536 | 433 | 184 | 378 | 3295 | | Slope: 111 |
| Par | 5 | 4 | 4 | 4 | 3 | 5 | 4 | 3 | 4 | 36 | WHITE | Rating: 69.5 |
| Handicap | 15 | 7 | 13 | 3 | 17 | 11 | 1 | 9 | 5 | x | | Slope: 109 |
| RED | 482 | 362 | 334 | 355 | 125 | 468 | 417 | 169 | 365 | 3077 | | |
| Par | 5 | 4 | 4 | 4 | 3 | 5 | 5 | 3 | 4 | 37 | RED | Rating: 73.0 |
| Handicap | 1 | 7 | 11 | 5 | 17 | 3 | 13 | 15 | 9 | x | | Slope: 115 |

| Hole | 10 | 11 | 12 | 13 | 14 | 15 | 16 | 17 | 18 | In | Totals | |
|---|---|---|---|---|---|---|---|---|---|---|---|---|
| BLUE | 512 | 353 | 391 | 421 | 174 | 486 | 226 | 375 | 437 | 3375 | BLUE | 6787 |
| WHITE | 499 | 334 | 376 | 409 | 157 | 473 | 216 | 359 | 413 | 3236 | WHITE | 6531 |
| Par | 5 | 4 | 4 | 4 | 3 | 5 | 3 | 4 | 4 | 36 | Par | 72 |
| Handicap | 16 | 18 | 8 | 2 | 12 | 14 | 6 | 10 | 4 | x | | |
| RED | 482 | 313 | 358 | 392 | 125 | 456 | 180 | 345 | 326 | 2977 | RED | 6048 |
| Par | 5 | 4 | 4 | 4 | 3 | 5 | 3 | 4 | 4 | 37 | Par | 74 |
| Handicap | 2 | 10 | 6 | 12 | 18 | 4 | 16 | 8 | 14 | x | | |

## JACK THOMPSON PAR-3 GOLF COURSE

**Course 41**
MAP I4 grid e9

9637 South Western Avenue
Los Angeles, CA 90047

Pro shop (213) 757-1650

- driving range
- ✓ **practice greens**
- power carts
- pull carts
- ✓ **golf club rental**
- locker rooms
- showers
- executive course
- accommodations
- food and beverages
- clubhouse

*Course information:* This public course has nine holes, par 27. The course is 1,008 yards.

*Play policy and fees:* Green fees are $4.25 weekdays and $5.50 weekends. Call for special rates.

*Location:* From Interstate 405 exit at Western Avenue and travel south about one mile to the course.

*Course description:* This par-3 course offers a good chance to sharpen up your short game. It is a popular course for juniors, seniors and beginners.

## LOS VERDES GOLF AND COUNTRY CLUB

**Course 42**
MAP I4 grid f7

**1964**
**William Francis Bell**

7000 West Los Verdes Drive
Rancho Palos Verdes, CA 90274

Pro shop (310) 377-0338
Starter (310) 377-7370

- ✓ **driving range**
- ✓ **practice greens**
- ✓ **power carts**
- ✓ **pull carts**
- ✓ **golf club rental**
- ✓ **locker rooms**
- ✓ **showers**
- executive course
- accommodations
- ✓ **food and beverages**
- ✓ **clubhouse**

**Len Kennett**
Professional

**Paul Rothwell**
Superintendent

*Course information:* This public course has 18 holes and par is 71. The course is 6,651 yards and rated 71.1 from the championship tees, and 6,273 yards and rated 69.0 from the regular tees. The slope ratings are 117 championship and 108 regular. Women's tees are 5,689 yards and rated 71.8. The slope rating is 118.

*Play policy and fees:* Green fees are $16.50 weekdays and $19.50 weekends. Carts are $17. Reservations are recommended. This course is available for outside tournaments.

*Location:* Travel on Interstate 405 to Rancho Palos Verdes. Exit on Hawthorne Boulevard and turn south and drive 11 miles to the Los Verdes Drive. Turn right and follow it to the club. Or, take Interstate 110 (Harbor Freeway) south to Pacific Coast Highway (Highway 1), then west to Hawthorne Boulevard. Turn south and drive 5.5 miles to Los Verdes Drive. Turn right and follow Los Verdes Drive around to the course.

*Course description:* This course offers one of the best golf values in the state. It has views of the Pacific Ocean matched only by Pebble Beach. The course is well maintained with excellent putting surfaces. The course record for men is 63, held by Ben Serns. The course record for women is 71. Numbers 13, 14 and 15 present a tough three-hole sequence, in addition to offering spectacular views of Catalina Island on clear days. The course is usually in quality condition.

## PALOS VERDES GOLF CLUB

**Course 43**
MAP 14 grid f8

**1924**
**George Thomas**

3301 Via Campesina
Palos Verdes Estates
CA 90274

Pro shop (310) 375-2759
Clubhouse (310) 375-2533

- driving range
- ✓ **practice greens**
- ✓ **power carts**
- pull carts
- ✓ **golf club rental**
- locker rooms
- showers
- executive course
- accommodations
- ✓ **food and beverages**
- ✓ **clubhouse**

**Richard Cox**
Professional

**Scott Young**
Superintendent

***Course information:*** This semi-private course has 18 holes and par is 71. The course is 6,221 yards and rated 70.8 from the championship tees, and 5,530 yards and rated 67.5 from the regular tees. The slope ratings are 129 championship and 121 regular. Women's tees are 5,530 yards and rated 76.3. The slope rating is 124.

***Play policy and fees:*** Outside play is accepted. Green fees are $85, carts included. Reservations are recommended.

***Location:*** Travel on Interstate 405 (San Diego Freeway) to Palos Verdes Estates. Exit on Hawthorne Boulevard and go west. Take Palos Verdes Drive north to Via Campesina and go left one-fourth of a mile to the club.

***Course description:*** This is a hilly course noted for its small, fast greens. Trees line the fairways. Water comes into play on one hole. The course offers spectacular ocean views, but with them come ocean breezes, as well. The course plays longer than its yardage, and has lots of character.

## DOMINGUEZ GOLF COURSE

**Course 44**
MAP 14 grid f9

19800 South Main Street
Carson, CA 90745

Pro shop (310) 719-1942

- ✓ **driving range**
- ✓ **practice greens**
- power carts
- ✓ **pull carts**
- ✓ **golf club rental**
- locker rooms
- showers
- executive course
- accommodations
- ✓ **food and beverages**
- ✓ **clubhouse**

**Brian Farkas**
**Leon Matthews**
Professionals

**Jose Castellanos**
Superintendent

***Course information:*** This short public course has 18 holes and par is 54. The course is 2,070 yards and rated 51.7 for 18 holes. No slope rating is available.

***Play policy and fees:*** Green fees are $6 weekdays for 18 holes and $4.50 weekdays for nine holes. Weekend and holidays green fees are $7 for 18 holes. Twilight rate is $5.25 after 5 p.m. for nine holes and $4.50 for 18. The course has lights and is open from 6 a.m. to 10 p.m.

***Location:*** From Interstate 405 north, exit on Main Street in Carson. The course is south of the freeway on your left.

***Course description:*** This tight course has a lot of gullies with some bunkers. It's a tough par-3 with undulating greens. It was built on landfill, which may have had some effect on the settling of the greens. It is managed by the American Golf Corporation.

## NEW HORIZONS GOLF COURSE

**Course 45**
MAP I4 grid f9

22727 Maple Avenue
Torrance, CA 90505

Pro shop (310) 325-3080

- driving range
- practice greens
- power carts
- pull carts
- golf club rental
- locker rooms
- showers
- executive course
- accommodations
- food and beverages
- clubhouse

*Course information:* This private course has nine holes and par is 27. The yardage and ratings were unavailable.

*Play policy and fees:* Current policy and green fees were also unavailable.

*Location:* Take Interstate 110 north to Torrance Boulevard. Follow Torrance Boulevard about one mile to maple Avenue. Turn right and go about three-fourths of a mile to the club.

*Course description:* This is a private course for residents of New Horizons. The course has narrow fairways and undulating greens, making it a difficult layout for anyone with shoddy iron play or an unsteady putting stroke.

## HARBOR PARK GOLF COURSE

**Course 46**
MAP I4 grid f9

1235 North Figueroa
Wilmington, CA 90744

Pro shop (310) 549-4953

- ✓ **driving range**
- ✓ **practice greens**
- ✓ **power carts**
- ✓ **pull carts**
- ✓ **golf club rental**
- locker rooms
- showers
- executive course
- accommodations
- ✓ **food and beverages**
- clubhouse

**Beverly Cox**
Manager

**Bob Murray**
Professional

**Randy Haney**
Superintendent

*Course information:* This public course has nine holes. Par is 72 for 18 holes. The course is 6,302 yards at 18 holes.

*Play policy and fees:* Green fees are $6.25 weekdays and $8.25 weekends. Carts are $8. Reservations are recommended.

*Location:* Take the Pacific Coast Highway (Highway 1) in Wilmington to Figueroa Street and drive about one-half mile to the course.

*Course description:* This is a long, nine-hole course. Keep the ball in play and there should be no problem. But when isn't that true? The greens can be difficult, especially in summer when they tend to dry out.

# ROLLING HILLS COUNTRY CLUB

**Course 47**
MAP 14 grid f9

**1970**
**Ted Robinson**

27000 Palos Verdes Dr. East
Rolling Hills Estate,
CA 90274

Pro shop (310) 326-7731
Clubhouse (310) 326-4343

driving range
✓ **practice greens**
✓ **power carts**
pull carts
✓ **golf club rental**
✓ **locker rooms**
✓ **showers**
executive course
accommodations
✓ **food and beverages**
✓ **clubhouse**

**Jack Hollis**
Professional

**Pat Chartrand**
Director

**Jim Neal**
Superintendent

***Course information:*** This private course has 18 holes and par is 70. The course is 6,081 yards and rated 69.8 from the championship tees, and 5,766 yards and rated 68.2 from the regular tees. The slope ratings are 122 championship and 119 regular. Women's tees are 6,081 yards and rated 73.7 from the championship tees, and 5,309 yards and rated 71.7 from the forward tees. The slope ratings are 130 championship and 126 forward.

***Play policy and fees:*** Members and guests only. Guest fees are $35 weekdays and $50 weekends. Carts are $18. This course is available for outside tournaments when sponsored by a member. No jeans allowed on the course. Tee times are not used.

***Location:*** South of Carson on Interstate 110, turn onto the Pacific Coast Highway west (Highway 1) and drive for 2.25 miles to Narbonne. Turn left and drive one mile to the club.

***Course description:*** This is a well-manicured course that appears short but is tricky because of narrow, tree-lined fairways. Watch out for the 181-yard 11th hole. The green is surrounded by a pond and it's filled with errant golf balls. Many holes feature large double greens and rolling fairways. The men's course record is 63, held by PGA Tour star John Cook, and the women's record is 67, held by Mary Enright.

# THE POINTE CATALINA ISLAND GOLF COURSE

**Course 48**
MAP I4 grid j7

P.O. Box 1564
Avalon, CA 90704

One Country Club Road
Avalon, CA 90704
Pro shop (310) 510-0530

driving range
✓ **practice greens**
✓ **power carts**
✓ **pull carts**
✓ **golf club rental**
✓ **locker rooms**
showers
✓ **executive course**
accommodations
✓ **food and beverages**
✓ **clubhouse**

**LaFata, Dave**
Professional

**Jose Morones**
Superintendent

***Course information:*** This resort course has nine holes. Par is 64 for 18 holes. The course is 4,201 yards and rated 60.5 from the regular tees. The slope rating is 97. Women's tees are rated 62.6 with a slope rating of 105.

***Play policy and fees:*** Outside play is accepted. Green fees are $10 for each nine holes. Carts are $20 for 18 holes and $10 for nine holes.

***Location:*** Take the boat from San Pedro Bay or Long Beach (Catalina Express of Catalina Cruises) to Catalina Island, 26 miles off the mainland. In the summer boats leave from Redondo and Newport Beaches. Helicopters are available from Long Beach and San Pedro.

***Course description:*** This scenic canyon course was opened in the late 1800s. Although short in length, the holes are narrow and demanding. Greens are small and surrounded by traps offering a challenge to any adventurous golfer. Celebrities have long been attracted to the course and William Wrigley of chewing gum fame sponsored tournaments here in the 1920s. The Catalina Island Junior Championship is held here during Easter week, and the Catalina Island Invitational is held here each October.

MAP ON PAGE 470

# MAP I5

(102 COURSES)

PAGES.. 506-583

SO-CAL MAP .....see page 466
adjoining maps
NORTH (H5).......see page 444
EAST (I6) ...........see page 584
SOUTH (J5) ........see page 668
WEST (I4) ...........see page 470

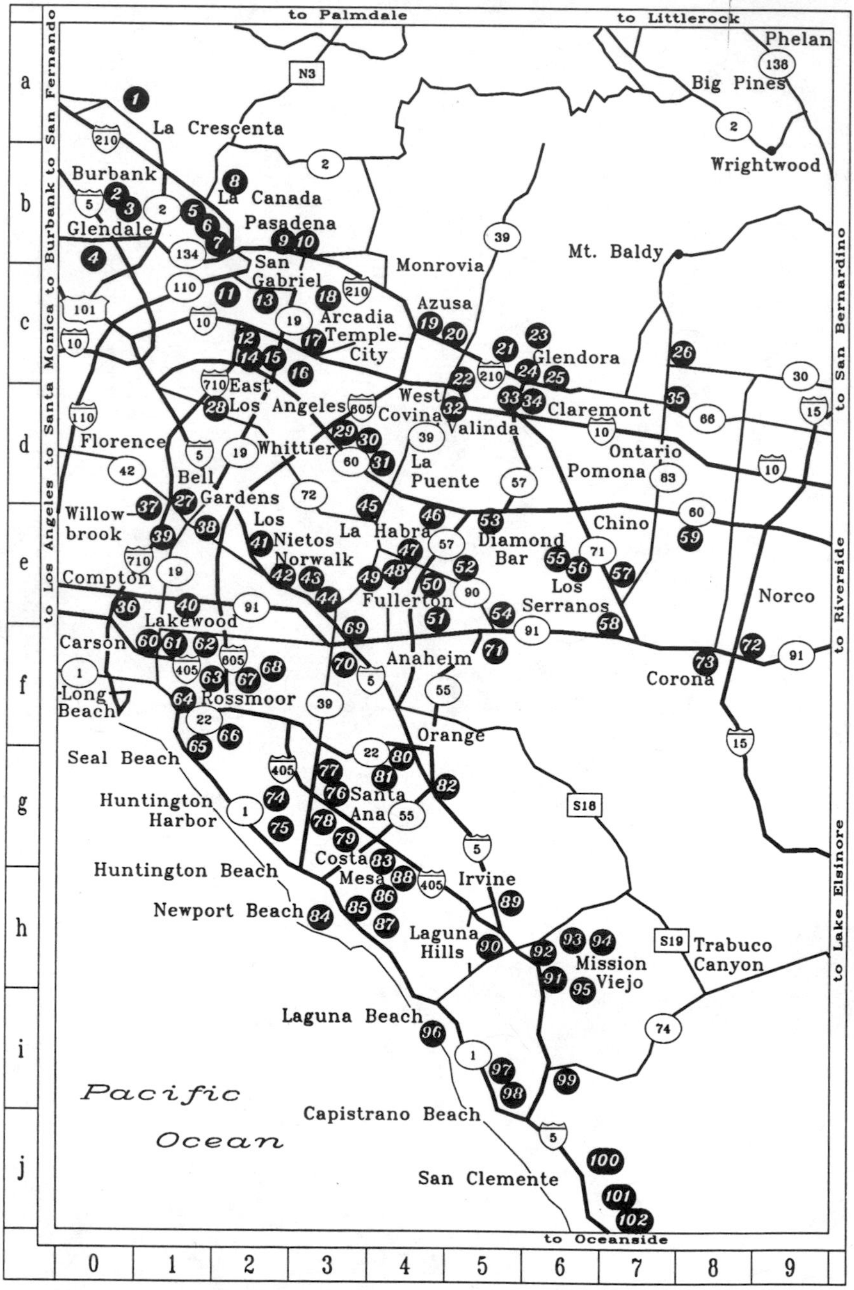

to Palmdale

to Littlerock

to Burbank to San Fernando

to Santa Monica to Los Angeles

to San Bernardino

to Riverside

to Lake Elsinore

to Oceanside

Phelan
Big Pines
Wrightwood
La Crescenta
Burbank
La Canada
Glendale
Pasadena
San Gabriel
Monrovia
Mt. Baldy
Azusa
Arcadia
Temple City
Glendora
East Los Angeles
West Covina
Valinda
Claremont
Florence
Whittier
La Puente
Ontario
Pomona
Bell Gardens
Willowbrook
Los Nietos
La Habra
Diamond Bar
Chino
Norwalk
Compton
Fullerton
Los Serranos
Norco
Lakewood
Carson
Anaheim
Corona
Long Beach
Rossmoor
Orange
Seal Beach
Huntington Harbor
Santa Ana
Costa Mesa
Irvine
Huntington Beach
Newport Beach
Laguna Hills
Mission Viejo
Trabuco Canyon
Laguna Beach
Pacific Ocean
Capistrano Beach
San Clemente

a b c d e f g h i j

0 1 2 3 4 5 6 7 8 9

## VERDUGO HILLS GOLF COURSE

**Course 1**
MAP I5 grid a0

6433 LaTuna Canyon Road
Tujunga, CA 91042

Pro shop (818) 352-1100
Starter (818) 352-3161

- ✓ **driving range**
- ✓ **practice greens**
- power carts
- pull carts
- ✓ **golf club rental**
- locker rooms
- showers
- ✓ **executive course**
- accommodations
- ✓ **food and beverages**
- ✓ **clubhouse**

**John Wells**
Manager

**Mike Reed**
Professional

***Course information:*** This public course has 18 holes and par is 54. The course is 1,805 yards. The course is not rated.

***Play policy and fees:*** Green fees are $7 weekdays and $10 weekends.

***Location:*** On Interstate 210 in Tujunga, take the Lowell Avenue exit. Drive one block and turn left on LaTuna Canyon Road. Veer left to the course, which is located at thc junction of LaTuna Canyon Road and Tujunga Canyon Road.

***Course description:*** This hilly, well-kept course has lots of trees and small greens. There are no bunkers or water to impede you or your ball. It's walkable. The longest hole is 140 yards. This course is considered to be one of the best conditioned par-3 courses in Southern California. The driving range is open until 10:30 p.m. and the last tee time is 9 p.m.

## DE BELL GOLF COURSE

**Course 2**
MAP I5 grid b0

1500 Walnut Avenue
Burbank, CA 91504

Pro shop (818) 845-5052
Clubhouse (818) 843-8666

- ✓ **driving range**
- ✓ **practice greens**
- ✓ **power carts**
- ✓ **pull carts**
- ✓ **golf club rental**
- ✓ **locker rooms**
- ✓ **showers**
- executive course
- accommodations
- ✓ **food and beverages**
- ✓ **clubhouse**

**Phil Scozzola**
Professional

***Course information:*** This public course has 18 holes and par is 71. The course is 5,813 yards and rated 66.8 from the regular tees. The slope rating is 109. Women's tees are 5,496 yards and rated 70.8. The slope rating is 118.

***Play policy and fees:*** Green fees for Burbank residents are $12 weekdays and $15 weekends. Non-resident green fees are $15 weekdays and $19 weekends. Carts are $18. Reservations are recommended.

***Location:*** From Interstate 5 take the Olive Avenue exit east about 2.5 miles to Walnut Avenue. Turn right on Walnut and follow it to the course.

***Course description:*** This is a fairly straight course with a minimum of sand traps and no water hazards. Although it is a short course, it is demanding, and course management is important. It has been called a thinking man's course.

## OAKMONT COUNTRY CLUB

**Course 3**
MAP I5 grid b0

***Course information:*** This private course has 18 holes and par is 72. The course is 6,758 yards and rated 73.2 from the championship tees, and 6,480 yards and rated 71.3 from the regular tees. The slope ratings are 130 championship, 124 regular. Women's yardage is 6,033 and rated 75. The slope rating is 128.

***Play policy and fees:*** Members and guests only. Green fees are $35 weekdays and $40 Fridays and weekends. Carts are $18.

***Location:*** From the Ventura Freeway take the Glendale Avenue exit and drive north on Verdugo/Canada Road for 3.5 miles to Country Club Drive. Turn left and drive one-half of a mile to the club.

***Course description:*** This mature course has tight fairways and well-maintained, tricky greens. Good ball placement is rewarded, even necessary; it is a shotmaker's course that has a lot of trees. All in all, a good test of golf. The LPGA Tour and Senior PGA Tour have held tournaments here in the past.

**1922**
3100 Country Club Drive
Glendale, CA 91208

Pro shop (818) 242-2050
Clubhouse (818) 242-3106

- ✓ **driving range**
- ✓ **practice greens**
- ✓ **power carts**
- pull carts
- golf club rental
- ✓ **locker rooms**
- ✓ **showers**
- executive course
- accommodations
- ✓ **food and beverages**
- ✓ **clubhouse**

**Greg Frederick**
Professional

**Dave Flaxbeard**
Superintendent

# GRIFFITH PARK GOLF COURSE

**Course 4**
MAP 15 grid b0

4730 Crystal Springs Drive
Los Angeles, CA 90027

Pro shop (213) 664-2255
Clubhouse (213) 663-2555

- ✓ **driving range**
- ✓ **practice greens**
- ✓ **power carts**
- ✓ **pull carts**
- ✓ **golf club rental**
- ✓ **locker rooms**
- ✓ **showers**
- ✓ **executive course** accommodations
- ✓ **food and beverages**
- ✓ **clubhouse**

**Tom Barber**
Professional

**Randy Haney**
Superintendent

***Course information:*** This public facility has two 18-hole courses and par is 72 on both. There is also a par-3 course (Los Felix), par 27, and an executive course (Roosevelt), par 33.

The Harding Course is 6,536 yards and rated 70.4 from the championship tees, and 6,317 yards and rated 69.1 from the regular tees. The slope ratings are 112 championship and 108 regular. Women's tees are 6,095 yards and rated 73.1. The slope rating is 118.

The Wilson Course is 6,942 yards and rated 72.7 from the championship tees, and 6,682 yards and rated 70.9 from the regular tees. The slope ratings are 115 championship and 109 regular. Women's tees are 6,483 yards and rated 76.0. The slope rating is 119.

***Play policy and fees:*** Green fees are $12 weekdays and $16 weekends. Carts are $16. Reservations are recommended. A Los Angeles Park and Recreation reservation card is required.

***Location:*** Take the Los Felix Boulevard West exit off Interstate 5. Turn right on Riverside Drive into Griffith Park and follow the signs for two more miles to the club.

***Course description:*** Both championship courses are fairly open with lots of trees lining the fairways. Water comes into play on both. The Wilson Course is the more difficult of the two championship courses. These courses are used for the annual Los Angeles City Amateur Championship. They receive substantially heavy play. The 18th at Harding parallels the Griffith Park Zoo, so expect zoo noises.

# CHEVY CHASE COUNTRY CLUB

**Course 5**
MAP I5 grid b1

**1927**
3067 E. Chevy Chase Drive
Glendale, CA 91206

Pro shop (818) 244-8461
Clubhouse (818) 246-5566

- driving range
- ✓ **practice greens**
- ✓ **power carts**
- pull carts
- golf club rental
- ✓ **locker rooms**
- ✓ **showers**
- ✓ **executive course**
- accommodations
- ✓ **food and beverages**
- ✓ **clubhouse**

**Derek MacArthur**
Professional

**Mark Campbell**
General Manager
Superintendent

***Course information:*** This private course has nine holes. Par is 66 for 18 holes. The course is 4,895 yards and rated 61.9 from the regular tees. The slope rating is 98.

***Play policy and fees:*** Members and guests only. Green fees are $20 weekdays and $25 weekends. Carts are $16.

***Location:*** From Highway 134 in Glendale, take Harvey exit and travel north for three blocks to Chevy Chase Drive. Turn right and drive two miles to the club.

***Course description:*** This course was built in 1927, and has a variety of holes that traverse the rolling terrain of this area. It is short and extremely tight, with out-of-bounds stakes on virtually every hole.

# BROOKSIDE GOLF COURSE

**Course 6**
MAP 15 grid b1

**1928**
**William Park Bell**

1133 Rosemont Avenue
Pasadena, CA 91103

Pro shop (818) 796-8151
Starter (818) 796-0177

- ✓ **driving range**
- ✓ **practice greens**
- ✓ **power carts**
- pull carts
- ✓ **golf club rental**
- ✓ **locker rooms**
- ✓ **showers**
- executive course
- accommodations
- ✓ **food and beverages**
- ✓ **clubhouse**

**John Wells**
Professional

**Dan Dau, Jr.**
Superintendent

***Course information:*** This public facility has two 18-hole courses. Par is 72 for the Number One Course, and 70 for the Number Two Course.

The Number One Course is 6,888 yards and rated 73.3 from the championship tees, and 6,661 yards and rated 71.6 from the regular tees. The slope ratings are 125 championship and 117 regular. Women's tees are 6,080 yards and rated 73.7. The slope rating is 117.

The Number Two Course is 5,689 yards and rated 66.3 from the regular tees. The slope rating is 104. Women's tees are 5,408 yards and rated 69.6. The slope rating is 108.

***Play policy and fees:*** Green fees for residents playing the Number One Course are $14 weekdays and $18 weekends. Green fees for non-residents playing the Number One Course are $25 weekdays and $30 weekends. Green fees for residents playing the Number Two Course are $11 weekdays and $15 weekends. Green fees for non-residents playing the Number Two Course are $20 weekdays and $25 weekends. Cart fees are $20. Reservations should be made one week in advance for weekday play. There is a special reservation system for weekends. Call ahead.

***Location:*** From Interstate 210 in Pasadena, take the Seco/Mountain exit. Travel south on Seco to Rosemont; the course is adjacent to the Rose Bowl.

***Course description:*** Number One is long and wide open with mature trees lining the fairways. A lake comes into play. Number Two is short and narrow. Well-placed bunkers guard both courses. The Los Angeles Open was held here in 1968. The Golden State Tour plays this course regularly each year. The Pasadena City Amateur is also played here. The Rose Bowl is directly next to the courses, which become parking lots during events there.

# ANNANDALE GOLF COURSE

**Course 7**
MAP I5 grid b1

*Course information:* This private course has 18 holes. See card below for yardage and rating information.

*Play policy and fees:* Members and guests only. Guests must be accompanied by members at time of play. Green fees are $35. Carts are $18.

*Location:* Take the San Rafael exit off Highway 134 in Pasadena. Turn left and drive one block to the entrance gate.

*Course description:* This hilly, narrow course is known for its fast, sloping greens. The memorable 14th and 16th holes are set in a canyon with a lake in front of the 16th green. Arnold Palmer plays here annually in a charity event. Rielly, the head professional, is a former president of the PGA of America.

One N. San Rafael Avenue
Pasadena, CA 91105

Pro shop (818) 795-8253
Clubhouse (818) 796-6125
Fax (818) 577-9643

- ✓ **driving range**
- ✓ **practice greens**
- ✓ **power carts**
- pull carts
- golf club rental
- ✓ **locker rooms**
- ✓ **showers**
- executive course
- accommodations
- ✓ **food and beverages**
- ✓ **clubhouse**

**Patrick Rielly**
Professional

**David Allec**
Superintendent

**Beda Hauelka**
Manager

| Hole | 1 | 2 | 3 | 4 | 5 | 6 | 7 | 8 | 9 | Out | | |
|---|---|---|---|---|---|---|---|---|---|---|---|---|
| BLUE | 338 | 412 | 408 | 404 | 171 | 458 | 460 | 334 | 165 | 3150 | BLUE | Rating: 71.9 |
| WHITE | 328 | 384 | 392 | 393 | 160 | 450 | 450 | 312 | 144 | 3013 | | Slope: 139 |
| Par | 4 | 4 | 4 | 4 | 3 | 5 | 4 | 4 | 3 | 35 | WHITE | Rating: 70.1 |
| Handicap | 11 | 5 | 3 | 7 | 15 | 13 | 1 | 9 | 17 | x | | Slope: 129 |
| RED | 320 | 371 | 392 | 380 | 151 | 434 | 447 | 298 | 137 | 2930 | | |
| Par | 4 | 4 | 4 | 4 | 3 | 5 | 5 | 4 | 3 | 36 | RED | Rating: 74.0 |
| Handicap | 11 | 5 | 3 | 7 | 15 | 1 | 13 | 9 | 17 | x | | Slope: 126 |

| Hole | 10 | 11 | 12 | 13 | 14 | 15 | 16 | 17 | 18 | In | Totals | |
|---|---|---|---|---|---|---|---|---|---|---|---|---|
| BLUE | 358 | 425 | 219 | 490 | 431 | 139 | 427 | 241 | 538 | 3268 | BLUE | 6418 |
| WHITE | 342 | 417 | 191 | 481 | 416 | 132 | 392 | 201 | 517 | 3089 | WHITE | 6102 |
| Par | 4 | 4 | 3 | 5 | 4 | 3 | 4 | 3 | 5 | 35 | Par | 70 |
| Handicap | 16 | 6 | 10 | 14 | 4 | 18 | 2 | 8 | 12 | x | | |
| RED | 315 | 409 | 184 | 464 | 397 | 125 | 367 | 176 | 503 | 2940 | RED | 5870 |
| Par | 4 | 5 | 3 | 5 | 5 | 3 | 4 | 3 | 5 | 37 | Par | 73 |
| Handicap | 8 | 10 | 14 | 2 | 12 | 18 | 6 | 16 | 4 | x | | |

## LA CANADA-FLINTRIDGE COUNTRY CLUB

**Course 8**
MAP 15 grid b2

5500 Godbey Drive
La Canada, CA 91011

Pro shop (818) 790-0155
Clubhouse (818) 790-0611

driving range
✓ **practice greens**
✓ **power carts**
pull carts
✓ **golf club rental**
✓ **locker rooms**
✓ **showers**
executive course
accommodations
✓ **food and beverages**
✓ **clubhouse**

**Mark Saatzer**
Professional

**Salvador Macias**
Superintendent

***Course information:*** This private course has 18 holes and par is 70. The course is 5,771 yards and rated 70.1 from the championship tees, and 5,514 yards and rated 69.0 from the regular tees. The slope ratings are 129 championship and 125 regular. Women's tees are 5,230 yards and rated 70. The slope rating is 118.

***Play policy and fees:*** Reciprocal play is accepted with members of other private clubs, otherwise members and guests only. Green fees are $28 weekdays and $35 weekends. Carts are $20. Reservations are recommended. This course is available for outside tournaments.

***Location:*** From Pasadena, drive west on Interstate 210 (Foothill Freeway) and take the Angeles Crest Highway exit. Drive north for 1.5 miles to Starlight Crest Drive. Turn right and drive one-fourth of a mile to Godbey Drive then turn right to the club.

***Course description:*** This short and narrow course makes up for lack of length with hills and tight fairways. Cart use is recommended for all but the bravest souls. On the back nine, watch for the par-5, 462-yard number 12. You tee off from an elevated tee to a narrow landing area, but first you must clear at least 160 yards of brush before you find a safe landing area. The hole then opens up and is reachable in two shots for longer hitters.

## ALTADENA TOWN AND COUNTRY CLUB

**Course 9**
MAP 15 grid b2

1456 East Mendocino Drive
Altadena, CA 91001

Pro shop (818) 797-3821
Clubhouse (818) 794-7679

✓ **driving range**
✓ **practice greens**
✓ **power carts**
✓ **pull carts**
✓ **golf club rental**
locker rooms
showers
executive course
accommodations
✓ **food and beverages**
✓ **clubhouse**

**Billy Gibbs**
Professional

**Lew Orwig**
Superintendent

***Course information:*** This public course has nine holes. Par is 72 for 18 holes. The course is 5,990 yards and rated 66.6 from the championship tees, and 5,680 yards and rated 65.2 from the regular tees. The slope ratings are 111 championship and 108 regular. Women's tees are 5,418 yards and rated 68. There is no slope rating.

***Play policy and fees:*** Green fees are $10 weekdays and $12 weekends for nine holes. Replay fees are $4 weekdays and $6 weekends. Carts are $10 for nine holes and $6 for replays.

***Location:*** Travel on Interstate 210 to the Lake Avenue exit in Pasadena. Drive 2.5 miles to Mendocino. Turn right and the course is 1.5 miles on the right.

***Course description:*** This is a flat, wide-open golf course with bunkers and some sloping fairways. The San Gabriel Mountains provide a pleasant backdrop when smog does not interfere.

## EATON CANYON GOLF COURSE

**Course 10**
MAP I5 grid b3

1150 North Sierra Madre Villa Avenue
Pasadena, CA 91107

Pro shop (818) 794-6773

- ✓ **driving range**
- ✓ **practice greens**
- ✓ **power carts**
- ✓ **pull carts**
- ✓ **golf club rental**
- locker rooms
- showers
- executive course
- accommodations
- ✓ **food and beverages**
- ✓ **clubhouse**

**David Brown**
Professional

**Lew Orwig**
Superintendent

*Course information:* This public course has nine holes. Par is 70 for 18 holes. The course is 2,862 yards and rated 65.8 from the championship tees, and 2,660 yards and rated 64.0 from the regular tees. The slope ratings are 111 championship and 108 regular. Women's tees are 2,453 yards and rated 69.3. The slope rating is 114.

*Play policy and fees:* Green fees are $10 for nine holes weekdays and $12 for nine holes weekends. Replay fees are $4 weekdays and $6 weekends Carts are $10 and $6 for replays.

*Location:* East of Pasadena on Interstate 210, take the Sierra Madre Boulevard exit. Drive under the freeway and head north on Sierra Madre Boulevard until it becomes Sierra Madre Villa. The course is located at 1150 North Sierra Madre Villa.

*Course description:* The first four holes are flat and the last five hilly on this tight course. There are lots of trees. The longest hole measures 483 yards.

## ARROYO SECO GOLF COURSE

**Course 11**
MAP I5 grid c2

1055 Lohman Lane
South Pasadena, CA 91030

Pro shop (213) 255-1506
Clubhouse (213) 254-5375

- ✓ **driving range**
- ✓ **practice greens**
- power carts
- ✓ **pull carts**
- ✓ **golf club rental**
- locker rooms
- showers
- ✓ **executive course**
- accommodations
- ✓ **food and beverages**
- ✓ **clubhouse**

**Horace Evans**
Professional

**John DeLaTorre**
Superintendent

*Course information:* This public course has 18 holes and par is 54. The course is 2,223 yards.

*Play policy and fees:* Green fees are $3.75 for nine holes and $5.75 for 18 holes weekdays, and $4 for nine holes and $6.50 for 18 holes weekends during the day. Night fees are $4.50 for nine holes and $7 for 18 holes.

*Location:* On Highway 110 (Pasadena Freeway) in South Pasadena, exit on Orange Grove Boulevard to the south. Drive one-fourth of a block and turn right on Mission and drive to the end. Look for the course sign.

*Course description:* This flat course has a small creek winding through the last holes. The holes range in distance from 88 yards to 165 yards. It is open at night.

# ALHAMBRA GOLF COURSE

**Course 12**
MAP I5 grid c2

**1956**
**William Francis Bell**

630 South Almansor Street
Alhambra, CA 91801

Pro shop (818) 570-5059
Clubhouse (818) 570-4600

- ✓ **driving range**
- ✓ **practice greens**
- ✓ **power carts**
- ✓ **pull carts**
- ✓ **golf club rental**
- locker rooms
- showers
- executive course
- accommodations
- ✓ **food and beverages**
- ✓ **clubhouse**

**Jerry Wisz**
Professional

**Zeke Avila, Jr.**
Superintendent

***Course information:*** This public course has 18 holes. The women's tournament tees are 5,092, rated 68.5, with a slope of 108. See card below for additional yardage and rating information.

***Play policy and fees:*** Green fees are $12 weekdays and $16.50 weekends. Seniors and juniors play for $6 on weekdays with a resident card. Carts are $16; Alhambra residents get a $1.50 discount. Reservations are recommended. Shirts and appropriate shoes required.

***Location:*** From downtown Los Angeles, take Interstate 10 east to the Garfield Avenue exit, turn right on Valley Boulevard and go one-half of a mile to Almansor Street. Turn left on Almansor and go three-fourths of a mile to the club.

***Course description:*** This short course features three par-5s and five par-3s. There are three lakes and 33 bunkers. The front nine is flat but easy to walk, with large groves of eucalyptus and black acacias. The back nine is composed of rolling hills with more sand and water. The two nines are distinctly different, although both have well-maintained greens. The greens are small and quick, requiring a soft touch. One unique feature of this course is the three-tiered, night-lighted driving range, believed to be America's first. This is a shot-maker's layout.

| Hole | 1 | 2 | 3 | 4 | 5 | 6 | 7 | 8 | 9 | Out | BLUE | Rating: 61.3 |
|---|---|---|---|---|---|---|---|---|---|---|---|---|
| BLUE | 283 | 469 | 254 | 255 | 289 | 483 | 125 | 151 | 334 | 2643 | | Slope: 94 |
| WHITE | 273 | 449 | 254 | 255 | 267 | 473 | 115 | 141 | 324 | 2551 | | |
| Par | 4 | 5/4 | 4 | 4 | 4 | 5 | 3 | 3 | 4 | 36/35 | WHITE | Rating: 61.6 |
| Handicap | 7 | 3 | 11 | 13 | 9 | 1 | 17 | 15 | 5 | x | | Slope: 91 |
| RED | 273 | 449 | 254 | 255 | 267 | 473 | 115 | 141 | 324 | 2551 | | |
| Par | 4 | 5 | 4 | 4 | 4 | 5 | 3 | 3 | 4 | 36 | RED | Rating: 67.3 |
| Handicap | 7 | 3 | 11 | 13 | 9 | 1 | 17 | 15 | 5 | x | | Slope: 105 |

| Hole | 10 | 11 | 12 | 13 | 14 | 15 | 16 | 17 | 18 | In | Totals | |
|---|---|---|---|---|---|---|---|---|---|---|---|---|
| BLUE | 285 | 162 | 348 | 186 | 291 | 131 | 490 | 272 | 398 | 2563 | BLUE | 5206 |
| WHITE | 275 | 146 | 306 | 158 | 271 | 117 | 400 | 272 | 376 | 2321 | WHITE | 4872 |
| Par | 4 | 3 | 4 | 3 | 4 | 3 | 5/4 | 4 | 4 | 34/33 | Par | 70/68 |
| Handicap | 14 | 16 | 6 | 8 | 12 | 18 | 2 | 10 | 4 | x | | |
| RED | 275 | 146 | 306 | 158 | 271 | 117 | 400 | 272 | 380 | 2325 | RED | 4876 |
| Par | 4 | 3 | 4 | 3 | 4 | 3 | 5 | 4 | 5 | 35 | Par | 71 |
| Handicap | 14 | 16 | 6 | 8 | 10 | 18 | 2 | 12 | 4 | x | | |

# SAN GABRIEL COUNTRY CLUB

**Course 13**
MAP 15 grid c2

***Course information:*** This private course has 18 holes. The course is 6,544 yards, rated 72.4, and has a slope of 133 from the tournament tees. See card below for additional yardage and rating information.

***Play policy and fees:*** Members and guests only. Guests must be accompanied by members during play. Green fees are $35 every day. Carts are $20. Reservations are recommended. Golfers must wear collared shirts. No jeans are allowed. Bermuda shorts to the knee are acceptable. Women must wear skirts or culottes.

***Location:*** Travel on Interstate 10 in San Gabriel and take the San Gabriel Boulevard exit. Drive north to Las Tunas Drive, turn left to the club.

***Course description:*** This historic course was built in 1904 and renovated in the mid-1970s by Robert Trent Jones, Jr. It plays longer than it looks because of the bunkers. Lots of mature trees line the fairways and the greens are well maintained. Fairways have been seeded with Kikuyu grass. Among the holes to watch for are the 437-yard seventh that features a dogleg right. Both sides of the fairway are out-of-bounds. The 420-yard 10th hole, which needs a second shot uphill to a heavily bunkered green, would give Ben Hogan nightmares. The course record of 59 is held by Bruce McCormick. The prestigious Cravens Invitational is held here each May and The Mission Bell tournament is played in October.

**1904**

411 East Las Tunas Drive
San Gabriel, CA 91775

Pro shop (818) 287-6052
Clubhouse (818) 287-9671
Starter (818) 287-4235
Fax (818) 287-4129

- ✓ **driving range**
- ✓ **practice greens**
- ✓ **power carts**
- pull carts
- ✓ **golf club rental**
- ✓ **locker rooms**
- ✓ **showers**
- executive course
- ✓ **accommodations**
- ✓ **food and beverages**
- ✓ **clubhouse**

**Michael Jon Kelley**
Professional

**Tony Cuellar**
Superintendent

**Cyrus Afshin**
Manager

| Hole | 1 | 2 | 3 | 4 | 5 | 6 | 7 | 8 | 9 | Out | BLUE | Rating: 70.6 |
|---|---|---|---|---|---|---|---|---|---|---|---|---|
| BLUE | 280 | 507 | 371 | 504 | 177 | 340 | 437 | 385 | 165 | 3166 | | Slope: 125 |
| WHITE | 272 | 486 | 363 | 484 | 163 | 323 | 422 | 365 | 157 | 3035 | | |
| Par | 4 | 5 | 4 | 5 | 3 | 4 | 4 | 4 | 3 | 36 | WHITE | Rating: 68.9 |
| Handicap | 17 | 7 | 9 | 3 | 11 | 13 | 1 | 5 | 15 | x | | Slope: 118 |
| RED | 272 | 486 | 363 | 484 | 163 | 323 | 422 | 365 | 157 | 3035 | | |
| Par | 4 | 5 | 4 | 5 | 3 | 4 | 5 | 4 | 3 | 37 | RED | Rating: 75 |
| Handicap | 11 | 1 | 7 | 3 | 15 | 9 | 13 | 5 | 17 | x | | Slope: 129 |

| Hole | 10 | 11 | 12 | 13 | 14 | 15 | 16 | 17 | 18 | In | Totals | |
|---|---|---|---|---|---|---|---|---|---|---|---|---|
| BLUE | 420 | 144 | 345 | 457 | 182 | 314 | 415 | 441 | 375 | 3093 | BLUE | 6259 |
| WHITE | 404 | 125 | 340 | 437 | 157 | 305 | 410 | 422 | 365 | 2965 | WHITE | 6000 |
| Par | 4 | 3 | 4 | 5 | 3 | 4 | 4 | 4 | 4 | 35 | Par | 71 |
| Handicap | 2 | 18 | 10 | 12 | 14 | 16 | 6 | 4 | 8 | x | | |
| RED | 404 | 125 | 340 | 437 | 157 | 305 | 410 | 422 | 365 | 2965 | RED | 6000 |
| Par | 5 | 3 | 4 | 5 | 3 | 4 | 5 | 5 | 4 | 38 | Par | 75 |
| Handicap | 10 | 18 | 12 | 2 | 16 | 14 | 8 | 4 | 6 | x | | |

## MONTEREY PARK GOLF COURSE

**Course 14**
MAP 15 grid c2

3600 Ramona Boulevard
Monterey Park, CA 91754

Pro shop (213) 266-4632
Clubhouse (213) 261-2241

- ✓ **driving range**
- ✓ **practice greens**
- power carts
- ✓ **pull carts**
- ✓ **golf club rental**
- locker rooms
- showers
- ✓ **executive course**
- accommodations
- ✓ **food and beverages**
- clubhouse

**Jay Hyon**
Professional

***Course information:*** This public course has nine holes. Par is 29. The course is 1,400 yards.

***Play policy and fees:*** Green fees are $4.50 weekdays and $5 weekends. Call for special rates.

***Location:*** From Interstate 710 (Long Beach Freeway) in Monterey Park, take the Ramona Boulevard exit. The course is directly off the freeway on Ramona Boulevard.

***Course description:*** This is an executive course consisting of seven par-3s and two 300-yard par-4s. The course and adjoining driving range are lighted for night play. Last tee time is 9 p.m. weekdays and 8 p.m. Sundays.

## WHITTIER NARROWS GOLF COURSE

**Course 15**
MAP 15 grid c2

8640 East Rush Street
Rosemead, CA 91770

Pro shop (818) 288-1044

- ✓ **driving range**
- ✓ **practice greens**
- ✓ **power carts**
- pull carts
- ✓ **golf club rental**
- locker rooms
- showers
- ✓ **executive course**
- accommodations
- ✓ **food and beverages**
- ✓ **clubhouse**

**Nick Cassa Jr.**
Professional

**Jerry Wolfington**
Superintendent

***Course information:*** This public course has 18 holes and par is 72. The course is 6,490 yards from the regular tees and rated 69.3. The slope is 112. Women's tees are 5,965 yards. The slope rating is 110. There is also a nine-hole course. At 18 holes, the course is 5,050 yards, par-68.

***Play policy and fees:*** Green fees are $15.50 weekdays and $19.50 weekends and holidays for the 18-hole course, and $7 weekdays and $9 weekends for the short course. Carts are $18.

***Location:*** Off Highway 60 in Rosemead, take the San Gabriel Boulevard exit and drive north to Walnut Grove Street. Drive to Rush Street and turn right to the course.

***Course description:*** The main course is flat and narrow with lots of trees and elevated greens, and is not especially difficult. The short course is flat and open.

# PICO RIVERA MUNICIPAL GOLF COURSE

*Course information:* This public course has nine holes and par is 29. The course is 1,400 yards.

*Play policy and fees:* Green fees are $4 weekdays before 6 p.m., and $5 weekends and holidays. Call for special rates.

*Location:* From Interstate 605, take the Beverly Boulevard exit onto San Gabriel River Parkway to Fairway Drive. The course is off Fairway Drive.

*Course description:* All the greens are elevated on this nice little course. The longest hole is 270 yards, which is number five. Finishing holes eight and nine are surrounded by lakes. The course is lighted for night play.

**Course 16**
MAP I5 grid c3

3260 Fairway Drive
Pico Rivera, CA 90660

Pro shop (310) 692-9933

- ✓ **driving range**
- ✓ **practice greens**
- power carts
- ✓ **pull carts**
- ✓ **golf club rental**
- locker rooms
- showers
- ✓ **executive course**
- accommodations
- ✓ **food and beverages**
- clubhouse

**John Sattler**
Professional

**Jerry Wolfington**
Superintendent

# ARCADIA PAR-3

*Course information:* This public course has 18 holes. The course is 1,898 yards.

*Play policy and fees:* Green fees are $6.75 weekdays and $8.25 weekends. Senior rates are $5.50.

*Location:* Off Interstate 10 in Arcadia, exit on Santa Anita Avenue and drive south for two miles until you reach Live Oak. Follow Live Oak east 1.5 miles to the course on your right.

*Course description:* This flat course has no bunkers or water. You tee off from mats. The course is lighted for night play and is open until 10 p.m. The last tee time is 8 p.m. Good practice for your irons.

**Course 17**
MAP I5 grid c3

620 East Live Oak
Arcadia, CA 91006

Pro shop (818) 443-9367

- ✓ **driving range**
- ✓ **practice greens**
- power carts
- ✓ **pull carts**
- ✓ **golf club rental**
- locker rooms
- showers
- executive course
- accommodations
- ✓ **food and beverages**
- clubhouse

**Greg Castleman**
Professional

**Jose Castelanos**
Superintendent

## SANTA ANITA GOLF COURSE

**Course 18**
MAP I5 grid c3

*Course information:* This public course has 18 holes and par is 71. The course is 6,823 yards and rated 70.2 from the regular tees. The slope rating is 106. Women's tees are 5,908 yards and rated 73.1. The slope rating is 121.

*Play policy and fees:* Green fees are $15.50 weekdays and $19.50 weekends. Carts are $18. Reservations are recommended one week in advance.

*Location:* Take Santa Anita Avenue off Interstate 210 and drive south to the course.

*Course description:* This is a well-maintained course with tight fairways, undulating and smallish greens and several well-placed traps. It is long and challenging. It has rolling terrain and is more of a links-style course without the ocean. The Santa Anita Race Track is next door and the San Gabriel Mountains provide a pleasant backdrop.

**1938**
405 S. Santa Anita Avenue
Arcadia, CA 91006

Pro shop (818) 447-7156

- ✓ **driving range**
- ✓ **practice greens**
- ✓ **power carts**
- ✓ **pull carts**
- ✓ **golf club rental**
- locker rooms
- showers
- executive course
- accommodations
- ✓ **food and beverages**
- ✓ **clubhouse**

**Bud Merriam**
Professional

**Dave Cuellar**
Superintendent

## RANCHO DUARTE GOLF CLUB

**Course 19**
MAP I5 grid c4

*Course information:* This public course has nine holes. Par is 31. The course is 1,800 yards.

*Play policy and fees:* Green fees are $6 weekdays and $8 weekends. Reservations are recommended a week in advance. Seniors are $4.

*Location:* Driving on Interstate 210 in Duarte, take Mount Olive Drive and go right on Huntington. At the first stop light, turn left on Las Lomas and drive 1/2 block to the course on the right.

*Course description:* This course offers undulating fairways and greens. It's well bunkered. There are five par-3s and four par-4s. The longest hole is 330 yards, so golfers can use their woods.

1000 Las Lomas
Duarte, CA 91010

Pro shop (818) 357-9981

- ✓ **driving range**
- ✓ **practice greens**
- power carts
- ✓ **pull carts**
- ✓ **golf club rental**
- locker rooms
- showers
- ✓ **executive course**
- accommodations
- ✓ **food and beverages**
- ✓ **clubhouse**

**Doug Ruff**
Professional

**Fred Mendoza**
Superintendent

# AZUSA GREENS COUNTRY CLUB

**Course 20**
MAP I5 grid c5

919 W. Sierra Madre Blvd.
Azusa, CA 91702

Pro shop (818) 969-1727
Clubhouse (818) 969-1729

- ✓ **driving range**
- ✓ **practice greens**
- ✓ **power carts**
- pull carts
- golf club rental
- locker rooms
- showers
- executive course
- accommodations
- ✓ **food and beverages**
- ✓ **clubhouse**

**Jerry Herrera**
Professional

**Jesus Padilla**
Superintendent

Vince Welsh, Mgr.

***Course information:*** This public course has 18 holes. See card below for yardage and rating information.

***Play policy and fees:*** Green fees are $16 weekdays and $25 weekends, carts included. Call for special rates. This course is available for outside tournaments.

***Location:*** From Pasadena, travel east on Interstate 210 to the Azusa Avenue exit. Drive north three miles to Sierra Madre Boulevard and turn left to the clubhouse.

***Course description:*** Set at the base of the San Gabriel Valley foothills, this course is fairly level with straight, tree-lined fairways.

| Hole | 1 | 2 | 3 | 4 | 5 | 6 | 7 | 8 | 9 | Out | | |
|---|---|---|---|---|---|---|---|---|---|---|---|---|
| BLUE | 414 | 370 | 210 | 296 | 472 | 208 | 448 | 406 | 166 | 2990 | BLUE | Rating: 67.5 |
| WHITE | 382 | 355 | 199 | 276 | 463 | 193 | 435 | 388 | 149 | 2834 | | Slope: 105 |
| Par | 4 | 4 | 3 | 4 | 5 | 3 | 4 | 4 | 3 | 34 | WHITE | Rating: 67.4 |
| Handicap | 7 | 13 | 5 | 15 | 9 | 11 | 1 | 3 | 17 | x | | Slope: 105 |
| RED | 375 | 340 | 160 | 224 | 424 | 176 | 424 | 373 | 121 | 2619 | | |
| Par | 4 | 4 | 3 | 4 | 5 | 3 | 5 | 4 | 3 | 35 | RED | Rating: 71.8 |
| Handicap | 9 | 11 | 13 | 5 | 1 | 15 | 3 | 7 | 17 | x | | Slope: – |

| Hole | 10 | 11 | 12 | 13 | 14 | 15 | 16 | 17 | 18 | In | Totals | |
|---|---|---|---|---|---|---|---|---|---|---|---|---|
| BLUE | 280 | 501 | 277 | 124 | 385 | 380 | 435 | 396 | 365 | 3143 | BLUE | 6133 |
| WHITE | 274 | 477 | 269 | 118 | 369 | 356 | 426 | 390 | 346 | 3025 | WHITE | 5859 |
| Par | 4 | 5 | 4 | 3 | 4 | 4 | 4 | 4 | 4 | 36 | Par | 70 |
| Handicap | 14 | 6 | 16 | 18 | 10 | 8 | 2 | 4 | 12 | x | | |
| RED | 260 | 459 | 263 | 110 | 349 | 336 | 421 | 340 | 327 | 2865 | RED | 5484 |
| Par | 4 | 5 | 4 | 3 | 4 | 4 | 5 | 4 | 4 | 37 | Par | 72 |
| Handicap | 14 | 2 | 16 | 18 | 8 | 12 | 6 | 4 | 10 | x | | |

# SIERRA LA VERNE COUNTRY CLUB

**Course 21**
MAP I5 grid c5

**1976**
**Dan Murray**

6300 Country Club Drive
La Verne, CA 91750

Pro shop (909) 596-2100
Clubhouse (909) 596-2100

- ✓ **driving range**
- ✓ **practice greens**
- ✓ **power carts**
- pull carts
- ✓ **golf club rental**
- ✓ **locker rooms**
- ✓ **showers**
- executive course
- accommodations
- ✓ **food and beverages**
- ✓ **clubhouse**

**Frank Dailey**
Manager

**Harry Sailor**
Professional

**Don Johnson**
Superintendent

***Course information:*** This private course has 18 holes and par is 71. The course is 6,337 yards and rated 73.1 from the championship tees, and 5,996 yards and rated 68.5 from the regular tees. The slope ratings are 127 championship and 119 regular. Women's tees are 5,606 yards and rated 72.3. The slope rating is 121.

***Play policy and fees:*** Members and guests only. Guests must be accompanied by a member. Green fees are $30 weekdays and $40 weekends. Carts are $17. Reservations are recommended. This course is available for outside tournaments.

***Location:*** From Pasadena, travel east on Interstate 210. Exit at Foothill Boulevard heading east and drive to Wheeler Road north. At Golden Hills Road turn east and continue to Country Club Road and head south to the club. From Orange County, take Highway 57 north to Foothill Boulevard exit and follow as directed above.

***Course description:*** Set in the foothills of La Verne, this course is both picturesque and challenging. The front nine is more open and not as difficult as the back nine, which requires accuracy with irons and good putting on the well-manicured greens. The greens are severe, however, and difficult to read direction and speed.

# GLENOAKS GOLF COURSE

**Course 2.2**
MAP I5 grid c5

***Course information:*** This public course has nine holes. Par is 54 for 18 holes. The course is 1,120 yards.

***Play policy and fees:*** Green fees are $4 weekdays and $5 weekends. Seniors are $3. Call for special women and junior day rates. The course does not take reservations—it's first come, first served.

***Location:*** From Highway 210 exit at Grand Avenue exit. Go one block to Glendora Avenue, turn right and go to Dawson Avenue. Turn right and you're at the course.

***Course description:*** This is a well-maintained par-3 course. The longest hole here is 188 yards, so leave your woods at home. Tennis and racketball courts are nearby.

200 West Dawson
Glendora, CA 91740

Pro shop (818) 335-7565

- ✓ **driving range**
- ✓ **practice greens**
- power carts
- ✓ **pull carts**
- ✓ **golf club rental**
- locker rooms
- showers
- executive course
- accommodations
- ✓ **food and beverages**
- clubhouse

**Howard J. Perrin**
Manager

**Bruce Perrin**
Professional

**Richard Rand**
Superintendent

| Hole | 1 | 2 | 3 | 4 | 5 | 6 | 7 | 8 | 9 | Total | | |
|---|---|---|---|---|---|---|---|---|---|---|---|---|
| BLUE | - | - | - | - | - | - | - | - | - | - | BLUE | Rating: -- |
| | | | | | | | | | | | | Slope: -- |
| WHITE | 88 | 125 | 188 | 155 | 156 | 110 | 116 | 87 | 95 | 1120 | | |
| Par | 3 | 3 | 3 | 3 | 3 | 3 | 3 | 3 | 3 | 27 | WHITE | Rating: -- |
| Handicap | 9 | 5 | 1 | 3 | 2 | 6 | 4 | 8 | 7 | x | | Slope: -- |
| RED | 88 | 125 | 188 | 155 | 156 | 110 | 116 | 87 | 95 | 1120 | | |
| Par | 3 | 3 | 3 | 3 | 3 | 3 | 3 | 3 | 3 | 27 | RED | Rating: -- |
| Handicap | 9 | 5 | 1 | 3 | 2 | 6 | 4 | 8 | 7 | x | | Slope: -- |

## SAN DIMAS CANYON GOLF CLUB

**Course 23**
MAP 15 grid c6

2100 Terrebonne Avenue
San Dimas, CA 91773

Pro shop (909) 599-2313
(909) 966-8547
Fax (909) 592-2587

- ✓ **driving range**
- ✓ **practice greens**
- ✓ **power carts**
- ✓ **pull carts**
- ✓ **golf club rental**
- locker rooms
- showers
- executive course
- accommodations
- ✓ **food and beverages**
- ✓ **clubhouse**

**George Landry**
Manager/Professional

**David Anderson**
Superintendent

***Course information:*** This public course has 18 holes and par is 72. The course is 6,315 yards and rated 70.1 from the championship tees, and 5,943 yards and rated 67.9 from the regular tees. The slope ratings are 119 championship and 108 regular. Women's tees are 5,549 yards and rated 72.3. The slope rating is 117.

***Play policy and fees:*** Green fees are $14 weekdays and $21 weekends. Carts are $20. Reservations are recommended. This course is available for outside tournaments.

***Location:*** Travel east on Interstate 210 (Foothill Freeway) and Highway 30 to the San Dimas Avenue exit. Travel north to Foothill Boulevard and turn right, and drive three-fourths of a mile to San Dimas Canyon Road. Go left and continue one mile to the Terrebonne Avenue entrance to Gray Oaks, then turn left to the club.

***Course description:*** This course offers a distinctive, interesting layout over a relatively level front nine and a hilly back nine. Four water hazards come into play. The 165-yard 16th hole is a real challenge. From an elevated tee, you hit over a lake to a green faced by a rock retaining wall and surrounded by mounds and pot bunkers. The course record is 66 for men and 70 for women.

## GLENDORA COUNTRY CLUB

**Course 24**
MAP 15 grid c6

310 South Amelia Avenue
Glendora, CA 91740

Pro shop (818) 335-3713

- ✓ **driving range**
- ✓ **practice greens**
- ✓ **power carts**
- ✓ **pull carts**
- ✓ **golf club rental**
- ✓ **locker rooms**
- ✓ **showers**
- executive course
- accommodations
- ✓ **food and beverages**
- ✓ **clubhouse**

**Dave Endorby**
Manager

**Robert Powell**
Professional

**Condie Lopez**
Superintendent

***Course information:*** This private course has 18 holes and par is 72. The course is 6,597 yards and rated 72.6 from the championship tees, and 6,377 yards and rated 71.2 from the regular tees. The slope ratings are 131 championship and 125 regular. Women's tees are 6,377 yards and rated 76.2 from the championship tees, and 5,992 yards and rated 75.1 from the regular tees. The slope ratings are 131 for both championship and regular.

***Play policy and fees:*** Members and guests only. Green fees are $35. Carts are $18 for two.

***Location:*** Travel east on Interstate 210. (Stay in the middle lane.) At the "End of Freeway/Foothill Boulevard" sign, take the Lone Hill exit and drive north for one-half mile to Alosta Avenue. Turn right and drive one-half mile to Amelia Avenue and turn left to the club.

***Course description:*** This picturesque course is set at the foot of the San Gabriel Mountains. The narrow, tree-lined fairways are fairly level and easy to walk. It is a traditional East Coast type of course, with gently rolling fairways and small greens.

## MARSHALL CANYON GOLF CLUB

**Course 25**
MAP 15 grid c6

**1966**
6100 North Stephens Ranch Road
La Verne, CA 91750

Pro shop (714) 593-6914
Clubhouse (714) 593-8211

- ✓ **driving range**
- ✓ **practice greens**
- ✓ **power carts**
- ✓ **pull carts**
- ✓ **golf club rental**
- locker rooms
- showers
- executive course
- accommodations
- ✓ **food and beverages**
- ✓ **clubhouse**

**Jamie Deffin**
Manager

**Pete Gray**
Professional

**A.B. Nunez**
Superintendent

***Course information:*** This public course has 18 holes. See card below for yardage and rating information.

***Play policy and fees:*** Green fees are $12.50 weekdays and $16.50 weekends. Twilight rates are $8.50 weekdays and $10.50 weekends after 4 p.m. Seniors play for $6.25 weekdays. Carts are $16. Reservations are recommended.

***Location:*** Take Interstate 210 east to Wheeler, then go north to Golden Hills. Go east on Golden Hills to Stephens Ranch Road and north to the course.

***Course description:*** This course is located in a canyon at the base of the San Gabriel Mountains. They offer a spectacular backdrop. The greens have a great deal of contour and are extremely tricky, particularly because of the mountains, which cause optical illusions. The par-3, 177-yard 11th hole plays over part of the canyon and is particularly scenic. The Pomona Valley Amateur Championship is held over Labor Day weekend. The course record is 59.

| Hole | 1 | 2 | 3 | 4 | 5 | 6 | 7 | 8 | 9 | Out | | |
|---|---|---|---|---|---|---|---|---|---|---|---|---|
| BLUE | 471 | 163 | 356 | 368 | 414 | 313 | 207 | 303 | 352 | 2947 | BLUE | Rating: 68.5 |
| WHITE | 462 | 154 | 340 | 356 | 404 | 304 | 195 | 290 | 342 | 2847 | | Slope: 111 |
| Par | 5 | 3 | 4 | 4 | 4 | 4 | 3 | 4 | 4 | 35 | WHITE | Rating: 67.2 |
| Handicap | 11 | 17 | 3 | 5 | 1 | 13 | 9 | 15 | 7 | x | | Slope: 107 |
| RED | 450 | 145 | 314 | 351 | 401 | 304 | 185 | 287 | 323 | 2760 | | |
| Par | 5 | 3 | 4 | 4 | 5 | 4 | 3 | 4 | 4 | 36 | RED | Rating: 72.3 |
| Handicap | 3 | 17 | 7 | 1 | 11 | 13 | 5 | 15 | 9 | x | | Slope: 117 |

| Hole | 10 | 11 | 12 | 13 | 14 | 15 | 16 | 17 | 18 | In | Totals | |
|---|---|---|---|---|---|---|---|---|---|---|---|---|
| BLUE | 482 | 177 | 318 | 424 | 352 | 376 | 175 | 460 | 404 | 3168 | BLUE | 6115 |
| WHITE | 469 | 161 | 297 | 417 | 342 | 351 | 161 | 405 | 393 | 2995 | WHITE | 5843 |
| Par | 5 | 3 | 4 | 4 | 4 | 4 | 3 | 5 | 4 | 36 | Par | 71 |
| Handicap | 6 | 18 | 14 | 2 | 10 | 8 | 16 | 12 | 4 | x | | |
| RED | 461 | 138 | 296 | 402 | 329 | 340 | 117 | 402 | 319 | 2304 | RED | 5564 |
| Par | 5 | 3 | 4 | 5 | 4 | 4 | 3 | 5 | 4 | 37 | Par | 73 |
| Handicap | 2 | 16 | 12 | 4 | 8 | 10 | 18 | 6 | 14 | x | | |

## UPLAND HILLS COUNTRY CLUB

**Course 26**
MAP 15 grid c8

**1983**
**Ted Robinson**

1231 East 16th Street
Upland, CA 91786

Pro shop (714) 946-4711
Clubhouse (714) 946-3057

- driving range
- ✓ **practice greens**
- ✓ **power carts**
- ✓ **pull carts**
- ✓ **golf club rental**
- ✓ **locker rooms**
- ✓ **showers**
- executive course
- accommodations
- ✓ **food and beverages**
- ✓ **clubhouse**

**Scott Chaffin**
Professional/Manager

**Jim Janisik**
Superintendent

***Course information:*** This semi-private course has 18 holes and par is 70. The course is 5,827 yards and rated 67.1 from the regular tees. The slope rating is 111. Women's tees are 4,813 yards and rated 66.5. The slope rating is 106.

***Play policy and fees:*** Outside play is accepted. Green fees are $26 weekdays and $34 weekends, including carts. This course is available for outside tournaments.

***Location:*** Travel east on Interstate 10 (San Bernardino Freeway) to Euclid Avenue in Upland. Turn north to 16th Street, then east for one mile to the club on the left.

***Course description:*** Located in the foothills, this relatively young course is fairly flat and easy to walk. Six lakes and fast greens add to the challenge. It is short and tight, causing lots of trouble, but it's always in good condition. Out-of-bounds stakes line both sides of the fairways on 15 holes.

## FORD PARK GOLF COURSE

**Course 27**
MAP 15 grid d1

8000 Park Lane
Bell Gardens, CA 90201

Pro shop (310) 927-8811

- ✓ **driving range**
- ✓ **practice greens**
- power carts
- ✓ **pull carts**
- ✓ **golf club rental**
- locker rooms
- showers
- executive course
- accommodations
- ✓ **food and beverages**
- clubhouse

**Tom Jackson**
Manager

***Course information:*** This public layout has nine holes, par is 27. The course is 1,017 yards.

***Play policy and fees:*** Green fees are $3.50 weekdays and $4 weekends. Juniors and seniors are $1.75 weekdays.

***Location:*** In Bell Gardens, take the Garfield Avenue exit off Interstate 5 and travel west about three miles to Park Lane. From there, take a right and you'll see the course.

***Course description:*** This is a short par-3 course, excellent for working on your short game. Leave your woods and long irons at home, though.

# MONTEBELLO GOLF COURSE

**Course 28**
**MAP I5 grid d2**

*Course information:* This public course has 18 holes and par is 71. The course is 6,601 yards and rated 70.4 from the championship tees, and 6,328 yards and rated 68.9 from the regular tees. The slope ratings are 114 championship and 103 regular. Women's tees are 5,967 yards and rated 72.6. The slope rating is 117.

*Play policy and fees:* Green fees are $14 weekdays and $18 weekends. Carts are $18. Reservations are recommended.

*Location:* In Montebello, travelling on Highway 60 (Pomona Freeway), exit at Garfield Avenue and drive south for one block. Turn right on Via San Clemente at the club sign.

*Course description:* Built in 1928, this flat course is one of the better maintained courses in the area. It is fairly long for a public course. Trees line many of the fairways, placing a premium on accuracy off the tees.

**1928**

PO Box 34
Montebello, CA 90640

901 Via San Clemente
Montebello, CA 90640

Pro shop (213) 723-2971
Clubhouse (213) 721-2311

- ✓ **driving range**
- ✓ **practice greens**
- ✓ **power carts**
- pull carts
- golf club rental
- locker rooms
- showers
- executive course
- accommodations
- ✓ **food and beverages**
- ✓ **clubhouse**

**Thomas Camacho**
Professional/Manager

**Henry Aguilar**
Superintendent

# CALIFORNIA COUNTRY CLUB

**Course 29**
MAP I5 grid d3

***Course information:*** This private course has 18 holes and par is 72. The course is 6,812 yards and rated 72.5 from the championship tees, and 6,522 yards and rated 70.8 from the regular tees. The slope ratings are 126 championship and 120 regular. Women's tees are 6,522 yards and rated 77.3 from the championship tees, and 6,169 yards and rated 75.0 from the forward tees. The slope ratings are 131 championship and 125 forward.

***Play policy and fees:*** Members and guests only. Green fees are $30 weekdays and $60 weekends. Carts are $17. This course is available for outside tournaments on Mondays, Thursday and Fridays.

***Location:*** From Los Angeles, travel on Highway 60 (Pomona Freeway) east to the Crossroads Parkway exit; left over freeway. Then left at the stoplight to Workman Mill Road. Turn right and go to Colcford Avenue, then left to the club.

***Course description:*** It is mostly a flat course except for a few elevated tees. Water hazards are minimal. It is a course built in the old traditional style. It plays extremely long, although it is fairly wide open.

**1956**
**William Park Bell**

PO Box 31
Whittier, CA 90608

1509 S. Workman Mill Road
Whittier, CA 90601

Pro shop (818) 333-4571
Clubhouse (310) 692-0421

- driving range
- ✓ **practice greens**
- ✓ **power carts**
- pull carts
- ✓ **golf club rental**
- ✓ **locker rooms**
- ✓ **showers**
- executive course
- accommodations
- ✓ **food and beverages**
- ✓ **clubhouse**

**Ric Rodriquez**
Professional

**Bob Johnson**

SOUTHERN I5

MAP ON PAGE 506

# WILDWOOD MOBILE COUNTRY CLUB

**Course 30**
MAP I5 grid d3

901 South 6th Avenue
Hacienda Heights, CA 91745
Office (818) 968-2338

- driving range
- ✓ **practice greens**
- power carts
- pull carts
- golf club rental
- locker rooms
- showers
- executive course
- accommodations
- food and beverages
- clubhouse

**Herb Middlemiss**
Manager

***Course information:*** This private course has nine holes. Par is 54 for 18 holes. The course is all par-3s.

***Play policy and fees:*** Members and guests only. This is a resident course. Memberships are available at $51 per year. There are no daily fees. No carts are allowed.

***Location:*** This course is located off of Highway 60 in Hacienda Heights. Take the Seventh Avenue exit north. At the first light, turn left on Clark Street, which runs into the course.

***Course description:*** This mostly flat course can be intimidating because it is so narrow. There's a fence on one side and mobile homes on the other.

| Hole | 1 | 2 | 3 | 4 | 5 | 6 | 7 | 8 | 9 | Out | | |
|---|---|---|---|---|---|---|---|---|---|---|---|---|
| BLUE | | | | | | | | | | | BLUE | Rating: -- |
| | | | | | | | | | | | | Slope: -- |
| WHITE | 63 | 128 | 123 | 116 | 143 | 175 | 133 | 193 | 116 | 1190 | | |
| Par | 3 | 3 | 3 | 3 | 3 | 3 | 3 | 3 | 3 | 27 | WHITE | Rating: -- |
| Handicap | 17 | 5 | 11 | 15 | 9 | 1 | 7 | 3 | 13 | x | | Slope: -- |
| RED | 63 | 128 | 123 | 116 | 143 | 175 | 133 | 137 | 116 | 1134 | | |
| Par | 3 | 3 | 3 | 3 | 3 | 3 | 3 | 3 | 3 | 27 | RED | Rating: - |
| Handicap | 17 | 7 | 11 | 15 | 9 | 1 | 3 | 5 | 13 | x | | Slope: – |

| Hole | 10 | 11 | 12 | 13 | 14 | 15 | 16 | 17 | 18 | In | Totals | |
|---|---|---|---|---|---|---|---|---|---|---|---|---|
| BLUE | - | - | - | - | - | - | - | - | - | - | BLUE | -- |
| WHITE | 63 | 128 | 123 | 116 | 143 | 175 | 133 | 193 | 116 | 1190 | WHITE | 2380 |
| Par | 3 | 3 | 3 | 3 | 3 | 3 | 3 | 3 | 3 | 27 | Par | 54 |
| Handicap | 18 | 6 | 12 | 16 | 10 | 2 | 8 | 4 | 14 | x | | |
| RED | 63 | 128 | 123 | 116 | 143 | 175 | 133 | 137 | 116 | 1134 | RED | 2268 |
| Par | 3 | 3 | 3 | 3 | 3 | 3 | 3 | 3 | 3 | 27 | Par | 54 |
| Handicap | 18 | 8 | 12 | 16 | 10 | 2 | 4 | 6 | 14 | x | | |

# INDUSTRY HILLS GOLF CLUB

**Course 31**
MAP I5 grid d4

1 Industry Hills Parkway
City of Industry, CA 91744

Pro shop (818) 965-0861
Reservation (818) 810-4653

- ✓ **driving range**
- ✓ **practice greens**
- ✓ **power carts**
- ✓ **pull carts**
- ✓ **golf club rental**
- ✓ **locker rooms**
- ✓ **showers**
- executive course
- ✓ **accommodations**
- ✓ **food and beverages**
- ✓ **clubhouse**

**Richard Stegall**
Professional

**Kent Davidson**
Superintendent

***Course information:*** This public club has two 18-hole courses. Par is 72 on the Eisenhower Course and 71 on the Zaharias Course.

The Eisenhower Course is 7,181 yards and rated 76.4 from the championship tees, and 6,735 yards and rated 73.5 from the regular tees. The slope ratings are 149 championship and 138 regular. Women's tees are 5,507 yards and rated 73.0. The slope rating is 126.

The Zaharias Course is 6,830 yards and rated 74.2 from the tournament tees, and 6,600 yards and rated 72.9 from the championship tees, and 6,124 yards and rated 70.3 from the regular tees. The slope ratings are 144 tournament, 137 championship and 130 regular. Women's tees are 5,394 yards and rated 71.8. The slope rating is 123.

***Play policy and fees:*** Green fees are $42 Monday through Thursday and $57 weekends. Cart included. Reservations are recommended.

***Location:*** Travel on Highway 60 to the Azusa Avenue exit north. Drive 1.5 miles to the cobblestones and turn left on Industry Hills Parkway and continue to the club. From Interstate 10 (San Bernardino Freeway) take Azusa Avenue exit; drive south on Azusa for three miles to cobblestones and turn right on Industry Hills Parkway to the club.

***Course description:*** Both courses are part of the Sheraton Hotel complex. The Eisenhower Course has been rated one of the top 25 public courses in the United States by *Golf Digest*. It's long and is an extremely demanding tract. Both courses can be exceedingly difficult, especially when the Kikuyu rough is thick. The greens are huge, but often tiered and undulating. U.S. Open qualifying is frequently held here. The Zaharias Course is tighter and trickier. A shot-maker will excel here. Both courses cover rolling and hilly terrain and make use of a funicular, imported from Switzerland to transport players.

# SOUTH HILLS COUNTRY CLUB

**Course 32**
MAP I5 grid d5

**1954**
**William Park Bell**

2655 South Citrus Avenue
West Covina, CA 91791

Pro shop (818) 332-3222
Clubhouse (818) 339-1231

- ✓ **driving range**
- ✓ **practice greens**
- ✓ **power carts**
- pull carts
- ✓ **golf club rental**
- ✓ **locker rooms**
- ✓ **showers**
- executive course
- accommodations
- ✓ **food and beverages**
- ✓ **clubhouse**

**Ron Erickson**
Manager

**Dave Carollo**
Professional

**Scott McColgan**
Superintendent

***Course information:*** This private course has 18 holes. See card below for yardage and rating information.

***Play policy and fees:*** Members and guests only. Guests must be accompanied by a member at time of play. Guest fees are $35 weekdays and $45 weekends. Carts are $16. Men must wear collared shirts. Jeans or shorts are not allowed. Women's skirts must be no shorter than four inches above the knee. No halters or tank tops are allowed.

***Location:*** From Los Angeles, travel on Interstate 10 (San Bernardino Freeway) to the Citrus Avenue exit and drive south for one mile to the club at the Lark Hill Drive intersection.

***Course description:*** This is a course for shot-makers. It requires precision iron play and a great imagination on and around the greens. The fairways are medium width over rolling terrain. A fair number of bunkers surround the well-groomed, fast greens. It is a right-to-left course favoring players who hook the ball. The Hustlers Invitational tournament is held here in April, the Mr. and Mrs. Invitational in August, and the Tres Dias in September.

| Hole | 1 | 2 | 3 | 4 | 5 | 6 | 7 | 8 | 9 | Out | WHITE | Rating: 71.1 |
|---|---|---|---|---|---|---|---|---|---|---|---|---|
| WHITE | 321 | 336 | 154 | 526 | 210 | 523 | 318 | 487 | 389 | 3264 | | Slope: 125 |
| GOLD | 298 | 320 | 139 | 494 | 193 | 498 | 307 | 468 | 376 | 3093 | | |
| Par | 4 | 4 | 3 | 5 | 3 | 5 | 4 | 5 | 4 | 37 | GOLD | Rating: 68.8 |
| Handicap | 11 | 7 | 17 | 1 | 13 | 9 | 15 | 5 | 3 | x | | Slope: 118 |
| RED | 286 | 312 | 122 | 454 | 170 | 476 | 300 | 429 | 356 | 2905 | | |
| Par | 4 | 4 | 3 | 5 | 3 | 5 | 4 | 5 | 4 | 37 | RED | Rating: 72.5 |
| Handicap | 11 | 7 | 17 | 5 | 15 | 1 | 13 | 9 | 3 | x | | Slope: 126 |

| Hole | 10 | 11 | 12 | 13 | 14 | 15 | 16 | 17 | 18 | In | Totals | |
|---|---|---|---|---|---|---|---|---|---|---|---|---|
| WHITE | 150 | 339 | 443 | 334 | 528 | 206 | 401 | 160 | 559 | 3120 | WHITE | 6384 |
| GOLD | 130 | 324 | 409 | 325 | 478 | 165 | 377 | 146 | 530 | 2884 | GOLD | 5977 |
| Par | 3 | 4 | 4 | 4 | 5 | 3 | 4 | 3 | 5 | 35 | Par | 72 |
| Handicap | 18 | 12 | 2 | 14 | 6 | 10 | 4 | 16 | 8 | x | | |
| RED | 122 | 286 | 407 | 301 | 449 | 137 | 371 | 131 | 494 | 2698 | RED | 5603 |
| Par | 3 | 4 | 4 | 4 | 5 | 3 | 4 | 3 | 5 | 35 | Par | 72 |
| Handicap | 16 | 12 | 2 | 10 | 4 | 18 | 6 | 14 | 8 | x | | |

# VIA VERDE COUNTRY CLUB

**Course 33**
MAP 15 grid d5

***Course information:*** This private course has 18 holes and par is 72. The course is 6,411 yards and rated 69.9 from the championship tees, and 6,129 yards and rated 68.7 from the regular tees. The slope ratings are 129 championship and 123 regular. Women's tees are 5,798 yards and rated 74.5. The slope rating is 121.

***Play policy and fees:*** Members and guests only. Green fees are $28 weekdays and $45 weekends. Carts are $18.

***Location:*** From San Bernardino, drive west on Interstate 10 (San Bernardino Freeway) to the Via Verde exit. Drive north one mile to Avenida Entrada and turn left. Drive three-fourths of a mile to the end and turn left to the club.

***Course description:*** This course, set on a hill, is well-bunkered with narrow fairways and rolling terrain. It is set within a residential community. The greens are extremely fast and usually in excellent condition. Water comes into play on two holes. It is primarily a target golf course: accuracy is imperative.

**1968**
1400 Avenida Entrada
San Dimas, CA 91773

Pro shop (714) 599-8486
Clubhouse (818) 966-4451

- ✓ **driving range**
- ✓ **practice greens**
- ✓ **power carts**
- pull carts
- golf club rental
- ✓ **locker rooms**
- ✓ **showers**
- executive course
- accommodations
- ✓ **food and beverages**
- ✓ **clubhouse**

**Tim Haas**
Professional

**Dal Lee**
Manager

**Rafael Martinez**
Superintendent

## MOUNTAIN MEADOWS GOLF COURSE

**Course 34**
MAP 15 grid d6

1875 Fairplex Drive
Pomona, CA 91768

Pro shop (714) 623-3704
Starter (714) 629-1166
Seniors (714) 623-2953

✓ **driving range**
✓ **practice greens**
✓ **power carts**
✓ **pull carts**
✓ **golf club rental**
locker rooms
showers
executive course
accommodations
✓ **food and beverages**
✓ **clubhouse**

**Kurt Knop**
Manager

**Joe Lerma**
Superintendent

*Course information:* This public course has 18 holes and par is 72. The course is 6,508 yards and rated 71.5 from the championship tees, and 6,141 yards and rated 68.4 from the regular tees. The slope ratings are 125 championship and 118 regular. Women's tees are 5,637 yards and rated 71.5. The slope rating is 117.

*Play policy and fees:* Green fees are $15.50 weekdays and $19.50 weekends. Carts are $18, plus a $5 refundable key deposit.

*Location:* Travel on Interstate 10 (San Bernardino Freeway) to the Fairplex Drive exit. Go north on Fairplex to the club.

*Course description:* This is a hilly course with numerous trees flanking the fairways. For scenery and difficulty, watch out for number 13. It's 226 yards and par-3 over a canyon and overlooking a part of the San Gabriel Valley. It is a great view on those rare days when there is no smog. The course overlooks the Los Angeles County Fairgrounds.

## RED HILL COUNTRY CLUB

**Course 35**
MAP 15 grid d8

**1921**
8358 Red Hill Country Club
Rancho Cucamonga, CA
91730

Pro shop (714) 982-4559
Clubhouse (714) 982-1358

✓ **driving range**
✓ **practice greens**
✓ **power carts**
✓ **pull carts**
golf club rental
✓ **locker rooms**
✓ **showers**
executive course
accommodations
✓ **food and beverages**
✓ **clubhouse**

**Jim Porter**
Professional

**Ernie Pacheco**
Superintendent

*Course information:* This private course has 18 holes and par is 72. The course is 6,621 yards and rated 71.9 from the championship tees, and 6,296 yards and rated 69.7 from the regular tees. The slope ratings are 121 championship and 116 regular. Women's tees are 6,020 yards and rated 75. The slope rating is 130.

*Play policy and fees:* Members and guests only. Guests must be accompanied by members at time of play. Guest fees are $35. Carts are $17. Golfers must wear collared shirts. Blue jeans and sweats are not allowed.

*Location:* Take Interstate 10 (San Bernardino Freeway) to the Euclid Avenue exit (west of San Bernardino) and drive north to Foothill Boulevard. Turn right and drive 1.5 miles to Red Hill Country Club Drive and turn left to the club.

*Course description:* This deceptive course offers a challenging test of golf. It is a traditional layout, void of railroad ties or other gimmicks. There are lots of trees and undulating greens. A point to remember: Two new ponds have been incorporated into holes seven and eight. It is a very pleasant course to play.

# VIRGINIA COUNTRY CLUB

**Course 36**
MAP 15 grid e0

***Course information:*** This private course has 18 holes. See card below for yardage and rating information.

***Play policy and fees:*** Members and guests only. Guest fees are $35 weekdays and $45 weekends. Carts are $16.

***Location:*** Travel on Interstate 405 to Long Beach Boulevard north. Turn left on San Antonio Road and right on Virginia Road.

***Course description:*** This is a medium-length, testy course designed in the old traditional style. This is a very private club, which counts among its members former American League All-Star Bobby Grich. The property is the site of Lynx's testing facility.

**1923**
**William Park Bell**

4602 Virginia Road
Long Beach, CA 90807

Pro shop (310) 424-5211
Clubhouse (310) 427-0924

- ✓ **driving range**
- ✓ **practice greens**
- ✓ **power carts**
- pull carts
- ✓ **golf club rental**
- ✓ **locker rooms**
- ✓ **showers**
- executive course
- accommodations
- ✓ **food and beverages**
- ✓ **clubhouse**

**II. Jeff Schlicht**
Manager

**Mike Bacica**
Professional

**Ray Davies**
Superintendent

| Hole | 1 | 2 | 3 | 4 | 5 | 6 | 7 | 8 | 9 | Out | BLUE | Rating: 71.1 |
|---|---|---|---|---|---|---|---|---|---|---|---|---|
| BLUE | 387 | 393 | 206 | 362 | 526 | 433 | 196 | 374 | 367 | 3244 | | Slope: 124 |
| WHITE | 378 | 373 | 192 | 347 | 511 | 412 | 160 | 368 | 354 | 3095 | | |
| Par | 4 | 4 | 3 | 4 | 5 | 4 | 3 | 4 | 4 | 35 | WHITE | Rating: 69.6 |
| Handicap | 3 | 5 | 13 | 15 | 9 | 1 | 17 | 7 | 11 | x | | Slope: 120 |
| RED | 358 | 262 | 186 | 333 | 415 | 402 | 125 | 352 | 334 | 2767 | | |
| Par | 4 | 4 | 3 | 4 | 5 | 5 | 3 | 4 | 4 | 36 | RED | Rating: 73.4 |
| Handicap | 3 | 17 | 11 | 13 | 7 | 5 | 15 | 1 | 9 | x | | Slope: 123 |

| Hole | 10 | 11 | 12 | 13 | 14 | 15 | 16 | 17 | 18 | In | Totals | |
|---|---|---|---|---|---|---|---|---|---|---|---|---|
| BLUE | 171 | 375 | 502 | 400 | 308 | 140 | 398 | 390 | 540 | 3224 | BLUE | 6468 |
| WHITE | 167 | 366 | 496 | 374 | 306 | 124 | 383 | 369 | 524 | 3109 | WHITE | 6204 |
| Par | 3 | 4 | 5 | 4 | 4 | 3 | 4 | 4 | 5 | 36 | Par | 71 |
| Handicap | 16 | 4 | 12 | 2 | 10 | 18 | 6 | 8 | 14 | x | | |
| RED | 159 | 351 | 495 | 349 | 304 | 107 | 367 | 353 | 489 | 2974 | RED | 5741 |
| Par | 3 | 4 | 5 | 4 | 4 | 3 | 4 | 4 | 5 | 36 | Par | 72 |
| Handicap | 16 | 4 | 2 | 14 | 12 | 18 | 8 | 6 | 10 | x | | |



MAP ON PAGE 506

# SOUTH GATE MUNICIPAL GOLF COURSE

Course 37
MAP I5 grid e1

**1959**
9615 Pinehurst Avenue
South Gate, CA 90280

Administration:
4900 Southern Ave.
South Gate, CA 90280

Pro shop (213) 564-1434

- driving range
- ✓ **practice greens**
- power carts
- pull carts
- golf club rental
- locker rooms
- showers
- executive course
- accommodations
- food and beverages
- clubhouse

**Dan Holmes**
Manager

**Cindy Tallen**
Superintendent

***Course information:*** This public course has nine holes. Par is 54 for 18 holes. See card below for additional yardage information.

***Play policy and fees:*** Green fees are $3.50 weekdays and $4.50 weekends for nine holes. Seniors play for $2.50.

***Location:*** From Highway 42 in South Gate, take the Central Avenue exit to Pinehurst, turn right and drive about one-half of a mile to the course.

***Course description:*** This is a par-3 course in which only irons are required. It features several large trees. It offers a driving cage, rather than a driving range.

| Hole | 1 | 2 | 3 | 4 | 5 | 6 | 7 | 8 | 9 | Out | | |
|---|---|---|---|---|---|---|---|---|---|---|---|---|
| BLUE | - | - | - | - | - | - | - | - | - | - | BLUE | Rating: -- |
| | | | | | | | | | | | | Slope: -- |
| WHITE | 82 | 99 | 105 | 102 | 100 | 120 | 136 | 156 | 110 | 1010 | | |
| Par | 3 | 3 | 3 | 3 | 3 | 3 | 3 | 3 | 3 | 27 | WHITE | Rating: -- |
| Handicap | 17 | 15 | 9 | 11 | 13 | 5 | 3 | 1 | 7 | x | | Slope: -- |
| RED | 82 | 99 | 105 | 102 | 100 | 120 | 136 | 156 | 110 | 1010 | | |
| Par | 3 | 3 | 3 | 3 | 3 | 3 | 3 | 3 | 3 | 27 | RED | Rating: -- |
| Handicap | 17 | 15 | 9 | 11 | 13 | 5 | 3 | 1 | 7 | x | | Slope: -- |

| Hole | 10 | 11 | 12 | 13 | 14 | 15 | 16 | 17 | 18 | In | Totals | |
|---|---|---|---|---|---|---|---|---|---|---|---|---|
| BLUE | - | - | - | - | - | - | - | - | - | - | BLUE | -- |
| WHITE | 82 | 99 | 105 | 102 | 100 | 120 | 136 | 156 | 110 | 1010 | WHITE | 2020 |
| Par | 3 | 3 | 3 | 3 | 3 | 3 | 3 | 3 | 3 | 27 | Par | 54 |
| Handicap | 18 | 16 | 10 | 12 | 14 | 6 | 4 | 2 | 8 | x | | |
| RED | 82 | 99 | 105 | 102 | 100 | 120 | 136 | 156 | 110 | 1010 | RED | 2020 |
| Par | 3 | 3 | 3 | 3 | 3 | 3 | 3 | 3 | 3 | 27 | Par | 54 |
| Handicap | 18 | 16 | 10 | 12 | 14 | 6 | 4 | 2 | 8 | x | | |

# LOS AMIGOS COUNTRY CLUB

**Course 38**
MAP I5 grid e1

**1966**
**Ron Reige**

7295 Quill Drive
Downey, CA 90242

Pro shop (213) 862-1717
Starter (213) 869-0302
Clubhouse (213) 923-9696

- ✓ **driving range**
- ✓ **practice greens**
- ✓ **power carts**
- ✓ **pull carts**
- ✓ **golf club rental**
- locker rooms
- showers
- executive course
- accommodations
- ✓ **food and beverages**
- ✓ **clubhouse**

**Mark Novorot**
Professional/Manager

**Jim Duffin**
Superintendent

***Course information:*** This public layout has 18 holes. See card below for yardage and rating information.

***Play policy and fees:*** Green fees are $12.50 weekdays and $16.50 weekends. Senior rates are $6.25. Carts are $18. Reservations are recommended. This course is available for outside tournaments.

***Location:*** From the Long Beach Freeway (Interstate 710), take the Imperial Highway east to Old River School Road. Turn left to the course on Quill Drive.

***Course description:*** This is a well-maintained public golf facility with large greens. It plays long, requiring good distance from fairway shots to reach the greens in regulation. The greens can be quick when baked under the hot summer sun. Water comes into play frequently. This is one of the busier courses in Southern California with about 135,000 rounds played annually.

| Hole | 1 | 2 | 3 | 4 | 5 | 6 | 7 | 8 | 9 | Out | | |
|---|---|---|---|---|---|---|---|---|---|---|---|---|
| BLUE | 512 | 402 | 160 | 364 | 377 | 376 | 151 | 493 | 240 | 3075 | BLUE | Rating: 67.5 |
| WHITE | 486 | 383 | 144 | 354 | 368 | 350 | 137 | 477 | 227 | 2958 | | Slope: 110 |
| Par | 5 | 4 | 3 | 4 | 4 | 4 | 3 | 5 | 3 | 35 | WHITE | Rating: 66.4 |
| Handicap | 5 | 1 | 15 | 3 | 7 | 11 | 17 | 13 | 9 | x | | Slope: 108 |
| RED | 499 | 370 | 145 | 346 | 362 | 350 | 132 | 486 | 225 | 2915 | | |
| Par | 5 | 4 | 3 | 4 | 4 | 4 | 3 | 5 | 4 | 36 | RED | Rating: 71.5 |
| Handicap | 1 | 5 | 15 | 9 | 7 | 11 | 17 | 3 | 13 | x | | Slope: 112 |

| Hole | 10 | 11 | 12 | 13 | 14 | 15 | 16 | 17 | 18 | In | Totals | |
|---|---|---|---|---|---|---|---|---|---|---|---|---|
| BLUE | 333 | 314 | 119 | 398 | 335 | 495 | 370 | 187 | 380 | 2931 | BLUE | 6006 |
| WHITE | 318 | 304 | 109 | 358 | 324 | 466 | 359 | 171 | 359 | 2828 | WHITE | 5786 |
| Par | 4 | 4 | 3 | 4 | 4 | 5 | 4 | 3 | 4 | 35 | Par | 70 |
| Handicap | 16 | 14 | 18 | 2 | 4 | 10 | 6 | 12 | 8 | x | | |
| RED | 315 | 303 | 115 | 366 | 319 | 473 | 351 | 149 | 340 | 2731 | RED | 5646 |
| Par | 4 | 4 | 3 | 4 | 4 | 5 | 4 | 3 | 4 | 35 | Par | 71 |
| Handicap | 12 | 14 | 18 | 6 | 10 | 2 | 4 | 16 | 8 | x | | |

## RIO HONDO COUNTRY CLUB

**Course 39**
MAP I5 grid e1

*Course information:* This public facility has 18 holes and par is 70. The course is 5,921 yards and rated 67.3 from the regular tees. The slope rating is 104. Women's tees are 5,576 and rated 71.3 from the regular tees. The slope rating is 115.

*Play policy and fees:* Green fees are $12 weekdays and $16 weekends. Carts are $18. Reservations are recommended.

*Location:* Take Interstate 710 (Long Beach Freeway) in Downey to the Firestone Boulevard exit. Drive east for one mile to Old River Road. Turn left and continue one-half of a mile to the club.

*Course description:* This is a level course with narrow, tree-lined fairways. It is not long, but the width of the fairways and size of the greens places a premium on accuracy. It's in great shape.

10629 Old River School Rd.
Downey, CA 90241

Pro shop (310) 927-2329
Starter (310) 927-2420

✓ **driving range**
✓ **practice greens**
✓ **power carts**
✓ **pull carts**
✓ **golf club rental**
✓ **locker rooms**
✓ **showers**
executive course
accommodations
✓ **food and beverages**
✓ **clubhouse**

**Bruce MacDonald**
Professional

**John Rodriquez**
Superintendent

## BELLFLOWER MUNICIPAL GOLF COURSE

**Course 40**
MAP I5 grid e1

*Course information:* This public course has nine holes. Par is 27. The course is 1,335 yards.

*Play policy and fees:* Green fees are $4 weekdays and $5 weekends. Those with a Bellflower senior's card pay $3 weekdays. Reservations are recommended.

*Location:* Take Highway 19 (Lakewood Boulevard) east to Compton Boulevard, turn right and go about one-half of a mile to the course.

*Course description:* This flat course is all par-3s, although it is not necessarily easy. Golfers can use virtually all their irons. The longest hole is 180 yards.

9030 E. Compton Boulevard
Bellflower, CA 90706

Pro shop (310) 920-8882

✓ **driving range**
✓ **practice greens**
power carts
✓ **pull carts**
✓ **golf club rental**
locker rooms
showers
✓ **executive course**
accommodations
✓ **food and beverages**
✓ **clubhouse**

**Bruce Martin**
Professional

# CANDLEWOOD COUNTRY CLUB

**Course 41**
MAP 15 grid e2

14000 E. Telegraph Rd.
Whittier, CA 90604

Pro shop (310) 941-5310
Clubhouse (310) 941-1228

- ✓ **driving range**
- ✓ **practice greens**
- ✓ **power carts**
- pull carts
- ✓ **golf club rental**
- ✓ **locker rooms**
- ✓ **showers**
- executive course
- accommodations
- ✓ **food and beverages**
- ✓ **clubhouse**

**Greg Johnson**
Professional

**Mike Caranci**
Superintendent

***Course information:*** This private course has 18 holes and par is 70. The course is 6,113 yards and rated 68.9 from the championship tees, and 5,889 yards and rated 67.9 from the regular tees. The slope ratings are 122 championship and 119 regular. Women's tees are 5,708 yards and rated 73.3. The slope rating is 126.

***Play policy and fees:*** Reciprocal play is accepted with members of other private clubs (have your pro call to make arrangements), otherwise members and guests only. Green fees are $30 weekdays and $45 weekends and holidays. Carts are $16. Reservations are recommended.

***Location:*** Travel on Interstate 605 (San Gabriel River freeway) to the Telegraph Road exit east and drive about 3.5 miles to the club.

***Course description:*** Lots of mature trees line the narrow fairways and a canal runs through the back nine. This course is not especially long, but it can be difficult in spots. Beware of number seven, a par-5, 545-yarder with a double dogleg with water in front of the green. The most difficult shot on this hole is the approach shot, which most likely will require a short iron over water to the sizeable green. But you're hitting downhill with out-of-bounds to the right and left—so beware.

# NORWALK GOLF COURSE

**Course 42**
MAP 15 grid e2

13717 Shoemaker Avenue
Norwalk, CA 90650

Pro shop (310) 921-6500

- driving range
- ✓ **practice greens**
- power carts
- ✓ **pull carts**
- ✓ **golf club rental**
- locker rooms
- showers
- ✓ **executive course**
- accommodations
- food and beverages
- clubhouse

**Dave Verhaaf**
Manager

***Course information:*** This public course has nine holes. Par is 27 for nine holes. The course is 960 yards or 1,920 for 18 holes.

***Play policy and fees:*** Green fees are $3 weekdays and $3.50 weekends. Seniors are $2 weekdays and $3 weekends.

***Location:*** Off Interstate 5 in Norwalk, exit on Rosecrans. Go east on Rosecrans to Shoemaker Street and left to the course.

***Course description:*** This pitch-and-putt course is excellent for beginners, seniors and those wishing to practice their short games. The longest hole is 130 yards.

# LA MIRADA GOLF COURSE

**Course 43**
MAP I5 grid e3

***Course information:*** This public course has 18 holes. See card below for yardage and rating information.

***Play policy and fees:*** Green fees are $15.50 weekdays and $19.50 weekends. Seniors are $7.75. Carts are $18. Reservations are recommended.

***Location:*** From Interstate 5, take Highway 39 east to Norwalk Boulevard. Go left on Norwalk for about one mile to La Mirada and follow it to the course.

***Course description:*** This is a well-maintained course with some trees. The greens are bunkered on most holes. Water comes into play on one hole, No. 10. Par-5s generally are reachable in two shots for longer hitters. This course permits fivesomes, so play, even during the week, can be slow, taking up to five hours.

**1961**
15501 East Alicante Road
La Mirada, CA 90638

Pro shop (310) 943-7123
Clubhouse (310) 943-3731
Fax (310) 947-5674

- ✓ **driving range**
- ✓ **practice greens**
- ✓ **power carts**
- ✓ **pull carts**
- ✓ **golf club rental**
- locker rooms
- showers
- executive course
- accommodations
- ✓ **food and beverages**
- clubhouse

**Randy Richardson**
Manager

**Robert Braga**
Professional

**Robert Linderman**
Superintendent

| Hole | 1 | 2 | 3 | 4 | 5 | 6 | 7 | 8 | 9 | Out | | |
|---|---|---|---|---|---|---|---|---|---|---|---|---|
| BLUE | 383 | 380 | 185 | 492 | 154 | 408 | 511 | 426 | 162 | 3101 | BLUE | Rating: 67.5 |
| WHITE | 370 | 368 | 174 | 488 | 150 | 400 | 495 | 421 | 151 | 3017 | | Slope: 114 |
| Par | 4 | 4 | 3 | 5 | 3 | 4 | 5 | 4 | 3 | 35 | WHITE | Rating: 66.6 |
| Handicap | 9 | 3 | 5 | 13 | 17 | 7 | 11 | 1 | 15 | x | | Slope: 112 |
| RED | 369 | 359 | 163 | 475 | 138 | 384 | 484 | 418 | 143 | 2933 | | |
| Par | 4 | 4 | 3 | 5 | 3 | 4 | 5 | 5 | 3 | 36 | RED | Rating: 71.7 |
| Handicap | 3 | 9 | 15 | 5 | 13 | 11 | 1 | 7 | 17 | x | | Slope: 115 |

| Hole | 10 | 11 | 12 | 13 | 14 | 15 | 16 | 17 | 18 | In | Totals | |
|---|---|---|---|---|---|---|---|---|---|---|---|---|
| BLUE | 355 | 180 | 545 | 165 | 340 | 323 | 472 | 133 | 368 | 2881 | BLUE | 5982 |
| WHITE | 345 | 155 | 532 | 152 | 334 | 306 | 450 | 122 | 357 | 2753 | WHITE | 5770 |
| Par | 4 | 3 | 5 | 3 | 4 | 4 | 5 | 3 | 4 | 35 | Par | 70 |
| Handicap | 8 | 4 | 2 | 10 | 16 | 14 | 12 | 18 | 6 | x | | |
| RED | 339 | 138 | 525 | 148 | 326 | 316 | 431 | 128 | 356 | 2699 | RED | 5632 |
| Par | 4 | 3 | 5 | 3 | 4 | 4 | 5 | 3 | 4 | 35 | Par | 71 |
| Handicap | 8 | 14 | 2 | 18 | 6 | 10 | 4 | 16 | 12 | x | | |

# BIG TEE GOLF COURSE

**Course 44**
MAP 15 grid e3

*Course information:* This public course has nine holes. Par is 27. The pitch-and-putt course is 1,098 yards.

*Play policy and fees:* Green fees are $4 weekdays before 5 p.m., $4.50 weekdays after 5.p.m., and $4.50 weekends for nine holes.

*Location:* On Highway 91 heading east in Buena Park, take the Beach Boulevard exit north and drive four miles into La Mirada Boulevard. The course is located on the corner of La Mirada and Beach Boulevard.

*Course description:* This beginner's course has the eighth hole as its longest at 160 yards. The course is flat and has many trees, as well as lights for night play.

5151 Beach Boulevard
Buena Park, CA 90621
Pro shop (714) 521-6300

- ✓ **driving range**
- ✓ **practice greens**
- power carts
- ✓ **pull carts**
- ✓ **golf club rental**
- locker rooms
- showers
- ✓ **executive course**
- accommodations
- ✓ **food and beverages**
- clubhouse

**Dick Sader**
Manager

**John Mahoney**
Professional

| Hole | 1 | 2 | 3 | 4 | 5 | 6 | 7 | 8 | 9 | Out | | |
|---|---|---|---|---|---|---|---|---|---|---|---|---|
| BLUE | | | | | | | | | | | BLUE | Rating: -- |
| | | | | | | | | | | | | Slope: -- |
| WHITE | 96 | 113 | 140 | 115 | 145 | 114 | 131 | 150 | 94 | 1098 | | |
| Par | 3 | 3 | 3 | 3 | 3 | 3 | 3 | 3 | 3 | 27 | WHITE | Rating: -- |
| Handicap | 15 | 11 | 1 | 7 | 5 | 13 | 3 | 9 | 17 | x | | Slope; -- |
| RED | 96 | 113 | 140 | 115 | 145 | 114 | 131 | 150 | 94 | 1098 | | |
| Par | 3 | 3 | 3 | 3 | 3 | 3 | 3 | 3 | 3 | 27 | RED | Rating: -- |
| Handicap | 15 | 11 | 1 | 7 | 5 | 13 | 3 | 9 | 17 | x | | Slope: -- |

| Hole | 10 | 11 | 12 | 13 | 14 | 15 | 16 | 17 | 18 | In | Totals | |
|---|---|---|---|---|---|---|---|---|---|---|---|---|
| BLUE | - | - | - | - | - | - | - | - | - | - | BLUE | -- |
| WHITE | 96 | 113 | 140 | 115 | 145 | 114 | 131 | 150 | 94 | 1098 | WHITE | 2206 |
| Par | 3 | 3 | 3 | 3 | 3 | 3 | 3 | 3 | 3 | 27 | Par | 54 |
| Handicap | 16 | 12 | 2 | 8 | 6 | 14 | 4 | 10 | 18 | x | | |
| RED | 96 | 113 | 140 | 115 | 145 | 114 | 131 | 150 | 94 | 1098 | RED | 2206 |
| Par | 3 | 3 | 3 | 3 | 3 | 3 | 3 | 3 | 3 | 27 | Par | 54 |
| Handicap | 16 | 12 | 2 | 8 | 6 | 14 | 4 | 10 | 94 | x | | |



MAP ON PAGE 506

# FRIENDLY HILLS COUNTRY CLUB

**Course 45**
MAP 15 grid e4

**8500 Villaverde Drive**
**Whittier, CA 90605**

**Pro shop (310) 693-3623**

- ✓ **driving range**
- ✓ **practice greens**
- ✓ **power carts**
- pull carts
- golf club rental
- ✓ **locker rooms**
- ✓ **showers**
- executive course
- accommodations
- ✓ **food and beverages**
- ✓ **clubhouse**

**William Cosgrove**
Manager

**Tom Schauppner**
Professional

**Jeff Beardsly**
Superintendent

***Course information:*** This private course has 18 holes and par is 70. The course is 6,400 yards and rated 72.1 from the championship tees, and 6,141 yards and rated 70.6 from the regular tees. The slope ratings are 135 championship and 128 regular. Women's tees are 5,639 yards and rated 68.4. The slope rating is 128.

***Play policy and fees:*** Members and guests only. Green fees are $40 weekdays and $50 weekends. Guests must be accompanied by a member. Reservations recommended.

***Location:*** From the Pomona Freeway (Highway 60) in Whittier, take the Hacienda Boulevard South exit and go south for three miles to Colima Road, turn right and drive 2 1/4 miles to Mar Vista. From there, go left to Villaverde Drive and the club.

***Course description:*** This club features rolling terrain, undulating greens and narrow fairways. The course gets off to a tough start at number one, a par-5, 558-yard heavyweight. The hole is straight uphill to a green heavily bunkered on both sides and a creek on the left. Play it straight or it will play you. The greens are treacherous. The course, in the hills above Whittier, is usually in immaculate condition.

# LOS ANGELES ROYAL VISTA GOLF COURSE

**Course 46**
MAP 15 grid e4

**1965**
20055 East Colima Road
Walnut, CA 91789

Pro shop (818) 965-1634
(800) 33GOLF3

- ✓ **driving range**
- ✓ **practice greens**
- ✓ **power carts**
- ✓ **pull carts**
- ✓ **golf club rental**
- ✓ **locker rooms**
- ✓ **showers**
- executive course
- accommodations
- ✓ **food and beverages**
- ✓ **clubhouse**

**John Welker**
Professional

**Dan Hornig**
Director

**Al Luna**
Superintendent

***Course information:*** This public course has 27 holes. Par is 71 on the East/North Course and 71 on the North/South Course. Par is 72 on the South/East Course.

The East/North Course is 6,221 yards and rated 69.0 from the championship tees, and 5,828 yards and rated 67.0 from the regular tees. The slope ratings are 115 championship and 108 regular. Women's tees are 5,521 yards and rated 71.4. The slope rating is 114.

The North/South Course is 5,939 yards and rated 67.6 from the championship tees, and 5,597 yards and rated 65.8 from the regular tees. The slope ratings are 110 championship and 105 regular. Women's tees are 5,308 yards and rated 70.4. The slope rating is 112.

The South/East Course is 6,152 yards and rated 68.5 from the championship tees, and 5,797 yards and rated 66.7 from the regular tees. The slope ratings are 112 championship and 105 regular. Women's tees are 5,606 yards and rated 71.6. The slope is rating 114.

***Play policy and fees:*** Outside play is accepted. Green fees are $14 weekdays and $25 weekends. Carts are $20. Reservations are recommended. No tank tops are allowed on the course.

***Location:*** From Los Angeles, travel on Highway 60 east to the Fairway Drive exit and turn right on the Brea Canyon cutoff. At Colima Road, turn left to the club.

***Course description:*** All the courses are moderately hilly with mature trees and some water. The South Course is the narrowest and moderately short and the East Course plays the longest. On the South Course, watch out for the second hole. It's a par-3, 199-yard wheeler-dealer that needs a delicate tee shot over a lake to a green tucked between two hills. The first hole on the East Course is the most difficult one with which to start, with water on the left, a major dogleg left after the tee shot, and a straight uphill approach to a shallow, extremely elevated green.

# HACIENDA GOLF CLUB

**Course 47**
MAP 15 grid e4

*Course information:* This private course has 18 holes. See card below for yardage and rating information.

*Play policy and fees:* Members and guests only. Guest fees are $35 weekdays and $45 weekends. Carts are $18. Proper attire for golfers is collared shirts and slacks. Bermuda shorts are acceptable.

*Location:* Travel on Highway 60 to La Habra Heights and exit on Hacienda Boulevard south. Drive four miles to East Road and turn left. Continue three-fourths of a mile to the club.

*Course description:* This course was built in 1922, during the golden age of golf. It is a classic old-school layout that is difficult with narrow, tree-lined fairways that traverse a rolling terrain. Number 16 is a real beauty. It's 194 yards over a lake to a two-tiered green. The USGA Women's Amateur Championship was held here in 1966. The McGregor Men's Tournament is held each June and the Jewel of the Canyon Invitational is played each August. It will host the 1994 Southern California Amateur Championship. The course record is 65 for men and 70 for women.

**1922**
**Max Behr**

718 East Road
La Habra Heights, CA 90631

Pro shop (310) 697-3610
Clubhouse (310) 694-1081
Fax (310) 694-4701

- ✓ **driving range**
- ✓ **practice greens**
- ✓ **power carts**
- pull carts
- ✓ **golf club rental**
- ✓ **locker rooms**
- ✓ **showers**
- executive course
- accommodations
- ✓ **food and beverages**
- ✓ **clubhouse**

**Jack Downing**
Manager

**Andy Thuney**
Professional

**Todd Coward**
Superintendent

| Hole | 1 | 2 | 3 | 4 | 5 | 6 | 7 | 8 | 9 | Out | | |
|---|---|---|---|---|---|---|---|---|---|---|---|---|
| BLUE | 410 | 433 | 325 | 187 | 460 | 202 | 516 | 448 | 392 | 3373 | BLUE | Rating: 73.2 |
| WHITE | 390 | 418 | 308 | 174 | 435 | 190 | 511 | 432 | 383 | 3242 | | Slope: 132 |
| Par | 4 | 4 | 4 | 3 | 4 | 3 | 5 | 4 | 4 | 35 | WHITE | Rating: 71.1 |
| Handicap | 9 | 5 | 15 | 11 | 1 | 17 | 13 | 3 | 7 | x | | Slope: 127 |
| RED | 369 | 339 | 286 | 128 | 362 | 175 | 494 | 427 | 373 | 2953 | | |
| Par | 4 | 4 | 4 | 3 | 4 | 3 | 5 | 5 | 4 | 36 | RED | Rating: 74.2 |
| Handicap | 9 | 13 | 7 | 17 | 5 | 11 | 1 | 15 | 3 | x | | Slope: 129 |

| Hole | 10 | 11 | 12 | 13 | 14 | 15 | 16 | 17 | 18 | In | Totals | |
|---|---|---|---|---|---|---|---|---|---|---|---|---|
| BLUE | 520 | 321 | 148 | 419 | 426 | 379 | 194 | 470 | 410 | 3287 | BLUE | 6660 |
| WHITE | 503 | 305 | 133 | 394 | 411 | 367 | 170 | 457 | 398 | 3138 | WHITE | 6380 |
| Par | 5 | 4 | 3 | 4 | 4 | 4 | 3 | 5 | 4 | 36 | Par | 71 |
| Handicap | 10 | 14 | 18 | 2 | 4 | 6 | 12 | 16 | 8 | x | | |
| RED | 470 | 259 | 122 | 370 | 401 | 330 | 131 | 440 | 357 | 2880 | RED | 5833 |
| Par | 5 | 4 | 3 | 4 | 4 | 4 | 3 | 5 | 4 | 36 | Par | 72 |
| Handicap | 6 | 14 | 18 | 4 | 2 | 10 | 16 | 8 | 12 | x | | |

# BREA GOLF COURSE

**Course 48**
MAP I5 grid e4

***Course information:*** This public course has nine holes. See card below for yardage information.

***Play policy and fees:*** Green fees are $5.50 weekdays and $6.50 weekends. Seniors pay $4 weekdays. Carts are $7. Reservations are recommended a week in advance.

***Location:*** From Highway 57 heading south toward Brea, take the Imperial Highway exit west to Brea Boulevard and turn left. At the second signal, turn right on West Fir, which will dead-end at the course.

***Course description:*** This mostly flat course has a storm channel running through its center. There are few trees. The course consists of two par-4s and seven par-3s.

**1958**
501 West Fir
Brea, CA 92621

Pro shop (714) 529-3003

- ✓ **driving range,**
- ✓ **practice greens**
- ✓ **power carts**
- pull carts
- ✓ **golf club rental**
- locker rooms
- showers
- ✓ **executive course**
- accommodations
- ✓ **food and beverages**
- clubhouse

**Dick Sader**
Manager

**Tony Lopez**
Professional

| Hole | 1 | 2 | 3 | 4 | 5 | 6 | 7 | 8 | 9 | Total | BLUE | Rating: -- |
|---|---|---|---|---|---|---|---|---|---|---|---|---|
| BLUE | - | - | - | - | - | - | - | - | - | - | | Slope: -- |
| WHITE | 132 | 167 | 310 | 132 | 385 | 183 | 139 | 114 | 121 | 1683 | | |
| Par | 3 | 3 | 4 | 3 | 4 | 3 | 3 | 3 | 3 | 29 | WHITE | Rating: -- |
| Handicap | 17 | 5 | 9 | 11 | 1 | 3 | 7 | 13 | 15 | x | | Slope: -- |
| RED | 122 | 120 | 290 | 125 | 319 | 131 | 128 | 86 | 110 | 1431 | | |
| Par | 3 | 3 | 4 | 3 | 4 | 3 | 3 | 3 | 3 | 29 | RED | Rating: -- |
| Handicap | 18 | 6 | 10 | 12 | 2 | 4 | 8 | 14 | 16 | x | | Slope: -- |

# FULLERTON GOLF CLUB

**Course 49**
MAP I5 grid e4

*Course information:* This public course has 18 holes. See card below for yardage and rating information.

*Play policy and fees:* Green fees are $14 weekdays and $18 weekends. Senior rates are $10. Twilight rates are $10. Carts are $18. Reservations are recommended.

*Location:* Exit Highway 91 at Harbor Boulevard in Fullerton. Go north for three miles to the course, just past the condo development, Greenview Terrace.

*Course description:* It is a tight, narrow course throughout which a creek meanders, coming into play on 14 holes. The course is generally in good condition. The Fullerton City Championship is played here. Golfers are likely to encounter the resident comedian, who plays there frequently and entertains other golfers with his jokes, some good, some bad. This course also features one of the best junior golf programs in Southern California.

**1961**
2700 N. Harbor Boulevard
Fullerton, CA 92635

Pro shop (714) 871-5141
Clubhouse (714) 871-7411

- ✓ **driving range**
- ✓ **practice greens**
- ✓ **power carts**
- ✓ **pull carts**
- ✓ **golf club rental**
- locker rooms
- showers
- executive course
- accommodations
- ✓ **food and beverages**
- ✓ **clubhouse**

**Hank Woodrome**
Professional

**Tom Ponce**
Superintendent

**Ryan Batzel**
Manager

| Hole | 1 | 2 | 3 | 4 | 5 | 6 | 7 | 8 | 9 | Out | | |
|---|---|---|---|---|---|---|---|---|---|---|---|---|
| BLUE | - | - | - | - | - | - | - | - | - | - | BLUE | Rating: -- |
| WHITE | 369 | 501 | 373 | 284 | 195 | 166 | 137 | 174 | 352 | 2551 | | Slope: -- |
| Par | 4 | 5 | 4 | 4 | 3 | 3 | 3 | 3 | 4 | 33 | WHITE | Rating: 65.1 |
| Handicap | 9 | 7 | 1 | 15 | 5 | 13 | 17 | 11 | 3 | x | | Slope: 105 |
| RED | 365 | 500 | 352 | 276 | 176 | 154 | 130 | 165 | 346 | 2464 | | |
| Par | 4 | 5 | 4 | 4 | 3 | 3 | 3 | 3 | 4 | 33 | RED | Rating: 70.1 |
| Handicap | 7 | 3 | 1 | 9 | 11 | 15 | 17 | 13 | 5 | x | | Slope: 112 |

| Hole | 10 | 11 | 12 | 13 | 14 | 15 | 16 | 17 | 18 | In | Totals | |
|---|---|---|---|---|---|---|---|---|---|---|---|---|
| BLUE | - | - | - | - | - | - | - | - | - | - | BLUE | -- |
| WHITE | 348 | 139 | 533 | 336 | 391 | 152 | 356 | 294 | 142 | 2691 | WHITE | 5242 |
| Par | 4 | 3 | 5 | 4 | 4 | 3 | 4 | 4 | 3 | 34 | Par | 67 |
| Handicap | 8 | 18 | 4 | 12 | 2 | 10 | 6 | 16 | 14 | x | | |
| RED | 321 | 131 | 497 | 326 | 382 | 146 | 342 | 285 | 138 | 2568 | RED | 5032 |
| Par | 4 | 3 | 5 | 4 | 4 | 3 | 4 | 4 | 3 | 34 | Par | 67 |
| Handicap | 8 | 18 | 6 | 10 | 4 | 16 | 2 | 12 | 14 | x | | |

# IMPERIAL GOLF COURSE

**Course 50**
MAP I5 grid e4

*Course information:* This public course has 18 holes and par is 72. The course is 6,376 yards and rated 70.0 from the championship tees, and 5,960 yards and rated 67.6 from the regular tees. The slope ratings are 118 championship and 111 regular. Women's tees are 5,581 yards and rated 71. The slope rating is 114.

*Play policy and fees:* Green fees are $15 weekdays and $20 weekends. Carts are $20. This course is available for outside tournaments.

*Location:* From Highway 60 (Pomona Freeway), take Highway 57 south and drive seven miles to the Imperial Highway exit east. From there, drive one-half of a mile to the course.

*Course description:* This course has several holes with out-of-bounds stakes and one red-tailed hawk that nests high in a tree near the first fairway and has been known to attack golfers hitting their tee shots right, near the tree. A regular here during the off-season is major league pitcher Charlie Hough. Eventually, the course will be shut down and another one built nearby to replace it.

PO Box 1150
Brea, CA 92621

2200 East Imperial Highway
Brea, CA 92621

Pro shop (714) 529-3923
Clubhouse (714) 524-0923

- ✓ **driving range**
- ✓ **practice greens**
- ✓ **power carts**
- ✓ **pull carts**
- ✓ **golf club rental**
- ✓ **locker rooms**
- ✓ **showers**
- executive course
- accommodations
- ✓ **food and beverages**
- ✓ **clubhouse**

**William Marsh**
Manager

**Bob Breeding**
Professional

**Bill Mague**
Superintendent

SOUTHERN I5

## ALTA VISTA COUNTRY CLUB

**Course 51**
MAP 15 grid e4

**1961**
**Harry Rainville**

777 East Alta Vista
Placentia, CA 92670

Pro shop (714) 528-1103
Clubhouse (714) 524-3319

- ✓ **driving range**
- ✓ **practice greens**
- ✓ **power carts**
- pull carts
- ✓ **golf club rental**
- ✓ **locker rooms**
- ✓ **showers**
- executive course
- accommodations
- ✓ **food and beverages**
- ✓ **clubhouse**

**Bill Marsh**
Manager

**Ted Debus**
Professional

**Ernie Hernandez**
Superintendent

***Course information:*** This private course has 18 holes and par is 72. The course is 6,361 yards and rated 69.8 from the championship tees, and 5,886 yards and rated 67.7 from the regular tees. The slope ratings are 115 championship and 107 regular. Women's tees are 5,851 yards and rated 70.5. The slope rating is 122.

***Play policy and fees:*** Reciprocal play is accepted with members of other private clubs after 12:30 p.m. weekdays and 1 p.m. weekends; otherwise members and guests only. Reciprocator fees are $35 weekdays and $45 weekends. Carts are $20. Reservations are required for reciprocators. This course is available for outside tournaments on Mondays only.

***Location:*** Travel on Highway 91 to Placentia and take the Kraemar Boulevard exit. Drive north two miles to Alta Vista Street and turn right. Turn left on Sue Drive and continue one-half block to the club.

***Course description:*** This is a flat course with mature trees, lots of out-of-bounds and some lakes. Homes line the perimeter. A redesign of the back nine is planned and the course is expected to be lengthened. Several members of the California Angels organization play out here frequently.

# BIRCH HILLS GOLF COURSE

**Course 52**
MAP I5 grid e5

*Course information:* This public course has 18 holes and par is 59. The course is 3,520 yards and rated 56.9. Slope rating is 86.

*Play policy and fees:* Green fees are $12 weekdays and $18 weekends for 18 holes. Carts are $14 weekdays and $16 weekends. Reservations are recommended one week in advance. Shirts are required.

*Location:* Driving south on Highway 57 from Brea, exit at Imperial Highway east. Turn left on Associated Road and right on Birch Street and drive to the course.

*Course description:* This short, executive course is hilly with good greens that can be tricky to putt. The course has five par-4s and golfers can hit their drivers—fairways are fairly wide. There is some water that comes into play on the front nine. The course is right across the street from Imperial Golf Course. It is an excellent course for seniors and extremely walkable.

2250 East Birch Street
Brea, CA 92621

Pro shop (714) 990-0201

- ✓ **driving range**
- ✓ **practice greens**
- ✓ **power carts**
- ✓ **pull carts**
- ✓ **golf club rental**
- locker rooms
- showers
- ✓ **executive course**
- accommodations
- ✓ **food and beverages**
- ✓ **clubhouse**

**Steve LaBarge**
Professional

**Larry Taylor**
Director

**Tony Harris**
Superintendent

# DIAMOND BAR GOLF COURSE

**Course 53**
MAP 15 grid e5

**1962**
22751 East Golden Springs
Diamond Bar, CA 91765

Pro shop (714) 861-8282
Clubhouse (714) 861-5757

- ✓ **driving range**
- ✓ **practice greens**
- ✓ **power carts**
- ✓ **pull carts**
- ✓ **golf club rental**
- locker rooms
- showers
- executive course
- accommodations
- ✓ **food and beverages**
- ✓ **clubhouse**

**Kevin McNece**
Professional

**Jim Pitmann**
Superintendent

***Course information:*** This public course has 18 holes and par is 72. The course is 6,819 yards and rated 71.6 from the championship tees, and 6,534 yards and rated 70.4 from the regular tees. The slope ratings are 122 championship and 119 regular. Women's yardage is 5,949 and rated 72.8. The slope rating is 117.

***Play policy and fees:*** Green fees are $15.50 weekdays and $19.50 weekends. Los Angeles County senior citizens play for $7.75 for 18 holes and $5 for nine holes. Carts are $18 for 18 holes and $11 for nine holes. Reservations are recommended. Shirts must be worn at all times.

***Location:*** From downtown L.A., take Highway 60 east 24 miles to Grand Avenue. Turn right and go one signal, then turn left to the course.

***Course description:*** This is a tree-lined course with water hazards on four holes and doglegs on several holes. It is usually calm in the morning, with the wind picking up in the afternoon and playing havoc with your ball. Number four is a perfect example. It is a 560-yard par-5 that plays directly into the wind. The course is fairly open so errant tee shots are salvageable. Efforts are made to define the fairways. Among the tournaments played here are the Diamond Bar Invitational in September and the Rotary Club Tournament in March.

## YORBA LINDA COUNTRY CLUB

**Course 54**
MAP I5 grid e5

**1957**
19400 Mountain View
Yorba Linda, CA 92686

Pro shop (714) 779-2467
Clubhouse (714) 779-2461

- ✓ **driving range**
- ✓ **practice greens**
- ✓ **power carts**
- pull carts
- ✓ **golf club rental**
- ✓ **locker rooms**
- ✓ **showers**
- executive course
- accommodations
- ✓ **food and beverages**
- ✓ **clubhouse**

**Gene Bevi**
Manager

**Tom Sargent**
Professional

**Larry Snyder**
Superintendent

*Course information:* This private course has 18 holes and par is 71. The course is 6,810 yards and rated 72.8 from the championship tees, and 6,492 yards and rated 70.5 from the regular tees. The slope ratings are 125 championship and 119 regular. Women's tees are 6,492 yards and rated 77.5 from the championship tees, and 5,918 yards and rated 74 from the forward tees. The slope ratings are 134 championship and 126 forward.

*Play policy and fees:* Members and guests only. Green fees are $40. Carts are $9 per person. This course is available for outside tournaments on Mondays only.

*Location:* Take the Riverside Freeway (Highway 91) to the Imperial Highway (Highway 90). Drive north to Kellogg and turn right to Mountain View and the club.

*Course description:* This old-style course is nestled between numerous homes. There are tree-lined fairways, some hills and bunkers and a little water. It's walkable. A new clubhouse and locker rooms were completed last year. For lessons, see head professional Tom Sargent, regarded as among the best instructors in Southern California. One is his pupils is Kellee Booth, considered the best junior girl in the country.

## WESTERN HILLS GOLF AND COUNTRY CLUB

**Course 55**
MAP I5 grid e6

1800 Carbon Canyon Road
Chino, CA 91709

Pro shop (714) 528-6661
Clubhouse (714) 528-6400

- ✓ **driving range**
- ✓ **practice greens**
- ✓ **power carts**
- pull carts
- ✓ **golf club rental**
- ✓ **locker rooms**
- showers
- executive course
- accommodations
- ✓ **food and beverages**
- ✓ **clubhouse**

**Brad Stormon**
Professional

**Vincent Vasquez**
Superintendent

*Course information:* This private course has 18 holes and par is 72. The course is 6,669 yards, rated 72.2 with a slope of 128 from the championship tees, and 6,370 yards, rated 70.6 with a slope of 122 from the regular tees. Women's tees are 6,370 yards, rated 77 with a slope of 134 from the championship tees, and 5,870 yards, rated 73.9 with a slope of 126 from the forward tees.

*Play policy and fees:* Reciprocal play is accepted with members of other private clubs Monday through Friday; otherwise members and guests only. Green fees are $25 weekdays and $40 weekends. Carts are $20. Available for outside tournaments on Mondays only.

*Location:* From Highway 71, take Chino Hills Parkway west to Carbon Canyon Road. Turn left and drive two miles to the club. From Highway 57, take Lambert Road east 11 miles to the club.

*Course description:* This rolling course has mature trees and is well-bunkered. There is a double green that serves two holes, numbers 12 and 14. Water comes into play on only one hole. The greens here are extremely difficult to read because the course is in a canyon. The U.S. Amateur qualifier has been held here in the past.

# LOS SERRANOS LAKES GOLF AND COUNTRY CLUB

**Course 56**
MAP 15 grid e6

15656 Yorba Avenue
Chino, CA 91709

Pro shop (714) 597-1711
Clubhouse (714) 597-1769

- ✓ **driving range**
- ✓ **practice greens**
- ✓ **power carts**
- ✓ **pull carts**
- ✓ **golf club rental**
- ✓ **locker rooms**
- ✓ **showers**
- executive course
- accommodations
- ✓ **food and beverages**
- ✓ **clubhouse**

**Kevin Sullivan**
Manager

**John Powell**
Professional

**Steven Hall**
Superintendent

***Course information:*** This public club has two 18-hole courses. Par is 74 on the South Course and 72 on the North Course.

The South Course is 7,007 yards and rated 73.6 from the championship tees, and 6,559 yards and rated 70.9 from the regular tees. The slope ratings are 129 championship and 122 regular. Women's tees are 5,935 yards and rated 71.9. The slope rating is 114.

The North Course is 6,292 yards and rated 69.5 from the championship tees, and 6,072 yards and rated 68.5 from the regular tees. The slope ratings are 116 championship and 112 regular. Women's tees are 5,880 yards and rated 71.8. The slope rating is 112.

***Play policy and fees:*** Green fees are $17 weekdays and $22 weekends. Carts are $20. This course is available for outside tournaments.

***Location:*** From Highway 60 (Pomona Freeway), take the Pomona-Corona/Highway 71 exit and travel south on Highway 71 for five miles to Los Serranos Road. Turn right to the club.

***Course description:*** The South Course is long and hilly and gets breezy in the afternoons. The North Course was built in the 1920s and is scenic and rolling. Jack Kramer, of tennis fame, owns these courses, which are among the better public courses in the area. The South Course has six par-5s, including the first two holes, each of them reachable in two for the longer hitter.

# EL PRADO GOLF COURSES

**Course 57**
MAP I5 grid e7

6555 Pine Avenue
Chino, CA 91710

Pro shop (714) 597-1753

- ✓ **driving range**
- ✓ **practice greens**
- ✓ **power carts**
- ✓ **pull carts**
- golf club rental
- locker rooms
- showers
- executive course
- accommodations
- ✓ **food and beverages**
- ✓ **clubhouse**

**Robert Bickford**
Director

**Joe McDermott**
Professional

**Dennis Jobert**
Superintendent

***Course information:*** This public facility has two 18-hole courses. Par is 72 on both.

The Butterfield Stage Course is 6,508 yards and rated 69.7 from the championship tees, and 6,251 yards and rated 68.4 from the regular tees. The slope ratings are 108 championship and 103 regular. Women's tees are 5,503 yards and rated 70. The slope rating is 118.

The Chino Creek Course is 6,671 yards and rated 71.1 from the championship tees, and 6,296 yards and rated 69.1 from the regular tees. The slope ratings are 114 championship and 108 regular. Women's tees are 5,596 yards and rated 70.6. The slope rating is 115.

***Play policy and fees:*** Green fees are $15 weekdays and $20 weekends and holidays. Carts are $20. Reservations are recommended.

***Location:*** From Los Angeles, travel east on Highway 60 (Pomona Freeway) to the Corona Freeway/Highway 71 exit. Turn right and drive six miles to Pomona Rincon Road and turn left and follow the signs.

***Course description:*** The Chino Creek Course is longer and a bit more challenging with water hazards and several out-of-bounds areas. It is straight forward, however. There are rolling hills and the course is very walkable. The Butterfield Stage Course is slightly shorter, flatter and more forgiving, making it receptive to beginning golfers. It, too, has water. Greens are usually well maintained. It often is not crowded during the week; golfers can walk up and usually get on, without a reservation.

# GREEN RIVER GOLF CLUB

**Course 58**
MAP 15 grid e7

**1958**
**William Francis Bell**
**Desmond Muirhead**

5215 Green River Drive
Corona, CA 91720

Pro shop (714) 737-7393
Clubhouse (714) 970-8411

- ✓ **driving range**
- ✓ **practice greens**
- ✓ **power carts**
- ✓ **pull carts**
- ✓ **golf club rental**
- ✓ **locker rooms**
- ✓ **showers**
- executive course
- accommodations
- ✓ **food and beverages**
- ✓ **clubhouse**

**Howard Smith**
Professional

**Buford Goins**
Superintendent

***Course information:*** This public facility has two 18-hole courses and par is 71 on both.

The Orange Course is detailed below.

The Riverside Course is 6,275 yards and rated 69.2 from the championship tees, and 6,013 yards and rated 67.9 from the regular tees. The slope ratings are 110 championship and 105 regular. Women's tees are 5,467 yards and rated 71.0. The slope rating is 115.

***Play policy and fees:*** Green fees are $16 weekdays, and $20 Fridays and weekends. Carts are $20. Reservations are recommended. This course is available for outside tournaments.

***Location:*** From the Riverside Freeway (Highway 91), take the Green River Drive exit north and travel one mile to the entrance.

***Course description:*** These two courses feature gently rolling slopes with many trees and lakes. An errant tee shot means trouble. The Santa Ana River runs through both courses. The first hole on the Orange Course features trees down the right side and the river down the left side. These courses are in a narrow valley with hills on each side and therefore can get quite windy.

Orange Course

| Hole | 1 | 2 | 3 | 4 | 5 | 6 | 7 | 8 | 9 | Out | BLUE | Rating: 70.4 |
|---|---|---|---|---|---|---|---|---|---|---|---|---|
| BLUE | 506 | 391 | 161 | 521 | 214 | 350 | 498 | 413 | 168 | 3222 | | Slope: 119 |
| WHITE | 497 | 382 | 151 | 507 | 198 | 342 | 488 | 394 | 157 | 3116 | | |
| Par | 5 | 4 | 3 | 5 | 3 | 4 | 5 | 4 | 3 | 36 | WHITE | Rating: 69.0 |
| Handicap | 11 | 3 | 13 | 7 | 5 | 15 | 17 | 1 | 9 | x | | Slope: 114 |
| RED | 488 | 373 | 136 | 486 | 142 | 334 | 429 | 356 | 124 | 2868 | | |
| Par | 5 | 4 | 3 | 5 | 3 | 4 | 5 | 4 | 3 | 36 | RED | Rating: 73.2 |
| Handicap | 3 | 5 | 17 | 1 | 13 | 11 | 9 | 7 | 15 | x | | Slope: 120 |

| Hole | 10 | 11 | 12 | 13 | 14 | 15 | 16 | 17 | 18 | In | Totals | |
|---|---|---|---|---|---|---|---|---|---|---|---|---|
| BLUE | 371 | 357 | 198 | 499 | 170 | 561 | 466 | 417 | 155 | 3194 | BLUE | 6416 |
| WHITE | 361 | 348 | 170 | 488 | 160 | 547 | 427 | 401 | 149 | 3051 | WHITE | 6167 |
| Par | 4 | 4 | 3 | 5 | 3 | 5 | 4 | 4 | 3 | 35 | Par | 71 |
| Handicap | 10 | 18 | 4 | 16 | 12 | 6 | 2 | 8 | 14 | x | | |
| RED | 358 | 322 | 146 | 475 | 127 | 529 | 406 | 376 | 137 | 2876 | RED | 5744 |
| Par | 4 | 4 | 3 | 5 | 3 | 5 | 5 | 4 | 3 | 36 | Par | 72 |
| Handicap | 10 | 12 | 16 | 4 | 18 | 2 | 6 | 8 | 14 | x | | |

# WHISPERING LAKES GOLF COURSE

**Course 59**
MAP I5 grid e8

2525 Riverside Drive
Ontario, CA 91761

Pro shop (909) 923-3673
Clubhouse (909) 923-3675

- ✓ **driving range**
- ✓ **practice greens**
- ✓ **power carts**
- ✓ **pull carts**
- ✓ **golf club rental**
- ✓ **locker rooms**
- ✓ **showers**
- executive course
- accommodations
- ✓ **food and beverages**
- ✓ **clubhouse**

**Dave Ferrell**
Professional

**Jim Noble**
Superintendent

***Course information:*** This public course has 18 holes and par is 72. The course is 6,666 yards and rated 71.4 from the championship tees, and 6,265 yards and rated 69.0 from the regular tees. The slope ratings are 122 championship and 114 regular. Women's tees are 5,987 yards and rated 73.0. The slope rating is 115. There is also an 18-hole, par-3 course.

***Play policy and fees:*** Green fees are $13 weekdays and $17 weekends. Carts are $16 weekdays and $18 weekends. Reservations are recommended.

***Location:*** Travel east of Los Angeles on Highway 60 to the Vineyard exit near Ontario. Turn right on Riverside Drive and travel two blocks and turn left to the club.

***Course description:*** This course has level terrain, mature trees and wide open fairways. It plays long because the ball gets little roll. The driving range has lights. It is among the least crowded courses in Southern California during the week. Often, reservations are not required.

# LAKEWOOD COUNTY GOLF COURSE

**Course 60**
MAP I5 grid f1

3101 Carson Street
Lakewood, CA 90712

Pro shop (310) 429-9711

- ✓ **driving range**
- ✓ **practice greens**
- ✓ **power carts**
- ✓ **pull carts**
- ✓ **golf club rental**
- locker rooms
- ✓ **showers**
- executive course
- accommodations
- ✓ **food and beverages**
- ✓ **clubhouse**

**Tom Petersen**
Manager

**Len Kennetts**
Professional

**John Castaneda**
Superintendent

***Course information:*** This public course has 18 holes and par is 72. The course is 6,992 yards and rated 71.6 from the championship tees. It is 6,435 yards and rated 70.1 from the regular tees. It is 5,920 yards and rated 74.1 from the women's tees. Slope ratings are 110, 105, and 121.

***Play policy and fees:*** Greens fees are $11 weekdays and $15 weekends. Reservations recommended. Be persistent and call early, any day.

***Location:*** Take the Lakewood Boulevard exit off Interstate 405 and head east. At Carson Street, turn left and drive about two miles to the club.

***Course description:*** This is a fairly flat course built alongside an 11-acre lake that brings water into play on holes 2, 9, 10, 11 and 12. It can be a noisy course, because it is located near Long Beach Airport. It is the site of the annual Queen Mary Open.

## SKYLINKS GOLF COURSE

**Course 61**
MAP I5 grid f1

*Course information:* This public course has 18 holes and par is 72. The course is 6,460 from the championship tees and rated 69.6, and 6,277 yards from the regular tees and rated 68.6. The slope ratings are 113 championship and 108 regular. Women's tees are 5,918 yards and rated 72.0. The slope rating is 113.

*Play policy and fees:* Green fees are $12.50 weekdays and $16 weekends for Long Beach residents, and $15.50 weekdays and $19 weekends for non-residents. Carts are $18. Pull carts are $3.

*Location:* Take Interstate 405 south to Long Beach. Exit on Lakewood Boulevard north. The course is located three blocks down on your right. It's across from the Long Beach Airport.

*Course description:* This course will give you a run of doglegs. It's mostly flat and it is walkable. It also can be noisy, because of air traffic at the nearby airport.

4800 Wardlow Road
Long Beach, CA 90808

Pro shop (310) 429-0030
Starter (310) 429-0030

✓ **driving range**
✓ **practice greens**
✓ **power carts**
✓ **pull carts**
✓ **golf club rental**
✓ **locker rooms**
✓ **showers**
executive course
accommodations
✓ **food and beverages**
✓ **clubhouse**

**Jamie Mulligan**
Professional

**Chris Leavitt**
Superintendent

## HEARTWELL GOLF PARK

**Course 62**
MAP I5 grid f1

*Course information:* This public course has 18 holes and par is 54. The course is 2,153 yards. It's all par-3s and rated 50.1.

*Play policy and fees:* Green fees are $6.75 weekdays and $8.25 weekends for 18 holes for Long Beach residents, and $8.25 weekdays and $9.75 weekends for 18 holes for non-residents. Carts are $7 for nine holes and $10 for 18 holes.

*Location:* Off Interstate 405 in Long Beach, take the Lakewood Boulevard exit north. Follow Lakewood two miles to Carson Street and turn right. The course is 1.5 miles on the right.

*Course description:* This well-conditioned course has elevated greens. The longest hole is the ninth at 140 yards. The course is lighted for night play. The driving range also has lights. This is a course Tiger Woods began playing virtually from infancy.

6700 East Carson Street
Long Beach, CA 90808

Pro shop (310) 421-8855

✓ **driving range**
✓ **practice greens**
✓ **power carts**
✓ **pull carts**
✓ **golf club rental**
locker rooms
showers
executive course
accommodations
✓ **food and beverages**
✓ **clubhouse**

**Dave McGrady**
Manager

**Roy Eversole**
Professional

## EL DORADO GOLF COURSE

**Course 63**
MAP I5 grid f1

**1955**
2400 Studebaker Road
Long Beach, CA 90815

Pro shop (310) 430-5411
Starter (310) 498-0977

- ✓ **driving range**
- ✓ **practice greens**
- ✓ **power carts**
- ✓ **pull carts**
- ✓ **golf club rental**
- locker rooms
- showers
- executive course
- accommodations
- ✓ **food and beverages**
- ✓ **clubhouse**

**Dan Yenny**
Professional

**Kevin Neal**
Superintendent

***Course information:*** This public course has 18 holes and par is 72. The course is 6,695 yards and rated 71.7 from the championship tees, and 6,427 yards and rated 68.9 from the regular tees. The slope ratings are 121 championship and 114 regular. Women's tees are 5,743 yards and rated 73.7. The slope rating is 118.

***Play policy and fees:*** Green fees are $12.50 weekdays and $16 weekends for Long Beach residents, and $15.50 weekdays and $19 weekends for non-residents. Carts are $18.

***Location:*** From Los Angeles, travel south on Interstate 405 (San Diego Freeway) to the Studebaker Road exit. Turn north and drive three-fourths of a mile to the club.

***Course description:*** This course is mostly level with lots of doglegs and trees at least 50 years old lining the fairways. Water comes into play on five holes. If the closing holes look reversed since the last time you played this course, don't worry. Number 17, formerly a par-5, is now par-3 and 169 yards; and number 18, formerly a par-3, is now a par-5 and 510 yards. Water has been added to the final hole for a finishing touch. The Queen Mary Open was held here until 1983. The Long Beach Open is played here annually.

## RECREATION PARK GOLF COURSE

**Course 64**
MAP I5 grid f1

5000 E. Anaheim Street
Long Beach, CA 90804

Pro shop (310) 494-5000
Coffee shop(310) 494-4333

- ✓ **driving range**
- ✓ **practice greens**
- ✓ **power carts**
- ✓ **pull carts**
- ✓ **golf club rental**
- locker rooms
- showers
- executive course
- accommodations
- food and beverages
- clubhouse

**Mez White**
Professional/Manager

**Jack Glant**
Superintendent

***Course information:*** This public course has 18 holes and par is 72. The course is 6,337 yards from the championship tees and rated 68.8. The slope is 108. It is 5,765 yards from the women's tees and rated 72.6 with a slope of 120.

***Play policy and fees:*** Green fees are $12.50 for 18 holes weekdays and $16 for 18 holes weekends for residents, and $15.50 for 18 holes weekdays and $19 for 18 holes weekends for non-residents. Reservations are recommended.

***Location:*** Follow the Pacific Coast Highway (Highway 1) north from Seal Beach and exit at Seventh Street. Drive one-half of a mile on Seventh to the course entrance.

***Course description:*** This course features rolling terrain and undulating greens. The course is fairly wide open, and features many trees. It is usually well maintained. This is where LPGA Tour player Laura Baugh learned to play, while becoming one of the best junior golfers and amateur golfers in the country.

## BIXBY VILLAGE GOLF COURSE

**Course 65**
MAP I5 grid f1

6180 Bixby Village Drive
Long Beach, CA 90803

Pro shop (310) 498-7003

- driving range
- practice greens
- power carts
- pull carts
- golf club rental
- locker rooms
- showers
- executive course
- accommodations
- food and beverages
- clubhouse

**Robert Jones**
Manager

***Course information:*** This public course has nine holes. Par is 29. The course is 1,539 yards. It is not rated.

***Play policy and fees:*** Green fees are $5.75 weekdays and $7 weekends. Replay rate is $4.25 weekdays and $5.50 weekends. Reservations are recommended one week in advance.

***Location:*** On Interstate 405 south in Long Beach, exit on Bellflower Boulevard and drive south. Veer left on the Pacific Coast Highway (Highway 1). Turn left on Bixby Village Drive and drive one-eighth of a mile to the course.

***Course description:*** This hilly course has undulating greens and two lakes. The longest hole is the par-4 fifth at 340 yards.

## LEISUREWORLD GOLF COURSE

**Course 66**
MAP I5 grid f2

13580 Saint Andrews
Seal Beach, CA 90740

Pro shop (310) 431-6586

- driving range
- practice greens
- power carts
- pull carts
- golf club rental
- locker rooms
- showers
- executive course
- accommodations
- food and beverages
- clubhouse

**Fred Cooper**
Director

***Course information:*** This private course has nine holes. Par is 54 for 18 holes. The course is 1,800 yards at 18 holes.

***Play policy and fees:*** Members only. This is a resident course. No reciprocal play is allowed.

***Location:*** On Interstate 405 heading south to Seal Beach, exit on Seal Beach Boulevard east. Turn left (south) and drive two blocks to the course on your right.

***Course description:*** This residential course is flat. A pond offers measurable excitement on four or five of the holes.

# OLD RANCH COUNTRY CLUB

**Course 67**
MAP 15 grid f2

***Course information:*** This private course has 18 holes. See card below for yardage and rating information.

***Play policy and fees:*** Members and guests only. Guest fees are $35 weekdays and $45 Fridays, weekends and holidays. Carts are $20. Reservations are required. Call the golf pro to arrange reciprocal play.

***Location:*** Near Long Beach, take the Seal Beach exit off Interstate 405 (San Diego Freeway) to the right. Drive one-half of a mile to Lampson Avenue. Turn right again and drive one-half of a mile to the club.

***Course description:*** This course is level, but don't let that fool you. Because of its proximity to the ocean, winds can greatly affect playing conditions. The holes are tight and the well-maintained greens are protected by water. The USGA Seniors Open qualifying event has been held here. The best holes on the course are the four finishing holes.

**1965**
**Ted Robinson**

3901 Lampson Avenue
Seal Beach, CA 90740

Pro shop (310) 596-4611
Clubhouse (310) 596-4425

- ✓ **driving range**
- ✓ **practice greens**
- ✓ **power carts**
- pull carts
- golf club rental
- ✓ **locker rooms**
- ✓ **showers**
- executive course
- accommodations
- ✓ **food and beverages**
- ✓ **clubhouse**

**Bill Elvins**
Manager

**Robert Silver**
Professional

**Don Parsons**
Superintendent

| Hole | 1 | 2 | 3 | 4 | 5 | 6 | 7 | 8 | 9 | Out | BLUE | Rating: 71.8 |
|---|---|---|---|---|---|---|---|---|---|---|---|---|
| BLUE | 337 | 371 | 168 | 545 | 316 | 383 | 211 | 537 | 402 | 3270 | | Slope: 124 |
| WHITE | 330 | 359 | 150 | 512 | 299 | 362 | 184 | 521 | 380 | 3097 | | |
| Par | 4 | 4 | 3 | 5 | 4 | 4 | 3 | 5 | 4 | 36 | WHITE | Rating: 69.4 |
| Handicap | 15 | 1 | 17 | 9 | 13 | 3 | 11 | 5 | 7 | x | | Slope: 114 |
| RED | 319 | 346 | 142 | 500 | 291 | 354 | 140 | 503 | 367 | 2962 | | |
| Par | 4 | 4 | 3 | 5 | 4 | 4 | 3 | 5 | 4 | 36 | RED | Rating: 73.4 |
| Handicap | 13 | 1 | 11 | 7 | 17 | 5 | 15 | 3 | 9 | x | | Slope: 128 |

| Hole | 10 | 11 | 12 | 13 | 14 | 15 | 16 | 17 | 18 | In | Totals | |
|---|---|---|---|---|---|---|---|---|---|---|---|---|
| BLUE | 375 | 135 | 383 | 380 | 530 | 205 | 400 | 413 | 524 | 3345 | BLUE | 6615 |
| WHITE | 347 | 126 | 364 | 353 | 503 | 160 | 362 | 380 | 504 | 3099 | WHITE | 6196 |
| Par | 4 | 3 | 4 | 4 | 5 | 3 | 4 | 4 | 5 | 36 | Par | 72 |
| Handicap | 12 | 18 | 8 | 16 | 2 | 14 | 4 | 10 | 6 | x | | |
| RED | 326 | 116 | 357 | 319 | 487 | 142 | 346 | 351 | 471 | 2915 | RED | 5877 |
| Par | 4 | 3 | 4 | 4 | 5 | 3 | 4 | 4 | 5 | 36 | Par | 72 |
| Handicap | 14 | 18 | 2 | 16 | 6 | 12 | 4 | 10 | 8 | x | | |

# NAVY GOLF COURSES LONG BEACH

**Course 68**
MAP I5 grid f2

**1966**
**Joe Williams**

5660 Orangewood Avenue
Cypress, CA 90630

Pro shop (310) 430-9913
Pro shop (714) 527-4401
Clubhouse (310) 431-4956
Fax (310) 594-5989

- ✓ **driving range**
- ✓ **practice greens**
- ✓ **power carts**
- ✓ **pull carts**
- ✓ **golf club rental**
- ✓ **locker rooms**
- ✓ **showers**
- ✓ **executive course** accommodations
- ✓ **food and beverages**
- ✓ **clubhouse**

**Paul Moreno**
Manager

**Dave Smith**
Professional

**Gilbert Quintero**
Superintendent

***Course information:*** This military course has 18 holes and par is 72. There is also a par-32, nine-hole executive course.

The Destroyer Course is detailed below.

The Cruiser is 4,031 yards and rated 55.8 from the regular tees. The slope rating is 85.

***Play policy and fees:*** Military personnel and guests only. Green fees are $6 to $10 for military personnel and $20 for guests. Carts are $15. Reservations are recommended one week in advance.

***Location:*** South on Interstate 405 (San Diego Freeway) bear right at the intersection with Garden Grove Freeway to Cypress-Valley View exit. Drive north 1.5 miles to Orangewood Avenue, then left to the course.

***Course description:*** Tree-lined fairways, numerous water hazards and offshore breezes add to the character and challenge of this course. Beware of the par-3, 185-yard ninth hole. Tee shots must carry over water to a bunker-lined green. Tiger Woods, the internationally-renowned junior golfer, learned to play here; his father, Earl, was a career serviceman. This is a busy course with 93,500 rounds played each year.

Destroyer Course

| Hole | 1 | 2 | 3 | 4 | 5 | 6 | 7 | 8 | 9 | Out | BLUE | Rating: 73.5 |
|---|---|---|---|---|---|---|---|---|---|---|---|---|
| BLUE | 399 | 339 | 529 | 378 | 361 | 571 | 413 | 392 | 185 | 3567 | | Slope: 129 |
| WHITE | 390 | 295 | 503 | 362 | 353 | 551 | 393 | 381 | 156 | 3384 | | |
| Par | 4 | 4 | 5 | 4 | 4 | 5 | 4 | 4 | 3 | 37 | WHITE | Rating: 71.2 |
| Handicap | 7 | 15 | 13 | 11 | 9 | 1 | 5 | 3 | 17 | x | | Slope: 123 |
| RED | 373 | 291 | 455 | 347 | 346 | 497 | 341 | 358 | 126 | 3134 | | |
| Par | 4 | 4 | 5 | 4 | 4 | 5 | 4 | 4 | 3 | 37 | RED | Rating: 72.5 |
| Handicap | 11 | 15 | 3 | 13 | 9 | 1 | 5 | 7 | 17 | x | | Slope: 117 |

| Hole | 10 | 11 | 12 | 13 | 14 | 15 | 16 | 17 | 18 | In | Totals | |
|---|---|---|---|---|---|---|---|---|---|---|---|---|
| BLUE | 362 | 180 | 373 | 518 | 422 | 163 | 443 | 216 | 560 | 3237 | BLUE | 6804 |
| WHITE | 357 | 162 | 352 | 495 | 410 | 156 | 434 | 202 | 543 | 3111 | WHITE | 6495 |
| Par | 4 | 3 | 4 | 5 | 4 | 3 | 4 | 3 | 5 | 35 | Par | 72 |
| Handicap | 6 | 16 | 14 | 8 | 4 | 18 | 2 | 12 | 10 | x | | |
| RED | 351 | 135 | 285 | 449 | 394 | 103 | 375 | 190 | 473 | 2755 | RED | 5889 |
| Par | 4 | 3 | 4 | 5 | 4 | 3 | 4 | 3 | 5 | 35 | Par | 72 |
| Handicap | 6 | 18 | 12 | 2 | 8 | 14 | 10 | 16 | 4 | x | | |

# LOS COYOTES COUNTRY CLUB

**Course 69**
MAP I5 grid f3

8888 Los Coyotes Drive
Buena Park, CA 90621

Pro shop (714) 523-7780
Clubhouse (714) 521-6171

- ✓ **driving range**
- ✓ **practice greens**
- ✓ **power carts**
- pull carts
- ✓ **golf club rental**
- ✓ **locker rooms**
- ✓ **showers**
- ✓ **executive course**
- accommodations
- ✓ **food and beverages**
- ✓ **clubhouse**

**Jeff Perkins**
Professional

**Bill Gallegos**
Superintendent

***Course information:*** This private club has 27 holes. Par is 72 on the Valley-Vista Course and 67 on the Vista-Lake and Lake-Valley courses.

The Valley-Vista Course is 6,965 yards and rated 73.7 from the championship tees, and 6,635 yards and rated 71.5 from the regular tees. The slope ratings are 129 championship and 119 regular. Women's tees are 6,195 yards and rated 75.0. The slope rating is 125.

The Vista-Lake Course is 5,272 yards and rated 64.6 from the regular tees. The slope rating is 100. Women's tees are 5,085 yards and rated 67. The slope rating is 111.

The Lake-Valley Course is 5,423 yards and rated 65.3 from the regular tees. The slope rating is 101. The women's tees are 5,099 yards and rated 68.4. The slope is 109.

***Play policy and fees:*** Reciprocal play is accepted with members of other private clubs, otherwise members and guests only. Fees for reciprocators are $45 weekdays. No reciprocal play on weekends. Guests on weekends are $60 weekends. Carts are $18 weekdays and $20 weekends. Reservations are required.

***Location:*** Take Highway 91 (Artesia Freeway) or Interstate 5 (Santa Ana Freeway) to the Beach Boulevard exit. Drive north for three miles from Highway 91 or two miles from Interstate 5 to Los Coyotes Drive and turn right, then continue one mile to the club.

***Course description:*** These courses are set around the top of a small hill. The rolling fairways are seeded with Kikuyu grass and the rough is brutal. All three layouts are well-bunkered and interesting. The Valley-Vista Course is the site of the annual Los Coyotes LPGA Classic, won twice by Nancy Lopez and once by Pat Bradley. It plays long from any set of tees.

## ANAHEIM "DAD" MILLER GOLF COURSE

**Course 70**
MAP I5 grid f3

PO Box 2366
Anaheim, CA 92804

430 North Gilbert Street
Anaheim, CA 92801

Pro shop (714) 774-8055
Reservation (714) 748-8900

- ✓ **driving range**
- ✓ **practice greens**
- ✓ **power carts**
- ✓ **pull carts**
- ✓ **golf club rental**
- locker rooms
- showers
- executive course
- accommodations
- ✓ **food and beverages**
- ✓ **clubhouse**

**Bob Johns**
Professional

**Gary Wimberly**
Superintendent

***Course information:*** This public course has 18 holes and par is 71. The course is 6,060 yards and rated 68.2 from the championship tees, and 5,805 yards and rated 67.0 from the regular tees. The slope ratings are 107 championship and 103 regular. Women's tees are 5,378 yards and rated 70.0. The slope rating is 107.

***Play policy and fees:*** Green fees are $16 weekdays and $20 weekends. After 12 noon, greens fees are $11 weekdays and $12 weekends. Call for special senior rates. Carts are $20. Reservations are recommended but can only be made through a computer reservation system—prior sign-up is required.

***Location:*** Travel on Interstate 5 (Santa Ana Freeway) to the Brookhurst Street exit. Drive south one-half of a mile to Crescent Avenue and turn right. Continue one-half of a mile to Gilbert Street and turn left to the course.

***Course description:*** This course is not long, except for the 595-yard, par-5 11th hole, but it is challenging for the average golfer. The tree-lined fairways are level and well kept for a public course. It's flat and easy to walk, but watch for the irrigation, which makes for a good challenge. It's always in good shape.

## ANAHEIM HILLS GOLF COURSE

**Course 71**
MAP I5 grid f5

6501 Nohl Ranch Road
Anaheim, CA 92807

Pro shop (714) 998-3041
Reservation (714) 748-8900

- ✓ **driving range**
- ✓ **practice greens**
- ✓ **power carts**
- pull carts
- ✓ **golf club rental**
- locker rooms
- showers
- executive course
- accommodations
- ✓ **food and beverages**
- ✓ **clubhouse**

**Don Poff**
Professional

**Don Lewis**
Superintendent

***Course information:*** This public course has 18 holes and par is 71. The course is 6,215 yards and rated 70.0 from the championship tees, and 5,966 yards and rated 68.4 from the regular tees. The slope ratings are 119 championship and 116 regular. Women's tees are 5,356 yards and rated 70.0. The slope rating is 115.

***Play policy and fees:*** Green fees are $16 weekdays and $20 weekends. Carts are $20. Reservations are recommended, but can be made only through a computer reservation system. Prior sign-up is required. This course is available for outside tournaments.

***Location:*** Take the Riverside Freeway (Highway 91) to the Imperial Highway exit south. Drive one-half of a mile to Nohl Ranch Road and turn left and travel 1.5 miles to the club.

***Course description:*** Most of the fairways are separated on this hilly course (only four are parallel). The greens are undulating and can be fast in the summer. The first hole is a short par-5, but because the tee is so elevated, tee shots hooking or slicing can easily wind up lost or out-of-bounds. It is a course in which local knowledge is imperative.

# CRESTA VERDE GOLF CLUB

**Course 72**
MAP 15 grid f8

**1927**
**Randolph Scott**

1295 Cresta Road
Corona, CA 91719

Pro shop (714) 737-2255

- ✓ **driving range**
- ✓ **practice greens**
- ✓ **power carts**
- ✓ **pull carts**
- ✓ **golf club rental**
- locker rooms
- showers
- executive course
- accommodations
- ✓ **food and beverages**
- ✓ **clubhouse**

**Mike McKinlay**
Professional

**Carlos Moreno**
Superintendent

***Course information:*** This public course has 18 holes and par is 71. The course is 5,694 yards and rated 67.3 from the championship tees, and 5,390 yards and rated 65.3 from the regular tees. The slope ratings are 111 championship and 102 regular. Women's tees are 5,026 yards and rated 69.1. The slope rating is 119.

***Play policy and fees:*** Green fees are $14 weekdays and $20 weekends. Senior rates are $10 on weekdays. Carts are $20. Carts are mandatory before 12 noon on weekends and holidays. Reservations are recommended one week in advance. This course is available for outside tournaments.

***Location:*** From the Riverside Freeway (Highway 91), take the Main Street North/Norco exit and travel north for one mile to Parkridge Avenue. Turn right and drive 1 1/4 miles to Termino Avenue, and turn left and drive to the club entrance.

***Course description:*** Here's a course with Hollywood history. Henry Fonda, Burt Lancaster and Randolph Scott started this course back in 1927. In fact, Scott, who was a star attraction at the early Bing Crosby National Pro-Am at Pebble Beach, is credited with being the architect. In recent years, the course has gone through some renovation. Three new water holes have been added (numbers eight, 15 and 18) for a total of four, and a new clubhouse was built in 1991. Power carts were also added in 1991. The course offers a rolling terrain with some steep slopes, many mature trees and winding fairways. It is not for the casual walker. The 17th hole has an elevated tee of 400 feet. The men's record stands at 61 and the women's at 72.

# MOUNTAIN VIEW COUNTRY CLUB

**Course 73**
MAP 15 grid f8

**1955**
2121 Mountain View Drive
Corona, CA 91720

Clubhouse (714) 737-9798
Pro shop (714) 633-0282

- ✓ **driving range**
- ✓ **practice greens**
- ✓ **power carts**
- ✓ **pull carts**
- ✓ **golf club rental**
- locker rooms
- showers
- executive course
- accommodations
- ✓ **food and beverages**
- ✓ **clubhouse**

**David Rietter**
Professional

**Frank Paullino**
Superintendent

***Course information:*** This public course has 18 holes and par is 72. The course is 6,487 yards and rated 70.6 from the championship tees, and 6,194 yards and rated 69.0 from the regular tees. The slope ratings are 118 championship and 112 regular. Women's tees are 5,405 yards and rated 70.4. The slope rating is 119.

***Play policy and fees:*** Green fees are $15 weekdays and $25 weekends. There are senior rates of $9 on weekdays with a cart. Carts are $20. Reservations are recommended. No tank tops, T-shirts, jeans or cut-offs.

***Location:*** From the Riverside Freeway (Highway 91), take the Serfas Club Drive exit and travel east 400 yards to Pinecrest. Turn left and drive to the club entrance at the end of the street.

***Course description:*** This course has tight fairways, tiny greens and lots of trees. The front nine winds through homes, while the back nine is hilly. It is a traditional course that offers a challenge to players of any skill level. This course annually hosts six Southern California Publinks team events. The course record is 61, shot before changes were made to the layout in the late 70s.

# MEADOWLARK GOLF COURSE

**Course 74**
MAP I5 grid g2

*Course information:* This public course has 18 holes. See card below for yardage and rating information.

*Play policy and fees:* Green fees are $16 weekdays and $21 weekends. Carts are $20. Reservations are recommended. Tee times are available 10 days in advance, beginning at 6 a. m.

*Location:* From South Orange County, travel north on Interstate 405 to the Warner Avenue exit and continue west for about four miles to Graham Street, then turn right to the club.

*Course description:* Established in the mid-1930s, this is a rolling course with narrow, tree-lined fairways. The greens are small, so shot placement is essential. There are several water hazards on the course. The course is located close to the ocean in Huntington Beach, and is subject to ocean breezes. The upside of this is that the air is usually clean and clear. This is a busy course, with 125,000 rounds per year.

16782 Graham Street
Huntington Beach
CA 92647

Pro shop (714) 846-1364
Clubhouse (714) 846-4450

- ✓ **driving range**
- ✓ **practice greens**
- ✓ **power carts**
- ✓ **pull carts**
- ✓ **golf club rental**
- locker rooms
- showers
- executive course
- accommodations
- ✓ **food and beverages**
- clubhouse

**Jack Henry**
Professional/Manager

**Guy Auxer**
Superintendent

| Hole | 1 | 2 | 3 | 4 | 5 | 6 | 7 | 8 | 9 | Out | BLUE | Rating: -- |
|---|---|---|---|---|---|---|---|---|---|---|---|---|
| BLUE | - | - | - | - | - | - | - | - | - | - | | Slope: -- |
| WHITE | 450 | 176 | 246 | 484 | 350 | 255 | 222 | 262 | 395 | 2840 | | |
| Par | 4 | 3 | 4 | 5 | 4 | 4 | 3 | 4 | 4 | 35 | WHITE | Rating: 66.2 |
| Handicap | 1 | 7 | 17 | 11 | 9 | 15 | 5 | 13 | 3 | x | | Slope: 104 |
| RED | 438 | 144 | 238 | 480 | 341 | 239 | 222 | 242 | 384 | 2664 | | |
| Par | 5 | 3 | 4 | 5 | 4 | 4 | 3 | 4 | 5 | 37 | RED | Rating: 71.2 |
| Handicap | 3 | 17 | 9 | 1 | 13 | 7 | 15 | 11 | 5 | x | | Slope: 116 |

| Hole | 10 | 11 | 12 | 13 | 14 | 15 | 16 | 17 | 18 | In | Totals | |
|---|---|---|---|---|---|---|---|---|---|---|---|---|
| BLUE | - | - | - | - | - | - | - | - | - | - | BLUE | -- |
| WHITE | 357 | 294 | 378 | 174 | 400 | 315 | 155 | 361 | 476 | 2910 | WHITE | 5750 |
| Par | 4 | 4 | 4 | 3 | 4 | 4 | 3 | 4 | 5 | 35 | Par | 70 |
| Handicap | 12 | 18 | 8 | 4 | 2 | 14 | 16 | 10 | 6 | x | | |
| RED | 354 | 287 | 364 | 166 | 392 | 302 | 146 | 352 | 440 | 2803 | RED | 5467 |
| Par | 4 | 4 | 4 | 3 | 4 | 4 | 3 | 4 | 5 | 35 | Par | 72 |
| Handicap | 10 | 14 | 6 | 16 | 4 | 8 | 18 | 12 | 2 | x | | |

## SEACLIFF COUNTRY CLUB

**Course 75**
MAP 15 grid g2

6501 Palm Avenue
Huntington Beach, CA 92648

Pro shop (714) 536-7575
Clubhouse (714) 536-8866

- ✓ **driving range**
- ✓ **practice greens**
- ✓ **power carts**
- pull carts
- ✓ **golf club rental**
- ✓ **locker rooms**
- ✓ **showers**
- executive course
- accommodations
- ✓ **food and beverages**
- ✓ **clubhouse**

**Perry Dickey**
Manager

**Terry Ferraro**
Professional

**Ben McBrien**
Superintendent

***Course information:*** This private course has 18 holes and par is 72. The course is 6,755 yards and rated 72.8 from the championship tees, and 6,480 yards and rated 70.8 from the regular tees. The slope ratings are 129 championship and 119 regular. Women's tees are 6,125 yards and rated 75.7 from the championship tees, and 5,585 yards and rated 73 from the forward tees. The slope ratings are 130 championship and 123 forward.

***Play policy and fees:*** Members and guests only. Guest fees are $35 weekdays and $50 weekends. Carts are $18. This course is available for outside tournaments on Mondays only.

***Location:*** In Huntington Beach, travel south on Interstate 405 (San Diego Freeway) to the Golden West exit. Turn right and drive seven miles to Palm Avenue. Turn right and drive to the club.

***Course description:*** This course was formerly a public layout, under the Huntington Seacliff name, and has been private for nine years. It was remodeled in the late 1980s and is long with undulating greens. It is well maintained.

## DAVID L. BAKER MEMORIAL GOLF COURSE

**Course 76**
MAP 15 grid g3

10410 Edinger Avenue
Fountain Valley, CA 92708

Pro shop (714) 531-5885

- ✓ **driving range**
- ✓ **practice greens**
- ✓ **power carts**
- ✓ **pull carts**
- ✓ **golf club rental**
- locker rooms
- showers
- ✓ **executive course**
- accommodations
- ✓ **food and beverages**
- ✓ **clubhouse**

**Joe Cannon**
Manager

**Jim Caspio**
Professional

**Arnie Pedia**
Superintendent

***Course information:*** This public course has 18 holes. Par is 62. The course 3,800 yards, rated 57.7 and has a slope ratingof 91.

***Play policy and fees:*** Green fees are $12 on weekdays and $17 on weekends. Ask about special senior rates. Power carts are $16 and pull carts are $2. Proper golf attire is required.

***Location:*** Off Highway 405, take the Brookhurst exit north for two mile, turn right on Edinger Avenue.

***Course description:*** Opened in 1989, this course has five lakes which come into play on nine holes.

# MILE SQUARE GOLF COURSE

**Course 77**
MAP I5 grid g3

PO Box 8347
Fountain Valley, CA 92708

Pro shop (714) 545-7106
Clubhouse (714) 968-4556

- ✓ **driving range**
- ✓ **practice greens**
- ✓ **power carts**
- ✓ **pull carts**
- ✓ **golf club rental**
- locker rooms
- showers
- executive course
- accommodations
- ✓ **food and beverages**
- ✓ **clubhouse**

**Steve Seals**
Professional

**Marty Bereki**
Superintendent

***Course information:*** This public course has 18 holes and par is 72. The course is 6,730 yards and rated 71.3 from the championship tees, and 6,466 yards and rated 69.9 from the regular tees. The slope ratings are 116 championship and 112 regular. Women's tees are 5,532 yards and rated 70.5. The slope rating is 109.

***Play policy and fees:*** Green fees are $16 weekdays and $20 weekends and holidays. Carts are $20. Reservations are recommended. This course is available for outside tournaments.

***Location:*** In Fountain Valley, take the Brookhurst Street/Fountain Valley exit off Interstate 405 (San Diego Freeway) and follow the Brookhurst Street north offramp. Continue north for one mile to Warner Avenue and turn right. Drive one-half of a mile to Ward Street and turn left to the course.

***Course description:*** This is a fairly open and level course. There are numerous mature trees, a small creek and three lakes that add to the course's challenge and scenery. You can find water off the fourth, 15th and 17th tees if you're not careful. The course is usually in decent condition. Afternoon breezes usually make the back nine difficult. The first hole is a good one to open with. It is a par-5, fairly wide open and flat. It provides a margin for error. Many fairways parallel one another, so errant tee shots can still be played.

# COSTA MESA GOLF AND COUNTRY CLUB

**Course 78**
MAP I5 grid g3

**1967**
**William Francis Bell**

PO Box 1829
Costa Mesa, CA 92626

1701 Golf Course Drive
Costa Mesa, CA 92626

Pro shop (714) 540-7500
Starter (714) 754-5267

- ✓ **driving range**
- ✓ **practice greens**
- ✓ **power carts**
- ✓ **pull carts**
- ✓ **golf club rental**
- ✓ **locker rooms**
- ✓ **showers**
- executive course
- accommodations
- ✓ **food and beverages**
- ✓ **clubhouse**

**Brad Booth**
Professional

**Mel Summer**
Superintendent

***Course information:*** This public facility has 36 holes. Par is 72 on the Los Lagos Course and 70 on the Mesa Linda Course.

The Los Lagos Course is 6,542 yards and rated 70.7 from the championship tees, and 6,233 yards and rated 69.0 from the regular tees. The slope ratings are 116 championship and 110 regular. Women's tees are 5,925 yards and rated 73.3. The slope rating is 118.

The Mesa Linda Course is 5,486 yards and rated 66.0 from the championship tees, and 5,041 yards and rated 63.5 from the regular tees. The slope ratings are 104 championship and 96 regular. Women's tees are 4,591 yards and rated 65.6. The slope rating is 102.

***Play policy and fees:*** Los Lagos green fees are $16 weekdays and $20 weekends. Carts are $20. Mesa Linda green fees are $14 weekdays and $17 weekends. Reservations are recommended.

***Location:*** Traveling south on Interstate 405 (near Huntington Beach and Costa Mesa), exit on Harbor Boulevard. Continue south one mile to Adams Avenue and turn right. Drive one-quarter of a mile to Mesa Verde Drive, turn left and then right on Golf Course Drive.

***Course description:*** Los Lagos is the older of the two courses and it features many trees, three lakes and a rolling layout. When the wind comes up, as it often does, this course can be extremely difficult. It is the site of the annual Costa Mesa City Championship. About five years ago, Mesa Linda was upgraded with the addition of bunkers and new undulating greens. It is a short, flat course that is excellent for seniors. The driving range is lighted for night practice.

## MESA VERDE COUNTRY CLUB

**Course 79**
MAP I5 grid g3

***Course information:*** This private course has 18 holes and par is 71. The course is 6,745 yards and rated 72.9 from the championship tees, and 6,285 yards and rated 70.5 from the regular tees. The slope ratings are 132 championship and 124 regular. Women's tees are 5,482 yards and rated 71.7. The slope rating is 124.

***Play policy and fees:*** Members and guests only. Green fees are $45 weekdays and $65 weekends. Carts are $20. This course is available for outside tournaments on Mondays only.

***Location:*** Travel south on Interstate 405 (San Diego Freeway) to Costa Mesa and take the Harbor Boulevard exit. Drive south and turn right on Baker Street. Continue three-quarters of a mile to Mesa Verde West and turn right on Club House Road.

***Course description:*** This mature course offers a variety of holes and hazards, and is easy walking. Number 18 is a par-3, 200-yard finisher with water in front to the right and out-of-bounds to the left. You must hit into the wind onto a sizeable green that slopes toward the water. Avoid being tight to the right or you're in the drink before you want to be. The course can be very difficult. The LPGA has played several tournaments here, including the Women's Kemper Open. It is the site of the 1993 U.S. Junior Girls Championship.

**1958**
3000 Club House Road
Costa Mesa, CA 92626

Pro shop (714) 549-0522
Clubhouse (714) 549-0377

- ✓ **driving range**
- ✓ **practice greens**
- ✓ **power carts**
- ✓ **pull carts**
- ✓ **golf club rental**
- ✓ **locker rooms**
- ✓ **showers**
- executive course
- accommodations
- ✓ **food and beverages**
- ✓ **clubhouse**

**James A. Walsh Jr.**
General Manager

**Art Schilling**
Professional

**Reed Yenny**
Superintendent

## RIVER VIEW GOLF COURSE

**Course 80**
MAP I5 grid g4

***Course information:*** This public course has 18 holes and par is 70. The course is 5,554 yards and rated 66.1 from the championship tees, and 5,288 yards and rated 64.4 from the regular tees. The slope ratings are 103 championship and 97 regular. Women's tees are 5,194 yards and rated 70.1. The slope is 112.

***Play policy and fees:*** Green fees are $12 weekdays and $17 weekends. Carts are $18. Reservations are recommended.

***Location:*** Travel south on Interstate 5 (Santa Ana Freeway) to the Bristol exit south to Santa Clara Street, then west to the club.

***Course description:*** This challenging, short course crisscrosses the bed of the Santa Ana River. The front nine requires good ball placement, and the back nine is wide open. Because of its proximity to the Santa Ana River, the course sometimes is subject to closing several of its holes during heavy rains.

1800 West 22nd Street
Santa Ana, CA 92706

Pro shop (714) 543-1115

- ✓ **driving range**
- ✓ **practice greens**
- ✓ **power carts**
- ✓ **pull carts**
- ✓ **golf club rental**
- locker rooms
- showers
- executive course
- accommodations
- ✓ **food and beverages**
- clubhouse

**Vince Lerma**
Professional

**James Mercer**
Superintendent

## WILLOWICK GOLF COURSE

**Course 81**
MAP I5 grid g4

*Course information:* This public course has 18 holes and par is 71. The course is 6,063 yards and rated 67.4 from the regular tees. The slope is 102. Women's tees are 5,742 yards and rated 71.6. The slope rating is 116.

*Play policy and fees:* Green fees are $13 weekdays and $20 weekends for 18 holes and $8 weekdays and $13 weekends for nine holes. Carts are $20. Reservations are recommended.

*Location:* In Santa Ana, take the Harbor exit off of Highway 22 (Garden Grove Freeway) and travel one mile south to Fifth Street. Turn left on Fifth Street and drive one-half mile and the course will be on your left.

*Course description:* This course is wide open and level with many trees and bunkers. It is an established course that has been a favorite of Southern Californians since the 1920s. It is short and walkable, good for exercising the legs. The course record is 61. It plays host to the annual Santa Ana City Championship.

3017 West Fifth Street
Santa Ana, CA 92703

Pro shop (714) 554-0672

- ✓ **driving range**
- ✓ **practice greens**
- ✓ **power carts**
- ✓ **pull carts**
- golf club rental
- ✓ **locker rooms**
- ✓ **showers**
- executive course
- accommodations
- ✓ **food and beverages**
- ✓ **clubhouse**

**Ken Kobayashi**
Professional

**Tom Pullium**
Professional

**Roy Haines**
Superintendent

## TUSTIN RANCH GOLF COURSE

**Course 82**
MAP I5 grid h3

*Course information:* This public course has 18 holes and par is 72. The course is 6,736 yards and rated 129 from the tournament tees, 6,376 yards and rated 70.8 from the championship tees and 6,004 yards and rated 68.8 from the regular tees. The slope ratings are 129 from the championship tees, 124 form the blue tees and 118 from the white tees. Forward tees are 5,204 yards and rated 64.6. The slope rating is 101.

*Play policy and fees:* Green fees are $65 Monday through Thursday and $85 Friday through Sunday, including carts (which are mandatory).

*Location:* Take I-5 to Jamboree Road exit. Go north to Irvine Blvd and turn left. Go to Tustin Ranch Road and turn right.

*Course description:* Architect Ted Robinson took a flat parcel of land and sculpted an excellent public course from it. Carts are not permitted on faiways, so the course is maintained in country club-quality condition. The signature hole is par-3 11th, which requires that the tee shot carry a pond that includes waterscapes, to a sloping tiered green.

**1989**
**Ted Robinson**

12442 Tustin Ranch Road
Tustin, CA 92680

Pro shop (714) 730-1611

- ✓ **driving range**
- ✓ **practice greens**
- ✓ **power carts**
- pull carts
- ✓ **golf club rental**
- locker rooms
- showers
- executive course
- accommodations
- ✓ **food and beverages**
- ✓ **clubhouse**

**Buck Page**
Professional/Gen. Manager

**Steven Plummer**
Superintendent

## SANTA ANA COUNTRY CLUB

**Course 83**
MAP I5 grid h3

**1929**
20382 Newport Blvd.
Santa Ana, CA 92707

Pro shop (714) 545-7260
Clubhouse (714) 556-3000

- ✓ **driving range**
- ✓ **practice greens**
- ✓ **power carts**
- pull carts
- ✓ **golf club rental**
- locker rooms
- showers
- executive course
- accommodations
- ✓ **food and beverages**
- ✓ **clubhouse**

**Mike Reehl**
Professional

**David Zahrte**
Superintendent

***Course information:*** This private course has 18 holes and par is 72. The course is 6,543 yards and rated 71.7 from the championship tees, and 6,212 yards and rated 69.6 from the regular tees. The slope ratings are 126 championship and 120 regular.

***Play policy and fees:*** Members and guests only. Accompanied guest fees are $50 and unaccompanied $75. Fees include carts.

***Location:*** Travel south on Interstate 405 to the Newport Freeway (Highway 55). Exit at Mesa Drive and turn left and drive 100 yards to Newport Boulevard. Turn left and drive 100 yards to the club.

***Course description:*** This course has many old trees and five lakes. It was built in 1929. When Fred Couples lived in Newport Beach, he played and practiced here frequently. Water comes into play on several holes. The course is relatively flat, exquisitely maintained, and sometimes noisy; John Wayne Airport is nearby.

## PELICAN HILL GOLF CLUB

**Course 84**
MAP I5 grid h3

**1991**
**Tom Fazio**

22653 Pelican Hill Road
Newport Coast, CA 92657

Pro shop (714) 760-0707

- ✓ **driving range**
- ✓ **practice greens**
- ✓ **power carts**
- pull carts
- ✓ **golf club rental**
- locker rooms
- showers
- executive course
- accommodations
- ✓ **food and beverages**
- clubhouse

**Jay Colliatie**
Director of Golf

**Rob Ford**
Professional

**George Druzisky**
Superintendent

***Course information:*** This resort course has 18 holes and par is 70. The course is 6,634 and rated 72.8 from the tournament tees, 6,305 yards and rated 70.8 from the blue tees, and 5,883 and rated 68.4 from the white tees. The slope ratings are 138 from the tournament tees, 130 from the blue tees and 119 from the white tees. Women's tees are 5,240 yards and rated 70.9. The slope rating is 121.

***Play policy and fees:*** Green fees are $105 Monday through Thursday and $125 Friday through Sunday, carts included.

***Location:*** Take I-405 or 55 Freeway to 73 Freeway toward Corona del Mar. Exit at MacArthur Blvd. and follow that to Pacific Coast Highway and turn left. Go to Newport Coast Drive and turn left.

***Course description:*** The Ocean Course, the first of two courses planned for Pelican Hill, offers spectacular ocean views from every hole. It was designed by noted architect Tom Fazio. The course is an adequate test of golf and a difficult one when the ocean breezes are stiff. More often, it is user-friendly. Construction already has begun on the second course, also designed by Fazio. It is scheduled to open late in 1993. Ultimately, one or both of these courses might become private.



MAP ON PAGE 506

## THE NEWPORT BEACH COUNTRY CLUB

**Course 85**
MAP I5 grid h3

*Course information:* This private course has 18 holes and par is 71. The course is 6,587 yards and rated 71.0 from the championship tees, and 6,232 yards and rated 68.9 from the regular tees. Women's yardage is 5,756 and rated 66.6. The slope ratings are 118 championship, 112 regular and 102 women.

*Play policy and fees:* Reciprocal play is accepted with members of other private clubs. Guest fees are $40 weekdays and $55 weekends. Carts are $20. Reservations are recommended.

*Location:* Travel north from Laguna Beach on Highway 1 past MacArthur Boulevard one-half mile.

*Course description:* This is an older, traditional course, with trees lining both sides of most of the fairways and water coming into play on only a few of the par-3s. It is located about a mile from the Pacific ocean, and therefore is subject to traditional ocean breezes, especially in the afternoon. Among the members here is comedian Joey Bishop, a long-time resident of Newport Beach. The course is owned by the prestigious Balboa Bay Club.

1600 East Coast Highway
Newport Beach, CA 92660

Pro shop (714) 644-9680
Clubhouse (714) 644-9550

✓ **driving range**
✓ **practice greens**
✓ **power carts**
pull carts
✓ **golf club rental**
✓ **locker rooms**
✓ **showers**
executive course
accommodations
✓ **food and beverages**
✓ **clubhouse**

**Jerry Anderson**
Director of Golf

**Monty Blodgett**
Professional

**Gregory Fox**
Superintendent

## NEWPORT BEACH GOLF COURSE

**Course 86**
MAP I5 grid h4

*Course information:* This public course has 18 holes and par is 59. The course is 3,450 yards and rated 51.5 from the regular tees. The slope rating is 83.

*Play policy and fees:* Green fees are $11 weekdays and $16 weekends.

*Location:* In Newport Beach from the Newport Freeway (Highway 55), exit at Highway 73/South Corona Del Mar and drive south to Irvine Avenue, turn right and drive one-half mile to the club.

*Course description:* This executive course offers well-maintained and well-contoured holes with bunkers and water that comes into play. The course is lighted and accepts starting times until 8 p.m. The course features five par-4s. The 18th hole is among the most difficult—225 yards, downhill. There are no grass tees here; golfers tee off from mats.

**1971**
**Robert Muir Graves**

PO Box 18426
Irvine, CA 92714

3100 Irvine Avenue
Newport Beach, CA 92660

Pro shop (714) 852-8689
Clubhouse (714) 852-8681

✓ **driving range**
✓ **practice greens**
power carts
✓ **pull carts**
✓ **golf club rental**
locker rooms
showers
✓ **executive course**
accommodations
✓ **food and beverages**
✓ **clubhouse**

**John Leonard**
Professional

**Manuel Mendoza**
Superintendent

## BIG CANYON COUNTRY CLUB

Course 87
MAP 15 grid h4

**1971**
One Big Canyon Drive
Newport Beach, CA 92660

Pro shop (714) 644-5404

- ✓ **driving range**
- ✓ **practice greens**
- ✓ **power carts**
- ✓ **pull carts**
- ✓ **golf club rental**
- ✓ **locker rooms**
- showers
- executive course
- accommodations
- ✓ **food and beverages**
- ✓ **clubhouse**

**Bob Lovejoy**
Professional

**Ray Layland**
Superintendent

***Course information:*** This private course has 18 holes and par is 72. The course is 6,937 yards and rated 73.9 from the championship tees, and 6,672 yards and rated 72.2 from the regular tees. Women's yardage is 5,788 and rated 67.5. The slope ratings are 137 championship and 130 regular.

***Play policy and fees:*** Members and guests only. Weekdays accompanied guest fees are $30, weekends $35. $75 for unaccompanied guests every day. Carts are $18 per person.

***Location:*** From Interstate 405, take the MacArthur Boulevard exit south and drive five miles to San Joaquin Hills Road. Turn right and drive to Big Canyon Drive.

***Course description:*** This course was built in 1971. It has a traditional layout with many trees and bunkers. There are several water hazards as well. It has rolling fairways and many blind shots to the greens. It is among the more exclusive country clubs in the state. When he is in town, junior star Tiger Woods often plays here, as does LPGA Tour player Sally Little.

## RANCHO SAN JOAQUIN GOLF COURSE

Course 88
MAP 15 grid h4

One Sandburg Way
Irvine, CA 92715

Pro shop (714) 786-5522

- ✓ **driving range**
- ✓ **practice greens**
- ✓ **power carts**
- ✓ **pull carts**
- ✓ **golf club rental**
- locker rooms
- showers
- executive course
- accommodations
- ✓ **food and beverages**
- ✓ **clubhouse**

**Andrew Valanis**
Manager

**Mitzi Sundberg**
Head Professional

**Mike Oren**
Superintendent

***Course information:*** This public course has 18 holes and par is 72. The course is 6,453 yards and rated 69.8 from the championship tees, and 6,229 yards and rated 68.8 from the regular tees. The slope ratings are 111 championship and 107 regular.

***Play policy and fees:*** Green fees are $23 Monday through Thursday; $35 Friday; and $45 including cart on Saturday, Sunday and holidays. Carts are included and mandatory on weekends. Carts are $20. Reservations are recommended. This course is available for outside tournaments.

***Location:*** Travel south on Interstate 405 to the Culver Drive exit west. Turn right on Sandburg Way and follow it to the end.

***Course description:*** This is an interesting and challenging course. It features large, undulating greens, hilly terrain and some water hazards. The par-5 fifth hole is among the best holes in Orange County. It requires a lay-up second shot with water on each side of the fairway. This course is maintained well, with an effort made to outline the fairways.

# EL TORO GOLF COURSE

**Course 89**
MAP I5 grid h5

***Course information:*** This military course has 18 holes. See card below for yardage and rating information.

***Play policy and fees:*** Military personnel and guests only. Green fees vary according to military status. Carts are $15.

***Location:*** Take the Santa Ana Freeway south from Santa Ana to the Sand Canyon exit east. At Trabuco Road turn south to the main gate and take the perimeter road south for 2.5 miles to the course.

***Course description:*** This relatively flat course has mature trees and a few doglegs. There is a strict dress code: no tank tops, cut-offs or clothing with obscene or anti-American sentiments. The course plays host to 75,000 rounds a year.

**1949**
**William Park Bell**

El Toro Marine
Memorial MCAS
Santa Ana, CA 92709

Pro shop (714) 726-2577

- ✓ **driving range**
- ✓ **practice greens**
- ✓ **power carts**
- ✓ **pull carts**
- ✓ **golf club rental**
- ✓ **locker rooms**
- ✓ **showers**
- executive course
- accommodations
- ✓ **food and beverages**
- ✓ **clubhouse**

**Wally Bradley**
Professional

**Elbert Turner**
Superintendent

| Hole | 1 | 2 | 3 | 4 | 5 | 6 | 7 | 8 | 9 | Out | | |
|---|---|---|---|---|---|---|---|---|---|---|---|---|
| BLUE | 397 | 512 | 417 | 384 | 433 | 31 | 228 | 497 | 195 | 3394 | BLUE | Rating: 71.5 |
| WHITE | 383 | 500 | 402 | 371 | 411 | 320 | 195 | 485 | 184 | 3251 | | Slope: 114 |
| Par | 4 | 5 | 4 | 4 | 4 | 4 | 3 | 5 | 3 | 36 | WHITE | Rating: 69.7 |
| Handicap | 5 | 11 | 3 | 7 | 1 | 15 | 13 | 9 | 17 | x | | Slope: 111 |
| RED | 368 | 452 | 358 | 340 | 344 | 283 | 155 | 445 | 155 | 2900 | | |
| Par | 4 | 5 | 4 | 4 | 4 | 4 | 3 | 5 | 3 | 36 | RED | Rating: 71.2 |
| Handicap | 3 | 5 | 1 | 11 | 7 | 13 | 17 | 9 | 15 | x | | Slope: 112 |

| Hole | 10 | 11 | 12 | 13 | 14 | 15 | 16 | 17 | 18 | In | Totals | |
|---|---|---|---|---|---|---|---|---|---|---|---|---|
| BLUE | 377 | 332 | 533 | 143 | 421 | 185 | 516 | 407 | 442 | 3356 | BLUE | 6750 |
| WHITE | 343 | 315 | 520 | 127 | 397 | 176 | 506 | 400 | 433 | 3217 | WHITE | 6468 |
| Par | 4 | 4 | 5 | 3 | 4 | 3 | 5 | 4 | 4 | 36 | Par | 72 |
| Handicap | 12 | 14 | 8 | 18 | 2 | 16 | 10 | 6 | 4 | x | | |
| RED | 324 | 274 | 443 | 120 | 419 | 166 | 318 | 365 | 328 | 2757 | RED | 5657 |
| Par | 4 | 4 | 5 | 3 | 5 | 3 | 4 | 4 | 4 | 36 | Par | 72 |
| Handicap | 12 | 14 | 8 | 18 | 6 | 16 | 10 | 2 | 4 | x | | |

# LAGUNA HILLS GOLF COURSE

**Course 90**
MAP 15 grid h5

*Course information:* This private facility has 27 holes and par is 71, 69 and 70 respectively for each of the 18-hole combinations listed.

The One and Two Combination is 5,849 yards and rated 66.5 from the regular tees. The slope rating is 100. Women's tees are 5,536 yards and rated 66.5. The slope rating is 113.

The Three and One Combination is 5,559 yards and rated 65.2 from the regular tees. The slope rating is 96. Women's tees are 5,369 yards and rated 65.2. The slope rating is 109.

The Two and Three Combination is 5,454 yards and rated 64.7 from the regular tees. The slope rating is 96. Women's tees are 5,331 yards and rated 64.7. The slope rating is 109.

*Play policy and fees:* Members and guests only. Green fees are $17 for guests. Carts are $16 for guests. Reservations are recommended.

*Location:* Take the El Toro Road exit off Interstate 5 and travel west to Moulton Parkway. Turn right and go one-quarter mile to the club.

*Course description:* Located in a retirement community, Leisure World, this rolling course is slightly hilly with mature trees. All three nines have different pars—36 for the first, 35 for the second, and 34 for the third.

PO Box 2307
Laguna Hills, CA 92653

24112 Moulton Parkway
Laguna Hills, CA 92653

Pro shop (714) 837-7630
Clubhouse (714) 951-2276

- ✓ **driving range**
- ✓ **practice greens**
- ✓ **power carts**
- ✓ **pull carts**
- ✓ **golf club rental**
- locker rooms
- showers
- executive course
- accommodations
- ✓ **food and beverages**
- ✓ **clubhouse**

**Robert Wilkinson**
Professional

**Mark Phillips**
Superintendent

# DOVE CANYON COUNTRY CLUB

**Course 91**
MAP I5 grid h6

**1990**
**Jack Nicklaus**

22682 Golf Club Drive
Dove Canyon, CA 92679

Pro shop (714) 858-2888
Clubhouse (714) 858-1800

- ✓ **driving range**
- ✓ **practice greens**
- ✓ **power carts**
- pull carts
- ✓ **golf club rental**
- ✓ **locker rooms**
- ✓ **showers**
- executive course
- accommodations
- ✓ **food and beverages**
- ✓ **clubhouse**

**Kevin Paluch**
Director of Golf

**Michael Coopman**
Superintendent

***Course information:*** This private course has 18 holes. Par is 71. The course is 6,902 yards and rated 75.0 from the tournament tees, 6,489 yards and rated 72.0 from the championship tees, and 5,917 yards and rated 68.0 from the regular tees. The slope ratings are 140 tournament, 133 championship and 120 regular. Women's tees are 5,472 yards and rated 71.2 from the championship tees, and 5,261 yards and rated 69.7 forward tees. The slope ratings are 122 championship and 119 forward.

***Play policy and fees:*** Reciprocal is not accepted. Members and guests only. Guest fees are $60 weekdays and $75 weekends and holidays, including cart and range balls. Reservations are required.

***Location:*** From Interstate 5 south, take the El Toro Road exit east. Drive to Santa Margarita Parkway. Turn south on Santa Margarita Parkway to Plano Trabuco and turn right. Take Plano Trabuco to Dove Canyon and turn left. Follow Dove Canyon to the guard gate and the course.

***Course description:*** This Jack Nicklaus course opened in August 1990, and the clubhouse followed in March 1991. This course backs up to the Cleveland National Forest, so count on plenty of wildlife. There are both barrancas and bunnies. The course is rolling, with some water and beautiful old oaks. The most notable water is at the 18th green, which features a waterfall and lake. This is a non-smoking course. It is among Nicklaus' more user-friendly courses, although from the championship tees, combined with tough pin placements, the course can play extremely difficult. Several members of the California Angels and other baseball teams are members here.

# CASTA DEL SOL GOLF COURSE

**Course 92**
MAP I5 grid h6

***Course information:*** This public course has 18 holes and par is 60. The course is 3,715 yards and rated 58.1 from the regular tees. The slope rating is 92. Women's tees are 3,413 yards and rated 58.1. The slope rating is 87.

***Play policy and fees:*** Green fees are $14 weekdays and $19 weekends. Carts are $17. Call for special afternoon rates.

***Location:*** Take the La Paz Road exit off Interstate 5 and travel east for one mile to Marguerite Parkway. Turn left and drive 1.5 miles to Casta del Sol Road and turn right and drive to the course.

***Course description:*** This rolling course has a couple of streams and lakes. It's a testy, short course but extremely busy, with more than 300,000 rounds played here a year.

**Ted Robinson**

27601 Casta del Sol Road
Mission Viejo, CA 92692

Pro shop (714) 581-0940
Clubhouse (714) 581-9701

- driving range
- ✓ **practice greens**
- ✓ **power carts**
- ✓ **pull carts**
- golf club rental
- locker rooms
- showers
- executive course
- accommodations
- ✓ **food and beverages**
- ✓ **clubhouse**

**R. James Ryan**
Manager

**Mary Rutledge**
Professional

**Brett Billeadeau**
Superintendent

# COTO DE CAZA GOLF COURSE

**Course 93**
MAP I5 grid h6

***Course information:*** This private course has 18 holes. The gold tees are 7,096 yards, rated 75.8, and have a slope of 146. See card below for additional yardage and rating information.

***Play policy and fees:*** Limited reciprocal play is accepted with members of other private clubs (have your pro call for arrangements); otherwise members and guests only. Green fees are $40 weekdays and $60 weekends with a member only. Carts are $19.

***Location:*** Take the El Toro exit off Interstate 5 and drive east to Santa Margarita Road in Coto de Caza. Turn right and drive five miles to Antonio and turn right to the club.

***Course description:*** Designed by Robert Trent Jones Jr., who retained Johnny Miller as a consultant, Coto is set in canyons in South Orange County and features native California oak trees. The 597-yard par-5 first hole requires a tee shot through a chute and over one of these canyons, with trees and more canyon guarding the left side. Among those who have given this course their stamp of approval is former Orange County resident Fred Couples, who played here shortly after the course opened in 1987. Among its members is Kellee Booth, generally regarded as the best junior girl in the country. A second course at Coto has been in the discussion stages for several years, with Jones expected to design that one as well. Coto is the site of the Orange County Amateur Championship.

**1987**
**Robert Trent Jones, Jr.**

25291 Vista del Verde
Coto de Caza, CA 92679

Pro shop (714) 858-2770
Clubhouse (714) 858-4100
Fax (714) 858-2797

- ✓ **driving range**
- ✓ **practice greens**
- ✓ **power carts**
- pull carts
- ✓ **golf club rental**
- ✓ **locker rooms**
- ✓ **showers**
- executive course
- accommodations
- ✓ **food and beverages**
- ✓ **clubhouse**

**Ed Merritt**
Manager

**Mike Mitzel**
Professional

**Larry Murphy**
Director

**Lee Hood**
Superintendent

| Hole | 1 | 2 | 3 | 4 | 5 | 6 | 7 | 8 | 9 | Out | | |
|---|---|---|---|---|---|---|---|---|---|---|---|---|
| BLUE | 576 | 331 | 385 | 176 | 522 | 169 | 381 | 389 | 272 | 3201 | BLUE | Rating: 72.8 |
| WHITE | 539 | 310 | 350 | 159 | 455 | 164 | 351 | 375 | 262 | 2965 | | Slope: 138 |
| Par | 5 | 4 | 4 | 3 | 5 | 3 | 4 | 4 | 4 | 36 | WHITE | Rating: 69.9 |
| Handicap | 1 | 9 | 5 | 3 | 13 | 15 | 7 | 11 | 17 | x | | Slope: 127 |
| RED | 429 | 288 | 308 | 135 | 426 | 143 | 291 | 336 | 239 | 2595 | | |
| Par | 5 | 4 | 4 | 3 | 5 | 3 | 4 | 4 | 4 | 36 | RED | Rating: 71.6 |
| Handicap | 1 | 9 | 7 | 5 | 13 | 17 | 11 | 3 | 15 | x | | Slope: 132 |

| Hole | 10 | 11 | 12 | 13 | 14 | 15 | 16 | 17 | 18 | In | Totals | |
|---|---|---|---|---|---|---|---|---|---|---|---|---|
| BLUE | 507 | 153 | 532 | 439 | 432 | 130 | 376 | 396 | 392 | 3357 | BLUE | 6558 |
| WHITE | 486 | 143 | 489 | 413 | 399 | 97 | 356 | 371 | 363 | 3117 | WHITE | 6082 |
| Par | 5 | 3 | 5 | 4 | 4 | 3 | 4 | 4 | 4 | 36 | Par | 72 |
| Handicap | 14 | 16 | 12 | 8 | 4 | 18 | 6 | 2 | 10 | x | | |
| RED | 440 | 115 | 455 | 361 | 370 | 87 | 296 | 333 | 317 | 2774 | RED | 5369 |
| Par | 5 | 3 | 5 | 4 | 4 | 3 | 4 | 4 | 4 | 36 | Par | 72 |
| Handicap | 14 | 16 | 4 | 10 | 8 | 18 | 6 | 2 | 12 | x | | |

# TIJERAS CREEK GOLF CLUB

**Course 94**
MAP I5 grid h6

***Course information:*** This public course has 18 holes and par is 72. The course is 6,601 yards and rated 71.8 from the championship tees and 6,220 yards and rated 69.4 from the regular tees. The slope ratings are 125 championship and 118 regular. Women's tees are 5,130 yards and rated 70.1. The slope rating is 115.

***Play policy and fees:*** Green fees are $45 weekdays and $70 weekends, cart included.

***Location:*** From the north, take I-5 south to the El Toro exit, then go east on El Toro for four miles. Turn right on Santa Margarita Parkway and go three miles to Avenida Empresa and turn right. Go to Avenida de Las Banderas and turn right. Take another right on Antonio parkway and follow it to the course. From the south, take I-5 north to Oso parkway exit and go east to Antonio Parkway. Turn left and go to Tijeras Creek Road and make another left.

***Course description:*** The course has distinictively different nines. The front nine winds through a housing development, while the back nine is surrounded by natural terrain that will not be developed. Deer have been spotted loitering on the back nine. Tijeras Creek is regarded as one of the best public courses in Orange County.

**1990**
**Ted Robinson**

29082 Tijeras Creek
Rancho Santa Margarita, CA
92688

Pro shop (714)589-9793

- ✓ **driving range**
- ✓ **practice greens**
- ✓ **power carts**
- pull carts
- ✓ **golf club rental**
- ✓ **locker rooms**
- ✓ **showers**
- executive course
- accommodations
- ✓ **food and beverages**
- ✓ **clubhouse**

**Doug Booth**
Professional

**Jim Fetterly**
Superintendent

# MISSION VIEJO COUNTRY CLUB

**Course 95**
MAP 15 grid h6

*Course information:* This private course has 18 holes. See card below for yardage and rating information.

*Play policy and fees:* Members and guests only. Green fees are $40 weekdays and $55 weekends. Carts are $16. This course is available for outside tournaments Mondays only.

*Location:* Take the Oso Parkway exit off Interstate 5, then travel east one-half mile to Country Club Drive and turn right to the club.

*Course description:* This is a long and demanding course. The fairways are hilly and parallel. The greens are well maintained, very fast, and largely elevated. It was once dubbed "Mission Impossible," by Johnny Miller; it is that difficult when set up for the pros.

**1967**
**Robert Trent Jones, Sr.**

26200 Country Club Drive
Mission Viejo, CA 92691

Pro shop (714) 582-1020
Clubhouse (714) 582-1550

- ✓ **driving range**
- ✓ **practice greens**
- ✓ **power carts**
- pull carts
- ✓ **golf club rental**
- ✓ **locker rooms**
- ✓ **showers**
- executive course
- accommodations
- ✓ **food and beverages**
- ✓ **clubhouse**

**Jeremy Dunkason**
Professional

**Mike Huck**
Superintendent

| Hole | 1 | 2 | 3 | 4 | 5 | 6 | 7 | 8 | 9 | Out | | |
|---|---|---|---|---|---|---|---|---|---|---|---|---|
| BLUE | 509 | 378 | 195 | 469 | 330 | 196 | 408 | 545 | 391 | 3421 | BLUE | Rating: 73.8 |
| WHITE | 489 | 366 | 177 | 430 | 320 | 177 | 376 | 525 | 376 | 3236 | | Slope: 138 |
| Par | 5 | 4 | 3 | 4 | 4 | 3 | 4 | 5 | 4 | 36 | WHITE | Rating: 71.3 |
| Handicap | 13 | 11 | 7 | 1 | 15 | 17 | 3 | 9 | 5 | x | | Slope: 126 |
| RED | 453 | 326 | 128 | 385 | 291 | 152 | 307 | 451 | 326 | 2819 | | |
| Par | 5 | 4 | 3 | 4 | 4 | 3 | 4 | 5 | 4 | 36 | RED | Rating: 73.2 |
| Handicap | 7 | 9 | 15 | 1 | 11 | 17 | 13 | 5 | 3 | x | | Slope: 126 |

| Hole | 10 | 11 | 12 | 13 | 14 | 15 | 16 | 17 | 18 | In | Totals | |
|---|---|---|---|---|---|---|---|---|---|---|---|---|
| BLUE | 398 | 394 | 417 | 194 | 519 | 371 | 196 | 488 | 416 | 3393 | BLUE | 6814 |
| WHITE | 378 | 368 | 402 | 179 | 497 | 361 | 170 | 472 | 393 | 3220 | WHITE | 6456 |
| Par | 4 | 4 | 4 | 3 | 5 | 4 | 3 | 5 | 4 | 36 | Par | 72 |
| Handicap | 2 | 12 | 4 | 16 | 6 | 10 | 18 | 14 | 8 | x | | |
| RED | 351 | 349 | 344 | 132 | 430 | 332 | 120 | 453 | 368 | 2879 | RED | 5698 |
| Par | 4 | 4 | 4 | 3 | 5 | 4 | 3 | 5 | 4 | 36 | Par | 72 |
| Handicap | 6 | 12 | 14 | 16 | 2 | 8 | 18 | 10 | 4 | x | | |

# ALISO CREEK GOLF COURSE

**Course 96**
MAP I5 grid i4

*Course information:* This resort course has nine holes. Par is 64 for 18 holes. The course is 4,148 yards and rated 57.2 for 18 holes from the regular tees. The slope rating is 104. Women's tees are 4,148 yards and rated 65.4. The slope rating is 109.

*Play policy and fees:* Green fees are $11 for nine holes weekdays and $12 for nine holes weekends. Reservations are required one week in advance. This course is available for outside tournaments.

*Location:* Take Interstate 5 or Interstate 405 southbound to Highway 133 (Laguna Freeway). Take Highway 133 (Laguna Freeway) west to Highway 1 (Pacific Coast Highway). Drive south on Highway 1 (Pacific Coast Highway) almost three miles to the green overpass. Take an immediate left turn at Ben Brown's sign. Northbound Interstate 5, take the Beach Cities exit. Drive north on Highway 1 (Pacific Coast Highway) about six miles. Turn right at the sign across from the Aliso State Beach Pier.

*Course description:* This 41-year-old course is set in a heavily-foliaged canyon, with a meandering creek. There are 19 bunkers and lots of trees. With the ocean just 400 yards away, a sea breeze adds to the quiet atmosphere.

**1951**

31106 Pacific Coast Highway
Laguna Beach, CA 92677

Pro shop (714) 499-1919
Office (714) 499-2271

- ✓ **driving range**
- ✓ **practice greens**
- ✓ **power carts**
- ✓ **pull carts**
- ✓ **golf club rental**
- ✓ **locker rooms**
- showers
- ✓ **executive course**
- accommodations
- ✓ **food and beverages**
- ✓ **clubhouse**

**Larry Brotherton**
Manager/Professional

**Severo Mercado**
Superintendent

# EL NIGUEL COUNTRY CLUB

**Course 97**
MAP I5 grid i5

*Course information:* This private course has 18 holes and par is 72. The course is 6,909 yards and rated 73.8 from the championship tees, and 6,635 yards and rated 71.8 from the regular tees. The slope ratings are 133 championship and 124 regular. Women's tees are 5,787 yards and rated 72.8. The slope rating is 120.

*Play policy and fees:* Members and guests only. Guest fees are $45 weekdays and $60 weekends. Carts are $16.

*Location:* Take the Crown Valley Parkway exit off Interstate 5 in Laguna Niguel and drive 4.5 miles to Clubhouse Drive. Turn left to the club.

*Course description:* This is a challenging course. It is well-bunkered with level fairways and lots of trees. The greens are some of the toughest west of the Rockies. You'll need a fortune teller to help you read them. The par-3 holes are exceptionally fine. Fairways and roughs are Kikuyu grass, which makes them unwieldy. The course is beautifully-maintained, and at one time was considered the finest course in Orange County. Atlanta Braves catcher Damon Berryhill is a member here.

23700 Clubhouse Drive
Laguna Niguel, CA 92677

Pro shop (714) 496-2023
Clubhouse (714) 496-5767

- ✓ **driving range**
- ✓ **practice greens**
- ✓ **power carts**
- pull carts
- golf club rental
- ✓ **locker rooms**
- ✓ **showers**
- executive course
- accommodations
- ✓ **food and beverages**
- ✓ **clubhouse**

**Paul Scodeller**
Professional

**Jim Bertoni**
Superintendent



MAP ON PAGE 506

# MONARCH BEACH GOLF LINKS

**Course 98**
MAP I5 grid i5

**1983**
**Robert Trent Jones, Jr.**

33080 Niguel Road
Dana Point, CA 92629

Pro shop (714) 240-8247

- driving range
- ✓ **practice greens**
- ✓ **power carts**
- pull carts
- ✓ **golf club rental**
- locker rooms
- showers
- executive course
- ✓ **accommodations**
- ✓ **food and beverages**
- ✓ **clubhouse**

**Chris Herald**
Professional

**Brian Sullivan**
Superintendent

***Course information:*** This resort course has 18 holes. See card below for yardage and rating information.

***Play policy and fees:*** Outside play is accepted. Green fees are $65 weekdays and $85 Friday through Sunday. Carts are included. Reservations are recommended.

***Location:*** Take the Crown Valley Parkway exit off Interstate 5. Drive 3.5 miles to Niguel Road, turn left and travel another three miles to the club.

***Course description:*** Most of the course offers a nice view of the ocean, and one hole runs alongside it. The course was built to conform nicely to the terrain. Watch for number 16. It's a par-5, 517-yard twister with a creek intersecting the fairway. To reach the green in regulation it is necessary to clear the creek twice. Long hitters might reach the green in two, but if they miss they will be appropriately penalized. The Ritz-Carlton is next to the course, which is located on both sides of Pacific Coast Highway. Among those who have played here are Ben Crenshaw, Mark Calcavecchia and O.J. Simpson.

| Hole | 1 | 2 | 3 | 4 | 5 | 6 | 7 | 8 | 9 | Out | BLUE | Rating: 69.9 |
|---|---|---|---|---|---|---|---|---|---|---|---|---|
| BLUE | 373 | 398 | 526 | 146 | 381 | 185 | 336 | 157 | 358 | 2860 | | Slope: 127 |
| WHITE | 346 | 342 | 496 | 127 | 354 | 137 | 305 | 133 | 330 | 2570 | | |
| Par | 4 | 4 | 5 | 3 | 4 | 3 | 4 | 3 | 4 | 34 | WHITE | Rating: 67.2 |
| Handicap | 7 | 3 | 1 | 15 | 5 | 13 | 11 | 17 | 9 | x | | Slope: 117 |
| RED | 306 | 303 | 456 | 90 | 323 | 105 | 268 | 117 | 288 | 2256 | | |
| Par | 4 | 4 | 5 | 3 | 4 | 3 | 4 | 3 | 4 | 34 | RED | Rating: 70.3 |
| Handicap | 5 | 7 | 1 | 15 | 3 | 13 | 11 | 17 | 9 | x | | Slope: 119 |

| Hole | 10 | 11 | 12 | 13 | 14 | 15 | 16 | 17 | 18 | In | Totals | |
|---|---|---|---|---|---|---|---|---|---|---|---|---|
| BLUE | 376 | 426 | 315 | 183 | 217 | 392 | 602 | 354 | 499 | 3364 | BLUE | 6224 |
| WHITE | 354 | 401 | 293 | 162 | 193 | 366 | 517 | 327 | 472 | 3085 | WHITE | 5655 |
| Par | 4 | 4 | 4 | 3 | 3 | 4 | 5 | 4 | 5 | 36 | Par | 70 |
| Handicap | 12 | 6 | 14 | 18 | 16 | 8 | 2 | 10 | 4 | x | | |
| RED | 319 | 346 | 258 | 132 | 164 | 340 | 499 | 296 | 436 | 2790 | RED | 5046 |
| Par | 4 | 4 | 4 | 3 | 3 | 4 | 5 | 4 | 5 | 36 | Par | 70 |
| Handicap | 4 | 14 | 12 | 18 | 10 | 6 | 2 | 8 | 16 | x | | |

# SAN JUAN HILLS COUNTRY CLUB

**Course 99**
MAP I5 grid i6

32120 San Juan Creek Road
San Juan Capistrano
CA 92675

Pro shop (714) 493-1167

- ✓ **driving range**
- ✓ **practice greens**
- ✓ **power carts**
- ✓ **pull carts**
- ✓ **golf club rental**
- locker rooms
- showers
- executive course
- accommodations
- ✓ **food and beverages**
- ✓ **clubhouse**

**Gary Bugg**
Professional

**Pete Gallardo**
Superintendent

***Course information:*** This public course has 18 holes and par is 71. The course is 6,003 yards and rated 68.3 from the regular tees. The slope rating is 114. Women's tees are 5,513 yards and rated 71.9. The slope rating is 120.

***Play policy and fees:*** Green fees are $16 weekdays and $32 weekends. Special rates are available after 1 p.m. weekdays and 2 p.m. weekends. Carts are $16. Reservations are recommended.

***Location:*** From Interstate 5, turn north on Highway 74 and go one-half mile to San Juan Creek Road.

***Course description:*** The front and back nines are as different as night and day. The front nine is flat with a number of trees lining the fairway. The back nine is hilly with an abundance of trees to get in your way. This course is fairly close to the ocean, so the air is clean, but afternoon winds can make the course difficult.

# SAN CLEMENTE GOLF COURSE

**Course 100**
MAP I5 grid j6

**1928**
**William Park Bell**

150 East Magdalena
San Clemente, CA 92672

Pro shop (714) 492-1997
Clubhouse (714) 492-3943

- ✓ **driving range**
- ✓ **practice greens**
- ✓ **power carts**
- ✓ **pull carts**
- ✓ **golf club rental**
- locker rooms
- showers
- executive course
- accommodations
- ✓ **food and beverages**
- ✓ **clubhouse**

**Dave Cook**
Professional

**Paul Linden**
Superintendent

***Course information:*** This public course has 18 holes and par is 72. The course is 6,431 yards and rated 70.1 from the championship tees, and 6,104 yards and rated 68.4 from the regular tees. The slope ratings are 119 championship and 112 regular. Women's tees are 5,727 yards and rated 72.1. The slope rating is 114.

***Play policy and fees:*** Green fees are $14 weekdays and $21 weekends. Twilight rates and resident discounts are available. Carts are $16. Reservations are recommended. This course is available for outside tournaments.

***Location:*** From San Diego, travel north on Interstate 5 and take Avenida Magdalena exit. Turn right on El Camino Real and go one block, then turn left on Magdelena to the course.

***Course description:*** This is a scenic course offering delightful ocean views. Hole 15, a par-3, 197-yarder has an elevated tee with a spectacular view of the Pacific Ocean. The men's course record is 64. The women's record is 69, set in 1989 by Jayne Thobois. The San Clemente City Championship is held here in October. The back nine is more enjoyable and challenging than the front nine. It is a heavily played course; reservations are often difficult to secure.

# PACIFIC GOLF CLUB

**Course 101**
MAP I5 grid j7

**1988**
**Gary Player**
**Carl Litton**

200 Avenida La Pata
San Clemente, CA 92672

Pro shop (714) 498-6604

- ✓ **driving range**
- ✓ **practice greens**
- ✓ **power carts**
- pull carts
- ✓ **golf club rental**
- ✓ **locker rooms**
- ✓ **showers**
- executive course
- accommodations
- ✓ **food and beverages**
- ✓ **clubhouse**

**Bob McCallister**
Professional

**Jesse Yukon**
Superintendent

***Course information:*** This private club has 27 holes and par is 72 for each of the 18-hole combinations.

The Royal Lytham/Muirfield Course is 6,516 yards and rated 73.1 from the tournament tees, 6,082 yards and rated 70.5 from the championship tees, and 5,499 yards and rated 67.4 from the regular tees. The slope ratings are 144 tournament, 134 championship and 125 regular. Women's tees are 5,402 yards and rated 65.8. The slope rating is 107.

The Carnoustie/Royal Lytham Course is 6,489 yards and rated 73.0 from the tournament tees, 5,992 yards and rated 70.1 from the championship tees, and 5,467 yards and rated 67.3 from the regular tees. The slope ratings are 144 tournament, 133 championship and 124 regular. Women's tees are 5,308 yards and rated 67.1. The slope rating is 111.

The Carnoustie/Muirfield Course is 6,759 yards and rated 74.5 from the tournament tees, and 6,272 yards and rated 71.4 from the championship tees, and 5,570 yards and rated 67.7 from the regular tees. The slope ratings are 146 tournament, 136 championship and 125 regular. Women's tees are 5,508 yards and rated 67.5. The slope rating is 114.

***Play policy and fees:*** Members and guests only. Reciprocal players must have their golf pro call on Monday through Thursday to arrange starting times. Reservations are recommended. No jeans are allowed. Golfers must wear collared shirts.

***Location:*** Take the Pico exit off Interstate 5 in San Clemente and travel two miles east to Avenida La Pata. Turn right and drive one mile to the club.

***Course description:*** This is a young course offering a traditional links layout that rolls through meadows. The first hole at Carnoustie gives some golfers a scare. It's an uphill par-4 to an undulating, sloping green. To make par, your second shot better be a good one. The course record at Carnoustie/Muirfield is 66, set by Gary Player on opening day. All three nines are distinctively different. Wind can be a factor here.

# SHORECLIFFS GOLF COURSE

**Course 102**
MAP I5 grid j7

*Course information:* This public course has 18 holes and par is 71. The course is 6.100 yards and rated 67.9 from the championship tees, and 5,577 yards and rated 67.0 from the regular tees. The slope ratings are 113 championship and 109 regular. Women's tees are 5,318 yards and rated 69.4. The slope rating is 112.

*Play policy and fees:* Green fees are $10 weekdays and $20 weekends. Carts are $16. Monday through Thursday, from 6 a. m. to 9 a. m., the cost is $26 for two, including cart.

*Location:* Take the Camino de Estrella exit off Interstate 5 and drive east to Avenida Vaquero. Turn right to the course.

*Course description:* This is a course that demands accuracy. It is short and tight, and meanders in and out of canyons. Hook a tee shot and you might find yourself in a canyon with the coyotes. There is much out-of-bounds and several water hazards. The yardage of this course makes it look deceptively easy. It isn't.

501 Avenida Vaquero
San Clemente, CA 92672

Pro shop (714) 492-1177

- ✓ **driving range**
- ✓ **practice greens**
- ✓ **power carts**
- ✓ **pull carts**
- ✓ **golf club rental**
- ✓ **locker rooms**
- ✓ **showers**
- executive course
- accommodations
- ✓ **food and beverages**
- ✓ **clubhouse**

**Fon Leong**
Manager

**Fred Pinion**
Superintendent



MAP ON PAGE 506

# MAP I6
(35 COURSES)

PAGES.. 584-611

SO-CAL MAP .....see page 466
adjoining maps
NORTH (H6).......see page 456
EAST (I7) ...........see page 612
SOUTH (J6) ........see page 672
WEST (I5) ...........see page 506

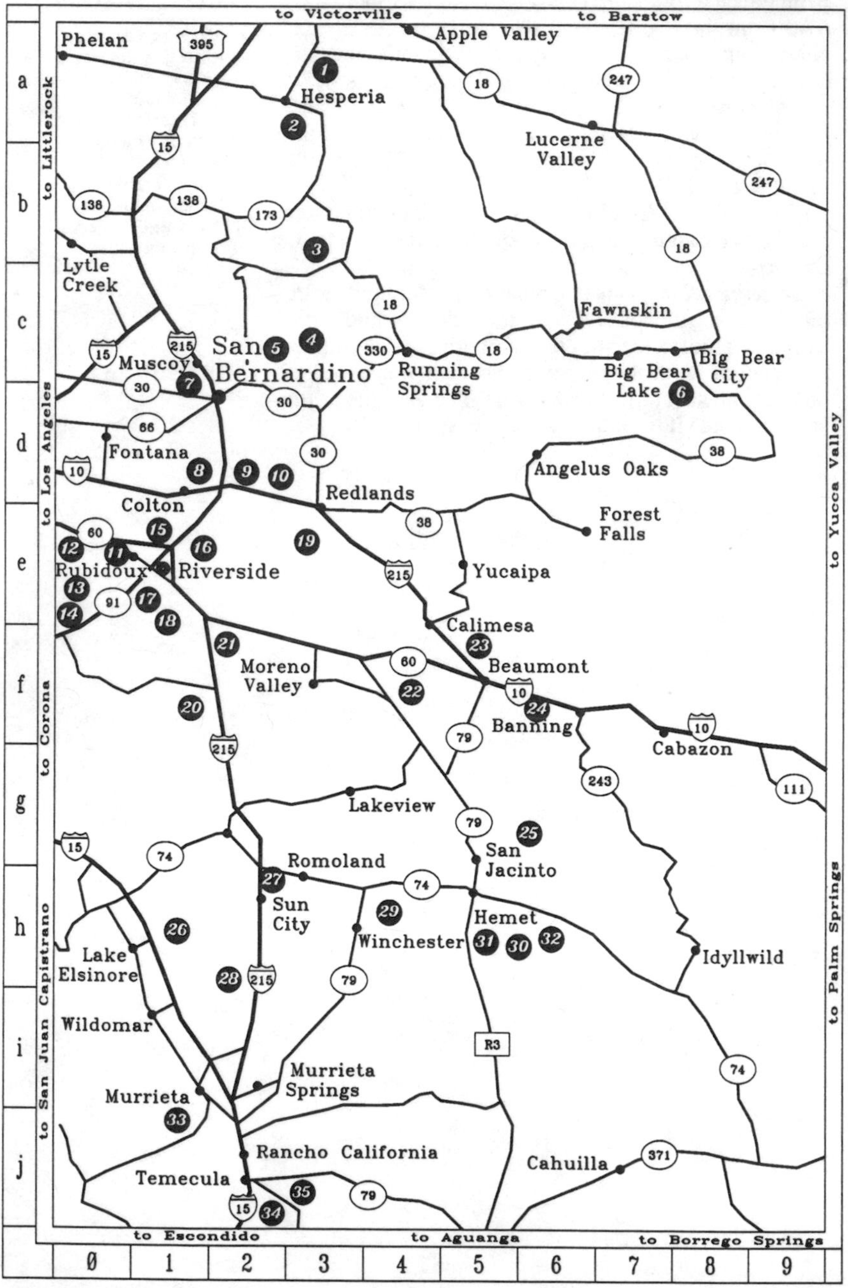

to Victorville
to Barstow
to Littlerock
to Los Angeles
to Corona
to San Juan Capistrano
to Yucca Valley
to Palm Springs
to Escondido
to Aguanga
to Borrego Springs

Phelan
395
Apple Valley
1
Hesperia
18
247
2
15
Lucerne Valley
247
138
138
173
3
18
Lytle Creek
18
Fawnskin
15
215
San Bernardino
5
4
330
Running Springs
18
Big Bear Lake
6
Big Bear City
Muscoy
7
30
30
66
Fontana
30
38
10
8
9
10
Angelus Oaks
Redlands
Colton
38
Forest Falls
60
15
16
19
12
11
Rubidoux
Riverside
215
Yucaipa
13
91
17
14
18
Calimesa
21
23
Moreno Valley
60
Beaumont
22
10
20
24
Banning
79
10
Cabazon
215
243
111
Lakeview
79
25
15
74
San Jacinto
Romoland
27
74
Sun City
29
Hemet
26
Winchester
31
30
32
Idyllwild
Lake Elsinore
28
215
79
Wildomar
R3
74
Murrieta Springs
Murrieta
33
Rancho California
371
Cahuilla
Temecula
35
79
15
34

a
b
c
d
e
f
g
h
i
j

0
1
2
3
4
5
6
7
8
9

# SPRING VALLEY LAKE COUNTRY CLUB

**Course 1**
MAP 16 grid a3

**1968**
**Robert Trent Jones, Jr.**

13229 Spring Valley Parkway
Victorville, CA 92392

Pro shop (619) 245-7921
Clubhouse (619) 245-5356

- ✓ **driving range**
- ✓ **practice greens**
- ✓ **power carts**
- ✓ **pull carts**
- ✓ **golf club rental**
- ✓ **locker rooms**
- ✓ **showers**
- executive course
- accommodations
- ✓ **food and beverages**
- ✓ **clubhouse**

**Gregg Combs,**
Professional

**Bob MacBeth**
Superintendent

*Course information:* This private course has 18 holes and par is 72. The course is 6,535 yards and rated 71.2 from the championship tees, and 6,179 yards and rated 69.3 from the regular tees. The slope ratings are 123 championship and 115 regular. Women's tees are 5,696 yards and rated 72.7. The slope rating is 122.

*Play policy and fees:* Reciprocal play is accepted with members of other private clubs, otherwise members and guests only. Green fees are $40. Carts arc included. Reservations are recommended. This course is available for outside tournaments. Mondays only.

*Location:* From Interstate 10, drive north on Interstate 15 to the Lucerne Valley exit. Turn right and travel east for five miles on Bear Valley Road to Spring Valley Parkway. Turn left through the big archway to Spring Valley Lake and turn left on Country Club Drive.

*Course description:* Traditionally in excellent condition, the course has plenty of water on the front and is relatively hilly on the back. It all toughens up when the winds blow, as they will. Greens are medium-sized, fast and true.

# HESPERIA GOLF AND COUNTRY CLUB

**Course 2**
MAP 16 grid a3

**1957**
**William Francis Bell**

17970 Bangor Avenue
Hesperia, CA 92345

Pro shop (619) 244-9301

- ✓ **driving range**
- ✓ **practice greens**
- ✓ **power carts**
- ✓ **pull carts**
- ✓ **golf club rental**
- locker rooms
- ✓ **showers**
- executive course
- accommodations
- ✓ **food and beverages**
- ✓ **clubhouse**

**Alex Rickards**
Manager

**Dick Renz**
Superintendent

*Course information:* This semi-private course has 18 holes and par is 72. The course is 6,996 yards and rated 74.6 from the championship tees, and 6,695 yards and rated 72.4 from the regular tees. The slope ratings are 133 championship and 127 regular. Women's tees are 6,136 yards and rated 73.9. The slope rating is 124.

*Play policy and fees:* Reciprocal play is accepted with members of other private clubs. Outside play is also accepted. Green fees are $15 weekdays and $20 weekends. Carts are $18. Reservations are recommended. This course is available for tournaments.

*Location:* From Interstate 10, travel 33 miles north on Interstate 15 to the Hesperia/Phelan exit. Turn right on Main Street and go 5.5 miles to "I" Avenue and turn right. Go 1.5 miles to Bangor Avenue and turn left.

*Course description:* This former PGA Tour stop offers a championship layout. It was designed and built 35 years ago and is still a tough test. The fairways are not parallel and are separated by mature trees. It's well bunkered and you'll find three lakes and a rolling terrain. Toughest hole is number 18, a par-4 440-yard stretch from the back tees that's guarded by trees on each side of the fairway. You have to be accurate through the trees. Ask Doug Sanders. Talk around the pro shop is Sanders once took a 12 on this hole. The trees have grown some since he encountered them, so watch out.

# LAKE ARROWHEAD COUNTRY CLUB

**Course 3**
MAP I6 grid b3

PO Box 670
Lake Arrowhead, CA 92352

250 Golf Course Road
Lake Arrowhead, CA 92352

Pro shop (714) 337-3515
Clubhouse (714) 337-2441

- ✓ **driving range**
- ✓ **practice greens**
- ✓ **power carts**
- pull carts
- golf club rental
- ✓ **locker rooms**
- ✓ **showers**
- executive course
- accommodations
- ✓ **food and beverages**
- ✓ **clubhouse**

**Dennis Murray**
Professional

**Emilio Castorena**
Superintendent

***Course information:*** This private course has 18 holes and par is 71. The course is 6,205 yards and rated 70.3 from the championship tees, and 5,957 yards and rated 68.9 from the regular tees. The slope ratings are 126 championship and 123 regular. Women's tees are 5,557 yards and rated 72.1. The slope rating is 128.

***Play policy and fees:*** Members and guests only. Green fees are $30 weekdays and $40 weekends. Carts are $20.

***Location:*** Drive northeast of San Bernardino on Interstate 215 to the Mountain Resorts exit. Continue to Highway 18 (Waterman Avenue) and turn left, following it through the Rimforest to the Blue Jay exit. Bear left to the stop signal, turn left and drive one-half mile to Grass Valley Road. Bear right and continue 1.5 miles to Golf Course Road. Turn left and drive 100 yards to the club.

***Course description:*** Originally a 1930s nine-hole course, it became a full 18 holes in 1959. The front nine is level and open while the back nine is hilly. There is a small lake on the course that comes into play. All the holes are dotted with bunkers. The course is open from April to November 1.

# ARROWHEAD COUNTRY CLUB

**Course 4**
MAP 16 grid c2

*Course information:* This private course has 18 holes. See card below for yardage and rating information.

*Play policy and fees:* Members and guests only. Green fees are $50. Carts are $16.

*Location:* From San Bernardino, travel east on Highway 30 to Waterman Avenue north. Drive for one-half mile and turn right on 34th Street. Continue to Parkside Drive and the entrance to the club.

*Course description:* This course, in one form or another, has been in existence since the 1920s, but became open for memberships in 1944. It has level terrain, mature trees and water hazards. It is set at the foot of the mountains in a desert area, so the heat can become unbearable. There is also swimming. In winter, several ski areas are open just a 30-minute drive into the San Bernardino Mountains above the course.

3433 Parkside Drive
San Bernardino, CA 92404

Pro shop (714) 882-1638
Clubhouse (714) 882-1735

- ✓ **driving range**
- ✓ **practice greens**
- ✓ **power carts**
- ✓ **pull carts**
- ✓ **golf club rental**
- ✓ **locker rooms**
- ✓ **showers**
- executive course
- accommodations
- ✓ **food and beverages**
- ✓ **clubhouse**

**Tom Miskell**
Professional

**R. John Martinez**
Superintendent

| Hole | 1 | 2 | 3 | 4 | 5 | 6 | 7 | 8 | 9 | Out | | |
|---|---|---|---|---|---|---|---|---|---|---|---|---|
| BLUE | 390 | 404 | 485 | 196 | 351 | 560 | 513 | 202 | 403 | 3504 | BLUE | Rating: 71.5 |
| WHITE | 373 | 372 | 465 | 165 | 344 | 551 | 494 | 202 | 387 | 3353 | | Slope: 123 |
| Par | 4 | 4 | 5 | 3 | 4 | 5 | 5 | 3 | 4 | 37 | WHITE | Rating: 69.4 |
| Handicap | 5 | 1 | 15 | 11 | 17 | 9 | 13 | 7 | 3 | x | | Slope: 114 |
| RED | 364 | 345 | 450 | 140 | 331 | 472 | 437 | 194 | 372 | 3105 | | |
| Par | 4 | 4 | 5 | 3 | 4 | 5 | 5 | 3 | 4 | 37 | RED | Rating: 72.8 |
| Handicap | 3 | 5 | 9 | 17 | 13 | 7 | 11 | 15 | 1 | x | | Slope: 120 |

| Hole | 10 | 11 | 12 | 13 | 14 | 15 | 16 | 17 | 18 | In | Totals | |
|---|---|---|---|---|---|---|---|---|---|---|---|---|
| BLUE | 194 | 499 | 212 | 487 | 338 | 174 | 420 | 363 | 382 | 3069 | BLUE | 6573 |
| WHITE | 176 | 479 | 195 | 470 | 325 | 140 | 401 | 347 | 361 | 2894 | WHITE | 6247 |
| Par | 3 | 5 | 3 | 5 | 4 | 3 | 4 | 4 | 4 | 35 | Par | 72 |
| Handicap | 8 | 18 | 4 | 16 | 6 | 14 | 2 | 10 | 12 | x | | |
| RED | 162 | 457 | 170 | 424 | 290 | 116 | 376 | 321 | 338 | 2654 | RED | 5759 |
| Par | 3 | 5 | 3 | 5 | 4 | 3 | 4 | 4 | 4 | 35 | Par | 72 |
| Handicap | 18 | 4 | 8 | 10 | 6 | 16 | 2 | 14 | 12 | x | | |

## SHANDIN HILLS GOLF CLUB

**Course 5**
MAP 16 grid c2

**1982**
**Cary Bickler**

3380 Little Mountain Drive
San Bernardino, CA 92407

Pro shop (714) 886-0669

- driving range
- ✓ **practice greens**
- ✓ **power carts**
- ✓ **pull carts**
- ✓ **golf club rental**
- locker rooms
- ✓ **showers**
- executive course
- accommodations
- ✓ **food and beverages**
- ✓ **clubhouse**

**Drew Boursaw**
Professional

**Rick Barnett**
Superintendent

***Course information:*** This public course has 18 holes and par is 72. The course is 6,517 yards and rated 70.3 from the championship tees, and 6,192 yards and rated 68.7 from the regular tees. The slope ratings are 120 championship and 114 regular. Women's tees are 5,592 yards and rated 71.6. The slope rating is 122.

***Play policy and fees:*** Green fees are $15 weekdays and $25 weekends. Carts are $10. Reservations are recommended.

***Location:*** From Los Angeles, travel east on Interstate 10 to Interstate 215. In San Bernardino, take the Mount Vernon/27th Street off-ramp and turn right on 27th Street, then immediately left on Little Mountain. Travel one mile to the club.

***Course description:*** This is a challenging course with 79 bunkers. The rough is well developed, so fairway placement is optimum. Narrow, tree-lined fairways lead from elevated tees to elevated greens. I-215 bisects the two nines, but scenic views of the San Bernardino Mountains abound.

## BEAR MOUNTAIN GOLF COURSE

**Course 6**
MAP 16 grid c8

43100 Goldmine Drive
Big Bear Lake, CA 92315

Pro shop (714) 585-8002

- ✓ **driving range**
- ✓ **practice greens**
- ✓ **power carts**
- ✓ **pull carts**
- ✓ **golf club rental**
- ✓ **locker rooms**
- showers
- executive course
- accommodations
- ✓ **food and beverages**
- ✓ **clubhouse**

**Mack Provart**
Professional

**Cliff Bell**
Superintendent

***Course information:*** This public course has nine holes. Par is 70 for 18 holes. The course is 5,528 yards from the championship tees for 18 holes and rated 65.0. It is 5,218 yards and rated 65 from the regular tees. The slope rating is 107. Women's tees are 4,398 yards and rated 65. The slope rating is 107.

***Play policy and fees:*** Green fees are $10 for nine holes and $14 for 18 holes weekdays, and $14 for nine holes and $20 for 18 holes weekends. Carts are $11 for nine holes and $16 for 18 holes.

***Location:*** In San Bernardino, take Highway 30 east to Highland Avenue. Drive north on Highway 330 to Highway 18, then east to Moonridge Road. Drive 1.25 miles to Club View Drive. Turn left on Goldmine Drive and left into the parking lot. It is about 40 miles from San Bernardino.

***Course description:*** The elevation here is 7,200 feet and the course closes when it snows. It offers long par-3s and gently rolling hills. In 1988, a lake was added in addition to tees for women. New clubhouse facilities are planned for summer of 1993. This course, now under new ownership, was formerly known as Goldmine Golf Course.

# EL RANCHO VERDE COUNTRY CLUB

**Course 7**
MAP 16 grid d1

PO Box 1234
Rialto, CA 92376

Foot of Country Club Drive
Rialto, CA 92376

Pro shop (714) 875-5346

- ✓ **driving range**
- ✓ **practice greens**
- ✓ **power carts**
- pull carts
- golf club rental
- locker rooms
- showers
- executive course
- accommodations
- ✓ **food and beverages**
- ✓ **clubhouse**

**Troy Burton**
Professional

**Pete Laws**
Superintendent

***Course information:*** This public course has 18 holes. The gold tees are 6,365 yards, rated 68.8 (men) and 76.3 (women), with slopes of 104 (men) and 126 (women). See card below for additional yardage and rating information.

***Play policy and fees:*** Green fees are $12 weekdays and $23 weekends. Carts are $18. Reservations are recommended. This course is available for tournaments.

***Location:*** From Los Angeles, drive east on Interstate 10 (San Bernardino Freeway) to Riverside Avenue in the town of Rialto. Then travel north six miles to Country Club Drive.

***Course description:*** This course offers gentle rolling hills with many pine and eucalyptus trees on the front nine and orange groves on the back nine. It boasts tough par-3s and a view of the San Bernardino Mountains. The 12th, for instance, is set 226 yards uphill, with an orange grove to the left and out-of-bounds to the right.

| Hole | 1 | 2 | 3 | 4 | 5 | 6 | 7 | 8 | 9 | Out | BLUE | Rating: 71.8 |
|---|---|---|---|---|---|---|---|---|---|---|---|---|
| BLUE | 381 | 455 | 516 | 195 | 393 | 438 | 498 | 389 | 167 | 3432 | | Slope: 112 |
| WHITE | 370 | 446 | 505 | 161 | 385 | 429 | 491 | 376 | 156 | 3319 | | |
| Par | 4 | 4 | 5 | 3 | 4 | 4 | 5 | 4 | 3 | 36 | WHITE | Rating: 70.3 |
| Handicap | 17 | 1 | 13 | 7 | 9 | 5 | 15 | 3 | 11 | x | | Slope: 106 |
| RED | 311 | 386 | 457 | 124 | 279 | 369 | 457 | 336 | 143 | 2862 | | |
| Par | 4 | 4 | 5 | 3 | 4 | 4 | 5 | 4 | 3 | 36 | RED | Rating: 71.9 |
| Handicap | 9 | 13 | 1 | 15 | 13 | 7 | 5 | 11 | 17 | x | | Slope: 118 |

| Hole | 10 | 11 | 12 | 13 | 14 | 15 | 16 | 17 | 18 | In | Totals | |
|---|---|---|---|---|---|---|---|---|---|---|---|---|
| BLUE | 378 | 368 | 226 | 415 | 512 | 168 | 389 | 430 | 526 | 3412 | BLUE | 6844 |
| WHITE | 367 | 353 | 209 | 406 | 503 | 149 | 377 | 420 | 512 | 3296 | WHITE | 6615 |
| Par | 4 | 4 | 3 | 4 | 5 | 3 | 4 | 4 | 5 | 36 | Par | 72 |
| Handicap | 10 | 8 | 2 | 6 | 18 | 12 | 16 | 4 | 14 | x | | |
| RED | 267 | 306 | 177 | 355 | 380 | 114 | 310 | 357 | 461 | 2727 | RED | 5589 |
| Par | 4 | 4 | 3 | 4 | 4 | 3 | 4 | 4 | 5 | 35 | Par | 71 |
| Handicap | 16 | 14 | 4 | 10 | 2 | 18 | 12 | 6 | 8 | x | | |

# COLTON GOLF CLUB

**Course 8**
MAP 16 grid d1

*Course information:* This short public course has 18 holes and par is 57. It is 3,095 yards long and rated 52.8. The slope is 82.

*Play policy and fees:* Green fees are $11 weekdays and $7 weekends for nine holes, and $11 weekdays and $12 weekends for 18 holes. Carts are $6 for nine holes and $10 for 18 holes weekdays, and $7 for nine holes and $12 for 18 holes weekends.

*Location:* Take Interstate 10 to Colton and exit at Riverside Avenue. Follow Riverside to Valley Boulevard, turn left and go about one mile to the course. You can take the Pepper exit off Interstate 10 and proceed to Valley Boulevard also.

*Course description:* This is an executive course, designed for those who want to test almost every club in the bag. There are three par-4s and 15 par-3s of varying length. When Sam Snead is in the area, this is where he plays. This Jones layout offers all his usual challenges in short form—sculpted, well-protected greens. A championship course from the fairway in.

**1966**
**Robert Trent Jones, Sr.**

1901 Valley Boulevard
Colton, CA 92324

Pro shop (714) 877-1712

- ✓ **driving range**
- ✓ **practice greens**
- ✓ **power carts**
- ✓ **pull carts**
- ✓ **golf club rental**
- locker rooms
- showers
- ✓ **executive course**
- accommodations
- ✓ **food and beverages**
- ✓ **clubhouse**

**Bob Mastalski**
Professional/Manager

# SAN BERNARDINO GOLF COURSE

**Course 9**
MAP 16 grid d2

**1969**
**Mike Murphy**

1494 South Waterman Avenue
San Bernardino, CA 92408

Pro shop (714) 825-1670
Clubhouse (714) 885-2414

- ✓ **driving range**
- ✓ **practice greens**
- ✓ **power carts**
- ✓ **pull carts**
- ✓ **golf club rental**
- locker rooms
- showers
- executive course
- accommodations
- ✓ **food and beverages**
- ✓ **clubhouse**

**Cheryl Thomas**
Professional

**Abel Moreno**
Superintendent

***Course information:*** This public course has 18 holes. See card below for yardage and rating information.

***Play policy and fees:*** Green fees are $12 weekdays and $19 weekends. Senior rates are $10 weekdays. Carts are $17. Reservations are recommended.

***Location:*** In San Bernardino, take Interstate 10 (San Bernardino Freeway) to the Waterman Avenue exit north and travel three-fourths of a mile to the course.

***Course description:*** This course has only two bunkers but five holes with water. Don't be fooled by the apparent short length of this course. Typically, scores here are higher on the average than on neighboring courses. Stay in the fairways or you're in tall rough. This is a thinking player's course. The men's course record is 60 and is held by Walt "Sonny" Hammond, set in 1985. The women's course record is 64 held by Kathy Dougherty. The San Bernardino County Men's Amateur Championships are held here each Labor Day Weekend.

| Hole | 1 | 2 | 3 | 4 | 5 | 6 | 7 | 8 | 9 | Out | BLUE | Rating: 67.2 |
|---|---|---|---|---|---|---|---|---|---|---|---|---|
| BLUE | 422 | 455 | 323 | 191 | 429 | 329 | 162 | 329 | 328 | 2968 | | Slope: 107 |
| WHITE | 415 | 445 | 317 | 176 | 419 | 320 | 152 | 319 | 318 | 2881 | | |
| Par | 4 | 5 | 4 | 3 | 4 | 4 | 3 | 4 | 4 | 35 | WHITE | Rating: 66.3 |
| Handicap | 3 | 11 | 13 | 7 | 1 | 15 | 17 | 9 | 5 | x | | Slope: 104 |
| RED | 404 | 404 | 308 | 154 | 409 | 304 | 137 | 304 | 308 | 2732 | | |
| Par | 5 | 5 | 4 | 3 | 5 | 4 | 3 | 4 | 4 | 37 | RED | Rating: 68.7 |
| Handicap | 5 | 1 | 11 | 13 | 3 | 15 | 17 | 9 | 7 | x | | Slope: 109 |

| Hole | 10 | 11 | 12 | 13 | 14 | 15 | 16 | 17 | 18 | In | Totals | |
|---|---|---|---|---|---|---|---|---|---|---|---|---|
| BLUE | 334 | 298 | 266 | 412 | 125 | 376 | 191 | 358 | 450 | 2810 | BLUE | 5778 |
| WHITE | 324 | 273 | 255 | 404 | 112 | 365 | 170 | 350 | 437 | 2690 | WHITE | 5571 |
| Par | 4 | 4 | 4 | 4 | 3 | 4 | 3 | 4 | 5 | 35 | Par | 70 |
| Handicap | 18 | 10 | 8 | 2 | 16 | 4 | 12 | 6 | 14 | x | | |
| RED | 308 | 244 | 248 | 384 | 104 | 294 | 148 | 334 | 426 | 2490 | RED | 5222 |
| Par | 4 | 4 | 4 | 4 | 3 | 4 | 3 | 4 | 5 | 35 | Par | 72 |
| Handicap | 8 | 16 | 10 | 2 | 18 | 6 | 14 | 12 | 4 | x | | |



MAP ON PAGE 584

# PALM MEADOWS GOLF COURSE

Course 10
MAP I6 grid d2

**1958**
Building 818, Norton AFB
San Bernardino, CA 92409

Pro shop (714) 382-2500
Clubhouse (714) 382-3421

- ✓ **driving range**
- ✓ **practice greens**
- ✓ **power carts**
- ✓ **pull carts**
- ✓ **golf club rental**
- ✓ **locker rooms**
- ✓ **showers**
- executive course
- accommodations
- ✓ **food and beverages**
- ✓ **clubhouse**

**"Sonny" Ryan**
Professional

**Don Combs**
Superintendent

***Course information:*** This military course has 18 holes and par is 72. The course is 6,659 yards and rated 71.5 from the championship tees, and 6,372 yards and rated 69.9 from the regular tees. The slope ratings are 115 championship and 111 regular. Women's tees are 5,794 yards and rated 72.5. The slope rating is 118.

***Play policy and fees:*** Military personnel and guests only. Green fees are $7 weekdays and $11 weekends for military. Guest green fees are $14 weekdays and $20 weekends. Carts are $12. Reservations are recommended. Golfers must wear appropriate attire.

***Location:*** Drive southeast of San Bernardino on Interstate 10 for about two miles to the Tippecanoe exit. Travel north for two miles to the main gate, and then go north one block to "A" Street and turn right. Drive to Fifth Street and turn right again. At the next stop sign, go right, then bear left to the course. Too complicated? Ask for instructions at the main gate.

***Course description:*** This course was carved out by civil engineers and the hard work of its early members. It's a scenic course with an easy, flat front nine and a tough back nine that gives players lots of trouble. The tee box and fairway at hole six run along the flight line of this Air Force base, causing unique hazards: Beware of low-flying F-4s. And try not to tee off while a plane is landing. The sheer noise might throw your swing off. The course records are 69 for men and 73 for the women.

# FAIRMOUNT PARK GOLF CLUB

**Course 11**
MAP I6 grid e0

2681 Dexter Drive
Riverside, CA 92501

Pro shop (714) 682-2202

- ✓ **driving range**
- ✓ **practice greens**
- ✓ **power carts**
- ✓ **pull carts**
- ✓ **golf club rental**
- locker rooms
- showers
- executive course
- accommodations
- ✓ **food and beverages**
- ✓ **clubhouse**

**Jim DeRosa**
Professional

**Glen Quirk**
Superintendent

***Course information:*** This public course has nine holes. Par is 72 for 18 holes. The course is 6,326 yards and rated 68.6 from the regular tees (18 holes). The slope rating is 103. Women's yardage and ratings were unavailable.

***Play policy and fees:*** Green fees are $6 for nine holes and $8 for 18 holes weekdays, and $8 for nine holes and $10 for 18 holes weekends. Carts are $9 for nine holes, and $15 for 18 holes.

***Location:*** From Los Angeles, travel east on Highway 60 (Pomona Freeway) to the city of Riverside. Take the Market Street exit to the course.

***Course description:*** This is an older course but it has character. Numerous mature palm and cypress trees line the level fairways. It's a fader's course with mean doglegs and more trees. Fortunately, there is a nice finishing hole because the first hole can be a rough start, thanks to a large tree in the middle of the fariway that requires your tee shot to either go over it or around it. Golden State Golf Centers took over management of the course in 1992 and undertook a $1 million renovation. Improvements include a 60-stall night-lighted driving range.

# INDIAN HILLS COUNTRY CLUB

**Course 12**
MAP I6 grid e0

**1967**
**William Park Bell**

5700 Clubhouse Drive
Riverside, CA 92509

Pro shop (714) 685-7443
Clubhouse (714) 685-6424

- driving range
- ✓ **practice greens**
- ✓ **power carts**
- pull carts
- ✓ **golf club rental**
- ✓ **locker rooms**
- ✓ **showers**
- executive course
- accommodations
- ✓ **food and beverages**
- ✓ **clubhouse**

**Don Willis**
Professional

**Scot Vlahos**
Superintendent

***Course information:*** This public course has 18 holes. See card below for yardage and rating information.

***Play policy and fees:*** Green fees are $16 weekdays and $23 weekends. Carts are $20 weekdays and $22 weekends. Reservations are recommended. This course is available for tournaments.

***Location:*** From Los Angeles, take Highway 60 (Pomona Freeway) east to the Van Buren/Etiwanda Avenue exit in Riverside. Travel south on Van Buren Boulevard for 4.5 miles to Limonite Avenue and turn left. Drive to Clay Street and turn left, then right on Lakeside Drive. Follow the signs to the club on top of the hill.

***Course description:*** This is a rolling course with numerous mature trees and no parallel fairways. The two nines loop out and back from the clubhouse. The greens are undulating and can be tough. Walking on this hilly course is for the adventurous.

| Hole | 1 | 2 | 3 | 4 | 5 | 6 | 7 | 8 | 9 | Out | BLUE | Rating: 70.0 |
|---|---|---|---|---|---|---|---|---|---|---|---|---|
| BLUE | 402 | 285 | 199 | 390 | 217 | 401 | 297 | 505 | 451 | 3147 | | Slope: 123 |
| WHITE | 400 | 278 | 176 | 379 | 162 | 386 | 292 | 495 | 437 | 3005 | | |
| Par | 4 | 4 | 3 | 4 | 3 | 4 | 4 | 5 | 4 | 35 | WHITE | Rating: 68.1 |
| Handicap | 5 | 15 | 7 | 3 | 11 | 9 | 17 | 13 | 1 | x | | Slope: 117 |
| RED | 387 | 274 | 165 | 368 | 158 | 397 | 287 | 488 | 423 | 2947 | | |
| Par | 4 | 4 | 3 | 4 | 3 | 5 | 4 | 5 | 5 | 37 | RED | Rating: 70.7 |
| Handicap | 5 | 9 | 11 | 7 | 15 | 17 | 13 | 3 | 1 | x | | Slope: 118 |

| Hole | 10 | 11 | 12 | 13 | 14 | 15 | 16 | 17 | 18 | In | Totals | |
|---|---|---|---|---|---|---|---|---|---|---|---|---|
| BLUE | 320 | 156 | 286 | 406 | 314 | 164 | 408 | 418 | 515 | 2987 | BLUE | 6134 |
| WHITE | 311 | 147 | 260 | 390 | 302 | 148 | 398 | 408 | 497 | 2861 | WHITE | 5866 |
| Par | 4 | 3 | 4 | 4 | 4 | 3 | 4 | 4 | 5 | 35 | Par | 70 |
| Handicap | 8 | 16 | 18 | 12 | 6 | 14 | 4 | 2 | 10 | x | | |
| RED | 307 | 137 | 240 | 376 | 291 | 133 | 383 | 330 | 418 | 2615 | RED | 5562 |
| Par | 4 | 3 | 4 | 4 | 4 | 3 | 4 | 4 | 5 | 35 | Par | 72 |
| Handicap | 5 | 9 | 11 | 7 | 15 | 17 | 13 | 13 | 1 | x | | |

# JURUPA HILLS COUNTRY CLUB

**Course 13**
MAP 16 grid e0

**1960**
**William Francis Bell**

6161 Moraga Avenue
Riverside, CA 92509

Pro shop (714) 685-7214
Clubhouse (714) 685-6682
Fax (714) 685-4752

- ✓ **driving range**
- ✓ **practice greens**
- ✓ **power carts**
- ✓ **pull carts**
- ✓ **golf club rental**
- locker rooms
- showers
- executive course
- accommodations
- ✓ **food and beverages**
- ✓ **clubhouse**

**Ron Robinson**
Professional/Manager

**Jason Taylor**
Professional

**Jim Fareio**
Superintendent

***Course information:*** This public course has 18 holes. Information on the white tees is not available. See card below for yardage and rating information.

***Play policy and fees:*** Green fees are $16 weekdays and $25 weekends. Twilight rates are $13.50 weekdays after 3 p.m. Carts are $22. Reservations are recommended one week in advance for weekends. This course is available for tournaments.

***Location:*** From Los Angeles, take Highway 60 (Pomona Freeway) east to the Van Buren/Etiwanda Avenue exit in Riverside. Travel east on Van Buren Boulevard for 4.5 miles and turn left on Limonite Avenue. Drive 1.5 miles to Camino Real. Turn right and drive to Linares. Then left one-half mile to the club.

***Course description:*** Trees of all sizes outline this fairly level course. Locally, the course is known for its well-kept, fast greens. It's a favorite spot for local tournaments. The SCPGA Senior's Championship is held here. Olin Dutra, the club's first pro, was a former U.S. Open champ. He and Gary McCord share the course record, 62.

| Hole | 1 | 2 | 3 | 4 | 5 | 6 | 7 | 8 | 9 | Out | BLUE | Rating: 68.1 |
|---|---|---|---|---|---|---|---|---|---|---|---|---|
| BLUE | 376 | 355 | 159 | 347 | 372 | 377 | 499 | 161 | 341 | 2987 | | Slope: 109 |
| WHITE | - | - | - | - | - | - | - | - | - | - | | |
| Par | 4 | 4 | 3 | 4 | 4 | 4 | 5 | 3 | 4 | 35 | WHITE | Rating: -- |
| Handicap | 5 | 1 | 13 | 3 | 9 | 7 | 15 | 17 | 11 | x | | Slope: -- |
| RED | 366 | 345 | 139 | 323 | 356 | 364 | 483 | 148 | 329 | 2853 | | |
| Par | 4 | 4 | 3 | 4 | 4 | 4 | 5 | 3 | 4 | 35 | RED | Rating: 71.4 |
| Handicap | 3 | 1 | 17 | 13 | 7 | 5 | 9 | 15 | 11 | x | | Slope: 117 |

| Hole | 10 | 11 | 12 | 13 | 14 | 15 | 16 | 17 | 18 | In | Totals | |
|---|---|---|---|---|---|---|---|---|---|---|---|---|
| BLUE | 363 | 441 | 336 | 378 | 134 | 512 | 362 | 368 | 141 | 3035 | BLUE | 6022 |
| WHITE | - | - | - | - | - | - | - | - | - | - | WHITE | -- |
| Par | 4 | 4 | 4 | 4 | 3 | 5 | 4 | 4 | 3 | 35 | Par | 70 |
| Handicap | 4 | 2 | 12 | 6 | 18 | 14 | 8 | 10 | 16 | x | | |
| RED | 350 | 429 | 327 | 358 | 121 | 507 | 350 | 354 | 124 | 2920 | RED | 5773 |
| Par | 4 | 5 | 4 | 4 | 3 | 5 | 4 | 4 | 3 | 36 | Par | 71 |
| Handicap | 2 | 14 | 12 | 8 | 16 | 10 | 4 | 6 | 18 | x | | |



MAP ON PAGE 584

## PARADISE KNOLLS

**Course 14**
MAP I6 grid e0

**1980**
9330 Limonite Avenue
Riverside, CA 92509

Pro shop (714) 685-7034

- driving range
- ✓ **practice greens**
- ✓ **power carts**
- ✓ **pull carts**
- ✓ **golf club rental**
- locker rooms
- showers
- executive course
- accommodations
- ✓ **food and beverages**
- ✓ **clubhouse**

**Margaret Wood**
Owner/Manager

**Jeff Jackson**
Superintendent

*Course information:* This public course has 18 holes and par is 72. The course is 6,191 yards and rated 68.3 from the regular tees. The slope rating is 104. Women's tees are 5,865 yards and rated 72.5. The slope rating is 117.

*Play policy and fees:* Green fees are $11.50 weekdays and $19 weekends. Call for senior weekdays rates. Carts are $19 weekdays and $21 weekends. Reservations are recommended. This course is available for outside tournaments.

*Location:* Travel east on Highway 60 (Pomona Freeway) to the Van Buren/Etiwanda Avenue exit and turn right onto Etiwanda. Drive about three miles to Limonite Avenue, turn left and proceed three miles to the course.

*Course description:* This is a pretty course with an interesting mix of mature eucalyptus, palm and pepper trees that act as natural dividers between fairways. The course is fairly level with parallel fairways and small greens.

## EL RIVINO COUNTRY CLUB

**Course 15**
MAP I6 grid e1

**1956**
Box 3369
Riverside, CA 92519

5530 El Rivino Road
Riverside, CA 92519

Pro shop (714) 684-8905

- driving range
- ✓ **practice greens**
- ✓ **power carts**
- pull carts
- golf club rental
- locker rooms
- showers
- executive course
- accommodations
- food and beverages
- ✓ **clubhouse**

**Dennis Burdo**
Professional

**William Anderson**
Superintendent

*Course information:* This public course has 18 holes and par is 72. The course is 6,422 yards and rated 69.5 from the championship tees, and 6,195 yards and rated 68.2 from the regular tees. The slope ratings are 109 championship and 102 regular. Women's tees are 5,848 yards and rated 72.0. The slope rating is 113.

*Play policy and fees:* Green fees are $15 weekdays and $27 weekends. Carts are $24. Reservations are recommended. This course is available for outside tournaments. Golfers must wear sleeved shirts. Short shorts and bathing suits are not allowed.

*Location:* From Los Angeles, travel east on Interstate 10 (San Bernardino Freeway) to the Cedar Avenue exit in Bloomington. Head south on Cedar Avenue for three miles to El Rivino Road and then turn east on El Rivino Road to the club.

*Course description:* Built in 1956, this wide open course has five lakes, level terrain and mature trees. The first hole is a long, 626-yard par-6 designed to scare off the fainthearted. If number one doesn't send you packing, wait until the fourth hole. The green is surrounded on three sides by water.

## RIVERSIDE GOLF CLUB

**Course 16**
MAP 16 grid e1

*Course information:* This public course has 18 holes and par is 72. The course is 6,760 yards and rated 72.0 from the championship tees, and 6,494 yards and rated 70.0 from the regular tees. The slope ratings are 122 championship and 116 regular. Women's tees are 6,200 yards and rated 73.0. The slope rating is 115 regular.

*Play policy and fees:* Green fees are $9 weekdays and $14 weekends. Call for special senior rates. Carts are $16. Reservations are recommended.

*Location:* Take the Columbia Avenue exit off the Riverside Freeway (Highway 91) and travel north on Orange Street to the club.

*Course description:* This course is long, but fairly level. It is lined with pine and mulberry trees. It is wide open, as are its largely level greens. A course John Daly would love.

1011 Orange Street
Riverside, CA 92517

Pro shop (714) 682-3748

- ✓ **driving range**
- ✓ **practice greens**
- ✓ **power carts**
- ✓ **pull carts**
- ✓ **golf club rental**
- locker rooms
- showers
- executive course
- accommodations
- ✓ **food and beverages**
- ✓ **clubhouse**

**Dennis Kahn**
Manager

**Howard Smith**
Professional

**Maurilio Briseno**
Superintendent

## VICTORIA GOLF CLUB

**Course 17**
MAP 16 grid e1

*Course information:* This private course has 18 holes and par is 72. The course is 6,483 yards and rated 71.3 from the championship tees, and 6,256 yards and rated 69.8 from the regular tees. The slope ratings are 125 championship and 121 regular. Women's tees are 5,849 and rated 73.3. The slope rating is 122.

*Play policy and fees:* Reciprocal play is accepted with members of other private clubs on Tuesdays, Thursdays and Fridays, otherwise members and guests only. Green fees are $35 with a member. Carts are $16. Reservations are required.

*Location:* In Riverside, take the Central Avenue exit off Highway 91 (Riverside Freeway) and travel east for one mile to the first traffic light (Victoria) and turn left. From there, go one-half mile to Arroyo Drive and turn right into the club entrance.

*Course description:* Roughly 90 years old, this course has that old- world look to it. There are many interesting holes. There is a lake on the first hole and a large creekbed meanders through the course. Accurate placement is crucial, especially off the tees.

**1903**
2521 Arroyo Drive
Riverside, CA 92506

Pro shop (714) 684-5035
Clubhouse (714) 683-5323

- ✓ **driving range**
- ✓ **practice greens**
- ✓ **power carts**
- ✓ **pull carts**
- golf club rental
- ✓ **locker rooms**
- ✓ **showers**
- executive course
- accommodations
- ✓ **food and beverages**
- ✓ **clubhouse**

**Jeff Cross**
Professional

**Lionel Guzman**
Superintendent

## CANYON CREST COUNTRY CLUB

**Course 18**
MAP I6 grid e1

975 Country Club Drive
Riverside, CA 92506

Pro shop (714) 274-7906
Clubhouse (714) 274-7900

- ✓ **driving range**
- ✓ **practice greens**
- ✓ **power carts**
- ✓ **pull carts**
- ✓ **golf club rental**
- ✓ **locker rooms**
- ✓ **showers**
- executive course
- accommodations
- ✓ **food and beverages**
- ✓ **clubhouse**

**Paul Hjulberg**
Professional

**Chris Seliga**
Superintendent

***Course information:*** This private course has 18 holes and par is 72. The course is 6,588 yards and rated 71.6 from the championship tees, and 6,331 yards and rated 70.1 from the regular tees. The slope ratings are 128 championship and 122 regular. Women's tees are 5,863 yards and rated 74.3. The slope rating is 129.

***Play policy and fees:*** Members and guests only. Green fees are $35 weekdays and $45 weekends. Carts are $10. Reservations are recommended.

***Location:*** In Riverside, take the Pennsylvania Avenue exit off Highway 60 and go west for about one-quarter mile to Canyon Crest Drive and turn left.

***Course description:*** This course is very hilly with lots of mature trees and numerous bunkers. Accurate shot placement is critical or your round could become a nightmare. A brush-filled dry creekbed runs through the course, lining six holes. Homes line the perimeter, which means out-of-bounds on nearly every hole. The slopes all went up in the last year. Carts are advisable because the hills make for strenuous walking.

## REDLANDS COUNTRY CLUB

**Course 19**
MAP I6 grid e3

**1897**
**A.E. Sterling**
**J.H. Fisher**

1749 Garden Street
Redlands, CA 92373

Pro shop (714) 793-1295
Clubhouse (714) 793-2661

- ✓ **driving range**
- ✓ **practice greens**
- ✓ **power carts**
- ✓ **pull carts**
- golf club rental
- ✓ **locker rooms**
- ✓ **showers**
- executive course
- accommodations
- ✓ **food and beverages**
- ✓ **clubhouse**

**Norman Bernard**
Professional

**Ray Navarro**
Superintendent

***Course information:*** This private course has 18 holes and par is 70. The course is 6,276 yards and rated 70.0 from the championship tees, and 6,061 yards and rated 69.0 from the regular tees. The slope ratings are 123 championship and 118 regular. Women's tees are 6,061 yards and rated 74.8 from the championship tees, and 5,730 yards and rated 73.0 from the forward tees. The slope ratings are 134 championship and 121 forward.

***Play policy and fees:*** Reciprocal play accepted. Otherwise, members and guests only. Guests must be accompanied by a member. Green fees are $20 weekdays and $25 weekends. Carts are $14. Reservations are recommended.

***Location:*** Take the Ford exit off Interstate 10 east of San Bernardino and travel south for 1.5 miles. Bear right at the fork on Garden Hill and turn left on Garden Street to the club.

***Course description:*** This course was originally built as a nine-hole layout by old money during the old days. In 1927 it was expanded to an 18-hole course under the direction of club member Raven Hornby and the consultation of Alister MacKenzie, according to club records. It has similar characteristics to the Lake Course at the Olympic Club and Cherry Hills. There are lots of oaks and many tall cypress and pine trees.

# GENERAL OLD GOLF COURSE

**Course 20**
MAP 16 grid f1

***Course information:*** This military course has 18 holes and par is 72. The course is 6,702 yards and rated 72.6 from the championship tees, and 6,423 yards and rated 70.6 from the regular tees. The slope ratings are 125 championship and 119 regular. Women's tees are 5,823 yards and rated 72.9. The slope is 118.

***Play policy and fees:*** Military personnel and guests only: active duty, retired military, Department of Defense employees and dependents. Call for various fees.

***Location:*** From Riverside drive southeast on Interstate 215 four miles to Van Buren Boulevard. That's the first exit past the main gate to March AFB. Turn right and drive one mile to Village West Drive and turn left to the golf course.

***Course description:*** General Peyton C. March, who was Chief of Staff during WW I, was once confronted with the logistical question of how the military was going to transport its troops across the Atlantic to the European front. "You can march them over there," he suggested in exasperation. Well, this Air Force Base boasts a course with just about as many logistical problems as the general faced more than 70 years ago. He didn't live long enough to see this course open for play, but chances are he would have appreciated its championship layout. There are numerous doglegs and bunkers, and although the water hazards don't match crossing the Atlantic on foot, there are seven holes that must be reached over or around water. The front nine is relatively flat and the back nine is up and down.

**1957**

March AFB
Village West Drive
Riverside, CA 92518

Pro shop (714) 653-7913

- ✓ **driving range**
- ✓ **practice greens**
- ✓ **power carts**
- ✓ **pull carts**
- ✓ **golf club rental**
- ✓ **locker rooms**
- ✓ **showers**
- executive course
- accommodations
- ✓ **food and beverages**
- ✓ **clubhouse**

**Dick Couts**
Professional

**Jerry Zigan**
Superintendent

# MORENO VALLEY RANCH GOLF CLUB

**Course 21**
MAP 16 grid f2

**1988**
**Pete Dye**

28095 John F. Kennedy Avenue
Moreno Valley, CA 92555

Pro shop (714) 924-4444

✓ **driving range**
✓ **practice greens**
✓ **power carts**
pull carts
✓ **golf club rental**
locker rooms
✓ **showers**
executive course
accommodations
✓ **food and beverages**
✓ **clubhouse**

**Ken Winn**
Professional

**Murray Nonhoff**
Superintendent

***Course information:*** This public facility has 27 holes and par is 36 on each nine.

The Lake/Valley Course is 6,898 yards and rated 74.4 from the tournament tees, 6,497 yards and rated 71.5 from the championship tees, and 5,933 yards and rated 68.9 from the regular tees. The slope ratings are 138 tournament, 126 championship and 119 regular. Women's tees are 5,246 yards and rated 69.8. The slope rating is 114.

The Mountain/Lake Course is 6,684 yards and rated 73.1 from the tournament tees, 6,389 yards and rated 70.9 from the championship tees, and 5,854 yards and rated 68.5 from the regular tees. The slope ratings are 135 tournament, 125 championship and 118 regular. Women's tees are 5,108 yards and rated 69.1. The slope rating is 112.

The Valley/Mountain tournament course is 6,898 yards, and rated 74.4 with a slope of 138. See card below for additional yardage and rating information.

***Play policy and fees:*** Green fees are $38 Monday through Thursday, and $55 Fridays and weekends. Carts are $16. Reservations are recommended seven days in advance.

***Location:*** From Highway 60, exit south on Moreno Beach Drive. Travel two miles to John F. Kennedy Avenue, then turn left and follow it to the course.

***Course description:*** This is a well-maintained course with fast sloping greens. The fairways are tight in some places, demanding accurate tee shots. The Valley and Lake Courses are rolling, with elevated tees and greens. The Mountain Course has lots of elevation changes and is much tighter.

Valley/Mountain Course

| Hole | 1 | 2 | 3 | 4 | 5 | 6 | 7 | 8 | 9 | Out | BLUE | Rating: 70.9 |
|---|---|---|---|---|---|---|---|---|---|---|---|---|
| BLUE | 427 | 143 | 499 | 333 | 434 | 425 | 509 | 125 | 320 | 3215 | | Slope: 125 |
| WHITE | 349 | 140 | 475 | 318 | 401 | 364 | 475 | 123 | 310 | 2955 | | |
| Par | 4 | 3 | 5 | 4 | 4 | 4 | 5 | 3 | 4 | 36 | WHITE | Rating: 68.5 |
| Handicap | 1 | 4 | 6 | 7 | 3 | 2 | 5 | 9 | 8 | x | | Slope: 118 |
| RED | 329 | 117 | 454 | 279 | 332 | 314 | 437 | 105 | 300 | 2667 | | |
| Par | 4 | 3 | 5 | 4 | 4 | 4 | 5 | 3 | 4 | 36 | RED | Rating: 69.7 |
| Handicap | 1 | 4 | 6 | 7 | 3 | 2 | 5 | 9 | 8 | x | | Slope: 113 |

| Hole | 10 | 11 | 12 | 13 | 14 | 15 | 16 | 17 | 18 | In | Totals | |
|---|---|---|---|---|---|---|---|---|---|---|---|---|
| BLUE | 333 | 374 | 150 | 359 | 404 | 489 | 165 | 515 | 334 | 3123 | BLUE | 6453 |
| WHITE | 279 | 334 | 144 | 343 | 380 | 472 | 115 | 498 | 313 | 2878 | WHITE | 5907 |
| Par | 4 | 4 | 3 | 4 | 4 | 5 | 3 | 5 | 4 | 36 | Par | 72 |
| Handicap | 8 | 4 | 9 | 5 | 1 | 2 | 7 | 3 | 6 | x | | |
| RED | 264 | 315 | 114 | 322 | 278 | 420 | 91 | 439 | 286 | 2529 | RED | 5246 |
| Par | 4 | 4 | 3 | 4 | 4 | 5 | 3 | 5 | 4 | 36 | Par | 72 |
| Handicap | 8 | 4 | 9 | 5 | 1 | 2 | 7 | 3 | 6 | x | | |

# PALM CREST RESORT AND COUNTRY CLUB

**Course 22**
MAP I6 grid f4

**1969**
**Desmond Muirhead**

15960 Gilman Springs Road
Moreno Valley, CA 923555

Pro shop (714) 654-2631
Clubhouse (714) 654-2727

- ✓ **driving range**
- ✓ **practice greens**
- ✓ **power carts**
- ✓ **pull carts**
- ✓ **golf club rental**
- ✓ **locker rooms**
- ✓ **showers**
- **executive course**
- **accommodations**
- ✓ **food and beverages**
- ✓ **clubhouse**

**Ken Joersz**
Professional

**Bill Phillips**
Superintendent

***Course information:*** This course is under new ownership. It has 18 holes and par is 72. The championship course is 6,875 yards and rated 73.8; the slope rating is 138. The regular course is 6,295 yards and rated 69.8; the slope rating is 122. The women's course is 5,291 yards and rated 70.4; the slope rating is 117.

***Play policy and fees:*** Green fees are Monday through Friday, $30, including cart; Saturday, Sunday and holidays, $50, including cart; twilight rates are $20 weekdays and $30 weekends with cart. Walking after 2 p.m. is $10. Rates are seasonal, corresponding to time changes. Call for new rates in 1993.

***Location:*** From Highway 91 take Highway 60 east about 14 miles to the Gilman Springs exit. Drive four miles south to the club.

***Course description:*** This course was formerly known as Quail Ranch Resort and Country Club, but changed its name to Palm Crest—and for good reason, too. The course was renovated in mid-1991 and 1,000 full-grown palm trees were planted in clusters around the greens and along the fairways. The Southern California Golf Association rated this course as one of its top 10 public golf facilities in 1988. It's a Scottish, links style course with rolling terrain and undulating greens. The PGA Tour School qualifier and the U.S. Open qualifier have been held here. Craig Stadler impressed the locals once when he finished a round in the dark and asked the pro staff if they would park their cars around the 18th green with their headlights on so he could finish his game. Gary McCord holds the course record with a 64.

# CALIMESA GOLF AND COUNTRY CLUB

**Course 23**
MAP I6 grid f5

1300 South Third Street
Calimesa, CA 92320

Pro shop (714) 795-2488

- ✓ **driving range**
- ✓ **practice greens**
- ✓ **power carts**
- ✓ **pull carts**
- golf club rental
- locker rooms
- showers
- executive course
- accommodations
- ✓ **food and beverages**
- ✓ **clubhouse**

**Lou Tendall**
Manager

**Michael Wysowski**
Professional

**Richard Hamilton**
Superintendent

***Course information:*** This public course has 18 holes and par is 70. The course is 5,914 yards and rated 67.9 from the championship tees, and 5,571 yards and rated 66.0 from the regular tees. The slope ratings are 111 championship and 103 regular. Women's tees are 5,214 yards and rated 69.2. The slope rating is 112.

***Play policy and fees:*** Green fees are $13 weekdays and $20 weekends. Carts are $18. Reservations are recommended one week in advance. This course is available for tournaments.

***Location:*** Travel eight miles east of Redlands on Interstate 10 to Calimesa. Turn east on County Line Road to Third Street and travel south to the club.

***Course description:*** This scenic little course is set in a canyon. It's up and down with mature trees and shows lots of character. You can have fun on this course. The entryway, lounge and dining facilities have all been recently remodeled.

# SUN LAKES COUNTRY CLUB

**Course 24**
MAP I6 grid f6

*Course information:* This semi-private course has 18 holes. The black tees are 7,017 yards, and are rated 74.3 with a slope of 132. The gold tees are 5,879 yards. See card below for additional yardage and rating information.

*Play policy and fees:* Outside play is accepted after 12 noon. Green fees for residents are $23 weekdays and $30 weekends, non-residents are $50, and guests are $40, carts included. Reservations are recommended.

*Location:* Take the Highlands Springs Avenue exit off Interstate 10 in Banning (east of San Bernardino) and travel south to Sun Lakes Boulevard. Head east and turn on Country Club Drive south and continue to the club.

*Course description:* This is a long course with a traditional layout. Bring sand-moving equipment—there are 104 bunkers. There are also seven lakes and smallish greens to make this challenging course even more difficult. The winds make this a real challenge, especially in winter, but the rough areas have been trimmed in recent years, making this a playable layout. It's the centerpiece of a planned community, which explains the resident, non-resident, and guest fees.

850 South Country Club Drive
Banning, CA 92220

Pro shop (714) 845-2135

- ✓ **driving range**
- ✓ **practice greens**
- ✓ **power carts**
- pull carts
- ✓ **golf club rental**
- ✓ **locker rooms**
- showers
- executive course
- accommodations
- ✓ **food and beverages**
- ✓ **clubhouse**

**Buddy Allin**
Professional

**Jess Padilla**
Superintendent

| Hole | 1 | 2 | 3 | 4 | 5 | 6 | 7 | 8 | 9 | Out | BLUE | Rating: 72.0 |
|---|---|---|---|---|---|---|---|---|---|---|---|---|
| BLUE | 353 | 563 | 420 | 365 | 164 | 516 | 416 | 171 | 376 | 3344 | | Slope: 128 |
| WHITE | 340 | 533 | 402 | 349 | 139 | 501 | 404 | 147 | 361 | 3176 | | |
| Par | 4 | 5 | 4 | 4 | 3 | 5 | 4 | 3 | 4 | 36 | WHITE | Rating: 70.4 |
| Handicap | 15 | 7 | 3 | 11 | 17 | 1 | 5 | 13 | 9 | x | | Slope: 123 |
| RED | 296 | 478 | 361 | 305 | 105 | 454 | 356 | 104 | 316 | 2775 | | |
| Par | 4 | 5 | 4 | 4 | 3 | 5 | 4 | 3 | 4 | 36 | RED | Rating: 72.7 |
| Handicap | 13 | 3 | 7 | 11 | 15 | 1 | 5 | 17 | 9 | x | | Slope: 118 |

| Hole | 10 | 11 | 12 | 13 | 14 | 15 | 16 | 17 | 18 | In | Totals | |
|---|---|---|---|---|---|---|---|---|---|---|---|---|
| BLUE | 361 | 362 | 418 | 164 | 391 | 535 | 353 | 165 | 524 | 3273 | BLUE | 6617 |
| WHITE | 345 | 352 | 408 | 151 | 375 | 521 | 339 | 132 | 510 | 3133 | WHITE | 6309 |
| Par | 4 | 4 | 4 | 3 | 4 | 5 | 4 | 3 | 5 | 36 | Par | 72 |
| Handicap | 16 | 8 | 2 | 14 | 6 | 10 | 18 | 12 | 4 | x | | |
| RED | 299 | 304 | 362 | 106 | 317 | 474 | 301 | 105 | 454 | 2722 | RED | 5497 |
| Par | 4 | 4 | 4 | 3 | 4 | 5 | 4 | 3 | 5 | 36 | Par | 72 |
| Handicap | 14 | 12 | 4 | 16 | 8 | 2 | 10 | 18 | 6 | x | | |

# SOBOBA SPRINGS COUNTRY CLUB

**Course 25**
MAP I6 grid g5

**1967**
**Desmond Muirhead**

1020 Soboba Road
San Jacinto, CA 92383

Pro shop (714) 654-9354
Clubhouse (714) 654-9357
Fax (714) 654-6068

- ✓ **driving range**
- ✓ **practice greens**
- ✓ **power carts**
- ✓ **pull carts**
- ✓ **golf club rental**
- ✓ **locker rooms**
- ✓ **showers**
- executive course
- accommodations
- ✓ **food and beverages**
- ✓ **clubhouse**

**Bob Yokoi**
Professional/Manager

**Jaime Barrera**
Superintendent

*Course information:* This semi-private course has 18 holes. See card below for yardage and rating information.

*Play policy and fees:* Reciprocal play is accepted with members of other private clubs. Outside play is accepted. Green fees are $36 for non-members weekdays and $42 for non-members weekends, $25 per day after 2 p.m., carts included. Reservations are recommended one week in advance. No reservations prior to 10 a.m. on Tuesdays, Wednesdays and Saturdays.

*Location:* Travel east of San Bernardino on Interstate 10 to the town of Beaumont. Then take Highway 60 to the San Jacinto-Hemet exit south to Soboba Road and head east to the club.

*Course description:* This is a fairly flat course but it plays long. There are lots of trees and six holes with water hazards. This course is a rare par-73.

| Hole | 1 | 2 | 3 | 4 | 5 | 6 | 7 | 8 | 9 | Out | BLUE | Rating: 73.5 |
|---|---|---|---|---|---|---|---|---|---|---|---|---|
| BLUE | 386 | 422 | 444 | 142 | 533 | 514 | 510 | 141 | 412 | 3504 | | Slope: 134 |
| WHITE | 372 | 361 | 416 | 130 | 513 | 487 | 455 | 137 | 388 | 3259 | | |
| Par | 4 | 4 | 4 | 3 | 5 | 5 | 5 | 3 | 4 | 37 | WHITE | Rating: 70.5 |
| Handicap (b/w) | 9/9 | 1/13 | 5/3 | 17/17 | 13/1 | 11/7 | 3/11 | 15/15 | 7/5 | x | | Slope: 123 |
| RED | 362 | 302 | 412 | 119 | 431 | 429 | 445 | 118 | 345 | 2963 | | |
| Par | 4 | 4 | 5 | 3 | 5 | 5 | 5 | 3 | 4 | 38 | RED | Rating: 73.1 |
| Handicap | 5 | 13 | 7 | 17 | 11 | 1 | 9 | 15 | 3 | x | | Slope: 123 |

| Hole | 10 | 11 | 12 | 13 | 14 | 15 | 16 | 17 | 18 | In | Totals | |
|---|---|---|---|---|---|---|---|---|---|---|---|---|
| BLUE | 365 | 384 | 410 | 200 | 411 | 212 | 497 | 345 | 498 | 3322 | BLUE | 6826 |
| WHITE | 350 | 370 | 393 | 143 | 331 | 194 | 478 | 337 | 485 | 3081 | WHITE | 6340 |
| Par | 4 | 4 | 4 | 3 | 4 | 3 | 5 | 4 | 5 | 36 | Par | 73 |
| Handicap (b/w) | 16/12 | 6/4 | 12/8 | 14/18 | 2/14 | 10/10 | 4/2 | 18/16 | 6/6 | x | | |
| RED | 344 | 332 | 386 | 118 | 307 | 158 | 425 | 325 | 471 | 2866 | RED | 5829 |
| Par | 4 | 4 | 4 | 3 | 4 | 3 | 5 | 4 | 5 | 36 | Par | 74 |
| Handicap | 8 | 6 | 4 | 18 | 12 | 16 | 10 | 14 | 2 | x | | |

## CANYON LAKE COUNTRY CLUB

**Course 26**
MAP I6 grid h1

**1968**
**Ted Robinson**

Box 4251
Canyon Lake, CA 92587

32001 Railroad Canyon Road
Canyon Lake, CA 92380

Pro shop (714) 244-2853

- ✓ **driving range**
- ✓ **practice greens**
- ✓ **power carts**
- pull carts
- ✓ **golf club rental**
- ✓ **locker rooms**
- ✓ **showers**
- executive course
- accommodations
- ✓ **food and beverages**
- ✓ **clubhouse**

**Gabe Hrab**
Professional

***Course information:*** This private course has 18 holes and par is 71. The course is 5,868 yards and rated 68.2 from the championship tees, and 5,609 yards and rated 66.7 from the regular tees. The slope ratings are 109 championship and 105 regular. Women's tees are 5,391 yards and rated 72.5. The slope rating is 126.

***Play policy and fees:*** Reciprocal play is accepted with members of other private clubs. Have your club pro call for arrangements. Green fees are $11 for members and $18 for guests. Carts are $14. Reservations are recommended. Golfers must wear collared shirts.

***Location:*** From Riverside, travel south on Interstate 215 to Newport Road, and turn right, heading west to the last stop and turn left. The club entrance is 300 yards past the traffic light.

***Course description:*** This hilly course is short and tight with many hidden greens. Watch for number 15. It is a par-3 185 yard hole with a drop of 200 feet off the tee to a green that's thankfully in sight. The green has trees and bunkers around it, so be straight.

## MENIFEE LAKES COUNTRY CLUB

**Course 27**
MAP I6 grid h2

**1989**
**Ted Robinson**

29875 Menifee Lakes Drive
Menifee, CA 92355

Pro shop (714) 672-3090
Clubhouse (714) 672-4824

- ✓ **driving range**
- ✓ **practice greens**
- ✓ **power carts**
- pull carts
- ✓ **golf club rental**
- locker rooms
- showers
- executive course
- accommodations
- ✓ **food and beverages**
- ✓ **clubhouse**

**Stan Gonzales**
Professional

**Mark Livingston**
Superintendent

***Course information:*** This semi-private course has 18 holes and par is 72. The course is 6,472 yards and rated 71.2 from the championship tees, and 6,075 yards and rated 69.0 from the regular tees. The slope ratings are 128 championship and 119 regular. Women's tees are 5,421 yards and rated 71.3. The slope rating is 119.

***Play policy and fees:*** Green fees are $35 weekdays and $45 weekends. Carts are included. Reservations are recommended.

***Location:*** From Perris, take the Newport Road exit off Interstate 215 South; follow it about one-half mile to Menifee Lakes Drive turn left and follow the road to the course.

***Course description:*** This Ted Robinson-designed course features tight fairways, plenty of signature water and sand. There are two practice holes reserved for club members in need of pre-round tune-ups and a marvelous driving range.

## CHERRY HILLS GOLF CLUB

**Course 28**
MAP 16 grid h2

**1962**
**Del Webb**

26583 Cherry Hills Boulevard
Sun City, CA 92586

Pro shop (714) 679-1182

- ✓ **driving range**
- ✓ **practice greens**
- ✓ **power carts**
- pull carts
- ✓ **golf club rental**
- locker rooms
- showers
- executive course
- accommodations
- ✓ **food and beverages**
- ✓ **clubhouse**

**Jim Christie**
Professional

**Antolin Coria**
Superintendent

***Course information:*** This semi-private course has 18 holes and par is 72. The course is 6,908 yards and rated 71.8 from the championship tees, and 6,483 yards and rated 69.4 from the regular tees. The slope ratings are 111 championship and 105 regular. Women's tees are 5,927 yards and rated 72.3 from the forward tees. The slope rating is 112. The women's championship course is 6,483 yards and rated 75.4; the slope rating is 119.

***Play policy and fees:*** Outside play is accepted. Green fees are $20. Carts are $16. Reservations are recommended.

***Location:*** In Sun City, take the McCall Boulevard/Sun City exit off Interstate 215 and travel west on McCall for one-quarter mile to Sun City Boulevard. Turn left and drive one-quarter mile to Cherry Hills Boulevard. Turn right and go one block to the club.

***Course description:*** The course is now contour-mowed. That new look plus numerous bunkers and a daily southern breeze in the afternoons have put some bite into this layout.

## COLONIAL COUNTRY CLUB

**Course 29**
MAP 16 grid h4

25115 Kirby Street
Hemet, CA 92545

Clubhouse (714) 925-2664

- driving range
- practice greens
- power carts
- pull carts
- golf club rental
- locker rooms
- showers
- ✓ **executive course**
- accommodations
- ✓ **food and beverages**
- ✓ **clubhouse**

***Course information:*** This private course has 18 holes and par is 60. The course is a short 3,200 yards from the regular tees.

***Play policy and fees:*** Members and guests only. Green fees are $3 for nine holes.

***Location:*** In Hemet, take Florida Avenue (Highway 74) to Warren Avenue, turn left and continue about three-fourths of a mile to Kirby Street, then turn right and follow Kirby to the course.

***Course description:*** This is a small executive course with a pair of par-4s. It is reserved for residents and guests of the adjoining mobile home park.

# SEVEN HILLS GOLF CLUB

Course 30
MAP I6 grid h5

**1970**
**Harry Rainville**

1537 South Lyon Avenue
Hemet, CA 93545

Pro shop (714) 925-4815

- ✓ **driving range**
- ✓ **practice greens**
- ✓ **power carts**
- ✓ **pull carts**
- ✓ **golf club rental**
- locker rooms
- showers
- executive course
- accommodations
- ✓ **food and beverages**
- ✓ **clubhouse**

**Rolf Metz**
Professional

**Mike Jauregui**
Superintendent

*Course information:* This public course has 18 holes and par is 72. The course is 6,618 yards and rated 70.7 from the championship tees, and 6,305 yards and rated 69.0 from the regular tees. The slope ratings are 118 championship and 114 regular. Women's tees are 5,771 yards and rated 70.5. The slope rating is 106.

*Play policy and fees:* Green fees are $17 weekdays and $21 weekends. Carts are $10 per player for 18 holes. Reservations are recommended one week in advance. This course is available for outside tournaments on a contractual basis.

*Location:* Take the Highway 79 exit off Interstate 10 east of San Bernardino and travel south to Highway 74 in Hemet. Turn left and drive to Lyon Avenue and then right to the club.

*Course description:* This is a flat course with trees and water. It is medium short with four water hazards and not an excess of bunkers. The greens are small, which makes the shots semi-demanding.

# ECHO HILLS GOLF CLUB

Course 31
MAP I6 grid h5

545 East Thornton Avenue
Hemet, CA 92543

Pro shop (714) 652-2203

- driving range
- ✓ **practice greens**
- ✓ **power carts**
- ✓ **pull carts**
- ✓ **golf club rental**
- locker rooms
- showers
- executive course
- accommodations
- ✓ **food and beverages**
- clubhouse

**William Bennington**
Owner

**Moon Park**
Manager

*Course information:* This public course has nine holes. Par is 70 for 18 holes. The course is 4,458 yards and rated 60.2 from the regular tees. The slope rating is 87.

*Play policy and fees:* Green fees are $7 for nine holes. Carts are $8 for two people for nine holes.

*Location:* From Interstate 215, take the Highway 74 exit to the town of Hemet and drive through town. Turn right on Buena Vista Street and drive 1.5 miles to Thorton Avenue then go left to the club.

*Course description:* This well-maintained, short course has narrow fairways and many mature trees.

# ARROYO FAIRWAYS GOLF COURSE

**Course 32**
MAP I6 grid h6

42751 East Florida
Hemet, CA 92544

Pro shop (714) 927-1610

- driving range
- ✓ **practice greens**
- power carts
- pull carts
- golf club rental
- locker rooms
- showers
- executive course
- accommodations
- food and beverages
- clubhouse

***Course information:*** This private course has 11 holes. The Lower Course is 1,848 yards for nine holes. The Upper Course, which is the same layout as the Lower Course with two different holes substituted, is 2,058 yards.

***Play policy and fees:*** Members and guests only. Green fees are $2 for nine holes and $3 for 18 holes any day.

***Location:*** In Hemet, follow Florida Avenue (Highway 74) east to the course.

***Course description:*** This is a pitch-and-putt layout reserved for residents and their guests staying at the adjoining mobile home park. It is well maintained with lots of trees and bunkers.

# BEAR CREEK GOLF AND COUNTRY CLUB

**Course 33**
MAP 16 grid j1

**1983**
**Jack Nicklaus**

22640 Bear Creek Drive North
Murrieta, CA 92362

Pro shop (714) 677-8631
Clubhouse (714) 677-8621

- ✓ **driving range**
- ✓ **practice greens**
- ✓ **power carts**
- pull carts
- ✓ **golf club rental**
- ✓ **locker rooms**
- ✓ **showers**
- executive course
- accommodations
- ✓ **food and beverages**
- ✓ **clubhouse**

**Eddie Brown,**
Professional

**Mike Greninger**
Superintendent

**John Dancoisne**
Manager

***Course information:*** This private course has 18 holes. The gold tees are 5,990 yards, and are rated 69.1 with a slope of 122. The green tees are 5,230 yards, and are rated 72.4 with a slope of 128 (women's). See card below for additional yardage and rating information.

***Play policy and fees:*** Limited reciprocal play is accepted with members of other private clubs, otherwise members and guests only. Green fees are $42 escorted and $77 unescorted, carts included. This course is available for outside tournaments. Proper dress code is strictly enforced.

***Location:*** Take Interstate 15 to the Clinton Keith exit in Murrieta then travel west to Bear Creek and turn north to the club.

***Course description:*** This championship course is aptly named because it is a bear. It was designed by Jack Nicklaus in 1983. It features a natural rolling terrain with pot bunkers, mounds and creeks. Water guards half the course and the greens are large and tricky. Nicklaus' favorite hole is the 435-yard, par-4 fourth hole. It has a split-level fairway divided by grass bunkers. The course was the site of the 1985 Skins Game and is used regularly for PGA Tour qualifying. It rates among the top 20 courses in the state, although the wind picks up considerably in the afternoons, often making this an angry bear. Immaculately conditioned, it hosts only about 35,000 rounds per year.

| Hole | 1 | 2 | 3 | 4 | 5 | 6 | 7 | 8 | 9 | Out | BLUE | Rating: 75.3 |
|---|---|---|---|---|---|---|---|---|---|---|---|---|
| BLUE | 412 | 424 | 499 | 414 | 434 | 132 | 433 | 172 | 547 | 3467 | | Slope: 143 |
| WHITE | 383 | 398 | 473 | 391 | 390 | 112 | 371 | 153 | 510 | 3181 | | |
| Par | 4 | 4 | 5 | 4 | 4 | 3 | 4 | 3 | 5 | 36 | WHITE | Rating: 71.6 |
| Handicap | 5 | 9 | 13 | 1 | 3 | 17 | 7 | 15 | 11 | x | | Slope: 136 |
| RED | 339 | 306 | 465 | 307 | 353 | 68 | 357 | 124 | 443 | 2762 | | |
| Par | 4 | 4 | 5 | 4 | 4 | 3 | 4 | 3 | 5 | 36 | RED | Rating: 73.9 |
| Handicap | 7 | 13 | 3 | 1 | 5 | 17 | 11 | 15 | 9 | x | | Slope: 133 |

| Hole | 10 | 11 | 12 | 13 | 14 | 15 | 16 | 17 | 18 | In | Totals | |
|---|---|---|---|---|---|---|---|---|---|---|---|---|
| BLUE | 414 | 531 | 210 | 351 | 532 | 424 | 210 | 425 | 428 | 3525 | BLUE | 6992 |
| WHITE | 398 | 483 | 174 | 330 | 496 | 396 | 164 | 392 | 408 | 3241 | WHITE | 6422 |
| Par | 4 | 5 | 3 | 4 | 5 | 4 | 3 | 4 | 4 | 36 | Par | 72 |
| Handicap | 4 | 6 | 16 | 14 | 8 | 2 | 18 | 12 | 10 | x | | |
| RED | 309 | 431 | 128 | 317 | 429 | 316 | 123 | 371 | 362 | 2786 | RED | 5548 |
| Par | 4 | 5 | 3 | 4 | 5 | 4 | 3 | 4 | 4 | 36 | Par | 72 |
| Handicap | 4 | 6 | 18 | 14 | 10 | 12 | 16 | 8 | 2 | x | | |



MAP ON PAGE 584

# TEMECULA CREEK INN GOLF COURSE

**Course 34**
MAP 16 grid j2

**1970**
**Ted Robinson**

PO Box 129
44-501 Rainbow Canyon Road
Temecula, CA 92390

Pro shop (714) 676-2405
Clubhouse (714) 676-5631
(619) 728-9100

- ✓ **driving range**
- ✓ **practice greens**
- ✓ **power carts**
- ✓ **pull carts**
- ✓ **golf club rental**
- ✓ **locker rooms**
- ✓ **showers**
- executive course
- ✓ **accommodations**
- ✓ **food and beverages**
- ✓ **clubhouse**

**Deane Manning**
Manager

**Michael Bratschi**
Professional

**Tim Ketterer**
Superintendent

***Course information:*** This resort facility has 27 holes.

The Creek/Oaks Course is 6,757 yards and rated 72.6 with a slope of 125 from the championship tees, and 6,344 yards and rated 69.8 with a slope of 115 from the regular tees. Women's tees are 5,737 yards and rated 72.8. The slope rating is 123.

The Oaks/Stone House Course is detailed below.

The Creek/Stone House Course is 6,580 yards and rated 71.8 with a slope of 131 from the championship tees, and 6,262 yards and rated 69.7 with a slope of 117 from the regular tees. Women's tees are 5,686 yards and rated 71.9. The slope rating is 120.

***Play policy and fees:*** Outside play is accepted. Hotel guests welcome. Green fees are $33 weekdays and $44 weekends, including cart. Reservations are recommended. This course is available for outside tournaments. Carts are $22. Inquire about twilight rates.

***Location:*** From the intersection of Highway 15 and Highway 79, travel east one-half mile to Pala Road and turn right. Drive to Rainbow Canyon Road and the course.

***Course description:*** A Ted Robinson-designed nine-hole course opened on April Fool's Day 1990, bringing to 27 the number of holes on this course. Each of the nines are distinctly different. They range in character from flat and rolling to hilly with lots of trees to more hills and more trees. A restful resort, Temecula is known for its sunny climate. The $75,000 Temecula Creek Open is staged in July. In 1992, both the U.S. Open and the U.S. Public Links held qualifying rounds here, a testament to this courses's challenging playability. An estimated 78,000 rounds a year are played here.

Oaks/Stonehouse

| Hole | 1 | 2 | 3 | 4 | 5 | 6 | 7 | 8 | 9 | Out | BLUE | Rating: 72.6 |
|---|---|---|---|---|---|---|---|---|---|---|---|---|
| BLUE | 372 | 498 | 171 | 404 | 443 | 212 | 520 | 411 | 405 | 3436 | | Slope: 130 |
| WHITE | 357 | 482 | 153 | 378 | 387 | 174 | 507 | 368 | 386 | 3192 | | |
| Par | 4 | 5 | 3 | 4 | 4 | 3 | 5 | 4 | 4 | 36 | WHITE | Rating: 70.1 |
| Handicap | 9/10 | 15/16 | 17/18 | 1/2 | 3/4 | 13/14 | 11/12 | 5/6 | 7/8 | x | | Slope: 116 |
| RED | 343 | 465 | 109 | 348 | 323 | 148 | 445 | 340 | 346 | 2867 | | |
| Par | 4 | 5 | 3 | 4 | 4 | 3 | 5 | 4 | 4 | 36 | RED | Rating: 72.4 |
| Handicap | 5/6 | 11/12 | 17/18 | 1/2 | 9/10 | 15/16 | 13/14 | 7/8 | 3/4 | x | | Slope: 125 |

| Hole | 10 | 11 | 12 | 13 | 14 | 15 | 16 | 17 | 18 | In | Totals | |
|---|---|---|---|---|---|---|---|---|---|---|---|---|
| BLUE | 505 | 352 | 402 | 331 | 180 | 416 | 351 | 165 | 555 | 3257 | BLUE | 6693 |
| WHITE | 488 | 333 | 380 | 315 | 165 | 396 | 333 | 153 | 540 | 3103 | WHITE | 6295 |
| Par | 5 | 4 | 4 | 4 | 3 | 4 | 4 | 3 | 5 | 36 | Par | 72 |
| Handicap | 11/12 | 9/10 | 3/4 | 13/14 | 15/16 | 1/2 | 7/8 | 17/18 | 5/6 | x | | |
| RED | 455 | 313 | 330 | 280 | 147 | 330 | 305 | 136 | 520 | 2816 | RED | 5683 |
| Par | 5 | 4 | 4 | 4 | 3 | 4 | 4 | 3 | 5 | 36 | Par | 72 |
| Handicap | 7/8 | 9/10 | 3/4 | 17/18 | 11/12 | 5/6 | 13/14 | 15/16 | 1/2 | x | | |

# RED HAWK GOLF CLUB

**Course 35**
MAP I6 grid j3

**1991**
**Ron Fream**

45100 Red Hawk Parkway
Temecula, CA 92592

Pro shop (714) 695-1424

- ✓ **driving range**
- ✓ **practice greens**
- ✓ **power carts**
- pull carts
- ✓ **golf club rental**
- locker rooms
- showers
- executive course
- accommodations
- ✓ **food and beverages**
- clubhouse

**Robin Kohlhaas**
Professional

**Bob Hall**
Superintendent

***Course information:*** This public course has 18 holes. Par is 72. The course is 7,070 yards and rated 75.3 from the tournament tees, 6,655 yards and rated 72.4 from the championship tees, and 6,130 yards and rated 69.6 from the regular tees. The slope ratings are 142 tournament, 133 championship and 125 regular. Women's tees are 5,460 yards and rated 72.4. The slope rating is 135.

***Play policy and fees:*** Green fees are $50 weekdays and $65 weekends. Twilight rates are $35, after 2 p.m. Carts are included. Reservations are required. This course is available for tournaments weekdays or after 12 noon weekends.

***Location:*** From Highway 15 in Temecula, take the Highway 79 South exit. Travel east on Highway 79 for 2.5 miles, then turn right on Red Hawk Parkway and drive straight to the course.

***Course description:*** This course was the site of the qualifying for 1992 U.S. Public Links Championship. Its rolling terrain features several elevated tees and greens. There are generous landing areas, but tiered and sloping greens present a real challenge.

# MAP I7

(65 COURSES)

PAGES.. 612-665


SO-CAL MAP .....see page 466

adjoining maps

NORTH .........................no map

EAST (I8) ...........see page 666

SOUTH (J7) ........see page 716

WEST (I6) ...........see page 584

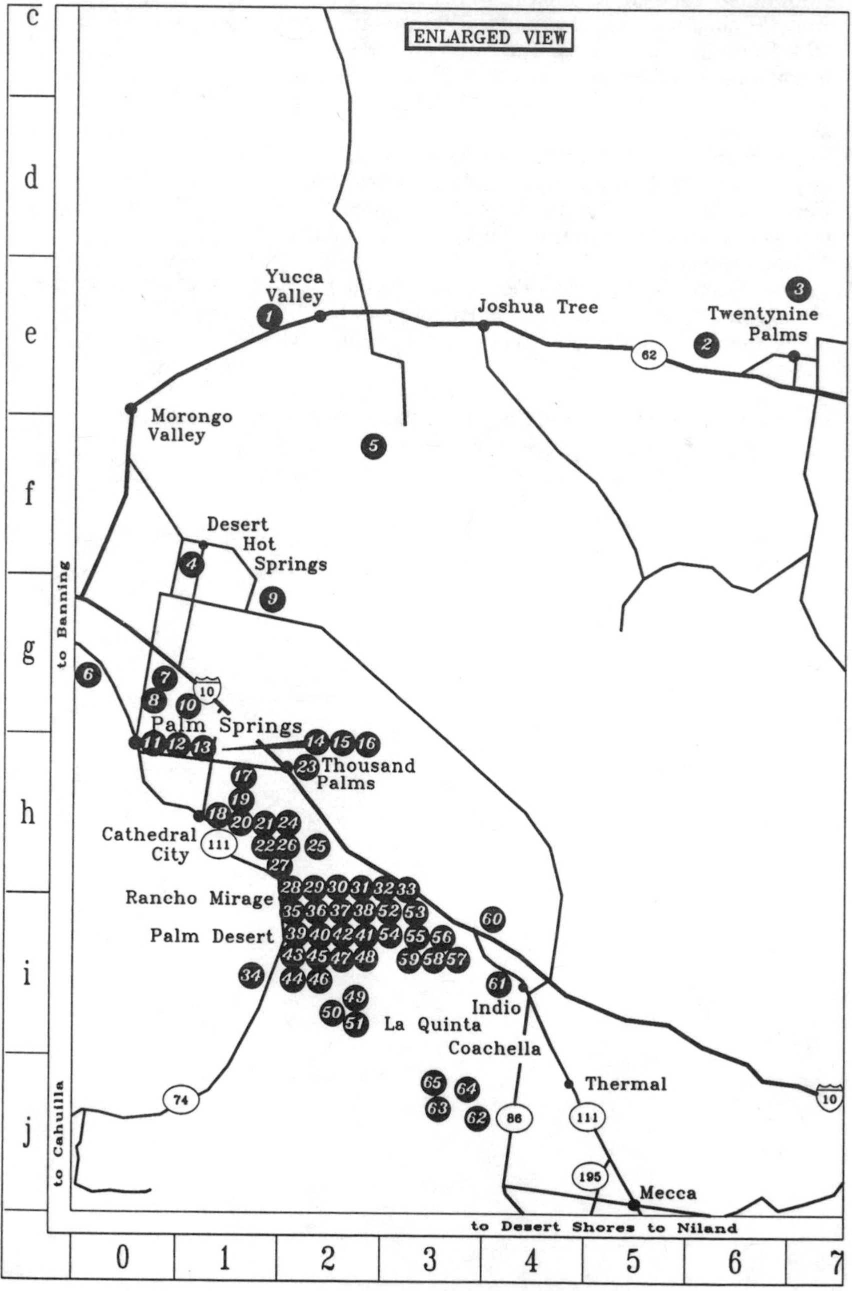

ENLARGED VIEW

c d e f g h i j

0 1 2 3 4 5 6 7

Yucca Valley 1

Joshua Tree

Twentynine Palms 2 3

62

Morongo Valley

5

Desert Hot Springs 4 9

to Banning

6 7 8 10

10

Palm Springs 11 12 13 14 15 16

23 Thousand Palms

17 19

18 20 21 24

Cathedral City 111 22 26 25

27

Rancho Mirage 28 29 30 31 32 33

35 36 37 38 52 53 60

Palm Desert 39 40 42 41 54 55 56

43 45 47 48 59 58 57

34 44 46 61

49 Indio

50 51 La Quinta

Coachella

65 64 Thermal

63 62 86 111 10

74

to Cahuilla

195

Mecca

to Desert Shores to Niland

# BLUE SKIES COUNTRY CLUB

**Course 1**
MAP I7 grid e1

**1957**
55-100 Martinez Trail
Yucca Valley, CA 92284

Pro shop (619) 365-0111

- ✓ **driving range**
- ✓ **practice greens**
- ✓ **power carts**
- ✓ **pull carts**
- ✓ **golf club rental**
- locker rooms
- showers
- executive course
- accommodations
- ✓ **food and beverages**
- ✓ **clubhouse**

**John Neubauer**
Professional

**Winston Bullock**
Assistant Professional

**Rusty Scott**
Superintendent

***Course information:*** This semi-private course has 18 holes and par is 71. The course is 6,430 yards and rated 70.1 from the championship tees, and 6,430 yards and rated 68.4 from the regular tees. The slope ratings are 117 championship and 109 regular. Women's tees are 5,769 yards and rated 70.9. The slope rating is 115 regular.

***Play policy and fees:*** Reciprocal play is accepted with members of other private clubs. Outside play is accepted. Green fees are $16 weekdays and $19 weekends and holidays. Seniors and active military rates are $11 weekdays and $14 weekends. Carts are $17 weekdays and $20 weekends for 18 holes. Reservations are recommended.

***Location:*** Take the Twenty Nine Palms/Yucca Valley exit off Interstate 10 and drive about 18 miles north on Highway 62. Turn left at the Yucca Inn sign and continue to the club.

***Course description:*** This upgraded course has tree-lined fairways and two lakes. The fairways are fairly open. Number three is a scenic lake hole. It is par-3 164 yards from an elevated tee hitting over the lake. The green is bunkered in the front and the tee is in a chute of trees. And what trees—towering cottonwoods and Chinese elms line every fairway.

# DESERT WINDS GOLF COURSE

**Course 2**
MAP I7 grid e6

Box 337
Twenty Nine Palms
CA 92277

Pro shop (619) 368-6132
Clubhouse (619) 368-7253

- ✓ **driving range**
- ✓ **practice greens**
- ✓ **power carts**
- ✓ **pull carts**
- ✓ **golf club rental**
- ✓ **locker rooms**
- ✓ **showers**
- executive course
- accommodations
- ✓ **food and beverages**
- ✓ **clubhouse**

**George Fisher**
Manager

***Course information:*** This military course has nine holes. Par is 72 for 18 holes. The course is 6,627 yards and rated 71.1 from the regular tees (18 holes). The slope rating is 119 regular. Women's tees are 5,691 yards. See card below for additional information.

***Play policy and fees:*** Military personnel and guests only. Reservations are required up to a week in advance for weekends and holidays. Civilian guests pay $9; military personnel pay $7.50 weekdays, $8 weekends. Retired military pay $6.50 weekdays, $7 weekends. Carts are $12. Juniors pay $5.

***Location:*** Take the Twenty Nine Palms/Yucca Valley exit off Interstate 10 and drive about 40 miles to the town of Twenty Nine Palms. Turn left at Adobe Road and drive five miles to the main gate at the Marine Combat Center. Continue through the main gate for three miles to the flashing light. Turn left and drive one-half mile to first paved road, then right to the course.

***Course description:*** If you like toying with the elements, this course is for you. It is built on the side of a hill in the middle of the desert. It is wide open but challenging with out-of-bounds areas, desert-style rough, and seasonal winds. Five ponds come into play, but during the summer, the water will be a welcome sight. Plans call for this course to expand to 18 holes. Approximately 20,000 rounds are played per year.

| Hole | 1 | 2 | 3 | 4 | 5 | 6 | 7 | 8 | 9 | Out | | |
|---|---|---|---|---|---|---|---|---|---|---|---|---|
| BLUE | - | - | - | - | - | - | - | - | - | - | BLUE | Rating: -- |
| | | | | | | | | | | | | Slope: -- |
| WHITE | 488 | 394 | 212 | 560 | 392 | 166 | 388 | 333 | 413 | 3362 | | |
| Par | 5 | 4 | 3 | 5 | 4 | 3 | 4 | 4 | 4 | 36 | WHITE | Rating: 71.1 |
| Handicap | 15 | 1 | 5 | 9 | 11 | 17 | 7 | 13 | 3 | x | | Slope: 119 |
| RED | 340 | 339 | 173 | 475 | 342 | 144 | 294 | 294 | 474 | 2875 | | |
| Par | 4 | 4 | 3 | 5 | 4 | 3 | 4 | 4 | 5 | 36 | RED | Rating: -- |
| Handicap | 7 | 1 | 15 | 3 | 9 | 17 | 11 | 13 | 5 | x | | Slope: -- |

| Hole | 10 | 11 | 12 | 13 | 14 | 15 | 16 | 17 | 18 | In | Totals | |
|---|---|---|---|---|---|---|---|---|---|---|---|---|
| BLUE | - | - | - | - | - | - | - | - | - | - | BLUE | -- |
| WHITE | 392 | 345 | 201 | 485 | 408 | 185 | 338 | 400 | 527 | 3265 | WHITE | 6627 |
| Par | 4 | 4 | 3 | 5 | 4 | 3 | 4 | 4 | 5 | 36 | Par | 72 |
| Handicap | 6 | 12 | 10 | 14 | 4 | 18 | 16 | 2 | 8 | x | | |
| RED | 334 | 331 | 142 | 411 | 375 | 160 | 328 | 324 | 411 | 2816 | RED | 5691 |
| Par | 4 | 4 | 3 | 5 | 4 | 3 | 4 | 4 | 5 | 36 | Par | 72 |
| Handicap | 8 | 4 | 16 | 2 | 12 | 18 | 14 | 10 | 6 | x | | |

## ROADRUNNER DUNES GOLF CLUB

**Course 3**
MAP I7 grid e7

PO Box 204
Twenty Nine Palms
CA 92277

4733 Desert Knoll Ave.
Twenty Nine Palms
CA 92277

Pro shop (619) 367-7610

- ✓ **driving range**
- ✓ **practice greens**
- ✓ **power carts**
- ✓ **pull carts**
- ✓ **golf club rental**
- locker rooms
- showers
- executive course
- accommodations
- ✓ **food and beverages**
- ✓ **clubhouse**

**Steve Barron**
Professional

**Randy Councell**
Superintendent

*Course information:* This public course has nine holes. Par is 72 for 18 holes. The course is 6,305 yards and rated 69.3 from the regular tees. The slope rating is 115. Women's tees are 5,574 yards and rated 70.2. The slope rating is 117.

*Play policy and fees:* During the week, green fees are $7.50 for nine holes and $11 for 18 holes, weekdays. Weekends are $10 for nine holes and $14 for 18 holes. The junior rate is $4.50 for nine holes and $7.50 for 18 holes. Senior rates are $6 for nine holes and $9 for 18. Carts are $6 for nine holes and $11 for 18 holes.

*Location:* Take the Twenty Nine Palms/Yucca Valley exit off Interstate 10 and drive about 40 miles to the town of Twenty Nine Palms. Turn left on Adobe Road and drive two miles. Turn right on Amboy and then left on Desert Knoll Avenue.

*Course description:* This challenging and short course has narrow fairways, small greens, grass bunkers and out-of-bounds on one side of every hole, both sides of three. The homes aren't up yet, so it's not claustrophobic. But it is tight.

## MISSION LAKES COUNTRY CLUB

**Course 4**
MAP I7 grid f1

**1971**
**Ted Robinson**

8484 Clubhouse Drive
Desert Hot Springs
CA 92240

Pro shop (619) 329-8061
Clubhouse (619) 329-6481

- ✓ **driving range**
- ✓ **practice greens**
- ✓ **power carts**
- pull carts
- ✓ **golf club rental**
- ✓ **locker rooms**
- ✓ **showers**
- executive course
- ✓ **accommodations**
- ✓ **food and beverages**
- ✓ **clubhouse**

**David Sarricks,**
Professional

**Bob Kennedy**
Superintendent

*Course information:* This semi-private course has 18 holes and par is 71. The course is 6,737 yards and rated 72.8 from the championship tees, and 6,396 yards and rated 70.6 from the regular tees. The slope ratings are 131 championship and 124 regular. Women's tees are 5,390 yards and rated 69.9. The slope rating is 109.

*Play policy and fees:* Outside play is accepted. Green fees are $50 weekdays and $55 weekends, carts included. During the summer, from June 1 to September 30, fees are $30 weekdays and $35 weekends. Reservations are recommended. Proper attire required on the course.

*Location:* Take the Indian Avenue exit off Interstate 10 at Palm Springs. Drive north to Mission Lakes Avenue east and turn north on Clubhouse Drive.

*Course description:* This is a high desert course which means you can expect searing sun and wicked wind. The greens are modern speed and there are three mountain holes. Long par-3s also make this a demanding course. Five par-3s are 200 yards or longer.

## THE FIELD GOLF CLUB

**Course 5**
MAP I7 grid f2

**1989**
**Robert Trent Jones, Jr.**

19300 Palm Drive
Desert Hot Springs
CA 92240

Pro shop (619) 251-5366

- ✓ **driving range**
- ✓ **practice greens**
- ✓ **power carts**
- pull carts
- ✓ **golf club rental**
- ✓ **locker rooms**
- ✓ **showers**
- executive course
- accommodations
- ✓ **food and beverages**
- ✓ **clubhouse**

**Rod Burreull**
Professional

**Jim Timke**
Superintendent

***Course information:*** This semi-private course has 18 holes and par is 72. The course is 6,876 yards and rated 74.1 from the championship tees, and 6,614 yards and rated 72.1 from the regular tees. The slope ratings are 135 championship and 129 regular. Women's tees are 5,359 yards and rated is 70.7. The slope rating is 119.

***Play policy and fees:*** Green fees are $55 weekdays and $65 weekends during peak season. Call for special seasonal rates. Reservations are recommended.

***Location:*** From Interstate 10 in Palm Springs, take Gene Autry Trail and cross over the freeway. When you cross the freeway, the name changes to Palm Drive. Continue on Palm Drive two miles to the course.

***Course description:*** This course has a unique Scottish-links design. Natural sand dunes and mesquite brush line the fairways. There is also an abundance of wildlife including jack rabbits, roadrunners, and coyotes in the surrounding desert. The par-3 fifth hole requires a long tee shot over a desert setting with a very undulating green and a mesquite backdrop. It's a terrific layout, very unusual for Southern California. But high winds and heat make this a distinctly un-Scottish experience.

## O'DONNELL GOLF CLUB

**Course 6**
MAP I7 grid g0

301 North Belardo Road
Palm Springs, CA 92262

Pro shop (619)325-2259

- driving range
- ✓ **practice greens**
- ✓ **power carts**
- pull carts
- ✓ **golf club rental**
- ✓ **locker rooms**
- showers
- executive course
- accommodations
- ✓ **food and beverages**
- ✓ **clubhouse**

**Sally Mahoney**
Professional

**Remedios Munoz**
Superintendent

***Course information:*** This private course has nine holes. Par is 70 for 18 holes. The course is 5,270 yards and rated 64.1 from the regular tees. The slope rating is 96. Women's tees are 5,350 yards and rated 66.0. The slope rating is 110.

***Play policy and fees:*** Members and guests only. Guest fees are $33, cart included.

***Location:*** From Interstate 10, take Highway 111 east on Palm Canyon Drive, into the town of Palm Springs. Turn west on Amado Road and drive one block to the club.

***Course description:*** This is a tranquil course in downtown Palm Springs set against the base of the mountains. It is a peaceful spot for some mellow golfing. This was the first course in the Springs, and a mecca for the Hollywood set 60 years ago. Today, it's a sporty course with two par-5s and a 207-yard par-3.

# PALM SPRINGS COUNTRY CLUB

**Course 7**
MAP I7 grid g0

2500 Whitewater Club Drive
Palm Springs, CA 92262

Pro shop (619 ) 323-8625
Clubhouse (619) 323-2626

- ✓ **driving range**
- ✓ **practice greens**
- ✓ **power carts**
- pull carts
- ✓ **golf club rental**
- ✓ **locker rooms**
- ✓ **showers**
- executive course
- ✓ **accommodations**
- ✓ **food and beverages**
- ✓ **clubhouse**

**Pete Bonestrell**
Professional

**Ramon Rublo**
Superintendent

***Course information:*** This resort layout has 18 holes and par is 72. The course is 6,396 yards and rated 72 from the championship tees, and 5,885 yards and rated 67 from the regular tees. The slope ratings are 110 championship and 102 regular. Women's tees are 5,885 yards and rated 67. The slope rating is 102.

***Play policy and fees:*** Reciprocal play is accepted with members of private clubs. Outside play is also accepted. Green fees are $20 weekdays and $30 weekends. Carts are included. Reservations are recommended. Call for seasonal rates.

***Location:*** Take the Palm Drive exit off Interstate 10 and drive south to Vista Chino. Turn right and drive one-half mile to the club entrance.

***Course description:*** This is a mature desert course with lots of trees. The well-conditioned greens are also well protected. Tee boxes have been enlarged.



MAP ON PAGE 612

## CANYON COUNTRY CLUB

**Course 8**
MAP I7 grid g0

***Course information:*** This private course has 18 holes and par is 72. The course is 6,819 yards and rated 73.5 from the tournament tees, 6,468 yards and rated 71.1. from the championship tees, and 6,041 yards and rated 68.8 from the regular tees. The slope ratings are 129 tournament, 122 championship and 114 regular. Women's tees are 5,862 yards and rated 72.9. The slope rating is 117.

***Play policy and fees:*** Members and guests only. Green fees are $65. Carts are $15. Reservations are recommended one day in advance. Call for special seasonal rates.

***Location:*** Take the Indian Avenue exit off Interstate 10 in Palm Springs and drive south to Murray Canyon. Turn left and drive six blocks to the club.

***Course description:*** This mature course is beautifully maintained. It's set among million-dollar homes with out-of-bounds markers on all but one hole.

1100 Murray Canyon Drive
Palm Springs, CA 92264

Clubhouse (619) 327-1321
Starter (619) 327-5831

- ✓ **driving range**
- ✓ **practice greens**
- ✓ **power carts**
- pull carts
- golf club rental
- ✓ **locker rooms**
- ✓ **showers**
- executive course
- accommodations
- ✓ **food and beverages**
- ✓ **clubhouse**

**David Reardon**
Professional

**Som Bali**
Superintendent

## SANDS RV COUNTRY CLUB

**Course 9**
MAP I7 grid g1

***Course information:*** This public course has nine holes. Par is 64 for 18 holes. The course is 5,254 yards and rated 57.5 from the regular tees (18 holes).

***Play policy and fees:*** Green fees are $12 for non-residents.

***Location:*** Take the Palm Drive exit north off Interstate 10. Turn right on Dillon Road and drive three-fourths of a mile to Bubbling Wells Road. The entrance to the motor home park and the course is on the corner.

***Course description:*** This is an executive course adjoining a motor home park. It is short and wide open with a few trees and no bunkers. It's a hacker's paradise. One little lake on number seven offers some relief.

**1983**
16400 Bubbling Wells Road
Desert Hot Springs
CA 92240

Pro shop (619) 251-1173

- ✓ **driving range**
- ✓ **practice greens**
- power carts
- ✓ **pull carts**
- ✓ **golf club rental**
- locker rooms
- showers
- ✓ **executive course**
- accommodations
- food and beverages
- clubhouse

**Bruce Rogers**
Superintendent

# DESERT PRINCESS COUNTRY CLUB

**Course 10**
MAP I7 grid g1

**1985**
**David Rainville**

28-555 Landau Boulevard
Cathedral City, CA 92234

Pro shop (619) 322-2280
Clubhouse (619) 322-1655

- ✓ **driving range**
- ✓ **practice greens**
- ✓ **power carts**
- pull carts
- ✓ **golf club rental**
- ✓ **locker rooms**
- ✓ **showers**
- executive course
- ✓ **accommodations**
- ✓ **food and beverages**
- ✓ **clubhouse**

**Barry Eiselman**
Manager

**David McKeating**
Professional

**Mike Kocour**
Superintendent

***Course information:*** This resort facility has 27 holes and par is 72 for each 18-hole combination.

Vista/Cielo Course is detailed below.

Cielo/Lagos Course is 6,587 yards and rated 71.2 from the tournament tees, 6,111 yards and rated 68.8 from the championship tees, and 5,663 yards and rated 66.2 from the regular tees. The slope ratings are 121 tournament, 117 championship and 110 regular. Women's tees are 5,394 yards, rated 70.1, slope 119.

Vista/Lagos Course is 6,687 yards and rated 71.8 from the tournament tees, 6,224 yards and rated 69.4 from the championship tees, and 5,805 yards and rated 67.2 from the regular tees. The slope ratings arc 123 tournament, 118 championship and 113 regular. Women's tees are 5,313 yards and rated 65.8. The slope rating is 118.

***Play policy and fees:*** June through May, green fees on weekdays are $60, weekends $75. June through September, weekdays are $30, weekends are $40. October through December 24, weekdays are $50, weekends are $60. Carts included. Reservations are recommended. A dress code does apply.

***Location:*** Take the Date Palm exit off Interstate 10 in Cathedral City. Turn right and drive 100 yards to Vista Chino. Turn right and drive 1.25 miles to Landau Boulevard. Go left to the club.

***Course description:*** Another nine holes have been added to this maturing course. The course is well maintained and mostly flat. Water comes into play on 17 holes. The new nine is placed in a wash and features six holes with a Scottish-links flair and three new water holes. The well-bunkered greens and bent grass make the course a challenge.

Vista/Cielo Course

| Hole | 1 | 2 | 3 | 4 | 5 | 6 | 7 | 8 | 9 | Out | BLUE | Rating: 70.0 |
|---|---|---|---|---|---|---|---|---|---|---|---|---|
| BLUE | 514 | 423 | 148 | 367 | 110 | 363 | 528 | 350 | 413 | 3216 | | Slope: 121 |
| WHITE | 490 | 399 | 142 | 340 | 87 | 343 | 505 | 325 | 396 | 3027 | | |
| Par | 5 | 4 | 3 | 4 | 3 | 4 | 5 | 4 | 4 | 36 | WHITE | Rating: 67.6 |
| Handicap | 3 | 1 | 7 | 2 | 9 | 6 | 4 | 8 | 5 | x | | Slope: 114 |
| RED | 465 | 373 | 130 | 289 | 74 | 297 | 453 | 280 | 363 | 2724 | | |
| Par | 5 | 4 | 3 | 4 | 3 | 4 | 5 | 4 | 4 | 36 | RED | Rating: 70.3 |
| Handicap | 1 | 3 | 8 | 5 | 9 | 6 | 2 | 7 | 4 | x | | Slope: 118 |

| Hole | 10 | 11 | 12 | 13 | 14 | 15 | 16 | 17 | 18 | In | Totals | |
|---|---|---|---|---|---|---|---|---|---|---|---|---|
| BLUE | 534 | 386 | 130 | 341 | 405 | 330 | 134 | 488 | 373 | 3103 | BLUE | 6319 |
| WHITE | 510 | 345 | 120 | 321 | 377 | 297 | 116 | 452 | 347 | 2885 | WHITE | 5912 |
| Par | 5 | 4 | 3 | 4 | 4 | 4 | 3 | 5 | 4 | 36 | Par | 72 |
| Handicap | 2 | 3 | 7 | 8 | 4 | 6 | 9 | 1 | 5 | x | | |
| RED | 464 | 290 | 105 | 284 | 361 | 281 | 109 | 431 | 324 | 2649 | RED | 5217 |
| Par | 5 | 4 | 3 | 4 | 4 | 4 | 3 | 5 | 4 | 36 | Par | 72 |
| Handicap | 1 | 3 | 8 | 7 | 4 | 6 | 9 | 2 | 5 | x | | |

## CANYON SOUTH GOLF COURSE

**Course 11**
MAP I7 grid h0

**1962**
**William Park Bell**

1097 Murray Canyon Drive
Palm Springs, CA 92264

Pro shop (619) 327-2019

- ✓ **driving range**
- ✓ **practice greens**
- ✓ **power carts**
- pull carts
- ✓ **golf club rental**
- ✓ **locker rooms**
- showers
- executive course
- accommodations
- ✓ **food and beverages**
- ✓ **clubhouse**

**Brian Morrison**
Professional

**Duke January**
Superintendent

*Course information:* This public course has 18 holes and par is 71. The course is 6,536 yards and rated 70.8 from the championship tees, and 6,205 yards and rated 68.6 from the regular tees. The slope ratings are 119 championship and 109 regular. Women's tees are 6,205 yards and rated 72.0. The slope rating is 109.

*Play policy and fees:* Green fees are $50 weekdays and $60 weekends during peak season. The rate is $30 after 2 p.m. Carts are included. Reservations are recommended one week in advance.

*Location:* Take the Indian Avenue exit off Interstate 10 in Palm Springs and drive south to Murray Canyon. Turn left and drive three blocks to the club.

*Course description:* Set in the Indian Canyons, this is one of the most scenic courses in the area. It's a good test of golf with some tough par-3s.

## MESQUITE GOLF AND COUNTRY CLUB

**Course 12**
MAP I7 grid h0

**1984**
**Bert Stamps**

2700 East Mesquite Avenue
Palm Springs, CA 92264

Pro shop (619) 323-1502
Clubhouse (619) 323-9377

- ✓ **driving range**
- ✓ **practice greens**
- ✓ **power carts**
- pull carts
- ✓ **golf club rental**
- ✓ **locker rooms**
- ✓ **showers**
- executive course
- accommodations
- ✓ **food and beverages**
- ✓ **clubhouse**

**Chris Hudson**
Professional

**Armando Arizmendez**
Director of Golf

*Course information:* This public course has 18 holes and par is 72. The course is 6,328 yards and rated 69.8 from the championship tees, and 5,944 yards and rated 67.9 from the regular tees. The slope ratings are 117 championship and 111 regular. Women's tees are 5,244 yards and rated 69.2. There is no slope rating.

*Play policy and fees:* Green fees are $55 weekdays and $65 weekends during peak season. Carts are included. Call for seasonal rates. Reservations are recommended two days in advance. This course is available for tournaments. No cut-offs or tank tops are allowed on the course. Golfers must wear collared shirts.

*Location:* Take the Palm Drive exit off Interstate 10 and drive south to Ramon Road and turn west. At Farrell, turn south and drive to the course at Mesquite Avenue.

*Course description:* This is a flat course with beautiful mountain scenery. It is well bunkered with eight small lakes and many palm trees. Mac O'Grady holds the course record with a 62. The course plays over and along a streambed, so it's considerably tougher when the water flows.

# FAIRCHILD'S BEL AIR GREENS

**Course 13**
MAP I7 grid h1

**1975**
1001 South El Cielo Road
Palm Springs, CA 92264

Pro shop (619) 327-0332

- ✓ **driving range**
- ✓ **practice greens**
- power carts
- ✓ **pull carts**
- ✓ **golf club rental**
- locker rooms
- showers
- ✓ **executive course**
- accommodations
- ✓ **food and beverages**
- ✓ **clubhouse**

**Bill Roberts**
Professional

**Anne Richardson**
Superintendent

***Course information:*** This public course has nine holes. Par is 32 for nine holes. The course is 1,675 yards for nine holes.

***Play policy and fees:*** Green fees are $10 any day during the summer season. Winter fees are $20 for nine holes and $25 for 18 holes (October through May). Pull carts are $2. Reservations are recommended.

***Location:*** In Palm Springs, take Highway 111 (East Palm Canyon Drive) to Escoba Drive. Follow Escoba about one-third of a mile to El Cielo and turn left, then go one-half mile to the course.

***Course description:*** This is a well-maintained, nine-hole course with small, quick greens and narrow fairways. It is one of the most scenic courses in the desert with mature trees and a lot of water. One of its main attractions is the air-conditioned driving range. Yes, it's true. Go give the micro-mister a try.



MAP ON PAGE 612

# PALM SPRINGS MUNICIPAL GOLF COURSE

**Course 14**
MAP I7 grid h1

**1959**
1885 Golf Club Drive
Palm Springs, CA 92264

Pro shop (619) 328-1005
Clubhouse (619) 328-1956

- ✓ **driving range**
- ✓ **practice greens**
- ✓ **power carts**
- ✓ **pull carts**
- ✓ **golf club rental**
- ✓ **locker rooms**
- showers
- executive course
- accommodations
- ✓ **food and beverages**
- ✓ **clubhouse**

**Mike Carroll**
Professional

**Terry Lortz**
Superintendent

*Course information:* This public course has 18 holes and par is 72. The course is 6,551 yards and rated 69.4 from the regular tees. The slope rating is 102. Women's tees are 6,044 yards and rated 71.9. The slope rating is 105.

*Play policy and fees:* Green fees are $35 daily, January 1 through May; $18 June 1 through September; $25 October 1 through December. The course closes for 6 weeks beginning September 1. Carts are $20. Reservations are recommended.

*Location:* In Palm Springs, take Palm Drive off Interstate 10 and drive south 4.5 miles to Ramon Road and turn left. Drive one-half mile to Crosley Road and turn right and then drive one mile to the club.

*Course description:* This well-maintained course is tree-lined, providing some much needed shade in the summer. It is fairly level with no bunkers. Leave your sandie at home. The Palm Springs City Seniors tournament is held here in November.

# LAWRENCE WELK'S DESERT OASIS GOLF AND TENNIS RESORT

**Course 15**
MAP I7 grid h1

**1975**
**David Rainville**
**Billy Casper**

34567 Cathedral Canyon Drive
Cathedral City, CA 92234

Pro shop (619) 328-6571
Clubhouse (619) 321-9000

- ✓ **driving range**
- ✓ **practice greens**
- ✓ **power carts**
- pull carts
- ✓ **golf club rental**
- ✓ **locker rooms**
- showers
- executive course
- accommodations
- ✓ **food and beverages**
- ✓ **clubhouse**

**Randy Kincaid**
Manager

**J.B. Kemp**
Professional

**Pete Isidoro**
Superintendent

***Course information:*** This semi-private course has 27 holes and par is 72 for each of three 18-hole combinations.

The Lakeview/Mountainview Course is 6,172 yards and rated 71.6 from the championship tees, and 6,177 yards and rated 69.5 from the regular tees. The slope ratings are 128 championship and 117 regular. Women's tees are 5,346 yards and rated 70.2. The slope rating is 118.

The Mountainview/Resort Course is 6,482 yards and rated 70.9 from the championship tees, and 6,067 yards and rated 68.7 from the regular tees. The slope ratings are 119 championship and 111 regular. Women's tees are 5,182 yards and rated 69.2. The slope rating is 117.

The Lakeview/Resort Course is 6,366 yards and rated 70.3 from the championship tees, and 6,021 yards and rated 68.5 from the regular tees. The slope ratings are 118 championship and 110 regular. Women's tees are 5,106 and rated 68.8. The slope rating is 116.

***Play policy and fees:*** Outside play is accepted. Green fees are $35 during the summer and $75 during peak season. Call for seasonal rates. Carts are included in fees. Reservations are recommended four days in advance. This course is available for outside tournaments. Proper attire is required.

***Location:*** Take the Date Palm exit off Interstate 10 and drive south to Dinah Shore Drive and turn right. Drive one mile to Cathedral Canyon Road and turn left, then continue south one mile to the club.

***Course description:*** Formerly known as Cathedral Canyon Country Club, this is a beautiful, tree-lined course which plays fairly tight and requires a variety of shot-making skills to score well. Refreshingly, water comes into play on almost every hole. The facility also boasts an 18-hole championship putting course.

# WESTIN MISSION HILLS RESORT

**Course 16**
MAP I7 grid h1

**1986**
**Pete Dye**

**1991**
**Gary Player**

71-501 Dinah Shore Drive
Rancho Mirage, CA 92270

Pro shops:
Dye (619) 328-3198
Player (619) 770-9496

- ✓ **driving range**
- ✓ **practice greens**
- ✓ **power carts**
- pull carts
- ✓ **golf club rental**
- ✓ **locker rooms**
- ✓ **showers**
- executive course
- ✓ **accommodations**
- ✓ **food and beverages**
- ✓ **clubhouse**

**John Herndon**
Director of Golf

**Roger Compton**
Director of Maintenance

***Course information:*** This resort facility has 36 holes. Par is 70 on the Pete Dye Course and par is 72 on the Gary Player Course.

The Pete Dye Course is 6,706 yards and rated 73.5 from the tournament tees, 6,196 yards and rated 70.3 from the championship tees, and 5,629 yards and rated 67.5 from the regular tees. The slope ratings are 137 tournament, 126 championship and 117 regular. Women's tees are 4,841 yards and rated 67.4. The slope rating is 107.

The Gary Player Course is 7,062 yards from the tournament tees, 6,643 yards from the championship tees, and 6,044 yards from the regular tees. Women's tees are 4,907 yards. The course has not been rated.

***Play policy and fees:*** Guests of the Westin Mission Hills Resort have priority on tees times. Public play is welcome. Green fees are seasonal. Call for rates. Reservations are recommended. These courses are available for outside tournaments for groups of 12 or more. Advance deposit required.

***Location:*** Take the Bob Hope Drive/Ramon Road exit off Interstate 10 and drive south on Bob Hope Drive to Dinah Shore Drive. Then turn right and drive one-half mile to the resort entrance.

***Course description:*** The Pete Dye Course is a links-style layout with rolling fairways and large, undulating greens. There are also numerous pot bunkers and railroad ties. The Gary Player Course, which opened in October 1991, is a championship course featuring nine lakes and four waterfalls on 12 of its holes. It is as challenging as the Pete Dye Course, but thankfully forgiving because the greens are not as severe or difficult and the wide fairways encourage the ball to roll greenward. Typical of a Player-designed course, each hole presents a different type of challenge.

# OUTDOOR RESORT AND COUNTRY CLUB

**Course 17**
MAP I7 grid h1

**1986**
**Kerry Johnston**

69-411 Ramon Road
Cathedral City, CA 92234

Pro shop (619) 324-4005

- driving range
- ✓ **practice greens**
- power carts
- ✓ **pull carts**
- ✓ **golf club rental**
- locker rooms
- showers
- executive course
- accommodations
- ✓ **food and beverages**
- ✓ **clubhouse**

**Kerry Johnston**
Professional

***Course information:*** This private course has 18 holes and par is 54. The course is 1,801 from the championship tees, and 1,771 yards from the regular tees. A nine-hole executive course is also available.

***Play policy and fees:*** Members and guests only. The guest fee is $7.50 for nine holes and $15 for 18 holes.

***Location:*** Take Interstate 10 to Date Palm Drive and turn left to Ramon Road. Go left and drive one-half mile to the course.

***Course description:*** This is a very short par-3 course with no hole over 145 yards. The greens are small and well protected. Johnston annually hosts a Skins Game with other local pros including Mac O'Grady and Mark Pfeil, and their best score is 3-under. Not just your garden variety par-3 course.

# DE ANZA PALM SPRINGS COUNTRY CLUB

**Course 18**
MAP I7 grid h1

**1971**
**Ted Robinson**

36-200 Date Palm Drive
Cathedral City, CA 92234

Pro shop (619) 324-7575
Clubhouse (619) 328-1315

- driving range
- ✓ **practice greens**
- ✓ **power carts**
- ✓ **pull carts**
- ✓ **golf club rental**
- ✓ **locker rooms**
- ✓ **showers**
- ✓ **executive course**
- accommodations
- ✓ **food and beverages**
- ✓ **clubhouse**

**Grant Kinman**
Manager

**Bobbie Reyes**
Superintendent

***Course information:*** This semi-private layout has 18 holes and par is 58. The course is a short 3,083 yards and rated 50.8 from the regular tees. The slope rating is 82. Women's tees are 2,517 yards and rated 50.8.

***Play policy and fees:*** Reciprocal play is accepted with members of other private clubs. Outside play is also accepted. Green fees are seasonal and range from $9 to $20. Carts are from $9 to $18. Reservations are recommended. No tank tops allowed on the course.

***Location:*** Take the Date Palm exit off Interstate 10 in Cathedral City and drive south for four miles to the club entrance on the left.

***Course description:*** This course is set in a retirement area, so it is quiet, private and walkable. Seven lakes dot the course and many trees line the fairways, including eucalyptus, olive and pine trees, some as old as 300 years. The 175-yard eighth hole is a standout. It takes an accurate tee shot over a beautiful lake. The green is guarded by trees on two sides. The Phil Harris Classic has been held here, and a tournament benefitting special and handicapped children is held annually. The course is closed for three weeks in late October.

# MISSION HILLS COUNTRY CLUB

**Course 19**
MAP I7grid h1

**1978**
**Arnold Palmer**
**Ed Seay**

**1988**
**Pete Dye**

**1970**
**Desmond Muirhead**

34-600 Mission Hills Drive
Rancho Mirage, CA 92270

Pro shop (619) 328-2153
Clubhouse (619) 321-8484

- ✓ **driving range**
- ✓ **practice greens**
- ✓ **power carts**
- pull carts
- ✓ **golf club rental**
- ✓ **locker rooms**
- ✓ **showers**
- executive course
- accommodations
- ✓ **food and beverages**
- ✓ **clubhouse**

**Chipper Cecil**
Professional

**Dave Johnson**
Superintendent

***Course information:*** This private facility has three 18-hole courses. Par is 72 on all of them.

The Arnold Palmer Course is 6,753 yards and rated 73.0 from the championship tees, and 6,218 yards and rated 70.0 from the regular tees. The slope ratings are 129 championship and 121 regular. Women's tees are 6,218 yards and rated 75.8 from the championship tees, and 5,482 yards and rated 71.6 from the forward tees. The slope ratings are 128 championship and 117 forward.

The Dinah Shore Course is 6,919 yards and rated 74.4 from the tournament tees, 6,582 yards and rated 72.2 from the championship tees, and 6,060 yards and rated 69.4 from the regular tees. The slope ratings are 141 tournament, 130 championship and 122 regular. Women's tees are 6,060 yards and rated 71.5 from the championship tees, and 5,079 yards and rated 68.5 from the forward tees. The slope ratings are 121 championship and 113 forward.

The Old Course is 7,246 yards and rated 75.5 from the tournament tees, and 6,880 yards and rated 73.4 from the championship tees, and 6,369 yards and rated 70.5 from the regular tees. The slope ratings are 137 tournament, 129 championship and 121 regular.

***Play policy and fees:*** Reciprocal play is accepted with members of other private clubs from June through September, otherwise members and guests only. Guest fees range from $35 to $150 depending on season. Fees for reciprocators range from $40 to $45. Carts are included. Reservations are recommended one day in advance.

***Location:*** Take the Date Palm Drive/Cathedral City exit off Interstate 10 and drive south for four miles to Gerald Ford Road. Turn left and drive 1.5 miles to the entrance.

***Course description:*** This is golf at its finest. The Arnold Palmer Course was designed by Arnie himself along with Ed Seay and opened in 1978. It's a links-style course that is relatively flat and heavily bunkered with bent grass greens. It's immaculate. The Dinah Shore Course was designed by Pete Dye and opened in 1988. It's a stadium-type course with big rolling hills and deep bunkers. The greens are small but undulating with bent grass. The rough and surrounding area consists of natural desert. The Old Course opened in 1970 and was designed by Desmond Muirhead. It is the home of the LPGA Nabisco Dinah Shore Tournament. It has rolling terrain, mature trees, undulating bermuda greens and is quite challenging. Amy Alcott owns a piece of this course and the pond at the 18th. Twice she's jumped it to celebrate victories.

## TAMARISK COUNTRY CLUB

**Course 20**
MAP I7 grid h1

**1952**
**William Park Bell**

70-240 Frank Sinatra Drive
Rancho Mirage, CA 92270

Pro shop (619) 328-2141

- ✓ **driving range**
- ✓ **practice greens**
- ✓ **power carts**
- pull carts
- golf club rental
- ✓ **locker rooms**
- ✓ **showers**
- executive course
- accommodations
- ✓ **food and beverages**
- ✓ **clubhouse**

**Dave Albrecht**
Professional

**Richard Sall**
Superintendent

***Course information:*** This private course has 18 holes and par is 72. The course is 6,818 yards and rated 72.8 from the championship tees, and 6,435 yards and rated 70.2 from the regular tees. The slope ratings are 125 championship and 115 regular. Women's tees are 6,044 yards and rated 73.8. The slope rating is 118.

***Play policy and fees:*** Members and guests only. Green fees are $30 with a member and $50 if sponsored. Carts are $20. This course closes for a portion of the summer. Call ahead.

***Location:*** Take the Bob Hope Drive/Ramon Road exit off Interstate 10 in Rancho Mirage, and drive south on Bob Hope Drive, and then turn right on Frank Sinatra Drive and travel one mile to the club on the right.

***Course description:*** This is one of the Bob Hope Classic tournament courses, and it's the second oldest course in the desert. It's a very challenging, mature course with lots of trees. The club's first golf pro was Ben Hogan.

## THE SPRINGS COUNTRY CLUB

**Course 21**
MAP I7 grid h1

**1975**
**Desmond Muirhead**

One Duke Drive
Rancho Mirage, CA 92270

Pro shop (619) 328-0590
Clubhouse (619) 324-8292

- ✓ **driving range**
- ✓ **practice greens**
- ✓ **power carts**
- pull carts
- ✓ **golf club rental**
- ✓ **locker rooms**
- ✓ **showers**
- executive course
- accommodations
- ✓ **food and beverages**
- ✓ **clubhouse**

**Doug Hart**
Professional

**Ross O'Fee**
Superintendent

***Course information:*** This private course has 18 holes and par is 72. The course is 6,637 yards and rated 72.3 from the championship tees, and 6,279 yards and rated 70.1 from the regular tees. The slope rating is 128. Women's tees are 5,607 yards and rated 71.6. The slope rating is 118.

***Play policy and fees:*** Members and guests only. The guest fees are $25 June through October and $50 the rest of the year. Carts are $20. Reservations are recommended.

***Location:*** Take the Bob Hope Drive/Ramon Road exit off Interstate 10 in Rancho Mirage and drive south on Bob Hope Drive four miles to the club entrance on the right.

***Course description:*** Water comes into play on 11 of the holes. The greens are well bunkered and undulating. The tree-lined fairways are well maintained.

## THE CLUB AT MORNINGSIDE

**Course 22**
MAP I7 grid h1

*Course information:* This private course has 18 holes and par is 72. The course is 6,776 yards and rated 73.6 from the tournament tees, 6,237 yards and rated 70.3 from the championship tees, and 5,530 yards and rated 66.5 from the regular tees. Women's tees are 6,237 yards and rated 75.6 from the championship tees, and 5,530 yards and rated 71.7 from the forward tees. The slope ratings are 132 championship and 123 forward.

*Play policy and fees:* Members and guests only. Green fees for guests are $40 with a member and $150 without a member. Carts are $12 per person. Pro shop closes at 11:30 a.m. during summer season.

*Location:* Take the Bob Hope Drive/Ramon Road exit off Interstate 10, and drive south on Bob Hope Drive. Turn right on Frank Sinatra Drive and travel one-half mile to Morningside Drive. Turn left and travel one-quarter mile to the club entrance on the right.

*Course description:* Jack Nicklaus designed this links-style course. It's immaculate and scenic. The golfer has the option to gamble or play it safe from every tee.

**Jack Nicklaus**

Morningside Drive
Rancho Mirage, CA 92270

Pro shop (619) 321-1555
Clubhouse (619 )324-1234
Starter (619) 321-1556

✓ **driving range**
✓ **practice greens**
✓ **power carts**
pull carts
✓ **golf club rental**
✓ **locker rooms**
✓ **showers**
executive course
accommodations
✓ **food and beverages**
✓ **clubhouse**

**Vernon Fraser**
Professional

**Cal Hardin**
Superintendent

## IVEY RANCH COUNTRY CLUB

**Course 23**
MAP I7 grid h2

*Course information:* This semi-private course has nine holes. Par is 70 for 18 holes. The course is 5,408 yards and rated 64.0 from the regular tees (18 holes). The slope rating is 100. Women's tees are 4,796 yards and rated 64.0. The slope rating is 114.

*Play policy and fees:* Outside play is accepted. Green fees vary with the seasons. Discounts available. Call for rates. Reservations are recommended one week in advance.

*Location:* Take the Monterey Avenue exit off Interstate 10 and drive east to Varner Road and then turn north and drive along the frontage road 1.5 miles to the club.

*Course description:* This well-maintained course has bent grass greens, some trees and fairly narrow fairways. It's a regulation nine-hole course, very sporty, with doglegs and out-of-bounds on several holes.

74-580 Varner Road
Thousand Palms, CA 92276

Pro shop (619) 343-2013

✓ **driving range**
✓ **practice greens**
✓ **power carts**
pull carts
✓ **golf club rental**
locker rooms
showers
executive course
accommodations
✓ **food and beverages**
✓ **clubhouse**

**Dennis Foster**
Professional

# RANCHO MIRAGE COUNTRY CLUB

**Course 24**
MAP I7 grid h2

**1984**
**Harold Heers Jr.**

38-500 Bob Hope Drive
Rancho Mirage, CA 92270

Pro shop (619) 324-4711
Clubhouse (619) 328-1444

- ✓ **driving range**
- ✓ **practice greens**
- ✓ **power carts**
- pull carts
- ✓ **golf club rental**
- ✓ **locker rooms**
- ✓ **showers**
- executive course
- accommodations
- ✓ **food and beverages**
- ✓ **clubhouse**

**Frank Goeckel**
Manager

**Brett Hartley**
Professional

**Abran Cabral**
Superintendent

***Course information:*** This private course has 18 holes and par is 70. See below for yardage and additional information.

***Play policy and fees:*** Reciprocal play is accepted with members of other private clubs. Green fees for guests range from $25 to $80. Carts are included. Reservations are recommended. Golfers are expected to wear appropriate golf attire. Closed during October.

***Location:*** Take the Bob Hope Drive/Ramon Road exit off Interstate 10 in Rancho Mirage, head south on Bob Hope Drive and drive four miles to the club entrance on the left.

***Course description:*** This gently rolling, sporty course has narrow fairways and small greens. Water comes into play on nine holes. And, because it's located centrally in the valley, there are views of the Santa Rosa and San Jacinto Mountains. It's a good test of golf for both the advanced and the beginning golfer.

| Hole | 1 | 2 | 3 | 4 | 5 | 6 | 7 | 8 | 9 | Out | | |
|---|---|---|---|---|---|---|---|---|---|---|---|---|
| BLUE | 315 | 101 | 360 | 471 | 447 | 142 | 469 | 416 | 313 | 3034 | BLUE | Rating: 69.5 |
| WHITE | 300 | 91 | 346 | 471 | 412 | 133 | 451 | 388 | 306 | 2898 | | Slope: 119 |
| Par | 4 | 3 | 4 | 5 | 4 | 3 | 4 | 4 | 4 | 35 | WHITE | Rating: 67.7 |
| Handicap | 11 | 17 | 9 | 7 | 3 | 15 | 1 | 5 | 13 | x | | Slope: 111 |
| RED | 292 | 77 | 338 | 403 | 383 | 125 | 391 | 306 | 280 | 2595 | | |
| Par | 4 | 3 | 4 | 5 | 4 | 3 | 4 | 4 | 4 | 35 | RED | Rating: 70.6 |
| Handicap | 13 | 17 | 9 | 7 | 3 | 15 | 1 | 5 | 11 | x | | Slope: 119 |

| Hole | 10 | 11 | 12 | 13 | 14 | 15 | 16 | 17 | 18 | In | Totals | |
|---|---|---|---|---|---|---|---|---|---|---|---|---|
| BLUE | 385 | 401 | 418 | 176 | 336 | 123 | 364 | 485 | 389 | 3077 | BLUE | 6111 |
| WHITE | 367 | 381 | 406 | 164 | 310 | 100 | 345 | 478 | 374 | 2925 | WHITE | 5823 |
| Par | 4 | 4 | 4 | 3 | 4 | 3 | 4 | 5 | 4 | 35 | Par | 70 |
| Handicap | 10 | 6 | 2 | 14 | 12 | 18 | 16 | 8 | 4 | x | | |
| RED | 355 | 356 | 389 | 145 | 299 | 79 | 324 | 432 | 335 | 2714 | RED | 5309 |
| Par | 4 | 4 | 4 | 3 | 4 | 3 | 4 | 5 | 4 | 35 | Par | 70 |
| Handicap | 10 | 4 | 2 | 16 | 12 | 18 | 14 | 8 | 6 | x | | |

# EMERALD DESERT COUNTRY CLUB

**Course 25**
MAP I7 grid h2

**1990**
**J. Laier, Jr.**

76-000 Frank Sinatra Drive
Palm Desert, CA 92260

Pro shop (619) 345-4770

driving range
✓ **practice greens**
✓ **power carts**
✓ **pull carts**
✓ **golf club rental**
locker rooms
showers
✓ **executive course**
accommodations
✓ **food and beverages**
clubhouse

**Clem Hernandez**
Superintendent

***Course information:*** This semi-private course has nine holes. Par is 62 for 18 holes. See below for yardage and additional information.

***Play policy and fees:*** Green fees are $15 for nine holes and $20 for 18 holes weekdays, and $20 for nine holes and $25 for 18 holes weekends. Carts are $15. Reservations are recommended.

***Location:*** From Interstate 10, take Monterey Avenue exit in Palm Desert to Frank Sinatra Drive, go east on Frank Sinatra approximately four miles to the course.

***Course description:*** This new course features six lakes, bent grass greens protected by numerous sand traps and narrow fairways. The par-4, 263-yard sixth hole demands good shot placement. The steeply elevated green is protected front and left by water.

| Hole | 1 | 2 | 3 | 4 | 5 | 6 | 7 | 8 | 9 | Out | BLUE | Rating: -- |
|---|---|---|---|---|---|---|---|---|---|---|---|---|
| BLUE | 153 | 187 | 272 | 135 | 268 | 263 | 161 | 257 | 127 | 1821 | | Slope: -- |
| WHITE | 132 | 169 | 256 | 105 | 262 | 259 | 143 | 248 | 106 | 1678 | | |
| Par | 3 | 3 | 4 | 3 | 4 | 4 | 3 | 4 | 3 | 31 | WHITE | Rating: -- |
| Handicap | 13 | 7 | 5 | 15 | 3 | 1 | 11 | 9 | 17 | x | | Slope: -- |
| RED | 95 | 165 | 171 | 100 | 253 | 254 | 141 | 243 | 97 | 1518 | | |
| Par | 3 | 4 | 4 | 3 | 4 | 4 | 3 | 4 | 3 | 32 | RED | Rating: -- |
| Handicap | 9 | 11 | 5 | 17 | 3 | 1 | 15 | 7 | 13 | x | | Slope: -- |

| Hole | 10 | 11 | 12 | 13 | 14 | 15 | 16 | 17 | 18 | In | Totals | |
|---|---|---|---|---|---|---|---|---|---|---|---|---|
| BLUE | 153 | 187 | 272 | 135 | 268 | 263 | 161 | 257 | 127 | 1821 | BLUE | 3644 |
| WHITE | 132 | 169 | 256 | 105 | 262 | 259 | 143 | 248 | 106 | 1678 | WHITE | 3358 |
| Par | 3 | 3 | 4 | 3 | 4 | 4 | 3 | 4 | 3 | 31 | Par | 62 |
| Handicap | 14 | 8 | 6 | 16 | 4 | 2 | 12 | 10 | 18 | x | | |
| RED | 95 | 165 | 171 | 100 | 253 | 254 | 141 | 243 | 97 | 1518 | RED | 3037 |
| Par | 3 | 4 | 4 | 3 | 4 | 4 | 3 | 4 | 3 | 32 | Par | 64 |
| Handicap | 10 | 12 | 6 | 18 | 4 | 2 | 16 | 8 | 14 | x | | |

# RANCHO LAS PALMAS COUNTRY CLUB

**Course 26**
MAP I7 grid h2

*Course information:* This semi-private facility has 27 holes and par is 71, 69 or 70 depending on the 18-hole combination played.

The North/South Course is 5,779 yards and rated 67.2 from the championship tees, and 5,569 yards and rated 65.7 from the regular tees. The slope ratings are 115 championship and 103 regular. Women's tees are 5,270 yards and rated 69.7 from the forward tees. The slope rating is 113.

The South/West Course is 5,427 yards and rated 65.6 from the championship tees, and 5,160 yards and rated 63.9 from the regular tees. The slope ratings are 106 championship and 97 regular. Women's tees are 4,782 yards and rated 66.8 from the forward tees. The slope rating is 110.

The West/North Course is 5,360 yards and rated 65.3 from the championship tees, and 5,129 yards and rated 63.7 from the regular tees. The slope ratings are 105 championship and 100 forward. Women's tees are 4,824 yards and rated 66.9 from the forward tees. The slope rating is 105.

**Ted Robinson**

42-000 Bob Hope Drive
Rancho Mirage, CA 92270

Pro shop (619) 568-0955
Clubhouse (619) 568-2727

- ✓ **driving range**
- ✓ **practice greens**
- ✓ **power carts**
- pull carts
- ✓ **golf club rental**
- ✓ **locker rooms**
- ✓ **showers**
- executive course
- ✓ **accommodations**
- ✓ **food and beverages**
- ✓ **clubhouse**

**Tom Gees**
Manager/Professional

**Ray Metz**
Professional

**Elazar Valdez**
Superintendent

*Play policy and fees:* Reciprocal play is accepted with members of other private clubs. A Marriott hotel is affiliated with this course, and hotel guests are welcome. Guest fees range from $70 to $85, including cart. Reservations are recommended three days in advance, one day in advance for reciprocators.

*Location:* Take the Bob Hope/Ramon Road exit off Interstate 10 and drive five miles south to the resort entrance on the left.

*Course description:* The North nine is the longest and has the most hills. The South nine is the narrowest and threads through condominiums. The West nine is the shortest and most scenic. It also has the most water. Numerous palm trees are spread throughout this well-maintained course.

## DESERT ISLAND GOLF AND COUNTRY CLUB

**Course 27**
MAP I7 grid h2

**1972**
**Desmond Muirhead**

71-777 Frank Sinatra Drive
Rancho Mirage, CA 92270

Pro shop (619) 328-0841
Clubhouse (619) 328-2111

- ✓ **driving range**
- ✓ **practice greens**
- ✓ **power carts**
- pull carts
- ✓ **golf club rental**
- ✓ **locker rooms**
- ✓ **showers**
- executive course
- accommodations
- ✓ **food and beverages**
- ✓ **clubhouse**

**Dennis Callahan**
Professional

**Keith Rogers**
Superintendent

***Course information:*** This private course has 18 holes and par is 72. The course is 6,684 yards and rated 71.6 from the championship tees, and 6,310 yards and rated 69.6 from the regular tees. The slope ratings are 121 championship and 114 regular. Women's tees are 5,604 yards and rated 66.4. The slope rating is 116.

***Play policy and fees:*** Members and guests only. Guest fees in-season are $55 with a member and $80 without a member. Guest fees out-of-season (June-October) are $45 with a member and $65 without a member. Carts are included. Closed in October. Reservations are recommended.

***Location:*** Take the Bob Hope Drive/Ramon Road exit off Interstate 10 and drive south on Bob Hope Drive to Frank Sinatra Drive. Turn right and drive one block to the entrance on the left.

***Course description:*** This is a well-maintained course set around an enormous lake with an island in the middle; condominiums are on the isalnd. It is challenging with narrow fairways and numerous bunkers surrounding the greens. There are also some panoramic views of the mountains. The design is interesting in that the course surrounds the enormous lake—and the condominiums are on the island, not on the course itself.

## PALM DESERT GREENS COUNTRY CLUB

**Course 28**
MAP I7 grid h2

73-750 Country Club Drive
Palm Desert, CA 92260

Pro shop (619) 346-2941
Clubhouse (619) 346-8005

- driving range
- ✓ **practice greens**
- ✓ **power carts**
- ✓ **pull carts**
- ✓ **golf club rental**
- ✓ **locker rooms**
- ✓ **showers**
- ✓ **executive course**
- accommodations
- ✓ **food and beverages**
- ✓ **clubhouse**

**Joe Casey**
Professional

***Course information:*** This private course has 18 holes and par is 63. The course is 4,088 yards and rated 59.6 from the regular tees. The slope rating is 90. Women's tees are 3,682 yards and rated 59.4 from the forward tees. The slope rating is 88.

***Play policy and fees:*** Members and guests only. Guests must be accompanied by members at time of play. Guest fees are seasonal and range from $15 to $30. Closed in October. Carts are $15. Reservations are recommended.

***Location:*** Take the Monterey Drive exit off Interstate 10 and drive south to Country Club Drive. Turn left to the club entrance.

***Course description:*** This 18-hole executive course is level with several lakes and mature trees. It's a sporty layout and in great shape.

## SUNCREST COUNTRY CLUB

**Course 29**
MAP I7 grid h2

*Course information:* This semi-private course has nine holes. Par is 66 for 18 holes. The course is 4,683 yards and rated 60.3 from the regular tees. The slope rating is 99. Women's tees are 3,930 yards and rated 63.2. The slope rating is 99.

*Play policy and fees:* Green fees are $15 for nine holes, $26 for 18 holes. Carts are $18. Reservations are recommended.

*Location:* Take the Monterey Drive exit off Interstate 10 and drive south to Country Club Drive. Turn left and travel one-half mile to the club on the left.

*Course description:* Set in Suncrest Park, this nicely-maintained course is flat with trees and two lakes. The elevation here is slightly higher than the surrounding courses and provides a nice view. The course record is 57. It is closed during September and October.

73-450 Country Club Drive
Palm Desert, CA 92260

Pro shop (619) 340-2467
Clubhouse (619) 346-5866

✓ **driving range**
✓ **practice greens**
✓ **power carts**
✓ **pull carts**
✓ **golf club rental**
✓ **locker rooms**
✓ **showers**
✓ **executive course**
accommodations
✓ **food and beverages**
✓ **clubhouse**

**Gary Stevenson**
Professional

**Robert Sanchez**
Superintendent

## SANTA ROSA COUNTRY CLUB

**Course 30**
MAP I7 grid h2

*Course information:* This private course has 18 holes and par is 67. The course is 5,443 yards and rated 65.6 from the regular tees. The slope rating is 103. Women's tees are 5,161 yards and rated 68.7 from the forward tees. The slope rating is 107.

*Play policy and fees:* Reciprocal play is accepted with members of other private clubs. Members and guests only. Guest fees are $50 in summer and $30 the rest of the year. Carts are $20 and mandatory for guests. Reservations are recommended two days in advance.

*Location:* Take the Monterey exit off Interstate 10 and drive south to Country Club Drive. Turn left and travel to Portola Avenue and turn left.

*Course description:* This desert course has tree-lined fairways and two large lakes. It's challenging and offers a view of the Santa Rosa Mountains. New tee boxes were the latest in a program to upgrade the course. A rarity in the desert, this course is 80 acres of golf course and clubhouse—no homes are built on or around it.

**1978**
**Leonard Gerkin**

PO Box 87
Palm Desert, CA 92260

38-105 Portola Avenue
Palm Desert, CA 92260

Pro shop (619) 568-5717

✓ **driving range**
✓ **practice greens**
✓ **power carts**
pull carts
✓ **golf club rental**
locker rooms
showers
executive course
accommodations
✓ **food and beverages**
✓ **clubhouse**

**Dennis Pogue**
Professional

**Scott Szydloski**
Superintendent

## DESERT FALLS COUNTRY CLUB

**Course 31**
MAP 17 grid h2

**1984**
**Ron Fream**

1111 Desert Falls Parkway
Palm Desert, CA 92260

Pro Shop (619) 341-4020
Clubhouse (619) 340-5646

- ✓ **driving range**
- ✓ **practice greens**
- ✓ **power carts**
- pull carts
- ✓ **golf club rental**
- ✓ **locker rooms**
- ✓ **showers**
- executive course
- accommodations
- ✓ **food and beverages**
- ✓ **clubhouse**

**Ray Miller**
Professional

**Phil Villalobos**
Superintendent

***Course information:*** This semi-private course has 18 holes and par is 72. The course is 7,017 yards and rated 75.0 from the championship tees, and 6,565 yards and rated 72.2 from the regular tees. The slope ratings are 145 championship and 133 regular. Women's tees are 5,288 yards and rated 71.0. The slope rating is 119.

***Play policy and fees:*** Outside play is accepted. Green fees are seasonal, ranging from $40 during the off-season (summer) to $120 during the high season (winter). Call for rates. Carts are included. Reservations are recommended. This course closes in October.

***Location:*** Take the Monterey Avenue exit off Interstate 10 and drive south to Country Club Drive. From there, turn left and travel two miles to the club.

***Course description:*** This course will really test your ability. It is long, and one of the few desert courses with a Scottish layout. The greens sport bent grass and are big enough to play football on. This course has served as a Stage I PGA Tour qualifying site. In November of 1992, it hosted Don Drysdale's PGA Senior Tour charity event. It is one of the best tracks in the Coachella valley.

## AVONDALE GOLF CLUB

**Course 32**
MAP 17 grid h2

**1969**
**Jimmy Hines**

75-800 Avondale Drive
Palm Desert, CA 92260

Pro shop (619) 345-3712
Clubhouse (619) 345-2727

- ✓ **driving range**
- ✓ **practice greens**
- ✓ **power carts**
- pull carts
- ✓ **golf club rental**
- ✓ **locker rooms**
- ✓ **showers**
- executive course
- accommodations
- ✓ **food and beverages**
- ✓ **clubhouse**

**Fred Scherzer**
Professional

**Carlos Lopez**
Superintendent

***Course information:*** This private course has 18 holes and par is 72. The course is 6,771 yards and rated 72.9 from the championship tees, and 6,386 yards and rated 70.7 from the regular tees. The slope ratings are 127 championship and 122 regular. Women's tees are 5,766 yards and rated 73.9. The slope rating is 125.

***Play policy and fees:*** Members and guests only. Green fees are $30 June 1 through mid-September, and $75 November 1 through May 31. The course is closed from mid-September to early November. Carts are included.

***Location:*** Take the Washington Street exit off Interstate 10 and drive south. Turn right on Country Club Drive and travel 2.5 miles to El Dorado. From there turn right to the course.

***Course description:*** This is not a typical desert course. There are water hazards and lots of trees dispersed on rolling terrain. This was formerly a semi-private course that went private in 1991.

# PALM VALLEY COUNTRY CLUB

**Course 33**
MAP I7 grid h2

**Ted Robinson**

76-200 Country Club Drive
Palm Desert, CA 92260

Pro shop (619) 345-2742

- ✓ **driving range**
- ✓ **practice greens**
- ✓ **power carts**
- pull carts
- ✓ **golf club rental**
- ✓ **locker rooms**
- ✓ **showers**
- ✓ **executive course**
- accommodations
- ✓ **food and beverages**
- ✓ **clubhouse**

**Malia Folquet**
Professional

***Course information:*** This private course has two 18-hole courses. Par is 72 on the South Course and 63 on the North Course.

The South Course is 6,471 yards and rated 71.1 from the championship tees, and 6,105 yards and rated 69.2 from the regular tees. The slope ratings are 125 championship and 119 regular. Women's tees are 5,429 yards and rated 70.7 from the forward tees. The slope rating is 125.

The North Course is 4,232 yards and rated 58.0 from the championship tees, and 3,909 yards and rated 56.2 from the regular tees. The slope ratings are 96 championship and 93 regular. Women's tees are 3,467 yards and rated 61.0. The slope rating is 99.

***Play policy and fees:*** Reciprocal play is accepted with members of other private clubs. During the summer, fees are $45 for the South Course and $35 for the North Course. During the peak winter season, fees are $85 for the South Course and $50 for the North course. Carts are included. Reservations are recommended one day in advance.

***Location:*** Take the Washington Street exit off Interstate 10 and drive south to Country Club Drive. Turn right and travel one mile to the club on the right.

***Course description:*** The South Course has quite a bit of undulation for a desert course and offers beautiful panoramic views of the area. The North Course is difficult for a short course with water hazards that come into play on 15 holes. It's a tough challenge for mid- to low-handicap players.

# BIGHORN GOLF CLUB

**Course 34**
MAP I7 grid i1

***Course information:*** This new private course has 18 holes. The gold tees are 6,848 yards, and are rated 74.4 with a slope of 147. See card below for additional yardage and rating information.

***Play policy and fees:*** Reciprocal play is not accepted. Members and guests only. Guests must be sponsored by a member. Guest fees are $100, including cart. Tee times are not necessary.

***Location:*** From Interstate 10 in Palm Desert exit on Monterey Avenue. Drive south until Monterey Avenue becomes Highway 74. The club is 3.5 miles south on Highway 74.

***Course description:*** This dramatic desert course is part of a private residential community. Carved into the Santa Rosa Mountains, with elevation changes ranging up to 400 feet, the course provides spectacular views of the mountains and the Coachella Valley. A clubhouse opened in the fall of 1992. Bighorn became the host of the PGA Skins Game, played annually on Thanksgiving weekend.

**1991**
**Arthur Hills**

255 Palowet Dr.
Palm Desert, CA 92260

Pro shop (619) 773-2468
Clubhouse (619) 341-4653

- ✓ **driving range**
- ✓ **practice greens**
- ✓ **power carts**
- pull carts
- ✓ **golf club rental**
- ✓ **locker rooms**
- ✓ **showers**
- executive course
- accommodations
- ✓ **food and beverages**
- ✓ **clubhouse**

**Tom Sullivan**
Manager

**Donnie Cude**
Professional

**Ruben Ramirez**
Superintendent

| Hole | 1 | 2 | 3 | 4 | 5 | 6 | 7 | 8 | 9 | Out | BLUE | Rating: 71.6 |
|---|---|---|---|---|---|---|---|---|---|---|---|---|
| BLUE | 490 | 346 | 494 | 173 | 270 | 480 | 343 | 161 | 405 | 3162 | | Slope: 136 |
| WHITE | 462 | 325 | 481 | 160 | 252 | 453 | 301 | 145 | 356 | 2935 | | |
| Par | 5 | 4 | 5 | 3 | 4 | 4 | 4 | 3 | 4 | 36 | WHITE | Rating: 67.9 |
| Handicap | 5 | 9 | 1 | 15 | 13 | 3 | 7 | 17 | 11 | x | | Slope: 123 |
| YELLOW | 418 | 302 | 436 | 87 | 228 | 335 | 259 | 110 | 256 | 2431 | | |
| Par | 5 | 4 | 5 | 3 | 4 | 4 | 4 | 3 | 4 | 36 | YEL-LOW | Rating: 70.0 |
| Handicap | 5 | 9 | 1 | 15 | 13 | 3 | 7 | 17 | 11 | x | | Slope: 123 |

| Hole | 10 | 11 | 12 | 13 | 14 | 15 | 16 | 17 | 18 | In | Totals | |
|---|---|---|---|---|---|---|---|---|---|---|---|---|
| BLUE | 373 | 162 | 508 | 405 | 399 | 492 | 381 | 145 | 391 | 3256 | BLUE | 6418 |
| WHITE | 310 | 139 | 459 | 350 | 341 | 471 | 342 | 143 | 352 | 2907 | WHITE | 5842 |
| Par | 4 | 3 | 5 | 4 | 4 | 5 | 4 | 3 | 4 | 36 | Par | 72 |
| Handicap | 2 | 16 | 4 | 10 | 12 | 6 | 14 | 18 | 8 | x | | |
| YELLOW | 300 | 96 | 425 | 315 | 312 | 433 | 306 | 101 | 321 | 2609 | YELLOW | 5040 |
| Par | 4 | 3 | 5 | 4 | 4 | 5 | 4 | 3 | 4 | 36 | Par | 72 |
| Handicap | 2 | 16 | 4 | 10 | 12 | 6 | 14 | 18 | 8 | x | | |

## THUNDERBIRD COUNTRY CLUB

**Course 35**
MAP I7 grid i2

**1952**
**Johnny Dawson**

Box 5005
Rancho Mirage, CA 92270

70-612 Highway 111
Rancho Mirage, CA 92270

Pro shop (619) 328-2161

- ✓ **driving range**
- ✓ **practice greens**
- ✓ **power carts**
- pull carts
- golf club rental
- ✓ **locker rooms**
- ✓ **showers**
- executive course
- ✓ **accommodations**
- ✓ **food and beverages**
- ✓ **clubhouse**

**Don Callahan**
Professional

**Bruce Duenow**
Superintendent

*Course information:* This private course has 18 holes and par is 71. The course is 6,460 yards and rated 71.5 from the championship tees, and 6,185 yards and rated 69.6 from the regular tees. The slope ratings are 126 championship and 119 regular. Women's tees are 5,854 yards and rated 73.9. The slope rating is 124.

*Play policy and fees:* Members and guests only. Guests must be accompanied by members at time of play. Green fees for guests are $35 from June to October and $100 the rest of the year. Carts are $22.

*Location:* Take the Bob Hope Drive/Ramon exit off Interstate 10, and drive south on Bob Hope Drive. Turn right on Country Club Drive and travel 1.5 miles to the club entrance on the left.

*Course description:* This is one of the very first and very exclusive courses in the area. It is the home of Gerry Ford.

## SUNRISE COUNTRY CLUB

**Course 36**
MAP I7 grid i2

**1971**
**Ted Robinson**

71-601 Country Club Drive
Rancho Mirage, CA 92270

Pro shop (619) 328-1139
Clubhouse (619) 328-6549

- ✓ **driving range**
- ✓ **practice greens**
- ✓ **power carts**
- pull carts
- ✓ **golf club rental**
- ✓ **locker rooms**
- ✓ **showers**
- ✓ **executive course**
- accommodations
- ✓ **food and beverages**
- ✓ **clubhouse**

**Jim Dayton**
Professional

**John Hernandez**
Superintendent

*Course information:* This private course has 18 holes and par is 64. The course is 3,841 yards and rated 57.3 from the regular tees. The slope rating is 90. Women's tees are 3,841 yards and rated 60.4 from the forward tees. The slope rating is 95.0.

*Play policy and fees:* Reciprocal play is accepted with members of other private clubs, otherwise members and guests only. Green fees are $30 for guests and $50 for reciprocators. Carts are $10 per player anytime. Reservations are recommended. Summer season hours are June 1 through October 1, 6 a.m. to 1 p.m.

*Location:* Take the Bob Hope Drive/Ramon Road exit off Interstate 10 and drive about six miles south on Bob Hope Drive. Then turn right on Country Club Drive and travel several yards to the entrance on the left.

*Course description:* This is a mature, 18-hole executive course with water and lots of sand. It boasts 10 par-4s and eight par-3s. If you drive the ball 180-190 yards and want to use every club in your bag, this is the course for you.

# CHAPARRAL COUNTRY CLUB

**Course 37**
MAP I7 grid i2

***Course information:*** This private course has 18 holes. See card below for yardage and rating information.

***Play policy and fees:*** Reciprocal play is accepted with members of other private clubs. The reciprocal fee is $50, $35 for guests. Carts are included. Reservations are recommended. Closed in October.

***Location:*** Take the Monterey Drive exit off Interstate 10 and drive south to Country Club Drive. Turn left and drive to Portola Road then turn right and drive 1.5 miles to the club.

***Course description:*** Known as the "Little Monster," this tough executive course is well bunkered with water on 13 holes. It's a shot-maker's course.

**Ted Robinson**

100 Chaparral Dr.
Palm Desert, CA 92260

Pro shop (619) 340-1501
Clubhouse (619) 340-1893

- ✓ **driving range**
- ✓ **practice greens**
- ✓ **power carts**
- pull carts
- ✓ **golf club rental**
- locker rooms
- showers
- ✓ **executive course**
- ✓ **accommodations**
- ✓ **food and beverages**
- ✓ **clubhouse**

**David M. James**
Professional

**John Rodriquez**
Superintendent

| Hole | 1 | 2 | 3 | 4 | 5 | 6 | 7 | 8 | 9 | Out | BLUE | Rating: 59.2 |
|---|---|---|---|---|---|---|---|---|---|---|---|---|
| BLUE | 309 | 152 | 188 | 195 | 320 | 215 | 315 | 149 | 201 | 2044 | | Slope: 108 |
| WHITE | 290 | 147 | 178 | 182 | 313 | 211 | 305 | 142 | 165 | 1933 | | |
| Par | 4 | 3 | 3 | 3 | 4 | 3 | 4 | 3 | 3 | 30 | WHITE | Rating: 57.9 |
| Handicap | 15 | 13 | 11 | 9 | 1 | 3 | 7 | 17 | 5 | x | | Slope: 100 |
| RED | 274 | 139 | 159 | 159 | 313 | 215 | 229 | 85 | 104 | 1677 | | |
| Par | 4 | 3 | 3 | 3 | 4 | 4 | 4 | 3 | 3 | 31 | RED | Rating: 57.8 |
| Handicap | 3 | 13 | 7 | 9 | 1 | 11 | 5 | 17 | 15 | x | | Slope: 98 |

| Hole | 10 | 11 | 12 | 13 | 14 | 15 | 16 | 17 | 18 | In | Totals | |
|---|---|---|---|---|---|---|---|---|---|---|---|---|
| BLUE | 203 | 275 | 212 | 278 | 204 | 275 | 129 | 115 | 181 | 1872 | BLUE | 3916 |
| WHITE | 198 | 248 | 183 | 272 | 197 | 260 | 111 | 100 | 162 | 1731 | WHITE | 3664 |
| Par | 3 | 4 | 3 | 4 | 3 | 4 | 3 | 3 | 3 | 30 | Par | 60 |
| Handicap | 4 | 14 | 6 | 10 | 2 | 8 | 16 | 18 | 12 | x | | |
| RED | 115 | 159 | 120 | 272 | 150 | 260 | 95 | 100 | 155 | 1426 | RED | 3103 |
| Par | 3 | 3 | 3 | 4 | 3 | 4 | 3 | 3 | 3 | 29 | Par | 60 |
| Handicap | 14 | 6 | 12 | 4 | 8 | 2 | 16 | 18 | 10 | x | | |

# THE LAKES COUNTRY CLUB

**Course 38**
MAP I7 grid i2

***Course information:*** This private facility has 27 holes and par is 72 for each of the 18-hole combinations.

The North/East Course is 6,414 yards and rated 70.6 from the championship tees, and 6,027 yards and rated 68.3 from the regular tees. The slope ratings are 122 championship and 109 regular. Women's tees are 5,396 yards and rated 70.8 from the forward tees. The slope rating is 123.

The South/North Course is 6,683 yards and rated 72.1 from the championship tees, and 6,278 yards and rated 69.4 from the regular tees. The slope ratings are 127 championship and 111 regular. Women's tees are 5,707 yards and rated 72.6 from the forward tees. The slope rating is 122.

The East/South Course is 6,607 yards and rated 71.6 from the championship tees, and 6,215 yards and rated 69.2 from the regular tees. The slope ratings are 125 championship and 110 regular. Women's tees are 5,697 yards and rated 72.6 from the forward tees. The slope rating is 123.

**1982**
**Ted Robinson**

161 Old Ranch Road
Palm Desert, CA 92260

Pro shop (619) 568-5674
Clubhouse (619) 568-4321

- ✓ **driving range**
- ✓ **practice greens**
- ✓ **power carts**
- pull carts
- ✓ **golf club rental**
- ✓ **locker rooms**
- ✓ **showers**
- executive course
- accommodations
- ✓ **food and beverages**
- ✓ **clubhouse**

**Mike Clifford**
Professional

**Ty Broadhead**
Superintendent

***Play policy and fees:*** Members and guests only. Guest fees are $56 with a member and $96 without, including cart. Unaccompanied guests are allowed Monday through Thursday. Reservations are recommended.

***Location:*** Take the Monterey Drive exit off Interstate 10 and drive south to Country Club Drive. Turn left and go three miles to the course.

***Course description:*** These well-bunkered courses have lots of water and spectacular views of the Santa Rosa Mountains. Two of the nines are set among the condos.

# MONTEREY COUNTRY CLUB

**Course 39**
MAP I7 grid i2

***Course information:*** This private facility has 27 holes and par is 72 or 71 for the 18-hole combinations.

The South/West Course is 6,185 yards and rated 69.2 from the championship tees, and 5,898 yards and rated 67.7 from the regular tees. The slope ratings are 116 championship and 108 regular. Women's tees are 5,417 yards and rated 71.6 from the forward tees. The slope rating is 123.

The East/West Course is 6,108 yards and rated 68.9 from the championship tees, and 5,790 yards and rated 67.2 from the regular tees. The slope ratings are 115 championship and 107 regular. Women's tees are 5,259 yards and rated 70.8 from the forward tees. The slope rating is 123.

The East/South Course is 6,005 yards and rated 68.3 from the championship tees, and 5,720 yards and rated 66.9 from the regular tees. The slope ratings are 114 championship and 106 regular. Women's tees are 5,226 yards and rated 70.4 from the forward tees. The slope rating is 124.

**1979**
**Ted Robinson**

41-500 Monterey Avenue
Palm Desert, CA 92260

Pro shop (619) 340-3885
Clubhouse (619) 568-9311

- ✓ **driving range**
- ✓ **practice greens**
- ✓ **power carts**
- pull carts
- ✓ **golf club rental**
- ✓ **locker rooms**
- ✓ **showers**
- executive course
- accommodations
- ✓ **food and beverages**
- ✓ **clubhouse**

**Terry Naughton**
Professional

**Shannon Cook**
Superintendent

***Play policy and fees:*** Reciprocal play is accepted with members of other private clubs. Green fees are $70 for guests unaccompanied by a member and $65 with a member. Green fees for reciprocators are $80. Carts are included. Reservations are required. Reciprocators call one day in advance.

***Location:*** Take the Monterey Avenue exit off Interstate 10, and drive south four miles to the club.

***Course description:*** This tight, target golf course has strategically placed bunkers and water hazards. The narrow fairways are lined with condos on both sides.

# PORTOLA COUNTRY CLUB

**Course 40**
MAP I7 grid i2

***Course information:*** This short private course has 18 holes and par is 54. The course is 2,167 yards. Women's tees are 1,913 yards.

***Play policy and fees:*** Members and guests only. Green fees are $10 weekdays and $15 weekends.

***Location:*** From Interstate 10 take Country Club Drive to Portola Avenue. Go left on Portola and follow it about one mile to the club.

***Course description:*** Situated on 27 acres, this par-3 course is somewhat rolling with many lakes and water hazards. It is situated in a mobile home park.

42-500 Portola Avenue
Palm Desert, CA 92260

Pro shop (619) 568-1592

- driving range
- ✓ **practice greens**
- power carts
- ✓ **pull carts**
- ✓ **golf club rental**
- locker rooms
- showers
- ✓ **executive course**
- accommodations
- food and beverages
- ✓ **clubhouse**

**Rusty Uhly**
Professional

**Juan Morieno**
Superintendent

SOUTHERN I7

# INDIAN WELLS GOLF RESORT

**Course 41**
MAP I7 grid i2

***Course information:*** This resort facility has two 18-hole courses with a par of 72 on both.

The East Course is detailed below.

The West Course is 6,478 yards and rated 70.3 from the championship tees, and 6,115 yards and rated 68.7 from the regular tees. The slope ratings are 116 championship and 109 regular. Women's tees are 6,115 and rated 74.0 from the championship tees, and 5,387 yards and rated 70.0 from the forward tees. The slope ratings are 120 championship and 110 forward.

***Play policy and fees:*** Green fees are $90 weekdays and $100 weekends from January through April, carts included. Prices vary during other months. Twilight rates are $30. Reservations are recommended. This course is available for outside tournaments. Green fees are subject to change in 1993-94.

***Location:*** From Interstate 10 take the Washington Street exit about one-half mile to Highway 111, turn right and follow Highway 111 to Indian Wells Lane and you'll see the course.

***Course description:*** Both courses were designed by Ted Robinson and feature beautiful greens, rolling fairways and a natural desert setting. Adjacent to both the Hyatt Grand Champions and Stouffer Hotels, the resort was awarded a silver medal listing in *Golf Magazine's* 1992 list of the nation's best resorts. There are many parallel fairways, but plenty of mounding to separate them fairly.

**1986**
**Ted Robinson**

44-500 Indian Wells
Indian Wells, CA 92210

Pro shop (619) 346-4653

- ✓ **driving range**
- ✓ **practice greens**
- ✓ **power carts**
- pull carts
- ✓ **golf club rental**
- ✓ **locker rooms**
- showers
- executive course
- ✓ **accommodations**
- ✓ **food and beverages**
- ✓ **clubhouse**

**Ron Cleveland**
Manager

**Jon Darrah**
Professional

**Glenn Miller**
Superintendent

East Course

| Hole | 1 | 2 | 3 | 4 | 5 | 6 | 7 | 8 | 9 | Out | BLUE | Rating: 71.6 |
|---|---|---|---|---|---|---|---|---|---|---|---|---|
| BLUE | 375 | 410 | 396 | 171 | 388 | 496 | 196 | 536 | 423 | 3391 | | Slope: 118 |
| WHITE | 353 | 370 | 376 | 151 | 361 | 482 | 165 | 497 | 391 | 3146 | | |
| Par | 4 | 4 | 4 | 3 | 4 | 5 | 3 | 5 | 4 | 36 | WHITE | Rating: 69.4 |
| Handicap | 13 | 3 | 9 | 17 | 11 | 5 | 15 | 1 | 7 | x | | Slope: 110 |
| RED | 319 | 330 | 339 | 135 | 321 | 430 | 139 | 437 | 342 | 2792 | | |
| Par | 4 | 4 | 4 | 3 | 4 | 5 | 3 | 5 | 4 | 36 | RED | Rating: 70.7 |
| Handicap | 13 | 9 | 7 | 15 | 11 | 3 | 17 | 1 | 5 | x | | Slope: 113 |

| Hole | 10 | 11 | 12 | 13 | 14 | 15 | 16 | 17 | 18 | In | Totals | |
|---|---|---|---|---|---|---|---|---|---|---|---|---|
| BLUE | 418 | 207 | 400 | 370 | 511 | 343 | 362 | 149 | 511 | 3271 | BLUE | 6662 |
| WHITE | 394 | 182 | 378 | 352 | 494 | 325 | 347 | 141 | 468 | 3081 | WHITE | 6227 |
| Par | 4 | 3 | 4 | 4 | 5 | 4 | 4 | 3 | 5 | 36 | Par | 72 |
| Handicap | 2 | 14 | 4 | 10 | 6 | 16 | 12 | 18 | 8 | x | | |
| RED | 353 | 151 | 332 | 290 | 436 | 297 | 322 | 112 | 436 | 2729 | RED | 5521 |
| Par | 4 | 3 | 4 | 4 | 5 | 4 | 4 | 3 | 5 | 36 | Par | 72 |
| Handicap | 2 | 14 | 10 | 8 | 4 | 16 | 12 | 18 | 6 | x | | |

# DESERT HORIZONS COUNTRY CLUB

**Course 42**
MAP I7 grid i2

**1979**
**Ted Robinson**

44-900 Desert Horizons Drive
Indian Wells, CA 92210

Clubhouse (619) 340-4646
Pro shop ext. 221 or 222
Starter (619) 340-4652

- ✓ **driving range**
- ✓ **practice greens**
- ✓ **power carts**
- pull carts
- ✓ **golf club rental**
- ✓ **locker rooms**
- ✓ **showers**
- executive course
- accommodations
- ✓ **food and beverages**
- ✓ **clubhouse**

**Paul Lemcke,**
Director of Golf

**Rick Ruppert**
Professional

**Mark Smith**
Superintendent

***Course information:*** This private course has 18 holes and par is 72. The course is 6,614 yards and rated 71.7 from the championship tees, and 6,117 yards and rated 68.9 from the regular tees. The slope ratings are 125 championship and 116 regular. Women's tees are 5,498 yards and rated 71.6. The slope rating is 121.

***Play policy and fees:*** Members and guests only. Green fees are $50 for guests accompanied by a member and $100 for guests unaccompanied by a member. This course is closed in October.

***Location:*** Travel one mile west of Indian Wells on Highway 111. At Desert Horizons Drive turn north and drive to the club.

***Course description:*** This championship course has more sand than Iwo Jima and lots of water. In other words, it is very challenging. Beware of number nine. It's a par-3, 210-yard brute that demands an 180-yard carry over water to a three-tiered, hour-glass green. The green is bunkered on the left, with water on the right. Ted Robinson lives in this development. The facility also features an 18-hole putting course complete with water and bunkers. Par is 44; the record is 40.



MAP ON PAGE 612

# SHADOW MOUNTAIN GOLF CLUB

**Course 43**
MAP I7 grid i2

**1959**
**Gene Sarazan**

PO Box 667
Palm Desert, CA 92260

73800 Ironwood
Palm Desert, CA 92260

Pro shop (619) 346-8242

- ✓ **driving range**
- ✓ **practice greens**
- ✓ **power carts**
- ✓ **pull carts**
- ✓ **golf club rental**
- ✓ **locker rooms**
- showers
- executive course
- accommodations
- ✓ **food and beverages**
- ✓ **clubhouse**

**Sherry Wilder**
General Manager/
Professional

**Gaylord Moller**
Superintendent

***Course information:*** This private course has 18 holes and par is 70. The course is 5,418 yards and rated 65.5 from the regular tees. The slope rating is 108. Women's tees are 5,418 yards and rated 70.7. The slope rating is 115.

***Play policy and fees:*** Reciprocal play is accepted with members of other private clubs. Green fees are $50 during the winter season and $25 during the summer season. Carts are included. Reservations are mandatory. Appropriate attire required. The course is closed during October.

***Location:*** Take the Monterey Avenue exit off Interstate 10 and drive south to Highway 111 in Palm Desert and turn left. At San Luis Rey Avenue turn right and drive to the end of the road. Turn left into the club.

***Course description:*** This course is well bunkered with some water and lots of palm trees. It's a challenging course for the average player. The men's course record is held by Fred Hawkins with a 55. Sherry Wilder holds the women's record with a 65. The 402-yard 17th hole which winds slightly uphill through rock gardens is the signature hole on this well-hidden gem. It's lined with 700 50-foot palm trees, but so protected it's the last place the wind blows or the rain falls.

## EL DORADO COUNTRY CLUB

**Course 44**
MAP I7 grid i2

**1957**
**Larry Hughes**

Fairway Drive
Indian Wells, CA 92210

Pro shop (619) 346-8081

- ✓ **driving range**
- ✓ **practice greens**
- ✓ **power carts**
- pull carts
- golf club rental
- ✓ **locker rooms**
- ✓ **showers**
- executive course
- accommodations
- ✓ **food and beverages**
- ✓ **clubhouse**

**Don Fairfield**
Professional

**Mike Mongiello**
Superintendent

***Course information:*** This private course has 18 holes and par is 72. The course is 6,702 yards and rated 72.6 from the championship tees, and 6,317 yards and rated 70.0 from the regular tees. The slope ratings are 123 championship and 116 regular. Women's tees are 5,942 yards and rated 76.2. The slope rating is 130.

***Play policy and fees:*** Members and guests only. The guest fees are $50 with a member and $150 without. Carts are $20. This course is formally open from November 1 to May 31.

***Location:*** Take the Monterey Avenue exit off Interstate 10 and drive south to Highway 111 in Palm Desert and turn left. At El Dorado Drive turn right and drive one-half mile to Fairway Drive. Turn right and drive one-half block to the club on the left.

***Course description:*** This is a mature course that is fairly level and with out-of-bounds areas on every hole. A fairway returns to the clubhouse every four to five holes for those in need of refreshments. This is probably the oldest course in the Palm Springs area south of Tamarisk. This course was in the Bob Hope PGA Tour rotation for almost 30 years.

## MARRAKESH COUNTRY CLUB

**Course 45**
MAP I7 grid i2

**1971**
**Johnny Dawson**

47 000 Marrakesh Drive
Palm Desert, CA 92260

Pro shop (619) 568-2660

- ✓ **driving range**
- ✓ **practice greens**
- ✓ **power carts**
- pull carts
- ✓ **golf club rental**
- locker rooms
- showers
- ✓ **executive course**
- accommodations
- ✓ **food and beverages**
- clubhouse

**Willie Gatherum**
Professional

**John Figgen**
Superintendent

***Course information:*** This short, semi-private course has 18 holes and par is 60. The course is 3,614 yards and rated 57.6 from the regular tees. The slope rating is 94. Women's yardage is 3,220 and rated 61.0. The slope rating is 104.

***Play policy and fees:*** Reciprocal play is accepted with members of other private clubs. The reciprocal fee is $45; a guest with a member is $25. Reservations are recommended. The course is closed in October.

***Location:*** Take the Monterey Avenue exit off Interstate 10 and drive south to Country Club Drive. Turn left at Portola Avenue and turn south to the club.

***Course description:*** This is a flat course with four lakes and many trees. You'll need every club in the bag on this fine little executive course. The longest of the six par-4s is 304 yards, and the par-3s range between 120 and 198 yards. But it's well-bunkered and has its share of trees, so it's a test.

# IRONWOOD COUNTRY CLUB

**Course 46**
MAP I7 grid i2

**Ted Robinson**
**North Course**
**1977**

**Desmond Muirhead**
**Ted Robinson**
**South Course**
**1973**

49-200 Mariposa Drive
Palm Desert, CA 92260

Pro shop (619) 568-4884
Clubhouse (619) 346-0551

- ✓ **driving range**
- ✓ **practice greens**
- ✓ **power carts**
- pull carts
- ✓ **golf club rental**
- ✓ **locker rooms**
- ✓ **showers**
- executive course
- ✓ **accommodations**
- ✓ **food and beverages**
- ✓ **clubhouse**

**John Hendricks**
Professional

**Ron Reed**
Superintendent

***Course information:*** This private facility has two 18-hole courses.

The South Course is 7,304 yards, and rated 76.2 with a slope of 136 from the tournament tees, See card below for additional yardage and rating information.

The North Course is par 70, 6,093 yards and rated 68.9 from the regular tees. The slope rating is 117. Women's tees are 5,980 yards and rated 69.6 from the forward tees. The slope rating is 113.

***Play policy and fees:*** Members and guests only. Guest fees are $75 with a member and $95 without during the winter season, and $55 with a member and $75 without during the summer season. Carts are included. Reservations are required. The course closes at 1 p.m. during the summer season. It is open all year. Proper attire required.

***Location:*** Take the Monterey Drive exit off Interstate 10 and drive south to Highway 111. Turn left and drive to Portola Avenue, then turn right and drive about two miles to the club.

***Course description:*** Situated above the desert floor, the South Course is very scenic. It's long and winds through the desert. Arnold Palmer was the original designer of the course, but after the great flood of the early 1970s it was reconstructed by Muirhead and Robinson. There are several tough holes from the back tees. The North Course is also very scenic with mountain and desert valley views. There are some water hazards and the fairways are lined with condos and homes, but it isn't as tough as the South Course, which has been rated among the nation's 100 toughest by the USGA.

South Course

| Hole | 1 | 2 | 3 | 4 | 5 | 6 | 7 | 8 | 9 | Out | BLUE | Rating: 73.5 |
|---|---|---|---|---|---|---|---|---|---|---|---|---|
| BLUE | 484 | 402 | 345 | 176 | 499 | 168 | 433 | 417 | 429 | 3353 | | Slope: 129 |
| WHITE | 461 | 390 | 334 | 159 | 487 | 156 | 416 | 404 | 405 | 3212 | | |
| Par | 5 | 4 | 4 | 3 | 5 | 3 | 4 | 4 | 4 | 36 | WHITE | Rating: 71.3 |
| Handicap | 17 | 3 | 9 | 11 | 13 | 15 | 1 | 7 | 5 | x | | Slope: 122 |
| RED | 412 | 325 | 310 | 134 | 471 | 123 | 363 | 363 | 351 | 2852 | | |
| Par | 5 | 4 | 4 | 3 | 5 | 3 | 4 | 4 | 4 | 36 | RED | Rating: 73.9 |
| Handicap | 11 | 9 | 13 | 17 | 1 | 15 | 3 | 7 | 5 | x | | Slope: 128 |

| Hole | 10 | 11 | 12 | 13 | 14 | 15 | 16 | 17 | 18 | In | Totals | |
|---|---|---|---|---|---|---|---|---|---|---|---|---|
| BLUE | 518 | 390 | 393 | 382 | 174 | 549 | 415 | 214 | 453 | 3488 | BLUE | 6841 |
| WHITE | 494 | 380 | 374 | 345 | 162 | 525 | 397 | 185 | 440 | 3302 | WHITE | 6514 |
| Par | 5 | 4 | 4 | 4 | 3 | 5 | 4 | 3 | 4 | 36 | Par | 72 |
| Handicap | 18 | 6 | 12 | 16 | 14 | 8 | 4 | 10 | 2 | x | | |
| RED | 474 | 353 | 362 | 329 | 109 | 490 | 373 | 168 | 366 | 3024 | RED | 5876 |
| Par | 5 | 4 | 4 | 4 | 3 | 5 | 4 | 3 | 4 | 36 | Par | 72 |
| Handicap | 6 | 14 | 10 | 12 | 18 | 2 | 4 | 16 | 8 | x | | |

# THE VINTAGE CLUB

**Course 47**
MAP I7 grid i2

**1980**
**Tom Fazio**

75-001 Vintage Drive West
Indian Wells, CA 92210

Pro shop (619) 568-0865
Clubhouse (619) 340-0500

- ✓ **driving range**
- ✓ **practice greens**
- ✓ **power carts**
- pull carts
- ✓ **golf club rental**
- ✓ **locker rooms**
- ✓ **showers**
- executive course
- accommodations
- ✓ **food and beverages**
- ✓ **clubhouse**

**Buddy Cook**
Professional

**Jeff Markow**
Superintendent

***Course information:*** This private facility has two 18-hole courses and par is 72 on both.

The Desert Course is 6,279 yards and rated 70.6 from the regular tees. The slope rating is 126. Women's tees are 5,718 yards and rated 68.4. The slope rating is 119.

The Mountain Course is 6,871 yards and rated 73.6 from the tournament tees, 6,456 yards and rated 70.8 from the championship tees, and 6,084 yards and rated 68.6 from the regular tees. The slope ratings are 129 tournament, 123 championship and 109 regular. Women's tees are 5,694 yards and rated 68.7. The slope rating is 118.

***Play policy and fees:*** Members and guests only. Guest fees are $50 with a member and $150 sponsored. Carts are $12.50 per rider.

***Location:*** Take the Monterey Avenue exit off Interstate 10 and drive south to Highway 111 in Palm Desert and turn left. At Cook Street, turn right and drive one-half mile to the club at the end of the road.

***Course description:*** The Desert Course is short but deceptive, requiring precise shot-making to the very small greens. It has a Scottish touch with deep pot bunkers, sand and shrubbery. The Mountain Course is a wide-open, easy-driving course with a British accent. It features deep pot bunkers, sprawling fairways, natural rock formations, citrus groves, indigenous shrubs, colorful flowers and waterfalls. The 379-yard, par-4 16th hole is flanked by three lakes and two greenside waterfalls, while the scenic 158-yard, par-3 17th is fronted by a lake and affords a panoramic view. This exclusive club was used for the Senior PGA Tour's Vintage Invitational between 1981-92. The seniors rated it the best groomed course on the senior tour and it is rated among the top 20 courses in the state. It's very private, very spectacular.

# INDIAN WELLS COUNTRY CLUB

**Course 48**
MAP I7 grid i2

**1955**
**Eddie Susella**

46-000 Club Drive
Indian Wells, CA 92210

Pro shop (619) 345-9774
Clubhouse (619) 345-2561

- ✓ **driving range**
- ✓ **practice greens**
- ✓ **power carts**
- pull carts
- ✓ **golf club rental**
- ✓ **locker rooms**
- ✓ **showers**
- executive course
- accommodations
- ✓ **food and beverages**
- ✓ **clubhouse**

**Neil Finch**
Professional/Director of Golf

**Doug Anderson**
Superintendent

***Course information:*** This private course has 27 holes and par is 72 on each of the four 18-hole combinations.

The Bob Hope Classic Course is 6,512 yards and rated 71.6 from the championship tees, and 6,153 yards and rated 69.4 from the regular tees. The slope ratings are 126 championship and 117 regular. Women's tees are 5,665 yards and rated 73.1. The slope rating is 127.

The Cove Course is 6,511 yards and rated 71.8 from the championship tees, and 6,212 yards and rated 69.9 from the regular tees. The slope ratings are 127 championship and 118 regular. Women's tees are 5,763 yards and rated 73.6. The slope rating is 127.

The North/Cove Course is 6,598 yards and rated 72.4 from the championship tees, and 6,208 yards and rated 70.0 from the regular tees. The slope ratings are 128 championship and 118 regular. Women's tees are 5,755 yards and rated 72.4. The slope rating is 128.

The West/North Course is 6,479 yards and rated 71.6 from the championship tees, and 6,094 yards and rated 69.3 from the regular tees. The slope ratings are 126 championship and 117 regular. Women's tees are 5,600 yards and rated 71.6. The slope rating is 126.

***Play policy and fees:*** Members and guests only. The green fee is $150 without a member and $75 with a member in season, half that after April; this includes cart and range fee. Country club attire required, Bermuda shorts permitted.

***Location:*** From Interstate 10 take the Monterey Avenue exit, go south to Highway 111, then east to Club Drive.

***Course description:*** The five layouts are distinctly different. The Classic 18 is the oldest and has tree-lined fairways. The West/Cove nine has a desert layout. The Cove nine is set at the base of the mountains. The Classic Course is contrived from a selection of holes from all three nines. Choose your poison. Bert Yancey holds the course record with a 61. The Bob Hope Classic is held here each year. The courses are not long, but demand accuracy.

# LA QUINTA HOTEL GOLF CLUB—DUNES COURSE

**Course 49**
MAP I7 grid i2

**1982**
**Pete Dye**

PO Box 29
La Quinta, CA 92253

50-200 Avenue Vista Bonita
La Quinta, CA 92253

Pro shop (619) 564-7610
Clubhouse (619) 564-3672

✓ **driving range**
✓ **practice greens**
✓ **power carts**
pull carts
✓ **golf club rental**
✓ **locker rooms**
✓ **showers**
executive course
✓ **accommodations**
✓ **food and beverages**
✓ **clubhouse**

**Greg Abadie**
Professional

**Mike Tellier**
Superintendent

***Course information:*** This semi-private course has 18 holes and par is 72. The course is 6,817 yards and rated 73.8 from the tournament tees, 6,251 yards and rated 70.6 from the championship tees, and 5,697 yards and rated 67.0 from the regular tees. The slope ratings are 139 tournament, 129 championship and 113 regular. Women's tees are 5,024 yards and rated 68.0. The slope rating is 114.

***Play policy and fees:*** Outside play is accepted. Members and guests have priority. There are reduced fees for hotel guests. Green fees range from $40 to $110 depending on time of year. Fees include cart and range fees. Reservations are recommended. Shorts are permitted on the course, although cut-offs are not allowed. Dress code enforced. Collared shirts are preferred.

***Location:*** Take the Washington Street exit off Interstate 10 and drive south past Highway 111 to Avenue 50 and turn right. Continue past Eisenhower Drive to the gate and follow the road to the club.

***Course description:*** This a traditional Pete Dye course. It is well bunkered with railroad ties and lots of water. PGA of America rated the 416-yard, par-4 17th one of country's toughest holes. The PGA Tour Qualifying School was held here in 1990. The California State Open was played here in 1990. *Golf Magazine* rated LaQuinta and its three courses a silver medalist for 1991-92.

# LA QUINTA HOTEL GOLF CLUB—MOUNTAIN COURSE

**Course 50**
MAP I7 grid i2

**1980**
**Pete Dye**

PO Box 29
La Quinta, CA 92253

50-200 Avenue Vista Bonita
La Quinta, CA 92253

Pro shop (619) 564-7610
Clubhouse (619) 564-3672

✓ **driving range**
✓ **practice greens**
✓ **power carts**
pull carts
✓ **golf club rental**
✓ **locker rooms**
✓ **showers**
executive course
✓ **accommodations**
✓ **food and beverages**
✓ **clubhouse**

**Greg Abadie**
Director of Golf

**Mike Tellier**
Superintendent

***Course information:*** This private course has 18 holes and par is 72. The course is 6,811 yards and rated 74.3 from the tournament tees, 6,402 yards and rated 71.4 from the championship tees, and 5,364 yards and rated 66.7 from the regular tees. The slope ratings are 146 tournament, 136 championship and 117 regular. Women's tees are 5,217 yards and rated 69.7. The slope rating is 115.

***Play policy and fees:*** Members and guests only. Guests must be accompanied by members. Guest fees vary according to time of year, but include cart and range fees. Reservations are recommended.

***Location:*** Take the Washington Street exit off Interstate 10 and drive south past Highway 111 to Avenue 50 and turn right. Drive past Eisenhower Drive to the gate and follow the road to the club.

***Course description:*** This is a challenging desert course noted for pot bunkers, rock formations, sand and water. The large, undulating greens are set naturally against the mountains. Accuracy is the key. Watch for the par-3 16th hole. The green is surrounded by mountain rocks. This has been the home of the World Cup and the PGA National Club Pro Championships and the California State Open. Golf pros and superintendents rate it the top course in the desert and it rates among the top 20 in the state. The Senior Skins Game was held here in 1989 featuring Arnold Palmer, Billy Casper, Chi Chi Rodriquez and Gary Player. Fred Couples holds the course record with a 63.

# LA QUINTA HOTEL GOLF CLUB—CITRUS COURSE

**Course 51**
MAP I7 grid i3

**1987**
**Pete Dye**

PO Box 942
La Quinta, CA 92253

50-503 Jefferson
La Quinta, CA 92253
Pro shop(619) 564-7620

✓ **driving range**
✓ **practice greens**
✓ **power carts**
pull carts
✓ **golf club rental**
locker rooms
showers
executive course
✓ **accommodations**
✓ **food and beverages**
✓ **clubhouse**

**Greg Abadie**
Director of Golf

**Rick Neal**
Professional

**Glen Martin**
Superintendent

***Course information:*** This semi-private course has 18 holes. The course is 7,106 yards, and rated 75.0 with a slope of 135 from the tournament tees. See card below for additional yardage and rating information.

***Play policy and fees:*** Outside play is accepted after 11 a.m. during the season and subject to availability, otherwise members and guests only. Guests must be accompanied by a member before 11 a.m. Hotel guest play is subject to availability after 11 a.m., although they have priority over outside play. Guest fees range from $40 to $110 depending on time of year. Cart and range fee are included. Reservations are recommended.

***Location:*** Take the Jefferson Street exit off Interstate 10 and drive south for three miles to the course.

***Course description:*** This is a level course carved out of a citrus orchard and it is anything but a lemon. In fact, this is one of the more scenic courses in the area. A typically challenging Pete Dye design, the course features rolling contours, bent grass greens, scenic views of the Santa Rosa Mountains. This layout has plenty of character with a mix of sand and water. It's a forgiving course if you don't try to outplay it.

| Hole | 1 | 2 | 3 | 4 | 5 | 6 | 7 | 8 | 9 | Out | | |
|---|---|---|---|---|---|---|---|---|---|---|---|---|
| BLUE | 379 | 495 | 189 | 440 | 359 | 392 | 139 | 340 | 363 | 3286 | BLUE | Rating: 70.9 |
| WHITE | 340 | 456 | 155 | 355 | 351 | 376 | 105 | 517 | 340 | 2995 | | Slope: 123 |
| Par | 4 | 5 | 3 | 4 | 4 | 4 | 3 | 5 | 4 | 36 | WHITE | Rating: 68.0 |
| Handicap | 9 | 11 | 7 | 1 | 15 | 3 | 13 | 5 | 17 | x | | Slope: 110 |
| RED | 287 | 418 | 104 | 316 | 326 | 319 | 99 | 450 | 288 | 2606 | | |
| Par | 4 | 5 | 3 | 4 | 4 | 4 | 3 | 5 | 4 | 36 | RED | Rating: 68.3 |
| Handicap | 9 | 11 | 7 | 1 | 15 | 3 | 13 | 5 | 17 | x | | Slope: 112 |

| Hole | 10 | 11 | 12 | 13 | 14 | 15 | 16 | 17 | 18 | In | Totals | |
|---|---|---|---|---|---|---|---|---|---|---|---|---|
| BLUE | 372 | 379 | 351 | 145 | 517 | 358 | 136 | 513 | 422 | 3193 | BLUE | 6479 |
| WHITE | 350 | 354 | 335 | 114 | 506 | 308 | 107 | 481 | 365 | 2920 | WHITE | 5915 |
| Par | 4 | 4 | 4 | 3 | 5 | 4 | 3 | 5 | 4 | 36 | Par | 72 |
| Handicap | 16 | 4 | 14 | 12 | 10 | 8 | 18 | 6 | 2 | x | | |
| RED | 314 | 280 | 290 | 94 | 435 | 277 | 74 | 414 | 322 | 2500 | RED | 5106 |
| Par | 4 | 4 | 4 | 3 | 5 | 4 | 3 | 5 | 4 | 36 | Par | 72 |
| Handicap | 16 | 4 | 14 | 12 | 10 | 8 | 18 | 6 | 2 | x | | |

# PALM DESERT RESORT COUNTRY CLUB

**Course 52**
MAP I7 grid i3

**1980**
**Joe Molleneaux**

77-333 Country Club Drive
Palm Desert, CA 92260

Pro shop (619) 345-2791
Clubhouse (619) 345-2781

- ✓ **driving range**
- ✓ **practice greens**
- ✓ **power carts**
- pull carts
- ✓ **golf club rental**
- ✓ **locker rooms**
- ✓ **showers**
- executive course
- ✓ **accommodations**
- ✓ **food and beverages**
- ✓ **clubhouse**

**Tom Bienek**
Professional

**Ray Cymbalisty**
Superintendent

***Course information:*** This semi-private course has 18 holes and par is 72. The course is 6,571 yards and rated 70.7 from the championship tees, and 6,288 yards and rated 69.2 from the regular tees. The slope ratings are 112 championship and 107 regular. Women's tees are 5,464 yards and rated 70.6 from the forward tees. The slope rating is 112.

***Play policy and fees:*** Outside play is accepted. Green fees are: November through May, Monday through Thursday, $65; Friday, Saturday and Sunday, $80. June through October, Monday through Thursday, $35; Friday, Saturday and Sunday, $45. Carts are included. Reservations are recommended. This course is available for outside tournaments. Golfers are not allowed to wear tank tops or cut-off pants. The course is open daily, however the pro shop is closed Mondays and Tuesdays during the summer season.

***Location:*** Take the Washington Street exit off Interstate 10, and drive south to Country Club Drive. Turn right and travel three-fourths of a mile to the club on the left.

***Course description:*** This course has fairly wide fairways, bent grass greens and nine lakes that come into play. It's well bunkered and in excellent condition. It challenges the good golfer as well as the average golfer.

# WOODHAVEN COUNTRY CLUB

**Course 53**
MAP I7 grid i3

***Course information:*** This private course has 18 holes. See card below for yardage and rating information.

***Play policy and fees:*** Reciprocal play is accepted with members of other private clubs. The fees for reciprocators are $40 June through September and $70 November through May 31. Green fees for guests accompanied by a member are $46 November through May and $32 June through September; the fees without a member are $55 November through May and $35 June through September. Carts are included. Reservations are recommended. Bermuda shorts are acceptable. The course is closed in October.

***Location:*** Take the Washington Street exit off Interstate 10 and drive south three-fourths of a mile to the club on the right.

***Course description:*** This is a well-maintained, challenging course that offers narrow fairways, trees, bunkers, small greens and some water. It's set among numerous condominiums.

**1985**
**Harold Heers Jr.**

41-555 Woodhaven Dr. East
Palm Desert, CA 92260

Pro shop (619) 345-7513
Clubhouse (619) 345-7636

- ✓ **driving range**
- ✓ **practice greens**
- ✓ **power carts**
- pull carts
- ✓ **golf club rental**
- ✓ **locker rooms**
- ✓ **showers**
- executive course
- accommodations
- ✓ **food and beverages**
- ✓ **clubhouse**

**Mark Range**
Professional

**Jim Holub**
Superintendent

| Hole | 1 | 2 | 3 | 4 | 5 | 6 | 7 | 8 | 9 | Out | | |
|---|---|---|---|---|---|---|---|---|---|---|---|---|
| BLUE | 358 | 368 | 133 | 382 | 254 | 152 | 478 | 384 | 356 | 2865 | BLUE | Rating: 66.6 |
| WHITE | 341 | 357 | 114 | 362 | 244 | 131 | 440 | 360 | 336 | 2865 | | Slope: 111 |
| Par | 4 | 4 | 3 | 4 | 4 | 3 | 5 | 4 | 4 | 35 | WHITE | Rating: 64.6 |
| Handicap | 9 | 7 | 17 | 1 | 15 | 13 | 5 | 3 | 11 | x | | Slope: 107 |
| RED | 341 | 357 | 114 | 362 | 244 | 115 | 440 | 360 | 336 | 2669 | | |
| Par | 4 | 4 | 3 | 4 | 4 | 3 | 5 | 4 | 4 | 35 | RED | Rating: 69.7 |
| Handicap | 9 | 7 | 17 | 1 | 15 | 13 | 5 | 3 | 11 | x | | Slope: 116 |

| Hole | 10 | 11 | 12 | 13 | 14 | 15 | 16 | 17 | 18 | In | Totals | |
|---|---|---|---|---|---|---|---|---|---|---|---|---|
| BLUE | 344 | 354 | 138 | 331 | 178 | 328 | 303 | 494 | 346 | 2816 | BLUE | 5681 |
| WHITE | 303 | 331 | 128 | 288 | 163 | 316 | 279 | 460 | 317 | 2585 | WHITE | 5270 |
| Par | 4 | 4 | 3 | 4 | 3 | 4 | 4 | 5 | 4 | 35 | Par | 70 |
| Handicap | 6 | 4 | 18 | 12 | 8 | 10 | 16 | 2 | 14 | x | | |
| RED | 303 | 331 | 128 | 288 | 163 | 316 | 279 | 460 | 317 | 2585 | RED | 5254 |
| Par | 4 | 4 | 3 | 4 | 3 | 4 | 4 | 5 | 4 | 35 | Par | 70 |
| Handicap | 12 | 4 | 18 | 6 | 16 | 10 | 14 | 2 | 8 | x | | |



MAP ON PAGE 612

# PALM DESERT COUNTRY CLUB

**Course 54**
**MAP 17 grid i3**

**1962**
**William Park Bell**

77-200 California Drive
Palm Desert, CA 92260

Pro shop (619) 345-2525

- ✓ **driving range**
- ✓ **practice greens**
- ✓ **power carts**
- ✓ **pull carts**
- ✓ **golf club rental**
- ✓ **locker rooms**
- ✓ **showers**
- ✓ **executive course**
- accommodations
- ✓ **food and beverages**
- ✓ **clubhouse**

**Nancy Little**
Professional

**Rafael Barajas**
Superintendent

***Course information:*** This semi-private course has 27 holes and par is 72 for 18 holes.

The Championship Course is 6,678 yards and rated 70.8 from the championship tees, and 6,375 yards and rated 69.5 from the regular tees. The slope ratings are 118 championship and 110 regular. Women's tees are 5,899 yards and rated 72.5 from the forward tees. The slope rating is 117.

The First and Third Nine is 5,435 yards and rated 65.1 from the championship tees, and 5,288 yards and rated 63.8 from the regular tees. The slope ratings are 100 championship and 94 regular. Women's tees are 4,987 yards from the forward tees.

The Second and Third Nine is 5,329 yards and rated 65 from the championship tees, and 5,257 yards and rated 63.6 from the regular tees. The slope ratings are 99 championship and 93 regular. Women's tees are 4,914 yards from the forward tees.

***Play policy and fees:*** Outside play is accepted. Hotel guests welcome. Green fees are $10 for the nine-hole course. The winter rates are: weekdays in the morning, $50; at noon, $45; after three p. m., $30. On weekends, the morning rate is $60, the noon rate is $50, and after three p.m., $30. Carts are $15. Reservations are recommended three days in advance. This course is available for outside tournaments. The course closes in October.

***Location:*** Take the Washington Street exit off Interstate 10 and turn right and drive 1.5 miles to Avenue of the Stars. Turn right and merge into California Drive and continue one mile to the club entrance.

***Course description:*** These are mature courses designed by Billy Bell. The wide, tree-lined fairways are well laid out and challenging. The executive nine, like the championship course, is lined with homes. Recent bunker, tree and flower bed additions have slightly boosted the ratings.

# THE OASIS COUNTRY CLUB

**Course 55**
MAP I7 grid i3

***Course information:*** This semi-private course has 18 holes and par is 60. The course is short at 3,617 yards and rated 57.3 from the championship tees, and 3,201 yards and rated 51.5 from the regular tees. The slope ratings are 90 championship and 84 regular. Women's tees are 3,201 yards and rated 57.6 from the championship tees, and 2,800 yards and rated 52.1 from the forward tees. The slope rating is 89 championship.

***Play policy and fees:*** Outside play is accepted. Green fees are $48 weekdays and $53 weekends. Carts are included. Reservations are recommended. This course is available for outside tournaments. The course is closed in October. During the summer months the pro shop closes at 2 p.m.

***Location:*** Take the Washington Street exit off Interstate 10 and drive south to Avenue 42. Turn right and drive one mile to the club.

***Course description:*** This is a fun and challenging executive course with some of the finest greens to be found in the desert. There are 22 lakes guarding six par-4s and 12 par-3s.

**1984**
**David Rainville**

42-330 Casbah
Palm Desert, CA 92260

Pro shop (619) 345-2715
Clubhouse (619) 345-5661

- ✓ **driving range**
- ✓ **practice greens**
- ✓ **power carts**
- ✓ **pull carts**
- ✓ **golf club rental**
- locker rooms
- showers
- ✓ **executive course**
- accommodations
- ✓ **food and beverages**
- ✓ **clubhouse**

**Daryl Boone**
Manager/Director of Golf

**Les Holt**
Superintendent

# BERMUDA DUNES COUNTRY CLUB

**Course 56**
MAP I7 grid i3

42-360 Adams Street
Bermuda Dunes, CA 92201

Pro shop (619) 345-2232
Clubhouse (619) 345-2771

- ✓ **driving range**
- ✓ **practice greens**
- ✓ **power carts**
- pull carts
- golf club rental
- locker rooms
- showers
- executive course
- accommodations
- ✓ **food and beverages**
- ✓ **clubhouse**

**Scott Walter**
Director of Golf

**Carl King**
Superintendent

***Course information:*** This private course has 27 holes and par is 72 for each 18-hole combinations.

The One and Two Course is 6,927 yards and rated 73.5 from the championship tees, and 6,542 yards and rated 70.8 from the regular tees. The slope ratings are 126 championship and 118 regular. Women's tees are 6,081 yards and rated 75.0. The slope rating is 126.

The One and Three Course is 6,716 yards and rated 72.2 from the championship tees, and 6,360 yards and rated 69.8 from the regular tees. The slope ratings are 123 championship and 115 regular. Women's tees are 5,857 yards and rated 74.0. The slope rating is 126.

The Two and Three Course is 6,749 yards and rated 72.4 from the championship tees, and 6,434 yards and rated 70.1 from the regular tees. The slope ratings are 124 championship and 116 regular. Women's tees are 6,016 yards and rated 74.8. The slope rating is 127.

***Play policy and fees:*** Members and guests only. Guest fees are $50 summer season and $65 during the winter. Carts are $24. It is closed in October.

***Location:*** Take the Washington Street exit off Interstate 10 and drive south to Avenue 42. Turn left and drive one mile to the club.

***Course description:*** This is not a typical desert course. It offers rolling hills with an assortment of trees guarding the fairways. There is some water. You can expect a lot of variation from hole to hole. It is one of the courses in the PGA Tour's Bob Hope Classic rotation.

# INDIAN SPRINGS COUNTRY CLUB

**Course 57**
MAP I7 grid i3

**1960**
46-080 Jefferson Street
La Quinta, CA 92253

Pro shop (619)775-3360
Clubhouse (619) 775-3363

- ✓ **driving range**
- ✓ **practice greens**
- ✓ **power carts**
- ✓ **pull carts**
- ✓ **golf club rental**
- locker rooms
- showers
- executive course
- accommodations
- ✓ **food and beverages**
- ✓ **clubhouse**

**Buzz Colton**
Manager

**Vic Martin**
Director of Golf

**Ben Gonzalez**
Superintendent

***Course information:*** This public course has 18 holes. See card below for yardage and rating information.

***Play policy and fees:*** Green fees are $30 weekdays and $35 weekends. Carts are included. Reservations are recommended. This course is available for outside tournaments. The course is closed during the summer season.

***Location:*** Take the Washington Street exit off Interstate 10 and drive south to Miller Avenue. Turn east on Jefferson Street and drive directly to the course.

***Course description:*** This older course has some trees and a few bunkers. There is a lot of sand off the fairway. Small greens demand a creative short game. It's a sporty, casual place with active men's and women's clubs.

| Hole | 1 | 2 | 3 | 4 | 5 | 6 | 7 | 8 | 9 | Out | | |
|---|---|---|---|---|---|---|---|---|---|---|---|---|
| BLUE | 324 | 466 | 194 | 387 | 482 | 524 | 377 | 448 | 373 | 3575 | BLUE | Rating: 69.5 |
| WHITE | 310 | 441 | 174 | 379 | 472 | 515 | 366 | 439 | 354 | 3450 | | Slope: 109 |
| Par | 4 | 4 | 3 | 4 | 5 | 5 | 4 | 4 | 4 | 37 | WHITE | Rating: 68.5 |
| Handicap | 15 | 1 | 17 | 5 | 13 | 7 | 9 | 3 | 11 | x | | Slope: 104 |
| RED | 305 | 432 | 160 | 370 | 462 | 505 | 358 | 430 | 326 | 3348 | | |
| Par | 4 | 5 | 3 | 4 | 5 | 5 | 4 | 5 | 4 | 39 | RED | Rating: 74.9 |
| Handicap | 15 | 5 | 17 | 3 | 11 | 1 | 7 | 13 | 9 | x | | Slope: 117 |

| Hole | 10 | 11 | 12 | 13 | 14 | 15 | 16 | 17 | 18 | In | Totals | |
|---|---|---|---|---|---|---|---|---|---|---|---|---|
| BLUE | 173 | 321 | 211 | 183 | 438 | 465 | 305 | 390 | 377 | 2863 | BLUE | 6438 |
| WHITE | 156 | 315 | 203 | 174 | 429 | 457 | 297 | 379 | 363 | 2773 | WHITE | 6223 |
| Par | 3 | 4 | 3 | 3 | 4 | 5 | 4 | 4 | 4 | 34 | Par | 71 |
| Handicap | 18 | 12 | 10 | 14 | 2 | 6 | 16 | 4 | 8 | x | | |
| RED | 146 | 305 | 198 | 130 | 425 | 452 | 290 | 372 | 357 | 2675 | RED | 6023 |
| Par | 3 | 4 | 3 | 3 | 5 | 5 | 4 | 4 | 4 | 35 | Par | 74 |
| Handicap | 14 | 10 | 8 | 18 | 6 | 2 | 16 | 4 | 12 | x | | |

## PALM ROYALE COUNTRY CLUB

**Course 58**
MAP 17 grid i3

**1985**
**Ted Robinson**

78-259 Indigo Drive
La Quinta, CA 92253

Pro shop (619) 345-9701
Clubhouse (619) 345-9703

- driving range
- ✓ **practice greens**
- power carts
- ✓ **pull carts**
- ✓ **golf club rental**
- ✓ **locker rooms**
- ✓ **showers**
- executive course
- accommodations
- ✓ **food and beverages**
- ✓ **clubhouse**

**John J. Marentette**
Professional

***Course information:*** This public course has 18 holes and par is 54. The course is 2,118 yards and rated 54.0 from the regular tees. Women's tees are 1,861. The rating was unavailable.

***Play policy and fees:*** Green fees are $20 during the season, November through April, and $15 before eight a. m., $10.50 after three p.m. Closed in October.

***Location:*** Take Interstate 10 and exit at Washington Street in La Quinta. Follow Washington to the club.

***Course description:*** This is a short par-3 course with water on nine holes. It's a scaled-down version of the Marriott Desert Springs courses, with palms backing the greens, 26 bunkers, grass moguls, and water treatments.

## LA QUINTA COUNTRY CLUB

**Course 59**
MAP 17 grid i3

**1959**
**Larry Hughes**

PO Box 99
La Quinta, CA 92253

77-750 Avenue 50
La Quinta, CA 92253

Pro shop (619) 564-4151

- ✓ **driving range**
- ✓ **practice greens**
- ✓ **power carts**
- pull carts
- golf club rental
- ✓ **locker rooms**
- ✓ **showers**
- executive course
- accommodations
- ✓ **food and beverages**
- ✓ **clubhouse**

**Jeff Jackson**
Professional

**William Baker**
Superintendent

***Course information:*** This private course has 18 holes and par is 72. The course is 6,854 yards and rated 73.8 from the championship tees, and 6,525 yards and rated 72.0 from the regular tees. The slope ratings are 133 championship and 129 regular. Women's tees are 6,136 yards and rated 74.5. The slope rating is 122.

***Play policy and fees:*** Members and guests only. Guests must be accompanied by members at time of play. Guest fee is $60. Carts are $20. The course is closed in October.

***Location:*** Take the Washington Street exit off Interstate 10 and drive south for six miles to Avenue 50 and turn right. Drive one mile to the club on the right.

***Course description:*** Larry Hughes designed this mature course. It has tree-lined fairways, lakes, bunkers and undulating greens. The emphasis is on driving accuracy. La Quinta is one of the courses in the Bob Hope Chrysler Classic of the PGA Tour rotation.

# INDIO GOLF COURSE

**Course 60**
MAP I7 grid i4

***Course information:*** This public course has 18 holes and par is 54. The course is 3,004 yards and rated 53.1 from the regular tees. The slope rating is 71. Women's tees are 2,662 yards and unrated.

***Play policy and fees:*** Green fees are $8 winter and $7 summer for 18 holes. Carts are $9 for 18 holes. Junior rate is $2 for nine holes. Reservations are recommended weekend mornings only. The course closes at 6 p.m. weekends.

***Location:*** Take the Jackson Street exit off Interstate 10 and drive north to Avenue 42 and turn right.

***Course description:*** This is a great little course. It is one of the longest par-3 courses in the country. The holes range from 110 to 240 yards, so bring your irons. There is one lake that intersects three holes, or four, depending on your shot. The course is night-lighted and the last weekday tee time is 7:30 p.m. for 18 holes.

PO Box X
Indio, CA 92202

83-040 Avenue 42
Indio, CA 92202

Pro shop (619) 347-9156

- ✓ **driving range**
- ✓ **practice greens**
- ✓ **power carts**
- ✓ **pull carts**
- ✓ **golf club rental**
- locker rooms
- showers
- executive course
- accommodations
- ✓ **food and beverages**
- ✓ **clubhouse**

**Scott Daniels**
Professional

SOUTHERN I7

# INDIAN PALMS COUNTRY CLUB

**Course 61**
MAP I7 grid i4

48-630 Monroe Street
Indio, CA 92201

Pro shop (619) 347-2326
Clubhouse (619) 347-0941

- ✓ **driving range**
- ✓ **practice greens**
- ✓ **power carts**
- pull carts
- ✓ **golf club rental**
- ✓ **locker rooms**
- showers
- executive course
- ✓ **accommodations**
- ✓ **food and beverages**
- ✓ **clubhouse**

**Homer Smith**
Director of Golf

**Toby Skeen**
Superintendent

***Course information:*** This semi-private course has 27 holes and par is 72 on each of the 18-hole combinations.

The Indian/Mountain Course is 6,807 yards and rated 72.0 from the championship tees, and 6,403 yards and rated 70.0 from the regular tees. The slope rating is 119. Women's tees are 5,858 yards and rated 72.4. The slope rating is 119.

The Mountain/Royal Course is 6,749 yards and rated 70.4 from the championship tees, and 6,284 yards and rated 69.5 from the regular tees. The slope rating is 115. Women's tees are 5,622 yards and rated 70.0. The slope rating is 116.

The Royal/Indian Course is 6,766 yards and rated 70.1 from the championship tees, and 6,279 yards and rated 69.4 from the regular tees. The slope rating is 115. Women's tees are 5,547 yards and rated 70.0. The slope rating is 116.

***Play policy and fees:*** Outside play is accepted. Green fees are $40 weekdays and $45 weekends during the winter season, and $30 weekdays and $35 weekends during the summer. There is a summer twilight rate of $25 any day after 1 p.m. Carts are included. Reservations are recommended.

***Location:*** Take the Monroe Street/Central Indio exit off Interstate 10 and drive south on Monroe for 2.5 miles to the club entrance.

***Course description:*** The original nine-hole course, called Indian Palms, was built in 1948 by world famous female aviatrix Jackie Cochran. It was built upon a ranch that once served as a retreat for the rich and famous of the 1940s and 1950s. Dwight Eisenhower wrote his memoirs here. The Mountain and the Royal nines were built around 1980. The Royal has eight holes on which water comes into play. All the courses have trees and natural growth along gently rolling terrain, leading to elevated greens.

# PGA WEST NICKLAUS RESORT



**1987**
**Jack Nicklaus**

56-150 PGA Boulevard
La Quinta, CA 92253

Pro shop (619) 564-7170
Clubhouse (619) 564-7429
Fax (619) 771-3109

- ✓ **driving range**
- ✓ **practice greens**
- ✓ **power carts**
- pull carts
- ✓ **golf club rental**
- ✓ **locker rooms**
- ✓ **showers**
- executive course
- accommodations
- ✓ **food and beverages**
- ✓ **clubhouse**

**Steve Walser**
Director of Golf

**Jeff Walser**
Professional

**Scott Lewis**
Superintendent

***Course information:*** This semi-private course has 18 holes. The course is 7,126 yards, and rated 75.5 with a slope of 138 from the black tees, and is 5,612 yards, and rated 72.1 with a slope (for women) of 124 from the gold tees. See card below for additional yardage and rating information.

***Play policy and fees:*** Outside play is accepted. Green fees April 12 until June are $85 weekdays and $110 weekends and holidays; June 1 through October fees are $60 weekdays and $75 weekends and holidays; November until December 26 they are $125 weekdays, weekends and holidays. Carts are included. Reservations are recommended one day in advance. This course is available for outside tournaments.

***Location:*** Take the Indio Boulevard/Jefferson Street exit off Interstate 10 and drive south to the end of Jefferson Street.

***Course description:*** A tamer version of the adjacent Stadium Course. There are Nicklaus's trademark elevated tees and Dye's trademark railroad ties, forced carries over water and huge, tiered greens. But none of it is quite as severe as in the Stadium Course, even if it looks that way from the tees. It can be as hard as you choose to make it, depending on what tees are used. The course has hosted the PGA Tour Qualifying School.

| Hole | 1 | 2 | 3 | 4 | 5 | 6 | 7 | 8 | 9 | Out | BLUE | Rating: 72.0 |
|---|---|---|---|---|---|---|---|---|---|---|---|---|
| BLUE | 381 | 397 | 167 | 506 | 324 | 412 | 473 | 146 | 438 | 3244 | | Slope: 129 |
| WHITE | 351 | 388 | 156 | 482 | 300 | 379 | 451 | 130 | 390 | 3027 | | |
| Par | 4 | 4 | 3 | 5 | 4 | 4 | 5 | 3 | 4 | 36 | WHITE | Rating: 69.2 |
| Handicap | 13 | 5 | 11 | 7 | 15 | 3 | 9 | 17 | 1 | x | | Slope: 122 |
| RED | 274 | 321 | 120 | 415 | 226 | 342 | 392 | 96 | 343 | 2529 | | |
| Par | 4 | 4 | 3 | 5 | 4 | 4 | 5 | 3 | 4 | 36 | RED | Rating: 69.0 |
| Handicap | 3 | 13 | 17 | 1 | 11 | 7 | 5 | 15 | 9 | x | | Slope: 116 |

| Hole | 10 | 11 | 12 | 13 | 14 | 15 | 16 | 17 | 18 | In | Totals | |
|---|---|---|---|---|---|---|---|---|---|---|---|---|
| BLUE | 328 | 488 | 165 | 381 | 387 | 504 | 433 | 184 | 432 | 3302 | BLUE | 6546 |
| WHITE | 321 | 482 | 151 | 330 | 346 | 455 | 366 | 159 | 400 | 3010 | WHITE | 6037 |
| Par | 4 | 5 | 3 | 4 | 4 | 5 | 4 | 3 | 4 | 36 | Par | 72 |
| Handicap | 18 | 12 | 16 | 10 | 6 | 8 | 4 | 14 | 2 | x | | |
| RED | 239 | 401 | 105 | 293 | 302 | 406 | 307 | 100 | 361 | 2514 | RED | 5043 |
| Par | 4 | 5 | 3 | 4 | 4 | 5 | 4 | 3 | 4 | 36 | Par | 72 |
| Handicap | 14 | 6 | 16 | 10 | 12 | 2 | 4 | 18 | 8 | x | | |

# PGA WEST NICKLAUS PRIVATE

**Course 63**
MAP 17 grid j3

**1987**
**Jack Nicklaus**

55-955 PGA Boulevard
La Quinta, CA 92253

Pro shop (619) 564-7100
Clubhouse (619) 564-7111
Fax (619) 771-2823

- ✓ **driving range**
- ✓ **practice greens**
- ✓ **power carts**
- pull carts
- ✓ **golf club rental**
- ✓ **locker rooms**
- ✓ **showers**
- executive course
- accommodations
- ✓ **food and beverages**
- ✓ **clubhouse**

**Mike Finnell**
Manager

**John Sheldon**
Professional

**Jeff Prichard**
**Dave Bergstrom**
Superintendents

***Course information:*** This private course has 18 holes. The course is 6,909 yards, and rated 75.1 with a slope of 142 from the tournament tees. See card below for additional yardage and rating information.

***Play policy and fees:*** Members and guests only. Guests must be accompanied by members at time of play. The fees are $75 weekdays, $125 weekends, in season.

***Location:*** Take the Indio Boulevard/Jefferson Street exit off Interstate 10 or Highway 111 and drive south to the end of Jefferson Street to PGA Boulevard.

***Course description:*** This is a unique course with flowers, tall desert grasses and water off the fairways. There are huge desert bunkers throughout the course. You may need a dune buggy to get in and out of these traps. Many fairways are defined with large mounds of grass. This course is the site of annual Titleist/Footjoy PGA Assistant Club Pro Championship staged in early October.

| Hole | 1 | 2 | 3 | 4 | 5 | 6 | 7 | 8 | 9 | Out | | |
|---|---|---|---|---|---|---|---|---|---|---|---|---|
| BLUE | 342 | 375 | 153 | 514 | 405 | 364 | 145 | 479 | 380 | 3157 | BLUE | Rating: 71.8 |
| WHITE | 294 | 345 | 126 | 460 | 329 | 343 | 142 | 442 | 337 | 2818 | | Slope: 132 |
| Par | 4 | 4 | 3 | 5 | 4 | 4 | 3 | 5 | 4 | 36 | WHITE | Rating: 69.7 |
| Handicap | 13 | 7 | 15 | 9 | 1 | 3 | 17 | 11 | 5 | x | | Slope: 119 |
| RED | 235 | 275 | 110 | 407 | 285 | 287 | 113 | 407 | 296 | 2415 | | |
| Par | 4 | 4 | 3 | 5 | 4 | 4 | 3 | 5 | 4 | 36 | RED | Rating: 68.6 |
| Handicap | 9 | 5 | 17 | 1 | 13 | 7 | 15 | 3 | 11 | x | | Slope: 119 |

| Hole | 10 | 11 | 12 | 13 | 14 | 15 | 16 | 17 | 18 | In | Totals | |
|---|---|---|---|---|---|---|---|---|---|---|---|---|
| BLUE | 385 | 175 | 375 | 472 | 344 | 390 | 492 | 183 | 395 | 3211 | BLUE | 6368 |
| WHITE | 326 | 151 | 324 | 437 | 308 | 352 | 443 | 155 | 350 | 2846 | WHITE | 5664 |
| Par | 4 | 3 | 4 | 5 | 4 | 4 | 5 | 3 | 4 | 36 | Par | 72 |
| Handicap | 8 | 18 | 6 | 16 | 14 | 12 | 2 | 10 | 4 | x | | |
| RED | 272 | 102 | 263 | 402 | 265 | 313 | 403 | 122 | 302 | 2444 | RED | 4859 |
| Par | 4 | 3 | 4 | 5 | 4 | 4 | 5 | 3 | 4 | 36 | Par | 72 |
| Handicap | 14 | 16 | 12 | 4 | 6 | 8 | 2 | 18 | 10 | x | | |

# PGA WEST—THE TPC STADIUM GOLF COURSE

**Course 64**
MAP I7 grid j3

**1986**
**Pete Dye**

56-150 PGA Boulevard
La Quinta, CA 92253

Pro Shop (619) 564-7170
Fax (619) 771-3109

- ✓ **driving range**
- ✓ **practice greens**
- ✓ **power carts**
- pull carts
- ✓ **golf club rental**
- ✓ **locker rooms**
- ✓ **showers**
- executive course
- accommodations
- ✓ **food and beverages**
- ✓ **clubhouse**

**Jeff Walser**
Professional

**Steve Walser**
Director of Golf

**Scott Lewis**
Superintendent

***Course information:*** This semi-private course has 18 holes. The course is 7,261 yards, and rated 77.3 with a slope of 151 from the tournament tees. See card below for additional yardage and rating information.

***Play policy and fees:*** Outside play is accepted. Green fees range between $100 for weekdays in April and May, to $175 between Christmas and mid-April. Carts and range balls are included. Reservations are recommended. Call Tee Time Central at (619) 564-6666 for reservations from October 31 to May 31. Men must wear collared shirts on the golf course. No blue jeans are allowed.

***Location:*** Take the Indio Boulevard/Jefferson Street exit off Interstate 10 or Highway 111 and drive south to the end of Jefferson Street to PGA Boulevard. Continue on PGA Boulevard to the Resort Golf House.

***Course description:*** This course opened in 1986 and immediately made its place in golf lore. It is packed with pot bunkers, sand, water and sidehill lies. Large, undulating greens with several tiers make putting a chore. Among the course highlights is a 19-foot-deep, greenside bunker that flanks the par-5 16th hole. The annual Skins Game was played here between 1986-1991. Lee Trevino holed out an eagle on number seven during the 1986 Skins Game and followed that with a hole-in-one on number 17 in 1987. The 1987 Bob Hope Chrysler Classic was held here. The course is considered one of the 100 greatest in the world. It is expensive, difficult, time-consuming in the busy season, deathly hot in summer, and one of the top 10 must-play courses in the country.

| Hole | 1 | 2 | 3 | 4 | 5 | 6 | 7 | 8 | 9 | Out | BLUE | Rating: 74.4 |
|---|---|---|---|---|---|---|---|---|---|---|---|---|
| BLUE | 377 | 349 | 446 | 171 | 512 | 223 | 319 | 526 | 430 | 3353 | | Slope: 139 |
| WHITE | 353 | 328 | 378 | 152 | 493 | 192 | 296 | 484 | 381 | 3057 | | |
| Par | 4 | 4 | 4 | 3 | 5 | 3 | 4 | 5 | 4 | 36 | WHITE | Rating: 71.2 |
| Handicap | 11 | 15 | 3 | 17 | 1 | 7 | 13 | 9 | 5 | x | | Slope: 130 |
| RED | 296 | 288 | 322 | 112 | 434 | 133 | 242 | 427 | 315 | 2569 | | |
| Par | 4 | 4 | 4 | 3 | 5 | 3 | 4 | 5 | 4 | 36 | RED | Rating: 70.3 |
| Handicap | 11 | 13 | 7 | 17 | 1 | 15 | 9 | 3 | 5 | x | | Slope: 124 |

| Hole | 10 | 11 | 12 | 13 | 14 | 15 | 16 | 17 | 18 | In | Totals | |
|---|---|---|---|---|---|---|---|---|---|---|---|---|
| BLUE | 381 | 593 | 346 | 198 | 375 | 439 | 521 | 147 | 400 | 3400 | BLUE | 6753 |
| WHITE | 351 | 530 | 309 | 171 | 349 | 407 | 479 | 128 | 383 | 3107 | WHITE | 6164 |
| Par | 4 | 5 | 4 | 3 | 4 | 4 | 5 | 3 | 4 | 36 | Par | 72 |
| Handicap | 12 | 2 | 16 | 10 | 18 | 8 | 6 | 14 | 4 | x | | |
| RED | 294 | 443 | 247 | 105 | 295 | 339 | 436 | 85 | 274 | 2518 | RED | 5087 |
| Par | 4 | 5 | 4 | 3 | 4 | 4 | 5 | 3 | 4 | 36 | Par | 72 |
| Handicap | 6 | 2 | 14 | 18 | 10 | 12 | 4 | 16 | 8 | x | | |



MAP ON PAGE 612

# PGA WEST
# ARNOLD PALMER COURSE

**Course 65**
MAP I7 grid j3

**1986**
**Arnold Palmer**

55-955 PGA Boulevard
La Quinta, CA 92253

Pro shop (619) 564-7100
Clubhouse (619) 564-7111
Fax (619)771-2823

- ✓ **driving range**
- ✓ **practice greens**
- ✓ **power carts**
- pull carts
- ✓ **golf club rental**
- ✓ **locker rooms**
- ✓ **showers**
- executive course
- accommodations
- ✓ **food and beverages**
- ✓ **clubhouse**

**Mike Finnell**
Manager

**John Sheldon**
Professional

**Jeff Prichard**
**Gerry Tarsitano**
Superintendents

***Course information:*** This private course has 18 holes. The course is 6,931 yards and rated 73.7 with a slope of 133 from the tournament tees. See card below for additional yardage and rating information.

***Play policy and fees:*** Members and guests only. Guests must be accompanied by members at time of play. The fees are $80 weekdays, $125 weekends in season.

***Location:*** Take the Indio Boulevard/Jefferson Street exit off Interstate 10 or Highway 111 and drive south to the end of Jefferson Street to PGA Boulevard.

***Course description:*** This demanding course is a tough track. It plays as long as any of the courses in this group, except perhaps the TPC Stadium Course. Bunkers distinguish the front nine, and hills the back nine. The last four holes are tight against the Santa Rosa Mountains. The tees are elevated above the large greens, just the way Arnie likes them. Some greens are backed by boulders. Along with three other area courses, this course annually hosts the Bob Hope Chrysler Classic on the PGA Tour in February.

| Hole | 1 | 2 | 3 | 4 | 5 | 6 | 7 | 8 | 9 | Out | | |
|---|---|---|---|---|---|---|---|---|---|---|---|---|
| BLUE | 405 | 490 | 156 | 373 | 207 | 531 | 390 | 317 | 421 | 3290 | BLUE | Rating: 70.7 |
| WHITE | 378 | 451 | 134 | 356 | 170 | 501 | 382 | 302 | 393 | 3067 | | Slope: 125 |
| Par | 4 | 5 | 3 | 4 | 3 | 5 | 4 | 4 | 4 | 36 | WHITE | Rating: 68.0 |
| Handicap | 11 | 9 | 15 | 13 | 7 | 5 | 1 | 17 | 3 | x | | Slope: 117 |
| RED | 317 | 402 | 90 | 287 | 102 | 433 | 309 | 262 | 330 | 2532 | | |
| Par | 4 | 5 | 3 | 4 | 3 | 5 | 4 | 4 | 4 | 36 | RED | Rating: 69.0 |
| Handicap | 5 | 11 | 15 | 1 | 17 | 7 | 9 | 13 | 3 | x | | Slope: 119 |

| Hole | 10 | 11 | 12 | 13 | 14 | 15 | 16 | 17 | 18 | In | Totals | |
|---|---|---|---|---|---|---|---|---|---|---|---|---|
| BLUE | 422 | 503 | 198 | 423 | 525 | 128 | 342 | 121 | 522 | 3184 | BLUE | 6474 |
| WHITE | 409 | 485 | 168 | 401 | 478 | 122 | 318 | 102 | 466 | 2949 | WHITE | 6016 |
| Par | 4 | 5 | 3 | 4 | 5 | 3 | 4 | 3 | 5 | 36 | Par | 72 |
| Handicap | 2 | 8 | 14 | 6 | 4 | 16 | 12 | 18 | 10 | x | | |
| RED | 268 | 402 | 126 | 307 | 456 | 81 | 275 | 82 | 446 | 2443 | RED | 4975 |
| Par | 4 | 5 | 3 | 4 | 5 | 3 | 4 | 3 | 5 | 36 | Par | 72 |
| Handicap | 12 | 8 | 14 | 6 | 2 | 16 | 10 | 18 | 4 | x | | |

MAP ON PAGE 612

# MAP I8
(1 COURSE)

PAGES.. 666-667

SO-CAL MAP .....see page 466
adjoining maps
NORTH ..........................no map
EAST ..............................no map
SOUTH (J8) ........see page 720
WEST (I7) ...........see page 612

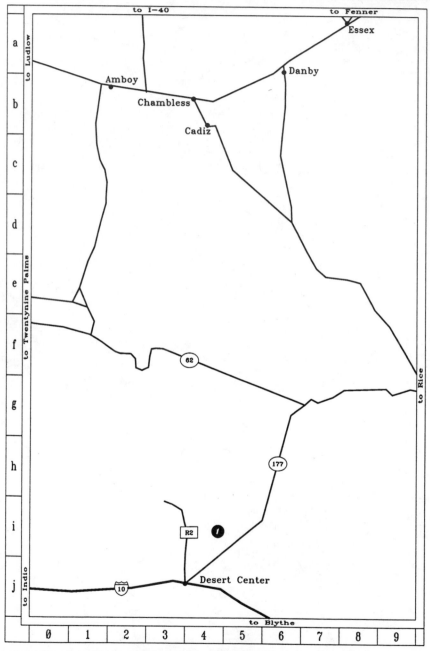

to I-40
to Fenner
Essex
Danby
to Ludlow
Amboy
Chambless
Cadiz
to Twentynine Palms
62
to Rice
177
R2
1
Desert Center
10
to Indio
to Blythe

a b c d e f g h i j

0 1 2 3 4 5 6 7 8 9

# LAKE TAMARISK GOLF CLUB

**Course 1**
MAP 18 grid i4

***Course information:*** This public course has nine holes. Par is 70 for 18 holes. The course is 5,932 yards and rated 66.9 from the regular tees for 18 holes. The slope rating is 100. Women's tees are 5,606 yards and rated 69.9. The slope rating is 104.

***Play policy and fees:*** Green fees are $12 for 18 holes. Carts are $9 for nine holes and $12 for 18 holes. Reservations are recommended January through April.

***Location:*** Travel east from Indio on Interstate 10 for about 50 miles and take the Desert Center Road exit north. Bear left onto Kaiser Road and drive 1.5 miles to the entrance.

***Course description:*** This is literally an oasis in the middle of the desert. Refreshing lakes line the course and palm trees and oleanders line the fairways. The course is fairly level and the tees and greens are elevated.

**1967**
**Robert Trent Jones, Sr.**

PO Box 315
Desert Center, CA 92239

26-251 Parkview Drive
Desert Center, CA 92239

Pro shop (619) 227-3203

- ✓ **driving range**
- ✓ **practice greens**
- ✓ **power carts**
- ✓ **pull carts**
- ✓ **golf club rental**
- locker rooms
- ✓ **showers**
- executive course
- accommodations
- food and beverages
- ✓ **clubhouse**

**Steve Jones**
Manager

# MAP J5
(5 COURSES)

PAGES.. 668-671

SO-CAL MAP .....see page 466
adjoining maps
NORTH (I5).........see page 506
EAST (J6) ...........see page 672
SOUTH..........................no map
WEST...........................no map

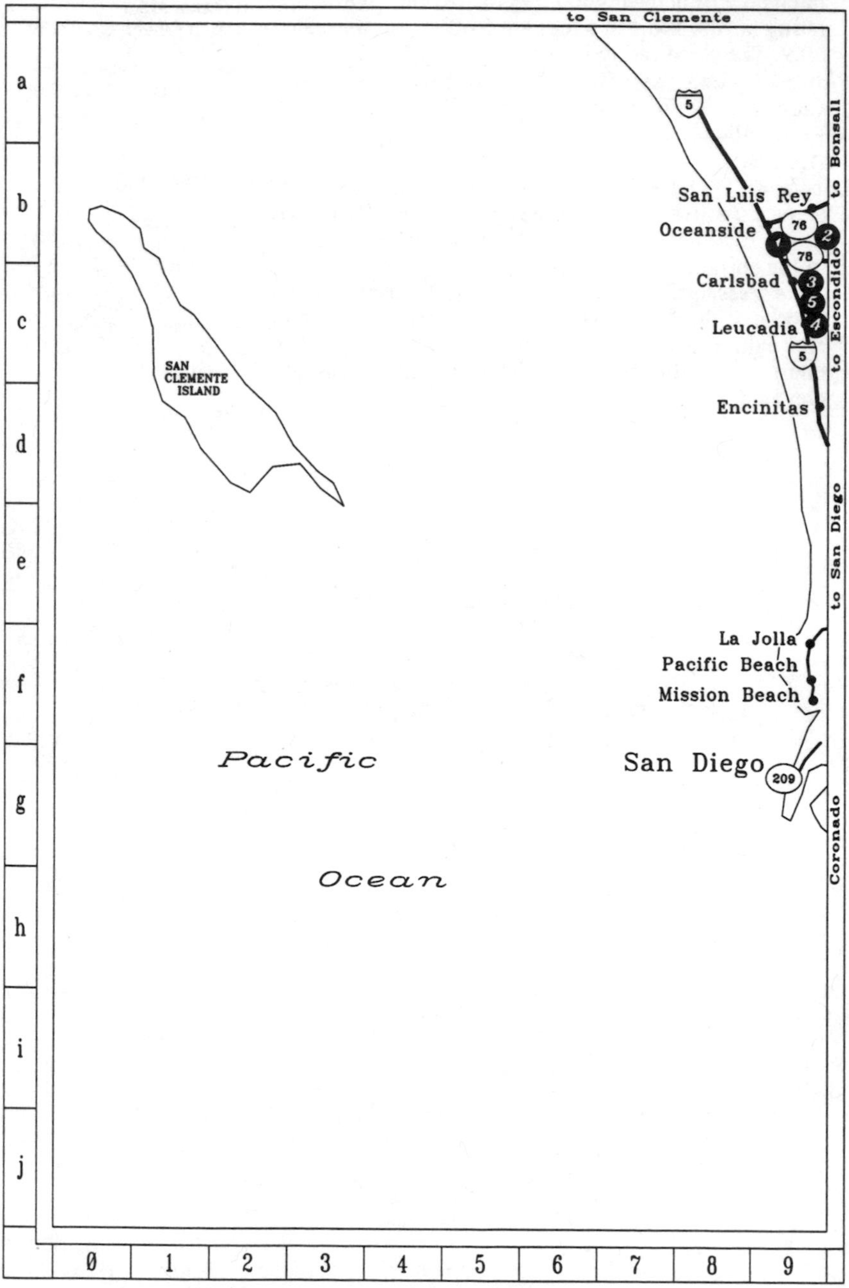

# CENTER CITY GOLF COURSE

**Course 1**
MAP J5 grid b9

*Course information:* This public course has 18 holes. Par is 65 for men, 66 for women. From the red tees, the course is 4,148 yards; from the blue tees, 4,641; and from the white tees 4,345 yards. and is unrated from the regular tees. The slope rating is 104 regular (18 holes). Women's tees are 2,450 yards and rated 33.3. There is no slope rating.

*Play policy and fees:* Green fees are $12 weekdays, and $15 weekends for 18 holes.

*Location:* In Oceanside, exit off Interstate 5 on Oceanside Boulevard. Drive inland. Stay in the left lane and turn left on Greenbrier. The course is one-quarter mile from the freeway.

*Course description:* Owner-operator Keehn designed a new nine which opened for play October 1, 1992. That has stretched the 35-year old course to executive length, including one par-5. The course is very hilly, with virtually every hole going up or down. The greens are on the large side—and there is only one bunker on the site.

PO Box 1088
Oceanside, CA 92054

2323 Greenbrier Street
Oceanside, CA 92054

Pro shop (619) 433-8590

- ✓ **driving range**
- ✓ **practice greens**
- ✓ **power carts**
- ✓ **pull carts**
- ✓ **golf club rental**
- locker rooms
- showers
- executive course
- accommodations
- ✓ **food and beverages**
- clubhouse

**Ludwig Keehn**
Manager

# EL CAMINO COUNTRY CLUB

**Course 2**
MAP J5 grid b9

*Course information:* This private course has 18 holes and par is 72. The course is 6,734 yards and rated 72.5 from the championship tees, and 6,362 yards and rated 70.0 from the regular tees. The slope ratings are 130 championship and 119 regular. Women's tees are 5,814 yards and rated 73.5. The slope rating is 120.

*Play policy and fees:* Reciprocal play is accepted with members of other private clubs. Hotel guests welcome. Green fees are $30 weekdays and $35 weekends. Carts are $19. Reservations are recommended.

*Location:* Take Interstate 5 to the Highway 78 exit in Oceanside, drive to the El Camino Real exit north and cross the overpass to Vista Way and turn right. Drive a one-quarter mile to the club.

*Course description:* This course offers a flat layout with plenty of trees and narrow fairways that offer little trouble. The course plays long, so be prepared. It's not laid out in a circle, but pretty close to it; there is out-of-bounds to the left of every hole. The 42-room El Camino Inn is virtually adjacent to the course.

**1958**
3202 Vista Way
Oceanside, CA 92056

Clubhouse (619) 757-2100
Pro shop (619) 757-0321

- driving range
- ✓ **practice greens**
- ✓ **power carts**
- ✓ **pull carts**
- ✓ **golf club rental**
- ✓ **locker rooms**
- ✓ **showers**
- executive course
- ✓ **accommodations**
- ✓ **food and beverages**
- ✓ **clubhouse**

**Tommy Jackson**
Professional

**Chris Bridge**
Superintendent

# LA COSTA RESORT AND SPA

**Course 3**
MAP J5 grid c9

***Course information:*** This private facility has two 18-hole courses and par is 72 on both.

The North Course is 6,987 yards and rated 74.8 from the tournament tees, 6,608 yards and rated 72.1 from the championship tees, and 6,269 yards and rated 69.9 from the regular tees. The slope ratings are 137 tournament, 128 championship and 121 regular. Women's tees are 5,939 yards and rated 74.0. The slope rating is 127.

The South Course is 6,894 yards and rated 74.4 from the tournament tees, 6,524 yards and rated 72.0 from the championship tees, and 6,198 yards and rated 69.8 from the regular tees. The slope ratings are 138 tournament, 129 championship and 121 regular. Women's tees are 5,612 yards and rated 72.1. The slope rating is 123.

***Play policy and fees:*** Members and guests only. Hotel guests welcome. Green fees are $75. Carts are $35. Reservations are required.

***Location:*** Travel 20 miles north of San Diego on Interstate 5 to the La Costa Avenue exit east. Drive 1.5 miles to El Camino Real and turn left to the club.

***Course description:*** The North Course is wide open and rolling while the South Course is tighter and more demanding. This is the site of the PGA Tour's Tournament of Champions. Parts of both courses are used to create the tournament layout.

**Dick Wilson**
**Joe Lee**

Costa del Mar Road
Carlsbad, CA 92009

Pro shop (619) 438-9111

- ✓ **driving range**
- ✓ **practice greens**
- ✓ **power carts**
- pull carts
- ✓ **golf club rental**
- ✓ **locker rooms**
- ✓ **showers**
- executive course
- ✓ **accommodations**
- ✓ **food and beverages**
- ✓ **clubhouse**

**Mike Sullivan**
Professional

**Harold Vaubel**
Superintendent

## RANCHO CARLSBAD GOLF COURSE

**Course 4**
MAP J5 grid c9

5200 El Camino Real
Carlsbad, CA 92008

Pro shop (619) 438-1772
(619) 438-9926

- ✓ **driving range**
- ✓ **practice greens**
- power carts
- ✓ **pull carts**
- ✓ **golf club rental**
- locker rooms
- showers
- ✓ **executive course**
- accommodations
- ✓ **food and beverages**
- ✓ **clubhouse**

**Craig Hunt**
Professional

**Ram Miramontes**
Superintendent

*Course information:* This public executive course has 18 holes and par is 56. The course is 2,100 yards.

*Play policy and fees:* Green fees are $6 weekdays and $10 weekends. After 1 p.m. in winter and 2 p.m. in summer, it's $6 weekdays, $8 weekends.

*Location:* From Interstate 5, take Highway 78 east to El Camino Real (County Road S-11). Then drive south to Rancho Carlsbad Drive and turn left to the course.

*Course description:* This is a well-maintained course with flat terrain. It's challenging for any caliber golfer. It's a tight, tree-lined course. If you hit a bad shot it costs, but a good shot is rewarded. The greens tend to be fast and for this reason they can be difficult to putt. The two par-4s are 260 and 225 yards.

## FOUR SEASONS RESORT AVIARA

**Course 5**
MAP J5 grid c9

**1991**
**Arnold Palmer**

7447 Batiquitos Drive
Carlsbad, CA 92009

Pro shop (619) 929-0077

- ✓ **driving range**
- ✓ **practice greens**
- ✓ **power carts**
- pull carts
- ✓ **golf club rental**
- ✓ **locker rooms**
- ✓ **showers**
- executive course
- accommodations
- ✓ **food and beverages**
- ✓ **clubhouse**

**Jim Bellington,**
Director of Golf

**Bill Crist,**
Professional

**Dick Rudolph**
Superintendent

*Course information:* This resort course has 18 holes. Par is 72. The course is 7,007 yards and rated 74.9 from the tournament tees, 6,591 yards and rated 71.8 from the championship tees, and 6,054 yards and rated 68.7 from the regular tees. The slope ratings are 141 tournament, 130 championship and 119 regular. Women's tees are 5,007 yards, rated 61.9 with a slope rating of 119.

*Play policy and fees:* Outside play is accepted. Green fees are $90 daily, cart included. Reservations are recommended six days in advance. This course is available for tournaments.

*Location:* From Interstate 5, take Poinsettia Avenue exit east to Batiquitos Drive. Drive south to the club.

*Course description:* An Arnold Palmer design, *Golf Magazine* rated it one of the 10 best new courses of 1991, and with good reason. It follows the coastal upland topography and features wide fairways and positively enormous greens. The course is in top condition.

# MAP J6

(53 COURSES)

PAGES.. 672-715

SO-CAL MAP .....see page 466
adjoining maps
NORTH (I6).........see page 584
EAST (J7) ..........see page 716
SOUTH.........................no map
WEST (J5) .........see page 668

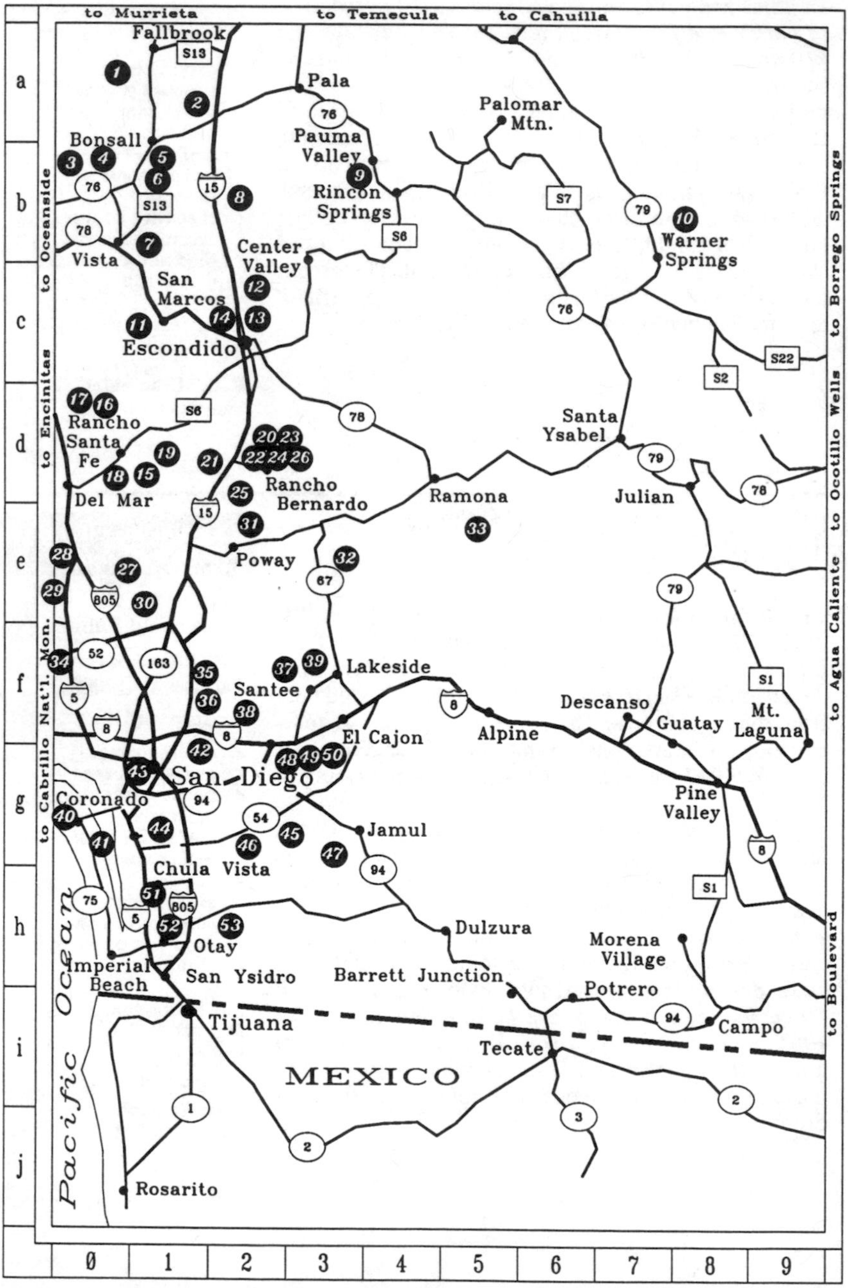

to Murrieta
to Temecula
to Cahuilla
to Oceanside
to Encinitas
to Cabrillo Nat'l. Mon.
to Borrego Springs
to Ocotillo Wells
to Agua Caliente
to Boulevard

Fallbrook
Pala
Palomar Mtn.
Bonsall
Pauma Valley
Rincon Springs
Warner Springs
Vista
San Marcos
Center Valley
Escondido
Rancho Santa Fe
Del Mar
Rancho Bernardo
Santa Ysabel
Ramona
Julian
Poway
Lakeside
Santee
El Cajon
Alpine
Descanso
Guatay
Mt. Laguna
San Diego
Coronado
Jamul
Pine Valley
Chula Vista
Otay
Dulzura
Morena Village
Imperial Beach
San Ysidro
Barrett Junction
Potrero
Campo
Tijuana
Tecate
MEXICO
Rosarito
Pacific Ocean

a b c d e f g h i j

0 1 2 3 4 5 6 7 8 9

# PALA MESA RESORT

**Course 1**
MAP J6 grid a0

**1964**
**Dick Rossen**

2001 South Highway 395
Fallbrook, CA 92028

Pro shop (619) 728-5881

- ✓ **driving range**
- ✓ **practice greens**
- ✓ **power carts**
- pull carts
- ✓ **golf club rental**
- locker rooms
- showers
- executive course
- ✓ **accommodations**
- ✓ **food and beverages**
- ✓ **clubhouse**

**Chris Starkjohann**
Professional

**Dale Hahn**
Superintendent

***Course information:*** This resort course has 18 holes and par is 72. The course is 6,461 yards and rated 72.0 from the championship tees, and 6,172 yards and rated 70.1 from the regular tees. The slope ratings are 131 championship and 125 regular. Women's tees are 5,814 yards and rated 74.5. The slope rating is 128 regular.

***Play policy and fees:*** Outside play is accepted. Hotel guests welcome. Green fees are $55 Mondays through Thursdays, and $70 Fridays and weekends. Carts are included. Reservations are recommended one week in advance.

***Location:*** From San Diego, drive north on Interstate 15 to the Highway 76. Turn left and drive to Old Highway 395. Turn right and drive two miles to the course.

***Course description:*** This scenic, mature course rolls through oak woodlands with tight fairways and fast greens. The course record is 62, set by host pro Chris Starkjohann in 1988. It's a pretty course, a little more demanding than your garden variety resort course. The inn, busiest in September and then February through April, has 132 newly refurbished rooms and all the usual amenities. It's 55 miles north of downtown San Diego, in the heart of avocado country.

# FALLBROOK GOLF CLUB

**Course 2**
MAP J6 grid a1

***Course information:*** This public course has 18 holes. See card below for yardage and rating information.

***Play policy and fees:*** Green fees are $22 weekdays and $30 weekends. Carts are $18. Reservations are recommended 10 days in advance. This course is available for outside tournaments.

***Location:*** From Interstate 15, take Highway 76 west two miles to Gird Road, drive north two miles to the course.

***Course description:*** This course features greens tightly guarded by sand. Shot-makers will score well here, especially those with a good short game. Live Oak Creek runs through the layout. It and the hundreds of live oak trees add to the course's beauty and challenge.

**1962**
**Harry Rainville**

PO Box 746
Fallbrook, CA 92028

2757 Gird Road
Fallbrook, CA 92028

Pro shop (619) 728-8334

- ✓ **driving range**
- ✓ **practice greens**
- ✓ **power carts**
- ✓ **pull carts**
- golf club rental
- locker rooms
- showers
- executive course
- accommodations
- ✓ **food and beverages**
- ✓ **clubhouse**

**Blair Cooke**
General Manager

**Ken Holloway**
Superintendent

| Hole | 1 | 2 | 3 | 4 | 5 | 6 | 7 | 8 | 9 | Out | | |
|---|---|---|---|---|---|---|---|---|---|---|---|---|
| BLUE | - | - | - | - | - | - | - | - | - | - | BLUE | Rating: -- |
| WHITE | 341 | 458 | 402 | 385 | 403 | 488 | 129 | 371 | 103 | 3080 | | Slope: -- |
| Par | 4 | 5 | 4 | 4 | 4 | 5 | 3 | 4 | 3 | 36 | WHITE | Rating: 69.8 |
| Handicap | 9 | 13 | 7 | 3 | 1 | 11 | 15 | 5 | 17 | x | | Slope: 117 |
| RED | 268 | 454 | 354 | 324 | 378 | 470 | 125 | 334 | 84 | 2791 | | |
| Par | 4 | 5 | 4 | 4 | 4 | 5 | 3 | 4 | 3 | 36 | RED | Rating: 71.6 |
| Handicap | 13 | 7 | 5 | 11 | 1 | 3 | 15 | 9 | 17 | x | | Slope: 119 |

| Hole | 10 | 11 | 12 | 13 | 14 | 15 | 16 | 17 | 18 | In | Totals | |
|---|---|---|---|---|---|---|---|---|---|---|---|---|
| BLUE | - | - | - | - | - | - | - | - | - | - | BLUE | -- |
| WHITE | 368 | 162 | 419 | 370 | 317 | 473 | 391 | 473 | 170 | 3143 | WHITE | 6223 |
| Par | 4 | 3 | 4 | 4 | 4 | 5 | 4 | 5 | 3 | 36 | Par | 72 |
| Handicap | 6 | 16 | 4 | 8 | 10 | 14 | 2 | 12 | 18 | x | | |
| RED | 339 | 151 | 380 | 325 | 274 | 434 | 355 | 403 | 145 | 2806 | RED | 5597 |
| Par | 4 | 3 | 4 | 4 | 4 | 5 | 4 | 5 | 3 | 36 | Par | 72 |
| Handicap | 6 | 16 | 2 | 10 | 14 | 8 | 4 | 12 | 18 | x | | |

# MARINE MEMORIAL GOLF COURSE

**Course 3**
MAP J6 grid b0

Buiding #18415
Camp Pendleton, CA 92055

Pro shop (619) 725-4704
Starter (619) 725-4756

- ✓ **driving range**
- ✓ **practice greens**
- ✓ **power carts**
- ✓ **pull carts**
- ✓ **golf club rental**
- ✓ **locker rooms**
- ✓ **showers**
- ✓ **executive course**
- accommodations
- ✓ **food and beverages**
- ✓ **clubhouse**

**John Clark**
Professional

**Phil Mata**
Superintendent

***Course information:*** This military course has 18 holes and par is 72. The course is 6,770 yards and rated 72.8 from the championship tees, and 6,379 yards and rated 70.2 from the regular tees. The slope ratings are 130 championship and 121 regular. Women's tees are 5,570 yards and rated 71.0. The slope rating is 118.

***Play policy and fees:*** Military personnel and guests only. Fees vary according to military personnel status.

***Location:*** From Highway 76 east of Oceanside, travel north on Douglas Drive 1.25 miles. Turn right on North River Road and drive 3.5 miles to the San Luis Rey entrance. From the Camp Pendleton main gate go one mile and turn left at the course sign.

***Course description:*** This is a relatively level course set in a peaceful valley. Some holes are strategically placed along the hills and slopes of the fairway. The fairways are tight and sand protects the greens.

# OCEANSIDE MUNICIPAL GOLF COURSE

**Course 4**
MAP J6 grid b0

825 Douglas Drive
Oceanside, CA 92056

Pro shop (619) 433-1360

- ✓ **driving range**
- ✓ **practice greens**
- ✓ **power carts**
- ✓ **pull carts**
- ✓ **golf club rental**
- locker rooms
- showers
- executive course
- accommodations
- ✓ **food and beverages**
- ✓ **clubhouse**

**Fred Wood**
Professional

**Chris Lemke**
Superintendent

***Course information:*** This public course has 18 holes and par is 72. The course is 6,450 yards and rated 70.8 from the championship tees, and 6,056 yards and rated 68.7 from the regular tees. The slope ratings are 118 championship and 109 regular. Women's tees are 5,398 yards and rated 70.3. The slope rating is 116.

***Play policy and fees:*** Green fees are $10 weekdays and $15 weekends. Carts are $16. Reservations are recommended 8 days in advance. This course is available for outside tournaments.

***Location:*** From Interstate 15 travel west on Highway 76 and turn right on Douglas Drive and go two miles to the course.

**Course description:** This course has level terrain, but water comes into play on 13 holes. The greens are fairly large. Mature trees line the fairways. The course offers a practice sand bunker for those in need. This is an American Golf Corporation property. That booming in the background is probably the Marines practicing artillery fire at nearby Camp Pendleton.

# SAN LUIS REY DOWNS GOLF AND COUNTRY CLUB

**Course 5**
MAP J6 grid b1

31474 Golf Club Drive
Bonsall, CA 92003

Pro shop (619) 758-9699
Clubhouse: (619) 758-3762

- ✓ **driving range**
- ✓ **practice greens**
- ✓ **power carts**
- ✓ **pull carts**
- ✓ **golf club rental**
- locker rooms
- showers
- executive course
- ✓ **accommodations**
- ✓ **food and beverages**
- ✓ **clubhouse**

**Greg Milligan**
Professional

**Gregg Swanson**
Superintendent

***Course information:*** This resort course has 18 holes and par is 72. The course is 6,750 yards and rated 72.6 from the championship tees, and 6,365 yards and rated 70.5 from the regular tees. The slope ratings are 128 championship and 122 regular. Women's tees are 5,493 yards and rated 71.4. The slope rating is 124.

***Play policy and fees:*** Outside play is accepted. Hotel guests are welcome. Green fees are $25 walking, $33 riding weekdays, and $40 weekends, which includes a mandatory cart. Reservations are recommended. This course is available for outside tournaments.

***Location:*** From Interstate I5, travel 4.5 miles west on Highway 76 to West Lilac Road in the town of Bonsall. Turn left over the bridge and bear left at the sign for San Luis Rey Downs. Continue for three-fourths of a mile to the golf resort.

***Course description:*** The San Luis Rey River snakes through this level course, where water comes into play on nine holes. Five par-3s and five par-5s add a twist to this generally tree-lined layout. A 26-room lodge is busy with winter visitors November through April. Adjacent to the course is the San Luis Rey Downs Training Center, where top-notch thoroughbred horses are trained. This helps draw the horsey set to play.

## VISTA VALLEY COUNTRY CLUB

**Course 6**
MAP J6 grid b1

**1978**
**Ted Robinson**

29354 Vista Valley Drive
Vista, CA 92084

Pro shop (619 )758-5275
Clubhouse (619) 758-2800

- ✓ **driving range**
- ✓ **practice greens**
- ✓ **power carts**
- ✓ **pull carts**
- golf club rental
- ✓ **locker rooms**
- ✓ **showers**
- executive course
- accommodations
- ✓ **food and beverages**
- ✓ **clubhouse**

**Phillip Machamer**
Professional

**Ronald Nolf**
Superintendent

***Course information:*** This private course has 18 holes and par is 71. The course is 6,411 yards and rated 71.3 from the championship tees, and 6,090 yards and rated 69.8 from the regular tees. The slope ratings are 128 championship and 122 regular. Women's tees are 5,630 yards and rated 74.4. The slope is 133.

***Play policy and fees:*** Reciprocal play is accepted with members of other private clubs. Members and guests only. Guest fees are $40 with a member and $60 without a member. Carts and range balls are included. Reservations are recommended seven days in advance.

***Location:*** From Interstate 15 take the Gopher Canyon Road exit and travel west for 2.5 miles to Vista Valley Drive. Turn left and drive one-half mile to the club.

***Course description:*** This course is nestled in a valley with a creek meandering through the hills. There are scenic mountain views. This is a good, challenging golf course for the low- and high-handicapper.

## SHADOW RIDGE COUNTRY CLUB

**Course 7**
MAP J6 grid b1

**1981**
**Ted Robinson**

1980 Gateway Drive
Vista, CA 92083

Pro shop (619) 727-7706
Clubhouse: (619) 727-7700

- ✓ **driving range**
- ✓ **practice greens**
- ✓ **power carts**
- pull carts
- ✓ **golf club rental**
- ✓ **locker rooms**
- ✓ **showers**
- executive course
- accommodations
- ✓ **food and beverages**
- ✓ **clubhouse**

**Hank George**
Professional

**Ed Mena**
Superintendent

***Course information:*** This private course has 18 holes and par is 72. The course is 6,059 yards and rated 73.3 from the championship tees, and 6,374 yards and rated 69.9 from the regular tees. The slope ratings are 124 championship and 114 regular. Women's tees are 5,693 yards and rated 73.3. The slope rating is 127.

***Play policy and fees:*** Members and guests only. Green fees are $49.50 including cart.

***Location:*** Travel north from San Diego on Interstate 5 or Interstate 15 to Highway 78. Take the Sycamore exit off Highway 78 and go south to Shadowridge Drive. Turn right and continue to Gateway Drive.

***Course description:*** This is a rolling layout with eucalyptus-lined fairways, several picturesque lakes and a beautiful finishing hole with a stone-edged lake set in front of the green.

# CASTLE CREEK COUNTRY CLUB

**Course 8**
MAP J6 grid b2

**1956**
**Jack Daray**

Route 2 Box 301
Escondido, CA 92026

8797 Circle "R" Drive
Escondido, CA 92026

Pro shop (619) 749-2422
Clubhouse (619) 749-2877

driving range
✓ **practice greens**
✓ **power carts**
✓ **pull carts**
✓ **golf club rental**
✓ **locker rooms**
✓ **showers**
executive course
✓ **accommodations**
✓ **food and beverages**
✓ **clubhouse**

**Michael Warren**
Manager

**Clayton Miller**
Professional

**Henry Hashimoto**
Superintendent

***Course information:*** This semi-private course has 18 holes. See card below for yardage and rating information.

***Play policy and fees:*** Outside play is accepted. Green fees are $20 weekdays and $40 weekends. Carts are $20. Reciprocal play is accepted.

***Location:*** From Interstate 15, take the Old Castle Road/Gopher Canyon Road exit and travel east. Turn left and drive one-half mile to the club.

***Course description:*** Castle Creek meanders through this well-maintained course. The front nine is flat and the back nine is hilly. There are numerous trees lining the fairways.

| Hole | 1 | 2 | 3 | 4 | 5 | 6 | 7 | 8 | 9 | Out | | |
|---|---|---|---|---|---|---|---|---|---|---|---|---|
| BLUE | 389 | 530 | 288 | 399 | 179 | 587 | 369 | 142 | 375 | 3258 | BLUE | Rating: 70.4 |
| | | | | | | | | | | | | Slope: 124 |
| WHITE | 365 | 519 | 269 | 385 | 159 | 537 | 354 | 126 | 367 | 3081 | | |
| Par | 4 | 5 | 4 | 4 | 3 | 5 | 4 | 3 | 4 | 36 | WHITE | Rating: 68.3 |
| Handicap | 7 | 9 | 13 | 3 | 15 | 1 | 11 | 17 | 5 | x | | Slope: 117 |
| RED | 361 | 500 | 226 | 377 | 134 | 480 | 290 | 120 | 342 | 2830 | | |
| Par | 4 | 5 | 4 | 4 | 3 | 5 | 4 | 3 | 4 | 36 | RED | Rating: 72.9 |
| Handicap | 9 | 3 | 13 | 5 | 15 | 1 | 11 | 17 | 7 | x | | Slope: 125 |

| Hole | 10 | 11 | 12 | 13 | 14 | 15 | 16 | 17 | 18 | In | Totals | |
|---|---|---|---|---|---|---|---|---|---|---|---|---|
| BLUE | 462 | 447 | 494 | 274 | 334 | 158 | 283 | 179 | 365 | 2996 | BLUE | 6254 |
| WHITE | 438 | 437 | 478 | 260 | 275 | 143 | 269 | 162 | 356 | 2818 | WHITE | 5899 |
| Par | 5 | 4 | 5 | 4 | 4 | 3 | 4 | 3 | 4 | 36 | Par | 72 |
| Handicap | 16 | 2 | 8 | 14 | 4 | 18 | 10 | 12 | 6 | x | | |
| RED | 428 | 415 | 457 | 239 | 257 | 134 | 226 | 158 | 332 | 2646 | RED | 5476 |
| Par | 5 | 5 | 5 | 4 | 4 | 3 | 4 | 3 | 4 | 37 | Par | 73 |
| Handicap | 6 | 4 | 2 | 12 | 10 | 18 | 14 | 16 | 8 | x | | |

# PAUMA VALLEY COUNTRY CLUB

**Course 9**
MAP J6 grid b3

**1960**
**Robert Trent Jones, Sr.**

Pauma Valley Drive
PO Box 206
Pauma Valley, CA 92061

Pro shop (619) 742-1230
Clubhouse (619) 742-3721

- ✓ **driving range**
- ✓ **practice greens**
- ✓ **power carts**
- pull carts
- golf club rental
- ✓ **locker rooms**
- ✓ **showers**
- executive course
- accommodations
- ✓ **food and beverages**
- ✓ **clubhouse**

**Bill Stutzer**
Professional

**Wayne Graf**
Superintendent

***Course information:*** This private course has 18 holes and par is 71. The course is 7,077 yards and rated 75.5 from the championship tees, and 6,468 yards and rated 71.4 from the regular tees. The slope ratings are 137 championship and 126 regular. Women's tees are 5,891 yards and rated 73.5. The slope rating is 122.

***Play policy and fees:*** Members and guests only. Green fees are $50. Carts are $20.

***Location:*** From Interstate 15 travel east on Highway 76 for 14 miles to the town of Pauma Valley. Turn right on Pauma Valley Drive and continue three-fourths of a mile to the club.

***Course description:*** Pick your trap; they are everywhere. This is a difficult course with more than 120 bunkers and is considered a ball striker's course. It's an original Robert Trent Jones, Sr. layout and plays very long. Very private, and all things considered, it's generally regarded as one of the top three courses in San Diego county. It has it all.

# WARNER SPRINGS RANCH

**Course 10**
MAP J6 grid b8

**1984**
**Ted Robinson**

Box 10
Warner Springs, CA 92086

31652 Highway 79
Warner Springs, CA 92086

Pro shop (619) 782-4270

- ✓ **driving range**
- ✓ **practice greens**
- ✓ **power carts**
- ✓ **pull carts**
- ✓ **golf club rental**
- ✓ **locker rooms**
- ✓ **showers**
- executive course
- accommodations
- ✓ **food and beverages**
- ✓ **clubhouse**

**Claude Waymire**
Professional

**David Waymire**
Superintendent

***Course information:*** This private course has 18 holes and par is 72. The course is 6,701 yards and rated 71.7 from the championship tees, and 6,252 yards and rated 69.1 from the regular tees. The slope ratings are 121 championship and 116 regular. Women's tees are 5,468 yards and rated 70.2. The slope rating is 119.

***Play policy and fees:*** Reciprocal play is accepted with members of other clubs. Green fees are $35 weekdays and $45 weekends for reciprocators. Carts are included. Reservations are a must. This course is available for outside tournaments. Proper golf attire required.

***Location:*** From Interstate 15 at Temecula, drive 38 miles south on Highway 79.

***Course description:*** This mature course traverses rolling, desert-mountain terrain and is fairly open. Three lakes come into play.

# LAKE SAN MARCOS COUNTRY CLUB

**Course 11**
MAP J6 grid c1

**1963**
**Gordon Frazar**

1750 San Pablo Drive
Lake San Marcos, CA 92069

Pro shop (619) 744-1310
Executive (619) 744-9092

- ✓ **driving range**
- ✓ **practice greens**
- ✓ **power carts**
- ✓ **pull carts**
- ✓ **golf club rental**
- locker rooms
- showers
- ✓ **executive course**
- ✓ **accommodations**
- ✓ **food and beverages**
- ✓ **clubhouse**

**Bob Hitzel**
Professional

**Ed Kelly**
Superintendent

***Course information:*** This resort course has 18 holes and par is 72. There is also an executive course. The course is 6,515 yards and rated 70.2 from the championship tees, and 6,272 yards and rated 69.2 from the regular tees. The slope ratings are 124 championship and 116 regular. Women's tees are 5,942 yards and rated 72.2. The slope rating is 130. The executive course is 2,700 yards. Women's tees are 2,226 yards.

***Play policy and fees:*** Reciprocal play is accepted with members of other private clubs, otherwise members and guests only. Hotel guests welcome. Green fees are $40 for hotel guests and $45 for all others. Carts are included. Reservations are recommended. Greens fees for the executive course are $11 before 3 p.m. and $7 after 3 p.m. For juniors 17-and-under the green fee is $5.

***Location:*** Take the Palomar Airport Road exit from Interstate 5. Travel seven miles east to Rancho Santa Fe Road and turn right. Continue to Lake San Marcos. To reach the executive course, continue to Camino del Arroyo. Turn left to the course.

***Course description:*** This gently rolling layout through a housing development is mature and well-maintained. The 610-yard third hole is a double dogleg known locally as the Monster. Greens, many of which are slightly elevated, are sloping, making ball positioning a key.

# MEADOW LAKE COUNTRY CLUB

**Course 12**
MAP J6 grid c2

10333 Meadow Glen East
Escondido, CA 92026

Pro shop (619) 749-1620
Clubhouse (619) 749-0983

- ✓ **driving range**
- ✓ **practice greens**
- ✓ **power carts**
- pull carts
- ✓ **golf club rental**
- ✓ **locker rooms**
- showers
- executive course
- accommodations
- ✓ **food and beverages**
- ✓ **clubhouse**

**Jim Gilbert**
Professional

**Mike Shaw**
Superintendent

***Course information:*** This semi-private course has 18 holes and par is 72. The course is 6,521 yards and rated 72.5 from the championship tees, and 6,312 yards and rated 71.0 from the regular tees. The slope ratings are 131 championship and 124 regular. Women's tees are 5,758 yards and rated 72.8. The slope rating is 123.

***Play policy and fees:*** Outside play is accepted. Green fees are $32 weekdays and $36 weekends, including carts. Green fees without golf carts are $22 weekdays and $26 weekends. Reservations are recommended seven days in advance.

***Location:*** 33 miles north of San Diego, take the Mountain Meadows exit off Interstate 15 and travel east 1.5 miles to the club located on Meadow Glen Way.

***Course description:*** This is a mountainous course with lots of doglegs. There are blind shots, but the variation between tight and open, demanding and forgiving makes this a sporty track. Don't be deceived by stated yardage—elevation changes call for every club in the bag.

# LAWRENCE WELK RESORT

**Course 13**
MAP J6 grid c2

**1986**
**David Rainville**

8860 Lawrence Welk Drive
Escondido, CA 92026

Pro shop (619) 749-3225

- driving range
- ✓ **practice greens**
- ✓ **power carts**
- ✓ **pull carts**
- ✓ **golf club rental**
- locker rooms
- showers
- ✓ **executive course**
- ✓ **accommodations**
- ✓ **food and beverages**
- ✓ **clubhouse**

**Cachi Trejo**
Professional

**Jim Brown**
Superintendent

***Course information:*** This resort has two 18-hole courses. Par is 62 on the Fountain Executive Course and 54 on the par-3 Oaks Course.

The Fountain Executive Course is 4,002 yards and rated 57.3 with a slope of 95 from the championship tees, and 3,581 yards and rated 54.6 with a slope of 89 from the regular tees. Women's tees are 3,099 yards and rated 58.1. The slope rating is 84.0.

The par-3 Oaks Course is 1,837 yards. Women's tees are 1,652 yards.

***Play policy and fees:*** Outside play is accepted. Green fees are $28 weekdays and $32 weekends for the Fountain Executive Course, including cart. Twilight rate for the Fountains Executive Course is $20 after 2 p.m. in summer and 1 p.m. in winter. Green fees are $12 any day for the Oaks Course. A cart is not required for the Oaks Course. Reservations are recommended. This course is available for outside tournaments.

***Location:*** 33 miles north of San Diego on Interstate 15 take the Mountain Meadow Road exit. Turn north on Champagne Boulevard and drive to the course entrance.

***Course description:*** The Fountains Executive Course is short and well maintained with narrow fairways. The men's course record is 57, held by Jim Robbyn. The Oaks Course is a challenging par-3 with century-old California oak trees lining the fairway and undulating greens.

# ESCONDIDO COUNTRY CLUB

**Course 14**
MAP J6 grid c2

**1962**
**Harry Rainville**

1800 West Country Club Lane
Escondido, CA 92026

Pro shop (619) 746-4212
Clubhouse (619) 743-3301

- ✓ **driving range**
- ✓ **practice greens**
- ✓ **power carts**
- pull carts
- ✓ **golf club rental**
- ✓ **locker rooms**
- ✓ **showers**
- executive course
- accommodations
- ✓ **food and beverages**
- ✓ **clubhouse**

**Tom Sims**
Professional

**Jose Canedo**
Senior Superintendent

*Course information:* This private course has 18 holes and par is 70. The course is 6,140 yards and rated 69.1 from the championship tees, and 5,884 yards and rated 67.7 from the regular tees. The slope ratings are 111 championship and 107 regular. Women's tees are 5,536 yards and rated 71.7. The slope rating is 124.

*Play policy and fees:* Members and guests only. Green fees are $30 weekdays and $40 weekends. Carts are $20.

*Location:* Take the Centre City Parkway off Interstate 15 two miles north of Escondido. Turn left on Country Club Lane and drive one mile to the club.

*Course description:* An American Golf Corporation property, it's sneaky hard, with hills, wind and subtle greens all in the mix—plus a stream that meanders through most of the course. Accuracy pays here, and patience. It doesn't look lethal, but it can be.

# HERITAGE HILLS COUNTRY CLUB

**Course 15**
MAP J6 grid d0

**1991**
**Joseph Lee**

6001 Camino Santa Fe
Rancho Santa Fe, CA 92067

Pro shop (619) 759-2720
Clubhouse (619) 759-5900

- ✓ **driving range**
- ✓ **practice greens**
- ✓ **power carts**
- pull carts
- golf club rental
- ✓ **locker rooms**
- ✓ **showers**
- executive course
- accommodations
- ✓ **food and beverages**
- ✓ **clubhouse**

**Bill Pennington**
General Manager

**Tim Moher**
Professional

**David Major**
Superintendent

*Course information:* This private course has 18 holes. Par is 72. The course is 6,950 yards from the tournament tees, and 6,508 yards from the championship tees with a rating of 74.4, and 5,972 yards from the regular tees with a rating of 71.2. Women's tees are 5,381 yards and rated 72.0. The slope rating of the championship tees is 133, the regular slope rating is 123, and the women's is 123.

*Play policy and fees:* Members and guests only. Reciprocal play is not accepted. Green fees were not available.

*Location:* Take the Via de la Valle exit off Interstate 5 and drive east to El Camino Real south. At San Dieguito Road, travel one mile and turn east. The course is about 600 yards east of the entrance to the Fairbanks Country Club.

*Course description:* This course opened in December, 1991. It features bent grass from tee to green and four lakes coming into play on four holes. The course is situated in a natural valley. There is a riparian of natural timbers and stands of old eucalyptus, plus new plantings. Last but not least, there are 80 bunkers with which to contend.

# RANCHO SANTA FE GOLF CLUB

**Course 16**
MAP J6 grid d0

PO Box 598
Rancho Santa Fe, CA 92067

Via de la Cumbre
Rancho Santa Fe, CA 92067

Pro shop (619) 756-3094
Clubhouse (619) 756-1174

- ✓ **driving range**
- ✓ **practice greens**
- ✓ **power carts**
- ✓ **pull carts**
- ✓ **golf club rental**
- ✓ **locker rooms**
- ✓ **showers**
- executive course
- ✓ **accommodations**
- ✓ **food and beverages**
- ✓ **clubhouse**

**Chuck Courtney**
Professional

**Tony Guerra**
Superintendent

***Course information:*** This private course has 18 holes and par is 72. The course is 6,911 yards and rated 74.3 from the championship tees, and 6,452 yards and rated 71.3 from the regular tees. The slope ratings are 137 championship and 129 regular. Women's tees are 5,869 yards and rated 74.8. The slope rating is 131.

***Play policy and fees:*** Members and guests only. Inn at Rancho Santa Fe guests are welcome to play at $90 per round, including cart. Reservations are recommended.

***Location:*** Take Interstate 5 to Lomas Santa Fe Drive and travel east for four miles on Highway 8 to the inn. Turn left on Avenida de Acacias and drive one-half mile to Via de la Cumbre, then go left one-half mile to the club.

***Course description:*** This course has some history. It was the original site of the Bing Crosby National Pro-Am and was the hangout of many Hollywood types during the 1940s and '50s. It has a rolling layout among mature trees with very little water. Regarded locally as one of the top courses in the country, if not Southern California, the design is a tribute to economy, demanding both strength and smarts. A true treasure.

# LOMAS SANTA FE COUNTRY CLUB

**Course 17**
MAP J6 grid d0

*Course information:* This private course has 18 holes and par is 72. There is also an executive course. The main course is 6,566 yards and rated 72.1 from the championship tees, and 6,163 yards and rated 69.6 from the regular tees. The slope ratings are 127 championship and 119 regular. Women's tees are 5,796 and rated 72.7. The slope rating is 120. The executive course is 2,380 yards. Women's tees are 2,119 yards.

*Play policy and fees:* Members and guests only. Green fees are $35 weekdays and $45 weekends. Carts are $9.50 per person. Executive green fees are $12 weekdays and $15 weekends for 18 holes. Carts are $14. Call for other special rates.

*Location:* Take the Lomas Santa Fe Drive exit off Interstate 5 and drive east one mile to the club. The executive course is on the north side.

*Course description:* This is a well-maintained course in a beautiful setting. The course offers rolling terrain with tight fairways. All new greens were constructed in 1991—and they're firm and true.

PO Box 1007
Solana Beach, CA 92075

Lomas Santa Fe Drive
at Highland
Solana Beach, CA 92075

Pro shop (619) 755-1547
Clubhouse (619) 755-6768
Executive (619) 755-0195

✓ **driving range**
✓ **practice greens**
✓ **power carts**
✓ **pull carts**
golf club rental
locker rooms
showers
✓ **executive course**
accommodations
✓ **food and beverages**
✓ **clubhouse**

**Robert Bellesi**
Professional

**Chris Lemke**
Superintendent

# FAIRBANKS RANCH COUNTRY CLUB

**Course 18**
MAP J6 grid d0

**1984**
**Ted Robinson**

PO Box 8055
Rancho Santa Fe, CA 92067

15150 San Dieguito Road
Rancho Santa Fe, CA 92067

Pro shop (619) 259-8819
Clubhouse (619) 259-8811

- ✓ **driving range**
- ✓ **practice greens**
- ✓ **power carts**
- pull carts
- ✓ **golf club rental**
- ✓ **locker rooms**
- ✓ **showers**
- executive course
- accommodations
- ✓ **food and beverages**
- ✓ **clubhouse**

**Richard "Tag" Merritt**
Professional

**Brian Darrock**
Superintendent

***Course information:*** This private course has 18 holes and par is 72. The course is 7,200 yards and rated 75.0, with a slope rating of 135 from the tournament tees, 6,666 yards and rated 71.8, from the white tees, and 6,200 yards and rated 69.1 from the gold tees. The slope ratings are 135 tournament, and 125 white and 113 gold. Women's tees are 5,911 yards and rated 76.7. The slope rating is 129.

***Play policy and fees:*** Members and guests only.

***Location:*** Take the Via de la Valle exit off Interstate 5 and drive east to El Camino Real south. At San Dieguito Road, travel one mile and turn east 1.5 miles.

***Course description:*** Ted Robinson designed this challenging course, which bears his trademarks: The greens are surrounded by mounds and palm trees, and there is quite a bit of water. This course was the site of the 1984 Olympic equestrian event. It can be about two shots tougher in the afternoon, but it's almost always in ideal condition. Fairbanks Ranch hosted the 1992 California Amateur.

# WHISPERING PALMS COUNTRY CLUB

**Course 19**
MAP J6 grid d1

**1965**
**David Rainville**
**North & South**

**1972**
**Larry Jones**
**East**

PO Box 3209
Rancho Santa Fe, CA 92067

4000 Concha de Golf
Rancho Santa Fe, CA 92067

Pro shop (619) 756-3255
Clubhouse (619) 756-2471

- driving range
- ✓ **practice greens**
- ✓ **power carts**
- ✓ **pull carts**
- ✓ **golf club rental**
- locker rooms
- showers
- executive course
- ✓ **accommodations**
- ✓ **food and beverages**
- ✓ **clubhouse**

**John Combs**
Professional

**Larry Jones**
Superintendent

***Course information:*** This resort club has 27 holes. Par is 72 for East/South and 71 for the South/North and North East courses.

The South/North Course is 6,346 yards and rated 69.7 from the championship tees, and 6,051 yards and rated 67.9 from the regular tees. The slope ratings are 112 championship and 105 regular. Women's tees are 5,603 yards and rated 71.7. The slope rating is 117.

The East/South Course is 6,443 yards and rated 70.2 from the championship tees, and 6,131 yards and rated 68.3 from the regular tees. The slope ratings are 112 championship and 105 regular. Women's tees are 5,705 yards and rated 72.6. The slope rating is 120.

The North/East Course is 6,141 yards and rated 68.8 from the championship tees, and 5,860 yards and rated 67.0 from the regular tees. The slope ratings are 110 championship and 103 regular. Women's tees are 5,514 yards and rated 71.7. The slope rating is 117.

***Play policy and fees:*** Outside play is accepted. Green fees are $23 weekdays and $28 weekends and holidays. Carts are $22. Reservations are recommended three days in advance. This course is available for outside tournaments.

***Location:*** Take the Valley Parkway (S-6) off Interstate 15 in Escondido and drive 10 miles west and turn left at Concha de Golf.

***Course description:*** This flat course is easy to walk, but the narrow fairways and long rough make it challenging. A river snakes through two of the nines. Known locally for its slow greens, the internationally acclaimed San Diego Academy of Golf is based here, and its students are on the course almost daily; they do not interfere with outside play.

# MIRAMAR MEMORIAL GOLF CLUB

**Course 20**
MAP J6 grid d2

***Course information:*** This military course has 18 holes and par is 72. The course is 6,685 yards and rated 72.1 from the championship tees, and 6,309 yards and rated 69.6 from the regular tees. The slope ratings are 122 championship and 114 regular. Women's white tees are 6,309 yards and rated 75.6. The slope rating is 128. Women's red tees are 5,899 yards and rated 73.3. The slope rating is 124.

***Play policy and fees:*** Military personnel and guests only. Green fees are based on military status.

***Location:*** Take Interstate 15 or State Road 163 12 miles north of San Diego to Miramar Way. Exit and drive west to main gate.

***Course description:*** This course is virtually adjacent to runways that are home to the Navy's "Top Gun" fighter pilots; the base was used in the movie. The course was originally built as an emergency landing area. Today, it's lined with trees. It's flat, but wind and rough make it a firm test.

**1963**
**Jack Daray**

PO Box 45312
San Diego, CA 92145

NAS Miramar
San Diego, CA 92145

Pro shop (619) 537-4155

- ✓ **driving range**
- ✓ **practice greens**
- ✓ **power carts**
- ✓ **pull carts**
- ✓ **golf club rental**
- ✓ **locker rooms**
- showers
- executive course
- accommodations
- ✓ **food and beverages**
- ✓ **clubhouse**

**Pam Procop**
Professional

**Gene Stoddard**
Superintendent

# CARMEL HIGHLAND GOLF AND TENNIS RESORT

**Course 21**
MAP J6 grid d2

**1986**
**Remodeled**
**Jack Daray**

PO Box 28565
San Diego, CA 92128

14455 Penasquitos Drive
San Diego, CA 92129

Pro shop (619) 672-2200

- ✓ **driving range**
- ✓ **practice greens**
- ✓ **power carts**
- pull carts
- ✓ **golf club rental**
- ✓ **locker rooms**
- ✓ **showers**
- executive course
- ✓ **accommodations**
- ✓ **food and beverages**
- ✓ **clubhouse**

**Michael Flanagan**
Director of Golf

**Mike Magnani**
Superintendent

***Course information:*** This resort course has 18 holes and par is 72. The course is 6,521 yards and rated 71.1 from the championship tees, and 6,108 yards and rated 68.9 from the regular tees. The slope ratings are 122 championship and 115 regular. Women's tees are 5,488 yards and rated 71.4. The slope rating is 119.

***Play policy and fees:*** Green fees are $30 weekdays plus cart. Carts are $10. Walking is optional on weekdays. Green fees are $50 weekends, including a mandatory cart. Senior rate during the week is $30, cart included. Reservations are recommended five days in advance. Proper golf attire is required.

***Location:*** Travel 20 miles north of San Diego on Interstate 15 to the Carmel Mountain Road exit. Drive west for one-quarter mile to Penasquitos Drive and turn right to the club entrance.

***Course description:*** This course is well groomed with exceptional greens. Water comes into play on four holes. The par-5 sixth hole has a lateral water hazard running alongside the fairway and a pond in front of the green. Hole eight is a long par-4 up a hill to a sloped green. This course has undergone significant improvement in recent years. Although most of it is up, down and sidehill, it is lush and most often in fine condition.



MAP ON PAGE 672

# RANCHO BERNARDO INN AND COUNTRY CLUB

**Course 22**
MAP J6 grid d2

**1962**
**William Francis Bell**

Box 28074
San Diego, CA 92128

17550 Bernardo Oaks Drive
San Diego, CA 92128

| | |
|---|---|
| Pro shop | (619) 487-0700 |
| Clubhouse | (619) 487-1611 |
| Executive | (619) 487-3021 |

- ✓ **driving range**
- ✓ **practice greens**
- ✓ **power carts**
- ✓ **pull carts**
- ✓ **golf club rental**
- locker rooms
- showers
- ✓ **executive course**
- ✓ **accommodations**
- ✓ **food and beverages**
- ✓ **clubhouse**

**Scott Mallory**
Director of Golf

**Bob Dobek**
Superintendent

***Course information:*** This resort course has 18 holes and par is 72. There is also a 27-hole executive course, Oaks North. The course is 6,458 yards and rated 70.6 from the championship tees, and 6,182 yards and rated 69.3 from the regular tees. The slope ratings are 122 championship and 118 regular. Women's tees are 5,448 yards and rated 71.2. The slope rating is 119.

***Play policy and fees:*** Outside play is accepted and hotel guests are welcome. The green fee is $44 weekdays, $54 weekends. Carts, mandatory only between nine a.m. and three p.m., are $11. Twilight rates are $20 weekdays, $25 weekends after two p.m. PST, three p.m. PDT. Reservations are recommended one week in advance. No jeans or running shorts allowed. Shirts must have collars and sleeves. Green fees for the executive course is $12 for nine holes and $18 for 18 holes weekdays, $15 for nine holes and $29 for 18 holes weekends.

***Location:*** Travel eight miles south of the town of Escondido on Interstate 15 to Rancho Bernardo Road east. Drive one mile to Bernardo Oaks Drive, and turn left to the inn and golf course.

***Course description:*** Set in a small valley and enclosed by homes, this course offers sloping fairways, a meandering creek and two lakes. Above all, accuracy is the key here. Rounds here can be time-consuming, with members playing early and plenty of difficulty on the course. The Inn, long a top-ranked tennis resort, has large nicely appointed accommodations and some of the best food in San Diego. One Minute Manager Golf School is based here.

## STONERIDGE COUNTRY CLUB

**Course 23**
MAP J6 grid d2

*Course information:* This private course has 18 holes and par is 72. The course is 6,286 yards and rated 69.9 from the championship tees, and 6,042 yards and rated 68.5 from the regular tees. The slope ratings are 118 championship and 111 regular. Women's tees are 5,679 yards and rated 72.0. The slope rating is 119.

*Play policy and fees:* Reciprocal play is accepted with members of other private clubs weekdays only. Green fees are $70 for reciprocators, including cart. Green fees are $60 for guests with members, including cart. Reservations are recommended.

*Location:* From Interstate 15 take the Rancho Bernardo Road exit and travel east for 2.5 miles to Stoneridge Country Club Lane.

*Course description:* The front nine is level and the back nine is hilly on this well maintained course. Afternoon winds can stiffen the challenge here. Stoneridge hosted the LPGA tour in 1988-92.

17166 Stoneridge Country Club Lane
Poway, CA 92064

Pro shop (619) 487-2117
Clubhouse (619) 487-2138

- ✓ **driving range**
- ✓ **practice greens**
- ✓ **power carts**
- pull carts
- golf club rental
- ✓ **locker rooms**
- ✓ **showers**
- executive course
- accommodations
- ✓ **food and beverages**
- ✓ **clubhouse**

**Ben Stewart**
Professional

**Delfino Cano**
Superintendent

## RANCHO BERNARDO GOLF CLUB

**Course 24**
MAP J6 grid d2

**Ted Robinson**

*Course information:* This private course has 18 holes and par is 72. The course is 6,468 yards and rated 70.3 from the tournament tees, 6,186 yards and rated 68.6 from the championship tees, and 5,663 yards and rated 65.9 from the forward tees. The slope ratings are 116 tournament, 109 championship and 103 regular. Women's tees are 5,546 yards and rated 71.9. The slope rating is 121.

*Play policy and fees:* Members and guests only. Guests must be accompanied by a member.

*Location:* Travel eight miles south of the city of Escondido on Interstate 15 to Rancho Bernardo Road east. Drive one mile to Bernardo Oaks Drive and turn left to the club.

*Course description:* This course has a fairly open layout where the short par-4s are uphill and the longer par-4s are downhill. It's known as hole-in-one paradise, although the par-3s range up to 190 yards.

12280 Greens East Road
San Diego, CA 92128

Pro shop (619) 487-1212
Clubhouse (619) 487-1134

- driving range
- ✓ **practice greens**
- ✓ **power carts**
- ✓ **pull carts**
- golf club rental
- locker rooms
- showers
- executive course
- accommodations
- ✓ **food and beverages**
- ✓ **clubhouse**

**Richard Carmody**
Professional

**Ken Williams**
Superintendent

# CARMEL MOUNTAIN RANCH GOLF COURSE

**Course 25**
MAP J6 grid d2

**1986**
**Ron Fream**

14050 Carmel Ridge Road
San Diego, CA 92128

Pro shop (619) 487-9224

- ✓ **driving range**
- ✓ **practice greens**
- ✓ **power carts**
- pull carts
- ✓ **golf club rental**
- ✓ **locker rooms**
- ✓ **showers**
- executive course
- accommodations
- ✓ **food and beverages**
- ✓ **clubhouse**

**Gary Glaser**
Professional

**Charles Reider**
Superintendent

***Course information:*** This semi-private course has 18 holes and par is 72. The course is 6,615 yards and rated 72.9 from the championship tees, and 6,217 yards and rated 70.5 from the regular tees. The slope ratings are 136 championship and 128 regular. Women's tees are 5,282 yards and rated 70.2. The slope rating is 121.

***Play policy and fees:*** Outside play is accepted. Green fees are $45 weekdays and $60 weekends. Carts are included. Reservations are recommended. This course is available for outside tournaments.

***Location:*** Take Interstate 15 to Carmel Mountain Road exit then take Highway 60 east to Highland Ranch Road and follow the signs to the clubhouse.

***Course description:*** The holes on this rolling, narrow course follow the contours of the hills. There are no parallel fairways. The greens are well kept and fast. Homes line virtually every fairway and there are some serious hills here, all of which demands accuracy, and patience.

# BERNARDO HEIGHTS COUNTRY CLUB

**Course 26**
MAP J6 grid d3

**1983**
**Ted Robinson**

16066 Bernardo Heights Prky.
San Diego, CA 92128

Pro shop (619) 487-3440
Clubhouse (619) 487-4022

- ✓ **driving range**
- ✓ **practice greens**
- ✓ **power carts**
- pull carts
- ✓ **golf club rental**
- ✓ **locker rooms**
- ✓ **showers**
- executive course
- accommodations
- ✓ **food and beverages**
- ✓ **clubhouse**

**Russ Bloom**
Professional

**Robert Steele**
Superintendent

***Course information:*** This private course has 18 holes and par is 72. The course is 6,748 yards and rated 72.5 from the championship tees, and 6,328 yards and rated 70.0 from the regular tees. The slope ratings are 125 championship and 118 regular. Women's tees are 5,624 yards and rated 73.2. The slope rating is 127.

***Play policy and fees:*** Reciprocal play is accepted with members of other private clubs. Green fees for guests are $25 weekdays and $40 weekends. Green fees for reciprocators are $50. Carts are $18. Reservations are recommended.

***Location:*** Take the Bernardo Center Drive exit off Interstate 15 and drive east to Bernardo Heights Parkway, then turn right to the club.

***Course description:*** This well-maintained course is hilly with a few trees, some water and fast greens. It hosted the LPGA in 1986-87. Homes and condos line many fairways, but are not intrusive. It's a big course, with large sloping greens.

# RANCHO SANTA FE FARMS GOLF CLUB

**Course 27**
MAP J6 grid e0

**1988**
**Perry Dye**

PO Box 5025
Rancho Santa Fe, CA 92067

8500 Saint Andrews Road
Rancho Santa Fe, CA 92067

Pro shop (619) 756-5585

- ✓ **driving range**
- ✓ **practice greens**
- ✓ **power carts**
- pull carts
- ✓ **golf club rental**
- ✓ **locker rooms**
- ✓ **showers**
- executive course
- accommodations
- ✓ **food and beverages**
- ✓ **clubhouse**

**John Schroeder**
Director of Golf

**Tommy Jacobs**
Senior Tour Representative

**Patrick Holden**
Superintendent

***Course information:*** This private course has 18 holes. The gold tees are 6,800 yards and are rated 73.8 with a slope of 140. The green tees are 4,847 yards and are rated 67.5 with a slope of 116. See card below for additional yardage and rating information.

***Play policy and fees:*** Members and guests only.

***Location:*** From Interstate 5, take the Carmel Valley Road exit and drive east four to five miles. Turn left on Rancho Santa Fe Road. At the dead end, turn right, the course is one-quarter mile.

***Course description:*** Members consider this maturing course a very private retreat. Michael Jordon and Janet Jackson are members. This very hilly course has three man-made lakes that come into play on five holes. This is one of the most scenic courses in the country. It demands accuracy to navigate rough-lined fairways and tiered greens, as well as some strength when the wind blows.

| Hole | 1 | 2 | 3 | 4 | 5 | 6 | 7 | 8 | 9 | Out | | |
|---|---|---|---|---|---|---|---|---|---|---|---|---|
| BLUE | 362 | 141 | 513 | 335 | 179 | 306 | 370 | 380 | 485 | 3071 | BLUE | Rating: 71.1 |
| WHITE | 323 | 129 | 482 | 309 | 166 | 289 | 330 | 351 | 430 | 2809 | | Slope: 131 |
| Par | 4 | 3 | 5 | 4 | 3 | 4 | 4 | 4 | 5 | 36 | WHITE | Rating: 68.6 |
| Handicap | 11 | 17 | 1 | 5 | 13 | 15 | 3 | 7 | 9 | x | | Slope: 121 |
| RED | 323 | 110 | 477 | 277 | 130 | 280 | 299 | 351 | 430 | 2677 | | |
| Par | 4 | 3 | 5 | 4 | 3 | 4 | 4 | 4 | 5 | 36 | RED | Rating: 71.6 |
| Handicap | 5 | 17 | 1 | 13 | 11 | 15 | 9 | 7 | 3 | x | | Slope: 125 |

| Hole | 10 | 11 | 12 | 13 | 14 | 15 | 16 | 17 | 18 | In | Totals | |
|---|---|---|---|---|---|---|---|---|---|---|---|---|
| BLUE | 411 | 367 | 495 | 381 | 163 | 364 | 171 | 430 | 508 | 3290 | BLUE | 6361 |
| WHITE | 390 | 339 | 457 | 358 | 145 | 314 | 154 | 402 | 481 | 3040 | WHITE | 5849 |
| Par | 4 | 4 | 5 | 4 | 3 | 4 | 3 | 4 | 5 | 36 | Par | 72 |
| Handicap | 4 | 12 | 6 | 8 | 18 | 14 | 16 | 2 | 10 | x | | |
| RED | 353 | 301 | 455 | 333 | 117 | 314 | 139 | 365 | 457 | 2834 | RED | 5511 |
| Par | 4 | 4 | 5 | 4 | 3 | 4 | 3 | 4 | 5 | 36 | Par | 72 |
| Handicap | 2 | 14 | 8 | 10 | 16 | 12 | 18 | 6 | 4 | x | | |

# TORREY PINES GOLF COURSE

**Course 28**
MAP J6 grid e0

***Course information:*** This public facility has two 18-hole courses and par is 72 on both.

The South Course is 7,033 yards and rated 74.6 from the championship tees, and 6,705 yards and rated 72.6 from the regular tees. The slope ratings are 136 championship and 130 regular. Women's tees are 6,463 yards and rated 77.2. The slope rating is 128.

The North Course is 6,647 yards and rated 72.1 from the championship tees, and 6,326 yards and rated 70.0 from the regular tees. The slope ratings are 129 championship and 119 regular. Women's tees are 6,118 yards and rated 73.5. The slope rating is 121.

***Play policy and fees:*** Green fees are $39.50 weekdays and $46 weekends. Carts are $22. Golf packages are available through the pro shop. Reservations are recommended seven days in advance. This course is available for outside tournaments. Waits can exceed two hours for those without a reservation.

***Location:*** From San Diego, drive north on Interstate 5 to Genesse and turn west to North Torrey Pines Road and turn north into the club.

***Course description:*** This is an excellent public facility. The South Course is wide open but it can be tough when the wind is blowing off the ocean. The North Course is shorter and more scenic. Both courses are used for the PGA Tour's Buick Invitational of California in February. The only water on either course fronts the 18th green on the South. Number 12 on the South Course at 486 yards into the wind has been rated the toughest hole in the country. The North Course is a good two shots easier.

**1957**
**William Francis Bell**

PO Box 9223
San Diego, CA 92109

11480 N. Torrey Pines Road
La Jolla, CA 92037

Pro shop (619) 452-3226
Clubhouse (619) 453-8148
Starter (619) 552-1784
Reservation (619) 570-1234

- ✓ **driving range**
- ✓ **practice greens**
- ✓ **power carts**
- ✓ **pull carts**
- ✓ **golf club rental**
- locker rooms
- showers
- executive course
- ✓ **accommodations**
- ✓ **food and beverages**
- ✓ **clubhouse**

**Joe DeBock**
Professional

**John Walter**
Superintendent

## LA JOLLA COUNTRY CLUB

**Course 29**
MAP J6 grid e0

*Course information:* This private course has 18 holes and par is 72. The course is 6,713 yards and rated 72.9 from the championship tees, and 6,254 yards and rated 70.2 from the regular tees. The slope ratings are 133 championship and 125 regular. Women's tees are 5,988 yards and rated 75.8. The slope rating is 134.

*Play policy and fees:* Members and guests only. Green fees are $40 weekdays and $60 weekends. Carts are $16.

*Location:* Take the Ardath Road exit (becomes Torrey Pines Road) off Interstate 5 north of San Diego and drive 3.25 miles. Turn left on Girard Street and then left on Pearl Street. Drive two blocks to High Street and turn right, then continue one block to the club.

*Course description:* This is an older traditional course perched on a bluff overlooking the Pacific. It is well maintained and relatively hilly with lots of trees and bunkers. When the wind picks up, it can be a tough course. The key here is accuracy—an ability to read the small, subtle and quick greens.

PO Box 1760
La Jolla, CA 92037

7301 High Avenue Extension
La Jolla, CA 92038

Pro shop (619) 454-2505
Clubhouse (619) 454-9601

- ✓ **driving range**
- ✓ **practice greens**
- ✓ **power carts**
- pull carts
- ✓ **golf club rental**
- ✓ **locker rooms**
- ✓ **showers**
- executive course
- accommodations
- ✓ **food and beverages**
- ✓ **clubhouse**

**Pete Coe**
Professional

**Carlos Gaines**
Superintendent

## SAN DIEGO NAVAL STATION GOLF COURSE

**Course 30**
MAP J6 grid e1

*Course information:* This military course has nine holes. Par is 54 for 18 holes. The course is 2,500 yards.

*Play policy and fees:* Green fees are according to military status.

*Location:* Going south on Interstate 5 take the Main Street exit. Cross Main Street and drive directly to the gate.

*Course description:* This is a short course with open fairways and small greens. Holes vary between 110 and 175 yards. It's all tucked snugly into the 32nd Street Naval Station just south of downtown San Diego.

MWR Code 10, NSGC
San Diego, CA 92136

Clubhouse (619) 556-7502

- ✓ **driving range**
- ✓ **practice greens**
- power carts
- ✓ **pull carts**
- ✓ **golf club rental**
- locker rooms
- showers
- executive course
- accommodations
- food and beverages
- clubhouse

# OAKS NORTH EXECUTIVE COURSE

**Course 31**
MAP J6 grid e2

**1971**
**Ted Robinson**

12602 Oaks North Drive
Rancho Bernardo, CA 92128

Pro shop (619) 487-3021
Clubhouse (619) 487-9148

✓ **driving range**
✓ **practice greens**
✓ **power carts**
✓ **pull carts**
✓ **golf club rental**
locker rooms
showers
✓ **executive course**
accommodations
✓ **food and beverages**
clubhouse

**Alice Herzog**
Manager

**Tom Wilson**
Professional

**Bob Dobeck**
Superintendent

***Course information:*** This public facility has 27 holes. There are three nines and each 18-hole combination is par 60.

The North/South course is 3,608 yards and rated 57.8. The slope rating is 88. Women's tees are 3,253 yards and rated 57.8. The slope rating is 86.

The South/East Course is 3,524 yards and rated 53.0. The slope rating is 87. Women's tees are 3,260 yards and rated 57.6. The slope rating is 87.

The North/East Course is 3,409 yards and rated 52.2. The slope rating is 86. Women's tees are 3,253 yards and rated 57.0. The slope rating is 85.

***Play policy and fees:*** Green fees are $14 for nine holes and $21 for 18 holes any day. Carts are $12 for nine holes and $17 for 18 holes. Dress code requires collared shirts, Bermuda-length shorts or slacks for men. No tank tops or short shorts for women.

***Location:*** Off Interstate 15 in Rancho Bernardo, take the Highland Valley Road/Pomerado exit and take it to Oaks North Drive. Turn left to the course.

***Course description:*** These executive courses have tight fairways and undulating greens. The courses have regulation par-4s and 3s, just no par-5s. Homes line some fairways. Greens are receptive—only two are tiered.

# MOUNT WOODSON COUNTRY CLUB

**Course 32**
MAP J6 grid e3

**1991**
**Landmark Signature**
**Lee Schmidt**

16302 North Woodson Drive
Ramona, CA 92065

Pro shop (619) 788-3555

- driving range
- ✓ **practice greens**
- ✓ **power carts**
- pull carts
- ✓ **golf club rental**
- locker rooms
- showers
- executive course
- accommodations
- ✓ **food and beverages**
- ✓ **clubhouse**

**Scott Bentley**
Professional

**Jon Marzolf**
Superintendent

***Course information:*** This semi-private course has 18 holes. Par is 70. This course is 6,180 yards and rated 68.8 from the championship tees, and 5,284 yards and rated 65.7 from the regular tees. The slope rating is 130 championship and 121 for the regular tees. Women's tees are 4,441 yards and rated 64.7. The slope rating is 108.

***Play policy and fees:*** Outside play is accepted. Green fees are $38 weekdays and $50 weekends. Carts are included. Twilight rates are $25 weekdays after 2 p.m., 1 p. m. during standard time, and $35 weekends after 3 p.m. Reservations recommended five days in advance. This course is available for outside tournaments.

***Location:*** From Interstate 5, take Poway Road east to Highway 67. Turn right on Highway 67 and drive for three miles to Archie Moore Road. Turn left to the club entrance.

***Course description:*** This course opened for play in late August, 1991. Tucked away in the mountains of Romona at the base of Mount Woodson, this course is spectacular in its natural setting. There are huge boulders, lakes and mature trees that pre-existed the construction of the course. There are numerous elevation changes. The 50-foot bridge that links the second green to the third tee is a landmark. Holes 13, 15 and 17 offer superb views of the valley below. Six lakes come into play. Both the fairways and the undulating greens are well bunkered. Bunkers at the greens are especially nice with white sand layered over a hard undersurface. There are no parallel fairways. It is short, but as the 130 slope rating indicates, a challenging course where accuracy is imperative off the tees and to the greens.

# SAN VICENTE INN AND GOLF CLUB

**Course 33**
MAP J6 grid e5

**1973**
**Ted Robinson**

24157 San Vicente Road
Ramona, CA 92065

Pro shop (619) 789-3477

- ✓ **driving range**
- ✓ **practice greens**
- ✓ **power carts**
- pull carts
- ✓ **golf club rental**
- locker rooms
- showers
- executive course
- ✓ **accommodations**
- ✓ **food and beverages**
- ✓ **clubhouse**

**Eric Ewing**
**Gordon Campbell**
Professionals

**Ken Sommermeyer**
Superintendent

***Course information:*** This semi-private resort course has 18 holes and par is 72. The course is 6,585 yards and rated 71.4 from the championship tees, and 6,180 yards and rated 69.2 from the regular tees. The slope ratings are 125 championship and 115 regular. Women's tees are 5,595 yards and rated 71.2. The slope rating is 125.

***Play policy and fees:*** Outside play is accepted. Green fees are $39 weekdays and $49 weekends, including cart. Twilight rates, after 1 p.m., are $20 to walk weekdays, and $23 to walk weekends. Reservations are recommended five days in advance. This course is available for outside tournaments.

***Location:*** From Main Street in downtown Ramona, drive south on 10th Street and continue for six miles to the San Diego Country Estates.

***Course description:*** This picturesque course is set in a valley and follows the topography of the land. Four lakes come into play on 14 of the holes, many of which are shaded by ancient live oaks. The sixth is a challenge: 329 yards uphill to the directional flag, then up to a bunkered green that slopes away. A 26-room lodge on site is crammed with winter guests from November through April.

# DE ANZA—MISSION BAY GOLF COURSE

**Course 34**
MAP J6 grid f0

2702 North
Mission Bay Drive
San Diego, CA 92109

Pro shop (619) 490-3370

- ✓ **driving range**
- ✓ **practice greens**
- ✓ **power carts**
- ✓ **pull carts**
- ✓ **golf club rental**
- locker rooms
- showers
- ✓ **executive course**
- accommodations
- ✓ **food and beverages**
- ✓ **clubhouse**

**Dori O'Rourke**
Professional

**Mark Mucerino**
Superintendent

***Course information:*** This public course has 18 holes. See card below for yardage information.

***Play policy and fees:*** Green fees are $7.50 for nine holes and $13 for 18 holes Monday through Friday, $8.50 for nine and $15 for 18 holes weekends. Carts are $9 for nine holes and $15 for 18 holes. Reservations are suggested.

***Location:*** Take Interstate 5 from San Diego and go west on Clairmont Drive and north on Mission Bay Drive to the course.

***Course description:*** Holes range between 72 and 293 yards, including four par-4s. Water and sand come into play often enough. The course is lighted for night play until 10 p.m. New management has greatly improved the course condition in the last two years. The course record is 48.

| Hole | 1 | 2 | 3 | 4 | 5 | 6 | 7 | 8 | 9 | Out | BLUE | Rating: -- |
|---|---|---|---|---|---|---|---|---|---|---|---|---|
| BLUE | - | - | - | - | - | - | - | - | - | - | | Slope: -- |
| WHITE | 268 | 91 | 138 | 98 | 125 | 72 | 277 | 139 | 129 | 1337 | | |
| Par | 4 | 3 | 3 | 3 | 3 | 3 | 4 | 3 | 3 | 29 | WHITE | Rating: -- |
| Handicap | 3 | 15 | 7 | 13 | 11 | 17 | 1 | 5 | 9 | x | | Slope: -- |
| RED | 244 | 79 | 122 | 82 | 111 | 63 | 251 | 123 | 105 | 1180 | | |
| Par | 4 | 3 | 3 | 3 | 3 | 3 | 4 | 3 | 3 | 29 | RED | Rating: -- |
| Handicap | 3 | 15 | 7 | 13 | 9 | 17 | 1 | 5 | 11 | x | | Slope: -- |

| Hole | 10 | 11 | 12 | 13 | 14 | 15 | 16 | 17 | 18 | In | Totals | |
|---|---|---|---|---|---|---|---|---|---|---|---|---|
| BLUE | - | - | - | - | - | - | - | - | - | - | BLUE | -- |
| WHITE | 251 | 135 | 145 | 138 | 105 | 122 | 123 | 135 | 293 | 1447 | WHITE | 2784 |
| Par | 4 | 3 | 3 | 3 | 3 | 3 | 3 | 3 | 4 | 29 | Par | 58 |
| Handicap | 4 | 12 | 6 | 8 | 18 | 16 | 14 | 10 | 2 | x | | |
| RED | 234 | 119 | 127 | 111 | 96 | 106 | 105 | 115 | 284 | 1297 | RED | 2477 |
| Par | 4 | 3 | 3 | 3 | 3 | 3 | 3 | 3 | 4 | 29 | Par | 58 |
| Handicap | 4 | 8 | 6 | 12 | 18 | 14 | 16 | 10 | 2 | x | | |

# NAVY GOLF COURSES MISSION GORGE

**Course 35**
MAP J6 grid f1

**1957**
**Jack Daray**

Friars Road
and Admiral Baker Road
San Diego, CA 92021

Pro shop (619) 556-5520
Clubhouse (619) 556-5502
Starter (619) 556-5521

- ✓ **driving range**
- ✓ **practice greens**
- ✓ **power carts**
- ✓ **pull carts**
- ✓ **golf club rental**
- ✓ **locker rooms**
- ✓ **showers**
- ✓ **executive course** accommodations
- ✓ **food and beverages**
- ✓ **clubhouse**

**Tim Bigham**
Operations Manager

**Howard Fisher**
Superintendent

***Course information:*** This military facility has two 18-hole courses. Par is 72 on the North Course and 70 on the South Course.

The North Course is 6,801 yards and rated 72.8 from the championship tees, and 6,486 yards and rated 70.3 from the regular tees. The slope ratings are 126 championship and 117 regular. Women's tees are 5,844 yards and rated 67.0. The slope rating is 109.

The South Course is 5,774 yards and rated 66.6 from the regular tees. The slope rating is 103. Women's yardage and ratings were unavailable.

***Play policy and fees:*** Military personnel and guests only. Green fees are $10 for military personnel. Guests are $15 weekdays and $20 weekends. Carts are $14.

***Location:*** Take the Interstate 5 off-ramp off Interstate 8, and drive north for one-quarter mile to the Friars Road East exit. Drive east to Admiral Baker Road and turn left past the security gate to the club.

***Course description:*** The North Course is the more interesting of the two and offers a variety of holes traversing rather hilly terrain. The South course is shorter and more level, but there are plans to extend this course to a par-72.

# STARDUST COUNTRY CLUB

**Course 36**
MAP J6 grid f1

*Course information:* This semi-private course has 27 holes and par is 72 for each 18-hole combination.

The Valley/Lake Course is 6,686 yards and rated 72.4 from the championship tees, and 6,383 yards and rated 70.2 from the regular tees. The slope ratings are 126 championship and 119 regular. Women's tees are 5,797 yards and rated 72.5. The slope rating is 120.

The River/Valley Course is 6,687 yards and rated 72.4 from the championship tees, and 6,384 yards and rated 70.2 from the regular tees. The slope ratings are 126 championship and 118 regular. Women's tees are 5,871 yards and rated 73.3. The slope rating is 122.

The Lake/River Course is 6,599 yards and rated 71.6 from the championship tees, and 6,303 yards and rated 69.8 from the regular tees. The slope ratings are 123 championship and 117 regular. Women's tees are 5,734 yards and rated 72.5. The slope rating is 120.

*Play policy and fees:* Reciprocal play is accepted with members of other private clubs. Hotel guests welcome. Green fees are $45 with cart for hotel guests and $50 for non-hotel guests. Reservations are recommended.

950 Hotel Circle
San Diego, CA 92108

Pro shop (619) 297-4796
Clubhouse (619) 298-0511

- ✓ **driving range**
- ✓ **practice greens**
- ✓ **power carts**
- ✓ **pull carts**
- ✓ **golf club rental**
- ✓ **locker rooms**
- ✓ **showers**
- executive course
- ✓ **accommodations**
- ✓ **food and beverages**
- ✓ **clubhouse**

**Cliff Crandall**
Director of Golf

**K.C. Crandall**
Professional

**Steve Parker**
Superintendent

*Location:* In Mission Valley, turn off Interstate 8 at the Stardust Hotel and Country Club sign.

*Course description:* These courses date back to the 1940s. They are flat with well-bunkered greens. The fairways tend to be narrow and demand good shot placement. The game starts on the greens, which are very quick. Water comes into play on four holes. Stardust hosted the PGA Tour in San Diego from 1955, when it was called Mission Valley Country Club, until 1968. It is well-known locally for its 45-stall night-lighted driving range. The golf course lease expires in June of 1994.



MAP ON PAGE 672

# CARLTON OAKS LODGE AND COUNTRY CLUB

**Course 37**
MAP J6 grid f2

**1989**
**Perry Dye**

9200 Inwood Drive
Santee, CA 92071

Pro shop (619) 448-8500
Clubhouse (619) 448-4242

✓ **driving range**
✓ **practice greens**
✓ **power carts**
pull carts
✓ **golf club rental**
locker rooms
showers
executive course
✓ **accommodations**
✓ **food and beverages**
✓ **clubhouse**

**Susan Reid**
Manager

**Rex Cole**
Professional

**Jim Timke**
Superintendent

***Course information:*** This resort course has 18 holes. The course is 7,088 yards and rated 75.7 with a slope of 144 from the tournament tees. Women's tees are 5,611 yards and rated 73.1 with a slope of 128 from the executive tees. See card below for additional yardage and rating information.

***Play policy and fees:*** Outside play is accepted and hotel guests are welcome. Green fees are weekdays January through June $50, weekends $65. July through December weekday fees are $40, weekends are $50. Carts are included. There are special rates in early morning and late afternoon. Reservations are recommended three days in advance. Collared shirts are required and shorts must be Bermuda length.

***Location:*** Take the Mission Gorge exit off Interstate 8, and drive north for 6.5 miles. Turn left at Mast Boulevard. Drive one-half mile and turn right on Carlton Oaks Drive. Continue one mile and turn right on Inwood Drive.

***Course description:*** The highest rated course in the county from the back tees, this terrific layout has it all—water, wind, rough, protected greens, waste areas—and depending on a player's ability, it's still very playable. One of the very best in the area. A 60-room lodge is on site.

| Hole | 1 | 2 | 3 | 4 | 5 | 6 | 7 | 8 | 9 | Out | BLUE | Rating: 72.2 |
|---|---|---|---|---|---|---|---|---|---|---|---|---|
| BLUE | 392 | 164 | 510 | 419 | 294 | 364 | 182 | 366 | 527 | 3218 | | Slope: 133 |
| WHITE | 377 | 146 | 496 | 381 | 263 | 341 | 137 | 336 | 500 | 2977 | | |
| Par | 4 | 3 | 5 | 4 | 4 | 4 | 3 | 4 | 5 | 36 | WHITE | Rating: 69.0 |
| Handicap | 3 | 17 | 5 | 1 | 13 | 7 | 15 | 11 | 9 | x | | Slope: 117 |
| RED | 289 | 103 | 356 | 275 | 173 | 232 | 78 | 225 | 425 | 2156 | | |
| Par | 4 | 3 | 5 | 4 | 3 | 4 | 3 | 4 | 5 | 36 | RED | Rating: 67.1 |
| Handicap | 15 | 13 | 7 | 9 | 5 | 11 | 17 | 1 | 3 | x | | Slope: 114 |

| Hole | 10 | 11 | 12 | 13 | 14 | 15 | 16 | 17 | 18 | In | Totals | |
|---|---|---|---|---|---|---|---|---|---|---|---|---|
| BLUE | 387 | 349 | 162 | 573 | 427 | 531 | 345 | 141 | 401 | 3316 | BLUE | 6534 |
| WHITE | 372 | 322 | 129 | 528 | 380 | 491 | 335 | 128 | 363 | 3048 | WHITE | 6025 |
| Par | 4 | 4 | 3 | 5 | 4 | 5 | 4 | 3 | 4 | 36 | Par | 72 |
| Handicap | 8 | 12 | 14 | 6 | 2 | 10 | 16 | 18 | 4 | x | | |
| RED | 295 | 260 | 81 | 436 | 307 | 420 | 215 | 91 | 287 | 2392 | RED | 4548 |
| Par | 4 | 4 | 3 | 5 | 4 | 5 | 4 | 3 | 4 | 36 | Par | 72 |
| Handicap | 14 | 6 | 12 | 10 | 4 | 8 | 18 | 16 | 2 | x | | |

# MISSION TRAILS GOLF COURSE

**Course 38**
MAP J6 grid f2

**1966**

Box 19402
San Diego, CA 92219

7380 Golfcrest Place
San Diego, CA 92219

Pro shop (619) 460-5400

- ✓ **driving range**
- ✓ **practice greens**
- ✓ **power carts**
- ✓ **pull carts**
- ✓ **golf club rental**
- locker rooms
- showers
- executive course
- accommodations
- ✓ **food and beverages**
- ✓ **clubhouse**

***Course information:*** This public course has 18 holes and par is 71. The course is 6,004 yards and rated 68.6 from the championship tees, and 5,604 yards and rated 66.3 from the regular tees. The slope ratings are 113 championship and 104 regular. Women's tees are 5,175 yards and rated 71.1. The slope rating is 120.

***Play policy and fees:*** Green fees are $18 weekdays and $24 on weekends. Senior rates $14 on weekdays only. Carts are $20. Shirts are required at all times. Reservations recommended one week in advance for the general public, and 10 days in advance for American Golf members.

***Location:*** In San Diego, drive on Interstate 8 to College Avenue, and turn north and drive one mile to Navajo Road. Turn right and drive two miles to Golfcrest Drive. Turn right and continue one-quarter mile to Golfcrest Place. Turn left into the club.

***Course description:*** Set in a little valley, the layout of this scenic course follows the contours of the land with two of the holes running alongside Lake Murray. Mature trees separate the fairways. It's a busy place, though most fairways are lined with mature trees. It's been upgraded considerably in recent years. A nice little challenge overall.

# WILLOWBROOK COUNTRY CLUB

**Course 39**
MAP J6 grid f3

**1955**
11905 Riverside Drive
Lakeside, CA 92040

Pro shop (619) 561-1061

driving range
✓ practice greens
✓ power carts
✓ pull carts
✓ golf club rental
locker rooms
showers
executive course
accommodations
✓ food and beverages
✓ clubhouse

**Spero Tzathas**
Manager

**Howard Fisher III**
Superintendent

***Course information:*** This public course has nine holes. See card below for yardage and rating information.

***Play policy and fees:*** Green fees are $12 for nine holes, $15 for 18 holes weekdays and $15 for nine holes and $20 for 18 holes weekends. Reservations are recommended. This course is available for outside tournaments.

***Location:*** Take Interstate 8 east from San Diego to the Highway 67 exit in El Cajon. Travel north to the Riverford Road exit (bear left). Make a left onto Riverford Road and then turn right onto Riverside Drive. The club is on the right hand side about one-half mile.

***Course description:*** This level course has water in play on four holes, five for the slightly errant. The 500-yard fifth can be a real monster if the afternoon winds pick up, and they often do. The 447-yard ninth features rough and water left off the tee, and trees straight ahead. Better have your power fade working here.

| Hole | 1 | 2 | 3 | 4 | 5 | 6 | 7 | 8 | 9 | Out | BLUE | Rating: 67.3 |
|---|---|---|---|---|---|---|---|---|---|---|---|---|
| BLUE | 306 | 362 | 116 | 292 | 500 | 379 | 172 | 381 | 447 | 2955 | | Slope: 107 |
| WHITE | - | - | - | - | - | - | - | - | - | - | | |
| Par | 4 | 4 | 3 | 4 | 5 | 4 | 3 | 4 | 5 | 36 | WHITE | Rating: -- |
| Handicap | 15 | 3 | 17 | 11 | 5 | 7 | 9 | 1 | 13 | x | | Slope: -- |
| RED | 310 | 279 | 112 | 242 | 461 | 380 | 89 | 314 | 448 | 2635 | | |
| Par | 4 | 4 | 3 | 4 | 5 | 4 | 3 | 4 | 5 | 36 | RED | Rating: 70.5 |
| Handicap | 9 | 11 | 15 | 13 | 3 | 1 | 17 | 7 | 5 | x | | Slope: 116 |

| Hole | 10 | 11 | 12 | 13 | 14 | 15 | 16 | 17 | 18 | In | Totals | |
|---|---|---|---|---|---|---|---|---|---|---|---|---|
| BLUE | 308 | 345 | 129 | 272 | 509 | 373 | 181 | 368 | 451 | 2936 | BLUE | 5891 |
| WHITE | - | - | - | - | - | - | - | - | - | - | WHITE | -- |
| Par | 4 | 4 | 3 | 4 | 5 | 4 | 3 | 4 | 5 | 36 | Par | 72 |
| Handicap | 16 | 4 | 18 | 12 | 6 | 8 | 10 | 2 | 14 | x | | |
| RED | 295 | 279 | 128 | 242 | 461 | 373 | 89 | 314 | 456 | 2637 | RED | 5272 |
| Par | 4 | 4 | 3 | 4 | 5 | 4 | 3 | 4 | 5 | 36 | Par | 72 |
| Handicap | 10 | 12 | 16 | 14 | 4 | 2 | 18 | 8 | 6 | x | | |

# CORONADO GOLF COURSE

**Course 40**
MAP J6 grid g0

***Course information:*** This public course has 18 holes. See card below for yardage and rating information.

***Play policy and fees:*** Green fees are $17. After 4 p.m. the green fees are $9. Carts are $18. Reservations are recommended.

***Location:*** From Interstate 5, take the Coronado Bridge west and turn left at the end of the bridge. Go left on Fifth Street to Glorietta Boulevard. Turn right to the club.

***Course description:*** Open fairways and large greens typify this course. It hosts a whopping 110,000 rounds annually but is in remarkably fine condition. Set beneath the Coronado Bridge, it has some of the best views of San Diego and its harbor.

**1958**
**Jack Daray**

PO Box 18055
Coronado, CA 92178

2000 Visalia Way
Coronado, CA 92118

Pro shop (619) 435-3121

- ✓ **driving range**
- ✓ **practice greens**
- ✓ **power carts**
- ✓ **pull carts**
- ✓ **golf club rental**
- locker rooms
- showers
- executive course
- accommodations
- ✓ **food and beverages**
- ✓ **clubhouse**

| Hole | 1 | 2 | 3 | 4 | 5 | 6 | 7 | 8 | 9 | Out | | |
|---|---|---|---|---|---|---|---|---|---|---|---|---|
| BLUE | 386 | 500 | 406 | 536 | 163 | 396 | 390 | 404 | 201 | 3382 | BLUE | Rating: 71.8 |
| WHITE | 368 | 485 | 389 | 516 | 136 | 380 | 371 | 383 | 179 | 3207 | | Slope: 124 |
| Par | 4 | 5 | 4 | 5 | 3 | 4 | 4 | 4 | 3 | 36 | WHITE | Rating: 70 |
| Handicap | 7 | 15 | 1 | 9 | 17 | 3 | 11 | 5 | 13 | x | | Slope: 118 |
| RED | 354 | 450 | 337 | 476 | 133 | 357 | 320 | 347 | 151 | 2925 | | |
| Par | 4 | 5 | 4 | 5 | 3 | 4 | 4 | 4 | 3 | 36 | RED | Rating: 73.7 |
| Handicap | 7 | 3 | 9 | 1 | 17 | 5 | 13 | 11 | 15 | x | | Slope: 126 |

| Hole | 10 | 11 | 12 | 13 | 14 | 15 | 16 | 17 | 18 | In | Totals | |
|---|---|---|---|---|---|---|---|---|---|---|---|---|
| BLUE | 409 | 137 | 300 | 543 | 391 | 175 | 370 | 427 | 499 | 3251 | BLUE | 6633 |
| WHITE | 382 | 135 | 285 | 524 | 378 | 166 | 359 | 411 | 470 | 3110 | WHITE | 6317 |
| Par | 4 | 3 | 4 | 5 | 4 | 3 | 4 | 4 | 5 | 36 | Par | 72 |
| Handicap | 8 | 18 | 16 | 6 | 4 | 12 | 10 | 2 | 14 | x | | |
| RED | 356 | 120 | 269 | 488 | 355 | 145 | 322 | 363 | 441 | 2859 | RED | 5784 |
| Par | 4 | 3 | 4 | 5 | 4 | 3 | 4 | 4 | 5 | 36 | Par | 72 |
| Handicap | 6 | 18 | 14 | 2 | 4 | 16 | 12 | 8 | 10 | x | | |

# SEA 'N' AIR

**Course 41**
MAP J6 grid g0

***Course information:*** This military course has 18 holes. See card below for yardage and rating information.

***Play policy and fees:*** Military personnel and guests only. Rates vary according to military rank and status. Reservations are recommended. This course is available for outside tournaments on a limited basis. Call for information.

***Location:*** Take the Coronado exit off Interstate 5 in San Diego and drive across the Coronado Bay Bridge through the toll gate. Continue on Third Avenue and turn left on Alameda Street. At Fourth Avenue, turn right through the main gate and drive one-quarter mile to Rogers Road and then left to the club.

***Course description:*** This flat course has undergone a considerable upgrade in recent years. Two unchanged features: three holes run along the ocean, making them truly links style, and they are directly below the flight path of planes attached to North Island NAS.

PO Box 180751
Coronado, CA 92178

Building 800, NAS North Is.
San Diego, CA 92135

Pro shop (619) 545-9659

- ✓ **driving range**
- ✓ **practice greens**
- ✓ **power carts**
- ✓ **pull carts**
- ✓ **golf club rental**
- ✓ **locker rooms**
- ✓ **showers**
- ✓ **executive course** accommodations
- ✓ **food and beverages**
- ✓ **clubhouse**

**Mike Jick**
Professional

**Patrick Shannon**
Superintendent

| Hole | 1 | 2 | 3 | 4 | 5 | 6 | 7 | 8 | 9 | Out | BLUE | Rating: 69.9 |
|---|---|---|---|---|---|---|---|---|---|---|---|---|
| BLUE | 500 | 280 | 268 | 411 | 362 | 563 | 195 | 360 | 341 | 3280 | | Slope: 113 |
| WHITE | 486 | 265 | 261 | 393 | 347 | 546 | 188 | 352 | 329 | 3167 | | |
| Par | 5 | 4 | 4 | 4 | 4 | 5 | 3 | 4 | 4 | 37 | WHITE | Rating: 68.8 |
| Handicap | 5 | 17 | 13 | 3 | 7 | 1 | 15 | 11 | 9 | x | | Slope: 109 |
| RED | 425 | 250 | 248 | 337 | 329 | 433 | 160 | 287 | 306 | 2775 | | |
| Par | 5 | 4 | 4 | 4 | 4 | 5 | 3 | 4 | 4 | 37 | RED | Rating: 70.8 |
| Handicap | 5 | 15 | 11 | 3 | 7 | 1 | 13 | 17 | 9 | x | | Slope: 113 |

| Hole | 10 | 11 | 12 | 13 | 14 | 15 | 16 | 17 | 18 | In | Totals | |
|---|---|---|---|---|---|---|---|---|---|---|---|---|
| BLUE | 393 | 163 | 544 | 173 | 393 | 487 | 356 | 191 | 349 | 3049 | BLUE | 6329 |
| WHITE | 382 | 155 | 528 | 161 | 384 | 477 | 347 | 185 | 339 | 2958 | WHITE | 6125 |
| Par | 4 | 3 | 5 | 3 | 4 | 5 | 4 | 3 | 4 | 35 | Par | 72 |
| Handicap | 4 | 18 | 2 | 14 | 6 | 10 | 8 | 16 | 12 | x | | |
| RED | 369 | 106 | 451 | 150 | 374 | 467 | 330 | 183 | 334 | 2764 | RED | 5539 |
| Par | 4 | 3 | 5 | 3 | 4 | 5 | 4 | 3 | 4 | 35 | Par | 72 |
| Handicap | 8 | 18 | 2 | 16 | 6 | 4 | 12 | 14 | 10 | x | | |

## COLINA PARK GOLF COURSE

**Course 42**
MAP J6 grid g1

***Course information:*** This is a par-3 public course. The par is 54 for 18 holes. The course is 1,252 yards.

***Play policy and fees:*** Green fees are $4. Juniors and seniors are $3 any day. Replay, or second rounds, are $2.

***Location:*** Take Interstate 805 to University Avenue and go east about 3.5 miles. At 52nd Street go left to the course. The course is on the right.

***Course description:*** This course has rolling fairways and undulating greens and trees. Lots of trees. It's carved into a neighborhood in the middle of the city. Bring your straight game. A delightful little track for seniors and juniors.

4085 52nd Street
San Diego, CA 92105

Pro shop (619) 582-4704

driving range
✓ **practice greens**
power carts
pull carts
✓ **golf club rental**
locker rooms
showers
executive course
✓ **accommodations**
food and beverages
✓ **clubhouse**

## PRESIDIO HILLS PITCH AND PUTT

**Course 43**
MAP J6 grid g1

**1932**
**William Park Bell**

***Course information:*** This public course has 18 holes. Par is 54. The course is 1,426 yards.

***Play policy and fees:*** Green fees are $6.

***Location:*** From Interstate 8 in San Diego, take the Taylor Street exit. Drive to Juan Street, turn left and drive one block to the course. The course is on the left.

***Course description:*** This is the oldest course of its kind in the San Diego area. It's been a family operation for many years. The grandfather of Donna Abrego was the first pro. This is a fun little pitch-and-putt course for tuning up the short game. There are full-grown sycamore trees keeping the course in welcome shade. The San Diego Junior Golf Association, one of the oldest and most successful in the nation, starts its youngsters here. For years after they made the PGA Tour, such players as Lou Hinkle and Morris Halalsky returned to have their short games polished here.

PO Box 10532
San Diego, CA 92210

4136 Wallace Street
San Diego, CA 92210

Clubhouse (619) 295-9476

driving range
✓ **practice greens**
power carts
pull carts
✓ **golf club rental**
locker rooms
showers
executive course
accommodations
✓ **food and beverages**
✓ **clubhouse**

**Donna Abrego**
Manager

## BALBOA PARK GOLF CLUB

**Course 44**
MAP J6 grid g1

***Course information:*** This public course has 27 holes. Par is 72 on the 18-hole course and 32 on the nine-hole course. The 18-hole course is 6,058 yards and rated 68.2 from the regular tees. The slope rating is 110. Women's tees are 5,391 yards and rated 69.8. The slope rating is 112.

***Play policy and fees:*** Call for fee structure which is being adjusted during reconstruction of the course. Reservations are recommended.

***Location:*** Take the Pershing Drive exit off Interstate 5 and drive east to 26th Street then turn right to Golf Course Drive and the club.

***Course description:*** Both courses play tight with small greens. The 18-hole course is undergoing a major renovation program; several holes at a time will be closed or temporary for up to two years beginning in early 1993. Still, the 60 year-old clubhouse offers one of the best 19th hole views anywhere.

**William Park Bell**

2600 Golf Course Drive
San Diego, CA 92102

Pro shop (619) 239-1632
Starter (619) 232-2470
Reservations (619) 570-1234

- ✓ **driving range**
- ✓ **practice greens**
- ✓ **power carts**
- ✓ **pull carts**
- ✓ **golf club rental**
- ✓ **locker rooms**
- ✓ **showers**
- ✓ **executive course**
- accommodations
- ✓ **food and beverages**
- ✓ **clubhouse**

**Jim Hillsbery**
Professional

**Gene Bianchi**
Superintendent

## BONITA GOLF CLUB

**Course 45**
MAP J6 grid g2

***Course information:*** This semi-private course has 18 holes and par is 71. The course is 6,287 yards and rated 69.3 from the championship tees, and 5,832 yards and rated 67.8 from the regular tees. The slope ratings are 110 championship and 104 regular. Women's tees are 5,442 yards and rated 69.6. The slope rating is 112.

***Play policy and fees:*** Outside play is accepted. Green fees are $15 weekdays and $22 weekends. Carts are $18. Reservations are recommended one week in advance. This course is available for outside tournaments.

***Location:*** Drive on Interstate 805 to the South Freeway East for 4.5 miles. At Sweetwater Road, turn right and drive three-fourths of a mile to the course.

***Course description:*** This flat course is set in a river valley and has a few doglegs. The friendly greens do not have any bunkers set directly in front of them. There are two lakes on the course and the breeze tends to pick up, but this is a user-friendly venue.

Box 455
Bonita, CA 91902

5540 Sweetwater Road
Bonita, CA 91902

Pro shop (619) 267-1103

- ✓ **driving range**
- ✓ **practice greens**
- ✓ **power carts**
- ✓ **pull carts**
- ✓ **golf club rental**
- locker rooms
- showers
- executive course
- accommodations
- ✓ **food and beverages**
- ✓ **clubhouse**

**Charles N. Hamilton III**
Manager

**Bill Nary**
Professional

**Robert Scribner**
Superintendent

# CHULA VISTA GOLF CLUB

**Course 46**
MAP J6 grid g2

***Course information:*** This public course has 18 holes and par is 73. The course is 6,788 yards and rated 72.7 from the championship tees, and 6,529 yards and rated 70.8 from the regular tees. The slope ratings are 125 championship and 116 regular. Women's tees are 5,859 and rated 72.7. The slope rating is 113.

***Play policy and fees:*** Green fees are $15 weekdays and $20 weekends. Carts are $20. Reservations are recommended.

***Location:*** Take the E Street exit off Interstate 805 in Chula Vista and travel east two miles to the club.

***Course description:*** This is a walkable, level course with five par-5s. It has large greens and wide open, rolling terrain. A creek meanders through most of the course, which adds to the test already presented by the usual afternoon breeze. Fivesomes are allowed on this busy American Golf Corporation property.

PO Box 403
Bonita, CA 92002

4475 Bonita Road
Bonita, CA 92002

Pro shop (619) 479-4141
Clubhouse (619) 427-9634

✓ **driving range**
✓ **practice greens**
✓ **power carts**
✓ **pull carts**
✓ **golf club rental**
locker rooms
showers
executive course
accommodations
✓ **food and beverages**
✓ **clubhouse**

**Ricke Crochet**
Manager

**John Gonzales**
Professional

**Steve Schroeder**
Regional Superintendent

# STEELE CANYON GOLF COURSE

**Course 47**
MAP J6 grid g3

**1991**
**Gary Player**

3199 Stonefield Drive
Jamul, CA 91935

Pro shop (619) 441-6900

- ✓ **driving range**
- ✓ **practice greens**
- ✓ **power carts**
- pull carts
- ✓ **golf club rental**
- locker rooms
- showers
- executive course
- accommodations
- ✓ **food and beverages**
- ✓ **clubhouse**

**Art Noehren**
Manager

**Jeffrey Johnson**
Professional

**David Buckles**
Superintendent

***Course information:*** This semi-private course has 27 holes. Par is 71.

Canyon-Ranch Course is 6,741 yards and rated 72.2 from the championship tees, 6,228 yards and rated 69.1 from the tournament tees, and 5,657 yards and rated 65.5 from the regular tees. The slope ratings are 125 championship, 116 tournament, and 109 regular. Women's tees are 4,656 yards and rated 66.6. The slope rating is 112.

Canyon-Meadow Course is 6,672 yards and rated 72.2 from the championship tees, 6,196 yards and rated 69.2 from the tournament tees, and 5,522 yards and rated 65.9 from the regular tees. The slope ratings are 134 championship, 122 tournament, and 115 regular. the women's tees are 4,814 yards and rated 67.9. The slope rating is 118.

Ranch-Meadow Course is 7,001 yards and rated 74.0 from the championship tees, 6,484 yards and rated 70.7 from the tournament tees, and 5,831 yards and rated 67.5 from the regular tees. The slope ratings are 137 championship, 125 tournament, and 118 regular. the women's tees are 5,026 yards and rated 69.5. The slope rating is 124.

***Play policy and fees:*** Green fees are $38 weekdays and $48 weekdays, including cart. Twilight rates are $23 weekdays and $25 weekends after 1 p.m. Reservations are recommended seven days in advance. No tee times for singles. This course is available for tournaments.

***Location:*** From Interstate 5 in San Diego, exit east on Interstate 94/Jamacha Road. Drive to Willow Glen Drive. Turn right and drive to Steele Canyon Drive. Turn right on Steele Canyon Drive to travel to Jamul Drive (the first traffic light). Turn left and drive one mile to the club.

***Course description:*** The Canyon Nine features several significant elevation changes. The Ranch Nine is somewhat flatter, but has a couple of carries over gulches. The new Meadow Nine places a premium on accuracy. The three combine for a top-flight layout.

# SUN VALLEY GOLF COURSE

**Course 48**
MAP J6 grid g3

5080 Memorial Drive
La Mesa, CA 92041

Pro shop (619) 466-6102

- driving range
- ✓ **practice greens**
- power carts
- ✓ **pull carts**
- ✓ **golf club rental**
- locker rooms
- showers
- executive course
- accommodations
- ✓ **food and beverages**
- clubhouse

***Course information:*** This public course has nine holes and par is 27. The course is 1,078 yards.

***Play policy and fees:*** Green fees are $3.50 for nine holes and $6 for 18 holes any day.

***Location:*** Take Interstate 8 east of San Diego to El Cajon Boulevard, go left to La Mesa Boulevard and follow it to Memorial Drive and the course.

***Course description:*** This course has open fairways and it's hilly. It's a part of a larger municipal park in a suburban San Diego neighborhood. The longest hole is 131 yards, the shortest, 96.

# SINGING HILLS COUNTRY CLUB AND LODGE

**Course 49**
MAP J6 grid g3

**1956**
**Spud Moorman**

**1980**
**Ted Robinson**

3007 Dehesa Road
El Cajon, CA 92019

Pro shop (619) 442-3425

- ✓ **driving range**
- ✓ **practice greens**
- ✓ **power carts**
- ✓ **pull carts**
- ✓ **golf club rental**
- ✓ **locker rooms**
- ✓ **showers**
- ✓ **executive course**
- ✓ **accommodations**
- ✓ **food and beverages**
- ✓ **clubhouse**

**Tom Addis III**
Professional/Director of Golf

**Tamo Maldanado**
Superintendent

***Course information:*** This semi-private club has two 18-hole courses. Par is 71 on the Oak Glen Course and 72 on the Willow Glen Course. A par-3 executive course is also available. This is also a resort.

The Oak Glen Course is 6,132 yards and rated 69.0 from the championship tees, and 5,749 yards and rated 66.9 from the regular tees. The slope ratings are 111 championship and 107 regular. Women's tees are 5,308 yards and rated 69.3. The slope rating is 112.

The Willow Glen Course is 6,608 yards and rated 71.9 from the championship tees, and 6,247 yards and rated 69.4 from the regular tees. The slope ratings are 124 championship and 114 regular. Women's tees are 5,585 yards and rated 71.4. The slope rating is 122.

***Play policy and fees:*** Reciprocal play is accepted with members of other private clubs. Outside play is accepted. Hotel guests welcome. Green fees are $25 weekdays and $30 weekends. Carts are $18. Reservations are recommended. This course is available for outside tournaments.

***Location:*** From Interstate 5 or Interstate 805, take Interstate 8 east to the Second Street exit in El Cajon. Turn right and turn left on Washington Street. Continue four miles to the course.

***Course description:*** *Golf Digest* ranks this course in the top 100 in the country. Mature trees line the flat straight fairways on the Oak Glen Course. The Willow Glen Course offers a rolling layout and is known for its elevated tee on the fourth hole and the par-3 12th with its tiered green beyond a lake ringed with flowers. One of the best and most popular facilities in the area with an award-winning pro shop and 104-room lodge on site.

# RANCHO SAN DIEGO GOLF COURSE

**Course 50**
MAP J6 grid g3

**1960**
**Spud Moorman**
**Bud Sears**

3121 Willow Glen Road
El Cajon, CA 92019

Pro shop (619) 442-9891

- ✓ **driving range**
- ✓ **practice greens**
- ✓ **power carts**
- ✓ **pull carts**
- ✓ **golf club rental**
- locker rooms
- showers
- executive course
- accommodations
- ✓ **food and beverages**
- ✓ **clubhouse**

**Bill Osgood**
Professional

**Norm Trivett**
Superintendent

***Course information:*** This public facility has two 18-hole courses.

The Ivanhoe Course is 7,089 yards and rated 74.4 from the championship tees, and 6,728 yards and rated 71.9 from the regular tees. The slope ratings are 129 championship and 115 regular. Women's tees are 5,624 yards and rated 72.0. The slope rating is 116.

The Monte Vista Course is 6,036 yards and rated 68.3 from the championship tees. The slope rating is 108. Women's tees are 5,407 yards and rated 73.1. The slope rating is 118.

***Play policy and fees:*** Green fees are $26 for Ivanhoe and $23 for Monte Vista weekdays, and $31 for Ivanhoe and $27 for Monte Vista weekends. Senior rates are $20 for Ivanhoe and $18 for Monte Vista Mondays through Thursdays. Carts are $19. Reservations are recommended two weeks in advance.

***Location:*** From Interstate 5 or Interstate 805, take Interstate 8 east to the Second Street exit in El Cajon. Drive south on Second Street for about four miles to Willow Glen Road and turn left to the club.

***Course description:*** These courses have a lot of trees, ponds and lakes, and even a river runs through in the winter. The Ivanhoe Course has a lot of doglegs and is one of the best maintained public courses in the area. The Monte Vista Course has tight fairways and is shorter.

# NATIONAL CITY GOLF COURSE

**Course 51**
MAP J6 grid h1

1439 Sweetwater Road
National City, CA 92050

Pro shop (619) 474-1400

- ✓ **driving range**
- ✓ **practice greens**
- ✓ **power carts**
- ✓ **pull carts**
- ✓ **golf club rental**
- locker rooms
- showers
- executive course
- accommodations
- ✓ **food and beverages**
- ✓ **clubhouse**

**Ann Gomez**
Manager

**Gary Roberts**
Professional

**Bobby Canedo**
Superintendent

***Course information:*** This public course has nine holes and par is 34. The course is 4,810 yards and rated 60.5 from the championship tees, and 4,440 yards and rated 59.9 from the regular tees. Women's tees are 4,000 yards and rated 60.5.

***Play policy and fees:*** Green fees are $7.50 for nine holes weekdays and $9.50 for nine holes weekends. The twilight rate after 5 p.m. is $5. The senior rate is $4 weekdays and $8 weekends. Reservations are recommended.

***Location:*** Follow Interstate 805 south to Sweetwater Road west which leads to the course.

***Course description:*** This course is extremely tight with out-of-bounds markers on almost every hole. The 525-yard second hole is very narrow and needs pinpoint placement for success. The course record is 55. Beware of the cat that hangs out near the first fairway. He steals balls.

# SAN DIEGO COUNTRY CLUB

**Course 52**
MAP J6 grid h1

***Course information:*** This private course has 18 holes and par is 72. The course is 6,887 yards and rated 74.2 from the championship tees, and 6,560 yards and rated 71.9 from the regular tees. The slope ratings are 133 championship and 127 regular. The forward tees are 4,946 yards and rated 68.9. The slope rating is 118. Women's championship tees are 6,137 yards and rated 75.5 and the regular tees are 4,946 yards and rated 68.9. Slope ratings are 131 championship and 118 regular.

***Play policy and fees:*** Members and guests only.

***Location:*** Take the "L" Street exit off Interstate 5 and drive 1.5 miles east to the club or take Telegraph Canyon/"L" Street exit off Interstate 805 and drive one mile west.

***Course description:*** This course is the last golf stop before reaching the Mexican border. It was built in the 1920s, making it the oldest private course in San Diego County, although new greens were built along with an enormous new clubhouse three years ago. Flat to gently rolling, it's an old-timey layout with new medium to large greens. This is the course in which PGA Tour great Billy Casper learned to play the game. It's also the site of the 1993 U.S. Women's Amateur in August.

88 "L" Street
Chula Vista, CA 91911

Pro shop (619) 422-0108
Clubhouse (619) 422-8895

- ✓ **driving range**
- ✓ **practice greens**
- ✓ **power carts**
- ✓ **pull carts**
- ✓ **golf club rental**
- ✓ **locker rooms**
- ✓ **showers**
- executive course
- accommodations
- ✓ **food and beverages**
- ✓ **clubhouse**

**Thomas Hust**
Professional

**Gary Dalton**
Superintendent

# EASTLAKE COUNTRY CLUB

**Course 53**
MAP J6 grid h2

**1991**
**Ted Robinson**

2375 Clubhouse Drive
Chula Vista, CA 91914

Pro shop (619) 482-5757

- ✓ **driving range**
- ✓ **practice greens**
- ✓ **power carts**
- pull carts
- ✓ **golf club rental**
- locker rooms
- showers
- executive course
- accommodations
- ✓ **food and beverages**
- ✓ **clubhouse**

**Mike Marcum**
General Manager/
Professional

**Sandy Clark**
Superintendent

***Course information:*** This public layout has 18 holes. The course is 6,606 yards and is rated 70.7 with a slope of 116 from the gold tees. Women's tees are 5,834 yards and rated 72.5 with a slope of 122 from the white tees. See card below for additional yardage and rating information.

***Play policy and fees:*** Green fees $25 weekdays and $40 weekends. Weekday twilight rates after 3 p.m. are $18 without a cart and $15 with a cart. Weekend twilight rates after 2 p.m are $26 without a cart and $33 with a cart. No pull carts allowed. Carts are $10 per person. Reservations are recommended. This course is available for tournaments.

***Location:*** Take Interstate 805 south to the Telegraph Canyon Road exit in Chula Vista. Drive east four miles to EastLake Greens Community/EastLake Parkway. Turn right and drive one-quarter mile to Clubhouse Drive. The club is on the right.

***Course description:*** There are four sets of tees on this course. There are undulating fairways, bent grass greens, and six lakes in play. These greens are huge, but not multi-tiered. The course is wide open, although afternoon winds can be tough. A good test for players of all abilities, depending on the tees they use.

| Hole | 1 | 2 | 3 | 4 | 5 | 6 | 7 | 8 | 9 | Out | | |
|---|---|---|---|---|---|---|---|---|---|---|---|---|
| BLUE | 302 | 363 | 310 | 154 | 530 | 415 | 160 | 365 | 513 | 3112 | BLUE | Rating: 68.7 |
| WHITE | 285 | 345 | 280 | 133 | 500 | 380 | 139 | 340 | 480 | 2882 | | Slope: 109 |
| Par | 4 | 4 | 4 | 3 | 5 | 4 | 3 | 4 | 5 | 36 | WHITE | Rating: 66.4 |
| Handicap | 15 | 5 | 17 | 7 | 3 | 1 | 13 | 11 | 9 | x | | Slope: 105 |
| RED | 255 | 295 | 270 | 111 | 440 | 340 | 122 | 310 | 425 | 2568 | | |
| Par | 4 | 4 | 4 | 3 | 5 | 4 | 3 | 4 | 5 | 36 | RED | Rating: 68.8 |
| Handicap | 13 | 9 | 11 | 17 | 1 | 5 | 15 | 7 | 3 | x | | Slope: 114 |

| Hole | 10 | 11 | 12 | 13 | 14 | 15 | 16 | 17 | 18 | In | Totals | |
|---|---|---|---|---|---|---|---|---|---|---|---|---|
| BLUE | 360 | 400 | 153 | 380 | 495 | 335 | 360 | 145 | 485 | 3113 | BLUE | 6225 |
| WHITE | 340 | 390 | 134 | 355 | 470 | 325 | 340 | 128 | 470 | 2952 | WHITE | 5834 |
| Par | 4 | 4 | 3 | 4 | 5 | 4 | 4 | 3 | 5 | 36 | Par | 72 |
| Handicap | 14 | 4 | 8 | 2 | 6 | 16 | 10 | 18 | 12 | x | | |
| RED | 320 | 315 | 113 | 300 | 425 | 280 | 285 | 102 | 410 | 2550 | RED | 5118 |
| Par | 4 | 4 | 3 | 4 | 5 | 4 | 4 | 3 | 5 | 36 | Par | 72 |
| Handicap | 8 | 10 | 14 | 6 | 2 | 12 | 16 | 18 | 4 | x | | |

MAP ON PAGE 672

# MAP J7
(2 COURSES)

PAGES.. 716-719

SO-CAL MAP .....see page 466
adjoining maps
NORTH (I7).........see page 612
EAST (J8) ...........see page 720
SOUTH..........................no map
WEST (J6) ..........see page 672

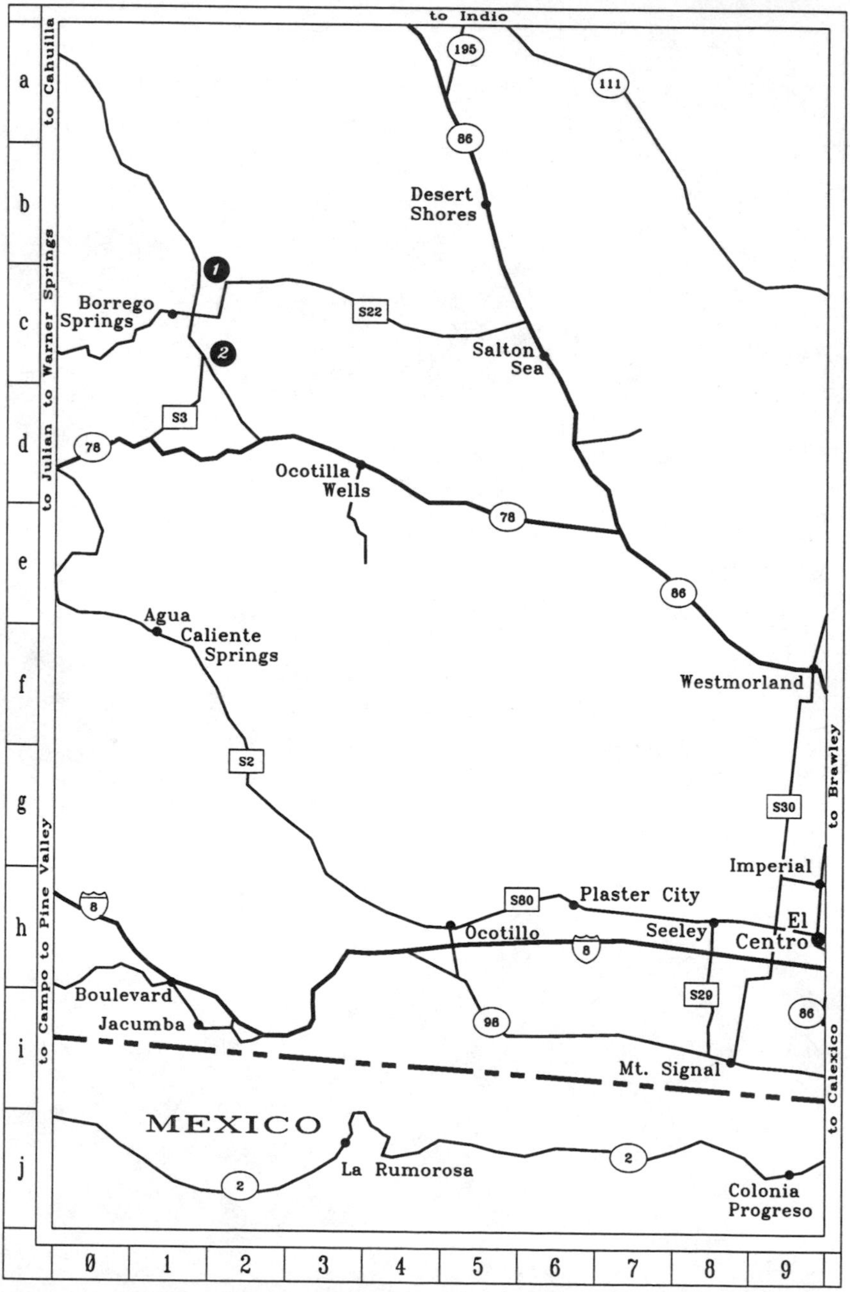

to Indio
195
111
86
to Cahuilla
Desert Shores
1
Borrego Springs
S22
2
Salton Sea
S3
78
to Julian to Warner Springs
Ocotilla Wells
78
86
Agua Caliente Springs
Westmorland
S2
to Brawley
S30
Imperial
S80
Plaster City
8
El Centro
Seeley
Ocotillo
8
to Campo to Pine Valley
Boulevard
S29
Jacumba
98
86
Mt. Signal
to Calexico
MEXICO
La Rumorosa
2
2
Colonia Progreso

a b c d e f g h i j

0 1 2 3 4 5 6 7 8 9

# DE ANZA DESERT COUNTRY CLUB

**Course 1**
MAP J7 grid c1

**1958**
**Tige Stanley**

PO Box 120
Borrego Springs, CA 92004

509 Catarina Drive
Borrego Springs, CA 92004

Pro shop (619)767-5577
Clubhouse (619)767-5105

- ✓ **driving range**
- ✓ **practice greens**
- ✓ **power carts**
- ✓ **pull carts**
- golf club rental
- ✓ **locker rooms**
- showers
- executive course
- accommodations
- ✓ **food and beverages**
- ✓ **clubhouse**

**Andy Gorton**
Manager

**Denny Mays**
Professional

**Tom Baty**
Superintendent

***Course information:*** This private course has 18 holes and par is 72. The course is 6,819 yards and rated 73 from the tournament tees, 6,438 yards and rated 70.5 from the championship tees, and 6,021 yards and rated 68.3 from the regular tees. The slope ratings are 131 tournament, 119 championship and 111 regular. Women's tees are 5,601 yards and rated 71.5. The slope rating is 115.

***Play policy and fees:*** Members and guests only. Fees for sponsored guests are $50. Carts are $16. Reservations are recommended. Course is open daily.

***Location:*** From Palm Canyon Drive in Borrego Springs, turn north on Ocotillo Circle and drive one-half mile to Lazy "S" Drive. Turn right and travel 1.5 miles to Pointing Rock Drive and turn right.

***Course description:*** This flat course has plenty of mature trees and two lakes. It's surrounded by homes. One of the toughest challenges of the course is number three, a 211-yard, par-3. You must hit over a lake and bunker to reach the green.

# RAMS HILL COUNTRY CLUB

**Course 2**
**MAP J7 grid c2**

***Course information:*** This semi-private course has 18 holes. See card below for yardage and rating information.

***Play policy and fees:*** Outside play is accepted. Green fees are $70 daily. Carts are included. Reservations are recommended three days in advance. This course is available for outside tournaments. The course is open from 6:30 a.m. to 6:30 p.m. during the summer season. Closed in September.

***Location:*** Travel on Interstate 10 or Highway 111 to Indio. Turn on Highway 86 to Salton City. Turn right on County Road S-22 to Borrego Valley Road, go left and drive six miles to the club.

***Course description:*** This is a long, well-maintained course with sloping, palm-lined fairways and seven scenic water holes. The course closes in September for fairway re-seeding. Rams Hill hosted the first round of qualifying for the 1992 U.S. Open and is scheduled to do so again.

**1982**
**Ted Robinson**

PO Box 664
Borrego Springs, CA 92004

1881 Rams Hill Road
Borrego Springs, CA 92004

Pro shop (619)767-5125

- ✓ **driving range**
- ✓ **practice greens**
- ✓ **power carts**
- ✓ **pull carts**
- ✓ **golf club rental**
- ✓ **locker rooms**
- ✓ **showers**
- executive course
- accommodations
- ✓ **food and beverages**
- ✓ **clubhouse**

**John Bell, Jr.**
Professional

**Bill Nestle**
Superintendent

| Hole | 1 | 2 | 3 | 4 | 5 | 6 | 7 | 8 | 9 | Out | BLUE | Rating: 74.0 |
|---|---|---|---|---|---|---|---|---|---|---|---|---|
| BLUE | 434 | 550 | 186 | 418 | 492 | 197 | 395 | 365 | 386 | 3423 | | Slope: 133 |
| WHITE | 398 | 518 | 164 | 385 | 468 | 168 | 371 | 349 | 357 | 3178 | | |
| Par | 4 | 5 | 3 | 4 | 5 | 3 | 4 | 4 | 4 | 36 | WHITE | Rating: 70.7 |
| Handicap | 5 | 11 | 13 | 1 | 17 | 15 | 3 | 9 | 7 | x | | Slope: 125 |
| RED | 351 | 466 | 141 | 337 | 430 | 140 | 327 | 315 | 330 | 2837 | | |
| Par | 4 | 5 | 3 | 4 | 5 | 3 | 4 | 4 | 4 | 36 | RED | Rating: 71.9 |
| Handicap | 7 | 1 | 17 | 3 | 5 | 15 | 13 | 9 | 11 | x | | Slope: 119 |

| Hole | 10 | 11 | 12 | 13 | 14 | 15 | 16 | 17 | 18 | In | Totals | |
|---|---|---|---|---|---|---|---|---|---|---|---|---|
| BLUE | 377 | 419 | 517 | 170 | 384 | 424 | 220 | 527 | 405 | 3443 | BLUE | 6866 |
| WHITE | 355 | 378 | 476 | 145 | 362 | 380 | 180 | 505 | 369 | 3150 | WHITE | 6328 |
| Par | 4 | 4 | 5 | 3 | 4 | 4 | 3 | 5 | 4 | 36 | Par | 72 |
| Handicap | 6 | 4 | 18 | 12 | 14 | 2 | 10 | 16 | 8 | x | | |
| RED | 331 | 343 | 436 | 133 | 323 | 332 | 156 | 460 | 343 | 2857 | RED | 5694 |
| Par | 4 | 4 | 5 | 3 | 4 | 4 | 3 | 5 | 4 | 36 | Par | 72 |
| Handicap | 10 | 4 | 6 | 18 | 12 | 14 | 16 | 2 | 8 | x | | |

MAP ON PAGE 716

# MAP J8
(2 COURSES)

PAGES.. 720-723

SO-CAL MAP .....see page 466
adjoining maps
NORTH (I8).........see page 666
EAST (J9) ..........see page 724
SOUTH.........................no map
WEST (J7) .........see page 716

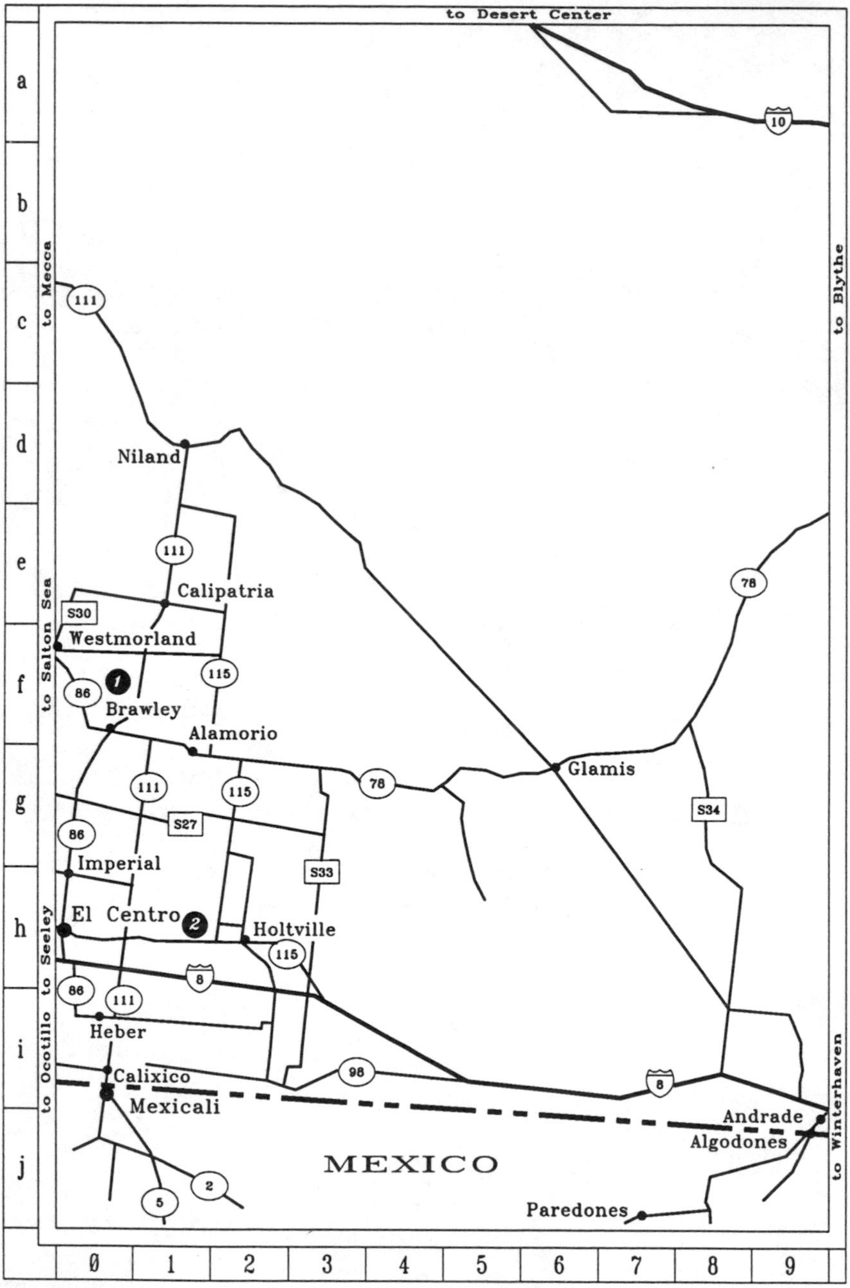

to Desert Center
to Mecca
to Salton Sea
to Ocotillo to Seeley
to Blythe
to Winterhaven

a
b
c
d
e
f
g
h
i
j

Niland
Calipatria
Westmorland
Brawley
Alamorio
Glamis
Imperial
El Centro
Holtville
Heber
Calixico
Mexicali
Andrade
Algodones
Paredones
MEXICO

10
111
S30
115
86
78
S27
S34
S33
8
98
2
5

1
2

0 1 2 3 4 5 6 7 8 9

# DEL RIO COUNTRY CLUB

**Course 1**
MAP J8 grid f0

**1906**

*Course information:* This semi-private course has 18 holes and par is 70. The course is 6,001 yards and rated 67.9 from the regular tees. The slope rating is 105. Women's tees are 5,738 yards and rated 72.8. The slope rating is 118.

*Play policy and fees:* Reciprocal play is accepted with members of other private clubs. Outside play is also accepted. Green fees are $25 weekdays and $30 weekends, carts included. Reservations are recommended.

*Location:* Travel east on Interstate 10 to the town of Indio and take Highway 86 south to Brawley. Take Highway 111 north and drive two miles to the course.

*Course description:* This course is short and tight, demanding strategic shot placement. It has fairly level terrain, tree-lined fairways, many doglegs and small greens. Del Rio hosts about 25,000 rounds annually. The highlight of the schedule is the Elmer Sears Lettuce Tournament, staged over four days in February; it's a storied 65-year old event.

102 East Del Rio Road
Brawley, CA 92227

Pro shop (619) 344-0085

- ✓ **driving range**
- ✓ **practice greens**
- ✓ **power carts**
- ✓ **pull carts**
- ✓ **golf club rental**
- locker rooms
- showers
- executive course
- accommodations
- ✓ **food and beverages**
- ✓ **clubhouse**

**Bob Gelesko**
Professional

**Cayteano Aguilera**
Superintendent

| Hole | 1 | 2 | 3 | 4 | 5 | 6 | 7 | 8 | 9 | Out | BLUE | Rating: -- |
|---|---|---|---|---|---|---|---|---|---|---|---|---|
| BLUE | - | - | - | - | - | - | - | - | - | - | | Slope: -- |
| WHITE | 520 | 414 | 225 | 424 | 198 | 336 | 258 | 353 | 294 | 3022 | | |
| Par | 5 | 4 | 3 | 4 | 3 | 4 | 4 | 4 | 4 | 35 | WHITE | Rating: 67.9 |
| Handicap | 9 | 3 | 11 | 1 | 13 | 7 | 17 | 5 | 15 | x | | Slope: 105 |
| RED | 511 | 406 | 217 | 414 | 189 | 323 | 244 | 344 | 287 | 2935 | | |
| Par | 5 | 5 | 4 | 5 | 3 | 4 | 4 | 4 | 4 | 38 | RED | Rating: 72.8 |
| Handicap | 1 | 11 | 15 | 7 | 17 | 5 | 13 | 9 | 3 | x | | Slope: 118 |

| Hole | 10 | 11 | 12 | 13 | 14 | 15 | 16 | 17 | 18 | In | Totals | |
|---|---|---|---|---|---|---|---|---|---|---|---|---|
| BLUE | - | - | - | - | - | - | - | - | - | - | BLUE | -- |
| WHITE | 185 | 385 | 492 | 206 | 375 | 365 | 145 | 473 | 353 | 2979 | WHITE | 6001 |
| Par | 3 | 4 | 5 | 3 | 4 | 4 | 3 | 5 | 4 | 35 | Par | 70 |
| Handicap | 10 | 2 | 8 | 16 | 6 | 4 | 18 | 12 | 14 | x | | |
| RED | 138 | 376 | 480 | 196 | 351 | 345 | 128 | 456 | 333 | 2803 | RED | 5738 |
| Par | 3 | 4 | 5 | 3 | 4 | 4 | 3 | 5 | 4 | 35 | Par | 73 |
| Handicap | 14 | 4 | 2 | 16 | 10 | 12 | 18 | 6 | 8 | x | | |



MAP ON PAGE 720

# BARBARA WORTH COUNTRY CLUB

**Course 2**
MAP J8 grid h1

**1920**
**Lawrence Hughes**

2050 Country Club Drive
Holtville, CA 92250

Pro shop (619) 356-5842
Clubhouse (619) 356-2806

- ✓ **driving range**
- ✓ **practice greens**
- ✓ **power carts**
- ✓ **pull carts**
- ✓ **golf club rental**
- locker rooms
- showers
- executive course
- ✓ **accommodations**
- ✓ **food and beverages**
- ✓ **clubhouse**

**John Hildreth**
Professional

**Randy Heasley**
Superintendent

***Course information:*** This semi-private course has 18 holes and par is 71. The course is 6,302 yards and rated 70.0 from the regular tees. The slope rating is 115. Women's tees are 5,879 yards and rated 72.6. The slope rating is 120.

***Play policy and fees:*** Reciprocal play is accepted with members of other private clubs. Outside play is accepted. Green fees are $14 weekdays and $18 weekends during the summer season, and $18 weekdays and $22 weekends during the winter season. Carts are $16. Reservations are recommended. This course is available for tournaments.

***Location:*** For reference, the club is 110 miles south of Palm Springs and 120 miles east of San Diego. Travel east from San Diego on Interstate 8 for about 125 miles to Bowker Road and turn left. At Highway 80, turn right and drive to the club.

***Course description:*** This older, desert course has tree-lined fairways, good putting greens and several ponds. It's nicely maintained. Have your bets won by the time you come to 17. It's 150 yards over water. And 18 covers 430 yards uphill to a small, well-bunkered green. This is a stay-and-play course, with more than a 104 motel rooms, three apartments and four executive suites. Tony Lema is said to have won his first professional event here.

MAP ON PAGE 720

# MAP J9

(1 COURSE)

PAGES.. 724-726

SO-CAL MAP .....see page 466
adjoining maps
NORTH ........................no map
EAST ............................no map
SOUTH..........................no map
WEST (J8) .........see page 720

# BLYTHE GOLF COURSE

**Course 1**
MAP J9 grid a2

***Course information:*** This public course has 18 holes and par is 72. The course is 6,567 yards and rated 70.7 from the regular tees. The slope rating is 109. Women's tees are 5,684 yards and rated 70.6 with a 110 slope.

***Play policy and fees:*** Green fees are $9 for nine holes, $15 for 18 holes. Carts are $7 per nine holes. Reservations are recommended.

***Location:*** Travel east of Palm Springs on Interstate 10 for 120 miles and take the Lovekin Boulevard exit north. Travel three miles to Sixth Avenue and turn left. At Defrain Boulevard turn right to the course.

***Course description:*** This nicely maintained course sits on top of a mesa overlooking the Palo Verde Valley. A moderate number of eucalyptus and pine trees line the fairways that go up and down the mesa. The 209-yard second hole drops 150 feet to a tiered green. The 384-yard seventh hole has a blind second shot, usually calling for two strong irons. Lots of character here.

**1968**
**Jack Bell**

PO Box 329
Blythe, CA 92226

Defrain Street
Blythe, CA 92226

Pro shop (619) 922-7272
Clubhouse (619) 922-8737

✓ **driving range**
✓ **practice greens**
✓ **power carts**
✓ **pull carts**
✓ **golf club rental**
locker rooms
showers
executive course
accommodations
✓ **food and beverages**
✓ **clubhouse**

**Willie Getchell**
Professional

**Frank Uyemura**
Superintendent

SOUTHERN J9

# INDEX

— B —

—C—

— C —

—E—

—G—

— L —

— M —

—O—

— P —

—Q—



—R—

— R —

—S—

— S —

— S —

—T—

—U—



—V—

—W—

—Y—

# A BARGAIN FOR YOU!

and our thanks

## *Hawaii Golf*

The Island Companion to *California Golf*

normally $16.95—now only $9.95

Since you've just purchased a copy of our new revised 1993-94 edition of California Golf and are about to enjoy all the courses in the Golden State, we'd like to offer you Hawaii as well!

All the courses in the Paradise State for only $9.95 (plus $3.00 for shipping and handling).

Just mail us this page with your check for $12.95,
or call 1-800-842-7477 with your Mastercard or Visa number.
Mail to: Foghorn Press, P.O. Box 77845, San Francisco, CA 94107